WORLD LIST
OF UNIVERSITIES

OTHER INSTITUTIONS
OF HIGHER EDUCATION
AND UNIVERSITY ORGANIZATIONS

EIGHTEENTH EDITION

LISTE MONDIALE
DES UNIVERSITES

AUTRES ETABLISSEMENTS
D'ENSEIGNEMENT SUPERIEUR
ET ORGANISATIONS UNIVERSITAIRES

DIX-HUITIEME EDITION

 # IAU AT A GLANCE

The **International Association of Universities**, founded in 1950, is a worldwide organization of nearly 1,000 member universities in over 120 countries. Its permanent Secretariat, the **International Universities Bureau** (IUB) with headquarters at Unesco House in Paris, provides a wide variety of services to member institutions.

<table>
<tr><td>

Activities and Services

* IAU-Unesco Information Centre and Clearinghouse on Higher Education
* Meetings, seminars
* Research and studies
* Promotion of academic mobility
* Credential evaluation
* Exchange of publications and materials
* Sponsorship of International Student Identity Card and International Academic Card

</td><td>

Publications

* International Handbook of Universities
* World List of Universities
* World Guide to Higher Education (prepared by IAU, published by Unesco)
* Studies and Monographs
* Higher Education Policy (quarterly)
* IAU Bulletin (bimonthly)

</td></tr>
</table>

Major Meetings Open to All Members

* Five-yearly General Conference. Determines IAU general policy and serves as a major forum on international higher education issues.

Ninth General Conference: 5–11 August 1990, University of Helsinki
Theme: **Universality, Diversity, Interdependence: The Missions of the University**

* Mid-Term Conference of Heads of Member Universities held between General Conferences.

Rio de Janeiro 1988
Theme: **International University Co-operation, A Critical Analysis: Failures, Successes, Perspectives**

(A full description of IAU is given on p. 610)

L'AIU EN BREF

Fondée en 1950, l'**Association internationale des Universités** (AIU) est une organisation mondiale regroupant près de mille universités membres dans plus de cent-vingt pays. Son Secrétariat permanent, le **Bureau international des Universités** (BIU), a son siège à la Maison de l'Unesco à Paris et assure aux institutions membres une large gamme de services.

<table>
<tr><td>

Activités et Services

* Centre d'information AIU-Unesco sur l'enseignement supérieur
* Réunions et séminaires
* Recherches et études
* Promotion de la mobilité académique
* Evaluation des diplômes
* Echanges de publications et documents
* Parrainage de la Carte internationale d'étudiant et de la Carte internationale d'enseignant

</td><td>

Publications

* International Handbook of Universities
* Liste mondiale des Universités
* Les Etudes supérieures (préparé par l'AIU, publié par l'Unesco)
* Etudes et Monographies
* Higher Education Policy (revue trimestrielle)
* Bulletin de l'AIU (bimestriel)

</td></tr>
</table>

Principales réunions ouvertes à tous les membres

* Conférence générale (quinquennale). Définit la politique générale de l'AIU et constitue une tribune mondiale pour la discussion des problèmes de l'enseignement supérieur.

IX ème Conférence générale: 5–11 août 1990, Université d'Helsinki
Thème: **Universalité, diversité, interdépendance: Les missions de l'université**

* Conférence intermédiaire des chefs des universités membres (entre les Conférences générales).

Rio de Janeiro 1988
Thème: **La Coopération universitaire internationale, une analyse critique: échecs, succès, perspectives**

(Une description complète de l'AIU est donnée p. 610)

WORLD LIST
OF UNIVERSITIES

EIGHTEENTH EDITION

LISTE MONDIALE
DES UNIVERSITES

DIX-HUITIEME EDITION

INTERNATIONAL ASSOCIATION OF UNIVERSITIES
ASSOCIATION INTERNATIONALE DES UNIVERSITES
1, rue Miollis, 75732 Paris Cedex 15

Editor/Rédacteur

F. EBERHARD

Assistant Editor/Rédactrice adjointe

ANN C. M. TAYLOR

Published biennially.
Eighteenth Edition 1990 published
in the United States and Canada by
STOCKTON PRESS
15 East 26th Street, New York, NY 10010

The Library of Congress has catalogued this
serial publication as follows:

Library of Congress Cataloging-in-Publication Data

World list of universities. Liste mondiale des universités.
    Paris, International Association of Universities.
        v. 24 cm.
Biennial.
    English and French.
    Continues: Liste mondiale.
    1.   Universities and colleges—Directories.   I. International Association
of Universities.   II. Title: Liste mondiale des universités.
L900.157   378   79-645502
ISBN 0-935859-86-1   MARC-S

Eighteenth Edition 1990 published in the United Kingdom by
MACMILLAN PUBLISHERS LTD (Journals Division)
Distributed by Globe Book Services Ltd,
Brunel Road, Houndmills, Basingstoke, Hants RG21 2XS

British Library Cataloguing in Publication Data

World list of universities. — 18th ed. –
    1989-90
    1.   Universities and colleges – Directories
    378′.0025   L900

Macmillan ISBN 0-333-47488-0
IAU ISBN 92-9002-051-2
ISSN 0084-1889

Typeset in Great Britain by Florencetype Ltd, Kewstoke, Avon
Printed and bound in Great Britain

For more detailed information about universities and other institutions of higher education, the following volumes, produced by officially recognized academic bodies, may be consulted:

Pour plus amples renseignements sur les universités et sur les autres établissements d'enseignement supérieur, on pourra se reporter aux volumes suivants, dont chacun est publié par un organisme académique reconnu:

AMERICAN UNIVERSITIES AND COLLEGES. Edited by the American Council on Education. 13th Edition, 1987. ISBN 089925179X. (Walter de Gruyter, Inc., 200 Saw Mill River Road, Hawthorne, NY 10532).

INTERNATIONAL HANDBOOK OF UNIVERSITIES. Edited by F. Eberhard. Macmillan ISBN 0-333-43642-3 IAU ISBN 92-9002-149-7 ISSN 0074-6215 (Macmillan Publishers Ltd for the International Association of Universities, 1, rue Miollis, 75732 Paris Cedex 15).

COMMONWEALTH UNIVERSITIES YEARBOOK. Edited by T. Craig. ISBN 0 85143 1135 ISSN 0069-7745 (Association of Commonwealth Universities, John Foster House, 36 Gordon Square, London WC1H 0PF). Distributed in North America by Stockton Press, 15 East 26th Street, New York, NY 10010.

★

FOREWORD

The *World List of Universities* is revised every two years in an attempt to remain up-to-date in relation to the continuingly rapid development of higher education in all parts of the world. The present edition, like its predecessors, is a world directory, including more than 9,000 universities and other institutions of higher education in 156 countries, and a guide to the principal national and international organizations concerned with higher education. In particular it includes information about bodies which have special responsibilities for interuniversity co-operation and for facilitating exchanges of academic staff and students.

Every effort has been made to ensure that the information published is authoritative, and the International Universities Bureau is grateful to central academic bodies and government departments in many countries and to the relevant international and regional organizations for their assistance in revising entries and providing new material.

The listing of institutions and organizations and the contents of the descriptive notes are based on information made available to the International Association of Universities. They do not imply any comment by the Association itself. For the first time, this edition also includes, as available, telephone, telefax, telex and cable details. If errors or omissions have occurred, corrections will be welcomed for inclusion in the next edition of the *World List of Universities*.

AVANT-PROPOS

La *Liste mondiale des Universités* est révisée tous les deux ans afin qu'elle reste autant que possible à jour par rapport au développement rapide et continu de l'enseignement supérieur dans le monde entier. Comme les précédentes, la présente édition constitue un répertoire mondial de plus de 9.000 universités et autres établissements d'enseignement supérieur de 156 pays et un guide des principales organisations nationales et internationales s'occupant d'enseignement supérieur. Elle comporte notamment des informations sur les organismes qui assument des responsabilités particulières en matière de coopération interuniversitaire et d'organisation des échanges d'enseignants et d'étudiants.

On s'est efforcé d'assurer aux informations publiées ici le maximum d'exactitude et le Bureau international des Universités remercie vivement les nombreux organismes universitaires nationaux et les services gouvernementaux, ainsi que les organisations internationales et régionales intéressées qui ont bien voulu l'aider à réviser et à renouveler sa documentation.

La liste des institutions et organisations et le contenu des notes descriptives reposent sur des renseignements communiqués à l'Association internationale des Universités et ne comportent aucun jugement propre de sa part. Pour la première fois, cette édition comporte aussi, si disponibles, les numéros de téléphone, téléfax, télex, et télégraphe. Si des erreurs ou des omissions se sont produites, toutes corrections seront accueillies avec reconnaissance en vue de la prochaine édition de la *Liste mondiale des Universités*.

TABLE OF CONTENTS
TABLE DES MATIERES

EXPLANATORY NOTE

The *World List of Universities* has been designed as a concise directory likely to be helpful in facilitating exchanges throughout the world of higher education. Its contents are arranged in two parts: the first contains information presented country by country about universities and other institutions of higher education and about national academic and student bodies; the second deals with international and regional organizations concerned with higher education.

PART ONE

Institutions and National Organizations

Information is classified under chapter headings for 156 countries and territories. These are placed in alphabetical order of their names in English, but indexes to both English and French names are provided (pages 701–706).

Each chapter begins with a list of the universities and other institutions of higher education in the country or territory concerned, and this is followed by information about national academic and student bodies.

(a) *Universities and other Institutions of Higher Education*

The terms "university" and "institution of higher education", as is well known, carry varying connotations. The selection of institutions for inclusion in the *World List of Universities* has, therefore, been based principally on the practices of the relevant national academic and educational bodies.

For countries with a considerable number of institutions, the entries are, as a rule, presented in two main groups:

(i) Universities (including where relevant technical universities and other multidisciplinary institutions having full university status);

(ii) Other Institutions of Higher Education.

In most cases, the second group is subdivided into institutions concerned with: Technical Education; Professional Education; Teacher Training; and General Education.

This classification has been adopted for the practical convenience of those consulting the *World List of Universities*, and should in no way be regarded as constituting an attempt at "evaluation" by the International Association of Universities. It should be noted that *independent* schools and faculties of theology have not been included, nor is reference made to military academies or similar institutions.

For each institution the following information is given: Its name (together with a translation into French or English where this appeared useful) and postal address; and the date (actual or legal) of its foundation. In a number of cases two or more dates are given; the first is that of the original foundation and the subsequent dates are those on which major changes took place, as for example a college founded in 1917 and accorded full university status in 1936.

Where appropriate, each entry also includes a note on the

composition of the institution by faculties, colleges, schools, departments or institutes. Abbreviations are used for both English and French terms and a bilingual key to them will be found on pages xvi–xxi. The information given in this way is simply indicative of the general nature of the institution and does not necessarily cover *all* principal fields of study. A Faculty of Medicine, for example, may or may not include dentistry, pharmacy or nursing; a Faculty of Philosophy covering the humanities may or may not include the social sciences. More detailed information may be found in another publication of the International Association of Universities, the *International Handbook of Universities*, and in its companion volumes, the *Commonwealth Universities Yearbook*, issued by the Association of Commonwealth Universities, London, and *American Universities and Colleges*, issued by the American Council of Education, Washington. Descriptions of university systems can be found in another reference work compiled by the International Association of Universities for Unesco: *World Guide to Higher Education: a comparative survey of systems, degrees and qualifications*, 1989, 3rd edition.

The title of the official (e.g., Secretary-General or Registrar) to whom general correspondence should usually be addressed is indicated for university institutions. It is given for the first university listed in each country and is the same for all universities of that country, unless otherwise stated.

Institutions marked with an asterisk (*) had been admitted to membership of the International Association of Universities.

(b) *National Academic and Student Bodies*

The second section of each chapter lists associations of universities; conferences or committees of rectors and vice-chancellors; associations of university teachers; university information offices; and students' associations and unions. Entries are also included for bodies which have special responsibility for matters related to the recognition of foreign degrees and diplomas. Where there is no such entry, such matters are usually dealt with either within the relevant Ministry of Education or Higher Education or by a national academic body such as a Conference of Rectors or National Council of Universities. Governmental agencies (usually Ministries of Education) able to provide information about higher education and National Commissions for Unesco are included as the last entry for each country or territory. Learned societies, scholarly bodies and other academic associations concerned with particular disciplines are not listed.

Many of these bodies have special responsibilities for facilitating academic interchange, offering services and assistance to foreign academic staff, graduates and students wishing to come to their respective countries or helping to arrange for their own students, graduates and academic staff to travel and work in universities abroad. In the few countries for which such bodies are not listed inquiries may be addressed directly to the universities themselves or to the Ministry of Education.

Descriptive notes are included for many of the principal organizations but not as a rule for those related to the international bodies which are described more fully in Part Two of the Volume. Where English is the language of the country concerned or the foreign language which may be used more commonly than French, the

descriptive note appears first in English followed, in italic print, by a translation into French. Conversely, the notes appear first in French when this is the dominant language and they are then followed by an English translation in italic print. Where international bodies have provided the addresses of their national branches or affiliates, they figure in the relevant chapters and connection with an international organization is indicated by the inclusion of its initials after the national names, e.g., Associazione nazionale Professori universitari di Ruolo (IAUPL).

United Nations University
European University Institute

The final section of Part One contains information about the United Nations University and the European University Institute.

PART TWO

This section constitutes a guide to the principal international and regional organizations concerned primarily with higher education. It includes entries for the International Association itself as well as for its nine Associate Members, and a special entry deals with the work of Unesco in this field. Descriptive notes in both English and French outline the history, aims, structure and activities of each organization; the texts for these notes, or the information for inclusion in them, were provided by the bodies themselves. A number of international organizations concerned with particular student activities are listed more briefly but, as in the case of the national chapters, references to learned societies, scholarly bodies and other academic associations concerned with particular disciplines have not been included.

NOTICE EXPLICATIVE

La *Liste mondiale des Universités* a été conçue comme un répertoire succinct susceptible de faciliter les échanges à travers le monde de l'enseignement supérieur dans son ensemble. Elle comprend deux parties: la première présente pays par pays des renseignements sur les universités et autres établissements d'enseignement supérieur, ainsi que sur les organismes universitaires et étudiants; la deuxième traite des organisations internationales et régionales s'occupant d'enseignement supérieur.

PREMIERE PARTIE

Etablissements et Organisations Nationales

Les renseignements sont classés par pays et territoires (au nombre de 156). Ceux-ci sont présentés dans l'ordre alphabétique de leur nom en anglais, mais un double index, anglais et français, est inclus (pages 701–706).

Chaque chapitre commence par une liste des universités et autres établissements d'enseignement supérieur dans le pays ou territoire intéressé, puis viennent des renseignements sur les organismes universitaires et étudiants nationaux.

(a) *Universités et autres institutions d'enseignement supérieur*

Les termes «université» et «institution d'enseignement supérieur» ont, on le sait, un contenu quelque peu variable selon les pays. La sélection des institutions figurant dans la *Liste mondiale des Universités* a été opérée principalement en fonction de l'usage des organismes académiques ou d'éducation des pays intéressés.

Pour les pays comptant un grand nombre d'institutions, celles-ci sont en règle générale réparties en deux rubriques principales:

(i) Universités (y compris, le cas échéant, les universités techniques et autres établissements pluridisciplinaires jouissant pleinement du statut universitaire;

(ii) Autres institutions d'enseignement supérieur.

Dans la plupart des cas, la seconde rubrique se trouve elle-même subdivisée en établissements d'enseignement technique; d'enseignement professionnel; de formation pédagogique; et d'enseignement général.

Cette classification n'a été adoptée que pour la commodité des usagers de la *Liste mondiale des Universités* et ne doit nullement être considérée comme une tentative «d'évaluation» de l'Association internationale des Universités. Il convient de noter que les écoles ou facultés *indépendantes* de théologie n'ont pas été mentionnées, non plus que les écoles de formation militaire.

On trouvera pour chaque institution les renseignements suivants: son nom (assorti, le cas échéant, de sa traduction anglaise ou française), son adresse et sa date (réelle ou légale) de fondation. Dans certains cas, deux dates ou plus sont indiquées: la première est la date primitive de fondation; les suivantes celles auxquelles des modifications importantes sont intervenues dans le statut de l'institu-

tion, comme, par exemple, un collège fondé en 1917, et qui a reçu le statut d'université en 1936.

Pour chaque institution, il est également fait mention, s'il y a lieu, de sa composition par facultés, collèges, écoles, départements ou instituts. A cette fin, des abréviations sont utilisées pour les termes tant anglais que français et on en trouvera le code, dans les deux langues, aux pages xvi–xxi. Ces indications ne font qu'indiquer le caractère général de l'établissement et n'embrassent pas nécessairement *toutes* les matières principales d'enseignement. C'est ainsi qu'une faculté de médecine peut ou non comporter une section d'odontologie, de pharmacie ou une école d'infirmières; une faculté de philosophie englobant les humanités peut ou non enseigner les sciences sociales. On trouvera à ce sujet des renseignements détaillés dans une autre publication de l'Association internationale des Universités, l'*International Handbook of Universities*, et dans l'ouvrage dont il constitue un complément, le *Commonwealth Universities Yearbook*, publié par l'Association of Commonwealth Universities, Londres, et *American Universities and Colleges*, publié par l'American Council on Education, Washington. Des descriptions des systèmes universitaires figurent dans un autre ouvrage de reférence préparé par l'Association internationale des Universités pour l'Unesco: *World Guide to Higher Education: a comparative survey of systems, degrees and qualifications*, troisième édition, 1989.

Le titre officiel de la personne à laquelle il convient habituellement d'adresser la correspondance générale (Secrétaire général, Registrar, etc.), est également indiqué pour les institutions universitaires. Il est donné pour l'université figurant en tête de la liste de chaque pays, et sauf indication contraire, il reste le même pour toutes les autres universités du pays considéré.

Les institutions marquées d'un astérisque (*) ont été admises à la qualité de membre de l'Association internationale des Universités.

(b) *Organismes nationaux universitaires et étudiants*

La deuxième section de chaque chapitre répertorie les associations d'universités, les conférences ou comités de recteurs et de vice-chanceliers, les associations d'enseignants universitaires, les bureaux d'information universitaire et les associations ou unions d'étudiants. Des notices ont également été incluses sur les organismes spécialement chargés de s'occuper des questions relatives à la reconnaissance des grades et diplômes étrangers. Dans les cas où il n'en existe pas, ces questions sont généralement réglées soit au sein du Ministère de l'Education ou de l'Enseignement supérieur concerné, soit par un organisme académique national (Conférence des Recteurs ou Conseil national des Universités, par exemple). Les services gouvernementaux (en général les ministères de l'éducation) qualifiés pour donner des renseignements en matière d'enseignement supérieur, ainsi que les Commissions nationales pour l'Unesco, ont été indiqués à la fin de la rubrique consacrée à chaque pays ou territoire. Les sociétés savantes, les organismes scientifiques et les associations académiques s'occupant de disciplines particulières, par contre, ne sont pas répertoriés.

Nombre de ces organismes s'emploient à faciliter les échanges universitaires, assurent des services aux enseignants, chercheurs et étudiants étrangers désireux de venir dans leurs pays respectifs ou apportent leur aide aux enseignants, chercheurs et étudiants nationaux désireux de travailler dans des universités étrangères.

Dans les quelques pays où aucun organisme de ce genre n'est mentionné, on pourra s'adresser directement aux universités elles-mêmes ou au ministère de l'éducation.

On trouvera des notes descriptives sur un grand nombre des organisations principales mais non, en règle générale, sur celles qui se rattachent aux organismes internationaux dont il est traité plus en détail dans la deuxième partie de l'ouvrage. Lorsque l'anglais est la langue du pays intéressé ou la langue étrangère la plus usitée, la note descriptive figure d'abord en anglais, suivie par une traduction française en italique. Inversement, la note paraît d'abord en français dans les cas où cette langue prédomine, et est alors suivie d'une traduction anglaise en italique. Là où les organismes internationaux ont indiqué les adresses de leurs sections ou adhérents nationaux, ceux-ci figurent sous les pays intéressés, leur lien avec une organisation internationale étant marqué par l'adjonction à leur nom du sigle de celle-ci: par ex. Associazione nazionale Professori universitari di Ruolo (IAUPL).

Université des Nations Unies
Institut Universitaire Européen

La dernière section de la première partie contient des renseignements sur l'Université des Nations Unies et l'Institut Universitaire Européen.

DEUXIEME PARTIE

Cette partie constitue un guide des principales organisations internationales et régionales s'occupant principalement d'enseignement supérieur. Elle comprend des rubriques consacrées tant à l'Association internationale elle-même qu'à ses neuf membres associés, ainsi qu'une rubrique traitant de l'œuvre de l'Unesco dans ce domaine. Des notes descriptives, données tant en anglais qu'en français passent brièvement en revue l'histoire, les buts, la structure et les activités de chaque organisme; les textes de ces notes ou les renseignements qui y figurent ont été fournis par les organismes eux-mêmes. Un certain nombre d'organisations internationales s'occupant de certaines activités particulières concernant les étudiants sont indiquées plus brièvement. Mais, pas plus que dans les chapitres consacrés aux différents pays, on n'a répertorié les sociétés savantes, les organismes scientifiques ou les associations académiques s'occupant de disciplines particulières.

ABBREVIATIONS—ABREVIATIONS

The following abbreviations have been used to indicate the composition of institutions by faculties, colleges, schools, departments, and institutes. Those of English terms appear in *italics* and are listed in column I; those of French terms appear in normal print and are listed in column II. The meaning of each abbreviation is given both in English (column III) and in French (column IV):

Les abréviations suivantes ont été utilisées pour indiquer la composition des établissements par facultés, collèges, écoles, départements et instituts. Les abréviations des termes anglais sont imprimées en *italique* dans la colonne I; et celles des termes français en caractères romains dans la colonne II. La signification de chaque abréviation est néanmoins donnée en anglais (colonne III) et en français (colonne IV):

acc	...	accountancy	comptabilité
...	dr	law	droit

Where abbreviations are hyphenated, they refer to faculties or departments with compound names:
Lorsque plusieurs abréviations sont jointes par un trait d'union, il s'agit de facultés ou départements à noms composés:

eco-soc	...	economics and social sciences	sciences économiques et sociales
...	phil-let	philosophy and letters	philosophie et lettres

ENGLISH	FRANCAIS	ENGLISH	FRANCAIS
A	A	Academy	Académie
acc	...	accountancy	comptabilité
acct	act	actuarial sciences	actuaries (sciences)
adm	adm	administration	administration
ad	ad	adult	adultes
aero	aéro	aeronautics	aéronautique
aff	aff	business/affairs	affaires
agr	agr	agronomy/agriculture	agronomie/agriculture
...	alim	food	alimentaire
Am	am	American	américain
an hus	...	animal husbandry	zootechnie
anc	anc	ancient	ancien
anim	anim	animal	animal
anth	anth	anthropology	anthropologie
app	app	applied	appliqué
arc	arc	architecture	architecture
archae	arché	archaeology	archéologie
...	arp	surveying	arpentage
arts	arts	arts/letters	lettres/arts
...	ass	insurance	assurances
astr	astr	astronomy	astronomie
athl	...	athletics	athlétisme
atm	atm	automation	automation
auto	auto	automobile	automobile
...	avic	aviculture	aviculture
ayur	...	ayurvedic medicine	médecine ayurvédique
B	...	Board(s)	Conseil(s)
...	ba	fine arts	beaux-arts
bact	bact	bacteriology	bactériologie

ENGLISH	FRANCAIS	ENGLISH	FRANCAIS
bank	banc	banking	bancaire
...	bât	building	bâtiment
...	bibl	library science	bibliothéconomie
bioch	bioch	biochemistry	biochimie
biol	biol	biology (sciences)	biologie (sciences)
bot	bot	botany	botanique
boudh	boud	Buddhism	bouddhisme
bui	...	building	bâtiment
bus	...	business	affaires
C	C	College	Collège
can	can	canon	canonique
cartog	cartog	cartography	cartographie
cath	cath	catholic	catholique
Ce	Ce	Centre	Centre
cer	cer	ceramics	céramique
ch	ch	chemistry (sciences)	chimie (sciences)
chir	chir	surgery	chirurgie
Chris	chré	Christian	chrétien
civ	civ	civil	civil
class	class	classics	classiques
clima	clima	climatology	climatologie
clin	clin	clinical	clinique
...	colon	colonial	colonial
com	com	commerce	commerce
...	comb	fuel	combustibles
commun	commun	communications	communications
...	comp	accountancy	comptabilité
comp	...	computer (sciences)/ computing	informatique
comty	comté	community	communauté
cons	cons	consular	consulaire
const	const	construction	construction
coop	coop	co-operative	coopérative
crim	crim	criminology	criminologie
cult	cult	culture	culture
cyb	cyb	cybernetics	cybernétique
D	D	Department/Division	Département/Division
decor	décor	decorative	décoration
dent	dent	dentistry	dentaire (art)
des	dess	design	dessin
dev	dév	development	développement
diet	diét	dietetics	diététique
dipl	dipl	diplomacy	diplomatie
div	...	divinity	théologie
...	doc	documentation	documentation
dom	dom	domestic	domestique
...	dr	law	droit
dram	dram	dramatic arts	dramatique (art)
...	E	School	Ecole
eccl	eccl	ecclesiastical	ecclésiastique
eco	éco	economics	économiques (sciences)
ecol	écol	ecology	écologie
ed	éd	education	éducation
elec	élec	electrical (engineering)	électrotechnique
electro	électro	electronics	électronique
...	élev	stockraising	élevage
energ	énerg	energetics	énergétique
eng	...	engineering	génie
...	ensg	education/teaching	enseignement
...	entrep	undertaking/business	entreprise

| --- | --- | --- | --- |
env	env	environmental	écologique
...	ét	studies	études
ethn	ethn	ethnology	ethnologie
...	étr	foreign	étranger
Eur	eur	Europe/European	europe/européen
...	évan	evangelical	évangélique
...	exp	expert	expert
expe	expé	experimental	expérimental
...	ext	abroad/foreign	extérieur
F	F	Faculty	Faculté
fa	...	fine arts	beaux-arts
fam	fam	family	familial
fash	...	fashion	mode
...	fem	feminine	féminin
...	ferm	brewing	fermentation
...	ferr	railway	ferroviaire
fgn	...	foreign	étranger
...	fiduc	accountancy	fiduciaire
...	fig	figurative arts	figuratifs (arts)
fin	fin	finance	finances
fish	...	fishery	pêche
...	fond	fundamental	fondamental
for	for	forestry	forestières (études)
fund	...	fundamental	fondamental
...	gé	engineering	génie
gen	gén	general	général
geod	géod	geodesy	géodésie
geog	géog	geography	géographie
geol	géol	geology	géologie
...	géom	geometry	géométrie
geophy	géophy	geophysics	géophysique
geosc	géosc	earth sciences	géosciences
Ger	ger	German	germanique
govt	...	government	gouvernement
grad	grad	graduate	gradué
graph	graph	graphic	graphique
heal	sa	health	santé
hist	hist	history	histoire .
hom	...	home	domestique
hort	hort	horticulture	horticulture
hous	...	household	ménagers (arts)
...	ht	high	haut(e)
hum	hum	humanities/human (sciences)	humaines(s) (sciences)
hyd	hyd	hydraulics	hydraulique
hyg	hyg	hygiene	hygiène
I	I	Institute	Institut
ind	ind	industry/industrial	industrie/industriel
...	inf	nursing	infirmières
infor	infor	information	information
...	inft	computer sciences	informatique
...	ing	engineer	ingénieur (sciences)
...	inor	inorganic	inorganique
ins	...	insurance	assurances
int	int	international	international
...	interp	interpretation	interprétariat
irrig	irrig	irrigation	irrigation
Isl	isl	Islamic	islamique
jour	jour	journalism	journalisme
...	jur	legal	juridique

ENGLISH	FRANCAIS	ENGLISH	FRANCAIS
L	L	Laboratory	Laboratoire
lab	lab	laboratory	laboratoire
lang	lang	language	langue
law	…	law	droit
let	let	letters	lettres
li	…	liberal	libéral
lib	…	library science	bibliothéconomie
ling	ling	linguistic(s)	linguistiques(s)
lit	lit	literature	littérature
mangt	…	management	gestion
mar	mar	maritime/marine	maritime/marine
…	march	merchandise	marchandises
…	masc	masculine	masculin
mater	matér	materials	matériaux
math	math	mathematics	mathématiques
mec	méc	mechanical (engineering)	mécanique (génie)
med	méd	medicine	médecine
medie	médié	medieval	médiéval
Medit	médit	Mediterranean	méditerranéen
…	mén	household	ménagers (arts)
met	mét	metallurgy	métallurgie
meteo	météo	meteorology	météorologie
microb	microb	microbiology	microbiologie
milit	…	military science	militaire (science)
mine	mine	mines/mining	mines/minier
miner	minér	mineralogy	minéralogie
mod	mod	modern	moderne
mus	mus	music	musique
nat	nat	natural (sciences)	naturelles (sciences)
nav	nav	naval	naval
…	nor	teacher training	normale (école)
nucl	nucl	nuclear	nucléaire
nurs	…	nursing	infirmières
nutr	nutr	nutrition	nutrition
…	obs	observatory	observatoire
obst	obst	obstetrics	obstétrique
occp	…	occupational	professionnel
oceanog	océanog	oceanography	océanographie
…	od	dentistry	odontologie
…	o-m	overseas	outre-mer
opt	opt	optics	optique
optom	optom	optometry	optométrie
org	org	organic	organique
orntl	orntl	oriental	oriental
…	ouv-pay	workers (industry-agriculture)	ouvrier-paysan
P	P	Programme	Programme
palae	paléo	palaeontology	paléontologie
pap	pap	paper technology	papeterie
…	pêch	fishery	pêche
ped	péd	pedagogics	pédagogie
pedi	pédi	pediatrics	pédiatrie
…	pédo	soil science	pédologie
…	pén	penal	pénal
pet	pét	petroleum	pétrole
phar	phar	pharmacy	pharmacie
phil	phil	philosophy	philosophie
phill	phill	philology	philologie
…	pho	phonetics	phonétique

ENGLISH	FRANCAIS	ENGLISH	FRANCAIS
phy	phy	physics	physique
phys	phys	physical (education)	physique (éducation)
physio	physio	physiotherapy	physiothérapie
pisci	pisci	pisciculture	pisciculture
plan	plan	planning	planification
plast	plast	plastic	plastique
pnt	pnt	painting	peinture
pol	pol	political science	politiques (sciences)
polytec	polytec	polytechnic	polytechnique
prac	prat	practical	pratique
prod	prod	production	production
prof	prof	professional	professionnel
prop	prop	propaedeutic	propédeutique
prot	prot	protestant	protestant
psyc	psyc	psychology	psychologie
publ	publ	public	publique/public
rad	rad	radiology	radiologie
recr	…	recreation	récréative (éducation)
…	rech	research	recherches
reg	rég	regional	régional
rel	rel	relations	relations
relig	relig	religion	religion
res	…	research	recherches
rur	rur	rural	rural
S	E	School	Ecole
…	sa	health	santé
…	sani	sanitary	sanitaire
sc	sc	science(s)	science(s)
…	scq	scientific	scientifique
sculp	sculp	sculpture	sculpture
sec	sec	secretarial studies	secrétariat
Sect	Sect	Section	Section
Sem	Sém	Seminary	Séminaire
serv	serv	service	service
soc	soc	social (sciences)	sociales (sciences)
socio	socio	sociology	sociologie
spe	spé	special	spécial
St, st	…	studies	études
stat	stat	statistics	statistique
stock	…	stockraising	élevage
…	stom	dentistry	stomatologie
…	sup	higher	supérieur
surg	…	surgery	chirurgie
surv	…	surveying	arpentage
synd	synd	syndicalism	syndicalisme
tec	tec	technical (sciences)	techniques (sciences)
techn	techn	technology	technologie
telec	téléc	telecommunications	télécommunications
tens	tens	tension	tension
tex	tex	textile	textile
theat	théât	theatre	théâtre
theo	théo	theology	théologie
theor	théor	theoretical	théorique
ther	thér	therapy/therapeutics	thérapeutique
topog	topog	topography	topographie
tour	tour	tourism	tourisme
…	trad	translation	traduction
trans	trans	transport	transports
…	trav	work	travail

ENGLISH	FRANCAIS	ENGLISH	FRANCAIS
trop	trop	tropical	tropical
U	U	University	Université
urb	urb	town-planning	urbanisme
ut	ut	Unit	Unité
vet	vét	veterinary medicine	vétérinaires (sciences)
vis	vis	visual	visuel
vit	vit	viticulture	viticulture
voc	...	vocational	professionnel
w	...	work	travail
west	...	western	occidental
wom	...	women	femmes
...	zoo	animal husbandry	zootechnie
zool	zool	zoology	zoologie

AFGHANISTAN
AFGHANISTAN

UNIVERSITIES — UNIVERSITES

*Kabul Pohantoon [Kabul U.], Kabul. (The Rector).   *1932, 1946, 1973*
Tel: 40341/3.
F : *med, phar, law, nat, lang-lit, Isl law, eng, agr, eco, vet, ed, stom, soc.*

University of Nengarhar, Jalalabad.   *1963*
  F : *med, agr, eng, ed.*
University of Islamic Studies, Kabul.   *1988*

OTHER INSTITUTIONS — AUTRES INSTITUTIONS

Kabul Polytechnic, Kabul.   *1967*
  F : *const, geol, electromec.*
Higher Agricultural Training Institute, Kabul.   *1971*
Communications Training Centre, Kabul.   *1964*
Institute of Finance and Management, Kabul.   *1971*
Junior Institute for Medical Education, Kabul.   *1979*
Higher Technical School, Balkh.   *1971*
Higher Technical School, Kabul.   *1974*
Institute of Pedagogy, Darull Aman Watt, Kabul.   *1983*
  D : *ch-biol, math, phy, Dari, Pashtu, English, soc st, lib.*
Balkh Higher Teachers' Training College, Balkh.   *1970*
Faryab Higher Teachers' Training College, Maimana City, Faryab Province.   *1978*
Helmand Higher Teachers' Training College, Lashkergah City, Helmand Province.   *1978*
Herat Higher Teachers' Training College, Herat City, Herat Province.   *1972*
Kandahar Higher Teachers' Training College, Kandahar City, Kandahar Province.   *1965*
Kundoz Higher Teachers' Training Institute, Kundoz.   *1970*
Nengarhar Higher Teachers' Training Institute, Jalalabad City, Nengarhar Province.   *1970*
Paktia Higher Teachers' Training Institute, Gerdiz City, Paktia Province.   *1970*

Parwan Higher Teachers' Training Institute, Parwan.
Roshan Higher Teachers' Training College, Shahi-de-Dosham sheera, Kabul.   *1965*
Samangan Higher Teachers' Training Institute, Aiback City, Samangan Province.   *1978*
Syed Jamaluddin Higher Teachers' Training College, Shier Shah Meena, Kabul.   *1941*
Takhar Higher Teachers' Training Institute, Kundoz City, Kundoz Province.
Institute of Physical Education and Sport, Kabul.   *1975*
Abu Haneefa Madrasa [I. of Religious Studies], Parwan Meena, Kabul.   *1964*
Abu Moslem Darul Uloom, Maimana City, Faryab Province.   *1936*
Arabic Darul Uloom, Andarahi Street, Kabul.   *1919*
Darul Uloom Asadea, Mazar-i-Shareef, Balkh Province.   *1936*
Fakhrul Madares Madrasa, Herat City.   *1933*
Jame Madrasa, Herat City.   *1923*
Mohammadia Madrasa, Kandahar City.   *1971*
Najmul Madares, Jalalabad City, Nengarhar Province.   *1931*
Ruhani Darul Uloom, Gerdiz City, Paktia Province.   *1972*
Takharistan Madrasa, Kundoz City.   *1939*

Democratic Youth Organization of Afghanistan –
  DYOA (IUS)
  Revolution Park, Kabul.
  Telex: 323 dem youth af
Ministry of Education
  Kabul.

Afghan National Commission for Unesco
  P.O. Box 717, Kabul.
  Tel: 717. Cables: unesco commission ministry education kabul

ALBANIA
ALBANIE

UNIVERSITIES — UNIVERSITES

Universiteti i Tiranës [U. de Tirana], Tiranë.
(M. le Recteur).   *1957*
Tél: 82–58. Télex: 060400/2211+
F : hist-phill, éco, pol-jur, nat, ing, gé civ, méd,
géol-mine, méc-élec.
  SECTION À BÉRAT.   *1968*
  ing.

  SECTION À ELBASAN.   *1970*
  ing, éco.
  SECTION À KORÇË.   *1969*
  ing, éco.
  SECTION À SHKODËR.   *1969*
  ing, éco.

OTHER INSTITUTIONS — AUTRES INSTITUTIONS

Instituti i Lartë Büjqësor [I. sup. d'Agriculture],
Tiranë.   *1951*
F : agr, vét, for, éco agr.
Instituti i Lartë Büjqësor, Korçë.   *1971*
F : agr.
Instituti i Lartë i Arteve [I. sup. des Arts],
Tiranë.   *1966*
F : arts fig, dram, mus, chorégraphie.
Instituti i Lartë i Kulturës Fizike «Vojo Kushi»

[I. sup. de Culture physique «Vojo Kushi»],
Tiranë.   *1958*
Instituti i Lartë Pedagogjik [I. sup. de Péda-
gogie], Elbasan. Tel: 27–82.   *1971*
phill-lit, math-phy, bioch.
Instituti i Lartë Pedagogjik, Gjirokastra.   *1971*
F : math-phy, hist-géog, bioch.
Instituti i Lartë Pedagogjik, Shkodra.   *1957*
F : phill-lit, bioch, math-phy, hist-géog.

**Union de la Jeunesse du Travail d'Albanie,
Section étudiante** — UJTA (IUS)
Boulevard Dëshmorët e Kombit, Tiranë.
Cables: brpsh tiranë.

*

Ministère de l'Education et de la Culture
Tiranë.
Commission nationale albanaise pour l'Unesco
Ministère des Affaires étrangères, Service de
l'Unesco, Tiranë.
Telex: 060400/4203+3. Cables: minjatm tirana.

REPUBLIC OF ALGERIA
REPUBLIQUE ALGERIENNE

UNIVERSITIES — UNIVERSITES

*Université d'Alger, 2 rue Didouche Mourad, Alger. (M. le Secrétaire général). *1909*
Tél: 64–69–70. Télex: 66529 unial dz
éco, dr-adm, jour, pol, soc-psyc, éd, orthophonie, bibl-doc, arché, hist, phil, lang-lit arabes, lang étr, trad-interp, sc méd.

*Université des Sciences et de la Technologie Houari Boumediène, B.P. 139, Dar-El-Beida, Alger. *1974*
Tél: 75–12–85. Télex: 54835 usta dz
I : math, phy, ch, biol, géol, électro.
E : ch.

Université d'Annaba, Annaba. *1975*
Tél: 83–34–29/30. Télex: 81847 uarto dz
éco, dr-adm, socio, lang-lit arabes, lang étr, biol, géol, sc exactes, ing, techn, sc méd.

Université de Constantine, Ain-El-Bey, Constantine. *1966, 1969*
Tél: 69–73–85. Télex: 92436 unczl dz
éco, dr-adm, socio, psyc-éd, lang étr, hist, lang-lit arabes, biol, vét, ind alim, géol, arc, sc exactes, phy, ch, sc méd, phys.

*Université d'Oran, Es Senia, Oran. *1961, 1966*
Tél: 38–79–67. Télex: 22993 uniorex oran
éco, dr-adm, soc-psyc, hist, démographie, lang-lit arabes, lang étr, biol-sc de la terre, sc méd, sc exactes, math, phy, ch.

Université des Sciences et de la Technologie d'Oran, Oran. *1974*

Tél: 34–19–63. Télex: 22701
électro-électrotec, méc, gé civ, optom.

Centre Universitaire de Batna, Batna. *1978*
Télex: 82070 ub dz
dr-adm, lang-lit arabes, biol, sc exactes, techn, éco, lang étr.

Centre Universitaire de Mostaganem, Mostaganem.
Tél: 26–46–62. Télex: 14022 uni mos
biol, sc exactes, phy.

*Instituts nationaux d'Enseignement supérieur de Sétif, Sétif. *1978, 1985*
Tél: 90–36–40. Télex: 86077 unset dz
éco, lang étr, biol, sc exactes, techn, arc, sc méd.

Centre Universitaire de Sidi-bel-Abbès, Sidi-bel-Abbès.
biol, sc exactes, phy.

Centre Universitaire de Tiaret, Tiaret (Tagdempt).
Tél: 28–62–18. Télex: 17062 cutia dz
sc exactes, biol.

Centre Universitaire de Tizi-Ouzou, Tizi-Ouzou.
Tél: 40–56–51. Télex: 76079 unive dz
éco, dr-adm, lang arabes, biol, sc exactes.

Centre Universitaire de Tlemcen, Tlemcen. *1974*
Télex: 18034 cut dz
éco, dr, lang-lit arabes, biol, sc exactes.

OTHER INSTITUTIONS — AUTRES INSTITUTIONS

Ecole normale supérieure, Kouba, Alger.
Ecole normale supérieure d'Enseignement polytechnique, Es Senia, Oran. *1970*
Ecole polytechnique d'Architecture et d'Urbanisme, El Harrach, Alger. *1970*
Ecole nationale vétérinaire, Avenue Pasteur, El-

Harrach, Alger.
Tél: 76–67–81
Institut national agronomique, El Harrach, Alger. *1966*
Tél: 76–19–87. Télex: 54802 ina dz.
Institut de Télécommunications d'Oran, Oran.

Ministère de l'Enseignement supérieur et de la Recherche scientifique
Route de Delly Brahim Ben Aknoun, Alger.
Tél: 64–47–54
Commission nationale algérienne pour l'Unesco et

l'Alecso
Ministère de l'Enseignement supérieur et de la Recherche scientifique, Route de Delly Brahim Ben Aknoun, Alger.
Tél: 64–47–54. Télex: 61460–66512

ANGOLA
ANGOLA

Universidade Agostinho Neto, Avenida 4 de Fevereiro 7, Caixa postal 815-C, Luanda. *1976* Tél: 37132. Télex: 3076 univela an

F : sc, méd, ing, dr, éco; agr (Huambo).
I : éd (Lubango).

Juventude do Partido-JMPL-JP (IUS), Avenida Comandante Valodia 152, Luanda. Tél: 33–81–92. Télex: 4116 jmpla jp an

*

Ministério da Educação
C.P. 1451, Luanda.
Tél: 37–010
Commission nationale angolaise pour l'Unesco
Ministère de l'Education, C.P. 1451, Luanda. Tél: 37–010. Télex: 4186 mirex an (attention comnat unesco)

ARGENTINA
ARGENTINE

UNIVERSITIES AND TECHNICAL UNIVERSITIES—
UNIVERSITES ET UNIVERSITES TECHNIQUES

Governmental Establishments—Etablissements publics

*Universidad de Buenos Aires, Viamonte 444, 1053 Buenos Aires. (Sr. Secretario General). *1821*
Tél: 311–9030. Télex: 18694 ibuba ar
F : agr, vét, arc-urb, ing, sc exactes-nat, pharbioch, éco, dr-soc, phil-let, méd, dent, psyc, soc.
Universidad Nacional de Catamarca, República 350, 4700 San Fernando del Valle de Catamarca. *1972*
Tél: (833) 2–5089
F : agr, sc app-techn, éco-adm, sc exactes-nat, hum, sa.
I : péd.
E : inf, arc.
Universidad Nacional del Centro de la Provincia de Buenos Aires, Pinto 399, 7000 Tandil (Buenos Aires). *1964, 1974*
Tél: 22062/3
F : vét, sc exactes, éco, hum; agr (Azul); ing; éco (Olavarría).

(Rectorado): commun soc, anth.
Universidad Nacional del Comahue, Buenos Aires 1400, Neuquén. *1964, 1971*
Tél: (943) 2–3596. Télex: 84266 uncnq ar
F : agr, ing, éco-adm, hum, tour; dr-soc (General Roca); éd (Cipolletti).
E : lang (General Roca).
Egalement 6 centres régionaux.
*Universidad Nacional de Córdoba, Obispo Trejo y Sanabria 242, 5000 Córdoba *1613*
Tél: (051) 46–418. Télex: 51822 bucor ar
F : arc-urb, sc exactes-phy-nat, ch, éco, dr-soc, phil-hum, méd, dent, agr, math-astr-phy.
I : tec.
E : serv soc, arts, lang, méd, diét, ing, inf, sa, inf, phonoaudiologie, kinésithér.
Universidad Nacional de Cuyo, Parque General San Martín, 5500 Mendoza. *1939*
Tél: (61) 253219. Télex: 55267 medoz ar
F : agr, ing, éco, pol-soc, phil-let, méd, dr, arts, dent.

I : phy (San Carlos de Bariloche).
E : mus, dess, théât, éd, arts plast, cer.
Egalement 2 centres régionaux.

Universidad Nacional de Entre Ríos, 8 de Junio 600, 3260 Concepción del Uruguay (Entre Ríos). *1973*
Tél: (442) 5573
F : agr, ing, éco, éd, bromatologie, serv soc, (Paraná); adm, alim (Concordía).

Universidad Nacional de Jujuy, Gorriti 237, 4600 San Salvador de Jujuy. *1973*
Tél: (882) 25617. Télex: 66102 tunju ar
F : agr, ing, éco, hum-soc.

Universidad Nacional de La Pampa, 9 de Julio 149, 6300 Santa Rosa (La Pampa). *1958, 1973*
Tél: 3109. Télex: 83132 ulpam ar
F : agr, vét, sc exactes-nat, éco, hum, ing.
D : phil-péd.

Universidad Nacional de La Patagonia «San Juan Bosco», Sarmiente 95, 5000 Comodoro Rivadavia (Chubut). *1973, 1980*
Tél: (967) 23396. Télex: 86022 unpcr ar
F : ing, éco, hum nat; éco, ing, nat, hum (Trelew); ing, nat, éco (Esquel); ing, nat (Puerto Madryn); ing, hum (Ushuaia).

Universidad Nacional de La Plata, Calle 7 No. 776, 1900 La Plata (Buenos Aires). *1890*
Tél: 215501. Télex: 31151 bulap ar
F : agr, vét, arc-urb, ing, sc exactes, nat, astr-géophy, éco, dr-soc, hum-éd, méd, ba, dent.
E : for, jour, obst, serv soc-sa.

Universidad Nacional de Litoral, Boulevard Pellegrini 2750, 3000 Sante Fe. *1889, 1919*
Tél: (42) 34461. Télex: 48153 inlit ar
F : éco, ing, gé ch, adm, dr-soc, bioch-biol, arc-urb; agr-vét (Esperanza).
I : mus.
E : péd, sa; alim (Reconquista, Gálvez).

Universidad Nacional del Lomas de Zamora, Camino de Cintura Km. 2, 1832 Lomas de Zamora (Buenos Aires). *1972*
Tél: 244–4358. Télex: 22067 calom ar
F : ing-agr, éco, ing, dr
(Rectorado): serv soc.

Universidad Nacional de Luján, Ruta 5Km. 70, 6700 Luján (Buenos Aires). *1972*
Tél: (323) 23171
D : agr, alim, adm, soc, éd, géo, hist.
Egalement 3 centres régionaux.

Universidad Nacional de Mar del Plata, Boulevard J.B. Albberdi 2695, 7600 Mar del Plata (Buenos Aires). *1961, 1975*
Tél: 39676. Télex: 398750 cop ar
F : dr, arc-urb, ing, éco-soc, sc exactes-nat, hum; agr (Balcarce).
E : psyc.
Ce : sa.

Universidad Nacional de Misiones, Junín 418, 3300 Posadas (Misiones). *1973*

Tél: (752) 26916. Télex: 76197
F : éco, sc exactes-nat-ch, hum-soc; ing-électro-méc, arts (Oberá); for (Eldorado).
E : inf.

Universidad Nacional del Nordeste, 25 de Mayo 868, 3400 Corrientes. *1956*
Tél: (783) 25060
F : agr, vét, sc exactes-nat-agr, dr-soc-pol, méd, dent; éd agr, for (Formosa); arc-urb, ing, éco, hum (Resistencia); gé ind agr (Presidente Roque Sáenz Peña).
I : dess, éd
(Rectorado): com, commun-tour.

Universidad Nacional de Río Cuarto, Campus Universitario, Enlace Rutas 6 y 36 Km. 603, 5800 Río Cuarto (Córdoba).
Tél: 24616. Télex: 54572 cunrc ar
F : agr-vét, ing, sc exactes-phy-ch-nat, éco, hum.

Universidad Nacional de Rosario, Córdoba 1814, 2000 Rosario (Santa Fe). *1968*
Tél: 49492. Télex: 4817 ciros ar
F : agr, sc exactes-ing, bioch-phar, arc-plan-dess, hum-arts, éco, dr, pol-rel int, méd, dent; vét (Casilda).

Universidad Nacional de Salta, Buenos Aires 177, 4400 Salta. *1972*
Tél: (87) 223200
F : techn, sc exactes, nat, éco-sc jur-soc, hum, sa.
Egalement 2 centres régionaux.

Universidad Nacional de San Juan, Avenida Libertador Gral-San Martín 1109 Oeste, 5400 San Juan. *1973*
Tél: 228750. Télex: 59100
F : ing, arc, sc exactes-nat-phy, soc, phil-hum-arts.

Universidad Nacional de San Luis, Lavalle 1189, 5700 San Luis. *1973*
Tél: 24689. Télex: 58125 unsl ar
F : ch-bioch-phar, phy math-nat, éd; ing-adm (Mercedes).

Universidad Nacional de Santiago del Estero, Avenida Belgrano 1912, 4200 Santiago del Estero. *1973*
Tél: (85) 222595. Télex: 64120 unset ar
F : agr-agroind, for, sc exactes-techn, hum.

Universidad Nacional del Sur, Avenida Colón 80, 8000 Bahía Blanca (Buenos Aires). *1956*
Tél: (91) 24986. Télex: 81712 dujor ar
D : agr, ing, électro, biol, géol, ch-ing ch, phy, éco, géog, hum, math, adm.

Universidad Provincial de La Rioja, Avenida Ortíz de Ocampo 1700, 5300 La Rioja. *1972*
Tél: 2–8836.
F : agr, adm, serv soc, péd, inf; for (Chamical); ing agr, éd (Chilecito).

Universidad Tecnológica Nacional, Sarmiento 440, 1041 Buenos Aires. *1959*

Tél: 394–9280. Télex: 48247 utnsf ar
Facultés régionales à : Avellaneda, Bahía
Blanca, Buenos Aires, Concepción del Uru-
guay, Córdoba, Delta, General Pacheco,
Haedo, La Plata, Mendoza, Paraná, Resisten-
cia, Rosario, San Nicolás, Santa Fe, San Miguel
de Tucumán.
Egalement 13 centres régionaux.
*Universidad Nacional de Tucumán, Calle Aya-
cucho 491, 4000 San Miguel de Tucumán. *1912*
Tél: 217123. Télex: 61–143 butuc ar

F : agr-zoo, arc-urb, sc exactes-techn, bioch-ch-
phar, éco, dr-soc, phil-let, dent, méd, nat, arts.
E : phys, arts mus, inf.
Academia Superior de Estudios Policiales,
Rosario 532, 1424 Buenos Aires. *1977*
Tél: 99–2426.
Escuela de Ingeniería Aeronáutica, Avenida
Fuerza Aérea Argentina Km. 51/2, Guarnición
Aérea, 5000 Córdoba. *1971*
Tél: 63958

Private Establishments—Etablissements privés

*Pontificia Universidad Católica Argentina
«Santa María de los Buenos Aires», Juncal
1912, 1116 Buenos Aires. *1959*
Tél: 44–1035
F : agr, phy-math-ing, soc-éco, dr-pol, phil-let,
théo, arts-sc mus; dr-soc (Rosario); hum-éd
(Mendoza).
I : cult.
Egalement 2 établissements annexes et 2
centres régionaux.
Universidad del Aconcagua, Catamarca 147, 5500
Mendoza. *1973*
Tél: 24–1257
F : éco-com, soc-adm, psyc, phonoaudiologie.
Universidad Argentina de la Empresa, Libertad
1340, 1016 Buenos Aires. *1972*
Tél: 42–1546
F : agr, ing, adm, éco, dr-soc.
Universidad Argentina «John F. Kennedy»
Bartolomé Mitre 1407, Buenos Aires. *1968*
Tél: 45–4338
E : adm, comp publ, pol, serv soc, jour-
commun, rel publ, socio, démographie-tour,
éd, psyc, arc, arts-théât, analyse des systèmes,
psycopéd.
*Universidad de Belgrano, Federico Lacroze
1959, 1426 Buenos Aires. *1970*
Tél: 772–4014/18. Télex: 18658
F : arc-urb, éco, dr-soc, hum, agr, ing, techn.
*Universidad Católica de Córdoba, Obispo Trejo
y Sanabria 323, 5000 Córdoba. *1959*
Tél: 42210; 38389
F : agr, arc, ing, ch, éco-adm, dr-soc, phil-hum,
méd, pol-rel int.
I : adm.
Universidad Católica de Cuyo, Avenida José I. de
la Roza 1516, Oeste, 5400 Rivadavia (San
Juan). *1963*
Tél: 230291
F : alim, éco, dr-soc, phil-hum; adm-tour (Men-
doza); serv soc (San Luis).
E : inf.
Universidad Católica de La Plata, Calle 13 No.
1227, 1900 La Plata. *1971*

Tél: 21–41291
F : arc, math app, éco, dr, soc, éd.
Universidad Católica de Salta, Casilla de Correo
18, 4428 Campo Castañares (Salta). *1968*
Tél: 219000
F : ing, éco-adm des aff, arts-sc, dr, arc-urb.
E : serv soc, phys, péd.
Universidad Católica de Santa Fe, Echagüe 7151,
3000 Santa Fe. *1960*
Tél: 63030
F : arc, éco, dr, éd, phil, hist, let, édaphologie.
*Universidad Católica de Santiago del Estero,
Libertad 321, Santiago del Estero. *1969*
Tél: (85) 21–3820
F : éco, pol-soc-jur, éd, math app.
**Universidad de Concepción del Uruguay «La
Fraternidad»**, 8 de Junio 522, 3260 Concepción
del Uruguay (Entre Ríos). *1971*
Tél: 7721
F : éco, arc-urb, agr.
(Rectorado): péd.
Universidad «Juan Agustín Maza», Salta 1690,
5500 Mendoza. *1963*
Tél: 251998
F : ing, phy-math, phar-bioch, jour; oenologie
(Rodeo del Medio).
E : nutr.
Universidad de la Marina Mercante, Billinghurst
376, 1174 Buenos Aires. *1974*
Tél: 871130
F : ing, adm-éco.
Universidad de Mendoza, Avenida Boulogne-
sur-Mer 665, 5500 Mendoza. *1962*
Tél: 247017
F : arc-urb, élec-électro, sc jur-soc.
Universidad de Morón, Cabildo 134, 1708 Morón
(Buenos Aires). *1972*
Tél: 629–2404
F : agr, ing, ch-nat-sc exactes, éco, dr-soc, phil-
let, arc, tour, arts, infor-commun.
E : inf.
I : ét des aff.
D : péd.
Universidad del Museo Social Argentino, Aven-

ida Corrientes 1723, 1042 Buenos Aires. *1961*
Tél: 40–6924
F : pol-jur-soc, serv soc, infor, eugénisme-hum, réinsertion soc.
E : choral, trad française.
Universidad del Norte «Santo Tomás de Aquino», 9 de Julio 165, 4000 San Miguel de Tucumán. *1958*
Tél: (81) 22–8805
F : éco, adm, sc jur-soc, adm, anth-psyc, ing, hum, phil, théo.
I : trav soc.
Universidad Notarial Argentina, Calle 51 No. 435, 1900 La Plata (Buenos Aires). *1968*
Tél: 212–9283
Sections à : Buenos Aires, Córdoba, Chaco, Pergamino, Santa Fe, Republica del Paraguay.
*Universidad del Salvador, Rodríguez Peña 640, 1020 Buenos Aires. *1959*
Tél: 495531. Télex: 18691 eiras ar
F : éd-commun soc, sc jur, soc, phil, hist-let, méd, psyc, psycpéd; théo, phil (San Miguel).
E : ét orntl, adm, art scénique, ch, comp publ, éco.
Centro de Altos Estudios en Ciencias Exactas, Avenida de Mayo 1396, 1085 Buenos Aires. *1968*
Tél: 373815
Escuela Universitaria de Teología, Pasaje Catedral 1750, 7600 Mar del Plata (Buenos Aires). *1964*
Tél: 28633
Instituto Tecnológico de Buenos Aires, Avenida Emilio Madero 351, 1106 Buenos Aires. *1960*
Tél: 34–7748

OTHER INSTITUTIONS — AUTRES INSTITUTIONS

Professional Education — Enseignement professionnel

Escuela Nacional de Bellas Artes «Rogelio Yrutia», Colón 428, Azul (Buenos Aires).
Escuela Nacional de Bellas Artes «Manuel Belgrano», Cerrito 1350, Buenos Aires.
Escuela Superior de Bellas Artes «Ernesto de la Cáreova», Avenida Costanera esq. Brasil, Buenos Aires.
Instituto Nacional de Bellas Artes «Prilidiano Pueyrredón», Las Heras 1749, Buenos Aires.
Instituto Santa Ana, Avenida del Libertador 6115/95, Buenos Aires.
dess, pnt, mus.
Instituto «Monseñor Juan M. Terrero», Calle II No. 675, La Plata (Buenos Aires).
arts vis.
Instituto del Profesorado Secundario de Artes Plásticas, La Rioja.
Escuela de Artes Visuales «Martín Malaharro», Funes 1357/71, Mar del Plata (Buenos Aires).
Instituto Superior del Profesorado «Antonio Ruíz de Montoya», Buenos Aires 285, Posadas (Misiones).
dess, pnt.
Academia de Bellas Artes, Tucumán 450, Resistencia (Chaco).
Escuela Provincial de Bellas Artes «Tomás Cabrera», Zuviría 465, Salta.
Academia Nacional de Bellas Artes del Norte «Juan Yepari», Avenida Belgrano Sur 1289, Santiago del Estero.
Escuela Nacional de Bibliotecarios, Biblioteca Nacional, Méjico 564, Buenos Aires.
Escuela Superior de Bibliotecología, Calle 44 Mo. 790, La Plata (Buenos Aires).
Escuela de Bibliotecología, San Martín 3459, Santa Fe.
Escuela Nacional de Cerámica, Bulnes 43, Buenos Aires.
Escuela de Cerámica de Mar del Plata, Dorrego 2081, Mar del Plata (Buenos Aires).
Escuela Nacional de Danzas, Esmeralda 285, Buenos Aires.
Escuela de Danzas Clásicas, Calle 10 entre 51 y 53, Mar del Plata (Buenos Aires).
Escuela Nacional de Arte Dramático, French 3614, Buenos Aires.
Escuela de Ciencias Económicas, La Rioja.
Instituto Superior de Ciencias Económicas, Ministerio de Gobierno, Justicia y Educación, Otero 369, San Salvador de Jujuy (Jujuy).
Escuela Superior de Enfermería, Saavedra 2149, Santa Fe.
Escuela Superior de Ciencias de la Información y Relaciones Públicas, Garibaldi 267, Mendoza.
Conservatorio de Música de Bahía Blanca, Dorrego 120, Bahía Blanca (Buenos Aires).
Conservatorio de Música «Julián Aguirre», Gral. Rodríguez 7672, Banfield (Buenos Aires).
Conservatorio Nacional de Música «Carlos López Buchardo», Callao 1521, Buenos Aires.
Conservatorio Municipal de Música «Manuel de Falla», Corrientes 1530, Teatro municipal, Gral. San Martín, Buenos Aires.
Conservatorio de Música de Chascomus, Lavalle 281, Chascomus (Buenos Aires).
Conservatorio de Música de Chivilcoy, Calle Frias 37, Chivilcoy (Buenos Aires).
Conservatorio de Música de La Plata, Calle 7 No.

1141, La Plata (Buenos Aires).
Conservatorio de Música, Dorrego 2071, Mar del Plata (Buenos Aires).
Instituto Cuyano de Cultura Musical, Boulogne-sur-Mer 1685, Mendoza.
Conservatorio Municipal «Manuel Aguirre», Rauch y Salta, Morón (Buenos Aires).
Escuela de Música, Avenida 9 de Julio, Resistencia (Chaco).
Instituto de Servicio Social de Avellaneda, French 146, Avellaneda (Buenos Aires).

Escuela de Servicio Social, Joaquín V. González 230, La Rioja.
Escuela Superior de Servicio Social, Julio A. Roca 343, Mendoza.
Instituto Superior de Servicio Social, Don Bosco 492, Gral. Roca, Río Negro.
Escuela de Servicio Social de Rosario, Córdoba 1770, Rosario (Santa Fe).
Escuela de Servicio Social, San Martín 2337, Santa Fe.

Teacher Training—Formation pédagogique

Instituto Nacional de Enseñanza Superior No. 1, Córdoba 1951, Buenos Aires.
Instituto Nacional de Enseñanza Superior No. 2, Gral Urquiza 269, Buenos Aires.
Instituto Nacional de Enseñanza Superior «Dr. Joaquín V. González», Rivadavia 3577 (San Juan).
Instituto Nacional de Enseñanza Superior «S. Eccleston», Figueroa Alcorta y Dorrego, Buenos Aires.
Instituto Nacional de Enseñanza Superior en L.V. «J.R. Fernández», Carlos Pellegrini 1455, Buenos Aires.
Instituto Nacional de Enseñanza Superior «J.B. Justo», Lascano 3810, Buenos Aires.
Instituto Nacional de Enseñanza Superior de Moreno, Ruta 7, Km. 35, Moreno.
Instituto Nacional de Enseñanza Superior de Azul, 25 de Mayo 783, Azul (Buenos Aires).
Instituto Nacional de Enseñanza Superior de City Bell, Nirvana Esq. 23, City Bell.
Instituto Nacional de Enseñanza Superior de Lincoln, Av. Leandro Alem 1950, Lincoln (Buenos Aires).
Instituto Nacional de Enseñanza Superior de Pehuajó, José Hernández 250, Pehuajó (Buenos Aires).
Instituto Nacional de Enseñanza Superior de Pergamino, Av. Colón 725, Pergamino (Buenos Aires).
Instituto Nacional de Enseñanza Superior de San Nicolás, Plaza 23 de Noviembre, San Nicolás (Santa Fe).
Instituto Nacional de Enseñanza Superior de Bell Ville, 25 de Mayo 135, Bell Ville (Córdoba).
Instituto Nacional de Enseñanza Superior de Capilla del Monte, Hipólito Yrigoyen 450, Capilla del Monte (Córdoba).
Instituto Nacional de Enseñanza Superior de Córdoba, Av. Colón 951, Córdoba.
Instituto Nacional de Enseñanza Superior de Cruz del Eje, Sarmiento 1155, Cruz del Eje (Córdoba).
Instituto Nacional de Enseñanza Superior de

Laboulaye, Independencia 475, Laboulaye (Córdoba).
Instituto Nacional de Enseñanza Superior de Villa María, Santiago del Estero 618 Villia María, (Córdoba).
Instituto Nacional de Enseñanza Superior de Concepión del Uruguay, Jordana 50, Concepcíon del Uruguay (Entre Ríos).
Instituto Nacional de Enseñanza Superior de Gualeguay-Melitó, Juárez 25, Gualeguay (Entre Ríos).
Instituto Nacional de Enseñanza Superior de Gualeguaychú, Gervasio Méndez 676, Gualeguaychú (Entre Ríos).
Instituto Nacional de Enseñanza Superior de Paraná, Corrientes y Urquiza, Paraná (Entre Ríos).
Instituto Nacional de Enseñanza Superior de Villa Hernandaria, Eva Perón 220 Villa Hernandarias (Entre Ríos).
Instituto Nacional de Enseñanza Superior de San Salvador de Jujuy, San Martín 750, San Salvador de Jujuy (Jujuy).
Instituto Nacional de Enseñanza Superior de La Rioja, Pelagio B. Luna 749, La Rioja.
Instituto Nacional de Enseñanza Superior de San Rafael, Barcala 14, San Rafael (Mendoza).
Instituto Nacional de Enseñanza Superior de Tupungato, Alte. Brown s/n, Tupungato (Mendoza).
Instituto Nacional de Enseñanza Superior de Eugenio Bustos, Arenales y Belgrano, Eugenio Bustos (Mendoza).
Instituto Nacional de Enseñanza Superior de San Juan, Av. Alem 31 Sur, San Juan.
Instituto Nacional de Enseñanza Superior de San Luis, Rivadavia 774, San Luis.
Instituto Nacional de Enseñanza Superior de Rosario, Corrientes 1191, Rosario (Santa Fe).
Instituto Nacional de Enseñanza Superior «Galileo Galilei» de Rosario, Bv. Oroño 1145 Rosario (Sante Fe).
Instituto Nacional de Enseñanza Superior de Santiago del Estero, Independencia 751,

Santiago del Estero.

Instituto Nacional de Enseñanza Superior de San Miguel de Tucumán, Muñecas 219, San Miguel de Tucumán (Tucumán).

Instituto Nacional de Enseñanza Superior de Ushuaia, 12 de Octubre 383, Ushuaia (Tierra del Fuego).

Instituto de Perfeccionamiento Docente, Rivadavia 880, Azul (Buenos Aires).

Instituto de Perfeccionamiento Docente, Vieytes 51, Bahía Blanca (Buenos Aires).

Instituto de Perfeccionamiento Docente, 9 de Julio 1158, Campana (Buenos Aires).

Instituto de Perfeccionamiento Docente, General Paz 8, Chivilcoy (Buenos Aires).

Instituto de Perfeccionamiento Docente, Calle 12 entre 67 y 68, La Plata (Buenos Aires).

Instituto de Perfeccionamiento Docente, 25 de Mayo 254, Lincoln (Buenos Aires).

Instituto de Perfeccionamiento Docente, Garibaldi 253, Lomas de Zamora (Buenos Aires).

Instituto de Perfeccionamiento Docente, Calle 24 No. 338, Mercedes (Buenos Aires).

Instituto de Perfeccionamiento Docente, Gutiérrez 515, Pehuajó (Buenos Aires).

Instituto de Perfeccionamiento Docente, 11 de Septiembre 812, Pergamino (Buenos Aires).

Instituto de Perfeccionamiento Docente, Belgrano y Almafuerte, Saladillo (Buenos Aires).

Instituto Nacional de Educación Física «Dr. Enrique Romero Brest», Avenida Libertador Gral. San Martín 7101, Buenos Aires.

Instituto Nacional de Educación Física «General Belgrano», Avenida Libertador Gral. San Martín 7101, Buenos Aires.

Instituto del Profesorado en Educación Física, Ministerio de Educación y Cultura, Poeta Lugones 447, Córdoba.

Instituto Nacional de Educación Física de Mendoza, Belgrado 441, Mendoza.

Instituto Superior del Profesorado en Educación Física, Chacabuco 1365, Rosario (Santa Fe).

Instituto Nacional de Educación Física de Santa Fe, San Jerónimo 3139, Santa Fe.

Instituto Nacional de Profesorado Secundario, Boulevard Belgrano y Junín, Catamarca.

Instituto Nacional Superior del Profesorado, Avenida de Mayo 1396, Buenos Aires.

Instituto Superior del Profesorado, San Martín 1152, Corondo (Santa Fe).

Instituto Superior del Profesorado «José Manuel Estrada», Mariano 1, Loza 824, Goya (Corrientes).

Instituto Superior del Profesorado (Idiomas y Letras), Mitre 929, Gral. Roca (Río Negro).

Instituto Superior del Profesorado de Misiones, Tucumán 448, Posadas (Misiones).

Instituto Superior del Profesorado, Alvear y Ludueña, Casilla de Correo 35, Reconquista (Santa Fe).

Instituto Superior del Profesorado (Ciencias Exactas) «Biblioteca D.F. Sarmiento», San Carlos de Bariloche (Río Negro).

Instituto Nacional del Profesorado Secundario «D.F. Sarmiento», Santiago del Estero 48 (Sur).

Instituto Nacional del Profesorado Secundario, Avenida Estrugamous 250, Venado Tuerto (Santa Fe).

Instituto Superior del Profesorado (Humanidades), San Martín 246, Viedma (Río Negro).

Instituto Superior del Profesorado de Villa Constitución, Gral. López 1331, Villa Constitución (Santa Fe).

Facultad de Antropología Escolar, Martínez de Rosas 829, Ciudad de Mendoza. *1971*

Escuela Normal de Maestras No. 6 y Profesorado de Economía Doméstica, Güemes 3859, Buenos Aires.

Instituto Superior de Educación de la Comunidad de la Capital Federal, Rodríguez Peña 744, Buenos Aires.

Instituto Superior de Educación Rural, Casilla de Correo 77, Tandil (Buenos Aires).

Escuela Normal de Maestros para Ciegos, Hipólito Yrigoyen 2850, Buenos Aires.

Instituto Superior de Especialización Docente para la Enseñanza Diferenciada, Calle 2 No. 639, La Plata (Buenos Aires).

Instituto Experimental del Mogólico, Carlos Calvo 3176, Buenos Aires.

Instituto de Psicopedagogía y Educación Diferenciada «Dr. Domingo Cabret», Hipólito Yrigoyen 115, Córdoba.

Instituto Nacional de Sordomudos «Profesor Bartolomé Ayrolo», Avenida Lincoln 4325, Buenos Aires.

Instituto Nacional de Niñas Sordomudas, Austria 2561–93, Buenos Aires.

Consejo de Rectores de Universidades Nacionales de Argentina

Le Conseil, créé en vertu d'un décret de 1977, remplace l'ancien Conseil créé en 1967. Il est composé des recteurs et des présidents des universités nationales. Ses réunions sont organisées par le Ministre, auquel le Conseil adresse des recommandations. Le Secrétariat des affaires universitaires du Ministère assure au Conseil des services d'ordre administratif.

Il appartient notamment au Conseil de coordonner les activités des universités; de formuler des recommandations relatives à la création, à la réorganisation ou à la suppression de facultés et de départements; de participer à la planification et à l'évaluation de la politique universitaire; d'adresser au Ministère des recommandations concernant le développement des universités nationales; de participer à des études portant sur la création, l'approbation et le fonctionnement des universités nationales, provinciales et privées; de formuler des recommandations applicables à toutes les universités dans les domaines de la recherche, de l'admission à l'enseignement supérieur, des règlements universitaires, du statut du personnel enseignant, etc . . .

The Council, established by decree in 1977, replaces the former Council set up in 1967. It is composed of the rectors and presidents of the national universities. Meetings of the Council are convened by the Minister to whom it makes recommendations. Administrative services for it are provided by the Secretariat of University Affairs of the Ministry.

The responsibilities of the Council include: coordination of the activities of the universities; the formulation of recommendations for the creation, reorganization or dissolution of faculties and departments; participation in the planning and evaluation of university policy; the making of recommendations to the Ministry for the development of national universities; participation in studies concerned with the creation, authorization and operation of national, provincial and private universities; the formulation of recommendations applicable to all universities in matters of research, *admissions, academic regulations and the status of academic staff, etc.*
Président: Guillermo G. Gallo.
Avenida Eduardo Madero 235, Buenos Aires.

Federación Argentina de Mujeres Universitarias (IFUW)
Rosario de Santa Fé 236, 5000 Córdoba.
Servicio Universitario Mundial (WUS)
Talcahuano 889, 1013 Buenos Aires.
Tél: 393–1537.
Federación Universitaria Argentina—FUA (IUS)
Córdoba 1814, Rosario 2000.
Télex: 41817 Att. FUA C. Díaz.
Agrupación de Profesionales de la Acción Católica Argentina (Pax Romana)
Président: Luis Llorens.
Secrétaire: Susana Rodríguez Villamil.
Avenida de Mayo 621, Buenos Aires.
Juventud Universitaria Católica (Pax Romana)
Zapiola 427, Bahía Blanca, Buenos Aires.
Movimiento Argentino de Juventud pro Naciones Unidas (ISMUN)
Cafferata 1240, Rosario, Santa Fe.
F.U.S.L.A. (WUJS)
Correspondant: 89 Chaussee De Vleurgut, 1050 Brussels (Belgium).
Tél: (2) 647–7279. Télex: 2065 b.

*

Ministerio de Educación y Justicia
Buenos Aires.
Tél: 423461. Télex: 22646 mejop ar
Comisión Nacional Argentina para la Unesco
Pizzurno 935, 1020 Buenos Aires.
Tél: 42–8487. Cables: conaplu buenos aires

AUSTRALIA
AUSTRALIE

UNIVERSITIES AND UNIVERSITY COLLEGES—
UNIVERSITES ET COLLEGES UNIVERSITAIRES

*University of Adelaide, GPO Box 498, Adelaide, South Australia 5001. (The Registrar). *1876*
Tel: (82) 223 4333. Telex: 89141 univad aa
F : *arts, sc, law, med, mus, agr sc, eng, dent, eco, arc & plan, math sc.*

*Australian National University, GPO Box 4, Canberra, A.C.T. 2601. *1946*
Tel: (62) 49 5111. Fax: (062) 48 9062. Telex: 62760 natuni aa. Cables: natuni canberra
F : *arts, sc, eco-com, law, Asian st.*
S : *biol sc, ch, Pacific st, phy sc, soc, med sc, earth sc* (all research).

Bond University, Private Bag 10, Gold Coast Mail Centre, Queensland 4217. *1987*
Tel: (75) 920411. Fax: (075) 39 8447 (In process of development)

Curtin University of Technology, GPO Box U1987, Perth, Western Australia 6001. *1967, 1987*
Tel: (9) 350 7700. Fax: (09) 458 4661. Telex & Cables: curtin university, perth
F : *arts, ed-soc, bus-adm, eng-sc, heal sc.*
> Muresk Agricultural College, Northam, Western Australia 6401. *1926, 1969*
> D : *agr.*
> Western Australian School of Mines, PO Box 597, Kalgoorlie, Western Australia 6430. *1903, 1969*
> D : *mineral exploration-mine, geol, mine-eng, met.*

*Deakin University, Victoria 3217. *1974*
Tel: (52) 471 111. Telex: 35625 duniv aa
S : *ed, arc, hum, sc, soc, mangt.*

*The Flinders University of South Australia, Bedford Park, South Australia 5042. *1965*
Tel: (8) 275 3911. Fax: (08) 276 8213. Telex: 89624 flindu aa. Cables: flinduniv adelaide
S : *math, soc, phy, biol, hum, med, earth sc, theo, ed.*

*Griffith University, Nathan, Queensland 4111. *1971*
Tel: (7) 275 7111. Fax: (07) 277 3759. Telex: 40362 aa. Cables: unigriff brisbane
S : *Australian env st, hum, mod Asian st, sc, soc-ind adm.*

James Cook University of North Queensland, Townsville, Queensland 4811. *1961, 1970*
Tel: (77) 81 4111. Fax: (077) 79 6371. Telex: 47009 unitown aa. Cables: university townsville
F : *arts, sc, eng, com-eco, ed.*
S : *ed.*

*La Trobe University, Bundoora, Victoria 3083. *1967*
Tel: (3) 479 1111. Telex: 33143 latrob aa. Cables: latrobe melbourne
S : *hum, soc, phy, biol, agr, behavioural sc, ed, eco, math-infor sc.*

Macquarie University, North Ryde, N.S.W. 2113. *1967*
Tel: (2) 805 7111. Fax: (02) 887 4752. Telex: 122377 macuni aa. Cables: macuni, north ryde
S : *behavioural sc, biol, earth sc, eco-fin st, English-ling, hist, phil-pol, math-phy, mod lang, ed, ch, law.*

University of Melbourne, Parkville, Victoria 3052. *1853*
Tel: (3) 344 4000. Fax: (03) 344 5104. Telex: 35185 unimelb aa. Cables: unimelb, parkville, victoria
F : *arts, sc, ed, law, med, eng, arc-plan, buitown & reg plan, mus, vet, eco-com, agr-for, dent sc.*

*Monash University, Clayton, Victoria 3168. *1958*
Tel: (3) 565 4000. Telex: 32691 monash aa. Cables: monashuni, melbourne
F : *arts, eng, eco-pol, med, sc, law, ed.*

Murdoch University, South Street, Murdoch, Western Australia 6150. *1975*
Tel: (9) 332 2211. Fax: (09) 332 2507. Telex: 92711 mulib aa
S : *math-phy sc, soc inquiry, env-life sc, vet, ed, human commun.*

University of New England, Armidale, N.S.W. 2351. *1938, 1954*
Tel: (67) 733333. Fax: (067) 733122. Telex: 166050. Cables: university, armidale
F : *arts, sc, rur sc, eco, ed, resource mangt.*

*University of New South Wales, GPO Box 1, Kensington, N.S.W. 2033. *1949, 1958*
Tel: (2) 697 2222. Fax: (02) 662 7471. Telex: 26054 aa. Cables: unitech, sydney
F : *arts, app sc, arc, eng, com, med, sc, milit,*

biol, law, prof st.
B. of st : *gen ed, sc math.*
W.S. & L.B. ROBINSON UNIVERSITY COL-
LEGE, GPO Box 334, Broken Hill, N.S.W.
2880. *1967*
F : *sc, mine-mineral sc.*
University College of the Northern Territory,
GPO Box 1341, Darwin, Northern Territory
5794. *1985*
Tel: (89) 462211. Fax: (089) 401460. Telex &
Cables: 84060 unicol aa
F : *arts, sc.*
University of Newcastle, Newcastle, N.S.W.
2308. *1951, 1965*
Tel: (49) 680401. Telex: 28194
F : *arts, sc, eng, eco-com, arc, math, ed, med.*
***University of Queensland**, St. Lucia, Queens-
land 4067. *1910*
Tel: (7) 377 1111. Fax: (07) 371 5896. Telex:
40315 univold aa. Cables: univold
F : *arts, sc, eng, com-eco, agr sc, law, med, vet,
ed, arc-plan, dent, mus, soc w.*
***University of Sydney**, Sydney, N.S.W. 2006.
1850
Tel: (2) 692 2222. Fax: (02) 692 4203. Telex:

26169 unisyd aa. Cables: unisyd, sydney
F : *arts, sc, law, med, eng, vet, agr, eco, arc,
dent, ed.*
B. of st : *div, mus, soc w.*
***University of Tasmania**, GPO Box 252C,
Hobart, Tasmania 7001. *1890*
Tel: (02) 202101. Fax: (002) 202186. Telex:
58150 untas aa. Cables: tasuni, hobart
F : *arts-lib, sc, law, eco-com, eng-surv, ed, agr
sc, med-phar, eco.*
S : *art.*
Conservatory : *mus.*
University of Western Australia, Nedlands,
Western Australia 6009. *1913*
Tel: (9) 380 3838. Fax: (09) 382 4649. Telex:
92992. Cables: uniwest, perth
F : *arts, sc, eng, law, agr, ed, med, dent, eco-
com.*
***University of Wollongong**, PO Box 1144,
Wollongong, N.S.W. 2500. *1962, 1975*
Tel: (42) 27 0555. Telex: 29022.
Cables: uniofwol
F : *eng, hum, math, sc, soc, com, ed.*
S : *arts-comty st.*

OTHER INSTITUTIONS – AUTRES INSTITUTIONS

Colleges of Advanced Education – Collèges de Formation avancée

Armidale College of Advanced Education, Mann
Street, Armidale, N.S.W. 2350. *1928*
Tel: (67) 734222
B. of st : *nurs, prof st, teacher ed.*
Avondale College, PO Box 19, Cooranbong,
N.S.W. 2265. *1897*
Tel: (49) 771107
S : *bus st, nurs, relig st, teacher ed.*
Ballarat College of Advanced Education, Gear
Avenue, Mt. Helen, Victoria 3350. *1976*
Tel: (53) 301800
F : *app sc, arts, bus, human st, eng, ed st.*
**Bathurst College of Technical and Further Educa-
tion**, Bathurst, N.S.W. 2007.
Telex: 14355 cabcae aa
F : *cartog.*
Bendigo College of Advanced Education, PO Box
199, Bendigo, Victoria 3550. *1976*
Tel: (54) 403222. Fax: (054) 403477. Telex:
38293 bencol aa
F : *arts, bus st, ed, eng-sc.*
Brisbane College of Advanced Education, 130
Victoria Park Road, Kelvin Grove, Queens-
land 4059. *1982*
Tel: (7) 3528153. Telex: 155355 cabcal aa
CARSELDINE CAMPUS.
soc-comty st, teacher ed.

KEDRON PARK CAMPUS
bus
KELVIN GROVE CAMPUS.
*creative & performing arts, early childhood
st, soc-comty st, teacher ed.*
MOUNT GRAVATT CAMPUS.
teacher ed.
Canberra College of Advanced Education, PO
Box 1, Belconnen, A.C.T. 2616. *1969*
Tel: (62) 52 2225. Telex: 62267 cancol aa
S : *adm st, app sc, env des, infor sc, li st, ed.*
Capricornia Institute of Advanced Education,
Rockhampton, Queensland 4700. *1971*
Tel: (79) 36 1177. Telex: 49476 ciae aa
S : *app sc, bus, hum, soc, eng, ed.*
Catholic College of Education Sydney, 40 Edward
Street, North Sydney, N.S.W. 2060.
Tel: (2) 929 0199
continuing ed, nurs ed, postgrad ed, teacher ed.
CASTLE HILL CAMPUS.
MOUNT SAINT MARY CAMPUS, Strathfield.
Tel: (2) 680 1977
Chisholm Institute of Technology, PO Box 197,
Caulfield East, Victoria 3145. *1982*
Tel: (3) 573 2000. Telex: 254087 citvic aa
F : *techn.*
S : *art-des, bus, ed, soc-behavioural st.*

Cumberland College of Health Sciences, PO Box 170, Lidcombe, N.S.W. 2141. *1973*
Tel: (2) 646 6444. Fax: (02) 646 4853
S : *commun disorders, nurs, occp ther, orthoptics, physio, med adm.*
D : *behavioural-gen st, biol sc.*

Darling Downs Institute of Advanced Education, c/o Darling Heights Post Office, Toowoomba, Queensland 4350. *1967, 1971*
Tel: (76) 30 1300. Telex: 40010 ddiae aa
S : *app sc, arts, bus st, eng, ed.*

Darwin Institute of Technology, PO Box 40146, Casuarina, N.T. 5792. *1974*
Tel: (89) 20 4211. Telex: 85235 dacol aa
Australian ling, bus, hum-soc, extension serv.

Footscray Institute of Technology, PO Box 64, Footscray, Victoria 3011. *1915*
Tel: (3) 688 4200. Telex: 36596 fitlex aa
F : *app sc, bus, gen st, eng.*

Gippsland Institute of Advanced Education, Switchback Road, Churchill, Victoria 3842. *1968*
Tel: (51) 22 0287. Telex: 222876
S : *bus, soc, eng, app sc, ed, vis arts.*

Hawthorn Institute of Education, 442 Auburn Road, Hawthorn, Victoria 3122. *1973*
Tel: (3) 818 0631. Telex: 37985 hawcol aa
teacher ed, grad st.

Institute of Catholic Education, 383 Albert Road, East Melbourne, Victoria 3002. *1974*
AQUINAS CAMPUS, BOX 650, Ballarat, Victoria 3350.
Tel: (53) 321904
tec teacher ed.
CHRIST CAMPUS, 17 Castlebar Road, Oakleigh, Victoria 3166.
Tel: (3) 568 2000
teacher ed.
MERCY CAMPUS, 251 Mt. Alexander Road, Ascot Vale, Victoria 3032.
Tel: (3) 376 2522
teacher ed.

Kuring-gai College of Advanced Education, PO Box 222, Lindfield, N.S.W. 2070. *1946*
Tel: (2) 467 9200. Telex: 72299 kxrc aa
S : *fin & adm st, teacher ed, lib & infor st, legal st, recr-comty st.*
P : *nurs.*

Kurri Kurri College of Technical and Further Education, Kurri Kurri, N.S.W 2007.
mine.

Lincoln Institute of Health Sciences, Lincoln Institute, 625 Swanston Street, Carlton, Victoria 3053. *1972*
Tel: (3) 347 6088
S : *med record adm, occp ther, orthoptics, physio, speech sc, prosthetics-orthoptics, nurs, behavioural sc, biol, ed adm-ed, podiatry.*
SCHOOL OF NURSING, 2–6 Slater Street,

Melbourne, Victoria 3004. *1950*
Tel: (3) 269 1700

Macarthur Institute of Education, PO Box 108, Milperra, N.S.W. 2214.
Tel: (2) 772 9200.
arts-gen st, bus-techn, comty-welfare st, ed-lang, nurs.

McAuley College, PO Box 247, Everton Park, Queensland 4053. *1955, 1976*
Tel: (7) 354 2166
continuing ed, postgrad ed, teacher ed.

Mackay College of Technical and Further Education, PO Box 135, Mackay, Queensland 4740.
Tel: (79) 513 400.
S : *sugar techn.*

Melbourne College of Advanced Education, 757 Swanston Street, Carlton, Victoria 3053.
1889, 1973, 1983
Tel: (3) 341 8111
D : *art-des, biol, bus, ch-phy, ed psyc, crafts, ed socio-soc st, geog, hist-pol, lang-lit, lib, math, media arts, mus, phil, phys, psyc.*
INSTITUTE OF EARLY CHILDHOOD DEVELOPMENT, 4 Madden Grove, Kew, Victoria 3101.
Tel: (3) 861 9798.

Mitchell College of Advanced Education, Bathurst, N.S.W. 2795. *1970*
Tel: (63) 31 1022
bus-publ adm, commun-li st, teacher ed, math, app sc-plan, nurs-heal adm, soc-welfare, external st.

Nepean College of Advanced Education, PO Box 10, Kingswood, N.S.W. 2750. *1973*
Tel: (4) 36 0222
S : *bus, teacher ed, arts, nurs.*

New South Wales Institute of Technology, PO Box 123, Broadway, N.S.W. 2007. *1965*
Tel: (2) 2 0930. Telex: 95004 nswit aa
F : *arc-bui, bus, eng, hum-soc, math-comp sc, sc, law.*

New South Wales State Conservatorium of Music, Macquarie Street, Sydney, N.S.W. 2000. *1916*
Tel: (2) 230 1222 (Sydney); (49) 2 3961 (Newcastle). Fax: (02) 230 1296
Branch in Newcastle.

Newcastle College of Advanced Education, PO Box 84, Waratah, N.S.W. 2298. *1949*
Tel: (49) 67 1388. Fax: (049) 676921. Telex: 28857 ncae aa
S : *teacher ed, vis-performing arts, paramed-comty welfare st.*

Northern Rivers College of Advanced Education, PO Box 157, Lismore, N.S.W. 2480. *1973*
Tel: (66) 21 2267. Fax: (066) 23 0706
S : *bus st, ed, arts sc st.*

Philip Institute of Technology *1982*
BUNDOORA CAMPUS, Plenty Road, Bundoora, Victoria 3083. *1937, 1968*

Tel: (3) 468 2200
S : *app sc-eng, art-des, bus, nurs, phys-leisure st, soc w.*
COBURG CAMPUS, PO Box 179, Coburg, Victoria 3058.   *1959, 1973*
Tel: (3) 350 4222
S : *bus, comty st, ed.*

Queensland Conservatorium of Music, PO Box 28, North Quay, Queensland 4000. *1957, 1971*
Tel: (7) 229 2650

Queensland Institute of Technology, GPO Box 2434, Brisbane, Queensland 4000.   *1965, 1971*
Tel: (7) 223 2111. Telex: 44699 qintec aa
S : *app sc, bui env, bus st, comp, eng, heal sc, law.*

Riverina-Murray College of Advanced Education, PO Box 588, Wagga Wagga, N.S.W. 2650.   *1972*
Tel: (69) 23 2222
S : *agr, app sc, ed, com, infor st, hum-soc, mangt, techn-arts, vis & performing arts.*

Royal Melbourne Institute of Technology, GPO Box 2476V, Melbourne, Victoria 3001.   *1887*
Tel: (3) 662 0611. Telex: 36406 rmit aa
F : *arc-bui, art, eng, app sc, bus, hum-soc.*
S (grad) : *mangt.*

Ryde College of Technical and Further Education, Ryde, N.S.W.
hort.

South Australian College of Advanced Education, 46 Kintore Avenue, Adelaide, South Australia 5000.
Tel: (8) 223 6170. Telex: 88420 saclib aa
art, des-app sc, bus, commun & cult st, ed-comty dev, heal, sc-ed, ed-hum, ed-fam st.

South Australian Institute of Technology, North Terrace, Adelaide, South Australia 5000.
1889, 1960
Tel: (8) 228 0211. Telex: 82565 iteca aa
S : *acc, app geol, arc-bui, bus adm, ch techn, civ elec, electro, mec, mine met, gen st, math-comp, occp ther, phar, phy, physio, soc st, surv, lib-infor mangt.*
Branch at Whyalla.

Swinburne Institute of Technology, PO Box 218, Hawthorn, Victoria 3122.   *1908, 1969*
Tel: (3) 819 8911. Telex: 37769 swinbn aa
F : *app sc, art, arts, bus, eng.*

Sydney College of Advanced Education, PO Box 129, Newtown, N.S.W. 2042.   *1982*
Tel: (2) 516 2966
INSTITUTE OF EARLY CHILDHOOD STUDIES.
INSTITUTE OF NURSING STUDIES.
INSTITUTE OF TECHNICAL AND ADULT TEACHER EDUCATION.
ST. GEORGE INSTITUTE OF EDUCATION.
primary & mus ed, gen & comty st.
SYDNEY INSTITUTE OF EDUCATION.

Sydney College of the Arts, PO Box 222, Glebe,

N.S.W. 2037.   *1975*
Tel: (2) 692 0266
des-vis arts.

Sydney Technical College, Mary Ann Street, Ultimo, N.S.W. 2007.
heal-bui surv, med radiography, met, arc, app sc, nucl med techn, podiatry, travel-tour, valuation, welfare w.

Tasmanian State Institute of Technology, PO Box 1214, Launceston, Tasmania 7250.   *1968*
Tel: (03) 26 0201. Telex: 58675 instec aa
bus, art, env des, eng, teacher ed, soc w, gen st, nurs.

Townsville College of Technical and Further Education, PO Box 980, Townsville, Queensland 4810.   *1969, 1972*
Tel: (77) 721400
comty welfare, bus, techn.

Victoria College, 221 Burwood Highway, Burwood, Victoria 3125.   *1981*
Tel: (3) 285 3333
BURWOOD CAMPUS.
bus, primary teacher ed, spe ed.
PRAHRAN CAMPUS.
art-des, bus.
RUSDEN CAMPUS.
app sc, secondary teacher ed.
TOORAK CAMPUS.
arts, primary teacher ed.

Victorian College of Agriculture and Horticulture, 166 Wellington Parade, East Melbourne, Victoria 3002.   *1983*
Tel: (3) 651 4242. Fax: (03) 417 6753
BURNLEY CAMPUS, Richmond.
Tel: (3) 810 8800
DOOKIE CAMPUS.
Tel: (58) 28 6371
GLENORMISTON CAMPUS.
Tel: (55) 92 5303
LONGERENONG CAMPUS, Dooen.
Tel: (53) 847208

Victorian College of Pharmacy Ltd, 381 Royal Parade, Parkville, Victoria 3052.   *1881*
Tel: (3) 387 7222

Victorian College of the Arts, 234 St. Kilda Road, Melbourne, Victoria 3004.   *1972*
Tel: (3) 616 9300
art, mus, dram, dance, opera.

Warrnambool Institute of Advanced Education, PO Box 423, Warrnambool, Victoria 3280.
1913, 1970
Tel: (55) 64 0111
F : *app sc-techn, art-des, bus, gen st, teacher ed.*

Western Australian College of Advanced Education, PO Box 217, Doubleview, Western Australia 6018.
Tel: (9) 387 9212
S : *arts-app sc, comty & lang st, ed, nurs.*
BUNBURY INSTITUTE.

Tel: (97) 21 6777
CHURCHLANDS CAMPUS.
Tel: (9) 387 9211
CLAREMONT CAMPUS.
Tel: (9) 383 0333
JOONDALUP CAMPUS, Wanneroo.
Tel: (9) 272 0444
MOUNT LAWLEY CAMPUS.

Tel: (9) 272 0444
A : *performing arts*.
NEDLANDS CAMPUS.
Tel: (9) 386 0222
Wollongong College of Technical and Further Education, Wollongong, N.S.W. 2500.
mine, met.

General Education – Enseignement général

Australian College of Physical Education, PO Box 46, Croydon, N.S.W. 2132.   *1979*
Tel: (2) 798 8022
teacher ed.

Australian Film and Television School, PO Box 126, North Ryde, N.S.W. 2113.   *1975*
Tel: (2) 887 1666

Australian Maritime College, PO Box 986, Launceston, Tasmania 7250.   *1978*
Tel: (03) 260711. Fax: (003) 260717. Telex: amc 58827
mar eng, fish techn, fish operations, naut st, naut sc, mar electro-radiocommun, hydro-graphic surv, shipping bus.

Canberra School of Art, PO Box 1561, Canberra City, A.C.T. 2601.   *1976*
Tel: (62) 46 7811

Canberra School of Music, PO Box 804, Canberra City, A.C.T. 2601.   *1965*
Tel: (62) 46 7811

Catholic Institute of Sydney, St. Patrick's College, Manly, N.S.W. 2095.   *1889, 1977*
Tel: (2) 977 6066
arts, theo.

Hawkesbury Agricultural College, Richmond, N.S.W. 2753.   *1891*
Tel: (45) 70 1333
S : *agr, mangt, food sc.*

Marcus Oldham Farm Management College, Private Bag 116, Mail Centre, Geelong, Victoria 3221.   *1962*
Tel: (52) 43 3533
farm mangt, horse mangt, external st.

The National Institute of Dramatic Art, PO Box 1, Kensington, N.S.W. 2033.   *1958*
Tel: (2) 663 3815

Orange Agricultural College, PO Box 883, Orange, N.S.W. 2800.   *1973*
Tel: (63) 62 4699
farm mangt, farm-sec st, env conservation, hort, horse mangt.

Queensland Agricultural College, Lawes, Queensland 4343.   *1897, 1971*
Tel: (75) 621011
B. of st : *tec st, undergrad st, postgrad-continuing st.*

Queensland College of Art, c/o PO Box 84, Morningside, Queensland 4170.   *1880*
Tel: (7) 395 9123
vis art.

Roseworthy Agricultural College, Roseworthy, South Australia 5371.   *1883, 1974*
Tel: (85) 248057

Signadou College of Education, PO Box 256, Dickson, A.C.T. 2602.   *1926, 1963, 1979*
Tel: (62) 47 9933
ed.

Australian Vice-Chancellors' Committee

The Committee, which dates its origins to a conference of Australian universities in 1920, is a consultative and advisory body for Australian university affairs. It consists of the Vice-Chancellors of 20 Australian universities. The objectives of the Committee are: a) to provide opportunities for universities to discuss matters of mutual concern; b) to review and advise on the problems and needs of universities, notably their relations with other educational institutions, the Australian Government and the community; c) to promote relations with universities in other countries, and in collaboration with the Australian Government, to assist universities and academics in developing countries to improve further their own capacities in teaching and research; d) to work in liaison with and consult with the Australian Government on matters relating to the Australian university sector; and e) to collect and disseminate information covering a wide range of subject areas reflecting the Australian and overseas demand for reports on issues confronting the Australian universities.

In order to achieve its objectives, the AVCC has appointed standing committees on research, education, planning and development, and public relations. The AVCC also appoints specialist working parties with particular terms of reference to examine specific matters, in such areas as the training of university administrators, student finances, and overseas student policies.

The AVCC is funded on an annual basis by contributions from the universities.

Le Comité des Vice-Chanceliers australiens, dont les origines remontent à une conférence des universités australiennes tenue en 1920, est un organisme consultatif formulant des recommandations en ce qui concerne les affaires universitaires australiennes. Il se compose des Vice-Chanceliers de vingt universités australiennes. Le Comité a pour objectifs: a) de fournir aux universités des possibilités de discuter de questions d'intérêt commun; b) de passer en revue les problèmes et les besoins des universités, notamment leurs relations avec d'autres institutions éducatives, avec le gouvernement australien et la collectivité, et de donner des conseils à cet égard; c) de promouvoir les relations avec les universités d'autres pays et, en collaboration avec le gouvernement australien, d'aider les universités et les enseignants des pays en voie de développement à continuer à améliorer leur potentiel en matière d'enseignement et de recherche; d) de travailler en liaison avec le gouvernement australien et de le consulter pour les questions relatives au secteur universitaire australien; et e) de rassembler et de diffuser des informations portant sur un très large éventail de domaines reflétant la demande qui se manifeste, en Australie et outre-mer, concernant les problèmes qui se posent aux universités australiennes.

Pour atteindre ses objectifs, l'AVCC a constitué des comités permanents chargés de s'occuper de la recherche de l'éducation, de la planification et du développement, et des relations publiques formuler des recommandations sur des questions telles que les relations industrielles, la recherche universitaire et les relations internationales. L'AVCC forme également des groupes de travail spécialisés qui ont pour mission particulière d'examiner des problèmes précis dans des domaines tels que la formation des administrateurs d'université, les budgets étudiants, et les politiques adoptées à l'égard des étudiants d'outre-mer.

L'AVCC est financé par des cotisations annuelles versées par les universités australiennes.

Chairman of Committee (1989–90): Prof. Brian Wilson, Vice-Chancellor, University of Queensland.

Deputy Chairman (1989): Prof. Laurie Nichol, Vice Chancellor, Australian National University.

Executive Director and Secretary: F.S. Hambly. GPO Box 1142, Canberra, A.C.T. 2601. Churchill House, 218 Northbourne Avenue, Braddon, A.C.T. 2601.

Tel: (62) 49 7577. Telex: 62180. Cables: vicom canberra.

Commonwealth Tertiary Education Commission

The Tertiary Education Commission, which was established by the Tertiary Education Commission Act on 22 June 1977, has replaced the three former tertiary commissions—the Universities Commission, the Commission on Advanced Education and the Technical and Further Education Commission.

The Commission's prime responsibility is to develop and recommend policies for federal financial support to the States across the three sectors of tertiary education in Australia— universities, colleges of advanced education and technical and further education institutions. Under its Act, the Commission is required to perform its functions with the object of promoting the balanced and co-ordinated development of tertiary education in Australia and the diversification of opportunities for tertiary education.

The Commission is assisted in its work by three statutory councils—the Universities Council, the Advanced Education Council and the Technical and Further Education Council. The Councils have been established to advise on matters relating to their respective sectors and are responsible for administering approved programmes of financial assistance.

Since its establishment, the Commission has submitted a number of reports to the Commonwealth Government in respect of financial assistance for tertiary education. These are *Recommendations for 1978, Report for 1979–81* (Volumes 1–4), and *Report for 1982–84 Triennium* (Volumes 1–4). The Commission has also conducted major inquiries into management education; nurse education and training; academic study leave in universities and colleges of advanced education; non-government business colleges; and staff development in the technical and further education sector.

Prior to 1974, the Federal Government shared financial responsibility with State Governments for universities and colleges of advanced education in Australia, according to an agreed formula. From 1 January 1974, the Federal Government took over full financial responsibility for these two sectors. In the technical and further education sector Federal funding is supplementary to State provisions.

La Commission du Commonwealth pour l'enseignement tertiaire, créée en date du 22 juin 1977, en vertu de la loi portant son nom, remplace les trois anciennes commissions pour l'enseignement tertiaire (Commission des Universités, Commission pour la Formation avancée, et Commission pour l'Enseignement technique et complémentaire).

La Commission a essentiellement pour but d'élaborer et de recommander des politiques relatives à l'octroi, par le gouvernement fédéral, d'un soutien financier aux Etats, dans les trois secteurs de l'enseignement tertiaire en Australie (universités, collèges de formation avancée, et institutions dispensant un enseignement technique et complémentaire). La loi stipule que la Commission doit, dans l'accomplissement de ses fonctions, avoir pour objet de promouvoir le développement équilibré et harmonieux de l'enseignement tertiaire en Australie et la diversification des possibilités de formation dans ce domaine.

Trois conseils statutaires assistent la Commission dans ses travaux: le Conseil des Universités, le Conseil pour la Formation avancée et le Conseil pour l'Enseignement technique et complémentaire. Les Conseils ont été créés afin de fournir des avis consultatifs sur des questions relatives à leurs domaines respectifs et ils sont chargés d'administrer les programmes d'aide financière qui ont été agréés.

Depuis sa création, la Commission a soumis au Gouvernement du Commonwealth un certain nombre de rapports sur l'aide financière à apporter à l'enseignement tertiaire. Il s'agit des Recommandations pour l'année 1978, *du* Rapport pour la période 1979–81 (vol. 1–4) *et du* Rapport pour le triennium 1982–84 (vol. 1–4). *La Commission a également effectué de grandes enquêtes sur l'enseignement de la gestion, l'enseignement et la formation dispensés aux infirmières, sur les congés d'éducation accordés par les universités et les collèges de formation avancée, sur les collèges d'enseignement commercial ne dépendant pas du gouvernement; et le recyclage des enseignants de l'enseignement technique et complémentaire.*

Avant 1974, le Gouvernement fédéral et les gouvernements des Etats se partageaient, selon une formule concertée, la responsabilité financière des universités et des collèges de formation avancée d'Australie. Depuis le 1er janvier 1974, le Gouvernement fédéral assume l'entière responsabilité financière de ces deux secteurs. Dans le secteur de l'enseignement technique et complémentaire le financement de source fédérale s'ajoute aux crédits des Etats.
Chairman: H. Hudson.
First Assistant Commissioner: L. Hennessy.
Benjamin Offices, Benjamin Way, Belconnen, A.C.T. 2616.
Tel: (62) 64 1133. Telex: 62585 tecom.

Higher Education Research and Development Society of Australasia

The Society was formed in August 1972 at a meeting at which it was resolved that the general objective of the Society be to promote research and development in higher education and that membership be opened to any person interested in that objective. A Constitution was adopted at the first General Meeting of the Society, which was held in August 1973.

A Conference and General Meeting has been held each year since 1975. The 1984 venue was Sydney, and the 1985 one Dunedin, New Zealand. Membership of the Society stands at about 400.

The Society produces a newsletter and publishes bibliographies, monographs, conference proceedings, *Research and Development in Higher Education*, and a twice-yearly journal *Higher Education Research and Development*.

La Société australasienne pour la recherche et le développement en matière d'enseignement supérieur a été fondée en août 1972 au cours d'une réunion où il fut décidé que l'objectif général de la Société serait de promouvoir la recherche et le développement en matière d'enseignement supérieur et que toute personne s'intéressant à cet objectif pourrait y adhérer. Les Statuts furent adoptés lors de la première Assemblée générale de la Société, tenue en août 1973.

Depuis 1975, la Société tient chaque année une Conférence et une Assemblée générale. Celles de 1984 ont eu lieu à Sydney, et celles de 1985 à Dunedin, Nouvelle-Zélande. La Société compte maintenant environ 400 membres.

La Société édite un bulletin d'information et publie des bibliographies, des monographies, les comptes rendus des débats de ses conférences, 'Research and Development in Higher Education', et sa revue intitulée 'Higher Education Research and Development' est publiée deux fois par an.
President: Dr. John Bowden, Centre for the Study of Higher Education, University of Melbourne, Parkville, Vic. 3052.
Tel (3) 660–2510.
HERDSA, c/o T.E.R.C., University of N.S.W., PO Box 1, Kensington, N.S.W. 2033.
Tel: (2) 697 4934. Fax: (02) 663 3420

Federation of Australian University Staff Associations (IAUPL)
Contact: 18 rue de Docteur Roux, 75015 Paris (France).
Tel: (33–1) 47–83–31
Australian Federation of University Women (IFUW)
PO Box 123, Nedlands, Western Australia 6009.
Australian Federation of University Graduates
Executive Secretary: D.D. Neilson.
c/o University of New South Wales, Box 1, Post

Office, Kensington, N.S.W. 2033.
Tertiary Catholic Federation of Australia (Pax Romana)
52 Malcom Street, Erskineville, N.S.W. 2042.
Australian Student Christian Movement (WSCF)
Australian S.C.M., Room 315/328 Hinders Street, Melbourne, Victoria 3000.
Australian Union of Jewish Students (WUJS)
Contact: 89 Chaussee De Vleurgat, 1050 Brussels (Belgium).
Tel: (2) 647 7279. Telex: 20625 b

*

Council on Overseas Professional Qualifications
PO Box 1407, Canberra City, A.C.T. 2601.
Tel: (62) 70 5711
Department of Foreign and Trade Affairs
Canberra City, A.C.T. 2601.
Tel: (62) 619111. Telex: 62007
Department of Education
PO Box 826, Woden, A.C.T. 2606.
Tel: (62) 83 7777
Australian National Commission for Unesco
Department of Education, PO Box 826, Woden, A.C.T. 2606.
Tel: (62) 83 7658. Fax: (062) 814476. Telex: 62116

AUSTRIA
AUTRICHE

*Karl-Franzens Universität Graz, Universitätsplatz 3, A-8010 Graz. *1585*
Tél: (316) 380–0. Télex: 311662 ubgraz a
F : théo cath, dr, soc-éco, méd, let, nat.
Universität Innsbruck, Innrain 52, A-6020 Innsbruck. *1669*
Tél: (5222) 507. Télex: 53708 ubibk a
F : théo cath, dr, soc-éco, méd, let, nat, gé civ-arc.
Universität Salzburg. Residenzplatz 1, A-5020 Salzburg. *1622, 1962*
Tél: (662) 44511. Télex: 633903 ubs a
F : théo cath, dr, let, nat.
*Universität Wien, Dr. Karl Lueger-Ring 1, A-1010 Wien. *1365*
Tél: (222) 4300–0. Télex:115619
F : théo cath, théo évan, dr, soc-éco, méd, hum, let, nat.
Technische Universität Graz, Rechbauerstrasse 12, A-8010 Graz. *1811*
Tél: (316) 7061–0. Télex: 311221 tugrz a
F : gé civ-arc, méc, élec, nat.
Montanuniversität Leoben, Franz Josef-Strasse 18, A-8700 Leoben. *1840*
Tél: (3842) 44511. Télex: 033322 mhbleo a
D : mine, mét, minér, petro-ch, mines, matiére synthétique, matér.
Technische Universität Wien, Karlsplatz 13, A-1040 Wien. *1815*
Tél: (222) 5601–0. Fax: 232–3222467. Télex: 131000 tvfwa a
F : gé civ, arc, méc, élec, nat.
Universität für Bodenkultur Wien [U. d'Agriculture], Gregor Mendel-Strasse 33, A-1180 Wien. *1872*
Tél: (222) 34–25–00. Cables: bodenkultur a–1180
D : agr, for, techn agr, ferm.
Veterinärmedizinische Universität Wien [U. vétérinaire], Linke Bahngasse 11, A-1030 Wien. *1767*
Tél: (222) 71–155
D : vét.
Wirtschaftsuniversität Wien [U. de Commerce], Augasse 2–6, A-1090 Wien. *1898*
Tél: (222) 34–05–25. Télex: 111–127 wuwa
D : com, soc-éco.
Universität Linz, Altenberger Strasse, A-4040 Linz-Auhof. *1962*
Tél: (732) 23–13–81. Télex: 2–2323 unilia a
F : dr, soc-éco, tec-nat.
Universität für Bildungswissenschaften Klagenfurt, Universitätsstrasse 67, A-9020 Klagenfurt. *1970*
Tél: (42–22) 23–7–30
F : let, hum.
Akademie der bildenden Künste in Wien [A. des Beaux-Arts], Schillerplatz 3, A-1010 Wien. *1692*
Tél: (222) 57–95–16
Hochschule für Musik und darstellende Kunst in Wien [A. de Musique et d'Art dramatique], Lothringerstrasse 18, A-1030 Wien. *1817*
Tél: (222) 56–16–85
Hochschule für Musik und darstellende Kunst in Graz [A. de Musique et d'Art dramatique], Leonhardstrasse 15, A-8010 Graz. *1962*
Tél: (316) 32–0–53/4

Hochschule für Musik und darstellende Kunst «Mozarteum» in Salzburg [A. de Musique et d'Art dramatique 'Mozarteum'], Mirabellplatz 1, A-5020 Salzburg. *1880*
Tél: (662) 75534–0
Hochschule für künstlerische und industrielle Gestaltung in Linz [A. des Arts appliqués],

Hauptplatz 8, A-4020 Linz. *1973*
Tél: (732) 27–34–85
Hochschule für angewandte Kunst in Wien [A. des Arts appliqués], Oskar Kokoschka Platz 2, A-1010 Wien. *1867*
Tél: (222) 71–111

Rektorenkonferenz

La Conférence des recteurs réunit à intervalles réguliers les recteurs de tous les établissements d'enseignement supérieur autrichiens, pour délibérer des problèmes touchant à l'enseignement supérieur.

The Conference of Rectors regularly brings together the rectors of all Austrian institutions of higher education in order to discuss problems affecting higher education.
Président: Dr. Walter Kemmerling.
Secrétaire général: Dr. Eva Glück.
Secrétariat général, Schottengasse 1, A-1010 Wien.
Tél: (0222) 63–06–22–0.

Fonds zur Förderung der wissenschaftlichen Forschung

La Fondation autrichienne pour la science a été créée en 1967 en vertu d'une loi fédérale.

La composition de ses trois organes constitutifs, l'Assemblée, le Conseil et le Comité exécutif, correspond à l'infrastructure de la recherche scientifique autrichienne institutionalisée. L'Assemblée regroupe les délégués des universités, des facultés, de l'Académie des Sciences et, depuis 1981, de toutes les autres institutions de recherche; les membres du Comité exécutif sont membres de droit de l'Assemblée et du Conseil. Les autres membres du Conseil, le principal organe de décision, sont élus par l'Assemblée et comprennent un représentant de chaque université, de l'Académie des sciences ainsi que, depuis 1981, des principaux milieux industriels et commerciaux et des institutions de recherche extra-universitaire. Les représentants des Ministères fédéraux des finances, de l'enseignement supérieur et de la recherche et du Fonds autrichien pour la recherche industrielle participent aux réunions, mais ne votent pas. Le Comité exécutif est composé de trois responsables, le président et deux vice-présidents, élus par l'Assemblée, ainsi que du président de la Conférence des recteurs autrichiens et du président de l'Académie des sciences, qui en sont membres de droit.

La Fondation soutient, dans tous les domaines de l'activité scientifique, les projets de recherche fondamentale scientifique des chercheurs ou des équipes de chercheurs; établit les projets prioritaires en matière de recherche et en assure la gestion, en collaboration avec la Conférence des Recteurs; soutient les jeunes chercheurs et encourage la publication de la documentation de caractère scientifique; fournit au Ministère fédéral de l'Enseignement supérieur et de la Recherche des services consultatifs pour les questions scientifiques; renseigne le public sur la politique de recherche et sur l'importance de la science; forme, avec le Fonds autrichien pour la recherche industrielle, le Conseil autrichien de la recherche *(Österreichische Forschungsförderungsrat)*, organe qui est chargé de coordonner l'expansion de la recherche scientifique appliquée et industrielle et du développement; fournit au gouvernement fédéral, aux gouvernements des états et au ministère fédéral des services consultatifs pour toutes les questions scientifiques.

The Austrian Science Foundation was established in 1967 by federal law.

Its three bodies, the Assembly, the Board and the Executive Committee reflect in composition the infrastructure of institutionalized scientific research in Austria. The Assembly consists of delegates of the Universities and Faculties and of the Academy of Sciences, and, since 1981, of all other research institutions; the members of the Executive Committee are ex officio members of the Assembly and the Board. The other members of the Board, the major decision-making body, are elected by the Assembly and include one representative of each University and of the Academy of Sciences, and, since 1981, also of the major interest groups and extra-university research institutions. Representatives of the Federal Ministry of Finance, of Higher Education and Research and of the Austrian Industrial Research Fund participate without vote. The Executive Committee comprises three officers, the President and two Vice-Presidents, elected by the Assembly and ex officio the Chairman of the Austrian Conference of Rectors and the President of the Academy of Sciences.

The Foundation promotes basic scholarly research projects of individual researchers and of research teams in all fields of scientific endeavour; establishes and administers research priorities in

collaboration with the Conference of Rectors; supports young researchers and the publication of science literature; advises the Federal Ministry of Higher Education and Research on scientific matters; provides information for the public on research policy and on the importance of science; and together with the Austrian Industrial Research Fund, forms the Österreichische Forschungsförderungsrat, Austrian Research Council, a body which co-ordinates the promotion of scholarly, applied, and industrial research and development and advises the Federal and the State governments and the Federal Ministry on all scientific matters.
Président: Prof. Dr. Kurt L. Komarek.
Vice-Présidents: Prof. Dr. Helmut Rauch; Prof. Dr. Moritz Csáky.
Secrétaire général: Dr. Raoul F. Kneucker.
Garnisongasse 7, A-1090 Wien.
Tél: (222) 42–12–36–0

Verband der wissenschaftlichen Gesellschaften Oesterreichs (VWGÖ)

L'Union des sociétés autrichiennes a pour but de réunir les sociétés scientifiques autrichiennes en vue d'encourager l'organisation du travail scientifique sur de plus larges bases. Elle favorise l'introduction dans la pratique, de conclusions de caractère scientifique en faisant paraître des publications et en organisant des conférences.

Périodiques: Oesterreichische Hochschulzeitung (dix fois par an) et un petit nombre d'autres publications spécialisées.

The Union of Austrian Societies seeks to bring together the Austrian scientific societies with the object of promoting the organization of scientific work on as broad a basis as possible. It supports the transfer of scientific results into practice through publications and lectures.

Journals: Oesterreichische Hochschulzeitung (ten times a year) and some other special publications.
Lindengasse 37, A-1070 Wien.
Tél: (222) 93–21–66

Oesterreichisches Komitee für Internationalen Studienaustausch

Le Comité autrichien d'échanges éducatifs internationaux a pour but d'encourager la collaboration internationale pour toutes les questions intéressant l'enseignement supérieur et les étudiants, en favorisant les échanges d'élèves, de jeunes gens, de professeurs, les stages d'été pour les étudiants, en vue de perfectionner leur formation professionnelle, ainsi que les vovages d'études et les camps de jeunesse.

The Austrian Committee for International Education Exchange seeks to encourage international co-operation in all matters concerning higher education and students, by promoting exchanges of students, young people and teachers, and by organizing summer courses for students to improve their professional training, study tours, and youth camps.
Président: Dr. jur. Leo Leitner.
Secrétaire: Rolf Kratochwill.
Türkenstrasse 4, A-1090 Wien IX.
Tél: (222) 3475–26

Oesterreichische Landesgruppe der IAUPL
Correspondant: 18, rue du Docteur Roux, 75015 Paris (France).
Tél: (33–1) 47–83–31–65

Verband der Akademikerinnen Oesterreichs (IFUW)
Présidente: Dr. Elfriede Sturm.
Reitschulgasse 2, A-1010 Wien.
Tél: (222) 533–90–80

Oesterreichische Hochschülerschaft –OH (WUS)
Schubertstrasse 2-4, A-8010 Graz.
Tél: (314) 90–22–047. Télex: 311662 ub graz

Büro für Studentwanderungen—BfSt
Schreyvogelgasse 3–5, A-1010 Wien 1.

Cartellverband der Katholischen Oesterreichischen Studentenverbindungen (Pax Romana)
Lerchenfeldstrasse 14, A1080 Wien.

Katholische Hochschuljugend Oesterreichs (Pax Romana)
Ebendorferstrasse 8–III, A1010 Wien.

Katholischer Akademiker-Verband Oesterreichs
Währingerstrasse 2–3, A-1090 Wien.

Evangelische Studentengemeinde (WSCF),
Schwarzspanierstrasse 13, A-1096 Wien.

Akademische Vereinigung für Aussenpolitik (ISMUN)
Président: Wolfgang Pircher.
Josefsplatz 6, Palais Palffy, A-1010 Wien.

Vereinigung Jüdischer Hochschüler in Oesterreich (WUJS)
Correspondant: 89 Chaussee De Vleurgat, 1050 Bruxelles (Belgique).
Tél: (2) 647–7279. Télex: 20625 b

*

Bundesministerium für Wissenschaft und Forschung (Ministère de la Science et de la Recherche —Ministry of Science and Research)
Wien.
Tél: (222) 531020. Télex: 111157 bmfwf a

Austrian National Commission for Unesco
Mentergasse 11, A-1070 Wien.
Tél: (222) 93–64–21. Cables: unescokom wien

BAHAMAS
BAHAMAS

College of The Bahamas, PO Box N4912, Nassau.
1974
Tel: 37930/3
D : *hum, nat, soc, techn, continuing ed-exten-*
sion serv, ed, bus-adm st.

Bahamas Hotel Training College, PO Box 4896, Nassau.
1973

Ministry of Education
Nassau.

BAHRAIN
BAHREIN

*****Bahrain University**, Manama.
1987
Tel: 682748. Telex: 9258 ucobah bn
Arabian Gulf University, PO Box 26809, Manama.
1986
Tel: 277209. Telex: 8674 agcp bn
C : *med & med sc.*

College of Health Sciences, Salmenia Medical Centre, PO Box 12, Manama.
1976
Telex: 8511 health bn
Hotel and Catering Training Centre, PO Box 22088, Muharraq.
1975
Tel: 32019. Telex: htc muharraq

Ministry of Education
PO Box 43, Manama.
Tel: 258400

Bahrain National Commission for Unesco
Ministry of Education, PO Box 43, Manama.
Tel: 259403. Fax: 272252. Telex: 9094 tarbia bn

BANGLADESH
BANGLADESH

UNIVERSITIES AND TECHNICAL UNIVERSITIES—
UNIVERSITES ET UNIVERSITES TECHNIQUES

Bangladesh Agricultural Research Institute, Joydebpur, Dhaka.   1976
Tel: 401013. Telex: 642401

Bangladesh Agricultural University, Mymensingh.   1961
Tel: pbx 4193. Cables: agrivarsity, mymensingh, bangladesh
F : *agr, vet, an hus, agr eco-rur socio, agr eng, fish.*
Also 2 affiliated institutions.

Bangladesh University of Engineering and Technology, Ramna, Dhaka 1205.   1961
Tel: 500252. Cables: engineering university, dhaka
F : *arc-plan, civ, elec-electro, eng, mec.*
I : *flood control.*

*University of Chittagong, University PO., Chittagong.   1966
Tel: pbx 210131/210134. Cables: chittagong university, bangladesh
F : *arts, sc, com, law, med, ed, soc.*
D : *Bengali, English, hist, Isl hist-cult, psyc, fa, Sanskrit-Pali, Arabic-Persian, acc, mangt, eco, pol, socio, phy, ch, math, stat, zoo, bot, marine biol, orntl lang.*
I : *marine biol, for.*
Also 97 affiliated colleges.

*University of Dhaka, Ramna, Dhaka 1205. (The Registrar).   1921
Tel: 500010–9. Cables: dhaka university, bangladesh
F : *arts, fa, sc, law, ed, med, com, soc, biol sc, postgrad med sc-res.*
D : *Bengali, English, Sanskrit & Pali, Arabic & Isl st, Urdu & Persian, hist, Isl hist & cult, phil, jour, lib, eco, pol, publ adm, socio, int rel, soc welfare, acc, mangt, marketing, fin, phy, app phy, ch, bio-ch, app ch, math, stat, bot, soil sc, geog, geol, zoo, phar, psyc, law.*
I : *bus adm, stat res & training, ed & res, soc welfare, nutr & res, mod lang, fa.*
BANGLADESH COLLEGE OF LEATHER TECHNOLOGY.
BARISAL MEDICAL COLLEGE.

COLLEGE OF HOME ECONOMICS.
COLLEGE OF NURSING.
COLLEGE OF PHYSICAL EDUCATION.
COLLEGE OF TEXTILE TECHNOLOGY.
DHAKA ENGINEERING COLLEGE.
DHAKA MEDICAL COLLEGE.
DENTAL COLLEGE.
INSTITUTE OF CARDIOVASCULAR DISEASES.
INSTITUTE OF CHILD HEALTH.
INSTITUTE OF DISEASES OF THE CHEST AND HOSPITAL.
INSTITUTE OF POSTGRADUATE MEDICINE.
SIR SALIMULLAH MEDICAL COLLEGE.
NATIONAL INSTITUTE OF EDUCATIONAL ADMINISTRATION EXTENSION AND RESEARCH.
NATIONAL INSTITUTE OF PREVENTIVE AND SOCIAL MEDICINE.
REHABILITATION INSTITUTE AND HOSPITAL FOR THE DISABLED.
TEACHERS' TRAINING COLLEGE.
TECHNICAL TEACHERS' TRAINING COLLEGE.
MYMENSINGH MEDICAL COLLEGE.
TEACHERS' TRAINING COLLEGE, Mymensingh.
TEACHERS' TRAINING COLLEGE FOR WOMEN, Mymensingh.
Also 187 affiliated colleges.

Islamic University, Tongi.   1986

Jahangirnagar University, Savar, Dhaka.   1976
Tel: 236078. Cables: university, savar, dhaka
F : *arts-hum, soc, math-phy.*
D : *Bengali, English, hist, eco, govt-politics, geog, math, stat, phy, ch.*

*University of Rajshahi, PO Rajshahi University, Rajshahi.   1953
Tel: 2441–9. Cables: university, rajshahi
F : *arts, sc, law, med, ed, eng, com.*
D : *Bengali, English, phil, hist, Isl hist & cult, pol, soc, soc w, eco, lang, Arabic, phy, app phy, stat, ch, app ch, bio-ch, geog, psyc, math, bot, zoo, geol-mine, acc, mangt, fin, marketing.*
I : *Bangladesh st.*
Also 165 affiliated colleges.

Bangladesh Federation of University Women (IFUW)
Road No. 6, Dhanmondi Residential Area, House 16/1, Dhaka 1205.
World University Service (WUS)
Secretary: Professor B.R. Khan.
Jahangirnagar University, Savar, Dhaka.
Tel: 509537. Telex: 642551 unic bg
SCM of Bangladesh (WSCF)
c/o Dhaka YMCA, 96–87 New Eskaton GPO Box 2041, Dhaka 1.
Bangladesh Students' Union—BSU (IUS)

31 Hossaini Dalan Road, Dhaka 11.
Telex: 642035 pco bj. Cables: unity dhaka (att. bsu)

*

Ministry of Education
Dhaka.
Tel: 415172
Bangladesh National Commission for Unesco
Ministry of Education, 1 Asian Highway, Palassy, Nilkhet, Dhaka 5.
Tel: 508432. Cables: unesconat dhaka

BARBADOS
BARBADE

*University of the West Indies** (see Jamaica, p. 235 and Trinidad and Tobago, p. 420).
Cave Hill Campus, PO Box 64, Bridgetown.
Tel: pbx 425–1310. Telex: 2257 univados wb

F : *law, arts-gen st, soc, nat.*
I : *soc-eco res, mass commun.*
D : *extra-mural st.*
S : *ed.*

Guild of Undergraduates—GU (IUS)
University of the West Indies, Cave Hill, PO Box 64, Bridgetown.

*

Ministry of Education and Culture
Jemmott's Lane, St. Michael.
Tel: 427–3272
Barbados National Commission for Unesco
Ministry of Education and Culture, Jemmott's Lane, St. Michael.
Tel: 427–3272 (ext. 213)

BELGIUM
BELGIQUE

UNIVERSITIES—UNIVERSITES

*Université Libre de Bruxelles, avenue F.D. Roosevelt 50, 1050 Bruxelles. (M. le Secrétaire). *1834, 1969*
Tél: (02) 642–2111. Télex: 23069 unilib b
F : phil-let, dr, sc, méd, sc app, soc-pol-éco, psyc-péd.
I : phill-hist orntl, ét eur, hist chré, aéro, téléc-élec, urb, phys, stat, trav.
I : phar, pho.
E : crim, sa publ.

*Vrije Universiteit Brussel, Campus Oefenplein, Pleinlaan 2, 1050 Brussel. *1969*
Tél: (02) 641–2111. Télex: 61051 vubco b
F : phil-let, dr, sc, méd-phar, sc app, soc-pol-éco, psych-péd.
I : phys, kin ésithér.

*Rijksuniversiteit te Gent, 25 St. Pietersnieuw-straat, 9000 Gent. *1816*
Tél: (091) 23–38–21. Télex: 12754 rugent b
F : phil-let, dr, sc, méd-phar, sc app, éco, agr, méd-vét, psyc-péd..
I : phys.
E : crim, management.

*Université de l'Etat à Liège, place du 20 août 7, 4000 Liège. *1816*
Tél: (41) 420080. Télex: 41397 univlg b
F : phil-let, dr, sc, méd-phar, phys, sc app, méd-vét, psyc, éco.
E : adm des aff, crim.

Université Catholique de Louvain, place de l'Université 1, 1348 Louvain-la-Neuve.
1425, 1834, 1969
Tél: (010) 43–21–11. Télex: 59516 uclac b
F : phil-let, sc, théo-can, dr, psyc-éd, sc, sc appl, éco-soc-pol, agr, méd-phar.
I : arc-hist d'art, relig, phil, phy, sc fam & sex, nat app, sc nucl & rad, math pure & appl, trav, phys, lang vivantes.
E : ét médié, crim, sa.
Ce : ét théât.

*Katholieke Universiteit Leuven, Naamsestraat 22, 3000 Leuven. *1425, 1834, 1969*
Tél: (016) 283811. Fax: (32–16) 284014. Télex: 25715 kulbib b
F : théo, dr can, dr, méd, phil-let, éco app-soc-psyc-péd, sc, sc app, agr.
I : phil, phar, phys, trav.

*Université de l'Etat à Mons, place du Parc 20, 7000 Mons. *1965, 1971*
Tél: (065) 37–31–11. Télex: 57764 uemons b
F : sc, éco app, méd-phar, psyc-péd.
E : trad-interp.
D : ling.

OTHER INSTITUTIONS—AUTRES INSTITUTIONS

Institutions with full University Status—
Etablissements assimilés aux universités

Rijksuniversitair Centrum te Antwerpen, Kasteel «Den Brandt» Beukenlaan, 12, 2000 Antwerpen. *1965*
Tél: (03) 8273707. Télex: 33362 nucabi b
F : sc, méd, éco app.

Universitaire Faculteiten Sint-Ignatius te Antwerpen, Venusstraat 35, 2000 Antwerpen. *1852, 1965*
Tél: (03) 231 6660. Télex: 33599 ufsia b
F : éco app, dr, phil-let, pol-soc.

Universitaire Faculteiten Sint-Aloysuis, 1, Vrij-heidslaan 17, 1080 Brussel. *1858, 1965, 1974*
Tél: (02) 42799–60
F : phil-let, dr, éco-soc-pol.

Facultés Universitaires Saint-Louis, boulevard du Jardin botanique 43, 1000 Bruxelles.
1858, 1965, 1974
Tél: (02) 21178–11
F : phil-let, dr, éco-sol-pol.
E : sc phil & relig.

Limburgs Universitair Centrum, Universitaire Campus, 3610 Diepenbeek. *1971*
Tél: (011) 22–99–61. Télex: 39948 luc b
F : méd, sc.

Faculté des Sciences Agronomiques de l'Etat à Gembloux, passage des Déportés 2, 5800

Gembloux. *1860*
Tél: (081) 62–21–11. Télex: 59432 isagx b
F : agr.
*Faculté Polytechnique de Mons, rue de Houdain
9, 7000 Mons. *1837*
Tél: (065) 33–1–91
F : sc appl.
D : math, phy, ch, mine, géol, mét, élec, méc,
arc, inft-gestion, inft-automatique.
I : sc nucl, lang vivantes.
Faculté Universitaire Catholique de Mons,
chaussée de Binche 151, 7000 Mons. *1896*

Tél: (065) 31–21–13
F : sc éco app, ing com, sc pol adm.
*Facultés Universitaires Notre-Dame de la Paix,
rue de Bruxelles 61, 5000 Namur. *1831*
Tél: (081) 22–90–61. Télex: 59222 facnam b
F : phil-let, sc, méd-phar, méd-vét, éco-soc, dr.
I : infor.
Universitaire Instelling Antwerpen, Universi-
teitsplein 1, 2610 Wilrijk. *1971*
Tél: (03) 828–25–28. Télex: 33646 uia b
F : sc, dr-pol-soc, phil-let, méd.

University level institututions—Establissements de niveau universitaire

Hoger Architectuurinstituut van het Rijk,
Mutsaertstraat 31, 2000 Antwerpen. *1952*
Institut supérieur d'Architecture Victor Horta,
Université Libre de Bruxelles, boulevard du
Triomphe, CP 248, Accès 5, 1050 Bruxelles.
Tél: (02) 640–00–15
Institut supérieur d'Architecture de l'Etat, Place
Flagey 19, 1050 Bruxelles.
Tél: (02) 64896–19
Institut supérieur d'Architecture St.-Luc, rue
d'Irlande 57, 1060 Bruxelles.
Tél: (02) 53734–19
Hoger Architectuurinstituut Sint-Lukas, Zwarte
Zustersstraat 34, 9000 Gent. *1953*
Tél: (091) 25–42–90
Stedelijk Architectuurinstituut «De Bijloke»,
Prof. J. Kluyskensstraat 6, 9000 Gent.
Tél: (091) 24–38–92
Provinciaal Hoger Architectuurinstituut, Uni-
versitaire Campus, Gebouw E, 3610 Diepen-
beek.
Tél: (011) 22–83–12
Institut supérieur d'Architecture St.-Luc, rue
Ste. Marie 40, 4000 Liège.
Tél: (041) 23–38–10
**Institut supérieur d'Architecture Lambert
Lombard**, rue Saint-Gilles 33, 4000 Liège.
Tél: (041) 52–42–40
**Institut supérieur d'Architecture de la Ville de
Mons**, rue d'Havré 88, 7000 Mons.
Tél: (065) 31–46–20
Institut supérieur d'Architecture St-Luc, chaus-
sée de Tournai 50, 7721 Ramegnies-Chin.
Industriele hogeschool van het Rijk [I. sup. de
Génie industriel], Nijverheidskaai 170, 1070
Brussel, Anderlecht. *1977*
Tél: (02) 520–18–10
Institut Gramme (Institut supérieur industriel),
Quai du Condroz 28, 4900 Angleur.
Tél: (041) 43–07–26
Stedelijke industriële hogeschool Antwerpen,
Paardenmarkt 94, 2000 Antwerpen. *1977*
Tél: (03) 231–50–36

Institut supérieur industriel de l'Etat, Chemin de
Weyler 2, 6700 Arlon.
Tél: (063) 22–05–17
Institut supérieur industriel de Bruxelles, Rue
Royale 154–158, 1000 Bruxelles.
Tél: (02) 21904–62
Institut supérieur industriel de l'I.I.F.-I.M.C.,
avenue Emile Gryson 1, 1070 Bruxelles.
Tél: (02) 523–20–80
Institut supérieur industriel ECAM & INRACI,
rue du Tir 14, 1060 Bruxelles. *1898*
Tél: (02) 539–38–10
Institut supérieur industriel du Hainaut, boule-
vard Solvay 31, 6000 Charleroi.
Katholieke industriële hogeschool voor Limburg,
Limburgs Universitaire Campus, 3610 Diepen-
beek. *1977*
Tél: (011) 22–21–42
Katholieke industriële hogeschool der Kempen,
Technische Schoolstraat 52, 2440 Geel.
Tél: (14) 58–55–65
**Katholieke industriële hogeschool Oost-Vlaan-
deren**, Gebr. De Smetstraat 1, 9000 Gent. *1977*
Tél: (091) 23–60–01
Industriële hogeschool van het Rijk C.T.L.,
Voskenslaan 270, 9000 Gent. *1977*
Tél: (091) 21–80–11
Industriële hogeschool van het Rijk B.M.E.,
Schoonmeersstraat 52, 9000 Gent. *1977*
Tél: (091) 21–38–31
Industriële hogeschool van het Rijk, Maast-
richterstraat 100, 3500 Hasselt. *1977*
Tél: (11) 22 14 77
Katholieke industriële hogeschool Antwerpen,
Salesianenlaan 1A, 2710 Hoboken. *1977*
Tél: (03) 828–16–40
Institut supérieur industriel de l'Etat, rue St.-
Victor 3, 5200 Huy.
Tél: (85) 21–48–26
Provinciale industriële hogeschool, Karel de
Goedelaan, 8500 Körtrijk. *1977*
Tél: (056) 21–64–55
Katholieke industriële hogeschool Groep T

Leuven, Vuurkruisenlaan 1, 3000 Leuven.
1977
Tél: (016) 23–08–50
Institut supérieur industriel liégeois, quai Gloesener 6, 4020 Liège.
Tél: (041) 41–13–85
Katholieke industriële hogeschool De Nayer-Mechelen, J. De Nayerlaan 5, 2580 Katelyne-Waver.
1977
Tél: (015) 31–69–44
Stedelijke industriële hogeschool Mechelen, Leopoldstraat 42, 2800 Mechelen.
Tél: (015) 41–22–11
Institut supérieur industriel de l'Etat, avenue Maistriau 8, Boîte A, 7000 Mons.
Tél: (065) 33–81–54. Cables: isiem mons
Institut supérieur industriel catholique du Hainaut, avenue de l'Hôpital 27h, 7000 Mons.
Tél: (065) 33–71–21
Katholieke industriële hogeschool West-Vlaanderen, Zeedijk 101, 8400 Oostende. *1977*
Tél: (059) 50–89–96
Institut supérieur industriel catholique du Luxembourg, Arts et Métiers Pierrard, 6760 Latour-Virton.
Tél: (063) 57–63–27
Handelshogeschool [E. sup. de Commerce], Korte Nieuwstraat 33, 2000 Antwerpen. *1934*
Tél: (03) 32–74–52
F : com (du soir).
Institut catholique des hautes Etudes commerciales de Bruxelles, boulevard Brand Whitlock 2, 1150 Bruxelles.
1931
Tél: (02) 73591–44
I : com.
Institut d'Enseignement supérieur Lucien Cooremans, place Anneessens 11, 1000 Bruxelles.
1911
Tél: (02) 51254–91
I : com (du soir).
E : trad-interp, adm (du soir).
Institut supérieur de Commerce St-Louis, rue du Marais 113, 1000 Bruxelles.
1927
Tél: (02) 21927–03
I : com (du soir).
Ecole des hautes Etudes commerciales et consulaires, rue Sohet 21, 4000 Liège.
1898
Tél: (041) 52–36–78
E : com.
Economische hogeschool St. Aloysius [E. sup. d'Economie], Sturmstraat 2, 1000 Brussel.
1934
Tél: (02) 21764–01

Economische hogeschool Limburg, Limburgse Universitaire Campus, Universiteitslaan, 3610 Diepenbeek.
1968
Tél: (011) 22–99–61
Vlaamse economische hogeschool Brussel, Koningstraat 284, 1210 Brussel.
1968
Tél: (02) 21765–10
Provinciaal hoger instituut voor bestuurswetenschappen [I. sup. d'Administration], Koningin Elisabethlei 18, 2018 Antwerpen.
1959
Tél: (03) 23728–00
Administratieve en economische hogeschool [I. sup. d'Administration et d'Economie], Trierstraat 84 bus 6, 1040 Brussel.
1949
Tél: (02) 230–21–95
I : adm, com (du soir).
Provinciaal hogeschool voor vertalers en tolken [I. des Etudes supérieures], Brusselsepoortstraat 93, 9000 Gent.
1968
Tél: (091) 23–94–51
Institut voor Tropische Geneeskunde, Nationalestraat 155, 2000 Antwerpen.
1931
Tél: (03) 23858–80. Télex: 31648 tropic b. Cables: metropical
Katholieke vlaamse hogeschool [I. sup. de Technologie], De Bomstraat 11, 2018 Antwerpen.
1968
Hoger institut voor vertalers en tolken [I. sup. de Traducteurs et d'Interprètes], Schildersstraat 41, 2000 Antwerpen.
Tél: (03) 23898–32
Rijkhogeschool voor vertalers en tolken, Trierstraat 84 bus 11, 1040 Brussel.
1964
Tél: (02) 23012–60
Institut supérieur de l'Etat de Traducteurs et d'Interprètes, rue Joseph Hazard 37, 1180 Bruxelles.
Tél: (02) 34551–33
Institut libre «Marie Haps» [Section langues et psychologie], rue d'Arlon 11, 1040 Bruxelles.
1965
Tél: (02) 51192–92
Ecole d'Interprètes internationaux, Avenue du Champ de Mors, 24, 7000 Mons.
Fondation Universitaire Luxembourgeoise, rue des Déportés 140, 6700 Arlon.
Tél: (063) 22–03–80. Télex: 42365 ful b
Universitaire protestantse theologische faculteit/ Faculté universitaire de théologie protestante, Bollandistenstraat 40/Rue des Bollandistes 40, 1040 Brussel/Bruxelles.
Evangelische theologische faculteit, St Jansbergsteenweg 91, 3030 Heverlee/Leuven.

Conseil Interuniversitaire de la Communauté Française (C.I.U.F.)
Le Conseil, créé par un décret du 3 avril 1980, modifié par les décrets des 30 juin 1982 et 30 mars

1983, est un organe de concertation entre les institutions universitaires belges de langue française. Il adresse, à cette fin, au ministre-membre de l'Exécutif de la Communauté Française, qui a

dans ses attributions l'enseignement, des avis et des propositions se rapportant à toutes les questions intéressant la collaboration entre les institutions universitaires de langue française.

Le Conseil agit, soit d'initiative, soit à la demande du Ministre ou d'une institution concernée. Il est habilité à prendre des initiatives visant à assurer une plus grande coopération entre les Facultés ou Départements universitaires. A cette fin, il peut créer des Commissions ou des Groupes de travail spécialisés et encourager des manifestations à caractère scientifique.

Le Conseil est composé de 35 personnes, dont 24 avec voix délibérative, qui sont le Recteur et des membres du Conseil d'administration des Universités et Institutions universitaires suivantes: l'Université de l'Etat à Liège, l'Université Catholique de Louvain, l'Université Libre de Bruxelles, l'Université de l'Etat à Mons, les Facultés Universitaires Notre-Dame de la Paix à Namur, la Faculté Universitaire Catholique de Mons, les Facultés Universitaires Saint-Louis à Bruxelles, la Faculté Polytechnique de Mons, la Faculté des Sciences Agronomiques de l'Etat à Gembloux. Siègent également, avec voix consultative, des représentants du Ministre-membre de l'Exécutif de la Communauté Française, Ministre de l'Education Nationale, et du Ministre de la Politique Scientifique ainsi que des délégués d'autres Institutions à caractère universitaire, du personnel scientifique et des étudiants.

The French Interuniversity Council, created by decree of 3 April 1980, modified by the decrees of 30 June 1982 and 30 March 1983, is the body linking the francophone university institutions in Belgium. To this end, it addresses, to the Minister-member of the Executive of the French Community, responsible, among other things, for education, opinions and proposals concerning all matters of collaboration between university faculties and departments. The Council acts either on its own initiative or at the request of the Minister or the institution involved. It is entitled to take initiatives with the object of promoting co-operation between university faculties or departments. To this end, it may form Commissions or specialized Working Groups and promote scientific events.

The 35 members of the Council (24 with the right to vote) are the Rectors and members of the administrative boards of the following universities and university institutions: Université de l'Etat à Liège; Université Catholique de Louvain; Université Libre de Bruxelles; Université de l'Etat à Mons; Facultés Universitaires Notre-Dame de la Paix à Namur; Faculté Universitaire Catholique de Mons; Facultés Universitaires Saint-Louis à Bruxelles; Faculté Polytechnique de Mons;

Faculté des Sciences Agronomiques de l'Etat à Gembloux. Representatives of the Minister-member of the Executive of the French Community, the Minister of Education, of the Minister for Science Policy, and representatives of other university level institutions, of academic staff and of students also serve on the Council but without right of vote.

Président (1986–88): Georges Verhaegen, Recteur de l'Université de libre Bruxelles.
5, rue d'Egmont, 1050 Bruxelles.
Tél: (02) 512–58–15. Télex: 25498 berefo b

Vlaamse Interuniversitaire Raad (VL.-I.R.)

Le Conseil Interuniversitaire Flamand a été créé en exécution d'un décret adopté fin 1976 par le Conseil culturel de la Communauté culturelle néerlandaise.

Dans le cadre des pouvoirs communautaires, le V.L.I.R. donne des avis et fait des propositions au Ministre de l'Education Nationale et/ou au Ministre de la Politique Scientifique. De plus, le Conseil interuniversitaire organise la concertation et la coopération entre les institutions universitaires flamandes.

Les trois universités flamandes dites 'complètes' (Rijksuniversiteit Gent, Katholieke Universiteit Leuven, Vrije Universiteit Brussel) sont représentées au Conseil interuniversitaire par deux membres, le recteur et un autre membre. Les cinq institutions universitaires dites 'in-complètes' (Universitaire Instelling Antwerpen, Rijksuniversitair Centrum Antwerpen, Universitaire Faculteiten Sint-Ignatius Antwerpen, Universitaire Faculteiten Sint-Aloysius, Limburgs Universitair Centrum) sont représentées chacune par son recteur. Un délégué du Ministre de l'Education nationale et un délégué du Ministre de la Politique Scientifique assistent aux séances du Conseil.

Le VL.I.R. élit son président pour une durée de deux ans.

The Flemish Interuniversity Council was created in 1976 by decree of the Cultural Council of the Flemish Cultural Community.

Within the framework of the competence of the Community the Council may advise and make proposals to the Minister of Education and to the Minister for Science Policy. The Council is responsible for organizing co-operation between the Flemish university institutions.

The three 'full' universities (Rijksuniversiteit Gent; Katholieke Universiteit Leuven; Vrije Universiteit Brussel) are each represented on the Council by two members, the Rector and one other person. Each of the five other university institutions (Universitaire Instelling Antwerpen; Rijksuniversitaire Centrum Antwerpen; Universitaire Faculteiten Sint-Ignatius Antwerpen;

Universitaire Faculteiten Sint-Aloysius; Limburgs Universitaire Centrum) is represented by its Rector. The meetings of the Council are attended by a representative of the Minister of Education and a representative of the Minister for Science Policy.

The Council elects its own president who serves for two years.

Président: L. De Meyer.
Directeur: J. Van der Perre.
Egmontstraat 5, 1050 Brussel.
Tél: (02) 521–91–10. Fax: (02) 513–25–52.
Télex: 25498

Fondation universitaire

Etablissement d'utilité publique créé par la loi du 6 juillet 1920, la Fondation poursuit l'avancement de la science. Elle ne professe aucune doctrine d'ordre philosophique ou politique.

Les ressources de la Fondation sont affectées à l'octroi de subsides pour tous objets se trouvant étroitement en rapport avec le développement de la haute culture scientifique dans le pays et l'amélioration de l'enseignement supérieur.

La Fondation alloue notamment des subsides pour favoriser la publication d'ouvrages et de revues scientifiques et pour aider des associations méritant, par leur activité et leur esprit d'initiative, l'appui qu'elles sollicitent.

En 1936, la Fondation a créé un Bureau de Statistiques universitaires qui publie chaque année un volume donnant les statistiques de l'enseignement universitaire ainsi que celles des diplômes de fin d'études délivrés par les établissements belges recensés dans le dit volume.

La Fondation a aménagé un Club où les savants belges et étrangers ont l'occasion de se rencontrer et de s'entretenir de leurs travaux. Le Club dispose d'une bibliothèque, de plusieurs salons et salles de conférences, réservés aux sociétés savantes, d'une salle de restaurant, d'une vingtaine d'appartements où peuvent résider les membres belges et étrangers, à l'occasion d'un séjour à Bruxelles.

Enfin, la Fondation collabore à la gestion des prix scientifiques suivants: Prix Scientifiques Louis Empain, Prix européens Emile Bernheim, Prix Fernand Collin.

The University Foundation, a public body, created by the law of 6 July 1920, promotes the advancement of learning. It has neither philosophical nor political doctrine.

The resources of the Foundation are used to subsidize undertakings of various kinds which are closely concerned with the development of higher learning and culture in the country and with the improvement of higher education.

In particular, the Foundation allows grants to

encourage the publication of learned works and reviews and to assist associations whose activities and spirit of initiative show them worthy of support.

In 1936 the Foundation created a Bureau of University Statistics which publishes annually a volume of statistics on higher education and on degrees and diplomas awarded by Belgian institutions of higher education.

The Foundation has organized a Club where Belgian and foreign scholars can meet and discuss their work. The Club has a library, several lounges and lecture rooms reserved for the use of academic societies, a restaurant, and some twenty apartments where Belgian and foreign members visiting Brussels may stay.

Lastly, the Foundation helps to administer the award of the following academic prizes: Prix Scientifiques Louis Empain, Prix européens Emile Bernheim, Prix Fernand Collin.

Président: Gilbert De Landsheere.
Administrateur Délégué: Louis Baeck.
11, rue d'Egmont, 1050 Bruxelles.
Tél: (02) 511–81–00

Fondation Francqui

Etablissement d'utilité publique, la Fondation Francqui a pour objet de favoriser le développement du haut enseignement et de la recherche scientifique en Belgique.

Elle décerne tous les ans le «Prix Francqui», d'un montant de 2.000.000 de francs, à un savant belge âgé de moins de cinquante ans, qui a apporté à la science une contribution importante dont la valeur a augmenté le prestige de la Belgique.

De plus, elle convie annuellement des savants belges et étrangers à donner, sous ses auspices, un enseignement en Belgique (Chaires Francqui). Elle peut en outre accorder discrétionnairement des subventions pour tout objet relatif au développement du haut enseignement ou de la recherche scientifique en Belgique.

The Francqui Foundation, a public body, seeks to encourage the development of higher education and research in Belgium.

It awards the annual 'Prix Francqui' (2,000,000 Frs), which goes to a Belgian scholar under 50 years of age who has enhanced Belgian prestige by making an important contribution to the advancement of learning.

Furthermore, every year it invites Belgian and foreign scholars to teach in Belgium under its auspices (Francqui Professorships). It may also, at its discretion, allow grants to finance work involving the advancement of higher education and research in Belgium.

Président: Jacques Grootwaert.

Administrateur Délégué: Pierre de Bie.
11, rue d'Egmont, 1050 Bruxelles.
Tél: (02) 511–81–00

Fonds national de la Recherche scientifique
Etablissement d'utilité publique, le Fonds national a pour but de favoriser la recherche scientifique en Belgique.
Les revenus du Fonds national sont affectés aux objets suivants: a) des subsides sont accordés à des chercheurs pour leur permettre de poursuivre leurs travaux; b) des subsides sont mis à la disposition de jeunes gens belges que leur valeur désigne à l'attention du Conseil et qui désirent se consacrer à la recherche scientifique; c) des subsides sont octroyés en vue de faciliter la présence de chercheurs belges à des congrès se tenant à l'étranger; d) des subsides peuvent en outre être accordés par le Conseil pour tout objet qui se trouve étroitement en rapport avec le développement de la recherche scientifique en Belgique.
The National Fund for Scientific Research, a public body, seeks to promote scientific research in Belgium.
The revenue of the Fund is used in the following ways: a) grants are made to scholars and research workers to help them in the pursuit of their work; b) grants are made to young Belgians whose ability has been brought to the attention of the Council and who wish to devote themselves to scientific research; c) subsidies are given to assist Belgian research workers attend congresses abroad; d) subsidies may also be given by the Council for other purposes closely related to the advancement of scientific research in Belgium.
Président (1987–1988): Arthur Bodson, Recteur de l'Université de l'Etat à Liège.
Secrétaire général: P. Levaux.
5, rue d'Egmont, 1050 Bruxelles.
Tél: (02) 512–58–15. Fax: (02) 513–25–52.
Télex: 25498 berefo b

Universitas Belgica (IAUPL)
Correspondant: 18, rue due Docteur Roux, 75015 Paris (France).
Tél: (33-1) 47–83–31–65

Fédération belge des Femmes diplômées des Universités (IFUW)
29, rue Blanche, 1050 Bruxelles.
Mouvement des Etudiants universitaires belges d'Expression française—MUBEF
61, rue Belliard, Bruxelles 4.
Vereniging der Vlaamse Studenten—VVS
Koopliedenstraat 20, Brussel 1.
Tourisme des Etudiants et de la Jeunesse MUBEF-YMCA, asbl.—TEJ
61, rue Belliard, Bruxelles 4.
Centre belge de Pax Romana
Margareta Square 1, Boîte 4, 1040 Bruxelles.
Conférence Olivaint de Belgique (Pax Romana)
Rue André Fauchille 12, 1150 Bruxelles.
Tél: (02) 7352050
Hoogstudenten Verbond voor Katholieke Aktie (Pax Romana)
Jan Stasstr. 2, 300 Leuven.
Paroisse universitaire de Louvain (Pax Romana)
9, place Hoover, 3000 Louvain.
International Student Chaplaincy (WSCF)
5, rue du Champ de Mars, 1050 Bruxelles.
Centre national pour l'Etude des Nations Unies et de la Coopération internationale (ISMUN)
c/o UNICEF/Basse Sambre, Rue Auguste Varet 27, 6268 Aiseau.
Union des Etudiants juifs de Belgique (WUJS)
89 Chaussee De Vleurgat, 1050 Bruxelles.
Tél: (02) 647–7279. Télex: 20625 b

*

Ministère de l'Education nationale
Cité Administrative de l'Etat, Bloc Arcades—4ᵉ étage, 1010 Bruxelles.
Tél: (02) 210–55–11. Télex: 64556 edunat b
Ministerie van Orderwijs Bestuur H.O./W.O.
Manhattan-Center, Toren 2, Kruisvaartenstraat 3, 1210 Brussel.
Tél: (02) 219–18–80/90 Post: 751–754
Commission nationale belge pour l'Unesco
Ministère des Affaires étrangères, Rue Quatre Bras 2, 1000 Bruxelles.
Tél: (02) 516–84–57. Télex: 21376. Cables: belext bruxelles

BELIZE
BELIZE

University College of Belize, Princess Margaret Drive, Belize City.   *1979*
Tel: (02) 45118
D : *arts, soc, nat, bus ed, eng, phar, const, fish, med & vet techn, ed.*
S : *agr.*
  BELIZE TECHNICAL COLLEGE SIXTH FORM, Freetown Road, Belize City.   *1974*
  D : *bus st, gen st, bui, eng.*

ST. JOHN'S COLLEGE SIXTH FORM, Princess Margaret Drive, Belize City.   *1952*
D : *arts, bus, sc.*
BELIZE TEACHERS' COLLEGE, Princess Margaret Drive, Belize City.   *1964*
D : *ed, academic, lang, prac subjects.*
BELIZE SCHOOL OF NURSING, Princess Margaret Drive, Belize City.   *1963*
F : *nurs, obst.*

Ministry of Education, Youth, Sport and Culture
Belmopan.
Tel: (08) 22324
Belize National Commission for Unesco

Ministry of Education, Youth, Sport and Culture, Belmopan.
Tel: (08) 2329

PEOPLE'S REPUBLIC OF BENIN
REPUBLIQUE POPULAIRE DU BENIN

*Université nationale du Bénin, B.P. 526, Cotonou.   *1970*
Tél: 36–00
F : *sa; sc-tec, let-arts-hum, sc jur-éco-pol, agr* (Abomey-Calavi).
  ECOLE NATIONALE D'ADMINISTRATION, Abomey-Calavi.
  Tél: 36–01–43
  INSTITUT NATIONAL D'ENSEIGNEMENT

D'EDUCATION PHYSIQUE ET SPORTIVE, B.P. 169, Porto-Novo.
COLLÈGE POLYTECHNIQUE UNIVERSITAIRE, Abomey-Calavi.
ECOLE NORMALE SUPÉRIEURE, Porto-Novo.
CENTRE RÉGIONAL DE DÉVELOPPEMENT SANITAIRE, Cotonou.
CENTRE BÉNINOIS DE LANGUES ÉTRANGÈRES, Cotonou.

Jeunesse Chrétienne Universitaire et Scolaire du Bénin (WSCF)
B.P. 34, Cotonou.
Tél: 21–29–30
Coopérative Universitaire des Etudiants—CUE (IUS)
Université nationale du Bénin, B.P. 526, Cotonou.
Télex: 5200 minaffet
Service de Documentation et d'Equivalence des

Diplômes
Ministère de l'Enseignements moyen et supérieur, B.P. 348, Cotonou.
Tél: 30–06–81
Ministère de l'Enseignement moyen et supérieur
Cotonou.
Tél: 30–19–91
Commission nationale béninoise pour l'Unesco
B.P. 520, Porto-Novo.
Tél: 21–25–30

BERMUDA
BERMUDES

Bermuda College, PO Box DV356, Devonshire
DVBX.   *1974*

Tel: 2–5205
D : *arts-sc, bus st, gen st, hotel techn, techn.*

Ministry of Education
P.O. Box HM1185, Hamilton.

Tel: (809) 236–6904

BOLIVIA
BOLIVIE

UNIVERSITIES AND TECHNICAL UNIVERSITIES—
UNIVERSITES ET UNIVERSITES TECHNIQUES

Universidad Católica Boliviana, Avenida 14 de
Septiembre 4807, Casilla 4805, La Paz.   *1966*
Tél: 78–31–48
D : éco, adm des aff, commun, phil, psyc.
I : rech psyc, rech socio.
E : ét coopératives.
Universidad Autónoma Gabriel René Moreno,
Plaza 24 de Septiembre, Casilla postal 702,
Santa Cruz.   *1880, 1938*
Tél: 4–2540
F : dr-pol-soc, éco, vét.
E : agr, ba.
I : techn.
*Universidad «Juan Misael Saracho»**, Avenida
Las Américas s/n, Casilla 51, Tarija.   *1946*
Tél: 3110/3111/3112
F : sc exactes-nat, techn.
E : dent, ing, dr-pol-soc-éco.
Universidad Mayor de San Andrés, Avenida
Villazón 1995, Casilla de Correo 6042, La
Paz.   *1830*
Tél: 35–94–90. Télex: 3252
F : arc-arts, dr-soc, hum-éd, sc exactes-nat,
techn, heal sc.
I : polytec, phy, ch, soc, ét bolivienes, hyd.
*Universidad Mayor de San Francisco Xavier**,
Calle Junín y Estudiantes 692, Casilla 212,
Sucre.   *1624*
Tél: 23245
F : dr-pol-soc, heal, sc.

D : lang mod, ba.
I : éco, socio, biol, rech cancer.
A : ballet.
Universidad Mayor de San Simón, Avenida
Oquendo-Sucre, Cochabamba.   *1832*
Tél: 25501
F : arc, bioch-phar, agr, éco, dr-soc-pol, méd,
dent.
E : agr.
Universidad Nacional Siglo XX, Edif. Fondo
Exploración Minera, Avenida Ecuador 2007,
La Paz.   *1984*
Universidad Técnica del Beni, Campus Universi-
tario, Casilla de Correo 38, Trinidad-Beni.
1967
Tél: 21590
F : zoo.
I : techn ind.
Universidad Técnica de Oruro, Avenida 6 de
Octubre 1209, Casilla 49, Oruro.   *1892, 1937*
Tél: 50100
F : techn, sc exactes-nat.
D : dr, éco, tour.
I : polytec.
Universidad Tomás Frías, Avenida del Maestro,
Casilla 36, Potosí.   *1892, 1937*
Tél: 2–7300
F : dr, éco, ing.
I : agr, com, aff soc & syndicalisme, tec.
A : ba, lang mod.

OTHER INSTITUTIONS—AUTRES INSTITUTIONS

Technical Education—Enseignement technique

Escuela Industrial Superior de la Nación «Pedro Domingo Murilla», La Paz.   *1942*
Tél: 2–2565

Professional Education—Enseignement professionnel

Escuela Superior de Bellas Artes, Calle Rosendo Gutiérrez 323, La Paz.   *1928*
Tél: 371141
Instituto Comercial Superior de la Nación «Federico Alvarez Plate», Ayacucho 6737, Cochabamba City.
Instituto Comercial Superior de la Nación, Calle Campero 94, La Paz.   *1944*
Tél: 37–32–96. Cables: incos
Colegio Nacional de Comercio «Felipe Leonor

Rivera»**, Santa Cruz.
Instituto Nacional de Comercio, Oruro City.
Colegio Nacional de Comercio, Tarija City.
Instituto Superior de Comercio, Trinidad City.
Escuela Nacional de Enfermería, Calle 16 de Julio 83, Obrajes, La Paz.
Conservatorio Nacional de Música, Avenida 6 de Agosto 2092, La Paz.   *1908*
Tél: 37–32–97

Teacher Training—Formation pédagogique

Escuela Normal Integrada Católica, Cochabamba.   *1949*
Instituto Superior de Educación, La Paz.
Escuela Normal Especializada Técnica, La Paz.   *1959*
Tel: 37–32–91
Instituto Normal Superior «Simón Bolívar», Villa IV Centenario, La Paz.   *1917, 1946*
Tél: 30–03–04
Instituto Normal Superior de Educación Física,

Calle Juande Vargas 311, La Paz.
Tél: 37–32–94
Escuela Normal Integrada «Enrique Finot», Avenida «Ejército esq., Aba Barba», Santa Cruz.   *1956*
Tél: 3416
Escuela Normal Integrada «Mariscal Sucre», Sucre.   *1909*
Instituto Superior de Educación Rural, Tarija.

Comité Ejecutivo de la Universidad Boliviana (CEUB)
Le CEUB a été créé au Vé Congrès national des Universités. If fonctionne régulièrement depuis 1982 comme l'instrument de coordination du système universitaire bolivien.
The Executive Committee of the Bolivian Universities was created at the Fifth National Congress of Universities. It has been regularly carrying out its tasks since 1982 as the coordinating institution of the Bolivian university system.
Secrétaire executif: Alfonso Via Reque.
Casilla postal 4722, La Paz.
Tél: 379967

Federación Boliviana de Mujeres Profesionales Universitarias (IFUW)
Casilla 6192, La Paz.
Confederación Universitaria Boliviana— CUB

(IUS)
Avenida Villazon, Edit. Cent «UMSA», La Paz.
Tél: 36–88–23. Télex: 3210 mir bv
Servicio Universitario Mundial (WUS), Casilla 3203, Cochabamba.
Tél: 29457
Juventud Universitaria Católica (Pax Romana)
Casilla 106, Potosí.
Movimiento Estudiantil Cristiano de Bolivia (WSCF)
Casilla 1146, Obrajes, La Paz.

*

Ministerio de Educación y Cultura
Avenida Arce 2408, La Paz.
Tél: 37–32–63
Comisión Nacional Boliviana para la Unesco
Ministerio de Educación y Cultura, La Paz.
Tél: 37–32–69

BOTSWANA
BOTSWANA

*University of Botswana, Private Bag 0022, Gaborone. *1976, 1982*
Tel: (31) 51151. Telex: 2429 bd. Cables: university, gaborone
F : *eco-soc st, ed, hum, sc.*
NATIONAL HEALTH INSTITUTE.

Tel: (31) 53031. Cables: sabaoki
AGRICULTURAL COLLEGE.
Tel: (31) 2381/2
Also affiliated teacher training colleges at: Francistown, Lobatse, Molepolole, Serowe, and Tlokweng.

Botswana Student Council—BSC (IUS)
PO Box 20988, Gaborone.
World University Service (WUS)
Naledi Segopolo & Associates, Suites 76, 8 & 9, Tswane House, PO Bag 237, Gaborone.
Tel: (31) 37–4002
Christian Council of Botswana (WSCF)
PO Box 355, Gaborone.
Botswana National Students' Union (ISMUN)
Secretary: Koobatile Kelebale.

Private Bag 0019, Gaborone.

*

Ministry of Education
Gaborone.
Tel: (31) 35–56–05. Cables: thuto
Botswana National Commission for Unesco
Ministry of Education, Gaborone.
Tel: (31) 35–56–05. Telex: thuto 2944 bd

BRAZIL
BRESIL

UNIVERSITIES—UNIVERSITES

Universidade Federal do Acre, Avenida Presidente Vargas 654, 69900 Rio Branco, AC. *1971*
Tel: (068) 2242397. Telex: 69–2532
I : *hum-let.*
F : *law, eco, let.*
*Universidade Federal do Alagoas, Praça Visconde de Sinimbu 206, 57000 Maceió, AL.
1961
Tel: (082) 2212801. Telex: 822307
Ce : *exact sc-nat, techn, biol, heal sc, hum-let-arts, app soc, agr.*
Universidad Federal do Amazonas, Avenida Getúlio Vargas 381, 69000 Manaus, AM. *1965*
Tel: (092) 2333600. Telex: 92–2554
I : *exact sc, hum-let, biol.*
F : *ed, heal sc, techn, soc st.*
Universidade Federal da Bahia, Rua Augusto Viana s/n, 40140 Salvador, BA. *1946*
Tel: (071) 2452811. Telex: 71–1978
I : *biol, phy, geosc, let, math, ch, heal sc.*

F : *arc, eco, law, ed, phar, phil-hum, med, dent.*
S : *adm, agr, nurs, vet, mus & theat art, nutr, polytec, fa, lib.*
Universidade de Bauru, Avenida Eng. Luiz Edmundo Carrijo Coube, 17033 Bauru, SP.
Tel: (0142) 232111. Telex: 14–2312
eng, arc-urb, sc, psyc, phys, techn, meteo, commun, civ const.
Universidad Regional de Blumenau, Avenida Antonio da Veiga, 89010 Blumenau, SC.
Tel: (0473) 228288. Telex: 47–3302
*Universidade de Brasília, Campus Universitário, Asa Norte, 70910 Brasília, DF. *1962*
Tel: (04) 2740022. Telex: 612730
I : *hum, exact sc, biol, commun, arc-urb.*
F : *heal sc, appl soc st, techn, ed.*
Universidade Braz Cubas, Rua Francisco Franco 133, 08700 Mogi das Cruzes, SP. *1984*
Tel: (011) 4696444. Telex: 11–39267
F : *law, eco-bus-adm, eng, phil-soc-let, arc-urb,*

soc commun.

Universidade Estadual de Campinas, Cidade Universitaria, «Zeferino Vaz», 13100 Campinas, SP. *1966*
Tel: (192) 391301. Telex: 19–1150
I : *biol, phil-hum, phy, math-stat-comp, ch, let, geosc, arts.*
F : *med, ed, nutr, agr, eng; eng* (Limeira); *dent* (Piracicaba).
Ce : *Brasilian st, phys, comp, techn, ch, med sc.*

*Pontifícia Universidade Católica de Campinas, Rodovio D. Pedro I, Km. 112, 13100 Campinas, SP. *1955*
Tel: (192) 520899. Telex: 19–1806
I : *arts-commun, exact sc, hum, phil-theol, let, psyc, biol.*
F : *lib, eco-acc-adm, techn, law-soc, ed, phys, nurs, dent, soc serv, med, arc-urb.*

Universidade de Caxias do Sul, Rua Francisco Getúlio Vargas, 95100 Caxias do Sul, RS. *1967*
Tel: (542) 2224133. Telex: 54–3734
Ce : *biol-heal sc, appl soc st, techn, hum-arts.*

Universidade Estadual do Ceará, Avenida Paranjana, 1700 Campus do Itaperi, 60715 Fortaleza, CE. *1977*
Tel: (85) 245–113. Telex: 85–2295
Ce : *app soc st, hum, sc-techn, heal sc, adm st.*

*Universidade Federal do Ceará, Avenida da Universidade 2853, 60000 Fortaleza, CE. *1954*
Tel: (85) 2230233. Telex: 85–1077
Ce : *hum, sc, techn, agr-fish, heal, app soc st, law-eco-ed.*

Universidade Federal do Espírito Santo, Avenida Fernando Ferrari, Goiabeiras, 29000 Vitória, ES. *1961*
Tel: (27) 2278118. Telex: 27–2330
F : *phar-bioch.*
Ce : *ge st, arts, techn, biomed, ed, phys, law-eco, agr.*

Universidade Estadual de Feira de Santana, Km. 03 BR 116, 44100 Feira de Santana, BA. *1976*
Tel: (75) 2241521. Telex: 75–2403
D : *app & soc, techn, heal, ed, let-arts, biol, hum-phil, exact sc.*

*Universidade Federal Fluminense, Rua Miguel de Frias, 9, Icaraí, 24220 Niterói, RJ. *1960*
Tel: (21) 7178080. Telex: 21–32076
Ce : *techn, app soc st, gen st, med.*
I : *ch, art-soc commun, phy, hum-phil, biomed-biol, geosc, let, math, law, ed.*
F : *law, eco, ed, dent, med, vet, phar.*
S : *eng, soc serv, nurs.*

Universidade de Fortaleza, Avenida Washington Soares s/n, 60810 Fortaleza, CE. *1973*
Tel: (85) 2392833. Telex: 85–3701
Ce : *hum, techn, heal sc, nat.*

Universidade Gama Filho, Rua Manoel Vitorino 625, 20740 Rio de Janeiro, RJ. *1972*
Tel: (212) 2697272

Ce : *exact sc-techn, hum, soc, biol-heal.*
F : *phil-sc-let.*
S : *eng, med.*

Universidade Católica de Goiás, Praça Universitária, 74000 Goiânia, GO. *1960*
Tel: (62) 2251188. Telex: 62–1276
law, ed, psyc, let, hist, soc serv, sc, arc-urb, biol, math, eco, acc, adm, nurs, phil, civ eng.

Universidade Federal de Goiás, Rodovia Goiânia Neropolis, 12, 74000 Goiânia, GO. *1963*
Tel: (62) 2610333. Telex: 62–2206
I : *biol, hum-let, math-phy, trop pathology, ch-geosc, arts.*
F : *law, ed, phar, med, dent.*
S : *agr-vet, eng.*

*Universidade de Ijui, Rua São Francisco 501, 98700 Ijui, RS. *1985*
Tel: (55) 3323211. Telex: 55–2210
I : *phil-let-arts, soc, exact sc-nat.*
Ce : *ed, app soc st, heal.*

Universidade Federal de Juiz de Fora, Rua Benjamin Constant 790, 36100 Juiz de Fora, MG. *1960*
Tel: (32) 2125966. Telex: 32–2365
I : *biol-geosc, exact sc, hum-let.*
F : *eco, law, eng, phar-bioch, med, ed, dent, soc serv.*

Universidade Estadual de Londrina, Campus Universitário, 86051 Londrina, PR. *1971*
Tel: (432) 275151. Telex: 43–2256
Ce : *biol, hum-let, exact sc, app soc st, heal, ed-commun-arts, techn, rur sc.*

Universidade Mackenzie, Rua Maria Antonia, 01222 São Paulo, SP. *1952*
Tel: (11) 2566611
S : *eng.*
F : *arc-urb, soc, let-ed, eco-adm-acc, law, techn, commun-arts, exact sc-techn.*

Universidade Federal do Maranhão, Largo dos Amores 351, 65000 São Luis, MA. *1966*
Tel: (98) 222331. Telex: 98–2214
I : *phil-hum, let-arts, sc-nat.*
F : *eco, med, law, nurs, phar, dent, soc serv, ed.*

Universidade Estadual do Maranhão, Cidade Universitária Paulo VI, 65000 São Luis, MA.
Tel: (98) 2250865
S : *adm, agr, eng, vet.*
F : *ed.*

Universidade Estadual de Maringá, Avenida Colombo, 3690, 87020 Maringá, PR.
Tel: (44) 224242. Telex: 44–2198
Ce : *techn, soci-eco, biol-heal sc, exact sc, hum-let-arts.*

Universidade Federal de Mato Grosso do Sul, Campus Universitário 649, 79100 Campo Grande, MT. *1970*
Tel: (67) 3873311. Telex: 67–2331
Ce : *biol-heal sc, exact sc-techn, hum-soc.*
(Corumbá, Aquidaúana, Dourados, Três

Lagoas).

Universidade Federal de Mato Grosso, Avenida Fernando Corrêa da Costa s/n, 78000 Cuiabá, MT. *1971*
Tel: (65) 3612211. Telex: 65–2371
Ce : *let-hum, exact sc-techn, soc, agr, biol-heal sc.*

*Pontifícia Universidade Católica de Minas Gerais, Avenida Dom José Gaspar 500, Caixa postal 2686, 30000 Belo Horizonte, MG. *1958*
Tel: (31) 3191144. Telex: 31–3339
Ce : *biol-heal sc, hum, exact sc, ch, soc.*
F : *commun, nurs-obst, law, eco, hum, dent.*
I : *polytec, psyc.*
S : *soc serv.*

*Universidade Federal de Minas Gerais, Avenida Antonio Carlos, 31270 Belo Horizonte, MG. *1892*
Tel: (31) 4418077. Telex: 31–2308
I : *biol, exact sc-phy, geosc.*
F : *eco, law, ed, phar-bioch, phil-hum, let, med, dent.*
S : *arc, eng, vet, phys, mus, fa, lib, nurs.*

Universidade de Mogi das Cruzes, Avenida Cândido Almeida Souza 200, 08700 Mogi das Cruzes, SP. *1964*
Tel: (11) 4695333
Ce : *exact sc-techn, biomed sc.*
F : *ed, eco-adm, med, dent, phys, eng, law, commun, arc-urb, geol.*
I : *phil-soc, let-arts, biol, psyc, sc.*
S : *nurs.*

Universidade Regional do Nordeste, Avenida Floriano Peixoto 718, 58100 Campina Grande, PB. *1967*
Tel: (83) 3210099. Telex: 83–3226
Ce : *hum-let-arts, sc-techn, biol-heal sc.*

*Universidade Federal de Ouro Prêto, Rua Diogo de Vasconcelos 122, 35400 Ouro Prêto, MG. *1969*
Tel: (31) 5512111. Telex: 31–2954
I : *exact sc, biol, hum, let, arts-arc.*
F : *app soc st, ed.*
S : *mine-met, phar.*

Universidade Federal do Pará, Rua Augusto Correa, 66000 Belém, PA. *1957, 1971*
Tel: (91) 2292088. Telex: 91–1013
Ce : *exact sc-nat, biol, phil-hum, let-arts, biomed, techn, socioeco, ed.*

Universidade Federal da Paraíba, Campus Universitário, 58000 João Pessôa, PB. *1960*
Tel: (83) 2247200. Telex: 83–2187
Ce : *hum-let-arts, techn, heal sc, exact sc-nat, ed, app soc; biol-heal, hum, techn-sc* (Campina Grande); *agr* (Areia); *tec ed* (Bananeiras).
F : *law* (Sousa); *phil-sc-let, eco* (Patos); *phil-sc-let* (Cajazeiras).

Pontifícia Universidade Católica do Paraná, Rua Imaculada Conceição 1155, 80000 Curitiba,

PR. *1959*
Tel: (41) 2230922. Telex: 41–0282
Ce : *theo-hum, legal-soc, exact sc, biomed.*
F : *adm-eco.*

Universidade Federal do Paraná, Rua XV de Novembro 1299, 80000 Curitiba, PR. *1912, 1974*
Tel: (41) 2642522. Telex: 41–5100
Sect : *exact sc, biol, hum-let-arts, ed, techn, agr, heal sc, app soc.*

Universidade de Passo Fundo, Campus Universitario, 99100 Passo Fundo, RS. *1968*
Tel: (54) 3132000. Telex: 54–5394
I : *exact sc-geosc, biol, phil-hum, arts.*
F : *agr, eco-adm, med, dent, ed, phys, law, eng.*

*Universidade Estadual Paulista «Júlio de Mesquita Filho», Praça da Se 108, 01001 São Paulo, SP. *1976*
Tel: (11) 327171. Telex: 11–31870
I : *biosc-let-exact sc* (São José do Rio Preto); *let-hist-psyc* (Assis); *ch* (Araraquara); *arts* (Planalto); *geosc, biosc* (Rio Claro); *hist-soc serv* (Franca).
F : *techn, mus; med, vet-agr-biol* (Botucatu); *eng* (Guaratinguetá); *phar, dent* (Araraquara); *phil-sc-let* (Araraquara, Assis, Franca, Marília, Presidente Prudente, Rio Claro, São José do Rio Prêto); *vet, agr* (Jaboticabal); *dent* (Araçatuba, São José dos Campos); *eng* (Ilha Solteira).

*Universidade Católica de Pelotas, Rua Félix da Cunha 412, 96100 Pelotas, RS. *1960*
Tel: (532) 253455. Telex: 53–2454
Ce : *soc, ed-hum, exact sc-techn, biol-heal sc.*

Universidade Federal de Pelotas, Campus Universitário, 96165 Pelotas, RS. *1969*
Tel: (532) 212033. Telex: 53–2302
I : *biol, ch-geosc, hum, let-arts, phy-math.*
F: *agr-zoo, vet, dom sc, dent, med, law, ed.*
S : *phys.*
Conservatory : *mus.*

Universidade Católica de Pernambuco, Rua do Principe 526, 50000 Recife, PE. *1943, 1951, 1973*
Tel: (81) 2317233. Telex: 81–2776
Ce : *theo-hum, techn, soc.*

Universidade Federal de Pernambuco, Avenida Professor Moraes Rego, 50739 Recife, PE. *1827, 1946*
Tel: (81) 2710344. Telex: 81–1267
Ce : *arts-commun, exact sc-nat, biol, phil-hum, ed, soc-app soc, heal sc, techn.*
F : *law.*

Universidade Federal Rural de Pernambuco, Avenida Dom Manoel de Medeiros, 50000 Recife, PE. *1947*
Tel: (81) 2685477. Telex: 81–1195
D : *ch, ed, rur techn, agr, biol, dom sc, let-hum, fish, anim physiology, vet, phy-math, zoo.*

Universidade Católica de Petrópolis, Rua Benjamin Constant 213, 25610 Petrópolis, RJ.
1954
Tel: (242) 425062. Telex: 21–31637
I : *arts-commun, theo-phil-hum, exact sc-nat.*
F : *law, eco-acc, adm, ed.*
S : *eng, rehabilitation.*
Universidade Metódista de Piracicaba, Rua Rangel Pestana 762, 13400 Piracicaba, SP.
1881, 1975
Tel: (194) 335011. Telex: 19–1914
Ce : *eco-acc-adm, soc commun, ed, hum, app sc, biol-heal sc, exact sc-techn.*
Universidade Federal do Piaui, Campus Universitário, 64000 Teresina, PI.
1971
Tel: (86) 2321212. Telex: 86–2271
Ce : *ed, techn, hum-let, heal sc, nat, agr.*
Universidade Estadual de Ponta Grossa, Praça Santos Dumont, 84100 Ponta Grossa, PR.
1970
Tel: (422) 243966. Telex: 42–2242
Sect : *bio-heal sc, exact sc-nat, let-hum.*
Universidade de Ribeirão Prêto, Avenida Costabile Romano 2201, 14095 Ribeirão Prêto, SP.
1971
Tel: (166) 6246300. Telex: 16–6036 asen
D : *soc commun, soc st, phys, mus, ed, sc, adm, let, plast arts, dent, tour.*
Universidade de Rio Grande, Rua Eng. Alfredo Huch 475, 96200 Rio Grande, RS.
1956
Tel: (532) 323300. Telex: 53–2373
Ce : *exact sc-techn, mar, let-arts, soc, biol-heal sc.*
Universidade Federal do Rio Grande do Norte, Avenida Hermes da Fonseca 780, BR. 101 Km. 1, 59000 Natal, RN.
1958
Tel: (84) 2311266. Telex: 84–2296
Ce : *app soc, hum-let-arts, techn, heal sc, exact sc, biosc.*
F : *jour.*
Universidade Regional do Rio Grande do Norte, Campus Universitário, 59600 Mossoró, RN.
1968
Tel: (84) 3214997. Telex: 84–3211
I : *hum, let-arts.*
F : *eco, ed, soc serv.*
*Pontifícia Universidade Católica do Rio Grande do Sul, Avenida Ipiranga 6681, Caixa postal 1429, 90620 Pôrto Alegre, RS.
1948
Tel: (512) 369400. Telex: 51–3349
I : *theo-relig sc, let-arts, psyc, phil-hum, biosc, math, phy, ch, geosc, comp.*
F : *soc serv, law, pol-eco, soc commun, ed, dent, adm-acc, eng, med, zoo.*
Universidade Federal do Rio Grande do Sul, Avenida Paulo Gama 110, 90049 Pôrto Alegre, RS.
1896
Tel: (512) 217033. Telex: 51–1055
I : *phy, geosc, math, ch, biosc, phil-hum, let, arts, hyd res, nutr.*

F : *arc, phar, med, dent, agr, vet, eco, lib-commun, law, ed.*
S : *eng, phys, nurs.*
*Pontifícia Universidade Católica do Rio de Janeiro, Rua Marquês de São Vicente 225, 22453 Rio de Janeiro, RJ.
1940
Tel: (21) 2749922. Telex: 21–31048
Ce : *theo-hum, soc, scq techn.*
S : *med* (postgrad).
Universidade do Estado do Rio de Janeiro, Avenida São Francisco Xavier 524, 20550 Rio de Janeiro, RJ.
1950
Tel: (21) 2848322
Ce : *biomed, techn, sc, ed-hum.*
I : *hum, phil-let, psyc-soc commun, phys, math-stat, phy, ch, geosc.*
F : *adm-fin, soc serv, law, eco, ed, eng.*
*Universidade Federal do Rio de Janeiro, Avenida Brigadeiro Trompowski s/n, 21941 Rio de Janeiro, RJ.
1922
Tel: (21) 2902112. Telex: 21–22924
I : *math, phy, ch, geosc, phil-soc, psyc, biomed, nutr.*
F : *arc-urb, let, ed, law, eco-adm, med, dent, phar.*
S : *fa, mus, commun, soc serv, phys, nurs.*
Universidade de Rio de Janeiro, Avenida Pasteur, 22290 Rio de Janeiro, RJ.
1890
Tel: (21) 2957794
Ce : *arts, hum, heal sc.*
Universidade Federal Rural do Rio de Janeiro, Km 47 da Antiga Rodovia Rio/São Paulo, 23460 Seropédica, RJ.
1943
Tel: (21) 7821210. Telex: 21–34411
I : *vet, for, exact sc, hum-soc, ed, techn, agr, biol, zoo.*
F : *teacher tr.*
Universidade Federal de Rondonia, Avenida Presidente Dutra, 78900 Porto Velho, Rondonia, RO.
1982
Tel: (69) 2233262. Telex: 69–2152
eco, acc, adm.
Universidade de Sagrado Coração, Rua Irma Arminda 1050, 17043 Bauru, SP.
Tel: (142) 232311
F : *mus, nurs, phil-sc-let.*
Universidade Católica do Salvador, Praça 2 de Julho 7, 40000 Salvador, BA.
1961
Tel: (712) 2452292
I : *exact sc-nat, phil-hum, let, mus, theo.*
F : *ed, law, ing, eco.*
S : *eng, soc serv, adm.*
*Universidade Federal de Santa Catarina, Campus Universitário 'Trindade', 88049 Florianópolis, SC.
1932, 1968, 1970
Tel: (482) 331000. Telex: 48–2240
Ce : *ed, techn, agr, socio-eco, phys, heal sc, biol, phy-math, commun, hum.*
Universidade para o Desenvolvimiento do Estado

de **Santa Catarina**, Madre Benvenuta 499, 88000 Florianopolis, SC.
Tel: (482) 332000. Telex: 48–2485
Universidad Santa Cecília dos Banderantes, Rua Oswaldo Cruz 250, 11100 Santos, S.P.
1961, 1969, 1986
Tel: (132) 344925
F : *plast arts, sc-techn, civ eng, ind eng, phys, com-adm, ed-hum, dent, med.*
Universidade Federal de Santa Maria, Cidade Universitária Km 9, 97100 Santa Maria, RS.
1961, 1970
Tel: (55) 2261616. Telex: 55–2230
Ce : *fund st, techn, biomed, rur sc, dr-eco-adm, arts let, phys, ped.*
Universidade de Santa Ursula, Rua Fernando Ferrari 75, 22231 Rio de Janeiro, RJ.
1938, 1970, 1975
Tel: (21) 5515542. Telex: 21–34929
Ce : *techn-phil-soc, ed, exact sc-techn, theo-phil, doc-let, hum-soc, biol, arc-arts.*
Universidade Católica de Santos, Rua Euclides da Cunha 241, 11060 Santos, SP.
Tel: (132) 373435. Telex: 13–1978
let, ed, hist, sc, psyc, phil, arc, eco, adm, acc, commun soc, law, soc serv, nurs-obst, math.
Universidade Federal de São Carlos, Avenida Washington Luiz-Km 235, 13560 São Carlos, SP.
1960, 1968
Tel: (162) 711100. Telex: 16–2369
Ce : *ed-hum, sc-techn, biol-heal sc, let-arts.*
Universidade de São Francisco, Avenida Francisco de Assis 218, 12900 Bragança Paulista, SP.
1967, 1985
Tel: (11) 4331500. Telex: 11–79949
F : *jur-acc-adm, phil-sc-let (2), ed, med, dent, law, eco-acc-adm-act; phil-sc-let, civ eng* (Itatiba).
*Universidade de São Paulo, Rua da Reitoria 109, 05508 São Paulo, SP.
1934
Tel: (11) 2110011. Telex: 11–36950
I : *biosc, phy, geosc, math-stat, astr-geophy, ch, psyc, biomed, atomic energ; math, phy-ch* (São Carlos).

F : *law, med, publ heal, phil-let, hum, phar, vet-zoo, arc-urb, eco-adm, dent, ed; med, nurs, phar-dent, phil-sc-let* (Ribeirão Prêto); *dent* (Bauru).
S : *nurs, commun-arts, polytec, phys; agr* (Piracicaba); *eng* (São Carlos); *nurs* (Ribeirão Prêto).
Pontifícia Universidade Católica de São Paulo, Rua Monte Alegre 984, 05014 São Paulo, SP.
1946
Tel: (11) 2630211
F : *commun-phil, soc-soc serv, law, psyc; biol.*
Ce : *eco-law-adm, hum, ed; math-phy, med-biol* (Sorocaba).
Universidade Federal de Sergipe, Campus Universitário, 49100 São Cristovão, SE.
1968
Tel: (79) 2241331. Telex: 79–2189
I : *let-arts-commun, phil-hum, ch, math-phy, biol.*
F : *eco-adm, ed, soc serv, med.*
Ce : *phys, biol-heal sc, app soc, ed-hum, exact sc.*
Universidade de Taubaté, Rua 4 de Março 432, 12100 Taubaté, SP.
1976
Tel: (122) 327555. Telex: 12–2251
F : *soc serv, phil-sc-let, eco-adm, law.*
S : *phys, eng.*
Ce : *biol-heal sc, exact sc-techn, hum-let.*
*Universidade Federal de Uberlândia, Avenida Engenheiro Diniz 1178, 38400 Uberlândia, MG.
1978
Tel: (34) 2350355. Telex: 34–3264
Ce : *biomed, hum-arts, exact sc-techn, ed.*
Universidade do Vale do Rio dos Sinos, Avenida Unisinos 950, 93020 São Leopoldo, RS.   *1969*
Tel: (512) 926333. Telex: 51–5106
Ce : *ed-hum, techn, exact sc, legal sc, commun, biomed, eco.*
*Universidade Federal de Viçosa, Avenida Peter Henry Rolfs, 36570 Viçosa, MG.   *1969*
Tel: (31) 899–2921. Telex: 31–1587
Ce : *exact sc-techn, hum-arts, agr, biol-heal, sc.*
S : *agr, for.*

OTHER INSTITUTIONS—AUTRES INSTITUTIONS

Public Institutions—Etablissements publics

Centro Brasileiro de Pesquisas Físicas Avenida Wenceslau Braz 71, Bolafigo, 2000 Rio de Janeiro, RJ.   *1962*
Centro de Educação Técnica da Utramig, Avenida Afonsa Peña 3400, 30000 Belo Horizonte, MG.   *1966*
Tel: (31) 2213677

Centro de Educação Técnica da Bahia, Estradas das Barreiras s/n, 40000 Salvador, BA.   *1980*
Tel: (71) 2311546
Centro de Educação Tecnologica da Bahia, Via Universitária, 43700 Simoes Filho, BA.   *1976*
Tel: (71) 5948400. Telex: 712335 cetf br
Centro de Ensino Superior do Vale do São

Francisco, Avenida Colonel Trapia 202, 56440 Belém do São Francisco, PE.
Tel: (81) 9361248

Centro Federal de Educação Tecnologica de Minas Gerais, Avenida Amazonas 30530, Gamaleira, Belo Horizonte, MG. *1972*
Tel: (31) 3331880. Telex: 313863 cf br

Centro Federal de Educaçao Tecnologica do Paraná, Avenida 7 de Setembro 3165, Centro, Curitiba, PR. *1973*
Tel: (41) 2245333. Telex: 415562 cfet br

Centro Federal de Educação Tecnologica do Rio de Janeiro, Avenida Maracaña 229, São Cristovão, 20271 Rio de Janeiro, RJ. *1966*
Tel: (21) 2489873

Centro Integrado de Ensino de Concordia, Rua Lauro Mueller 21, 89700 Concordia, SC.
nurs, biol, acc.

Centro Polivalente de Tecnologia de Sobral, Avenida da Universidade s/n, 62100 Sobral, CE. *1971*
Tel: (85) 6110023

Escola de Administração de Vitoria da Conquista, Estrada do Bem Querer Km. 04, 45100 Vitoria da Conquista, BA. *1980*
Tel: (73) 4221143

Escola de Artes Plásticas, Avenida Amazonas 6252, 30000 Belo Horizonte, MG. *1954*
Tel: (31) 3320807

Escola de Biblioteconomia e Documentação de São Carlos, Rua São Sebastião, 13560 São Carlos, SP.
Tel: (162) 721308

Escola de Ciências Médicas de Alagoas, Avenida Siqueira Campos 2095, 57000 Maceió, AL. *1970*
Tel: (82) 2214646

Escola de Educação Física de São Carlos, Rua São Sebastião, 13560 São Carlos, SP.
Tel: (162) 721308

Escola de Enfermagem, Rua Teresina 495, 69000 Manaus, AM. *1949*
Tel: (92) 2347088

Escola de Enfermagem Magalhães Barata, Avenida José Bonifácio 1289, 66000 Belém, PA. *1945*
Tel: (91) 2290236

Escola de Engenharia de Piracicaba, Avenida Mons. Martinho Salgot 560, 13400 Piracicaba, SP. *1969*
Tel: (94) 233444

Escola de Farmácia e Odontologia de Alfenas, Rua Gabriel Monteiro da Silva, 37130 Alfenas, MG. *1914*
Tel: (35) 9211011. Telex: 313496 efoa br

Escola de Música, Rua Ouro Prêto, 30000 Belo Horizonte, MG. *1954*
Tel: (31) 3373274

Escola de Música do Espírito Santo, Avenida Princesa Isabel 610, 29000 Vitoría, ES. *1971*
Tel: (27) 2220195

Escola de Música e Belas Artes do Paraná, Rua Emiliano Perneta 179, 80000 Curitiba, PR. *1948*
Tel: (41) 2231129

Escola Nacional de Saúde Pública, Rua Leopoldo Bulhoes 1480, 21041 Manguinhoes, RJ.

Escola de Zootecnia de Itapetinga, Praça Primavera, 45700 Itapetinga, BA.
Tel: (73) 2611720

Escola Federal de Engenharia de Itajubá, Rua Colonel Renno 7, 37500 Itajubá, MG.
Tel: (35) 6221966. Telex: 03134-85 efei br

Escola Nacional de Ciencias Estatísticas, Rua André Cavalcanti 106, 20231 Rio de Janeiro, RJ. *1953*
Tel: (21) 2247677

Escola Paulista de Medicina, Rue Botucatu 740, 04023 São Paulo, SP. *1933*
Tel: (111) 5726033

Escola Politécnica da Fundação de Ensino Superior de Pernambuco, Praça do Internacional, 50000 Recife, PE. *1912*
Tel: (81) 2272855

Escola Superior de Administração e Gerencia, Avenida Madre Bevenuta s/n, 88000 Florianopólis, SC. *1966*

Escola Superior de Agricultura de Lavras, Campus Universitário, 37200 Lavras, MG. *1908*
Tel: (35) 8213900. Telex: 312937 esag br

Escola Superior de Agricultura de Mossoro, BR-110, Km-47, 59600 Mossoro, RN. *1968*
Tel: (84) 3211765. Telex: 843152 esua br

Escola Superior de Ciências Agrarias de Rio Verde, Rua São Sebastião, 76200 Rio Verde, GO.
Tel: (62) 6212019

Escola Superior de Ciências Contábeis e Administrativas, Campus Universitário, 88800 Criciúma, SC. *1975*
Tel: (484) 381411

Escola Superior de Educação Física de Avare, Praça Altino Arantes 163, 18700 Avare, SP. *1973*
Tel: (147) 221133

Escola Superior de Educação Física de Cruzeiro, Rua Dr. José R.A. Sobrinho 191, 12700 Cruzeiro, SP. *1970*
Tel: (12) 5441865

Escola Superior de Educação Física de Goias, Avenida Anhanguera 1420, 74000 Goiânia, GO. *1963*
Tel: (62) 2611443

Escola Superior de Educação Física de Jundiaí, Praça Prof. Lazaro Miranda Duarte, 13200 Jundiaí, SP. *1974*
Tel: (11) 4347955

Escola Superior de Educação Física de Recife, Rua Arnobio Marques, 50000 Recife, PE. *1946*
Tel: (81) 2225075

Escola Superior de Educação Física do Pará, Avenida 1 de Dezembro 817, 66000 Belém, PA. *1970*
Tel: (91) 2260436

Escola Superior de Educação Física e Desportos de Criciúma, Rua Pascoal Meller, 88800 Criciúma, SC. *1974*
Tel: (484) 381411

Escola Superior de Educação Física e Desportos de Joinville, Campus Universitário 144, Bom Reitro, 89200 Joinville, SC. *1970*
Tel: (474) 253200

Escola Superior de Estudos Sociais, Rua Padre Gattone 112, 88350 Brusque, SC. *1973*
Tel: (473) 551200

Escola Superior de Tecnologia de Criciúma, Rua Pascoel Meller, 88000 Criciúma, SC. *1975*
Tel: (484) 381411

Faculdade de Administração de Empresas do Alto Vale do Itajaí, Rua Dr. Guilherme Gemballa 13, 89160 Rio do Sul, SC. *1967*
Tel: (47) 8220988

Faculdade de Administração e de Ciências Contábeis de Arapongas, 86700 Arapongas, PR.
Tel: (432) 523730

Faculdade de Administração e Economia de São João da Boa Vista, Avenida Dr. Oscar Piraja Martins 15, 13870 São João da Boa Vista, SP. *1963*
Tel: (196) 233022

Faculdade de Agronomia do Médio São Francisco, Avenida Edgard Chastinet Guimarães s/n, 48900 Juázeiro, BA. *1962*
Tel: (75) 8112363

Faculdade de Agronomia Luiz Meneghel, Rodovia Br. 369, KM-54-Saida P/Andira, 86360 Bandirantes, PR. *1971*
Tel: (437) 421123. Cables: agrofal

Faculdade de Ciências Administrativas de Joinville, Campus Universitário 144, Dom Retiro, 89200 Joinville, SC. *1971*
Tel: (474) 253200

Faculdade de Ciências Administrativas de Poços de Caldas, Avenida Padre Francisco Cletos Cox s/n, 37700 Poços de Caldas, MG. *1973*
Tel: (35) 7214954

Faculdade de Ciências Administrativas, Econômicas e Contábeis Vale Itajaí, Rua Uruguai 458, 88300 Itajaí, SC. *1979*
Tel: (473) 441500

Faculdade de Ciências Agrarias do Pará, Avenida Perimetral s/n, 66000 Belém, PA. *1951*
Tel: (91) 2261922. Telex: 911892 fagp br

Faculdade de Ciências Biologicas de Araras, Avenida Universitária s/n, 13600 Araras, SP.
1975

Tel: (195) 411411

Faculdade de Ciências Contábeis de Curitibanos, Avenida Leoberto Leal, 89520 Curitibanos, SC. *1977*
Tel: (482) 450724

Faculdade de Ciências Contábeis de Sobral, Avenida da Universidade, 62100 Sobral, CE.
1970
Tel: (85) 6111827

Faculdade de Ciências Contábeis e Administrativas de Cachoeiro do Itapemirim, Rodovia Cachoeiro Muqui, 29300 Cachoeiro do Itapemirim, ES. *1971*

Faculdade de Ciências Contábeis, Econômicas e Administrativas de Videira, Rua 10 de Marco, 89560 Videira, SC. *1973*
Tel: (49) 5330488

Faculdade de Ciências de Administração de Limoeiro, Avenida Jeronimo Heraclio, 55700 Centro, Limoeiro, PE. *1976*
Tel: (81) 6280563

Faculdade de Ciências de Administração de Pernambuco, Avenida Abdias de Carvalho s/n, 50000 Recife, PE. *1956*
Tel: (81) 2285644

Faculdade de Ciências de Administração de Petrolina, Avenida Dom Bosco, 56300 Petrolina, PE.
Tel: (81) 9611075

Faculdade de Ciências e Educação de Criciúma, Rua Pascoel Meller, 88800 Criciúma, SC. *1970*
Tel: (484) 381090

Faculdade de Ciências e Humanidades de Pato Branco, Rua Itacolomi 1550, Balbinotti, 85500 Pato Branco, PR. *1975*
Tel: (462) 241348

Faculdade de Ciências e Letras de Avare, Praça Altino Arantes 163, 18700 Avare, SP. *1969*
Tel: (147) 221133

Faculdade de Ciências e Letras de Bragança Paulista, Rua Conselheiro Rodrigues Alves 249, 12900 Bragança Paulista, SP. *1968*
Tel: (11) 4332418

Faculdade de Ciências e Letras de Campo Mourão, Avenida Comendador N. Marcondes 1972, 87300 Campo Mourão, PR. *1974*
Tel: (44) 8231880

Faculdade de Ciências e Letras de Mafra, Avenida Presidente Nereu Ramos 1071, 89300 Mafra, SC. *1973*
Tel: (476) 420059

Faculdade de Ciências Econômicas, Administrativas e Contábeis de Belo Horizonte, Cobre, 30310 Belo Horizonte, MG. *1966*
Tel: (31) 2271388

Faculdade de Ciências Econômicas, Contábeis e Administrativas de Lages, Avenida Castelo Branco, 88500 Lages, SC. *1966*
Tel: (492) 221020

Faculdade de Ciências Econômicas, Administrativas e Contábeis de São João del Rei, Praça Frei Orlando 170, 36300 São João del Rei, MG.
1972
Tel: (32) 3711397

Faculdade de Ciências Econômicas de Anápolis, Avenida Juscelino Kubitschek 146, 77100 Anápolis, GO.   *1962*
Tel: (62) 3243962

Faculdade de Ciências Econômicas de Joinville, Campus Universitário 144, 89200 Joinville, SC.   *1965*
Tel: (474) 253200

Faculdade de Ciências Econômicas e Administrativas de Franca, Avenida Major Nicacio 2433, 14400 Franca, SP.   *1951*
Tel: (16) 7224104

Faculdade de Ciências Econômicas e Administrativas de Osasco, Rua Narciso Sturlini 111, 06000 Osasco, SP.   *1965*
Tel: (11) 8032955

Faculdade de Ciências Econômicas e Administrativas de Santo André, Avenida Principe de Gales 821, 09000 Santo André, SP.   *1954*
Tel: (11) 4493093

Faculdade de Ciências Humanas Arnaldo Busato, Rua de Faculdade 2550, 85900 Toledo, PR.
Tel: (452) 52–3535

Faculdade de Ciências Humanas de Belo Horizonte, Rua Aimores 2679, 30000 Belo Horizonte, MG.   *1971*
Tel: (31) 3379855

Faculdade de Ciências Humanas de Francisco Beltrão, Rua João de Barro 212, 85600 Francisco Beltrão, PR.   *1976*
Tel: (465) 221233

Faculdade de Ciências Humanas de Marechal Candido Rondon, Rua Costa e Silva s/n, 85960 Marechal Candido Rondon, PR.
Tel: (45) 543216

Faculdade de Ciências Humanas do Cabo, Rua do Campo, 54500 Cabo, PE.
Tel: (81) 5210400

Faculdade de Ciências Jurídicas e Sociais do Vale de Itajaí, Rua Uruguai 458, 88300 Itajaí, SC.
1965
Tel: (473) 441500

Faculdade de Ciências Médicas de Pernambuco, Rua Arnobio Marques, 50000 Recife, PE. *1950*
Tel: (81) 2211554

Faculdade de Ciências Sociais Aplicadas de Foz do Iguacu, Rua Silvino dal Bo, 85890 Foz do Iguacu, PR.
Tel: (455) 732290

Faculdade de Direito de Cachoeíro de Itapemirim, Rua Mario Imperial 56, 29300 Cachoeíro de Itapemirim, ES.   *1966*
Tel: (27) 5220128

Faculdade de Direito de Conselheiro Lafaiete, Praça Barão de Queluz 11, 36400 Conselheiro Lafaiete, MG.   *1970*
Tel: (31) 7211069

Faculdade de Direito de Franca, Avenida Major Niçacio 2377, 14400 Franca, SP.   *1957*
Tel: (16) 222010

Faculdade de Direito São Bernardo do Campo, Rua Java 425, 09700 São Bernardo do Campo.
1965
Tel: (11) 4580222

Faculdade de Educação, Ciências e Letras de Irati, Rua Cel Pires 826, 84500 Irati, PR.   *1975*
Tel: (424) 221381

Faculdade de Educação de Jaoçaba, Campus Universitário, 896000 Jaoçaba, SC.   *1976*
Tel: (493) 220615

Faculdade de Educação de Mossoro, Praça Miguel Faustino, 59600 Mossoro, RN.   *1963*

Faculdade de Educação de Sobral, Avenida da Universidade, 62100 Sobral, CE.
Tel: (85) 6112213

Faculdade de Educação Física da Alta Araraquarense, Rua Oito 854, 15777 Santa Fe do Sul, SP.   *1972*
Tel: (17) 6312921

Faculdade de Educação Musical do Paraná, Rua Alminante Barroso 78, 80000 Curitiba, PR.
1968
Tel: (41) 2237490

Faculdade de Enfermagem e Obstetrícia de Itajaí, Rua Uruguai 458, 88300 Itajaí, SC.
Tel: (473) 441500

Faculdade de Enfermagem de Jequié, Avenida José Moreira Sobrinho, 45200 Jequié, BA.
Tel: (73) 5251673

Faculdade de Enfermagem e Obstetrícia de Passos, Rua Juca Stockler 1130, 37900 Passos, MG.   *1981*
Tel: (35) 5212714

Faculdade de Enfermagem e Obstetrícia de Sobral, Avenida da Universidade, 62100 Sobral, CE.   *1972*
Tel: (55) 6112583

Faculdade de Enfermagem Nossa Senhora das Graças, Rua Arnobio Marques, 50000 Recife, PE.   *1945*
Tel: (81) 2221933

Faculdade de Engenharia Civil de Itajubá, Rua Zequinha Luiz, 37500 Itajubá, MG.   *1973*
Tel: (35) 6222315

Faculdade de Engenharia Civil de Passos, Avenida Juca Stockler, 37900 Passos, MG.
Tel: (35) 5212971

Faculdade de Engenharia de Barretos, Avenida Prof. Roberto Frade Monte, 14780 Barretos, SP.   *1966*
Tel: (173) 226411

Faculdade de Engenharia de Joinville, Campus Universitário, 89200 Joinville, SC.   *1965*

Faculdade de Engenharia Industrial de São João del Rei, Praça Frei Orlando 170, 36300 São João del Rei, MG. *1976*
Tel: (32) 3711397

Faculdade de Farmacia e Bioquímica do Espiríto Santo, Avenida Cleto Nunes 133, 29000 Vitória, EP.
Tel: (27) 2234344

Faculdade de Filosofia, Ciências e Letras de Adamantina, Rua Nove de Julho 730, 17800 Adamantina, SP. *1968*
Tel: (189) 211176

Faculdade de Filosofia, Ciências e Letras de Alegre, Rua Belo Amorim 100, 29500 Alegre, ES. *1973*
Tel: (27) 5521412

Faculdade de Filosofia, Ciências e Letras de Araxa, Avenida Amazonas, 38180 Araxa, MG. *1973*
Tel: (34) 6611920

Faculdade de Filosofia, Ciências e Letras de Boa Esperança, Rua Marechal Floriano Peixoto, 37170 Boa Esperança, MG. *1973*
Tel: (35) 9611223

Faculdade de Filosofia, Ciências e Letras de Cabo Frio, Avenida Prof. Julia Kubitschek s/n, 28900 Cabo Frio, RJ. *1974*
Tel: (246) 431567

Faculdade de Filosofia, Ciências e Letras de Carangola, Praça dos Estudiantes 23, 36800 Carangola, MG. *1972*
Tel: (32) 7411969

Faculdade de Filosofia, Ciências e Letras de Catanduva, Rua Maranhão, 15800 Catanduva, SP. *1967*
Tel: (175) 5222323

Faculdade de Filosofia, Ciências e Letras de Guarabira, PB 75 Km. 1, 58200 Guarabira, PB. *1970*
Tel: (83) 2711451

Faculdade de Filosofia, Ciências e Letras de Itajubá, Rua Zequinha Luiz, 37500 Itajubá, MG. *1965*
Tel: (35) 6221291

Faculdade de Filosofia, Ciências e Letras de Itumbiara, Avenida de Furnas, 76100 Itumbiara, GO.
Tel: (62) 4313669

Faculdade de Filosofia, Ciências e Letras de Joinville, Campus Universitário, 89200 Joinville, SC. *1968*
Tel: (474) 253200

Faculdade de Filosofia, Ciências e Letras de Mandaguari, Rua São Paulo 315, 86970 Mandaguari, PR. *1967*
Tel: (442) 331356

Faculdade de Filosofia, Ciências e Letras de Patos de Minas, Rua Irmão Exuperancio 800, 38700 Patos de Minas, MG. *1970*

Tel: (34) 8213561

Faculdade de Filosofia, Ciências e Letras de Patrocínio, Rua Artur Botelho 403, 38740 Patrocínio, MG. *1974*
Tel: (34) 8313737

Faculdade de Filosofia, Ciências e Letras de Poços de Caldas, Avenida Padre Francis Cletus Cox, 37700 Poços de Caldas. *1966*
Tel: (34) 7214954

Faculdade de Filosofia, Ciências e Letras de Santo André, Avenida Principe de Gales 821, 09000 Santo André, SP. *1966*
Tel: (11) 4493158

Faculdade de Filosofia, Ciências e Letras de São José do Rio Pardo, Avenida Dep. Eduardo Vicente Nasser 1020, 13720 São José do Rio Pardo, SP. *1966*
Tel: (19) 8611704

Faculdade de Filosofia, Ciências e Letras do Vale do Itajai, Rua Uruguai 458, 88300 Itajai, SC. *1965*
Tel: (67) 441500

Faculdade de Filosofia da Cidade de Goiás, Rua Maximiano Mendes s/n, 76600 Goiás, GO. *1972*

Faculdade de Filosofia de Passos, Avenida Juca Steckler 1130, 37900 Passos, MG. *1965*
Tel: (35) 5212714

Faculdade de Filosofia de Rio Verde, Rua Senador Martins Borges 269, 76200 Rio Verde, GO. *1973*
Tel: (62) 6211839

Faculdade de Formação de Professores de Alagoinhas, Praça Rui Berbosa s/n, 48100 Alagoinhas, BA. *1972*
Tel: (75) 421139

Faculdade de Formação de Professores de Araripina, Rua 11 de Setembro 163, 56280 Araripina, PE. *1977*
Tel: (81) 9311283

Faculdade de Formação de Professores de Arcoverde, Rua Gumercindo Cavalcante s/n, 56500 Arcoverde, PE. *1970*
Tel: (81) 8210574

Faculdade de Formação de Professores de Belo Jardim, Dr. Henrique do Nascimento s/n, Boa Vista, 55150 Belo Jardim, PE. *1976*
Tel: (81) 7261929

Faculdade de Formação de Professores de Garanhuns, Praça Souto Filho 696, Heliopolis, 55399 Garanhuns, PE. *1967*
Tel: (81) 7611343

Faculdade de Formação de Professores de Goiana, Rua Poco do Rei s/n, 55900 Goiana, PR. *1978*
Tel: (81) 6260517

Faculdade de Formação de Professores de Jacobina, Rua da Aurora, 44700 Jacobina, BA. *1981*

Tel: (71) 6212307
Faculdade de Formação de Professores de Jequie, Rua José Moreira Sobrinho s/n, 45200 Jequie, BA.   *1977*
Tel: (73) 5251552
Faculdade de Formação de Professores de Mata Sul, BR 101 Km. 117 Sul, 55545 Palmares, PE.
Tel: (81) 6610086
Faculdade de Formação de Professores de Nazare da Mata, Rua Professor Americo Brandão 43, 55800 Nazare da Mata, PE.   *1967*
Tel: (81) 6331350
Faculdade de Formação de Professores de Primeiro Grau de Penedo, Rua 15 de Novembro, 57200 Penedo, AL.   *1972*
Tel: (82) 5512694
Faculdade de Formação de Professores de Primeiro Grau de Serra Talhada, Avenida Afonso Magalhães, 56900 Serra Talhada, PE.
Tel: (81) 8311090
Faculdade de Formação de Professores de Santo Antonio de Jesus, Santo Antonio de Jesus, 44570 Santo Antonio de Jesus, BA.
Tel: (75) 7312338
Faculdade de Formação de Professores de São Gonçalo, Rua Dr. Francisco Portela 794, 24400 São Gonçalo, RJ.   *1973*
Tel: (21) 7122005
Faculdade de Formação de Professores de Vitória da Conquista, Do Bem Querer Km. 4, 45100 Vitória da Conquista, BA.   *1972*
Tel: (73) 4221143
Faculdade de Medicina de Jundiaí, Rua Francisco Telles 250, 13200 Jundiaí, SP.   *1967*
Tel: (11) 4375726
Faculdade de Medicina do Triangulo Mineiro, Praça Manuel Terra s/n, 38100 Uberaba, MG.
                                                        1954
Tel: (34) 3333800
Faculdade de Odontologia de Nova Friburgo, Rua Sylvio H. Braune 22, 28600 Nova Friburgo, RJ.   *1971*
Tel: (245) 222916
Faculdade de Odontologia de Pernambuco, Avenida Gal Newton Cavalcanti 146, 54750 Recife, PE.   *1957*
Tel: (822) 2713088
Faculdade de Tecnologia de São Paulo, Praça Cel. Fernando Prestes 30, 01124 São Paulo, SP.
Tel: (11) 2279443
Faculdade de Tecnologia de Sorocaba, Avenida Eng. Carlo Reinaldo Mendes, 18100 Sorocaba, SP.
Tel: (152) 326881
Faculdade Estadual de Ciências Econômicas de Apucarana, Rodovia do Café BR 376, 86800 Apucarana, PR.   *1961*
Tel: (434) 222071
Faculdade Estadual de Direito do Norte Pioneiro,

Avenida Manoel Ribas 711, 86400 Jacarèzinho, PR.   *1968*
Tel: (437) 220862
Faculdade Estadual de Educação Física de Jacarèzinho, Avenida Getúlio Vargas 2, 86400 Jacarèzinho, PR.   *1972*
Tel: (437) 220498
Faculdade Estadual de Filosofia, Ciências e Letras de Cornélio Procópio, Avenida Portugal 340, 86300 Cornélio Procópio, PR.   *1966*
Tel: (435) 232922
Faculdade Estadual de Filosofia, Ciências e Letras de Guarapuava, Presidente Zacarias 875, Santa Cruz, 85100 Guarapuava, PR.   *1970*
Tel: (427) 231869
Faculdade Estadual de Filosofia, Ciências e Letras de Jacarèzinho, Rua Padre Melo 1200, 86400 Jacarèzinho, PR.   *1960*
Tel: (437) 220643
Faculdade Estadual de Filosofia, Ciências e Letras de Paranaguá, Rua Commendor Correa Junior 81, 83300 Paranaguá, PR.   *1960*
Tel: (414) 221242
Faculdade Estadual de Filosofia, Ciências e Letras de União da Vitória, Praça Colonel Amazonas s/n, Caixa postal 234, 84600 União da Vitória, PR.   *1960*
Tel: (425) 224433.
Faculdade Estadual de Medicina do Pará, Trav. 14 de Abril 1462, 66000 Belém, PA.   *1971*
Tel: (91) 2293046
Faculdade Federal de Ciências Médicas de Porto Alêgre, Rua Prof. Sarmento Leite 245, 90000 Porto Alêgre, RS.   *1961*
Tel: (51) 2248615
Faculdade Federal de Odontologia de Diamantina, Rua da Glória 187, 39100 Diamantina, MG.   *1954*
Tel: (37) 9311024
Faculdade Municipal de Administração e Ciências Econômicas de União da Vitória, Avenida Bento Munhoz da Rocha Neto 3856, União da Vitória, PR.   *1975*
Tel: (4) 5221837
Faculdade Municipal de Educação, Ciências e Letras de Cascavel, Rua Jardim Universitário, 85800 Cascavel, PR.   *1972*
Faculdade Municipal de Educação, Ciências e Letras de Paranavaí, Avenida Gabriel Esperidião, 87700 Paranavaí, PR.   *1966*
Tel: (444) 220943
Faculdade Olindense de Formação de Professores, Avenida Getúlio Vargas 1360, Novo, 53000 Olinda, PE.   *1973*
Tel: (81) 4290957
Faculdades Reunidas de Administração, Ciências Contábeis, e Ciências Econômicas de Palmas, Rua Dr. Bernardo Ribeiro Viana 903, 84670 Palmas, PR.   *1980*

Tel: (462) 621287

Instituto de Ciências, Letras e Artes de Tres Corações, Avenida Castelo Branco 82, Chacara das Rosas, 37410 Tres Corações, MG. *1968*
Tel: (35) 2313924

Instituto de Educação de Minas Gerais, Rua Pernambuco s/n, 30130 Belo Horizonte, MG. *1970*
Tel: (31) 2229637

Instituto de Ensino Superior de Caceres, Praça Duque de Caxias s/n, 78700 Caceres, MG. *1968*
sc, lang, soc st.

Instituto de Ensino Superior de Mococa, Praça Madre Cabrini 87, Vila Mariano, 13730 Mococa, SP. *1973*
Tel: (19) 6550340
lib, ped.

Instituto de Matemática Pura e Aplicada, Edificio Lélio Gama, 22460 Rio de Janiero, RJ. *1952*
Tel: (21) 2210440

Instituto de Pesquisas Espasciais de São José dos Campos, Avenida dos Astronauts 1758, 12200 São José dos Campos, SP.
Tel: (18) 2228333. Telex: 01133530

Instituto Municipal de Ensino Superior de Presidente Prudente, Rua Robert Simonsen 300, 19100 Presidente Prudente, SP. *1971*

Instituto Municipal de Ensino Superior de São Caetano do Sul, Avenida Goiás 3400, Barcelona, 09500 São Caetano do Sul, SP. *1968*
Tel: (11) 4531577
adm-acc, soc-commun, eco, law.

Instituto Rio Branco, Esplanade dos Ministerios, 70170 Brasília, DF.
Tel: (61) 2116194. Cables: exteriores
dipl.

Instituto Superior de Ciências, Artes e Humanidades de Lavras, Rua Padre José Poggel 506, Centenario, 37200 Lavras, MG. *1969*
Tel: (35) 8212230

Instituto Tecnólogico de Aeronáutica, Praça Mar. Eduardo Gomes, 12225 São José dos Campos, SP. *1948*
Tel: (123) 219883. Telex: 01133393

Private Institutions—Etablissements privés

Centro Cibernetico Gay-Lursac, Rua Eduardo Luiz Gomes 134, 24020 Niterói, RJ. *1976*
Tel: (21) 719747

Centro de Ciências Humanas e Sociais, Rua Mariz e Barros 612, 20270 Rio de Janeiro, RJ. *1973*
Tel: (21) 2843749

Centro de Educação Técnica do Instituto Americano de Lins, Rua Tenente Florencio Pupo Neto 200, 16400 Lins, SP. *1973*
Tel: (14) 222223

Centro de Ensino Superior, Estrada Chapeco, São Carlos Km. 7, 89800 Chapeco, SC. *1972*
Tel: (49) 7222033
D : *acc, adm, ed.*

Centro de Ensino Superior de Erexim, Avenida Sete de Setembro 1621, 99700 Erexim, RS. *1975*
Tel: (54) 3211943
soc st, let, sc, eco-adm, ped, ed.

Centro de Ensino Superior de Jaragua do Sul, Avenida dos Immigrantes, 89250 Jaragua do Sul, SC.
Tel: (473) 720983

Centro de Ensino Superior de Juiz de Fora, Rua Halfeld 1179, 36100 Juiz de Fora, MG. *1972*
Tel: (32) 2118683
sc, arts, soc, let, ped, psyc, biol.

Centro de Ensino Superior de Sant' Ana do Livramento, Avenida Daltro Filho 1537, 97570 Sant' Ana do Livramento, RS. *1981*
Tel: (55) 2421621
I : *agrotec.*
F : *eco-acc, ed.*

Centro de Ensino Superior de São Carlos, Avenida José Pereira Lopes 252, 13560 São Carlos, SP. *1972*
Tel: (16) 2711255
soc, acc, adm, ind arts, exact sc, ped, law.

Centro de Ensino Superior Plinio Mendes dos Santos, Rua Ceará 333, 79100 Campo Grande, MT. *1976*
Tel: (67) 3827660
acc, adm-eco-com, law.

Centro de Ensino Unificado de Brasília, EQN 707/709, Campus Universitário Asa Norte Comercial, 70351 Brasília, DF. *1968*
Tel: (612) 2721010
F : *law, phil-sc-let, eco-adm, ed.*

Centro de Estudos Superiores do Carmo, Rua Egydio Martins 181, 11030 Santos, SP.
Tel: (132) 361735
phy, sc, ch, ed.

Centro de Estudos Superiores de Londrina, Rua Juscelino Kubitschek 1260, 86100 Londrina, PR. *1972*
Tel: (432) 272150
soc, psyc, exact sc, ed.

Centro de Estudos Superiores de Maceió, Rua Conego Machado, 57055 Maceió.
Tel: (82) 2215008
F : *phil-sc-let, adm-acc, law, eco.*
I : *psyc.*
S : *sc-ped, techn.*

Centro de Estudos Superiores do Esta do Pará, Avenida Alcindo Cacela 287, 66000 Belém, PA. *1974*

Tel: (91) 2232100
adm, law, eco.
Centro de Formação de Professores de Disciplinas Especializadas, Avenida Cussy de Almeida 187, 16100 Araçatuba, SP.   *1976*
Tel: (186) 231188
Centro Educacional La Salle de Ensino Superior, Avenida Victor Barreto 2288, 92000 Canoãs, RS.
Tel: (512) 724411
soc st, let, ped.
Centro Integrado de Ensino Superior de Alegrete, Praça Getúlio Vargas, 97540 Alegrete, RS.
Tel: (55) 4221105
Centro Superior de Ciências Sociais de Vila Velha, Rua Sete de Setembro 70, Centro, 92010 Vila Velha, ES.   *1976*
Tel: (27) 2291661
Centros Integrados de Ensino Superior de Farias Brito, Praça Tereza Cristina 1, 07000 Guarulhos, SP.
Tel: (11) 2093688
F : *phil-sc-let, ed, arc-urb, plast arts-commun, nurs-midwifery.*
Conjunto Universitário Candido Mendes (Sociedade Brasileira de Instrução), Praça XV de Novembro 101, Centro, 20010 Rio de Janeiro.   *1902*
Tel: (21) 2226201
F: *pol-eco (2), law (2), ed, law-eco-adm-acc, adm; eco-adm- acc* (Campos); *bus adm* (Nova Friburgo).
Conservatório Brasileiro de Música, Avenida Graça Aranha 57, 12-andar, 20030 Rio de Janeiro, RJ.   *1936*
Tel: (212) 2406131
Conservatório Dramático e Musical de São Paulo, Rua Conselheiro Crispiniano, 01037 São Paulo, SP.   *1941*
Tel: (11) 2239231
Conservatório de Música de Niterói, Rua São Pedro 96, 24000 Niterói, RJ.   *1914*
Conservatório Musical de Santos, Rua Dr. Egydio Martins, 11100 Santos, SP.   *1927*
Tel: (132) 361735
Curso de Estudos Sociais de Jaguarão, Rua 15 de Novembro, 96300 Jaguarão, RS.
Tel: (532) 611868
Escola Baiana de Processamento de Dados, Avenida Cardeal da Silva 132, 40000 Salvador, BA.
data processing.
Escola Brasileira de Administração Pública, Praia de Botafogo 190, 20000 Rio de Janeiro, RJ.   *1952*
Tel: (21) 551–3599
Escola de Administração de Empresas de Bahia, Avenida Cardeal da Silva 132, 40000 Salvador, BA.   *1972*
Tel: (71) 2352068

Escola de Administração de Empresas, Avenida Nove de Julho 2029, 01313 São Paulo, SP.   *1954*
Tel: (11) 2842311. Telex: (11) 53148
Escola de Administração e Informatica de Santa Rita do Sapucaí, Avenida Antonio de Cassisa 472, 37540 Santa Rita do Sapucaí, MG.   *1971*
Escola de Biblioteconomia, Avenida Dr. Arnaldo de Senna, 37290 Formigá, MG.   *1968*
Tel: (37) 3212997
Escola de Ciências Contábeis, Fazenda Tres Poços s/n, 27180 Volta Redonda, RJ.   *1974*
Tel: (243) 422313
Escola de Ciências Médicas de Volta Redonda, Fazenda Tres Poços-est., Pinheiral/Volta Redonda, 27180 Volta Redonda, RJ.   *1974*
Tel: (243) 426404
Escola de Educação Física de Assis, Avenida Doctor Doria 204, 19800 Assis, SP.   *1970*
Tel: (183) 222552
Escola de Educação Física de Bauru, Praça 9 de Julho 1–51, 17100 Bauru, SP.   *1952*
Tel: (142) 233911
Escola de Educação Física de São Carlos, Rua S. Sebastião s/n, 13560 São Carlos, SP.   *1949*
Tel: (162) 721320
Escola de Educação Física de Volta Redonda, Rua 21 s/n, Santa Cecilia 27180 Volta Redonda, RJ.   *1911*
Tel: (243) 421560
Escola de Enfermagem Santa Emilia de Rodat, Praça Caldas Brandão s/n, 58000 João Pessoa, PB.   *1959*
Tel: (83) 2212925
Escola de Enfermagem Wenceslau Braz, Avenida Cesário Alvim 472, 37500 Itajubá, MG.   *1955*
Tel: (35) 6220930
Escola de Engenharia de Lins, Avenida Nicolau Zarvos 1925, 16400 Lins, SP.   *1964*
Tel: (145) 222300
Escola de Engenharia de Vassouras, Avenida Expedicionario Oswaldo de Almeida Ramos 280, 27700 Vassouras, RJ.
Tel: (244) 711595
Escola de Engenharia de Volta Redonda, Rua Luiz Alves Pereira, 27180 Volta Redonda, RJ.
Tel: (243) 422313
Escola de Engenharia Electro-Mecânica da Bahia, Avenida Joana Angelica 1381, 40000 Salvador, BA.   *1934*
Tel: (71) 2416922
Escola de Engenharia Industrial de São José dos Campos, Avenida Barão do Rio Branco 882, 12200 São José dos Campos, SP.   *1968*
Tel: (123) 219144
Escola de Engenharia Kennedy, Rua José Dias Vieira 46, 30000 Belo Horizonte, MG.   *1963*
Tel: (31) 4471761
Escola de Engenharia Mauá, Estrada das Lagrimas 2035, 09500 São Caetano do Sul,

SP. *1962*
Tel: (11) 442–1900
Escola de Engenharia Veiga de Almeida, Rua Ibiturana 108, 20271 Rio de Janeiro, RJ. *1972*
Tel: (21) 2646172
Escola de Medicina de Santa Casa de Misericorda de Vitória, Avenida N. Sra, da Penha s/n, Caixa postal 36, 29000 Vitória, ES. *1968*
Tel: (27) 2278679
Escola de Medicina e Saúde Pública, Rua Frei Henrique 08, 40000 Salvador, BA. *1953*
Tel: (71) 2434623
Escola de Medicina Souza Marquêz, Rua do Catete 6, 22220 Rio de Janeiro, RJ. *1970*
Tel: (21) 2524172
Escola de Odontologia de Volta Redonda, Rua Luiz A. Pereira 76, 27180 Volta Redonda, RJ. *1970*
Tel: (243) 431556
Escola de Sociologia e Politica de São Paulo, Rua General Jardim 522, Vila Buarque, 01223 São Paulo, SP. *1933*
Tel: (11) 2561552
Escola Guignard, Avenida Alfonso Pena, 30130 Belo Horizonte, MG.
Tel: (31) 2268511
Escola Superior de Administração de Negócios, Avenida Humberto de Alencar Castelo Branco, 3740, 09700 São Bernardo do Campo, SP. *1965*
Tel: (11) 4195833
Escola Superior de Administração de Negócios ESAN, Rua São Joaquim 163, Liberdade, 01508 São Paulo, SP. *1941*
Tel: (11) 2780955
Escola Superior de Agrimensura de Minas Gerais, Rua Aquilles Lobo 524, 30000 Belo Horizonte, MG. *1968*
Tel: (31) 2246494
Escola Superior de Agronomia e Ciências de Machado, Praça Olegario Maciel, 37750 Machado, MG. *1968*
Tel: (35) 9311866
Escola Superior de Agronomia de Paraguaçu Paulista, Rua Prof. Jayme Monteiro, 19700 Paraguaçu Paulista, SP. *1974*
Tel: (18) 3611953
Escola Superior de Artes Santa Marcelina, Rua Dr. Costa Leite 548, 18600 Botucatu, SP. *1974*
Tel: (14) 9220577
Escola Superior de Ciências Contábeis e Administrativas de Ituiutaba, Avenida Geraldo Alves Tavares 1980, 38300 Ituiutaba, MG. *1970*
Tel: (34) 2612838
Escola Superior de Educação Física da Alta Paulista, Rua Mandaguaris 274, 17600 Tupã, SP. *1971*
Tel: (144) 421218
Escola Superior de Educação Física de Muzam-

binho, Rua Dinah s/n, 37890 Muzambinho, MG. *1971*
Tel: (35) 5711155
Escola Superior de Educação Física de São Caetano do Sul, Rua Amazonas 2000, 09500 São Caetano do Sul, SP. *1971*
Tel: (11) 4413233
Escola Superior de Educação Física e Desportos de Catanduva, Avenida Paulo de Faria s/n, 15800 Catanduva, SP. *1973*
Tel: (175) 227656
Escola Superior de Educação Física e Técnicas Desportivas de Andradina, Rua Amazonas 571, 16900 Andradina, SP. *1973*
Tel: (187) 222706
Escola Superior de Educação Física e Técnicas Desportivas de Araçatuba, Rua Francisco Braga 414, 16100 Araçatuba, SP. *1971*
Tel: (186) 235128
Escola Superior de Estatística da Bahia, Avenida Levigildo Filgueiras, 40000 Salvador, BA.
Tel: (71) 2450611
Escola Superior de Propaganda e Marketing de São Paulo, Avenida Rui Barbosa, 01326 São Paulo, SP. *1975*
Tel: (11) 2846388
soc commun.
Escola Superior de Relações Públicas de Pernambuco, Avenida Conselheiro Rosa e Silva 839, 50000 Recife, PE. *1968*
Tel: (81) 2225802
Faculdade Adventista de Educação, Est Itapecerica da Serra Km-23, 05835 São Paulo, SP. *1973*
Tel: (11) 5114011
Faculdade Adventista de Enfermagem, Est Itapeceria da Serra Km-23, 05835 São Paulo, SP. *1969*
Tel: (11) 5114011
Faculdade Anhanguera de Ciências Humanas, Rua Piragibe Leite 456, Cidade Jardim, 74000 Goiânia, GO. *1972*
Tel: (62) 2513688
Faculdade Anhembi Morumbi, Rua Casa do Ator 90, 04546 São Paulo, SP. *1981*
Tel: (11) 5330588
Faculdade «Auxilium» de Filosofia, Ciências e Letras, Rua Nicolau Zarvos 754, 16400 Lins, SP. *1957*
Tel: (145) 222733
Faculdade Brasileira de Ciências Jurídicas, Praça de República 60, 20211 Rio de Janeiro, RJ. *1953*
Tel: (21) 2311965
Faculdade Camaquense de Ciências Contábeis e Administrativas, Rua Alvaro Macedo 105, 96180 Camaquã, RS. *1969*
Tel: (00) 6711640
Faculdade Católica de Administração e Economia, Rua 24 de Maio 135, 80000 Curitiba,

PR.   *1959*
Tel: (41) 2334222
**Faculdade Católica de Ciências Econômicas da
Bahia**, Avenida Joana Angelica, 40000 Nazare,
BA.
Tel: (71) 2435832
Faculdade de Administração Champagnat, Rua
Professor Estevão Pinto 400, Serra, 30000 Belo
Horizonte, MG.   *1974*
Tel: (31) 2234998
adm.
**Faculdade de Administração, Ciências Contábeis
e Econômicas de Teresopolis**, Avenida Albert
Torres 11, 25950 Teresopolis, RJ.   *1975*
Tel: (21) 7423152
**Faculdade de Administração, Ciências Econôm-
icas e Contábeis de Natal**, Rua Serido, 59000
Natal, RN.   *1981*
Tel: (84) 222314
**Faculdade de Administração da Fundação
Armando Alvares Penteado**, Rua Alagoas 903,
01242 São Paulo, SP.   *1973*
Tel: (11) 8264233
Faculdade de Administração da Guanabara, Rua
General Severino 159, Botafogo, 22290 Rio de
Janeiro, RJ.   *1977*
Tel: (21) 2953099
Faculdade de Administração de Capivari, Rua
Barão do Rio Branco 374, 13360 Capivari,
SP.   *1972*
Tel: (194) 911694
**Faculdade de Administração de Empresas
Amador Aguiar**, Rua Narcisco Sturlini 883,
06010 Osasco, SP.   *1972*
Tel: (11) 8016840
**Faculdade de Administração de Empresas de
Aračatuba**, Rua Mato Grosso, 16100 Arača-
tuba, SP.   *1969*
Tel: (186) 235128
**Faculdade de Administração de Empresas de
Catanduva**, Rua do Seminario 281, 15800
Catanduva, SP.   *1972*
Tel: (175) 222405
**Faculdade de Administração de Empresas de
Governador Valadares**, Rua José de Tassis s/n,
Vila Bretas, 35100 Governador Valadares,
MG.   *1975*
Tel: (332) 213006
**Faculdade de Administração de Empresas de
Jahú**, Rua Tenente Navarro 642, 17200 Jahú,
SP.   *1972*
Tel: (146) 223435
**Faculdade de Administração de Empresas de Joã
Pessoa**, BR 230 Km. 22, 58000 Joã Pessoa,
PB.   *1973*
Tel: (83) 2241418
**Faculdade de Administração de Empresas de
Santos**, Rua Armando de S. Oliveira 150,
11050, Santos, SP.   *1969*

Tel: (13) 351311
**Faculdade de Administração de Empresas Rio-
pretense**, Rua Saldanha Marinho 2038, 15100
São José do Rio Prêto, SP.   *1971*
Tel: (172) 325355
**Faculdade de Administração de Empresas e Ciên-
cias Contábeis Campos Salles**, Rua Nossa
Senhora da Lapa 284, 05072 São Paulo, SP.
                                                       1973
Tel: (11) 2606477
Faculdade de Administração de Joaçaba, Campus
Universitário, 89600 Joaçaba, SC.   *1972*
Tel: (495) 220288
Faculdade de Administração de Pinhal, Avenida
Hélio Vergueiro Leite s/n, 13990 Espirito Santo
do Pinhal, SP.   *1972*
Tel: (196) 513604
Faculdade de Administração e Informática,
Avenida Antonio de Cassia 472, 37540 Santa
Rita do Sapucaí, MG.
Tel: (35) 6311219
**Faculdade de Administração e Ciências Contábeis
de Guarulhos**, Rua Doctor Solon Fernandes
155, Vila Rosalia, 07000 Guarulhos, SP.   *1971*
Tel: (11) 2093233
**Faculdade de Administração e Ciências Contábeis
Nove de Julho**, Rua Diamatina 302, 02117 São
Paulo, SP.   *1985*
Tel: (11) 2648843
**Faculdade de Administração e Ciências Contábeis
Tibiriça**, Largo São Bento s/n, 01029 São
Paulo, SP.   *1972*
Tel: (11) 1375485
**Faculdade de Administração e Finanças de
Machado**, Praça Olegario Maciel 25, 37750
Machado, MG.   *1972*
Tel: (35) 9311866
**Faculdade de Administração e Finanças do Norte
de Minas**, Avenida Rui Braga, 39400 Montes
Claros, MG.   *1972*
Tel: (38) 2218687
Faculdade de Administração Hospitalar, Aven-
ida Duquesa de Goias 735, 05686 São Paulo,
SP.   *1974*
Tel: (11) 5311620
Faculdade de Administração São Marcos, Aven-
ida Nazare 900, 04262 São Paulo, SP.   *1972*
Tel: (11) 2745711
Faculdade de Administração Tres de Maio, Aven-
ida Avai 370, 98910 Tres de Maio, RS.   *1976*
Tel: (535) 1061
**Faculdade de Agronomia e Zootecnica Manoel
Carlos Gonçalves**, Avenida Helio Vergueiro
Leite s/n, 13990 Espirito Santo do Pinhal,
SP.   *1969*
Tel: (196) 513579
Faculdade de Arquitetura de Barra do Pirai,
Rodovia Benjamin Ielpo, 27100 Barra do Pirai,
RJ.

Tel: (244) 421533
Faculdade de Arquitetura e Urbanismo de Tupa, Avenida dos Universitários, 17600 Tupa, SP. *1981*
Tel: (144) 421784
Faculdade de Artes Alcantara Machado, Praça Tres Corações 300, 05608 São Paulo, SP. *1975*
Tel: (11) 2702433
Faculdade de Artes da Fundação Brasileira de Teatro, SDS Bloco C Ed. FBT, 70300 Brasília, DF. *1981*
Tel: (61) 2260188
Faculdade de Artes Plásticas, Rua Alagoas 903, 01242 São Paulo, SP. *1963*
Tel: (11) 8264233
Faculdade de Belas Artes de São Paulo, Praça da Luz 2, 01120 São Paulo, SP. *1925*
Tel: (11) 2299422
Faculdade de Biblioteconomia e Documentação, Rua Martiniano de Carvalho, 01321 São Paulo, SP. *1940*
Tel: (11) 2842489
Faculdade de Biologia e Psicologia Maria Theresa, Rua Visconde do Rio Branco 869, 24020 Niterói, RJ. *1975*
Tel: (21) 7190660
Faculdade de Ciências Administrativas, Contábeis e Econômicas de Umuarama, Praça Mascarenhas de Moraes s/n, 87500 Umuarama, PR. *1980*
Tel: (446) 23164333
Faculdade de Ciências Administrativas de Canoinhas, Rua Robert Ehlke s/n, 89460 Canoinhas, SC. *1973*
Tel: (476) 220436
Faculdade de Ciências Administrativas e Comercio Exterior do Paraná, Rua Desembargador Westphalen, 80000 Curitiba, PR. *1975*
Tel: (41) 2247375
Faculdade de Ciências Administrativas e Contábeis de Atibaia, Avenida de 9 de Julho 288, 12940 Atibaia, SP. *1972*
Tel: (11) 4844140
Faculdade de Ciências Administrativas e Contábeis Paulo Eiro, Rua Barão de Cotegipe 111, 04721 São Paulo, SP. *1972*
Tel: (11) 5238522
Faculdade de Ciências Administrativas e Contábeis Tabajara, Avenida Jandira 455, 04080 São Paulo, SP. *1972*
Tel: (11) 2404397
Faculdade de Ciências Administrativas e Econômicas, Rua Itororo 800, Centro, 89500 Caçador, SC. *1977*
Tel: (49) 6620536
Faculdade de Ciências Administrativas Maria de Magalhães Pinto, Ladeira da Freguesia 196, 22700 Rio de Janeiro, RJ. Tel: (21) 3926646.
Faculdade de Ciências Agrarias de Alfenas,

Rodovia MG 179 Km. 0, Alfenas, MG. *1979*
Tel: (35) 9211977
Faculdade de Ciências Contábeis, Administrativas e Econômicas do ICNPF, Rua Tamoios 792, 30000 Belo Horizonte, MG. *1972*
Tel: (31) 2018811
Faculdade de Ciências Contábeis de Araçatuba, Rua Mato Grosso, 16100 Araçatuba, SP. *1975*
Tel: (186) 235128
Faculdade de Ciências Contábeis de Caratinga, Rua João Pinheiro 286, 35300 Caratinga, MG. *1972*
Tel: (33) 3213377
Faculdade de Ciências Contábeis de Itapetininga, Avenida João Barth s/n, 18200 Itapetininga, SP. *1966*
Tel: (152) 710485
Faculdade de Ciências Contábeis de Lucélia, Avenida Internacional 3000, 17780 Lucélia, SP. *1972*
Tel: (189) 511289
Faculdade de Ciências Contábeis de Ponte Nova, Rua dos Vereadores, 35430 Ponte Nova, MG. *1873*
Tel: (31) 8812580
Faculdade de Ciências Contábeis de Rio Claro, Rua Nove 15, 13500 Rio Claro, SP. *1972*
Tel: (195) 342887
Faculdade de Ciências Contábeis de Salvador, Rua do Salete 50, 40000 Salvador, BA. *1966*
Tel: (71) 2414861
Faculdade de Ciências Contábeis e Administração de Empresas, Avenida Ernani Cardoso 345, 21310 Rio de Janeiro, RJ. *1971*
Tel: (21) 3906365
Faculdade de Ciências Contábeis e Administrativas «Cruizeiro do Sul», Avenida Dr. Ussiel Cirilo, 08060 São Paulo, SP. *1973*
Tel: (11) 2971777
Faculdade de Ciências Contábeis e Administrativas de Avare, Praça Padare Tavares 46, 18700 Avare, SP. *1975*
Tel: (147) 221677
Faculdade de Ciências Contábeis e Administrativas de Lins, Rua Dom Bosco 265, 16400 Lins, SP. *1972*
Tel: (14) 5121625
Faculdade de Ciências Contábeis e Administrativas de Marília, Avenida Hygino Muzzy Filho 529, 17500 Marília, SP. *1970*
Tel: (144) 330833
Faculdade de Ciências Contábeis e Administrativas de Rolândia, Rua Dom Pedro 11, 400, 86600 Rolândia, PR. *1974*
Tel: (432) 562362
Faculdade de Ciências Contábeis e Administrativas de Santa Rosa, Rua Santos Dumont 820, 98900 Santa Rosa, RS. *1976*
Tel: (55) 5121659

48 BRAZIL—BRESIL

Faculdade de Ciências Contábeis e Administrativas de Sorocaba, Avenida Gen. Osorio 215, 18165 Sorocaba, SP. *1966*
Tel: (152) 323062

Faculdade de Ciências Contábeis e Administrativas de Taquara, Rua Julio de Castilhos 2084, 95600 Taquara, RS.
Tel: (51) 6421256

Faculdade de Ciências Contábeis e Administrativas de Votuporanga, Rua Pernambuco 1624, 15500 Votuporanga, SP. *1973*
Tel: (174) 223700

Faculdade de Ciências Contábeis e Administrativas «Machado Sobrinho», Rua Constantino Paleta 203, 36100 Juiz de Fora, MG. *1969*
Tel: (32) 2111477

Faculdade de Ciências Contábeis e Administrativas «Moraes Júnior», Rua Buenos Aires 283, 20061 Rio de Janeiro, RJ. *1964*
Tel: (21) 2245613

Faculdade de Ciências Contábeis e Administrativas São Judas Tadeu, Rua Don Diego de Souza, 100-Bloc AB, 90000 Pôrto Alegre, RS. *1970*
Tel: (51) 2407888

Faculdade de Ciências Contábeis e Administrativas São Paulo Apostolo, Rua José Bonifacio 140, 20771 Rio de Janeiro, RJ. *1974*
Tel: (21) 2492266

Faculdade de Ciências Contábeis e Administrativas de Tupã, Rua Cherentes 36, 17600 Tupã, SP. *1970*
Tel: (144) 422620

Faculdade de Ciências Contábeis e Administração de Varginha, Rua Catanduvas 173, 37100 Varginha, MG. *1971*

Faculdade de Ciências Contábeis e Atuariais da Alta Noroeste, Avenida Cussy de Almeida 187, 16100 Araçatuba, SP. *1974*
Tel: (180) 231188

Faculdade de Ciências da Saúde Barão de Maua, Rua Ramos de Azevedo, 14100 Ribeirão Prêto, SP.
Tel: (16) 6254935

Faculdade de Ciências da Saúde de Presidente Prudente, Rua José Bongiovani 700, 19100 Presidente Prudente, SP.
Tel: (18) 2225666

Faculdade de Ciências da Saúde do Instituto Pôrto Alêgre, Cel Joaquim Pedro Salgado 80, 90000 Pôrto Alêgre, RS. *1971*
Tel: (51) 231300

Faculdade de Ciências da Saúde e Sociais, Rua Pereira da Silva, 20230 Rio de Janeiro, RJ.
Tel: (21) 2254470

Faculdade de Ciências da Saúde São Camilo, Avenida Nazare 1501, 04263 São Paulo, SP. *1975*
Tel: (11) 2724760

Faculdade de Ciências de Administração de Garanhuns, Rua Ernesto Dourado, 55300 Garanhuns, PE. *1977*
Tel: (81) 7611596

Faculdade de Ciências de Barretos, Avenida Prof. Roberto Frade Monte, 14780 Barretos, SP. *1969*
Tel: (17) 3226411

Faculdade de Ciências e Letras «Cruzeiro do Sul», Avenida Dr. Ussiel Cirilo, 08060 São Paulo, SP.
Tel: (11) 2871777

Faculdade de Ciências e Letras de Araras, Rua Quadra H., 13600 Araras, SP. *1974*
Tel: (195) 413047

Faculdade de Ciências e Letras de Matão, Rua Cesario Mota 644, 15990 Matão, SP. *1975*
Tel: (162) 821226

Faculdade de Ciências e Letras de Osorio, Rua Lobo da Costa 1042, 95520 Osorio, RS. *1981*

Faculdade de Ciências e Letras de Ribeirão Pires, Rua Comendador João Ugliengo 12, 09400 Ribeirão Pires, SP. *1973*
Tel: (11) 4592634

Faculdade de Ciências e Letras de Votuporanga, Rua Pernambuco 1624, 15500 Votuporanga, SP. *1968*
Tel: (174) 223700

Faculdade de Ciências e Letras Padre Anchieta, Rua Dom Jesus de Pirapora 140, 13200 Jundiaí, SP. *1973*
Tel: (11) 4348444

Faculdade de Ciências e Letras Plinio Augusto do Amaral, Rua Luiz Leite 232, 13900 Amparo, SP. *1971*
Tel: (192) 702918

Faculdade de Ciências e Pedagogia de Lages, Avenida Castelo Branco, 88500 Lages, SC. *1970*
Tel: (492) 221216

Faculdade de Ciências Econômicas, Administrativas e Contábeis de São Sebastião do Paraíso, Avenida Wenceslau Braz, 37950 São Sebastião do Paraíso, MG.. *1971*
Tel: (35) 5311998

Faculdade de Ciências Econômicas, Contábeis, e Administração de Emprêsas Camilo Castelo Branco, Rua Carolina Fonseca, 08230 São Paulo, SP. *1972*
Tel: (11) 2050099

Faculdade de Ciências Econômicas, Contábeis, e Administração de Emprêsas Padre Anchieta, Avenida Dr. Andoniro Ladeira 94, 13200 Jundiaí, SP. *1966*
Tel: (11) 4376165

Faculdade de Ciências Econômicas, Contábeis e Administrativas de Barbacena, Rua Monsenhor José Augusto 203, Alto da Fabrica, Barbacena, MG. *1966*

Tel: (32) 3313182
Faculdade de Ciências Econômicas, Contábeis e Administrativas de Visconde do Rio Branco, Avenida Ruy Bouchardet s/n, 36520 Visconde do Rio Branco, MG. *1972*
Tel: (32) 5511600
Faculdade de Ciências Econômicas, Contábeis e Administrativas de Nova Iguaçu, Rua Itaiara 301, 26150 Nova Iguaçu, RJ. *1972*
Tel: (21) 7614440
Faculdade de Ciências Econômicas, Contábeis e Administrativas «Prof. de Placido e Silva», Avenida Dr. Vicente Machado, 80000 Curitiba, PR. *1974*
Tel: (41) 2338423
Faculdade de Ciências Econômicas da Região dos Vinhedos, Alameda João dal Sasso, 95700 Bento Gonçalves, RS. *1974*
Tel: (54) 2521188
Faculdade de Ciências Econômicas de Bauru, Praça 9 de Julho, 17100 Bauru, SP. *1961*
Tel: (142) 236290
Faculdade de Ciências Econômicas de Colatina, Avenida Brasil, 29700 Colatina, ES. *1970*
Tel: (27) 7220533
Faculdade de Ciências Econômicas de Divinópolis, Praça do Mercado 191, 35500 Divinópolis, MG. *1969*
Tel: (37) 2215921
Faculdade de Ciências Econômicas de Itauna, Avenida Governador Magalhes Pinto, 35680 Itauna, MG. *1966*
Tel: (37) 2419255
Faculdade de Ciências Econômicas de Patos, Rua Antenor Navarro, 58700 Patos, PB.
Tel: (83) 4212819
Faculdade de Ciências Econômicas de São Gabriel, Rua Barão do Cambai 550, 97300 São Gabriel, RS. *1977*
Faculdade de Ciências Econômicas de São Paulo, Avenida da Libertade, 01502 São Paulo, SP. *1932*
Tel: (11) 2770122
Faculdade de Ciências Econômicas de Valença, Praça Visconde do Rio Prêto 401, 27600 Valença, RJ. *1968*
Tel: (0244) 520910
Faculdade de Ciências Econômicas do Alto Taquari, Rua João Tallini, 95900 Lajeado, RS. *1969*
Tel: (51) 7142835
Faculdade de Ciências Econômicas do Sul de Minas, Avenida Presidente Tancredo de Almeida Neves, 37500 Itajubá, MG. *1965*
Tel: (35) 6221122
Faculdade de Ciências Econômicas do Triângulo Mineiro, Praça Tomas Ulhoa 07, 38100 Uberaba, MG. *1966*
Tel: (34) 3324043

Faculdade de Ciências Econômicas «Dom Bosco», Estrada Resenda Riachuelo, 27500 Resende, RJ. *1968*
Tel: (243) 541140
Faculdade de Ciências Econômicas e Administrativas de Guaratinguetá, Avenida Pedro de Toledo 195, 12500 Guaratinguetá, SP. *1973*
Tel: (12) 5222911
Faculdade de Ciências Econômicas e Administrativas de Presidente Prudente, Praça Raul Furquim s/n, 19100 Presidente Prudente, SP. *1970*
Tel: (182) 334744
Faculdade de Ciências Econômicas e Administrativas de São José de Rio Prêto, Avenida Bady Bassitt, 15100 São José de Rio Prêto, SP. *1962*
Tel: (172) 321622
Faculdade de Ciências Gerenciais da Una, Rua Aimores, 30140 Belo Horizonte, MG.
Tel: (31) 2265677.
Faculdade de Ciências Humanas de Curvelo, Raimunda de Souza Marques, 35790 Curvelo, MG.
Tel: (37) 7211835
Faculdade de Ciências Humanas de Itabira, Rua Dr. Sizenando de Barros 90, 35900 Itabira, MG. *1981*
Tel: (31) 8313770
Faculdade de Ciências Humanas de Olinda, Largo da Misericordia s/n, 53000 Olinda, PE. *1973*
Tel: (81) 4292679
Faculdade de Ciências Humanas do Sul Paulista, Rua Prof. Rivadavia Marques Júnior 338, 18400 Itapeva, SP. *1976*
Tel: (155) 220605
Faculdade de Ciências Humanas e Sociais de Curitiba, Rua Tobias de Macedo Júnior 333, Bairro de Santo Inacio, 80000 Curitiba, PR. *1975*
Tel: (41) 2328683
Faculdade de Ciências Humanas Esuda, Avenida João de Barros, Boa Vista, 50000 Recife, PE. *1974*
Tel: (81) 2214866
Faculdade de Ciências Jurídicas e Sociais, João Luiz Ribeiro de Morais, 58000 João Pessoa, PB. *1973*
Tel: (83) 2241418
Faculdade de Ciências Jurídicas e Sociais de Barbacena, Rua Monsenhor José Augusto 203, 36200 Barbacena, MG. *1974*
Tel: (32) 3313102
Faculdade de Ciências Jurídicas e Sociais Vianna Junior, Avenida dos Andradas 415, 36100 Juiz de Fora, MG. *1970*
Tel: (32) 2122940
Faculdade de Ciências, Letras e Educação de Presidente Prudente, Rua José Bongiovani 700,

Cidade Universitária, 19100 Presidente Prudente, SP.   *1972*
Tel: (18) 2225666
Faculdade de Ciências Médicas de Minas Gerais, Alameda Ezequiel Dias 275, 30000 Belo Horizonte, MG.   *1951*
Tel: (31) 2229066
Faculdade de Ciências Médicas de Nova Iguaçu, Avenida Abilio Augusto Tavora 2134, 26000 Nova Iguaçu, RJ.   *1977*
Tel: (21) 7678605
Faculdade de Ciências Médicas de «Santa Casa de São Paulo», Rua Dr. Cesário Motta Júnior 112, 01221 São Paulo, SP.   *1963*
Tel: (11) 2207288
Faculdade de Ciências Médicas de Santos, Rua Oswaldo Cruz, 11045 Santos, SP.   *1967*
Tel: (132) 351148
Faculdade de Ciências Médicas «Dr. José António Garcia Coutinho», Avenida Alfredo Custodio de Paula 320, 37550 Pouso Alegre, MG.   *1969*
Tel: (35) 4213504
Faculdade de Ciências Políticas e Econômicas de Cruz Alta, Parada Benito, 98100 Cruz Alta, RS.   *1960*
Tel: (55) 3223933
Faculdade de Comunicação da FAAP, Rua Alagoas 903, Pacaembu, 02142 São Paulo, SP.   *1972*
Tel: (11) 8264233
Faculdade de Comunicação e Turismo Helio Alonso, Rua Muniz Barreto, 22251 Rio de Janeiro, RJ.   *1972*
Tel: (21) 5515695
Faculdade de Comunicação Social Casper Libero, Avenida Paulista 900, 01310 São Paulo, SP.
1947
Tel: (11) 2874322
Faculdade de Comunicação Social e Turismo de Santo Amaro, Rua Prof. Eneas de Siqueiro Neto 340, 04829 São Paulo, SP.   *1975*
Tel: (11) 5209611
Faculdade de Desenho Industrial de Maua, Rua Alonso Vasconcelos Pacecho, Vila Vitória, 09300 Maua, SP.   *1975*
Tel: (11) 4162166
Faculdade de Direito da Alta Paulista, Rua Mandaguaris 1010, 17600 Tupã, SP.   *1970*
Tel: (144) 421862
Faculdade de Direito de Anápolis, Avenida Universitária, 77100 Anápolis, GO.   *1968*
Tel: (623) 3246517
Faculdade de Direito de Araçatuba, Rua Mato Grosso 1146, 16100 Araçatuba, SP.   *1971*
Tel: (186) 234088
Faculdade de Direito de Bauru, Praça 9 de Julho 1—51, 17100 Bauru, SP.   *1953*
Tel: (142) 233911
Faculdade de Direito de Campos, Rua Tenente

Colonel Cardoso 349, 28100 Campos, RJ. *1960*
Tel: (247) 233350
Faculdade de Direito de Caruarú, Avenida Portugal 385, 55100 Caruarú, PE.   *1959*
Tel: (81) 7212155
Faculdade de Direito de Colatina, Avenida Guarapari s/n, 29700 Colatina, ES.   *1967*
Tel: (27) 7222311
Faculdade de Direito de Cruz Alta, Parada Benito, 98100 Cruz Alta, RS.   *1969*
Tel: (55) 3223933
Faculdade de Direito de Curitiba, Rua Emiliano Perneta 268, 80000 Curitiba, PR.   *1952*
Tel: (41) 2232986
Faculdade de Direito de Guarulhos, Rua Dr. Solon Fernandes 155, 07000 Guarulhos, SP.
1968
Tel: (11) 2093233
Faculdade de Direito de Itaúna, Rua São Sebastião 676, 35680 Itaúna, MG.   *1966*
Tel: (37) 2412788
Faculdade de Direito de Itú, Avenida Tiradentes s/n, 13300 Itú, SP.   *1969*
Tel: (11) 409114
Faculdade de Direito de Joinville, Rua São José 490, 89200 Joinville, SC.   *1980*
Tel: (474) 228577
Faculdade de Direito de Marília, Avenida Hygino Muzzy Filho 529, 17500 Marília, SP.   *1970*
Tel: (144) 330833
Faculdade de Direito de Nova Iguaçu, Avenida Abilio Augusto Tavora 2134, 26000 Nova Iguaçu, RJ.   *1974*
Tel: (21) 7677176
Faculdade de Direito de Olinda, Rua de São Bento 200, 53000 Olinda, PE.   *1971*
Tel: (81) 4291300
Faculdade de Direito de Osasco, Rua Narciso Sturlini 883, 06010 Osasco, SP.   *1969*
Tel: (11) 8016507
Faculdade de Direito de Pinhal, Avenida Helio Vergueiro Leite s/n, 13990 Espírito Santo do Pinhal, SP.   *1966*
Tel: (196) 513604
Faculdade de Direito de Presidente Prudente, Praça Raul Furquim s/n, 19100 Presidente Prudente, SP.   *1961*
Tel: (182) 334744
Faculdade de Direito de Santo Ângelo, Rua Gaspar da Silveira Martins s/n, 98800 Santo Ângelo, RS.   *1963*
Tel: (55) 3121477
Faculdade de Direito de São Carlos, Rua Dr. Marino da Costa Terra, 13560 São Carlos, SP.   *1968*
Tel: (162) 717222
Faculdade de Direito de São João da Boa Vista, Rua Gen. Osorio 433, 13870 São João da Boa Vista, SP.   *1967*

Tel: (19) 6233012
Faculdade de Direito de Sete Lagoas, Avenida Marechal Castelo Branco, 35700 Sete Lagoas, MG. *1970*
Tel: (31) 9212022
Faculdade de Direito de Sorocaba, Rua Dra. Ursulina L. Torres 123, 18100 Sorocaba, SP. *1957*
Tel: (152) 322975
Faculdade de Direito de Teófilo Otôni, Rua Frei Dimas 111, 39800 Teófilo Otôni, MG. *1971*
Tel: (33) 5213111
Faculdade de Direito de Umuarama, Praça Mascarenhas de Moraes s/n, 87500 Umuarama, PR. *1980*
Tel: (446) 231643
Faculdade de Direito de Valença, Rua Sargento Vitor Hugo 219, 27600 Valença, RJ. *1968*
Tel: (244) 520284
Faculdade de Direito de Varginha, Rua José Gonsalves Pereira, 37100 Varginha, MG. *1966*
Tel: (35) 2211900
Faculdade de Direito do Norte de Minas, Avenida Rui Braga, 39400 Montes Claros, MG. *1965*
Tel: (38) 2212400
Faculdade de Direito do Oeste de Minas, Rua Minas Gerais 900, 35500 Divinópolis, MG. *1966*
Tel: (37) 2215975
Faculdade de Direito do Sul de Minas, Avenida João Beraldo 430, 37550 Pouso Alegre, MG. *1960*
Tel: (35) 4211339
Faculdade de Direito do Vale do Rio Doce, Rua Artur Bernardes, 35100 Governador Valadares, MG. *1969*
Tel: (33) 2600621
Faculdade de Direito Padre Anchieta, Rua Bom Jesus de Pirapora 140, 13200 Jundiaí, SP. *1969*
Tel: (11) 4348444
Faculdade de Direito Prof. Milton Campos, Avenida Carandai 587, 30000 Belo Horizonte, MG. *1975*
Tel: (31) 2248543
Faculdade de Economia da Fundação Armando Alvares Penteado, Rua Alagoas 903, Picaembu, 01242 São Paulo, SP. *1974*
Tel: (11) 8264233
Faculdade de Economia e Finanças do Rio de Janeiro, Praça da República 62, 20211 Rio de Janeiro, RJ. *1916*
Tel: (21) 2311965
Faculdade de Economia, Finanças e Administração de São Paulo, Rua Altinopolis 147, 02334 São Paulo, SP. *1943*
Tel: (11) 2676244
Faculdade de Economia «São Luís», Rua Haddock Lobo 400, 01414 São Paulo, SP. *1948*

Tel: (11) 2573022
Faculdade de Educação, Campus do Ipe, 58000 João Pessoa, PB. *1980*
Tel: (83) 2241418
Faculdade de Educação Antonio A. Reis Neves, Rua 20, 383, 14780 Barretos, SP. *1973*
Tel: (173) 225733
Faculdade de Educação Campos Salles, Rua Nossa Senhora da Lapa 284, 05072 São Paulo, SP. *1971*
Tel: (11) 2606472
Faculdade de Educação, Ciências e Artes Dom Bosco de Monte, Rua Agosto Chiesa 679, 15150 Monte Aprazivel, SP. *1972*
Tel: (17) 2751736
Faculdade de Educação, Ciências e Letras, SEP SUL EQ 912/712 Lote 4, Plano Piloto, 70390 Brasília DF. *1973*
Faculdade de Educação, Ciências e Letras da Região dos Vinhedos, Alameda João dal Sasso, 95700 Bento Gonçalves, RS. *1974*
Tel: (54) 2521188
Faculdade de Educação, Ciências e Letras do Alto Taquari, Estrada Lajeado Arroio do Meio Km, Vila Jardim, 95900 Lajeado, RS. *1969*
Tel: (51) 7142835
Faculdade de Educação, Ciências e Letras de Moji Mirim, Avenida Praça da Bandeira 11, 13800 Miji Morim, SP. *1973*
Tel: (192) 620839
Faculdade de Educação, Ciências e Letras de Uberlândia, Rua Barão de Camargos 695, 38400 Uberlândia, MG. *1975*
Tel: (34) 2364066
Faculdade de Educação, Ciências e Letras Don Domenico, Rua Dr. Arthur Costa Filho 20, 11400 Guaruja, SP. *1973*
Tel: (132) 862617
Faculdade de Educação, Ciências e Letras, Hebraico Brasileira Renascença, Rua Prates 790, Bom Retiro, 01121 São Paulo, SP. *1975*
Tel: (11) 2286450
Faculdade de Educação, Ciências e Letras Notre Dame, Barão da Torre 308, Ipanema, 22411 Rio de Janeiro, RJ. *1973*
Tel: (21) 2873740
Faculdade de Educação, Ciências e Letras Olavio Bilac, Avenida Lusitania 169, 21011 Rio de Janeiro, RJ. *1975*
Tel: (21) 2605552
Faculdade de Educação, Ciências e Letras Urubupunga, Avenida Cel. Jonas Alves de Mello 1660, 15370 Pereira Barreto, SP. *1973*
Tel: (18) 611825
Faculdade de Educação de Assis, Avenida Doctor Doria, 19800 Assis, SP.
Tel: (183) 222552
Faculdade de Educação da Bahia, Rua da Mangueira, 40000 Salvador, BA. *1967*

Tel: (71) 2438826
Faculdade de Educação de Fatima do Sul, Rua Tenente Antonio João 1410, 79700 Fatima do Sul, MS. *1980*
Tel: (67) 4237544
Faculdade de Educação de Guaratinguetá, Avenida Pédro de Toledo 195, 12500 Guaratinguetá, SP. *1974*
Tel: (12) 5222284
Faculdade de Educação de João Monlevade, Rua Tiete 100, 35930 João Monlevade, MG. *1972*
Tel: (31) 8514784
Faculdade de Educação de Joinville, Rua São José 490, 89200 Joinville, SC. *1973*
Tel: (474) 228577
Faculdade de Educação e Ciências Pinheirense, Rua Cardeal Arcoverde 1097, Pinheiros, 05407 São Paulo, SP. *1975*
Tel: (11) 8136570
Faculdade de Educação e Letras São Judas Tadeu, Clarimundo de Melo 79, 20740 Rio de Janeiro, RJ. *1974*
Tel: (21) 2898749
Faculdade de Educação Física, Campus Universitário, 58000 João Pessoa, PB. *1972*
Tel: (83) 2241418
Faculdade de Educação Física de Barra Bonita, Rua João Gerin 275, 17340 Barra Bonita, SP. *1973*
Tel: (146) 410300
Faculdade de Educação Física de Batatais, Rua Dom Bosco 466, 14300 Batatais, SP. *1970*
Tel: (16) 7614777
Faculdade de Educação Física de Cruz Alta, Parada Benito, 98100 Cruz Alta, RS. *1972*
Tel: (55) 3222933
Faculdade de Educação Física de Lins, Rua Dom Bosco 265, 16400 Lins, SP. *1972*
Tel: (14) 5221625
Faculdade de Educação Física de Santo Amaro, Rua Prof. Eneas de Siqueira Neto 340, Rio Bonito Santo Amaro, 04829 São Paulo, SP. *1976*
Tel: (11) 5209611
Faculdade de Educação Física de Santo André, Travesse Cisplatina 20, 09000 Santo André, SP. *1970*
Tel: (11) 4490700
Faculdade de Educação Física de Sorocaba, Rua da Penha 680, 18100 Sorocaba, SP. *1971*
Tel: (152) 320684
Faculdade de Educação Física do Clube Naútico Mogiano, Rua Cabo Diogo Oliver 758, Ponte Grande, 08700 Mogi das Cruzes, SP. *1972*
Tel: (11) 469588
Faculdade de Educação Física do Norte do Paraná, Rua Piauí 399, 86100 Londrina, PR. *1973*
Tel: (43) 2234202

Faculdade de Educação Osorio Campos, Rua Prof. Alfredo G. Filgueiras, 28500 Nilopolis, RJ. *1974*
Tel: (21) 7910135
Faculdade de Educação Padre Anchieta, Avenida Dr. Adoniro Ladeira, 13200 Jundiaí SP. *1968*
Tel: (11) 4376165
Faculdade de Educação São Luis, Rua Floriano Peixoto 873, 14870 Jaboticabal, SP. *1972*
Tel: (11) 220530
Faculdade de Enfermagem e Obstetrícia de Araras, Avenida Universitaria, 13600 Araras, SP.
Tel: (195) 411411
Faculdade de Enfermagem e Obstetrícia de Fernandópolis, Avenida Teotonio Vilela, 15600 Fernandópolis, SP.
Tel: (174) 421602
Faculdade de Enfermagem e Obstetrícia de Guarulhos, Rua Barão de Mauá 600, 07000 Guarulhos, SP.
Tel: (11) 2093719
Faculdade de Enfermagem e Obstetrícia Dom Domenico, Rua Dr. Arthur Costa Filho 20, 11400 Guaruja, SP.
Tel: (132) 862617
Faculdade de Enfermagem Luiza Marillac, Rua Dr. Satamini 245, 20270 Rio de Janeiro, RJ.
Tel: (21) 2343692
Faculdade de Enfermagem Nossa Senhora Medianeira, Avenida Presidente Vargas 2377, 97100 Santa Maria, RS. *1955*
Tel: (55) 2211726
Faculdade de Enfermagem São José, Avenida Nazare, 04263 São Paulo, SP. *1959*
Tel: (11) 2724760
Faculdade de Engenharia Civil de Alfenas, Rodovia MG 179 Km. 0, 37130 Alfenas, MG. *1974*
Tel: (35) 9211977
Faculdade de Engenharia Civil de Araraquara, Avenida Brasil 782, 14800 Araraquara, SP. *1970*
Tel: (162) 321748
Faculdade de Engenharia Civil de Barra do Piraí, Rodovia Benjamin Ielpo, Km. 11, 27100 Barra do Piraí, RJ. *1968*
Tel: (244) 421243
Faculdade de Engenharia Conselheiro Algacyr Munhoz Maeder, Rua José Bongiovani 700, 19100 Presidente Prudente, SP.
Tel: (18) 2225666
Faculdade de Engenharia da Fumec, Rua Cobre, 30000 Belo Horizonte, MG.
Tel: (31) 2212800
Faculdade de Engenharia da Fundação Armando Alvares Penteado, Rua Alagoas 903, 01242 São Paulo, SP. *1967*
Tel: (11) 665918

Faculdade de Engenharia de Agrimensura de Araraquara, Avenida Brasil 782, 14800 Araraquara, SP. *1965*
Tel: (162) 321748

Faculdade de Engenharia de Agrimensura de Pirassunya, Avenida dos Academicos 1, 13630 Pirassununga, SP.
Tel: (195) 613845

Faculdade de Engenharia de Itaúna, Rua São Sebastião, 35680 Itaúna, MG. *1968*
Tel: (37) 2412788

Faculdade de Engenharia de Sorocaba, Rodovia Sen. José Ermirio de Moraes, Km. 1.5, 18100 Sorocaba, SP. *1976*
Tel: (152) 329712

Faculdade de Engenharia Industrial, Avenida Humberto de Alencar Castelo Branco 3972, 09700 São Bernardo do Campo, SP. *1946*
Tel: (11) 4190220

Faculdade de Engenharia Química de Lorena, Rodovia Lorena/Itajuba, 12600 Lorena, SP. *1971*
Tel: (125) 523113. Telex: 0122318

Faculdade de Engenharia São João do Rio Prêto, Avenida Bady Bassitt 3777, 15100 São José do Rio Prêto, SP. *1977*
Tel: (172) 321622

Faculdade de Engenharia São Paulo, Rua Arabe, 04042 São Paulo, SP. *1975*
Tel: (11) 8811022

Faculdade de Engenharia Souza Marquês, Avenida Ernani Cardoso 335, 21310 Rio de Janeiro, RJ. *1967*
Tel: (21) 3906365

Faculdade de Estudos Sociais Aplicados de Aracajú, Rua Estancia 362, 49000 Aracajú, SP. *1976*
Tel: (79) 2224477

Faculdade de Estudos Sociais Regina Coeli, Rua Conselheiro Ferraz, 20710 Rio de Janeiro, RJ.
Tel: (21) 2646172

Faculdade de Farmácia e Bioquímica de Presidente Prudente, Rua José Buongiovani 700, 19100 Presidente Prudente, SP. *1978*
Tel: (18) 2225666

Faculdade de Filosofia «Bernardo Sayão», Avenida Universitária Km-3, 77100 Anápolis, GO. *1961*
Tel: (62) 3244025

Faculdade de Filosofia, Ciências e Letras «Barão de Mauá», Rua Ramos de Azevedo 423, 14100 Ribeirão Prêto, SP. *1968*
Tel: (16) 6254935

Faculdade de Filosofia, Ciências e Letras Camilo Castelo Branco, Rua Carolina Fonseca, 08230 São Paulo, SP.
Tel: (11) 2005009

Faculdade de Filosofia, Ciências e Letras Carlos Queiroz, Avenida Cel Clementino Gonçalves 1651, 18900 Santa Cruz do Rio Pardo, SP. *1971*
Tel: (143) 721173

Faculdade de Filosofia, Ciências e Letras da Alta Sorocabana, Praça Raul Furquin s/n, 19100 Presidente Prudente, SP. *1973*
Tel: (182) 334744

Faculdade de Filosofia, Ciências e Letras da Fundação de Ensino Superior de Itaúna, Rua Professor Francisco Santiago 275, 35680 Itaúna, MG. *1966*
Tel: (37) 2413921

Faculdade de Filosofia, Ciências e Letras da Fundação Norte de Minas de Ensino Superior, Rua Coronel Celestino 75, 39400 Montes Claros, MG. *1964*
Tel: (38) 2212651

Faculdade de Filosofia, Ciências e Letras de Alfenas, Rodovia MG. 179, 37130 Alfenas, MG. *1972*
Tel: (35) 9211977

Faculdade de Filosofia, Ciências e Letras de Araçatuba, Rua Mato Grosso 1141, 16100 Araçatuba, SP. *1966*
Tel: (186) 234088

Faculdade de Filosofia, Ciências e Letras de Araguari, Avenida Minas Gerais 1889, 38440 Araguari, MG. *1968*
Tel: (34) 2413900

Faculdade de Filosofia, Ciências e Letras de Arapongas, Rua des Garças 290, 86700 Arapongas, PR. *1968*
Tel: (432) 521056

Faculdade de Filosofia, Ciências e Letras de Barra do Piraí, Rodovia Benjamin Ielpo, Km. 11, 27100 Barra do Piraí, RJ. *1968*
Tel: (244) 421533

Faculdade de Filosofia, Ciências e Letras de Bebedouro, Rua Prof. Orlando F. de Carvalho 325, 14700 Bebedouro, SP. *1970*
Tel: (173) 421100

Faculdade de Filosofia, Ciências e Letras de Belo Horizonte, Avenida Antonio Carlos 521, 30000 Belo Horizonte, MG. *1964*
Tel: (31) 4426955

Faculdade de Filosofia, Ciências e Letras de Caratinga, Avenida São José 49, 35300 Caratinga, MG. *1968*
Tel: (33) 3212930

Faculdade de Filosofia, Ciências e Letras de Caruarú, Rua Azevedo Coutinho, 55100 Caruarú, PE. *1961*
Tel: (81) 7212611

Faculdade de Filosofia, Ciências e Letras de Cataguases, Praça Rui Barbosa 86, 36770 Cataguases, MG. *1972*
Tel: (32) 4213109

Faculdade de Filosofia, Ciências e Letras de Colatina, Avenida Brasil, 29700 Colatina, ES.
Tel: (27) 7220533

Faculdade de Filosofia, Ciências e Letras de Cruz Alta, Campus Universitário, 98100 Cruz Alta, RS. *1974*

Faculdade de Filosofia, Ciências e Letras de Duque de Caxias, Avenida Presidente Kennedy 9422, 25000 Duque de Caxias, RJ. *1972*
Tel: (21) 7713942

Faculdade de Filosofia, Ciências e Letras de Formiga, Avenida Dr. Arnaldo de Senna, 37290 Formiga, MG. *1967*
Tel: (37) 3212997

Faculdade de Filosofia, Ciências e Letras de Governador Valadares, Campus Universitário, 35030 Governador Valadares, MG. *1971*
Tel: (332) 213090

Faculdade de Filosofia, Ciências e Letras de Guarulhos, Rua Barão de Mauá 600, 07000 Guarulhos, SP. *1971*
Tel: (11) 2093533

Faculdade de Filosofia, Ciências e Letras de Guaxupe, Avenida D. Floriana s/n, 37800 Guaxupe, MG. *1964*
Tel: (35) 5511696

Faculdade de Filosofia, Ciências e Letras de Itapetininga, Avenida João Barth s/n, 18200 Itapetininga, SP. *1968*
Tel: (15) 2710503

Faculdade de Filosofia, Ciências e Letras de Itararé, Rua João Batista Veiga 1725, 18460 Itararé, SP. *1973*
Tel: (155) 321330

Faculdade de Filosofia, Ciências e Letras de Ituverava, Rua Cel. Flausino Barbosa Sandoval 1259, 14500 Ituverava, SP. *1971*
Tel: (16) 7292326

Faculdade de Filosofia, Ciências e Letras de Jahú, Rua Tenente Navarro 642, 17200 Jahú, SP. *1966*
Tel: (146) 223435

Faculdade de Filosofia, Ciências e Letras de Jales, Avenida Francisco Jales 567, 15700 Jales, SP. *1970*
Tel: (17) 6321620

Faculdade de Filosofia, Ciências e Letras de Jandaia do Sul, Rua dos Patriotas, 86900 Jandaia do Sul, PR. *1967*
Tel: (43) 4321113

Faculdade de Filosofia, Ciências e Letras de Macae, Rua Tenente Rui Lopes Ribeiro 200, 28700 Macae, RJ. *1974*
Tel: (247) 620965

Faculdade de Filosofia, Ciências e Letras de Moema, Avenida Divino Salvador 12, 04078 São Paulo, SP. *1971*
Tel: (11) 5425888

Faculdade de Filosofia, Ciências e Letras de Nova Iguaçu, Avenida Abilio Augusto Tavora, 26000 Nova Iguaçu, RJ.
Tel: (21) 7677221

Faculdade de Filosofia, Ciências e Letras de Ouro Fino, Rodovia MG 290 Km. 59 Ouro Fino, 37570 Ouro Fino, MG. *1972*
Tel: (35) 4411426

Faculdade de Filosofia, Ciências e Letras de Palmas, Rua Dr. Bernardo Ribeiro Viana 903, 84670 Palmas, PR. *1969*
Tel: (462) 621287

Faculdade de Filosofia, Ciências e Letras de Patos, Rua Horacio Nobrega, 58700 Patos, PB. *1970*
Tel: (83) 4212606

Faculdade de Filosofia, Ciências e Letras de Penápolis, Campus Universitário, 16300 Penápolis, SP. *1967*
Tel: (186) 522315

Faculdade de Filosofia, Ciências e Letras de Pirajú, Rua João Hailer 408, 18800 Pirajú, SP. *1975*
Tel: (143) 512078

Faculdade de Filosofia, Ciências e Letras de Presidente Wenceslau, Avenida Carlos Platzeck, 19400 Presidente Wenceslau, SP.
Tel: (182) 712373

Faculdade de Filosofia, Ciências e Letras de Registro, Rua São Francisco Xavier 165, 11900 Registro, SP. *1972*
Tel: (138) 212411

Faculdade de Filosofia, Ciências e Letras de Rio de Janeiro, Avenida Ernani Cardoso 335, 21310 Rio de Janeiro, RJ. *1968*

Faculdade de Filosofia, Ciências e Letras de Santiago, Vinte de Setembro 2410, 97700 Santiago, RS. *1969*
Tel: (55) 2511715

Faculdade de Filosofia, Ciências e Letras de Santo Amaro, Rua Prof. Eneas de S. Neto 340, 04829 São Paulo, SP. *1970*
Tel: (11) 5209611

Faculdade de Filosofia, Ciências e Letras de São Bernardo de Campo, Rua Americo Brasiliense 49, 09700 São Bernardo do Campo, SP. *1971*
Tel: (11) 4433277

Faculdade de Filosofia, Ciências e Letras de São Borja, Avenida Bernardo de Mello, 97670 São Borja, RS. *1970*
Tel: (55) 4311687

Faculdade de Filosofia, Ciências e Letras de São Caetano do Sul, Rua Amazonas, 95000 São Caetano do Sul, SP.
Tel: (11) 4413233

Faculdade de Filosofia, Ciências e Letras de São João da Boa Vista, Rua Cristiano Osorio 10, 13870 São João da Boa Vista, SP. *1971*
Tel: (196) 233833

Faculdade de Filosofia, Ciências e Letras de Sete Lagoas, Avenida Marechal Castelo Branco, 35700 Sete Lagoas, MG.
Tel: (31) 9212022

Faculdade de Filosofia, Ciências e Letras de **Sorocaba**, Avenida General Osório 35, 18165 Sorocaba, SP. *1954*
Tel: (152) 327153

Faculdade de Filosofia, Ciências e Letras de **Tatui**, Rua Prof. Cracy Gomes, 18270 Tatui, SP. *1971*
Tel: (152) 510460

Faculdade de Filosofia, Ciências e Letras de Tupã, Avenida dos Universitarios, 17600 Tupã, SP. *1968*
Tel: (152) 510460

Faculdade de Filosofia, Ciências e Letras de Ubá, Praça São Januario 276, 36500 Ubá, MG. *1970*
Tel: (32) 5321447

Faculdade de Filosofia, Ciências e Letras de **Umuarama**, Praça Mascarenhas de Moraes 29, 87500 Umuarama, PR. *1972*
Tel: (446) 231643

Faculdade de Filosofia, Ciências e Letras de **Uruguaiana**, Domingos de Almeida 3225, 97500 Uruguaiana, RS. *1959*
Tel: (55) 4121683

Faculdade de Filosofia, Ciências e Letras de **Valença**, Rua Sargento Vitor Hugo 219, 27600 Valença, RI. *1967*

Faculdade de Filosofia, Ciências e Letras de **Varginha**, Rua Maria B. Resende 78, 37100 Varginha, MG. *1966*
Tel: (35) 2212358

Faculdade de Filosofia, Ciências e Letras de **Vassouras**, Avenida Exp. Oswaldo de A. Ramos, 27700 Vassouras, RJ. *1971*
Tel: (244) 711595

Faculdade de Filosofia, Ciências e Letras de Volta Redonda, Rua Gov. Luiz Monterra 81, 27180 Volta Redonda, RJ. *1972*
Tel: (243) 424530

Faculdade de Filosofia, Ciências e Letras do Alto São Francisco, Avenida Formiga, 35595 Luz, MG. Tel: (37) 4211494.

Faculdade de Filosofia, Ciências e Letras do ICNPF, Rua Tamoios, 30000 Belo Horizonte, MG.
Tel: (31) 2018811

Faculdade de Filosofia, Ciências e Letras Dom Bosco, Estrada Resende/Riachuelo Km-1, 27500 Resende, RJ. *1974*
Tel: (243) 541140

Faculdade de Filosofia, Ciências e Letras Dom Bosco, Rua Santa Rosa 536, 98900 Santa Rosa, RS. *1970*
Tel: (55) 5121183

Faculdade de Filosofia, Ciências e Letras Eugenio Pacelli, Rua Joaquim Roberto Duarte, 37550 Pouso Alegre, MG. *1972*
Tel: (35) 4211736

Faculdade de Filosofia, Ciências e Letras **Imaculada Conceição**, Rua Andradas 1614,

97100 Santa María, RS. *1955*
Tel: (55) 2212792

Faculdade de Filosofia, Ciências e Letras José Olympio, Rua Dom Bosco 466, 14300 Batatais, SP. *1973*
Tel: (16) 7614777

Faculdade de Filosofia, Ciências e Letras «**Madre Gertrudes de São José**», Avenida Monte Castelo 03, 29300 Cachoeiro do Itapemirim, ES. *1966*
Tel: (27) 5225425

Faculdade de Filosofia, Ciências e Letras «**Mater Divinae Gratiae**», Rua Monsenhor J. Augusto 203, 36200 Barbacena, MG. *1966*
Tel: (32) 3313182

Faculdade de Filosofia, Ciências e Letras Ministro Tarso Dutra, Avenida Alcides Chacon Couto 395, 1790-0 Dracena, SP. *1969*
Tel: (18) 8211191

Faculdade de Filosofia, Ciências e Letras «**Nossa Senhora do Patrocinio**», Rua Madre Maria Basília 965, 13300 Itú, SP. *1959*
Tel: (11) 4822547

Faculdade de Filosofia «Nossa Senhora do Sion», Rua Padre Nattuzzi, 37400 Campanha, MG. *1973*
Tel: (35) 2611187

Faculdade de Filosofia, Ciências e Letras Nove de Julho, Rua Diamantina 302, 02117 São Paulo, SP. *1972*
Tel: (11) 2648843

Faculdade de Filosofia, Ciências e Letras Prof. Carlos Pasquale, Rua Oriente 123, 03016 São Paulo, SP. *1972*
Tel: (11) 2279239

Faculdade de Filosofia, Ciências e Letras «**Prof. José A. Vieira**», Praça Olegario Maciel 25, 37750 Machado, MG. *1968*
Tel: (35) 9311866

Faculdade de Filosofia, Ciências e Letras «**Prof. Nair Fortes Abu-Merhy**», Avenida 18 de Julho 210, 36660 Além Paraíba, MG. *1973*
Tel: (32) 4622951

Faculdade de Filosofia, Ciências e Letras «**Santa Marcelina**», Rua do Bomfim, 36880 Muriae, MG. *1961*
Tel: (32) 7211026

Faculdade de Filosofia, Ciências e Letras São Marcos, Avenida Nazare, 04262 São Paulo, SP.
Tel: (11) 2745711

Faculdade de Filosofia, Ciências e Letras Tibirica, Largo São Bento, 01029 São Paulo, SP.
Tel: (11) 2808531

Faculdade de Filosofia, Ciências e Letras Tuiuti, Rua Marcelino Champagnat, 80000 Curitiba, PR. *1973*
Tel: (41) 2253131

Faculdade de Filosofia, Ciências e Letras Veiga de Almeida, Rua São Francisco Xavier 124, 20550

Rio de Janeiro, RJ. *1974*
Tel: (21) 2646172
Faculdade de Filosofia de Campo Grande,
Estrada da Caroba 685, Campo Grande, 23000
Rio de Janeiro, RJ. *1961*
Tel: (21) 3941230
Faculdade de Filosofia de Campos, Avenida da
Visc. de Alvarenga s/n, 28100 Campos, RJ.
1961
Tel: (247) 228043
Faculdade de Filosofia de Fortaleza, Avenida
Dom Manoel, 60000 Fortaleza, CE. *1973*
Tel: (85) 2267525
Faculdade de Filosofia de Itaperuna, Rua Major
Porphiro Henriques 41, Itaperuna, RJ. *1968*
Tel: (249) 220610
Faculdade de Filosofia do Crato, Rua del Antonio
Luiz, 63100 Crato, CE.
Tel: (85) 5210511
Faculdade de Filosofia do Recife, Avenida Conde
da Boa Vista 921, 50000 Recife, PE. *1941*
Tel: (81) 2226344
Faculdade de Filosofia do Vale do São Patricio,
Praça Alvaro de Melo, Rua 21, 76700 Ceres,
GO. *1976*
Tel: (62) 7211318
Faculdade de Filosofia Dom José de Sobral, Praça
da Universidade s/n, 62100 Sobral, CE. *1961*
Tel: (85) 6112213
Faculdade de Filosofia e Letras, Travessa
Mercedes Mourão 77, 39100 Diamantina, MG.
1968
Tel: (37) 9311922
**Faculdade de Filosofia Nossa Senhora Imaculada
Conceição**, Rua Senador Salgado Filho 7427,
94400 Viamão, RS. *1957*
Tel: (51) 2851177
**Faculdade de Filosofia «Nossa Senhora Median-
eira»**, Rua Haddock Lobo 440, 01414 São
Paulo, SP. *1955*
Tel: (11) 2573022
Faculdade de Filosofia «Santa Dorotéia», Rua
Monsenhor Miranda 86, 28600 Nova Friburgo,
RJ. *1967*
Tel: (245) 222900
**Faculdade de Fisiotérapia de Presidente
Prudente**, Rua José Bongiovani 700, 19100
Presidente Prudente, SP. *1981*
Tel: (18) 2225666
Faculdade de Fonoaudiologia, Rua 18 de
Outubro, Rio de Janeiro, RJ.
Tel: (21) 2082095
**Faculdade de Formação de Professores Bethen-
court da Silva**, Rua Frederico Silva, 20230 Rio
de Janeiro, RJ.
Tel: (21) 2215708
**Faculdade de Formação de Professores de Petro-
lina**, BR 203 Km 2 s/n, Predio, 56300 Petrolina,
PE. *1969*

**Faculdade de Formação de Professores de Prim-
eiro Grau de Arapiraca**, Rua Governador Luiz
Cavalcante s/n, Alto do Cruzeiro, 57300
Arapiraca, AL. *1971*
Tel: (82) 5213786
**Faculdade de Formação de Professores de Vitória
de Santo Antão**, Lot São Vicente Ferrer s/n,
Caja, 55600 Vitória de Santo Antão, PE. *1972*
Tel: (81) 5231020
**Faculdade de Formação de Professores e Especial-
istas em Educação**, Rua Julio de Castilho,
96180 Camaqua, RS. *1980*
Tel: (51) 6711640
**Faculdade de Formação de Professores do
Instituto Americano de Lins**, Rua Tenente
Florencio Puppo Neto 200, Jardim Americano,
Lins, SP. *1970*
Tel: (14) 5222223
**Faculdade de Formação de Professores São Judas
Tadeu**, Rua Dom Diego de Souza 100, Cristo
Redentor, 90000 Pôrto Alegre, RS. *1976*
Tel: (51) 2407888
Faculdade de Formação Profissional Integrada,
Avenida Ernani do Amaral Peixoto 836, 24020
Niterói, RJ. *1973*
Tel: (21) 7194455
let, sc, soc st, art, adm, acc, eco, stat.
Faculdade de Humanidades Pedro II, Rua
Pirauba s/n, 20940 São Cristovão, RJ. *1970*
Tel: (21) 5806426
Faculdade de Letras e Educação de Vacaria,
Avenida Presidente Kennedy 2020, Vila
Militar, 95200 Vacaria, RS. *1974*
Tel: (54) 2312055
Faculdade de Medicina de Barbacena, Plaça
Antonio Carlos s/n, 36200 Barbacena, MG.
1971
Tel: (32) 3312966
Faculdade de Medicina de Campos, Rua Alberto
Torres 217, 28100 Campos, RJ. *1967*
Tel: (24) 7226788
Faculdade de Medicina de Catanduva, Avenida
São Vicente de Paula, 15800 Catanduva, SP.
1970
Tel: (17) 5223280
Faculdade de Medicina de Itajubá, Rua Cel.
Reno Júnior 368, 37500 Itajubá, MG. *1968*
Tel: (35) 6221100
Faculdade de Medicina de Marília, Avenida
Monte Carmelo, 17500 Marília, SP. *1967*
Tel: (144) 331744
Faculdade de Medicina de Petrópolis, Rua
Machado Fagundes 326, 25710 Petrópolis, RJ.
1967
Tel: (242) 427017
Faculdade de Medicina de Santo Amaro, Rua
Prof. Eneas de Siqueira Netto 340, 04829 São
Paulo, SP. *1970*
Tel: (11) 5209611

Faculdade de Medicina de Teresópolis, Avenida Alberto Torres 111, 25950 Teresópolis, RJ. *1970*
Tel: (21) 7423152
Faculdade de Medicina de Valença, Praça Balbina Fonseca 186, 25960 Valença, RJ. *1968*
Tel: (244) 520163
Faculdade de Medicina de Vassouras, Rua Dr. Joaquin Teixeira Leite 53, 27700 Vassouras, RJ. *1969*
Tel: (244) 711595
Faculdade de Medicina do «ABC», Avenida Principe de Gales, 09000 Santo André, SP. *1969*
Tel: (11) 4493347
Faculdade de Medicina do Norte de Minas, Avenida Rui Braza, 39400 Montes Claros, MG. *1969*
Tel: (38) 2216355
Faculdade de Música Carlos Gomes, Rua Pirapitingui 162, 01508 São Paulo, SP. *1963*
Tel: (11) 5713100
Faculdade de Música «Mãe de Deus», Avenida São Paulo 651, 86100 Londrina, PR. *1965*
Tel: (432) 235440
Faculdade de Música Palestrina, Rua Gen. Vitorino 305, 90000 Pôrto Alegre, RS. *1968*
Tel: (51) 2273811
Faculdade de Música Santa Cecilia, Praça Barão do Rio Branco 59, 12400 Pindamonhangaba, SP. *1975*
Tel: (12) 2425755
Faculdade de Música Santa Marcelina, Rua Dr. Costa Leite 548, 18600 Botucatu, SP. *1963*
Tel: (14) 9220577
Faculdade de Nutrição, Rua Dr. Lauro de Oliveira 71, 90000 Pôrto Alegre, RS.
Tel: (51) 2317720
Faculdade de Odontologia Camilo Castelo Branco, Rua Carolina Fonseca, 08230 São Paulo, SP.
Tel: (11) 2050099
Faculdade de Odontologia de Barretos, Avenida Prof. Roberto Frade Monte 389, 14700 Barretos. *1984*
Tel: (173) 226411
Faculdade de Odontologia de Campos, Avenida Visc. de Alvarenga 143, 28100 Campos, RJ. *1972*
Tel: (247) 230616
Faculdade de Odontologia de Caruaru, Avenida Portugal 385, 55100 Caruaru, PE. *1959*
Tel: (81) 7210258
Faculdade de Odontologia de Governador Valadares, Rodovia MG-4 Km. 3, 35100 Governador Valadares, ME. *1975*
Tel: (332) 700430
Faculdade de Odontologia de Itaúna, Rua Zeze Lima, 35680 Itaúna, MG. *1966*

Tel: (37) 2412289
Faculdade de Odontologia de Lins, Rua Tenente Florencia Pupo Neto 200, 16400 Lins, SP. *1954*
Tel: (145) 222223
Faculdade de Odontologia de Presidente Prudente, Rua José Bongiovani 700, 19100 Presidente Prudente, SP. *1974*
Tel: (18) 2225666
Faculdade de Odontologia de Santo Amaro, Rua Prof. Eneias de Siqueira Neto 340, Santo Amaro, 04829 São Paulo, SP. *1976*
Tel: (11) 5200611
Faculdade de Odontologia de Valença, Rua Carneiro de Mendonça 139, 27600 Valença, RJ. *1968*
Tel: (244) 521216
Faculdade de Odontologia João Prudente, Avenida Universitária Km-3, 77100 Anápolis, GO. *1971*
Tel: (62) 3244729
Faculdade de Pedagogia, Ciências e Letras de Caçador, Rua Itoro, 89500 Caçador, SC. *1972*
Tel: (49) 6620536
Faculdade de Reabilitação, Rua Uaruma 80, Higienopolis, 21050 Rio de Janeiro, RJ. *1977*
Tel: (21) 2601556
Faculdade de Reabilitação Tuiuti, Rua Marcelino Champagnat, 80000 Curitiba, PR. *1981*
Tel: (41) 2253131
Faculdade de Serviço Social de Araraquara, Rua Padre Duarte 1463, 14800 Araraquara, SP. *1972*
Tel: (162) 220733
Faculdade de Serviço Social de Bauru, Praça 9 de Julho 1–51, 17100 Bauru, SP. *1963*
Tel: (142) 236319
Faculdade de Serviço Social de Lins, Rua Dom Lucio 165, 16400, Lins, SP. *1959*
Tel: (145) 223966
Faculdade de Serviço Social de Piracicaba, Rua Boa Morte 1865, 13400 Piracicaba, SP. *1963*
Tel: (194) 222332
Faculdade de Serviço Social de Uberlândia, Rua Mercedes Brasileiro 129, 38400 Uberlândia, MG. *1972*
Tel: (34) 2364066
Faculdade de Serviço Social do Rio de Janeiro, Rua Conselheiro Ferraz, 20710 Rio de Janeiro, RJ. *1955*
Tel: (21) 2646172
Faculdade de Serviço Social e de Saúde, Rua Itororo 800 Centro, 89500 Caçador, SC. *1977*
Tel: (49) 6620536
Faculdade de Tecnologia de Rio Claro, Rua Nove 1864, 13500 Santa Cruz, SP. *1981*
Tel: (195) 346320
Faculdade de Turismo Embaixador Paschoel Carlos Magno, Rua Ibiturana, 20271 Rio de Janeiro, RJ.

Tel: (21) 2646172
Faculdade de Zootécnia de Uberaba, Rua Dom
Luiz Santana 115, 38100 Uberaba, MG.   *1975*
Tel: (34) 3331188
**Faculdade Dom Bosco de Filosofia, Ciências e
Letras**, Praça D. Helvécio 74, 36300 São João
Del Rei, MG.   *1954*
Tel: (32) 3714744
Faculdade Educação de Assis, Avenida Dr. Doria
204, 19800 Assis, SP.   *1972*
Tel: (183) 222552
Faculdade Espírito Santense de Administração,
Rua Anselmo Serrat 199, 29000 Vitória, ES.
                                        1973
Tel: (27) 2225344
Faculdade Evangélica de Medicina do Paraná,
Rua Princesa Isabel 1580, 80000 Curitibá, PR.
                                        1969
Tel: (44) 2232633
**Faculdade Ibero-Americana de Letras e Ciências
Humanas**, Avenida Brigadeiro Luis Antonio
871, 01317 São Paulo, SP.   *1971*
Tel: (11) 370071
Faculdade Luzwell, Avenida Chibaras 74,
Moema, 04076 São Paulo, SP.   *1972*
Tel: (11) 5491611
Faculdade Marcelo Tupinamba, Rua Vergueiro,
04010 São Paulo, SP.
Tel: (11) 5496899
Faculdade Mozarteum de São Paulo, Rua Nava
dos Portugueses, 02462 São Paulo, SP.
Tel: (11) 9500788
**Faculdade Niteroiense de Educação, Letras e
Turismo**, Rua Visconde de Rio Branco 123,
24020 Niterói, RJ.   *1976*
Tel: (21) 7170513
**Faculdade Niteroiense de Formação de Profess-
ores**, Rua Visconde do Rio Branco 123, 24020
Niterói, RJ.   *1972*
Tel: (21) 7170513
Faculdade Olindense de Administração, Rua do
Bonfim 37, 53000 Olinda, PE.   *1972*
Tel: (81) 4291052
Faculdade para Executivos, Avenida Junqueira
Aires, 59000 Natal, RN.
Tel: (84) 2226557
Faculdade Paulista de Arte, Rua Martiniano de
Carvalho 864, 01321 São Paulo, SP.   *1957*
Tel: (11) 2873213
**Faculdade Paulista de Serviço Social de São
Caetano do Sul**, Avenida Paraíso 600, 09500
São Caetano do Sul, SP.   *1966*
Tel: (11) 4532911
Faculdade Paulista de Serviço Social, Rua Lopes
Chaves 273, 01154 São Paulo, SP.   *1940*
Tel: (11) 1660246
Faculdade Paulistana de Ciências e Letras, Rua
Madre Cabrini 36, 04020 São Paulo, SP. *1972*
Tel: (11) 5493033

**Faculdade Pôrto-Alegrense de Ciências Contábeis
e Administrativas**, Avenida Arnaldo Bohrer
253, 90000 Pôrto Alegre, RS.   *1971*
Tel: (512) 343533
**Faculdade Pôrto-Alegrense de Educação, Ciên-
cias e Letras**, Avenida Elias Mandel, 91300
Pôrto Alegre, RS.   *1968*
Tel: (512) 344522
**Faculdade Regional de Medicina de São José do
Rio Prêto**, Avenida Brigadeiro Faria Lima,
15100 São José do Rio Prêto, SP.
Tel: (172) 325733
**Faculdade Riopretense de Filosofia, Ciências e
Letras**, Rua Ipiranga 3460, 15100 São José do
Rio Prêto, SP.   *1972*
Tel: (17) 321646
Faculdade Salesiana de Educação Física, Rua
Santa Rosa, 98900 Santa Rosa, RS.
Tel: (55) 5121683
**Faculdade Salesiana de Filosofia, Ciências e
Letras**, Rua Dom Bosco 284, Caixa postal 29,
12600 Lorena, SP.   *1952*
Tel: (12) 5522033
Faculdade Salesiana de Tecnologia, 13100
Campinas, SP.   *1981*
Tel: (192) 422188
Faculdade Santa Marcelina, Rua Dr. Emilio
Ribas, 05006 São Paulo, SP.   *1938*
Tel: (11) 8269718
D : *ed, ind arts, hum-ped, mus.*
Faculdades Associadas de Ipiranga, Avenida
Nazare 993, 04263 São Paulo, SP.
Tel: (11) 2948555
F : *adm-eco-acc, phil-sc-let.*
Faculdades Associadas de São Paulo, Rua José
Antonio Coelho 879, Vila Mariana, 04011 São
Paulo, SP.   *1975*
Tel: (11) 5498233
F : *adm, comp, ed.*
Faculdades Canoenses, Rua Miguel Tostes,
92000 Canõas, RS.
Tel: (512) 725599. Telex: 0513378 cels br.
F : *adm-acc, arc-urb.*
Faculdades Capital, Rua Colonel Joviniano
Brandão, 03127 São Paulo, SP.   *1970*
Tel: (11) 2735011
F : *adm-acc-eco-stat, let-hum.*
**Faculdades da Associação Educacional do Litoral
Santista**, Avenida Rangel Pestana, 11500
Cubatão, SP.
Tel: (132) 322060
F : *tour, acc.*
Faculdades da Zona Leste de São Paulo, Rua
Cesario Galero 432, 03071 São Paulo, SP.
Tel: (11) 9413499
dr-arc-adm, phil-sc-let, ed.
Faculdades de Barra Mansa, Rua Vereador P. de
Carvalho 267, 27400 Barra Mansa, RJ.   *1966*
Tel: (243) 220222

adm, soc commun, nurs, law, phil-sc-let.
Faculdades de Itapetininga, Rodovia Raposo
Tavares 161, 18200 Itapetininga, SP.   *1969*
Tel: (152) 2710284
F : *law; soc commun, adm, phys.*
Faculdades do Grande Dourados, Rua Balbina de
Matos 2121, 79100 Dourados, MT.
Tel: (67) 4213121
**Faculdades do Instituto Educacional Teresa
Martin**, Rua Antonieta Leitão 129, 02925 São
Paulo, SP.   · *1981*
Tel: (11) 8578222
F : *sc-let, lib.*
Faculdades Integradas Alcantara Machado,
Praça Tres Corações 300, 05608 São Paulo,
SP.   *1972*
Tel: (11) 8145044
F : *commun, sc-let.*
Faculdades Integradas Augusto Motta, Avenida
Paris 72, 21041 Rio de Janeiro, RJ.   *1970*
Tel: (21) 2809422
F : *soc st, hum-let-arts, ed, eng, rehabilitation.*
Faculdades Integradas Bennett, Rua Marques de
Abrantes 55, 22230 Rio de Janeiro, RJ.   *1971*
Tel: (21) 2458000
F : *adm, arc-urb, eco, dr.*
Faculdades Integradas Castelo Branco, Avenida
Santa Cruz 1665, Realengo, 21710 Rio de
Janeiro, RJ.   *1973*
Tel: (21) 3311207
F : *ed-sc-let, phys.*
Faculdades Integradas Colegio Moderno, Trav.
Quintino Bocaiuva 1808, 66040 Belém, PA.
                                     1974
Tel: (91) 2232111
F : *adm, acc, eco.*
Faculdades Integradas Católicas de Brasília,
Areas Complementares, 72000 Taguatinga,
DF.   *1974*
Tel: (61) 5635000
F : *techn, hum.*
Faculdades Integradas de Cruzeiro, Rua Dom
Bosco 35, Centro, 12700 Cruzeiro, SP.   *1972*
Tel: (125) 441603
F : *adm, phil-sc-let.*
**Faculdades Integradas de Educação Física e
Técnicas Desportivas**, Rua Solon Fernandes
155, 0700 Guaralhos, SP.   *1972*
Tel: (11) 2093233
Faculdades Integradas de Marília, Avenida
Hygino Muzzi Filho 1001, 17500 Marília, SP.
Tel: (14) 338088
F : *eco, ed, phys, psyc, soc serv, dent.*
Faculdades Integradas de Ourinhos, Rua Arlindo
Luz 800, 19900 Ourinhos, SP.
Tel: (14) 3222033
F : *sc-let, bus adm.*
Faculdades Integradas de Santa Cruz do Sul, Rua
Cel. Oscar J. Jost 1551, 96800 Santa Cruz do

Sul, RS.
Tel: (51) 7131011
F : *acc-adm, law, phil-sc-let.*
S : *phys.*
Faculdades Integradas de Santo Angelo, Rua
Universidade das Missoes 393, 98800 Santo
Angelo, RS.   *1976*
Tel: (55) 3121599
F : *acc-adm, phil-sc-let.*
Faculdades Integradas de São Gabriel, Rua
Barão do Cambai 550, 97300 São Gabriel,
RS.   *1970*
Tel: (55) 2321042
sc, soc, commun, ed, eco-adm.
Faculdades Integradas de São Gonçalo, Rua
Lambari 10, Trindade, 24400 São Gonçalo,
RJ.   *1976*
Tel: (21) 7010505
nutr, phys, sc-let.
Faculdades Integradas de São José dos Campos,
Praça Candido Dias Castejon, 12200 São José
dos Campos, SP.
Tel: (123) 222355
Faculdades Integradas de Uberaba, Avenida
Guilherme Ferreira 217, 38100 Uberaba, MG.
                                     1972
Tel: (34) 3322322
F : *law, dent, phys, eng, commun.*
I : *hum, phil-hum, let, sc.*
**Faculdades Integradas do Instituto Ritter dos
Reis**, Rua Santos Dumont, 92120 Canoas, RS.
                                     1977
Tel: (512) 724149
F : *law, arc-urb.*
Faculdades Integradas Estacio de Sá, Rua do
Bispo 83, 20261 Rio de Janeiro, RJ.   *1970*
Tel: (21) 2843321
F : *law, eco-adm, soc commun, archae-
museology, teacher tr, tour, phil-sc-let.*
**Faculdades Integradas Hebraico Brasileira
Renascença**, Rua Prates 790, 01121 São Paulo,
SP.   *1975*
Tel: (11) 2286450
F : *lang, ed, sc, hotel mangt, comp.*
Faculdades Integradas Ibirapuera, Avenida Irai,
04082 São Paulo, SP.
Tel: (11) 5332022
Faculdades Integradas Moacyr Sreder Bastos,
Rua Engenheiro Trindade 229, 23000 Rio de
Janeiro, RJ.   *1976*
Tel: (21) 3941063
F : *eco-adm-acc, las, sc.*
Faculdades Integradas Rui Barbosa, Rua
Rodrigues Alves 932, Centro, 16900 Adradina,
SP.
Tel: (18) 6223492
F : *phil-sc-let, eco.*
Faculdades Integradas Silva e Souza, Rua Uranos
735, Ramos, 21060 Rio de Janeiro, RJ.   *1971*

Tel: (21) 2606422
arc-urb, ind des, stat.
Faculdades Integradas Teresa D'Avila, Avenida
Peixoto de Castro, 12600 Lorena, SP.
Tel: (125) 522888
Faculdades Integradas Teresa D'Avila, Rua
Siqueira Campos 483, 09020 Santo André,
SP. *1976*
Tel: (11) 4497477
F : *artistic ed, dom ed, lib.*
Faculdades Integradas Tiradentes, Rua Lagarto
264, 49000 Aracajú, SP. *1972*
F : *eco-adm-acc, soc commun, law.*
**Faculdades Metodistas Integradas Izabela
Hendrix**, Rua Bahia 2020, 30000 Belo Hori-
zonte, MG. *1972*
Tel: (31) 3376973
F : *phil-sc-let, arc-urb.*
Faculdades Metropolitanas Unidas, Rua Tagua
150, 01508 São Paulo, SP. *1968*
Tel: (11) 2702433
ed, soc serv, eco, bus adm-acc, phil-sc-let, law.
Faculdades Oswaldo Cruz, Rua Brigadeiro
Galvão 540, Barra Funda, São Paulo, SP. *1967*
Tel: (11) 8254266
F : *phil-sc-let, adm-eco-acc.*
E : *ch.*
Faculdades Reunidas Nuño Lisboa, Avenida
Ministro Edgard Romero 807, 21361 Rio de
Janeiro, RJ. *1971*
Tel: (21) 32765–15
F : *eng, acc-adm, ch.*
Faculdades São Judas Tadeu, Rua Taquari,
31660 São Paulo, SP. *1971*
Tel: (11) 9481677
F : *agr, biol heal-sc, let, exact sc-techn, hum.*
Faculdades Unidas Católicas de Mato Grosso,
Avenida Mato Grosso, 79100 Campo Grande,
MG. *1962*
Tel: (67) 3824261
F : *phil-sc-let, law, eco-acc-adm, soc.*
Faculdades Unidas de Bagé, Rua Tupy Silveira
2099, 96400 Bagé, RS. *1974*
Tel: (532) 422244
F : *fa, phys, law, phil-sc-let, agr, vet.*
Faculdades Unidas Grande Rio, Rua Marques de
Herval 1160, 25000 Duque de Caxias, RJ. *1972*
Tel: (217) 7714251
I : *soc st.*
F : *ed-sc-let, heal sc.*
**Federação das Escolas Superiores de Ilheus e
Itabuna**, Rodovia Ilheus-Itabuna, Km. 16,
45660 Ilheus, BA. *1974*
Tel: (73) 2313222
F : *law, eco, phil.*
Federação das Faculdades Celso Lisboa, Rua 24
de Mãio 797, 20951 Rio de Janeiro, RJ. *1972*
Tel: (21) 2014722
F : *eco-adm-acc, let-ped, psyc sc.*

**Federação das Faculdades Isoladas de Arara-
quara**, Rua Voluntarios da Patria 1309,
Centro, 14800 Araraquara, SP.
Tel: (16) 220499
F : *ed-soc st, eco-adm, law.*
**Federação de Escolas Faculdades Integradas
Simosen**, Rua Ibitiuva 151, 21710 Rio de
Janeiro, RJ. *1971*
Tel: (21) 3313022
F : *ed-sc-let, eco-act-adm.*
Federação de Escolas Superiores do ABC, Rua do
Sacramento, 09720 São Bernardo do Campo,
SP. *1971*
Tel: (11) 4573733
F : *adm, hum-let, soc commun, dent, phil-sc-let.*
**Federação de Estabelecimentos de Ensino
Superior em Novo Hamburgo**, Rua Maurício
Cardoso 510, 93300 Novo Hamburgo, RS. *1970*
Tel: (512) 933144
F : *fa, acc, ed, commun, tour, archae.*
S : *adm, phys.*
Ce : *techn.*
**Instituto Brasileiro de Estudos e Pesquisas
Gastroenterologicas**, Rua Dr. Seng 320, 01331
São Paulo, SP.
Tel: (11) 2882119
Instituto de Ciências Humanas de Santo Amaro,
Rua Prof. Eneas de S. Neto 340, Santo Amaro,
03071 São Paulo, SP. *1977*
Tel: (11) 5209611
Instituto de Ciências Sociais, EQS 704/904, BL A
LOTES ABC, 70390 Brasília, DF. *1967*
Tel: (61) 2232055
Instituto de Ciências Sociais de Americana, Rua
Dom Bosco 100, 13470 Americana, SP. *1972*
Tel: (194) 613367
Instituto de Ciências Sociais do Paraná, Rua
General Carneiro 216, 80000 Curitiba, PR.
1938
Tel: (41) 2643311
Instituto de Ciências Sociais e Aplicadas, SGAS
910 LOTE 32, 70390 Brasília, DF. *1981*
Tel: (51) 2439241
Instituto de Ensino de Engenharia Paulista, Rua
Doctor Bacelar, Mirandopolis, 04043 São
Paulo, SP. *1977*
Tel: (11) 5786455
Instituto de Ensino Superior do Alto Uruguai,
Rua Assis Brasil, 98400 Frederico Westphalen,
RS. *1970*
Tel: (55) 3441168
let, adm, acc, law, stat, soc-hum.
Instituto de Ensino Superior e Pesquisa, Campus
Universitario, 35500 Divinopolis, MG. *1966*
Tel: (37) 2212799
phil.
Instituto de Ensino Superior Santo André, Rua
Delfim Moreira 40, Centro, 09000 Santo
André, SP. *1972*

Tel: (11) 4499277
acc.

Instituto de Física Teórica de São Paulo, Rua Pamplona 145, 01405 São Paulo, SP.
1952, 1969
Tel: (11) 2885643

Instituto de Odontologia Paulista, Rua Doctor Bacelar, 04026 São Paulo, SP. *1981*
Tel: (11) 5786455
dent.

Instituto de Psicologia, BR 230 Km. 22 Blocos E/F, 58000 João Pessoa, PB. *1972*
Tel: (83) 2241418

Instituto de Tecnologia de Governador Valadares, Rua Moreira Sales, 35030 Governador Valadares, MG. *1968*
Tel: (332) 213090

Instituto Nacional de Telecomunicações de Santa Rita do Sapucai, Avenida João de Camargo 510, 37540 Santa Rita do Sapucai, MG. *1965*
Tel: (35) 6311788

Instituto Superior de Ciências Aplicadas, Via 147 Limeira Piracicaba, 13480 Limeira, SP. *1970*
Tel: (19) 4415367

Instituto Superior de Ensino e Pesquisa de Ituiutaba, Avenida Rio Grande c/ Rua Bahia,

38300 Ituiutaba, MG.
Tel: (35) 2613344

Instituto Superior de Estudos Sociais Clovis Bevilacqua, Avenida Lusitania 169, 21011 Rio de Janeiro, RJ. *1973*
Tel: (21) 2605552

Instituto Unificado Paulista, Rua Luis Goes 2211, Mirandopolis, 04043 São Paulo, SP. *1972*
Tel: (11) 5786455
psyc, let, soc commun, ped.

União das Faculdades Francanas, Anel Viario, 14400 Franca, SP. *1972*
Tel: (16) 7221444
sc-ed-techn, plast des, phil-sc-let.

Unidas Escolares de Instituição Moura Lacerda, Rua Padre Euclides 995, Campos Elisios, 14085 Ribeirão Prêto, SP. *1969*
Tel: (16) 6361010
F : *phil-sc-let, eco, arc-urb; phys* (Jaboticabal).

Unidas Integradas de Ensino Superior do Vale do Jacui, Rua Major Ouriques 2284, 96500 Cachoeira do Su, RS. *1970*
Tel: (51) 7224399
F : *eco-acc-adm, phil-sc-let.*
S : *phys, arts.*

Conselho de Reitores das Universidades Brasileiras (CRUB)

The Council of Brazilian University Rectors, created in 1966, is a private non-profit body which is composed of their rectors (as full members) and their former rectors (as honorary members). Its aims are: to promote the study of problems relative to the development of higher education and to seek solutions to them; to collaborate with the public authorities for the improvement of education and culture; to develop scholarly work and the creation of new technology in the universities; to help raise the cultural and technical standards of the academic staff and administrative personnel; to act as a permanent body for co-ordinating exchanges of experience and information between Brazilian universities; to promote the organization of congresses, conferences, seminars and other meetings; and to maintain exchanges with foreign universities and cultural bodies.

The supreme organ is the Plenary Council under the authority of which function the Presidency, the Executive Directorate and the Finance Committee.

Le Conseil des Recteurs des Universités brésiliennes, créé en 1966, est un organisme de droit privé, à but non lucratif, qui rassemble les universités brésiliennes, représentées par leurs

recteurs (en qualité de membres effectifs) ainsi que par les exrecteurs (en qualité de membres honoraires). Il a pour but de promouvoir les études sur les problèmes relatifs au développement de l'enseignement supérieur et de proposer des solutions visant à les résoudre; de collaborer avec les pouvoirs publics, en vue du perfectionnement de l'éducation et de la culture; de développer l'activité scientifique et la création de technologies nouvelles dans les universités; de contribuer à l'élévation du niveau culturel et technique du corps enseignant et du personnel administratif des universités; de jouer le rôle d'organe permanent de coordination des universités brésiliennes, en permettant la réalisation d'échanges d'expériences et d'informations; de promouvoir l'organisation de congrès, conférences, séminaires et autres rencontres propres à favoriser le perfectionnement des activités universitaires; et d'entretenir les échanges avec les universités et organismes culturels étrangers.

L'organe suprême est le Conseil plénier sous l'autorité duquel fonctionnent la Présidence, le Directoire exécutif et le Comité des finances.

President: Eduardo José Pereira Coelho.

Secretary-General: Ademar Arcângelo Cirimbelli.

Avenida W/3 Norte, Quadra 516, Lote 09, Setor de Entidades de Utilidade Pública 70770

Brasília, D.F.
Tel: (61) 272–2960. Telex: 611972 crub br

Coordenação do Aperfeiçoamento de Pessoal de Nivel Superior (CAPES)
The 'Federal Agency for Post-Graduate Education' (CAPES) is an agency for the co-ordination of Graduate Studies in Brazil, thus monitoring the scientific development in Brazilian universities. It is the largest agency in the country devoted to awarding Master's and Doctoral fellowships both in Brazil and abroad. As a result of its mandate, CAPES yearly evaluates every Brazilian Graduate Programme. Seed money is available to support promising activities and programmes. In addition, it sponsors experimental programmes and innovation in teaching. In the recent past it has helped to deploy the human resources of graduate schools to help government and public enterprises.

La "Coordination Nationale pour les Etudes de Post-Graduation" (CAPES) est un organisme qui coordonne les études de 'post-graduation' au Brésil et améliore le niveau scientifique dans les universités brésiliennes. Elle est également la plus grande organisation nationale pour l'octroi des bourses d'études pour la formation postgraduée au Brésil et à l'étranger. Elle est aussi chargée d'évaluer les programmes de post-graduation. Elle aide financièrement les projets et activités qu'elle juge prometteurs. Parallèlement, elle encourage des programmes expérimentaux et la mise au point des innovations dans l'enseignement. Ces dernières années la CAPES a contribué à la mobilisation des ressources humaines venant de cours de post-graduation pour le perfectionnement des projets du Gouvernement et des entreprises publiques.

General Director: Edson Machado de Sousa.

Ministério da Educação, Anexo 1, 4° andar, Caixa postal 3540, 70070 Brasília, DF.
Tel: (61) 214–8852. Telex: (61) 2018 copn br

Associação Brasileira de Mulheres Universitárias (IFUW)
Praça Mahatma Gandhi 2, Z c-06, 20031 Rio de Janeiro, RJ.

World University Service (WUS)
Rua da Gloria 332–1, 01510 São Paulo, SP.
Tel: (0511) 284–6879. Telex: (38) 11–32892 epsp br

União Nacional dos Estudantes (IUS)
Rua Demetrio Ribeiro 777/401, 90010 Pôrto Alegre, RS.

Intelectuales Católicos de Brasil (Pax Romana)
Correspondent: Prof. Candido Mendes de Almeida.
Faculdade de Direito, Praça 15 de Novembro 101, Rio de Janeiro, RJ.

Movimento de Estudantes Cristãos (WSCF)
Rua Marques de Abrantes 55, 22230 Rio de Janeiro, RJ.

Mesa Universitario de São Paulo (WUJS)
Contact: 89 Chaussee de Vleurgat, 1050 Brussels (Belgium).
Tel: (2) 647–7279. Telex: 20625.

*

Ministerio de Educação
Brasília, DF. Tel: (61) 214–8444.

Instituto Brasileiro de Educação, Ciências e Cultura
Palácio Itamarati, 196 Avenida Marechal Floriano 196, 20080 Rio de Janeiro, RJ.
Tel: (21) 263–9919. Telex: 2122563 ibecc rio de janeiro

BRUNEI DARUSSALAM
BRUNEI DARUSSALAM

Universiti Brunei Darussalam, Gadong, Bandar Seri Begawan 3187, Brunei Darussalem. *1985* Tél: 2-27001. Fax: 2-27003. Télex: bu 2725 unibrun. Cables: universiti brunei F : *arts-sc, ed.*

INSTITUT PENDIDIKAN SULTAN HASSANAL BOLKIAH [Sultan Hassanal Bolkiah I. of Education], P.O. Box 601, Bandar Seri Begawan, Brunei Darassalam. *1984*

Department of Education
Brunei.

BULGARIA
BULGARIE

UNIVERSITIES—UNIVERSITES

*Plovdivski universitet «Paissii Hilendarski» [U. de Plovdiv «Paissii Hilendarski»], Ul. Tzar Asséne 25, Plovdiv 4000. *1962, 1971* Tél: 3-36-61. Télex: 44251 pu bg F : math, éd, ch-biol, phy, ét soc.
*Sofiiski universitet Kliment Ohridski [U. de Sofia «Clément d'Ochrida»], Bul. Ruski 15, Sofia 1000. (M. le Recteur). *1888* Tél: 85-81. Télex: 23296 suko bg

F : phil, péd, hist, phill slave, phill occidentale, géol-géog, dr, ch, phy, mathméc, biol, jour, ét soc.
*Velikotarnovski universitet «Kiril i Metodi» [U. de Veliko Tarnovo «Cyril et Méthode»], Ul. 'Teodosius Tirnovo' 2, Veliko Tarnovo. *1963, 1971* Tél: 2-04-89 F : hist, phill, ba, éd.

OTHER INSTITUTIONS—AUTRES INSTITUTIONS
Technical Education—Enseignement technique

Vìsš himikotehnologičeski institut [I. sup. de Technologie chimique], Ul. Guéorgui Dimitrov 4, Bourgas. *1963* Tél: 6-01-19. Télex: 83689 techn ch, ét soc.
Vìsš himikotehnologičeski institut, Boul. "Clment Ochrid" 8, Darvénitza, Sofia. *1945* Tél: 62-41-41 F : techn org, techn inor, mét, ét soc.
Vìsš institut po hranitelna i vkusova promišlenost [I. sup. d'Industrie alimentaire], Bul. Vladimir I. Lénin 26, Plovdiv. *1948, 1953*

Tél: 4-18-11. Télex: 44 669 vihup bg F : techn, tec, ét soc.
Vìsš institut po arkitectura i stoitelstvo [I. sup. d'Architecture et de Construction], Bul. Christo Smirnenski 2, Sofia. *1942, 1953* Tél: 66-17-71. Télex: 23 574 F : gé civ, hyd, arc, géod, ét soc.
Vìsš mašinno-elektrotehničeski institut «V.I. Lenin» [I. sup. électrotechnique et mécanique 'V.I. Lenin'], 'Hristo Botev' Student Township, Sofia. *1945, 1953* Tél: 65-30-11

F : élec, méc, trans-commun, radio-électro, méc-énerg, automation, const de machine, ét soc.

Visš mašinno-elektrotehničeski institut. Ul. V. Kolarov 1, Varna. *1963*
Tél: 8-01-61. Cables: vmei
F : méc-const nav, élec-électro-automation, const de machine, ét soc.

Visš minno-géoložki institut [I. sup. des Mines et de Géologie], Darvénitza, Sofia. *1953*
Tél: 6-25-81
F : mine, géol, ét soc.

Visš mašinno elektrotehničeski institut, Ul. Hadji Dimitr 4, Gabrovo. *1964*
F : const de machines et d'instruments, électrotec, ét soc.

Visš tecničesko učilišče «Angel Kančev» [E. sup. Technique 'Angel Kunchev'], Ul. Komsomolska 8, Roussé. *1954*
Tél: 44-71.
F : techn méc, mécanisation de l'économie rurale, élec-électro-automation, ét soc.

Visš lesotehničeski institut [I. sup. de Technologie forestière], Boul. 'Climent Ochrid' 10, Darvénitza, Sofia. *1925, 1955*
Tél: 63-01

Professional Education—Enseignement professionnel

Visš ikonomičeski institut «Karl Marx» [I. sup. de Sciences économiques 'Karl Marx'], Studentski grad, Sofia. *1920*
Tél: 63 381. Télex: 22040 ii bg
F : éco gén, infor éco, ind-agr, march-trans.

Visš finansovo-stopanski institut «D.A. Cenov» [I. sup. d'Economie et de Finances], Ul. Emil Tchakarov 2, Svištov. *1936*
Tél: 2-46-82. Télex: 66684 vfsi bg
F : comp, fin.

Visš institut za narodno stopanstvo «Dimitar Blagoev» [I. sup. d'Economie nationale 'Dimitar Blagoev'], Boul. 'Lenin 77', Varna. *1920*
Tél: 2-33-81. Télex: 70382
F : comp, march, ét soc.

Visš medicinski Institut [I. de Médecine], Ul. Georgi Sofiyski 1, Sofia. *1918*
Tél: 51–72–82
F : stom, phar, méd.

Visš medicinski Institut, Ul. V. Aprilov 15a, Plovdiv. *1945*
Filiale à Pozardjik.

Visš medicinski Institut, Ul. Marindrinov 55, Varna. *1961*
Filiale à Tolbuhin.

Visš medicinski Institut, Ul. Karl Marx 1, Pleven. *1974*
Tél: 29 175. Télex: 34590

Visš medicinski Institut, Ul. Armeyska 7, Stara Zagora. *1982*

Visš selskostopanski institut «Vassil Kolarov» [I. sup. d'Agriculture 'Vassel Kolarov'], Ul. Mendeleev 12, Plovdiv. *1945*
Tél: 34-98. Télex: 04405

Visš institut po zootehnika i veterinarna medicina [I. sup. de Zootechnie et de Médecine vétérinaire], Ul. Dimitar Blagoev 62, Stara Zagora. *1922*
Tél: 2-80-31. Télex: 88465 vsizm bg

Teacher Training—Formation pédagogique

Visš institut za fizičeska kultura «G. Dimitrov'» [I. sup. de Culture physique 'G. Dimitrov'], Ul. Tina Kirkova 1, Sofia. *1942*
Tél: 88-15-11

Visš pedagogičeski institut [I. sup. de Pédagogie], Ul. Maritsa 16, Blagoevgrad. *1983*

Visš pedagogičeski institut, Šumen 9700. *1971*

F : nat-math, phill, péd, ét soc.

Institut za čuždestranni «G.A. Nasser» [I. pour les étudiants étrangers 'G.A. Nasser'], Ul. Assen Velchev 27, Sofia.
Egalement 12 autres établissements de formation pédagogique.

General Education— Enseignement général

Visš institut za isobrazitelni izkustva «N. Pavlovič» [I. sup. des Beaux-Arts], Sipka 1, Sofia. *1921, 1954*
Tél: 88-17-01
F : *ba, arts app.*

Visš institut za theatralno izkustvo «Kristu Sarafov» [I. sup. d'Art dramatique], Ul. G.S.
Rakovski 108, Sofia. *1948*
Tél: 87-98-62

Balgarska daržavna konservatoria [Conservatoire national bulgare], Ul. Klement Gotvald 11, Sofia. *1921*
Tél: 44-20-79
F : mus, théorie de la mus, compositeurs, chefs

d'orchestre, chefs de chorale.
Visš muzikalno-pedagogičeski institut [I. sup. Musico-Pédagogie], Ul. 'Todor Samodumov 2, Plovdiv. *1971*

National Student Council of Bulgaria— NSCB (IUS)
Bul. A. Stamboliisky 11, Sofia.
Tél: 84-81. Télex: 22552 ckdkms bg
Bureau d'Excursions internationales de la Jeunesse—BEIJ
10 Kaloyan, Sofia.
Bulgarian Patriarchate (WSCF)
4 Oborishte Street, 1090 Sofia
Tél: (02) 87-56-11

*

Commission pour l'Equivalence des Diplômes de fin d'Etudes secondaires
Bul. A. Stamboliisky 18, Sofia.

Tél: 22-83-11
Institut des Sciences de la Communication, Sofia.
Institut de Tourisme international, Ul. Karadja 32, Varna.

Tél: 84-81
Commission pour l'Equivalence des Diplômes d'Etudes supérieures et des Cours de Qualification après Diplômes
Bul. V. Tchapaev 55a, Sofia.
Commission supérieure d'Attestation pour l'Equivalence des Grades scientifiques
Bul. V. Tchapaev 55a, Sofia.
Ministère de l'Education nationale
Bul. A. Stamboliisky 18, Sofia.
Tél: 84-81. Télex: 22384 mnp sf bg
Commission nationale de la République populaire de Bulgarie pour l'Unesco
Ul. Rakovsky 96b, B.P. 386, Sofia 1000.
Tél: (02) 87-54-49. Cables: bulunesco sofia

BURKINA FASO
BURKINA FASO

Université de Ouagadougou, B.P. 7021, Ouagadougou. *1965, 1969, 1974*
Tél: 30-70-64. Télex: 5270 bf uniouaga
INSTITUT DES SCIENCES HUMAINES ET SOCIALES, Ouagagougou. *1965, 1980, 1985*
hist-arché, géog, socio, phil, psyc.
INSTITUT SUPÉRIEUR DES LANGUES, DES LETTRES ET DES ARTS, Ouagadougou.
1965, 1985
INSTITUT DE MATHÉMATIQUES ET DE PHYSIQUES, Ouagadougou. *1975*
INSTITUT DE CHIMIE, Ouagadougou. *1985*
INSTITUT DE DÉVELOPPEMENT RURAL, Ouagadougou. *1973, 1985*
INSTITUT DES SCIENCES DE LA NATURE, Ouagadougou. *1980, 1985*
hydro-géol, agro-ind.
INSTITUT UNIVERSITAIRE DE TECHNOLOGIE, Ouagadougou. *1970*
gestion des entrep, sec de direction.
ECOLE SUPÉRIEURE DE DROIT, Ouagadougou. *1975*

ECOLE SUPÉRIEURE DES SCIENCES ECONOMIQUES, Ouagadougou. *1975*
INSTITUT DES SCIENCES DE L'EDUCATION, Ouagadougou. *1985*
ECOLE SUPÉRIEURE DES SCIENCES DE LA SANTÉ, Ouagadougou. *1980*
Institut de la Réforme et de l'Action pédagogique, B.P. 7043, Ouagadougou. *1965, 1976*
Tél: (33) 63-63. Télex: mineduc 5293
Ecole nationale d'Administration et de Magistrature, B.P. 7013, Ouagadougou. *1959, 1984*
Tél: 33-46-10
Institut national des Sports, B.P. 7035, Ouagadougou.
Ecole Inter-Etats d'Ingénieurs de l'Equipement rural, B.P. 2023, Ouagadougou.
Tél: (33) 35-28. Télex: 5266 ei er
Ecole Inter-Etats des Techniciens supérieurs de l'Hydraulique et de l'Equipement rural, B.P. 594, (Kamboinse)—Ouagadougou.
Tél: (33) 42-47. Télex: 5266 uv

Commission nationale des Equivalences, des Titres et des Diplômes

B.P. 7021, Ouagadougou.
Tél: 33-34-62

Ministère de l'Enseignement supérieur et de la
  Recherche Scientifique
Ouagadougou.
Tél: 30-77-56

Commission nationale burkinabé pour l'Unesco
Boîte postale 7046, Ouagadougou.
Tél: (33) 46-84. Télex: 5555 secgouv

BURMA
BIRMANIE

UNIVERSITIES AND UNIVERSITY INSTITUTIONS—
UNIVERSITES ET INSTITUTIONS UNIVERSITAIRES

Arts and Science University of Mandalay, University P.O., Mandalay. (The Registrar).
1958, 1964
Tel: 659
F : *arts, sc.*
Moulmein University, Moulmein.   *1953, 1986*
Tel: (32) 21180
arts, sc, mar sc.
Arts and Science University of Rangoon, University P.O., Rangoon.   *1920, 1964*
Tel: Auto 31144
F : *arts, sc.*
Institute of Agriculture, Ye Zin, Pyinmana.
1937, 1946, 1958, 1964, 1975
Tel: 98
Institute of Animal Husbandry and Veterinary Science, Rangoon.   *1964*
Rangoon Institute of Technology, Gyogon, Insein.   *1964*
Tel: 40526
Workers' College, Botataung Pagoda Road, Rangoon.   *1964*

Akyab College, Akyab.   *1973*
arts, sc.
Bassein College, Bassein.   *1958*
Magwe College, Magwe.   *1958*
Institute of Dental Medicine, Shwedagon Pagoda Road, Rangoon.   *1964, 1974*
Institute of Economics, University P.O., Rangoon.   *1964*
Institute of Education, University P.O., Rangoon.   *1930, 1946, 1964*
Institute of Medicine, Mandalay.   *1964*
Institute of Medicine I, Godwin Road, Rangoon.
1964
Institute of Medicine II, Mingaladon P.O., Rangoon.   *1964*
arts, sc.
Myitkyina College, Myitkyina.   *1963*
arts, sc.
Taunggyi College, Taunggyi.   *1961*
arts, sc.

OTHER INSTITUTIONS—AUTRES INSTITUTIONS

Technical Education—Enseignement technique

Government Technical Institute, Insein.   *1890*
Government Technical Institute, Kalaw.   *1968*

Government Technical Institute, Mandalay. *1955*

Professional Education—Enseignement professionnel

State Agricultural Institute, Pyinmana.   *1954*
State Agricultural Institute, Thaton.   *1967*
Institute for Foreign Languages, University

Avenue, Rangoon.   *1963*
Institute of Para-Medical Sciences, General Hospital Compound, Rangoon.   *1964*

Teacher Training—Formation pédagogique

State Teachers' Training School, Bogalay. *1970*
State Teachers' Training School, Kyaukpyu. *1953*
State Teachers' Training College, Mandalay. *1952*
State Teachers' Training School, Meiktila. *1953*
State Teachers' Training College, Moulmein. *1953*
State Teachers' Training School, Myaungmya. *1953*
State Teachers' Training School, Myitkyina. *1962*

State Teachers' Training School, Prome. *1968*
State Teachers' Training College, Kanbe, Rangoon. *1947*
State Teachers' Training School, Thinkangyun, Rangoon. *1969*
State Teachers' Training School, Sagaing. *1968*
State Teachers' Training School, Taunggyi. *1964*
State Teachers' Training School, Thegon, Prome District. *1965*
State Teachers' Training School, Toungoo. *1967*

The Universities' Central Council
The Council is composed of 43 members and formulates policy in matters of university expansion, planning and administration.
Le Conseil se compose de 43 membres et élabore la politique en matière d'expansion, de planification et d'administration universitaires.
Rangoon.

The Universities' Academic Council
The Council is composed of 45 members and formulates policy on academic matters and co-ordinates all academic matters between institutions of higher learning.
Le Conseil comprend 45 membres et élabore la politique en matière d'enseignement et de recherche et assure la coordination entre les institutions d'enseignement supérieur.
Rangoon.

Student Christian Movement of Burma (WSCF)
601 Prome Road, G.P.O. 1400, Rangoon.
Tel: 732-90

*

Ministry of Education, Department of Higher Education
Theinbyu Street, Rangoon.
Tel: (95) 31 590. Cables: versity rangoon
Ministry of Union Culture
Rangoon, c/o Ministry of Information.
Tel: (95) 31553
Burmese National Commission for Unesco
Department of Higher Education, Ministry of Education, Office of the Ministers, Theinbyu Street, Rangoon.
Tel: 85-011 (ext. 91). Cables: unesco commission ministry education rangoon

BURUNDI
BURUNDI

*Université du Burundi, B.P. 1550, Bujumbura.
(M. le Recteur).   *1960, 1977*
Tél: (22) 3288. Télex: 5161
F : dr, let-hum, sc, éco-adm, méd, agr, psyc-sc
de l'éd, sc app.
I : tec sup, péd, phys-sports.
Ecole de Journalisme, B.P. 2393, Bujumbura.
Tél: (22) 6295
Ecole nationale de Police, B.P. 2636, Bujumbura.

formation des Officiers.
Ecole supérieure de Commerce, B.P. 1440,
Bujumbura.
Tél: (22) 4520
Institut supérieur d'Agriculture, B.P. 61, Gitega.
Tél: 2335
Institut supérieur des Techniques d'Aménage-
ment et d'Urbanisme, B.P. 2720, Bujumbura.
Tél: (22) 3694

Unirundi (IAUPL)
Correspondant: 18, rue du Docteur Roux, 75015
Paris (France).
Tél: (33-1) 47-83-31-65
Union de la Jeunesse Révolutionnaire Burund-
aise—UJRB, Commission Estudiantine (IUS)
B.P. 475, Bujumbura.
Télex: 5057 bdi (att. ujrb-ce)

Ministère de l'Education nationale
Bujumbura.
Tél: (22) 218
Commission nationale du Burundi pour l'Unesco
Ministère de l'Education nationale, B.P. 1990,
Bujumbura.
Tél: 4517. Télex: (22) 5166 mineduc bdi

*

CAMBODIA[1]
CAMBODGE[1]

UNIVERSITIES—UNIVERSITES

Université Phnôm-Penh, 133 Moha Vithei Preah
Bat Norodam, Phnôm-Penh.   *1960, 1970*
F : dr-éco, méd-sc paraméd, phar, let-hum, sc,
éd, com, dent.
I : lang mod.
E : éd.
Université technique, Angle Vithei Moat Chrouk
et Vithei Hing Pén, Phnôm-Penh.   *1965, 1970*
F : ing, gé civ, élec.

I : techn.
Université des Sciences Agronomiques, Chamcar
Daung (Kandal).   *1965, 1970*
F : agr, for, vét, socio-éco rur, pêch.
Université bouddhique, B.P. 117, Quai Sisowath,
Phnôm-Penh.   *1954, 1970*
Université des Beaux-Arts, Moha Vithei de
l'URSS, Phnôm-Penh.   *1965, 1970*

---

(1) No recent information having been received from the Cambodian authorities, the list of institutions is
reproduced in the form published in the preceding edition of this volume.

(1) Aucune information n'ayant été reçue récemment des autorités du Cambodge, la liste des institutions est
reproduite sous une forme identique à celle figurant dans l'édition précédente de ce volume.

Revolutionary Youth Association (IUS)
Phnôm-Penh.

*

Ministère de l'Education nationale et des Beaux-Arts
Phnôm-Penh.

CAMEROON
CAMEROUN

*Université de Yaoundé, B.P. 337, Yaoundé. (M. le Vice-Chancelier). *1962*
Tél: 22-07-44. Télex: 8384 u y kn
F : dr-éco, let-hum, sc.
  ECOLE NORMALE SUPÉRIEURE, B.P. 47, Yaoundé. *1961*
  CENTRE UNIVERSITAIRE DES SCIENCES DE LA SANTÉ, B.P. 337, Yaoundé. *1969*
  ECOLE NATIONALE SUPÉRIEURE POLYTECHNIQUE, B.P. 738, Yaoundé. *1971, 1975*
  INSTITUT DES RELATIONS INTERNATIONALES, B.P. 1637, Yaoundé. *1972*
  ECOLE SUPÉRIEURE DES SCIENCES ET TECHNIQUES DE L'INFORMATION, B.P. 1328, Yaoundé. *1970, 1982*
Centre Universitaire de Douala, B.P. 2071, Douala. *1977*
Tél: 42-62-19. Télex: 6140 kn
  ECOLE NORMALE SUPÉRIEURE DE L'ENSEIGNEMENT TECHNIQUE, B.P. 1872, Douala. *1979*
  ECOLE SUPÉRIEURE DES SCIENCES ÉCONOMIQUES ET COMMERCIALES, B.P. 1931, Douala. *1979*
Centre Universitaire de Dschang, Dschang. *1960, 1970*
Télex: 7013 kn
  ECOLE NATIONALE SUPÉRIEURE AGRONOMIQUE, Yaoundé. *1960, 1975*
  INSTITUT DES TECHNIQUES AGRICOLES, B.P. 110, Dschang. *1977*
Centre Universitaire de Ngaoundéré, B.P. 454,

Ngaoundéré. *1977*
Tél: 25-12-45. Télex: 7645 kn
  ECOLE NATIONALE SUPÉRIEURE DES INDUSTRIES AGRO-ALIMENTAIRES DU CAMEROUN, B.P. 455, Ngaoundéré. *1982*
Centre Universitaire de Buéa, Buéa. *1977*
  ECOLE SUPÉRIEURE DE TRADUCTION ET D'INTERPRÉTARIAT (ASTI) *1985*
Ecole nationale de l'Administration et de la Magistrature, B.P. 1180, Yaoundé. *1959, 1962*
Tél: 22-37-54
Ecole nationale supérieure de Police, B.P. 148, Yaoundé.
Ecole supérieure des Postes et Télécommunications, B.P. 1186, Yaoundé.
Tél: 22-37-00
Ecole nationale supérieure des Travaux publics, B.P. 510, Yaoundé. *1982*
Institut de Développement informatique Africain, B.P. 6316, Yaoundé. *1982*
Tél: 22-04-06. Télex: 8653 kn
Institut de Formation et de Recherche démographiques, B.P. 1556, Yaoundé. *1972*
Tél: 22-24-71
Institut international des Assurances, B.P. 1575, Yaoundé.
Institut national de la Jeunesse et des Sports, B.P. 1016, Yaoundé.
Institut de Statistiques, de Planification et d'Economie appliquée, B.P. 294, Yaoundé. *1973*
Tél: 22-01-34

Ministère de l'Enseignement supérieur et de la Recherche scientifique
Yaoundé.
Tél: 23 18 50. Télex: 8418 mesres kn
Commission nationale de la République du

Cameroun pour l'Unesco
Ministère de l'Education nationale, Yaoundé.
Tél: 2340 50 (postes 501 & 510). Télex: mineduc 8551 kn yaoundé

CANADA
CANADA

UNIVERSITIES AND OTHER INSTITUTIONS
OF HIGHER EDUCATION (1)—
UNIVERSITES ET AUTRES ETABLISSEMENTS
D'ENSEIGNEMENT SUPERIEUR (1)

Acadia University, Wolfville, Nova Scotia
B0P 1X0.   *1838*
Tel: (902) 542-2201
F : *sc, arts, ed, mus, theo, mangt.*
S : *bus, comp sc, eng, ed, hom eco, mus, phys-recr, sec.*
D : *fa, relig.*
Also 1 affiliated college.
The University of Alberta, Edmonton, Alberta
T6G 2E1.   *1906*
Tel: (403) 432-3111. Fax: (403) 432-7219.
Telex: 037-2979
F : *agr-for, arts, bus, dent, ed, eng, hom eco, law, lib, med, nur, phar, phys, rehab med, sc.*
D : *art-des, mus, relig.*
Also 5 affiliated colleges.
Athabasca University, Box 10,000, Athabasca, Alberta T0G 2R0.   *1970*
Tel: (403) 675-6111. Fax (403) 675-2166. Telex: 037-41714 athauedm
Bishop's University, Lennoxville, Quebec J1M 1Z7.   *1843*
Tel: (819) 569-9551. Fax: (819) 822-1092.
Telex: 058-36168
F : *bus adm, hum, nat-math, soc.*
Also 1 affiliated institution.
Brandon University, Brandon, Manitoba R7A 6A9.   *1899*
Tel: (204) 728-9520. Fax: (204) 727-0942.
Telex: 07-502721
F : *arts, sc, ed, mus.*
D : *native st, relig.*
*The University of British Columbia, 2075 Wesbrook Mall, Vancouver, British Columbia V6T 1W5.   *1908*
Tel: (604) 228-2211. Fax: (604) 224-8588.
Telex: 04-51233.
F : *app sc, agr, arts, com-bus, dent, ed, for, law, med, phar, sc.*
S : *audiology and speech sc, arc, hom eco, lib, nurs, phys, rehab med, soc w.*

D : *mus, theat.*
Also 4 affiliated institutions.
British Columbia Open University, 7671 Alderbridge Way, Richmond, British Columbia V6X 1Z9.   *1988*
Tel: (604) 660-2224. Fax: (604) 660-2272
Brock University, Merrittville Highway, St. Catharines, Ontario L2S 3A1.   *1964*
Tel: (416) 688-5550. Fax: (416) 688-2789.
Telex: 061-5133
F : *ed, hum, math, soc, sc.*
S : *adm, env & urb st, phys-recr, app hum dev.*
D : *Canadian st, comp sc, fa.*
*The University of Calgary, 2500 University Drive, North West, Calgary, Alberta T2N 1N4.   *1966*
Tel: (403) 220-5110. Fax: (403) 282-7298.
Telex: 038-21545
F : *ed, eng, env des, fa, hum, law, mangt, med, nurs, phys, sc, soc, soc w.*
D : *mus, relig.*
Also 2 related colleges.
Camrose Lutheran College, 4901–46 Avenue, Camrose, Alberta T4V 2R3.   *1985*
Tel: (403) 679-1100
University College of Cape Breton, P.O. Box 5300, Sydney, Nova Scotia B1P 6L2.   *1974*
Tel: (902) 539-5300. Fax: (902) 562-0119
F : *art-sc, techn & trades.*
*Carleton University, Ottawa, Ontario K1S 5B6.
                                                 1942
Tel: (613) 564-4321. Fax: (613) 564-7149.
Telex: 053-4232
F : *arts, eng, sc, soc.*
S : *arc, bioch, Canadian st, bus, ind des, int aff, comp sc, ind des, jour, publ adm, soc w.*
D : *mus, pol.*
Ecole des hautes Etudes commerciales, 5255, avenue Decelles, Montréal, Québec H3T 1V6.
                                                 1907
Tél: (514) 340-6000. Fax: (514) 340-6314

---

(1) Excluding institutions granting degrees only in Theology.
(1) A l'exclusion des institutions ne conférant de grades qu'en théologie.

F : adm des aff, com.

*Concordia University, 1455 de Maisonneuve Boulevard West, Montreal, Quebec H3G 1M8.
1974
Tel: (514) 848-2424. Fax: (514) 848-3494. Telex: 05-25517
F : *arts-sc, com-adm, eng, fa, comp.*
D : *Canadian st.*

Dalhousie University, Halifax, Nova Scotia B3H 3J5.
1818
Tel: (902) 424-2211. Fax: (902) 424-2319. Telex: 019-21863
F : *adm, arts, sc, dent, heal professions, law, med, mangt.*
S : *bus, dental hyg, nurs, pharm, occp ther, phy, publ adm, soc w, ed, heal, physio.*
D : *ed, eng, mus, pol.*
Also 3 associated universities.

Collège dominicain de philosophie et de théologie, 96, avenue Empress, Ottawa, Ontario K1R 7G2.
1909
Tél: (613) 233-5696
F : théo.
D : phil.
I : pastorale.

University of Guelph, Guelph, Ontario N1G 2W1.
1964
Tel: (519) 824-4120. Fax: (519) 824-945. Telex: 069-56540
F : *arts, fam, sc, soc.*
C : *agr, arts, vet.*
S : *eng, hotel & food adm, landscape arc.*
D : *fa.*

The King's College, 10766-97 Street, Edmonton, Alberta T5H 2M1.
1979
F : *hum, soc.*

University of King's College, Halifax, Nova Scotia B3H 2A1.
1789
Tel: (902) 422-1271
F : *arts, sc, theo, jour.*
Also 1 associated institution.

Lakehead University, Oliver Road, Thunder Bay, Ontario P7B 5E1.
1965
Tel: (807) 343-8110. Fax (807) 343-8023. Telex: 073-4594
F : *arts, ed, sc.*
S : *bus adm, eng, for, lib, nurs, recr, phys.*

Laurentian University of Sudbury/Université Laurentienne de Sudbury, Ramsey Lake Road, Sudbury, Ontario P3E 2C6.
1960
Tel: (705) 675-1151. Fax: (705) 673-6519. Telex: 0677-569
F : *hum, sc, soc, eng.*
S : *com, ed, eng, nurs, phys, soc w.*

UNIVERSITÉ DE SUDBURY/UNIVERSITY OF SUDBURY, Ramsey Lake Road, Sudbury, Ontario P3E 2C6.
1914
Tel: (705) 673-5661. Fax: (705) 673-6519. Telex: 067-7569

D : *phil, relig, native st, folklore.*
Also 3 affiliated colleges, 1 constituent college, and 3 federated universities.

*Université Laval, Cité universitaire, Québec, Québec G1K 7P4.
1663
Tél: (418) 656-2131. Fax: (418) 656-2809. Télex: 051-31621
F : adm, agr-alim, arts, dr, éd, for-géod, let, méd, phil, sc-gé, soc, théo.
E : arc, arts-vis, méd-dent, sc-inf, mus, phar, psyc, serv soc.

The University of Lethbridge, 4401 University Drive, Lethbridge, Alberta T1K 3M4.
1967
Tel: (403) 328-2111. Fax: (403) 329-2022. Telex: 038-49357
F : *art-sc, ed.*
S : *nurs, fa, mangt.*
D : *mus, phys.*

*McGill University, 845 Sherbrooke Street West, Montreal, Quebec H3A 2T5.
1821
Tel: (514) 398-4455. Fax: (514) 391-3596. Telex: 052-00510
F : *agr, arts, dent, ed, eng, law, mangt, med, mus, relig, sc.*
S : *arc, comp sc, lib, nurs, physical & occp ther, soc w, urb, diet-nutr, occp-heal.*
D : *agr eng.*
Also 3 affiliated colleges, and 1 constituent college.

McMaster University, Hamilton, Ontario L85 4L8.
1887
Tel: (416) 525-9140. Telex: 061-8347
F : *bus, eng, hum, heal sc, sc.*
S : *nurs, soc w, phys.*
C : *theo.*
Also 1 affiliated institution.

The University of Manitoba, Winnipeg, Manitoba R3T 2N2.
1877
Tel: (204) 474-8880. Fax: (204) 269-6629. Telex: 075-87721
F : *adm, agr, arc, arts-sc, dent, ed, eng, hum eco, law, med, phar, phys, recr.*
S : *fa, mus, nurs, phys, soc w, agr.*
D : *interior des, env st, phys ther.*

COLLÈGE UNIVERSITAIRE DE SAINT-BONIFACE, 200 avenue de la Cathédrale, Saint Boniface, Manitoba R2H 0H7. *1818*
Tél: (204) 233-0210. Télex: cn/cp

ST. JOHN'S COLLEGE, 400 Dysart Road, The University of Manitoba Campus, Winnipeg, Manitoba R3T 2M5. *1866*
Tel: (204) 474-8531

ST. PAUL'S COLLEGE, 430 Dysart Road, Winnipeg, Manitoba R3T 2M6. *1926*
Tel: (204) 474-8575. Fax: (204) 269-6629. Telex: 07-587721

Also 1 affiliated college, 2 approved teaching centres, and 1 constituent college.

Memorial University of Newfoundland, Elizabeth

Avenue, St. John's Newfoundland A1C 5S7.
1925
Tel: (709) 737-8000. Fax: (709) 737-4569.
Telex: 016-4101
F : *arts, ed, eng-app sc, med, sc, bus adm.*
S : *nurs, phys, soc w, fa, phar.*
D : *for, comp sc.*
Also 1 affiliated college and 1 regional college.

Université de Moncton, Moncton, Nouveau-Brunswick E1A 3E9.   *1963*
Tél: (506) 858-4000. Télécopieur: (506) 858-4379.
F : adm, arts, ed, sc-ing, soc.
E : sc dom, sc inf, dr.

***Université de Montréal**, C.P. 6128, Succursale A, Montréal, Québec H3C 3J7.   *1878*
Tél: (514) 343-6111. Fax: (514) 343 5976
Télex: 055-61359.
F : aménagement, arts-sc, dr, méd, vét, dent, éd, mus, phar, inf, théo.
E : adm, crim.
D : bibl, urb.
Egalement 2 écoles affiliées.

Mount Allison University, Sackville, New Brunswick E0A 3C0.   *1839*
Tel: (506) 364-2200
F : *arts-sc.*
D : *com, ed, fa, eng-comp sc, mus, sec, relig.*

Mount Saint Vincent University, Halifax, Nova Scotia B3M 2J6.   *1873*
Tel: (902) 443-4450. Fax: (902) 445-3960.
Telex: cn 111cp
F : *hum-sc.*
D : *pub rel, relig.*

University of New Brunswick, P.O. Box 4400, Fredericton, New Brunswick E3B 5A3.   *1785*
Tel: (506) 453-4666. Fax: (506) 453-4599.
Telex: 014-46202
F : *adm, arts, ed, eng, for, law, nurs, phys, sc.*
S : *comp sc.*
    St. Thomas University, P.O. Box 4569, Fredericton, New Brunswick E3B 5G3.
1910
    Tel: (506) 452-7700. Telex: 014-46202
Also 1 affiliated institution.

Nova Scotia Agricultural College, Truro, Nova Scotia B2N 5E3.   *1905*
Tel: (902) 895-1571. Fax: (902) 893-4601.
Telex: 019-34532
D : *agr.*

Nova Scotia College of Art and Design, 5163 Duke Street, Halifax, Nova Scotia B3J 3J6.   *1887*
Tel: (902) 422-7381. Fax: (902) 425-2420.
Telex: 019-21591
D : *des, fa.*

Ontario Institute for Studies in Education, 252 Bloor Street West, Toronto, Ontario M5S 1V6.   *1965*
Tel: (416) 923-664. Fax: (416) 926-4725. Telex:

06217720
D : *ed.*

***Université d'Ottawa/University of Ottawa**, Ottawa, Ontario K1N 6N5.   *1848*
Tel: (613) 564-3311. Fax: (613) 564-5829.
Telex: 053-3338
F : adm, arts, dr civ, éd, sa, soc.
E : inf, hum phys.
D : arts vis, mus.
Egalement 1 université fédérée.

Ecole polytechnique de Montréal, Case postal 6079, succursale A, Montréal, Québec H3C 3A7.   *1873*
Tél: (514) 340-4711. Télécopieur: (514) 340-4440. Télex: 05-24146
F : *ing.*

University of Prince Edward Island, 550 Charlottetown, Prince Edward Island C1A 4P3.   *1969*
Tel: (902) 566-0439. Fax: (902) 566-0420.
F : *arts, ed, sc, bus adm, vet.*
D : *eng, fa, hom eco, mus.*

***Université du Québec**, 2875 boulevard Laurier, Ste-Foy, Québec G1V 2M3.   *1968*
Tél: (418) 657-3551. Fax: (418) 657-3551 poste 2271. Télex: 051-31623
E : adm, publ.
F : adm, arts app, ba, dess env, dr, éd, ing, let, sa, sc-hum-soc, sc app & pures, serv comty & publ.
I : microbiol, rech scq, techn.
    Université du Québec à Chicoutimi, 555, boulevard de l'Université, Chicoutimi, Québec G7H 2B1.
    Tél: (418) 545-5011. Fax: (418) 545-5012. Télex: 051-36108
    Université du Québec à Hull, Case postale 1250, Succursale B, Hull, Québec J8X 3X7.
    Tél: (819) 595-3900. Fax: (819) 595-3924
    Université du Québec à Montréal, Case postale 8888, Succursale A, Montréal, Québec H3C 3P8.
    Tél: (514) 282-3000. Fax: (514) 282-3095. Télex: 051-31623
    Université du Québec à Rimouski, 300, avenue des Ursulines, Rimouski, Québec G5L 3A1.
    Tél: (418) 723-1986. Fax: (418) 724-1525. Télex: 051-31623
    Université du Québec à Trois-Rivières, 3351 boulevard des Forges, Case postale 500, Trois-Rivières, Québec G9A 5H7.
    Tél: (819) 376-5011. Fax: (819) 376-5012. Télex: 051-31623
    Université du Québec en Abitibi-Témiscamingue, 42 Monseigneur Rhé-aume est, C.P. 700, Rouyn, Québec J9X 5E4.

Tél: (819) 762-0971

ECOLE NATIONALE D'ADMINISTRATION PUBLIQUE, 945, rue Wolfe, Sainte-Foy, Québec G1V 3J9.
Tél: (418) 657-2845. Fax: (418) 657-2620.
Télex: 051-31623

ECOLE NATIONALE DE TECHNOLOGIE SUPÉRIEURE, 4750, avenue Henri-Julien, Montréal, Québec H2T 1R0.
Tél: (514) 289-8800
Egalement 1 collège affilié.

*Queen's University at Kingston, Kingston, Ontario K7L 3N6.   *1841*
Tel: (613) 545-2000. Fax: (613) 545-6300.
Telex: 009-6100
F : *app sc, arts-sc, bus, ed, law, med, nurs.*
S : *ind rel, phys, publ adm, rehab, ther, urb & reg plan.*
D : *mus.*
Also 1 related college.

Redeemer Reformed Christian College, R.R. 1, Highway 53 West, Ancaster, Ontario L9G 3N6   *1980*
Tel: (416) 648-2131
D : *lang, fa, sc, soc.*

*The University of Regina, Regina, Saskatchewan S4S 0A2.   *1959*
Tel: (306) 584-4111. Fax: (306) 586-9862
Telex: 961-000.
F : *adm, arts, ed, eng, sc, soc w, phys st.*
S : *jour.*
D : *mus, vis arts.*

CAMPION COLLEGE, c/o The University of Regina, Regina, Saskatchewan S4S 0A2.   *1917*
Tel: (306) 586-4242

LUTHER COLLEGE, c/o The University of Regina, Saskatchewan S4S 0A2.   *1913*
Tel: (306) 585-5333. Fax: (306) 586-9862

SASKATCHEWAN INDIAN FEDERATED COLLEGE, 127 College West, The University of Regina, Regina, Saskatchewan S4S 0A2.   *1976*
Tel: (306) 584-8333
Also 2 affiliated colleges.

Ryerson Polytechnic Institute, 350 Victoria Street, Toronto, Ontario M5B 2K3.   *1948*
Tel: (416) 979-5000. Fax: (416) 979-5155.
Telex: 06-528056
F : *app arts, arts, bus, comty serv, techn.*
D : *jour, nurs, sec sc, soc w.*

Université Sainte-Anne, Pointe-de-l'Eglise, Nouvelle-Ecosse B0W 1M0.   *1890*
Tél: (902) 769-2114. Fax: (902) 769-2496.
Télex: 019-385-06
D : *com, éd, hum-soc, sc.*

St. Francis Xavier University, Antigonish, Nova Scotia B2G 1C0.   *1853*
Tel: (902) 863-3300

F : *arts-sc.*
D : *bus adm, mus, nurs.*
Also 1 related college.

St. Mary's University, Halifax, Nova Scotia B3H 3C3.   *1802*
Tel: (902) 420-5400. Fax: (902) 420-5561.
Telex: 019-22679
F : *arts, com, ed, sc.*
D : *bus adm, mangt, relig.*
Also 1 affiliated college.

Université Saint-Paul/Saint Paul University, 223 Main Street, Ottawa, Ontario K1S 1C4.   *1866*
Tél: (613) 236-1393. Télex: cn/cp
F : *dr can, phil, théo.*
Egalement 1 établissement affilié.

University of Saskatchewan, Saskatoon, Saskatchewan S7N 0W0.   *1909*
Tel: (306) 244-4343. Fax: (306) 373-6088.
Telex: 074-2659
C : *arg, arts-sc, com, dent, ed, eng, hom eco, law, med, nurs, phar, phys, vet.*
S : *phys ther, agr.*
D : *mus*

ST. THOMAS MORE COLLEGE, 1437 College Drive, Saskatoon, Saskatchewan S7N 0W6.   *1936*
Tel: (306) 966-8900
Also 5 affiliated colleges.

Université de Sherbrooke, Cité universitaire, 2500 boulevard Université, Sherbrooke, Québec J1K 2R1.   *1954*
Tél: (819) 821-7000. Télex: bibuniv shb 058-36149
F : *let-hum adm, dr, éd, méd, phys, sc, sc app, théo.*
E : *mus.*
D : *serv soc, inf.*

Simon Fraser University, Burnaby, British Columbia V5A 1S6.   *1963*
Tel: (604) 291-3111
F : *arts, ed, sc, app sc, bus adm.*
D : *commun, comp sc, crim, kinesiology.*

Technical University of Nova Scotia, P.O. Box 1000, Halifax, Nova Scotia B3J 2X4.   *1907*
Tel: (902) 429-8300. Fax: (902) 429-2179.
Telex: tuns 019-21566
F : *arc, eng.*
S : *comp sc.*

University of Toronto, Toronto, Ontario M5S 1A1.   *1827*
Tel: (416) 978-2011. Fax: (416) 9783-938.
Telex: cnp 623887 gedogy tor
F : *app sc-eng, arc, arts-sc, dent, ed, for, law, lib, mangt, med, mus, nurs, phar, soc w.*
S : *phys.*
D : *comp sc, stat.*

UNIVERSITY OF ST. MICHAEL'S COLLEGE, 81 St. Mary Street, Toronto, Ontario M5S 1J4.   *1852*

Tel: (416) 926-1300. Telex: cn/cp
UNIVERSITY OF TRINITY COLLEGE, Toronto,
Ontario M5S 1H8.   *1852*
Tel: (416) 978-2522. Fax: (416) 978-8182.
Telex: 055-24428
VICTORIA UNIVERSITY, 73 Queen's Park,
Toronto, Ontario M5S 1K7.   *1836*
Tel: (416) 585-4524. Telex: 049-7222
Also 6 constituent colleges, 4 federated col-
leges, and 3 other related institutions.
Trent University, Peterborough, Ontario
K9J 7B8.   *1963*
Tel: (705) 748-1011. Fax: (705) 748-1246.
Telex: 06-962824
F : *arts-sc.*
Trinity Western University, 7600 Glover Road,
Langley, British Columbia V3A 4R9.   *1962*
Tel: (604) 888-7511
D : *bus, fa, hum, nat, phys, relig, soc, ed.*
Also 1 affiliated institution.
University of Victoria, PO Box 1700, Victoria,
British Columbia V8W 2Y2.   *1902*
Tel: (604) 721-7211. Fax: (604) 721-8653.
Telex: 049-7222
F : *arts-sc, ed, fa, law, eng, hum-soc dev.*
D : *mus, nurs, publ adm, soc w.*
University of Waterloo, Waterloo, Ontario
N2L 3G1.   *1957*
Tel: (519) 885-1211. Fax: (519) 888-4521.
Telex: 069-55259
F : *arts, eng, env st, sc, hum kinetics, math.*
S : *arc, optom, urb & reg plan, acc.*
D : *comp sc, fa.*
UNIVERSITY OF ST. JEROME'S COLLEGE,
Waterloo, Ontario N2L 3G3.   *1865*
Tel: (519) 884-8110. Telex: 06-955 259
Also 3 affiliated colleges.
The University of Western Ontario, London,
Ontario N6A 3K7.   *1878*
Tel: (519) 679-2111. Fax: (519) 661-3292.
Telex: 064-7134

F : *arts, dent, ed, eng, law, lib, med, mus, nurs,
phys, sc, soc, app heal sc.*
D : *sec, bus adm, jour.*
BRESCIA COLLEGE, 1285 Western Road,
London, Ontario N6G 1H2.   *1919*
Tel: (519) 432-8353. Telex: 111
HURON COLLEGE, London, Ontario
N6G 1H3.   *1863*
Tel: (519) 438-7224. Telex: 064-7134
KING'S COLLEGE, 266 Epworth Avenue,
London, Ontario N6A 2M3.   *1955*
Tel: (519) 433-3491. Telex: 064-7134
Wilfrid Laurier University, Waterloo, Ontario
N2L 3C5.   *1911, 1960*
Tel: (519) 884-1970. Fax: (519) 886-9351
F : *arts-sc, bus-eco, mus, soc w.*
D : *bus adm, relig.*
*University of Windsor, Windsor, Ontario N9B
3P4.   *1857*
Tel: (519) 253-4232. Fax: (519) 973-7050.
Telex: 064-77684
F : *arts, bus adm, ed, eng, human kinetics, law,
sc, soc.*
S : *comp sc, mus, nurs, soc w, vis arts, dram.*
D : *hom eco, relig.*
Also 2 affiliated colleges and 1 federated
university.
*The University of Winnipeg, 515 Portage
Avenue, Winnipeg, Manitoba R3B 2E9.   *1871*
Tel: (204) 786-7811
F : *art-sc, theo.*
I : *urb st.*
Also 1 associated institution.
*York University, 4700 Keele Street, North
York, Ontario M3J 1P3.   *1959*
Tel: (416) 736-2100. Fax: (416) 736-5641.
Telex: 065-24736
F : *adm, arts, ed, env st, fa, sc.*
S : *law.*
D : *Canadian st, soc w.*
Also 10 constituent colleges.

**Association of Universities and Colleges of
Canada/Association des Universités et Collèges du
Canada**

Since 1911, the Association has served as the
national organization of degree-granting institutions. It was incorporated under an Act of
Parliament in 1965 with a mandate «to foster
and promote the interests of higher education
in Canada». To this end, the Association co-
ordinates national initiatives undertaken by its
members and represents the concerns of the
university community to governments, the
general public and at national and international
fora. It provides for the study and discussion of
issues in higher education and facilitates the

exchange of ideas and information among its
members. In 1988, 87 institutions held membership in the association.

Publications include: the biennial Directory of
Canadian Universities; the annual Academic and
Administrative Officers at Canadian Universit-
ies; the biennial Awards for Graduate Study; the
Directory of Canadian University Resources for
International Development; the monthly news-
magazine University Affairs; the quarterly news-
letters, Canadian Universities in International
Development; the Government Relations News-
letter; and the bi-weekly Notes from AUCC.

*Depuis 1911, l'Association sert d'organisation
nationale aux établissements qui confèrent des*

grades. Elle a été constituée en corporation en vertu d'une loi du Parlement en 1965, «pour favoriser et faire progresser les intérêts de l'enseignement supérieur au Canada». A cette fin, l'Association coordonne les initiatives nationales de ses établissements membres et fait valoir les intérêts de la communauté universitaire auprès des gouvernements et du grand public et à l'occasion de forums nationaux et internationaux. Elle sert de tribune pour l'étude et la discussion de questions concernant l'enseignement supérieur et facilite l'échange d'idées et de renseignements entre ses membres. En 1988, quatre-vingt-sept établissements étaient membres de l'Association.

Parmi ses publications, il y a lieu de mentionner: le Répertoire des universités canadiennes, publication biennale; Dirigeants et administrateurs des universités canadiennes, publication annuelle; le Répertoire canadien des bourses d'études supérieures, publication biennale; le Répertoire des ressources des universités canadiennes pour le développement international; le journal mensuel Affaires Universitaires; les Universités et le développement international (trimestriel); le Bulletin des relations avec les gouvernements; et Info de l'AUCC, bulletin publié toutes les deux semaines.

President/Président: Dr. Arnold Naimark, President, The University of Manitoba.

Executive Director/Directeur général: Dr. Claude Lajeunesse.

151 Slater Street, Ottawa, Ontario K1P 5N1.

Tel: (613) 563-1236. Fax: (613) 563-9745. Telex: 053-3329. Cables: canuf ott

Conférence des Recteurs et des Principaux des Universités du Québec/Conference of Rectors and Principals of Quebec Universities

Le Conseil d'administration de la Conférence regroupe vingt personnes dont le recteur de chacun des établissements universitaires du Québec et des vice-recteurs. Un ensemble de comités et de souscomités composés de vice-recteurs, de professeurs, de directeurs de départements ou de services examine et fait au Conseil d'administration des recommandations concernant toutes les questions d'ordre pédagogique, financier et administratif susceptibles d'avoir une incidence sur le fonctionnement des universités.

The Administrative Board of the Conference comprises 20 members, including the rector of each university and vice-rectors. A series of committees and sub-committees composed of vice-rectors, professors, heads of departments or services, examine all educational, financial and administrative questions likely to affect the functioning of the universities and makes recommendations to the Administrative Board.

Président: Gilles Cloutier, Recteur, Université de Montréal.

Directeur général: Richard Pérusse.

C.P. 952, Succursale Place du Parc, Montréal, Québec H2W 2N1.

Tél: (514) 288-8524. Télex: 5560944 crepuq mtl

Council of Ontario Universities/Conseil des Universités de l'Ontario

The Council, formerly the Committee of Presidents of Universities of Ontario, was established in 1962 to promote co-operation among the provincially assisted universities of Ontario and between them and the Provincial Government and, generally, to work for the improvement of higher education in Ontario. Originally, members were the presidents of the provincially assisted universities. The membership of the Council, as reconstituted in 1970, comprises the executive heads and academic colleagues elected by the senior academic body of each of the provincially assisted universities in Ontario which have power to grant university degrees in more than one field.

The Council meets every month or two during the academic year to deliberate matters of concern for the system of Ontario universities. It is aided in its deliberations by advice from numerous specialized subcommittees and affiliates.

Le Conseil des universités de l'Ontario, anciennement Comité des Présidents des Universités de l'Ontario, a été créé en 1962 pour promouvoir la coopération des universités de l'Ontario subventionnées par la province, tant entre elles qu'avec le gouvernement provincial, et, plus généralement, pour travailler à l'amélioration de l'enseignement supérieur dans l'Ontario. A l'origine en étaient membres les présidents des universités subventionnées par la province. Les membres du Conseil, remodelé en 1970, sont les chefs des universités et des professeurs élus par le corps enseignant supérieur de chaque université de l'Ontario subventionnée par la province et habilitée à conférer des grades universitaires dans plus d'une discipline.

Le Conseil se réunit à peu près tous les deux mois pendant l'année universitaire pour discuter des sujets concernant les universités de l'Ontario. Il est aidé dans ses délibérations par les avis de nombreux sous-comités spécialisés et de groupes affiliés.

Chairman: Harry W. Arthurs, President, York University.

Executive Director: Dr. Edward J. Monahan.

Suite 8039, 130 St. George Street, Toronto, Ontario M5S 2T4.

Tel: (416) 979-2165. Fax: (416) 979-8635

Association of Atlantic Universities/Association des Universités de l'Atlantique (AAU)

Founded in 1964, the Association comprises 19 institutions in Canada's four Atlantic provinces, plus the University of the West Indies. Its governing body is the AAU Council, comprising the President of each member institution.

The Association also maintains semi-formal links with some 15 Atlantic university administrative groups, e.g. AAU Business Officers, Librarians, Directors of Physical Plants.

Fondée en 1964, l'Association comprend 19 institutions se trouvant dans les quatre provinces atlantiques du Canada, auxquelles s'ajoute l'Université des Antilles. Son organe directeur est le Conseil de l'AAU, formé des Présidents de chacune des institutions membres.

L'Association entretient également des relations de caractère semiformel avec une quinzaine de groupements administratifs des universités des provinces atlantiques, réunissant par exemple des responsables d'administration, des bibliothécaires, des directeurs de bâtiments.

Chairman: Dr. Leslie Harris, Memorial University.

Executive Director: Dr. John R. Keyston.

Suite 300, 1668 Barrington Street, Halifax, Nova Scotia B3J 2A2.

Tel: (902) 425-4230

Canadian Bureau for International Education/ Bureau canadien de l'éducation internationale

The Bureau (CBIE), founded in 1966, is a national non-profit organization which promotes international development and intercultural understanding through a broad range of educational activities and programmes in Canada and abroad. It works to encourage international involvement by Canadian educational institutions. It conducts research projects, organizes conferences, seminars and professional development workshops, and operates educational exchanges. CBIE also acts as an agent in developing and administering training programmes on a contract basis.

The Bureau operates an overseas student reception service from mid-August to mid-September each year at Canada's main international airports, and provides assistance to Third World students in emergency financial difficulty. It offers professional development resources such as workshops and study tours. CBIE is a link between educational institutions, governments and embassies on foreign student issues.

The Bureau also develops and operates travel and study programmes in Canada and abroad. Through International Work-camps young people over 17 have an opportunity to spend 2–4 weeks in another country working on a volunteer group community project. The Bureau coordinates sending Canadians abroad and placing foreign volunteers in Canadian camps.

CBIE acts as an agent and administrator for educational institutions, Canadian and foreign governments and their agencies, international corporations and private organizations. In conjunction with Canadian institutions, it will develop programmes to meet the educational and training needs of other countries.

The Council of Second Language Programmes in Canada is an organization of English and French Language intensive and immersion programmes offered by CBIE member institutions.

Publications: International Education Magazine (six times a year); Study in Canada; International Students Handbook; Annual Report; pamphlet on language programmes in Canada. Publications list available on request.

Le Bureau, fondé en 1966, est une organisation nationale à but non lucratif qui encourage le développement international et les relations interculturelles par l'intermédiaire d'une vaste gamme d'activités et de programmes éducatifs au Canada et à l'étranger. Son travail consiste à encourager la participation internationale des établissements éducatifs canadiens. Il organise des projets de recherche, des conférences, des séminaires et des ateliers de perfectionnement professionnel et s'occupe d'échanges éducatifs. Le BCEI sert également d'organe de liaison dans le développement et l'administration des programmes de formation sur une base contractuelle.

Le Bureau organise un service d'accueil des étudiants d'outre-mer dans les principaux aéroports internationaux canadiens. Ce service fonctionne de la mi-août à la mi-septembre chaque année. Il offre également de l'aide aux étudiants du Tiers-Monde qui ont des difficultés financières imprévues, ainsi que des moyens de perfectionnement professionnel tels que des ateliers et des voyages d'études. Le BCEI est un lien entre les établissements éducatifs, les gouvernements et les ambassades pour tout ce qui concerne les étudiants étrangers.

Le Bureau développe et dirige également des programmes de voyages et d'études au Canada et à l'étranger. Grâce aux Chantiers internationaux les jeunes de plus de 17 ans peuvent passer de 2 à 4 semaines dans un pays étranger en vue de participer à un projet communautaire bénévole. Le BCEI coordonne l'envoi à l'étranger des jeunes du Canada ainsi que le placement des bénévoles étrangers dans des chantiers au Canada.

Le BCEI sert de représentant et d'administrateur pour les établissements éducatifs, les gouvernements canadiens et étrangers et leurs

institutions, corporations internationales et les organisations privées. Conjointement avec les établissements canadiens, le Bureau développe des programmes qui répondront aux besoins de formation et d'éducation d'autres pays.

Le Conseil des programmes de langues secondes au Canada est une organisation regroupant des programmes intensifs et d'immersion en anglais et en français offerts par les établissements membres du BCEI.

Publications: Le Magazine de l'éducation internationale (six fois par an); Les études au Canada (dépliant); Rapport annuel; dépliant sur les programmes de langue au Canada. Liste de publications disponible sur demande.

President/Président: Dr. Gilles Boulet, President, Université du Québec.

Executive Director/Directrice générale: Marnie Girvan.

85 Albert, Suite 1400, Ottawa, Ont. K1P 6A4.

Tel: (613) 237-4820. Telex: 053-3255 cble ott

Canadian Society for the Study of Higher Education/La Société canadienne pour l'étude de l'enseignement supérieur

The Society was formed in 1970 to provide the means of communication among those persons conducting or using research in postsecondary education. Members include faculty and students in universities and community colleges, administrators and trustees, professionals in government departments and agencies, and others with an interest in Canadian higher education.

The main activities of the Society are the holding of an annual conference and the publication of the Canadian Journal of Higher Education. The journal publishes scholarly articles on a variety of topics and in a variety of academic disciplines related to higher education, and bibliographical information of value to persons interested in the study of higher education. The principal focus of interest is on Canadian higher education, but not to the exclusion of developments taking place in other countries of direct concern to Canadian higher education. A quarterly Bulletin reports on the work of the different committees, news from funding agencies, conferences, etc.

La Société a été fondée en 1970 pour servir de tribune d'échange aux membres des diverses disciplines universitaires et aux personnes occupant des postes administratifs qui effectuent ou utilisent des recherches sur l'enseignement supérieur. Parmi les membres de la Société on retrouve des présidents d'université et de collèges communautaires ainsi que enseignants et des étudiants, des professionnels au sein de ministères et d'organismes gouvernementaux et d'autres

personnes qui s'intéressent à l'enseignement supérieur au Canada.

Les principales activités de la Société consistent en l'organisation d'une conférence annuelle et en la publication de la "Revue canadienne de l'enseignement supérieur." Cette revue publie des articles sur une vaste gamme de sujets appartenant à diverses disciplines de l'enseignement supérieur, ainsi que des informations bibliographiques précieuses pour les personnes qu'intéresse l'étude de l'enseignement supérieur. Son centre principal d'intérêt est l'enseignement supérieur canadien, sans toutefois exclure ce qui peut se passer à l'étranger et qui a une influence directe sur l'enseignement supérieur canadien. Le 'Bulletin' trimestriel rend compte des travaux des divers comités, donne des nouvelles sur les organismes de financement, les conférences, etc.

President: Naomi Hersom, President and Vice-Chancellor, Mount Saint Vincent Uniterstiy, Halifax.

Secretary/Treasurer: Dr. Norm Uhl, Mount St. Vincent University, Halifax.

Secretariat: 151 Slater Street, Suite 1001, Ottawa, Ontario K1P 5N1.

Tel: (613) 563-1236 (Ext. 269 or 270). Fax: (613) 563-7736. Electronic mail: clements a cosy. guelph

CUSO

CUSO was established in 1961 as an independent non-profit organization to provide professionally and technically qualified Canadians to meet the changing requirements of developing countries. Today, in addition to maintaining more than 350 volunteers in 35 countries, it funds, administers and staffs a wide range of projects supporting the development efforts of those countries, and is also involved in development education in Canada. CUSO is a 'middle-level placement' programme operating under the plans and priorities of the countries with which it co-operates. It is not a relief, religious or emergency aid organization, but aims at long-term development. CUSO has programmes and projects in Africa, Asia, the Caribbean, Latin America, and the South Pacific.

Universities and colleges still play a role in the recruitment and initial selection of personnel for overseas assignments through a network of 30 local committees across Canada. These committees, some of which are on university campuses, operate on a voluntary basis, and are usually composed of faculty and student members, returned CUSO personnel, representatives of the participating countries and members of the local community wherever possible. In addition, many committees are involved in fund raising and

development education activities. The programme is administered through an Ottawa based secretariat and regional offices both in Canada and overseas.

CUSO receives a substantial part of its finances from the Canadian International Development Agency; an equal amount is contributed by overseas governments and agencies in the form of CUSO workers' salaries and housing supplements. The balance comes in the form of contributions from individuals, corporations, foundations, community groups, and provincial governments.

Le CUSO, créé en 1961, est une organisation indépendante et à but non lucratif qui offre à des Canadiens qualifiés professionnellement et techniquement la possibilité de répondre aux besoins changeants des pays en voie de développement. Maintenant, outre le fait qu'il entretient plus de 350 coopérants en poste dans 35 pays, il subventionne, fournit la main-d'oeuvre nécessaire, et administre un grand nombre de projets qui complètent l'effort que déploient ces pays en vue de se développer. Le CUSO s'occupe aussi d'éducation au développement au Canada. Le CUSO est un programme d'assistance en cadres moyens qui s'effectue en fonction des plans et des priorités définis par les pays avec lesquels il coopère. Ce n'est pas une organisation de secours, religieux ou destiné à remédier à des situations d'urgence mais plutôt une organisation de développement à long terme. Le CUSO a des programmes et projets en Afrique, en Asie, aux Caraïbes, en Amérique latine et dans le Pacifique Sud.

Par l'intermédiaire d'un réseau de 30 comités locaux à travers le Canada, les universités et collèges jouent néanmoins un rôle pour le recrutement et la présélection du personnel à affecter outremer. Ces comités, dont certains exercent leur activité sur les campus universitaires, travaillent bénévolement et se composent ordinairement d'enseignants et d'étudiants, coopérants de retour qui représentent les pays participants, ainsi que des membres de la collectivité locale partout où cela est possible. Plusieurs de ces comités s'occupent également de recueillir des fonds et participent à diverses activités en éducation du public. Le secrétariat d'Ottawa ainsi que les bureaux régionaux tant du Canada que d'outre-mer sont chargés de l'administration.

Le CUSO reçoit une part importante de ses fonds de l'Agence canadienne pour le développement international; un montant égal lui est versé par des gouvernements et des institutions outremer sous forme de traitements des personnes engagées au CUSO et par indemnités de résidence. Le reste provient des contributions de personnalités, de sociétés, fondations, associations et gouvernements provinciaux.

Chairman of the Board: Gary Warner.
Executive Director: Chris Bryant.
CUSO, 135 Rideau Street, Ottawa, Ontario K1N 9K7.
Tel: (613) 563-1242. Telex: 053-4706. Cables: cusott

Canadian Council for International Co-operation (CCIC)/Conseil canadien pour la coopération internationale (CCCI)

Founded in 1968, the Council's purpose is to promote and mobilize greater Canadian participation in global development. Its main thrust of activity is to support the individual and collective programmes of other voluntary agencies. Approximately one hundred organizations comprise the membership of CCIC. Individuals may also belong. The Council acts as a focal point for voluntary agency relations with other sectors of Canadian society and with developmental institutions in other countries and at the international level. CCIC is the co-ordinating and service council for Canadian voluntary and non-governmental organizations working in international development.

The Annual Meeting decides broad policy and programme and elects a Board of directors from the membership. The Board meets three times a year to govern activities and is assisted by two standing committees, Programme and Finance/Organization. Regional committees across the country, again drawn from the membership, provide services and programmes at a more local level. A Secretariat in Ottawa implements the national programme. CCIC is supported by its membership fees, donations and a contribution from the Canadian International Development Agency (CIDA).

CCIC monitors and analyses government policies and actions relevant to voluntary agencies and international development, channels this information to its membership, and provides a mechanism for non-governmental organizations to voice their interests to government. It promotes development education in Canada through support to the work of the development education constituency. The regional committees have the primary responsibility for co-ordinating, informing and organizing activities best suited to the needs of groups in each region.

The Council facilitates its three programme mandates with a communications system that includes a monthly *Newsletter*, notices on events and issues, reports on meetings and workshops, and occasional directories and studies on voluntary agency activities.

Mis sur pied en 1968, le Conseil a pour objectif de susciter et promouvoir la participation accrue des Canadiens au développement mondial. Son action vise principale-ment à soutenir les programmes individuels et collectifs des autres organismes bénévoles. Le CCCI regroupe une centaine d'organismes ainsi que des membres à titre personnel. Il veut servir d'instrument de communication entre le secteur des organismes bénévoles et les autres secteurs de la société canadienne, ainsi que les agences de développe-ment d'autres pays et au niveau international. Le CCCI est un regroupement d'organismes béné-voles et non gouvernementaux canadiens qui travaillent au développement international.

L'Assemblée annuelle adopte les grandes lignes de sa politique et de son programme et élit un Conseil d'administration composé de membres du CCCI. Ce Conseil siège trois fois l'an pour diriger les activités, muni de l'aide de deux comités permanents, celui des Programmes et celui des Finances et de l'Organisation. De par le pays, des comités régionaux, composés également de membres du CCCI, fournissent des services et des programmes au niveau régional. Le Secrétariat d'Ottawa veille à l'exécution du programme national. Le CCCI est financé par des contribu-tions de ses membres, des dons et une subvention de l'Agence canadienne de développement inter-national (ACDI).

Le CCCI observe et analyse les politiques et initiatives gouvernementales qui touchent les organismes bénévoles et le développement inter-national, communique ces informations à ses membres et fait fonction de porte-parole des organismes non gouvernementaux auprès du gouvernement. Il contribue à l'éducation du public au Canada en soutenant les travaux de ses membres en matière d'éducation au développe-ment. Il revient en premier lieu aux comités régionaux d'assurer la coordination, l'informa-tion et l'organisation des activités les mieux adaptées aux groupes de chaque région.

Pour faciliter l'exécution de son mandat, le Conseil est doté d'un système de communications qui comprend un bulletin mensuel, des circulaires sur les événements et questions de l'heure, des rapports sur des réunions et ateliers et la publica-tion intermittente de répertoires et d'études sur les activités des organismes bénévoles.

President: Thomas Kines.
Secretary-General: Richard Harmston.
200 Isabella Street, Ottawa, Ontario K1S 1V7.
Tel: (613) 236-4547. Telex: 534313

Canadian International Development Agency (CIDA)/Agence canadienne de développement international (ACDI)

The Canadian International Development Agency (CIDA) was formed in 1968 to administer most of Canada's official foreign development assistance programme. It grew out of the earlier External Aid Office and reports to Parliament through the Secretary of State for External Affairs. Disbursements for official development assistance during the fiscal year 1982-83 totalled more than $1.68 billion.

During 1982, there were 869 students and trainees from developing countries studying in Canada under CIDA programmes. In addition, 593 Canadian advisers and educators were serving abroad through CIDA. Under a unique feature of Canada's technical training pro-gramme, 752 students and trainees were studying at institutions in 'first' or 'third' countries under CIDA sponsorship in the 1982-83 academic year—358 in their own countries, and 394 in other developing countries.

Canada also participates in the Common-wealth Scholarship and Fellowship Plan estab-lished in 1958 to give promising Commonwealth students the opportunity to study in other member countries. One-quarter of the annual scholarships are provided by Canada. There were 290 students under the plan in Canada in Sept-ember 1982.

Since 1972 CIDA has provided approximately 15 scholarships on an annual basis for Canadians interested in careers in development assistance.

L'Agence canadienne de développement inter-national (ACDI) administre la majeure partie de l'aide publique du Canada aux pays en voie de développement. Elle a succédé, en 1968, au Bureau de l'aide extérieure et elle fait rapport de ses activités au Parlement par l'intermédiaire du Secrétaire d'Etat aux Affaires extérieures. Les dépenses d'aide au Tiers Monde pour l'année 1982-1983 se sont chiffrées à plus de 1,68 milliard de dollars.

Au cours de l'année 1982, il y avait 869 étudiants et stagiaires de pays en voie de développement qui étudiaient au Canada en bénéficiant des program-mes de l'ACDI. De plus, l'ACDI a envoyé 593 coopérants et éducateurs canadiens dans le Tiers Monde. Une caractéristique unique du pro-gramme canadien de formation technique a été l'attribution de bourses, par l'ACDI, à 752 étud-iants et stagiaires pour étudier dans leur propre pays ou dans un pays tiers au cours de l'année académique 1982-1983—358 dans leur propre pays et 394 dans un pays tiers en développement.

Le Canada participe également à la mise en oeuvre du Plan de bourses du Commonwealth qui, depuis 1958, permet à des étudiants doués de celui-ci d'aller acquérir une formation supérieure dans d'autres pays membres que les leurs. Un quart des bourses annuelles est fourni par le

Canada. En septembre 1982, 290 étudiants bénéficiaient de ce plan au Canada même.

Depuis 1972, l'ACDI a accordé une quinzaine de bourses annuelles à de jeunes Canadiens souhaitant faire carrière dans la coopération au développement international.

Place du Centre, 200 Promenade du Portage, Hull, Québec K1A 0G4.

Tel: (819) 997-5456. Fax: (819) 953 54-69.

Telex: 053-4140 cida hull

International Development Research Centre (IDRC)/Centre de recherches pour le développement international (CRDI)

The International Development Research Centre is a corporation created by the Parliament of Canada in 1970 to stimulate and support scientific and technical research by developing countries for their own benefit.

The fields of investigation to which IDRC gives its financial and professional support include: farming; food storage, processing, and distribution; forestry; fisheries; animal sciences; energy; tropical diseases; water supplies; health services; education; population studies; economics; communications; urban policies; science and technology policy; information systems; and earth and engineering sciences.

Although IDRC is funded entirely by the Canadian Parliament, its operations are guided by an international 21-member Board of Governors. The Centre's Headquarters are in Ottawa. Regional Offices are located in Africa, Asia, Latin America, and the Middle East.

Le Centre de recherches pour le développement international, est une corporation instituée en 1970 par le Parlement du Canada pour encourager et subventionner des recherches techniques et scientifiques réalisées par les pays en développement pour leur propre bénéfice

Les domaines d'étude auxquels le CRDI prête une aide professionnelle et financière concernent: l'agriculture; l'entreposage, le traitement et la distribution des vivres; la sylviculture; les pêches; la zootechnie; l'énergie; les maladies tropicales; l'approvisionnement en eau; les services de santé; l'éducation; la démographie; l'économie; les communications; les politiques urbaines; les politiques scientifiques et technologiques; les sciences de la terre et les systèmes d'information.

Bien que les fonds du CRDI proviennent d'une subvention du gouvernement du Canada, le Centre est dirigé par un Conseil des gouverneurs international, formé de 21 personnes. Établi à Ottawa, le Centre a des bureaux régionaux en Afrique, en Asie, en Amérique latine et au Moyen-Orient.

President/Président: Ivan L. Head.

Secretary/Sécretaire: Robert Auger.

250 Albert Street, P.O. Box 8500, Ottawa, Ontario K1G 3H9.

Tel: (613) 236-6163. Telex: 053-3753. Cables: recentre

Association of Universities and Colleges of Canada International Division/Association des Universités et Collèges du Canada division internationale

The former International Development Office/Secretariat pour de développement international, established in 1978 to enhance the role of Canadian universities in international development no longer exists as such. It is now the development Programmes Section of the AUCC International Division.

The general mandate of the International Division is to promote and facilitate the international initiatives of Canadian universities. To this end, the division serves as a point of contact between Canadian universities, overseas educational institutions, and federal and provincial government agencies or departments within Canada and abroad.

Grants from the Canadian International Development Agency (CIDA), the International Development Research Centre (IDRC), fees from member institutions, and specific project or programme funds from external sources provide the financial support for the division to pursue its goals.

There are an administrative group and two sections within the division: Academic Relations, which is responsible for scholarly exchanges and liaison with universities and diplomatic missions abroad, and Development Programmes, which is responsible for the activities directly related to Canada's Official Development Assistance programmes.

Publications: International Division Annual Report; quarterly newsletter Canadian Universities in International Development; quarterly newsletter Synergy: Canadian Initiatives for International Health; an occasional newsletter of the Thailand Institutional Linkages programme Thai Links; an occasional newsletter of the Canada/China Universities Linkage Programme; Directory of Canadian University Resources for International Development; conference reports —the most recent International Development: Sharing Concerns.

L'ancien International Development Office/Secrétariat pour le développement international, créé en 1978 pour accroître le rôle des universités canadiennes dans le développement international, n'existe plus en tant que tel. Il est maintenant remplacé par la Section des Programmes de

développement de la division internationale de l'AUCC.

Le mandat général de la Division internationale consiste à promouvoir et à faciliter les initiatives des universités canadiennes sur le plan international. A cette fin, la Division sert de centre de liaison entre les universités canadiennes, les établissements d'enseignement à l'étranger, et les organismes ou les ministères dépendant des gouvernements fédéral et provinciaux, qu'ils soient situés au Canada ou à l'étranger.

Les subventions versées par l'Agence canadienne de développement international (ACDI), le Centre de recherches pour le développement international (CRDI), les cotisations des établissements membres ainsi que des fonds provenant de sources extérieures et expressément destinés à un projet ou à un programme déterminé assurent à la Division l'assistance financière dont elle a besoin pour poursuivre ses objectifs.

En plus de l'administration, la Division compte deux sections: la Section des relations académiques, chargée des échanges d'universitaires et de la liaison avec les universités et les missions diplomatiques à l'étranger, et la Section des programmes de développement, chargée des activités directement liées au Programme officiel du Canada.

Publications: Rapport annuel de la division internationale; le bulletin trimestriel des universités canadiennes et le développement international; le bulletin trimestriel Synergie: les initiatives canadiennes dans le domaine de la santé internationale; un bulletin occasionnel publié par le programme de jumelage institutionnel entre les universités canadiennes et les établissements thaïlandais; le bulletin occasionnel du Programme de jumelage entre les universités canadiennes et les universités chinoises; Répertoire des Ressources des universités canadiennes pour le développement international; des rapports de conférences: le plus récent:

Exchange de vues et de préoccupations en matière de développement international.
Director/Directeur: John W. Berry.
151 Slater, Ottawa, Ontario K1P 5N1.
 Tel: (613) 563-1236. Fax: (613) 563-9745.
 Telex: 053-3329. Cables: canuf ottawa

Canadian Association of University Teachers (IAUPL)
Contact: 18 rue du Docteur Roux, 75015 Paris (France)
Tel: (33-1) 47-83-31-65

Canadian Federation of University Women (IFUW)
55 Parkdale Avenue, Ottawa, Ontario K1Y 1E5.

World University Service
Executive Director: William McNeill.
P.O. Box 3000 Stn. C, Ottawa, Ontario K1Y 4MB.
Tel: (613) 725-3121. Telex: 053-3691 wuscan ott

Student Christian Movement of Canada/Association chrétienne des Etudiants canadiens (WSCF)
7 Hart House Circle, Toronto, Ontario M5S 1A1.
Tel: 416) 596-71-02

World Union of Jewish Students (WUJS)
Contact: 89 Chaussee De Vleurgat, 1050 Brussels (Belgium).
Tel: (02) 647-7279. Telex: 20625

*

Dominion Bureau of Statistics
Education Division, Ottawa, Ontario.
Tel: (613) 990-81-16

Canadian Commission for Unesco/Commission canadienne pour l'Unesco
99 Metcalfe, Ottawa, Ontario K1P 5V8.
Tel: (613) 237-34000. Telex: 053-4573 cancon-arts ott

CENTRAL AFRICAN REPUBLIC
REPUBLIQUE CENTRAFRICAINE

*Université de Bangui, B.P. 1450, Bangui. *1970*
Tél: (61) 20-00
F : dr-éco, sc, let-hum, sa.
INSTITUT SUPÉRIEUR DE DÉVELOPPEMENT RURAL, B.P. 909, Bangui.
INSTITUT POLYTECHNIQUE, B.P. 1450, Bangui.
mine-géol, const.

INSTITUT UNIVERSITAIRE DE GESTION DES ENTREPRISES, B.P. 1450, Bangui.
ECOLE NORMALE SUPÉRIEURE, B.P., Bangui.
INSTITUT DE RECHERCHE POUR L'ENSEIGNEMENT DES MATHÉMATIQUES, B.P. 1450, Bangui.
INSTITUT DE LINGUISTIQUE APPLIQUÉE, B.P. 1450, Bangui.

Ministère de l'Education nationale et de l'Enseignement supérieur
B.P. 1583, Bangui.
Tél: 61-4300. Télex: mineduc 5333 rc bangui
Commission nationale centrafricaine pour

l'Unesco
Ministère de l'Education nationale et de l'Enseignement supérieur, B.P. 1583, Bangui.
Tél: 61-43-00. Télex: mineduc 5333 rc bangui

CHAD
TCHAD

*Université du Tchad, Avenue Mobutu, B.P. 1117, N'Djaména. *1971*
Tél: 2176
F : let-hum, sc jur-éco-gestion, sc exactes et app.
I : élev, éd.
INSTITUT NATIONAL DES SCIENCES DE L'EDUCATION.
INSTITUT NATIONAL DES SCIENCES HUMAINES, B.P. 503, N'Djaména.
ECOLE NORMALE SUPÉRIEURE, P.O. Box 460, N'Djaména.
Ecole nationale d'Administration et de Magistra-

ture, B.P. 758, N'Djaména. *1963*
Tél: 2707
Ecole nationale des Travaux publics, N'Djaména. *1965*
Institut des Techniques de l'Elevage, B.P. 433, N'Djaména. *1952*
Institut de Recherches du Coton et des Textiles exotiques, route de Farcha, B.P. 764, N'Djaména. *1932*
Office de la Recherche scientifique et technique d'Outre-Mer [ORSTOM], B.P. 65, N'Djaména.

Ministère de l'Education nationale
B.P. 731, N'Djaména.
Tél: 51-44-76
Commission nationale tchadienne pour l'Unesco

Ministère de l'Education nationale, B.P. 731, N'Djaména.
Tél: 51-46-71. Cables: Unesco ndjamena

CHILE
CHILI

UNIVERSITIES AND TECHNICAL UNIVERSITIES—
UNIVERSITES ET UNIVERSITES TECHNIQUES

Universidad de Antofagasta, Antonio Toro 851, Casilla 170, Antofagasta. *1981*
Tél: 22 66 52. Télex: 325093 uantof ck
F : ing, éd-hum, sa, sc.
I : rech océanog.

Universidad Arturo Prat, Filomena Valenzuela 704, Casilla 121, Iquique. *1984*
Tél: 23533. Télex: 323126 unapi ck
F : mar, sc, ing, éco-adm, éd-hum.

Universidad de Atacama, Avenida J.F. Kennedy 485, Casilla 240, Copiapó. *1981*
Tél: (52) 2005
F : ing, hum-éd.
E : techn.
I : rech scq & techn.

Universidad de Bío-Bío, Campus Universitario, Avenida Collao 1202, Casilla 5-c, Concepción. *1981*
Tél: 238984
F : arc-const, ing, sc-hum.
F : arc, const civ, ing.
Ce : dév arc-const, ind for, ét énerg.

Universidad Central, Avenida José Joaquín Prieto 10–001, San Bernardo. *1983*
Tél: 583116
E : arc, pol-adm, const civ, dr, éd, gé com, psyc.

Universidad de Chile, Avenida Libertador Bernardo O'Higgins 1058, Casilla 10-D, Santiago. *1738, 1842*
Tél: (562) 89539
F : agr-for, arc-urb, arts, sc ch-phar, éco-adm, phy-math, hum-éd, mus-dram, dr, phil, méd, vét, dent.
E : hum, soc, jour, arc, agr, for, vét, ch-phar-bioch, comp, éco-adm, ing-sc, dr, sa, méd, dent, mus, géog.
I : nutr-alim, ét int, pol, mus, rel de trav, rech matér.

Universidad Austral de Chile, Campus Universitario Isla Teja, Casilla 567, Valdivia. *1954*
Tél: 39-11. Télex: 271035 unaus cl
F : agr, vét, for, méd, sc, phil-hum, éco-adm.
E : agr, gé for, vét, méd, inf, obst, techn méd, éco agr, gé du son, stat, sc, phy-math, gé com, gé civ-inft, bioch, péd; éd (Ancud).
Ce : techn du lait.

***Pontificia Universidad Católica de Chile**,

Avenida Libertador Bernardo O'Higgins 340, Santiago. *1888*
Tél: 22-53-46. Télex: 240395 pucva cl
F : agr, arc-ba, biol, éco-adm, soc, dr, éd, phil, hist-géog-pol, ing, let, math, méd, ch, théo.
E : arc, dess, art, théât, adm, psyc, trav soc, dr, éd, const civ, ing, jour, inf, méd; kinésithér, péd, techn méd, tec for (Maule); dr, éd, tec mar (Talcahuano); éd (Temuco); éd (Villarrica); éd (Curico).
I : ét urb, mus, éco, socio, phil, pol, géog, hist, let.

Universidad de Concepción, Barros Arana 631, Casilla 20-C, Concepción. *1920*
Tél: 225346. Télex: 260005 teuco cl
F : sc, agr-for, biol-ressource nat, éco-adm, sc jur-soc, éd, hum-art, phar, ing, méd, dent.

Universidad «Finis Terrae», Grajales 1898, Santiago. *1988*
E : dr, gé com.

Universidad Diego Portales, Avenida Ejército Libertador 260, Santiago. *1983*
Tél: 696431
E : dr, psyc, gé com, comp, gé de l'exécution.

Universidad Gabriela Mistral, Avenida Ricardo Lyon 1177, Santiago. *1981*
Tél: 2257497
D : dr, psyc, éd, ing.

Universidad de La Frontera, Francisco Salazar 01145, Casilla 54-D, Temuco. *1981*
Tél: 237776. Télex: 267038 unfro cl
F : méd, ing, éd-hum, sc jur-adm-soc, agr.
I : inft.

Universidad «Las Condes», Avenida Las Condes 12500, Las Condes. *1988*
E : éco, adm des entrep, jur.

Universidad de La Serena, Colina El Pino s/n, Casilla 599, La Serena. *1981*
Tél: 211868. Télex: 220044 unise cl
F : ing, hum, sc.

Universidad de Magallanes, Angamos esq. Zenteno, Casilla 113-D, Punta Arenas. *1981*
Tél: 24523. Télex: 380004 umag ck. Cables: umag
F : ing, ét gén.
I : Patagonia.

Universidad «Mayor», Pedro de Valdivia 624,

Providencia. *1988*
F: arc-const, for, ing, éd techn.
Universidad Metropolitana de Ciencias de la Educación, Avenida José Pedro Alessandri 774, Santiago. *1985*
Tél: 2257731
F : phil-éd, soc-let, sc, arts-phys.
I : entomologie.
Universidad del Norte, Avenida Angamos 0610, Casilla 1280, Antofagasta. *1956, 1964*
Tél: 251611. Télex: 225097 unort cl. Cables: udelnorte
F : arc, sc, éco, éd, ing; mar (Coquimbo).
Universidad de Playa Ancha de Ciencias de la Educación, Avenida Playa Ancha 850, Valparaíso. *1985*
Tél: 255321
D : hum, phys-arts, sc exactes-nat, éd.
*****Universidad de Santiago de Chile**, Avenida Ecuador 3469, Casilla 4637, Santiago. *1947, 1981*
Tél: 761011
F : ing, sc, éco-adm, hum.
E : techn.
Universidad de Talca, 2 Norte 685, Casillas 721 y 747, Talca.
Tél: (56) 31682
F : sc, hum, ing, agr-for.
I : rech env.
Universidad de Tarapacá, Calle 18 de Septiembre

2222, Casilla 287, Arica. *1981*
Tél: 42600. Télex: 221036 untar cl. Cables: untar cl
F : adm-éco, sc, éd, hum-let, ing.
I : agr, anth-arc.
Universidad Técnica «Federico Santa María», Avenida Los Placeres 401, Casilla 110-V, Valparaíso. *1926*
Tél: 660176. Télex: 230338 utfsm cl
F : ing, sc, éco-adm.
E : ing (Viña de Mar, Talcahuano).
Universidad de Valparaíso, Errázuriz esq. General Cruz s/n, Casilla 123-V, Valparaíso. *1981*
Tél: 213071
F : arc, sc jur-éco-soc, méd.
E : arc, const civ, dess, dr, serv soc, gé com, comp, méd, dent, inf-obst, ch-phar.
I : ét hum, math-phy, océanog.
Universidad Católica de Valparaíso, Avenida Brasil 2950, Casilla 4059, Valparaíso. *1928, 1929*
Tél: 251024. Télex: 230389 ucval cl
F : arc-urb, sc-math, sc jur-soc, phil-éd, ing, éco-adm, ressources nat.
E : agr, alim, mar, géog, gé com, com, gé inft, const civ, trans, gé ch, méc, gé ind, élec, gé bioch, mus, phys, péd, serv soc, arc.
I : art, biol, sc relig, phy, math, ch, éd, phil, hist, lit-lang, géog.

OTHER INSTITUTIONS—AUTRES INSTITUTIONS

Public Institutions—Etablissements publics

Instituto Profesional de Osorno, Avenida Fuchslocher s/n, Casilla 933, Osorno. *1981*
Tél: 21-94-53-77
D : alim, sc exactes-nat, soc-adm, éd, hum-art; éd (Puerto Mott).

Instituto Profesional de Santiago, Dieciocho 161, Casilla 9845, Santiago. *1981*
Tél: 6964123
E : adm, bibl, trav soc, dess, techn, const, inft.
D : ét gén.

Private Institutions—Etablissements Privés

Instituto Profesional «Adolfo Matthei», Avenida Alcalde René Soriano s/n., Osorno. *1981*
Instituto Profesional «Adventista», Fundo «Las Mariposas», Camino Tanilvoro Km. 12, Coihueco. *1982*
Instituto Profesional Blas Cañas, Curicó 465, Santiago. *1981*
Instituto Profesional «Campus», Manuel Montt 948, Providencia. *1983*
Tél: 393032
Institute Profesional «Diego Portales», Maipú 301, Concepción. *1988*

Instituto Profesional «D.V.O.C.», Rebeca Matte 018, Santiàgo. *1983*
Instituto Profesional «Chileño Británico de Cultura», Santa Lucía 124, Santiago. *1982*
Tél: 1382156
Institute Profesional «De La Arancania», Andrés Bello esq., General Lagos s/n, Temuco. *1987*
Instituto Profesional «Del Pacífico», Avenida Las Condes 11121, Las Condes. *1982*
Tél: 395655
Instituto Profesional «Educares», Luis Rodríguez Velasco 4746, Santiago. *1981*

Instituto Profesional «Escuela de Comunicación», Ricardo Lyon 227, Providencia. *1982*
Instituto Profesional «Escuela de Contadores Auditores de Santiago», Providencia 1933, Providencia. *1982*
Instituto Profesional «Guillermo Subercaseaux», Agustinas 1476, Santiago. *1982*
Institute Profesional «IACC», Avenida Salvador 1222, Providencia. *1987*
Instituto Profesional 'INACAP', Chesterton 7028, Las Condes. *1981*
Instituto Profesional «IPEVE», República 237, Santiago. *1981*
Instituto Profesional «Libertador de Los Andes», Avenida Libertador Bernardo O'Higgins 197, Los Andes. *1981*
Instituto Profesional «Luis Galdames», María Luisa Santander 466, Providencia. *1984*
Instituto Profesional «Manpower», Estados Unidos 395, Santiago. *1981*
Tél: 514359
Instituto Profesional de la Salud «PROPAM», Pedro de Valdivia 176, Providencia. *1987*
Instituto Profesional Providencia, Bernarda Morín 495, Providencia. *1982*
Tél: 741453
Instituto Profesional «Teatro La Casa», Romero 2421, Santiago. *1982*
Tél: 92672
Instituto Profesional de «Viña del Mar», Montana 800, Viña del Mar. *1985*
Instituto Profesional «VIPRO», Padre Mariano 94, Providencia. *1987*
Instituto Profesional «Wilhelm von Humboldt», Avenida Kennedy 6150, Las Condes. *1988*
Instituto Profesional «Del Maule», Santa Rosa s/n, Talca. *1988*

Consejo de Rectores Universidades Chilenas

Créé par une loi de 1954, le Conseil a pour mission d'assurer la coordination des universités chiliennes, qui sont toutes représentées en son sein par leur recteur. Dans le cadre d'une nouvelle loi adoptée en 1964 pour élargir la portée de ses objectifs, le Conseil assure maintenant, en outre, des services aux institutions d'enseignement supérieur par ses études en matière de recherche. Quatre Départements et dix Commissions fonctionnent en permanence, sous le contrôle direct du Secrétaire général, dans les vastes secteurs d'intérêt pour les universités. Ces organismes effectuent des études techniques; rassemblent des données statistiques sur l'enseignement supérieur; publient des informations et des études; conçoivent des politiques d'enseignement et de recherche; analysent les besoins et les problèmes nouveaux qui se font jour au Chili dans le domaine de l'enseignement supérieur. Le Conseil élabore ainsi des propositions à l'intention des universités chiliennes et leur assure des services consultatifs, ce qui lui permet de mieux réaliser ses propres objectifs en matière d'enseignement et de recherche (qui ont été définis en toute autonomie et toute indépendance), tout en soutenant et en renforçant leurs tâches d'enseignement, leur protection du point de vue juridique, et leurs relations internationales. Des consultations avec des particuliers, des institutions, des organisations régionales et nationales, et des organismes publics ou privés s'occupant, à divers égards, du développement de la nation permettent d'autre part d'améliorer la gestion et l'administration des universités chiliennes, qui est l'un des objectifs du Conseil.
The Council of Chilean University Rectors was
established by law in 1954 for the purpose of providing co-ordination between the Chilean universities, each of which is represented on it by its rector. In 1964 a new law was adopted in order to broaden the scope of its objectives and the Council now also serves higher education institutions through its research studies and services. Four Departments and ten Commissions operate permanently in large areas of the universities' interests, under the direct administration of the General Secretary. These units conduct technical studies; assemble statistical data on higher education; publish information and studies; design teaching and research policies; and identify and interpret new and emerging problems and needs in higher education in the country. The Council thus makes proposals and gives advice to the Chilean universities, leading to a better achievement of its own clearly autonomous and independently defined educational and research objectives, as well as safeguarding and strengthening the universities' academic work, legal protection, and international relations. The Council's purpose of promoting improvement in the organization and administration of the Chilean universities is also accomplished through consultation with individuals, institutions, regional and national organizations, and public or private agencies related in various ways to the nation's development.

Secrétaire général: Hugo Araneda Dorr.
Moneda 673, 8° piso, Casilla 14798, Santiago.
Tél: 383-137

Consejo de Institutos Profesionales Privados
Avenida Ricardo Lyon 891, Santiago.
Tél: 38-47-74

Servicio Universitario Mundial (WUS)
Almirante Pastene 12, Providencia, Santiago.
Tél: 740825
Consejo de Presidentes de Federaciones Universitarias de Chile — CPFUCH (IUS)
Fernando Reyes, Castillo Velasco 2530, Nuñoa, Santiago.
Asociación de Universitarios Católicos (Pax Romana)
Villavicencio 337, Santiago.
Movimiento Estudiantil Cristiano de Chile (WSCF)
Casilla 27019, Correo 27, Santiago.
World Union of Jewish Students (WUJS)

Correspondant: 89 Chaussee De Vleurgat, 1050 Brussels (Belgium)
Tél: (02) 647-7279. Télex: 20625

*

Ministerio de Educación Pública
Santiago.
Tél: 39-40-51. Télex: 240-567 meduc cl
Comisión Nacional Chilena de Cooperación con la Unesco
Oficina de Relaciones Internacionales, Ministerio de Educación Pública, Santiago.
Tél: 39-40-51. Télex: 240-567 meduc cl

PEOPLE'S REPUBLIC OF CHINA
REPUBLIQUE POPULAIR DE CHINE

UNIVERSITIES AND TECHNICAL UNIVERSITIES — UNIVERSITES ET UNIVERSITES TECHNIQUES

Anhui University, Ximenwei Hefei, Anhui Province.
Tel: (551) 62655
D : *lang-lit, hist, phil, eco, law, lib, for lang, math, phy, ch, biol, radio-electro, comp.*
Anhui Normal University, Wuhu, Anhui Province.
Tel: (553) 2065
D : *lang-lit, pol, hist, for lang, mus-fa, ch, ed, biol, geog, math, phy, phys.*
Anhui University of Labour, District of Xuancheng, Anhui Province.
Beijing University, Loudouqiao, Hadian District, Beijing, Beijing Municipality.
1898, 1945, 1952, 1977
Tel: (1) 28471. Telex: 22239 pkuni cn
D: *math, mec, phy, radio-electro, geophy, ch, biol, geol, geog, comp, psyc, lang-lit, hist, archae, phil, eco, law, int pol, lib, socio.*
Beijing Agricultural University, Yuan Mingyuan West Road, Haidian District, Beijing, Beijing Municipality.
Beijing Normal University, 19 Xinjiekouwai Street, Beijing, Beijing Municipality.
Tel: (1) 656531
D : *ed, lang-lit, hist, phil, eco, for lang-lit, math, phy, radio-electro, astr, ch, biol, geog, lib, psyc, phys, art ed.*
Beijing Polytechnical University, 100 Pingleyuan, Chaoyang District, Beijing, Beijing Munici-

pality.   *1960*
Tel: (1) 784631
D : *eng.*
Beijing University of Foreign Studies, 2 North Xisanhuan Avenue, Haidan District, P.O. Box 8110, Beijing Municipality.   *1941, 1954*
Tel: (1) 890351
D : *lang-lit.*
Beijing University of Iron and Steel Technology, 30 Xneynan Lu, Beijing, Beijing Municipality.
1952
Tel: (1) 2017441. Telex: 22036 biaat cn
Chengdu University of Science and Technology, Mozi Bridge, Chengdu, Sichuan Province.
1954
Tel: (28) 52911. Telex: 60166 cust cn
D : *mec, elec, comp-atm techn, ch eng, hyd eng, met mater, mec, app math-mangt, ch, soc-hum.*
China Capital Medical University, 10 Sitoutiao, Beijing, Beijing Municipality.
Tel: (1) 339484
China Textile University, 1882 Yanan West Road, Shanghai (Shanghai Municipality) *1951*
Tel: (21) 522430
Chinese University of Political Science and Law, 41 Xueyuan South Road, Haidian District, Beijing, Beijing Municipality.
Tel: (1) 2015517
*Chongqing University, Shapingba, Chongqing, Sichuan Province.   *1929*

Tel: (811) 661185. Telex: 6234

D : *mec (2), elec, mine, met, commun eng, comp-atm, app math, app phy, app ch, mangt eng.*

East China Normal University, 3663 Zhongshan Road, Shanghai 200062, Shanghai Municipality.

Tel: (21) 548461. Telex: 333 28 ecnu cn

D : *ed, pol ed, phil, eco, lang-lit, hist, for lang, lib-infor, math, stat, phy, electro, ch, biol, comp, psyc, geog, env sc, phys, fa.*

East China Technical University of Water Resources, Xikang Road 1, Nanjing 210024, Jiangsu Province.   *1952*

Tel: (25) 32106. Telex: 34101 ectuw cn

D : *hyd eng, geol-surv, arc eng, mangt, mec.*

East China University of Chemical Technology, 130 Meilong Road, Shanghai 201107, Shanghai Municipality.   *1952*

Tel: (21) 380811. Telex: 33428 ecict cn

D : *ch eng, bioch eng, env eng, atm-elec, math, phy, ch, lang for sc & techn, soc, comp.*

Fudan University, 220 Handan Road, Shanghai, Shanghai Municipality.

Tel: (21) 484906. Telex: 33317 huafu cn

D: *lang-lit, for lang-lit, hist, jour, eco, world eco, int pol, law, phil, math, appl math, stat, phy, electro, atomic nucl sc, ch, biol, comp, mangt sc, mater sc.*

Fujian Normal University, 23 Linghou Road, Lunshan District, Fuzhou, Fujian Province.

Tel: (591) 41616

D : *ed, pol ed, lang-lit, hist, geog, biol, math, phy, ch, phys, mus, fa, for lang.*

Fuzhou University, Industrial Road, Fuzhou, Fujian Province.   *1958*

Tel: (591) 55874

D : *math, comp, phy, ch, civ & arc eng, geol-mine eng, mec, elec, ch eng, lang, ind mangt, fin-eco.*

Gansu Agricultural University, District of Wuwei, Gansu Province.

Gansu Normal University, Lanzhou, Gansu Province.

Gansu University of Technology, 57 Langongping, Qilihe District, Lanzhou, Gansu Province.

Tel: (931) 35951

Guangxi University, Nanning, Guangxi Autonomous Region of Zhuang Nationality.

Tel: (771) 28823

D : *phil, eco, law, for lang, ch ind, mine-met, math, phy, ch, light ind, lang-lit, eng.*

Guangxi Normal University, Guilin, Guangxi Autonomous Region of Zhuang Nationality.

Tel: (771) 2915)

D: *lang-lit, for lang, hist, phys, math, phy, ch, biol, ed.*

Guizhou University, Huaxi, Guiyang, Guizhou,

Guizhou Province.

Tel: (851) 2218

D : *math, phy, ch, lang-lit, hist, law, for lang, phil.*

Hangzhou University, 34 Tien Mu Shan Road, Hangzhou, Zhejiang Province.   *1958*

Tel: (571) 81224. Telex: 9600

D : *phil, eco, law, lang-lit, hist, ed, psyc, math, phy, ch, biol, geog, phy.*

Hainan University, Haikou, Guandong Province.

Harbin Polytechnical University, 166 West Dazhi Street, Harbin, Heilongjiang Province.

Tel: (451) 33051

Harbin Normal University, 24 Hexing Road, Nangang District, Harbin, Heilongjiang Province.

Tel: (451) 62912

Harbin Medical University, 1 Baojian Road, Nangang District, Harbin, Heilongjian Province.

Tel: (451) 62941

Harbin University of Science and Technology, 22 Xeufei Road, Nangang District, Harbin, Heilongjian Province.

Tel: (451) 61081

Hebei University, 1 Hezuo Road, Baodang, Hebei Province.

Tel: 2929

D : *lang-lit, hist, eco, for lang-lit, law, ed, lib, math, phy, ch, biol, electro.*

Hebei Agricultural University, Nanguan Baodan, Hebei Province.

Tel: 2956

Hebei Normal University, Yuhua Road, Shijiazhuang, Hebei Province.

Tel: (311) 49941

D : *lang-lit, pol ed, hist, ed, for lang, math, phy, ch, biol, geog, phys, mus, fa.*

Hebei University of New Medicine, 48 Changan West Road, Shijiazhuang, Hebei Province.

Tel: (311) 48744

Hefei Polytechnical University, Tunxi Road, Hefei, Anhui Province.

Tel: (551) 74711

Heilongjian University, 24 Xue Fu Road, Nankang District, Harbin, Heilongjian Province.

Tel: (451) 64940

D : *lang-lit, hist, phil, eco, law, for lang-lit, lib-infor, math, comp, phy, ch.*

Heilongjiang August 1st University of Land Reclamation, District of Mishan, Heilongjian Province.   *1958*

D : *agr, mec, lang.*

Henan Normal University, Jianshe Road, Xinxing, Henan Province.

Tel: 54921

D : *math, comp, phy, ch, for lang, lang-lit, pol ed, phys, ed.*

Huanan Normal University, Guangzhou, Guandong Province.
Huazhong Agricultural University, Wuhan, Hubei Province. *1952, 1985*
Tel: (27) 875681
Hunan University, Yuelushan, Changsha, Hunan Province.
Tel: (731) 83171
D : *civ eng, mec, elec, eco adm eng, ch eng, env eng, comp, ind eng, arc, appl phy-math, for lang, hum-soc.*
Inner Mongolia University, Daxue Road, Xincheng District, Hohhot, Inner Mongolia Autonomous Region.
Tel: (471) 43141
D : *lang-lit, Chinese lang-lit, hist, phil, eco, law, for lang, math, phy, ch, biol, electro.*
Inner Mongolia Normal University, Hohhot, Inner Mongolia Autonomous Region.
Jiangxi University, Disi Jiaotong Road, Nanchang, Jiangxi Province. *1958*
Tel: (791) 67800
D : *lang-lit, jour, law, hist, eco, math, phy, ch, biol, fgn lang & lit, phil, comp.*
Jiangxi Agricultural University, Meiling, Nanchang, Jiangxi Province.
Tel: (791) 53923
Jiangxi Normal University, Disi Jiaotong Road, Nanchang, Jiangxi Province. *1953, 1983*
Tel: (791) 67802
D : *lang-lit, hist, pol ed, for lang, ed, mus, pnt, math, comp, phy, ch, geog, ed, commun.*
Jilin University, 77 Jiefang Road, Changchun, Jilin Province. *1946*
Tel: (431) 25187. Telex: 83040 jlv cn
D : *math, phy, ch, comp, biol, lang-lit, hist, eco, law, phil, pol.*
S : *grad.*
Jilin Agricultural University, Jingyue Xiang, Nanguan District, Changchun, Jilin Province. *1949*
Tel: (431) 42112
D : *agr, an hus, hort, agr mec, agr eco.*
Jilin Polytechnical University, Changchun, Jilin Province.
Tel: (431) 27044. Telex: 83016 booth cn
Jinan University, Shipai, Guangzhou, Guandong Province. *1906*
Tel: (20) 774511
D : *eco, med, arts, sc, eng, fgn lang & lit, lang & lit, jour, hist, ch, phy, biol, math, comp.*
Jishou University, District of Jishou, Hunan Province.
Lanzhou University, 78 Tianshui Road, Lanzhou, Gansu Province.
Tel: (931) 22991
D : *lang-lit, jour, hist, eco, phil, law, for lang-lit, lib, math-mec, phy, radiophy-comp, mater sc, mod phy, ch.*

Liaoning University, Chongshan West Road, Huanggu District, Shenyang, Liaoning Province. *1958*
Tel: (24) 62541
Nanjing University, 22 Hantou Road, Nanjing, Jiangsu Province.
Tel: (25) 33307. Telex: 34151 prcnu cn
Nanjing Forestry University, Jiangsi Province. *1952, 1984*
Tel: (25) 43161
*Nankai University, Weijin Road 94, Tianjin, Tianjin Municipality. *1919*
Tel: (22) 331640. Telex: 23133 nanki cn
D : *lang-lit, hist, phil, eco, mangt, fgn lang-lit, math, phy, ch, biol, elec, comp, env sc, lib, pol, law, fin, tour, soc.*
Ningxia University, 21 Wencui Road, Yinchunan, Hui Ningxia Autonomous Region.
Tel: (951) 77800
Norman Bethune University of Medical Sciences, 6 Xinmin Street, Changchun, Jilin Province. *1939*
Tel: (431) 55911
D : *med, dent.*
Northeast Normal University Changchun, Jilin Province. *1950*
Tel: (431) 27056
D : *ed, lang-lit, hist, math, biol.*
*Northeast University of Technology, Shenyang, Liaoning Province. *1923*
Tel: (24) 483081. Telex: 80033 neit cn
D : *mine eng, met, mec (2), atm, comp-eng, mangt eng, math, phy, ch, fgn lang, phys, soc.*
*Northern Jiaotong University, Shangyuancun, Xizhimenwai, Beijing, Beijing Municipality. *1909*
Tel: (1) 890561
D : *telec, civ eng, mec, trans, elec, mangt eng, app math-phy, eco.*
Northwest University, East Daxue Road, Xi'an Shaanxi Province.
Tel: (29) 25036. Telex: 70005 nwuvs cn
D : *lang-lit, hist, for lang-lit, phil, eco, math, comp, phy, ch, biol, geog, geol, ch eng.*
Northwestern Agricultural University, Yangling, Shaanxi Province. *1934, 1939, 1985*
Tel: (910) 6007
*Northwestern Polytechnical University, Xi'an 710036, Shaanxi Province. *1957*
Tel: (29) 53351. Telex: 70185 nwtuy cn
D : *mar eng, mater sc, aero eng, comp sc, atm, math, phy, mec, soc sc.*
Overseas Chinese University, Quanzhou, Fujian Province.
Tel: (595) 4921
D : *eng, comp, app math, app phy, app ch, Chinese cult, ind & com mangt, for lang, tour, arts, law.*
People's University of China, 39 Haidian Road,

Haidian District, Beijing, Beijing Municipality.
Tel: (1) 285431. Telex: 0086
D : *phil, hist of Chinese communist party, int pol, eco, plan eco, stat, ind eco, agr eco, trade eco, publ fin.*

Qinghai Normal University, 38, Wu Si Street, Xining, Qinghai Province.   *1956, 1984*
Tel: (971) 55451

Qinghua University, 1 Qinghuayuan, Haidian District, Beijing, Beijing Municipality.
Tel: (1) 282451. Telex: 22617 qhtsc cn
D: *eng, comp-techn.*

Shaanxi Normal University, Xi'an, Shaanxi Province.
Tel: (29) 52946
D : *pol ed, lang-lit, ed, hist, for lang, math, phy, ch, biol, geog, phys, comp.*

Shandong University, 5 Hungjialou Town, Jinan, Shandong Province.   *1901*
Tel: (531) 43861
D : *lang-lit, hist, fgn lang & lit, eco, phil, soc, law, math, phy, opt, electro, comp, biol, mangt, socio, lib, aerospace tec, English.*

Shandong Normal University, 38 Wenhua East Road, Jinan, Shandong Province.
Tel: (531) 43711. Telex: 39103 bthjh cn c/o na. 59
D : *ed, pol, lang-lit, hist, for lang, math, comp, phy, ch, biol, geog, arts, phys.*

Shandong Polytechnical University, Wenhua Road, Jinan, Shandong Province.   *1951*
Tel: (531) 25081
D : *mec, met, elec, comp-eng, hyd eng, mangt.*

Shanghai University, 1220 Xin Zha Road, Shanghai, Shanghai Municipality.   *1983*
C : *li arts, eng, bus mangt, fa, int bus, pol.*

Shanghai Fisheries University, 334 Jun Gond Road, Shanghai Municipality.
                            1921, 1952, 1985
Tel: (21) 413090. Telex: 33001 bthsha cn

Shanghai Jiaotong University, 1954 Huashan Road, Shanghai, Shanghai Municipality.
Tel: (21) 310310. Telex: 33262 jiash cn
D: *mar eng, elec, comp, electro, mater sc, app math, app phy, app ch, biol, ind for eco trade, for lang of sc & techn, lit-arts, civ eng, soc-eng.*

Shanghai Polytechnical University, 149 Yanchang Road, Shanghai, Shanghai Municipality.
Tel: (21) 650744

Shanghai Second Medical University, 280 South Chongqing Road, Shanghai, Shanghai Municipality.   *1952*
Tel: (21) 260760

Shanghai University of Science and Technology, South Gate, Jiading Town, Shanghai, Shanghai Municipality.
Tel: (21) 952932

Shantou University, Shantou, Guandong Province.

Shanxi University, 36 Wucheng Road, Taiyuan, Shanxi Province.
Tel: (351) 73441

Shanxi Agricultural University, Taigu, Shanxi Province.
Tel: 241

Shanxi Coal and Chemical Industrial University, Taiyuan, Shanxi Province.
Tel: (351) 66602

Shenzhen University, Nanton, Shenzhen, Guandong Province.   *1983*
Tel: 60277

Sichuan University, Wangjianglou, Chengdu, Sichuan Province.
Tel: (28) 54111. Telex: 60159 scun cn

Sichuan Teachers' University, Shahebo, Chengdu, Sichuan Province.   *1952, 1986*

South China Agricultural University, Wushan, Guanghzou, Guangdong Province. *1952, 1984*
Tel: (20) 774881

Southwest China Jiaotong University, District of Emei, Sichuan Province.
Tel: 2361
D : *civ eng, arc, mec (2); elec, comp-eng, mater eng, trans, mangt eng, eng mec, app phy, app math, soc.*

Southwest University of Forestry, District of Anning, Kunming, Yunnan Province.   *1939*
Tel: (87) 28606

Suzhou University, Shizi Street, Suzhou, Jiangsu Province.
Tel: (512) 23614

*Taiuyan University of Technology, Taiyuan, Shanxi Province.   *1902*
Tel: (351) 66701
D : *hyd eng, mec (2), elec, telec, comp-eng, ch, app ch, math-mec, civ & env eng, mangt.*

Talimu University of Agriculture and Land Reclamation, District of Akesu, Xingjiang, Oygur Autonomous Region.

Tianjin University, 92 Weijin Road, Nankai District, Tianjin, Tianjin Municipality.   *1955*
Tel: (22) 332250
D : *ch, app ch, ch eng, elec, atm, mec, arc, civ eng, hyd eng, mar eng, mangt eng, phy, math, hum-soc, fgn lang.*
S : *grad.*

Tianjin Normal University, Weijin Road, Hexi District, Tianjin, Tianjin Municipality.
Tel: (22) 334713

Tongji University, 1239 Siping Road, Shanghai, Shanghai Municipality.
Tel: (21) 462121. Telex: 33488 tjidc cn

Tongji Medical University, Hang Kong Lu, Wuhu, Hubei Province.   *1907, 1951, 1985*
Tel: 356811

University of International Business and Econ-

omics, Beijing, Beijing Municipality.
1954, 1984
Tel: (1) 462161. Telex: 22019 cchdp cn
University of Medicine of China, Shenyang, Liaoning Province. *1931*
Tel: 32578
University of Science and Technology of China, 24 Jin Zhai Road, Hefei, Anhui Province. *1958*
Tel: 63300
D : *math, phy, ch, mec, elec-telec, geol, biol.*
Wuhan University, Luojia Hill, Wuchang, Wuhan, Hubei Province.
Tel: (27) 812712
Wuhan Technical University of Surveying and Mapping, 39 Loyu Road, Wuhan, Hubei Province. *1956*
Tel: (27) 75571. Telex: 402/0 wtusm cn
Wuhan University of Iron and Steel Technology, Wuhan, Hubei Province. *1958*
Tel: (27) 663212
D : *mine, met, mec, atm, ch, mangt.*
Xiamen University, Xiamen, Fujian Province.
Tel: (592) 25102. Telex: 0633
Xi'an Jiaotong University, 26 Xianning Road, Xi'an, Shaanxi Province. *1896*
Tel: (29) 721011. Telex: 70123 xjtu cn
D : *mangt, mec, energ, elec, telec, comp sc, mater, arc, ch, math, phy, fgn lang, soc.*
Xingjiang University, Urumqi, Xingjiang, Oygur Autonomous Region.
Tel: (991) 22929
D : *lang-lit, hist, pol, law, fgn lang, math, phy, ch, biol, geog.*
Xingjiang Normal University, Urumqi, Xinjiang, Oygur Autonomous Region.
Xiangtan University, Xiangtan, Hunan Province.
Tel: 24812
D : *lang-lit, hist, eco, phil, fgn lang, law, math, phy, ch, ch eng, mec, comp, lib.*
Xizang (Tibet) University, Lhasa, Xizang (Tibet) Autonomous Region.
Yan'an University, Yan'an, Shaanxi Province.

Yanbian University, Yanji, Jilin Province.
Tel: (433) 3167
D : *pol, lang, hist, for lang, math, phy, ch, phys, geog, arts, ind eng.*
Yunnan University, 52 Cuihu Road, North Kunming, Yunnan Province.
Tel: (871) 26578
D : *lang-lit, hist, pol, law, eco, for lang-lit, math, phy, ch, biol, comp, radio electro, geophy.*
Yunnan Agricultural University, District of Xundian, Yunnan Province.
Tel: (871) 23901
Zhejiang University, Hangzhou, Zhejiang Province. *1897*
Tel: (571) 21701. Telex: 35040 zufao cn
D : *app math, phy, ch, mec, geol, elec, ch, civ eng, telec, opt, mater techn, thermophy eng, comp, mangt, soc, lang.*
Zhejiang Agricultural University, Hangzhou, Zhejiang Province. *1910, 1960*
Tel: (571) 42605. Telex: 351016 zau cn
Zhejiang Medical University, Hangzhou, Zhejiang Province. *1921, 1960*
Tel: (571) 22501. Telex: 35036 zmu cn
Zhejiang Normal University, Jinhua City, Zhejiang Province. *1965, 1985*
Tel: 23801
D : *lang-lit, for lang, pol ed, hist, math, phy, ch, biol, geog, phys, mus.*
Zhengzhou University, 129 Daxue Road, Zhengzhou, Henan Province.
Tel: (371) 46455
D: *lang-lit, jour, hist, pol, law, phil, eco, fgn lang, math, phy, ch, electro, comp, lib.*
*Zhongshan (Sun-Yat-Sen) University, Guangzhou, Guandong Province. *1924, 1926*
Tel: (20) 446300. Telex: 44604 zsufo cn
D : *mangt, anth, biol, ch, lang-lit, comp sc, eco, fgn lang-lit, geol, hist, law, math, mec, meteo, phil, phy, telec, soc, lib.*

OTHER INSTITUTIONS—AUTRES INSTITUTIONS

Anhui (Province)

Anhui Institute of Technology, Liu-An Road, Hefei.
Tel: (551) 7553
Anhui Electrical and Mechanical Institute, Wuhu.
Huainan Mining Institute, Huainan.
Tel: 4797
Maanshan Institute of Iron and Steel Technology, Maanshan.
Hefei Institute of Geology, Hefei.
Anhui Agricultural Institute, Hefei.

Wannan Agricultural Institute, Xuancheng.
Anhui Medical College, Hefei.
Bengbu Medical College, 108 Zhi Huai Road, Bengbu 233000.
Tel: (552) 4412
Wannan Medical College, Wuhu.
Tel: (553) 5947
Anhui College of Traditional Chinese Medicine, Wuhu.
Anqing Teachers College, Anqing.
Fuyang Teachers College, Fuyang.
Huaibei Teachers College for Coal, Huaibei.
Chaohu Teachers School, Chaohu.

Chuzhou Teachers School, Chuzhou.
Huainan Teachers School, Huainan.
Huizhou Teachers School, Tunxi.
   Tel: 3130
Liuan Teachers School, District of Liuan.
Wuhu Teachers School, Wuhu.
Xuzhou Teachers School, Xuzhou.
Anhui Institute of Finance, Bengbu.
Maanshan School of Commerce, Maanshan.
Tongling School of Finance and Economics, Tongling.

Beijing (Municipality)

Beijing Institute of Aeronautics and Astronautics, 37 Xue Yuan Road, Beijing.
   Tel: (1) 7251. Telex: 22036 biaat cn
Beijing Institute of Agricultural Mechanization, Beijing.
Beijing Institute of Chemical Fibres, Heping Street, Chaoyang District, Beijing.
   Tel: (1) 466931
Beijing Institute of Chemical Technology, 15 Beisanhuan East Road, Chaoyang District, Beijing.
   Tel: (1) 464089
Beijing Institute of Civil Engineering and Architecture, Beijing.
Beijing Institute of Forestry, Beijing.
   Tel: (1) 277179. Telex 9131
Beijing Institute of Light Industry, Beijing.
   Tel: (1) 892497
Beijing Institute of Posts and Telecommunications, 42 Xueyuan Road, Hai Dian District, Beijing.
   Tel: (1) 664549. Telex: 222341 buptf cn
Beijing Institute of Technology, 7 Baishiqiao, Haidian District, Beijing.
   Tel: (1) 890321. Telex: 22011 bit cn
Beijing Metallurgical Institute of Mechanical and Electrical Engineering, Beijing.
Beijing Technical School of Electronics, Beijing.
Beijing Technical School of Meteorology, Beijing.
Beijing Technical School of Petrochemical Technology, Beijing.
Beijing Printing Institute, Beijing.
   Tel: (1) 9233981. Telex: 3469
Beijing Agricultural Institute, Beijing.
Beijing Medical College, Beijing.
Beijing Medical College N° 2, Beijing.
Beijing College of Traditional Chinese Medicine, 11 Beihuandong Road, Chaoyang District, Beijing.
   Tel: (1) 462731
Beijing Teachers College, Huayuancun, Haidian District, Beijing.
   Tel: (1) 890841
Beijing Teachers College of Physical Education, No 21 Bei San Huan West Road, Hai Dian District, Beijing.
   Tel: (1) 5522
Beijing Second Foreign Languages Institute, Dingfuzhuang, Chaoyang District, Beijing.
   Tel: (1) 571331
Beijing Language Institute, Xueyuan Road, Haidian District, Beijing.
   Tel: (1) 2017531
Beijing Broadcasting Institute, Dinfuzhuang, Beijing.
   Tel: (1) 571461
Beijing Institute of Commerce, 11 Fu Cheng Road, Beijing.
   Tel: (1) 890341
Beijing Institute of Economics, Hongmiao, Chaoyangmen, Beijing.
   Tel: (1) 593831
Beijing Institute of Finance and Trade, 68 Tsao Ling Front Street, Hsuan Wu District, Beijing.
   Tel: (1) 1631
Beijing Institute of Procurements and Handling of Commodities, Beijing.
Central Institute of Finance, 19 Xueyuan South Road, Xizhimenwai, Beijing.
   Tel: (1) 891562
Foreign Affairs College, 24 Zhan Lan Road, Beijing.
   Tel: (1) 890151
Institute of International Politics, Beijing.
Institute of International Relations, Poshangchun, Haidian District, Beijing.
   Tel: (1) 285631
Beijing Institute of Physical Culture, Yuanmingyuan East Road, Beijing.
   Tel: (1) 282231
Central Academy of Arts and Crafts, 34 Donghuan North Road, Beijing.
   Tel: (1) 596391
Central Academy of Fine Arts, 5 Xiaoweihutong, Dongcheng District, Beijing.
   Tel: (1) 596391
Central Conservatory of Music, 43 Baojia Road, Xicheng District, Beijing.
   Tel: (1) 667120
Institute of Chinese Music, Beijing.
Institute of Chinese Operas, Beijing.
Central Academy of Drama, 39 Dong Mianhua Lane, Jiaodaoku, Beijing.
   Tel: (1) 445269
Beijing Film Academy (BFA), Zhu-xin-zhuang, Beijing.
Beijing Dancing Academy, Beijing.
Central Institute for Nationalities, 27 Baishiqiao Road, Haidian District, Beijing.
   Tel: (1) 890771

Fujian (Province)

Fujian School of Civil Engineering, Fuzhou.

Jimei Navigation Institute, Xiamen.
  Tel: (592) 28151
Fujian Forestry College, Xiqing, Nanping.
  Tel: 4982
Fujian Agricultural College, Fuzhou.
  Tel: (591) 50721
Xiamen Institute of Aquatic Products, Xiamen.
Fujian Medical College, Central 817 Road,
  Fuzhou.
  Tel: (591) 57861
Fujian College of Traditional Chinese Medicine,
  Fuzhou.
Fuqing Teachers School, Fuqing.
Fuzhou Teachers School, Fuzhou.
Jimei Teachers School, Xiamen.
Nanping Teachers School, Nanping.
Ningde Teachers School, District of Ningde.
Quanzhou Teachers School, Quanzhou.
Zhangzhou Teachers School, Zhangzhou.
Fujian Institute of Physical Culture, Xiamen.

Gansu (Province)

Lanzhou Railway Institute, 3 West Anning Road,
  Lanzhou.
  Tel: (931) 66221
Lanzhou Medical College, 7 Donggang West
  Road, Lanzhou.
  Tel: (931) 24311
**Lanzhou College of Traditional Chinese
  Medicine**, Lanzhou.
Northwest Teachers College, 51 Anning East
  Road, Lanzhou.
  Tel: (931) 66151
Lanzhou Teachers School, Lanzhou.
Qingyang Teachers School, District of Qingyang.
Tianshui Teachers School, Tianshui.
Zhangye Teachers School, District of Zhangye.
Lanzhou Institute of Commerce, Lanzhou.
Northwest Institute of Nationalities, 4 Xibeixin-
  cun, Lanzhou.
  Tel: (931) 24011

Guangdong (Province)

Guangdong Institute of Technology, 729 East
  Dong Road, Guangzhou.
  Tel: 776597
Guangdong Machinery Institute, Guangzhou.
South China (Huanan) Institute of Technology,
  Wushan, Guangzhou 7003.
  Tel: (20) 774433
South China College of Tropical Agriculture,
  District of Danxian, Hainan.
Zhanjiang Agricultural School, Zhanjiang.
Zhanjiang Fisheries College, 40 Jiefang Road,
  Zhanjiang.
  Tel: 21233
Foshan School of Veterinary Medicine, Foshan.

Guangzhou Medical College, Guangzhou.
Zhanjiang Medical College, Zhanjiang.
Zhongshan (Sun-Yat-Sen) Medical College, 74
  Zhongshanerlu, Guangzhou.
  Tel: (20) 778223
**Guangzhou College of Traditional Chinese
  Medicine**, 10 Jichang Road, San Yuan Li,
  Guangzhou.
  Tel: (20) 661233
Guangdong College of Medicine and Pharmacy,
  Baoggang, Haizhou District, Guangzhou.
  Tel: 429040
Guangzhou Teachers College, Guangzhou.
Foshan Teachers School, Foshan.
Hanshan Teachers School, District of Chaoan.
Huiyang Teachers School, Huiyang.
Jiaying Teachers School, Meixian.
  Tel: 23624
Leizhou Teachers School, Zhanjiang.
  Tel: 38255
Shaoguan Teachers College, Da Tang Road,
  Shaoguan.
  Tel: 5707
**Teachers School for Hainan Li and Miao Auton-
  omous Zhou**, Tongshen.
Zhaoqing Education College, Xing Hu, Zhaoqing
  City.
  Tel: 23071
**Guangzhou Institute of Foreign Languages
  (GIFL)**, Huangpodong, Guangzhou.
  Tel: (20) 662303
Guangdong Institute of Finance and Economics,
  Guangzhou.
Guangzhou Institute of Foreign Trade,
  Guangzhou.
Guangzhou Institute of Physical Education,
  Maoer Hill, Shaheding, Guangzhou.
Guangzhou Conservatory of Music, Guangzhou.
Guangzhou Academy of Fine Arts, 257 Chang-
  gang East Road, Haizhou District, Guang-
  zhou.
  Tel: (20) 449883
Guandong Institute of Nationalities, Guangzhou.

*Guangxi (Autonomous Region of Zhuang
  Nationality)*

Guangxi Institute of Technology, Nanning.
Guilin Institute of Electronics, Guilin.
Guilin Institute of Geology, Guilin.
  Tel: 2796
Guangxi Agricultural College, Nanning.
  Tel: (771) 21223
Guangxi Medical College, Taoyuan Road, Nan-
  ning.
  Tel: (771) 21477
**Guangxi College of Traditional Chinese Medi-
  cine**, Nanning.
Youijiang Medical College for Nationalities,

Baise.
Guilin Medical School, Guilin.
Nanning Teachers College, Nanning.
Hechi Teachers School, Yishan.
Nanning Teachers School, Nanning.
Yulin Teachers School, Yulin.
Guangxi Youjiang Teachers School for National-ities, Baise.
Guangxi Academy of Arts, Nanning.
Guangxi Institute of Nationalities, Nanning.

Guizhou (Province)

Guizhou Institute of Technology, Caijiaguan, Guiyang.
Tel: (851) 42756
Guizhou Agricultural College, Huaxi, Guiyang.
Tel: (851) 2319
Guiyang Medical College, Beying Road, Guiyang.
Tel: (851) 23948
Zunyi Medical College, Waihuan Road, Zunyi.
Tel: 3191
Guiyang College of Traditional Chinese Medi-cine, 8 Shidong Road, Guiyang.
Tel: (851) 22633
Guiyang Teachers College, Guiyang.
Anshun Teachers School, Anshun.
Bijie Teachers School, Bijie.
Tongren Teachers School, District of Tongren.
Xingyi Teachers School, District of Xingyi.
Zunyi Teachers School, Zunyi.
Southeast Guizhou Teachers School for National-ities, District of Kaili.
South Guizhou Teachers School for Nationalities, Duyun.
Guizhou Institute of Finance and Economics, Guiyang.
Guizhou Institute of Nationalities, Guiyang.

Hebei (Province)

Hebei Institute of Chemical Technology, Shijiaz-huang.
Hebei Institute of Civil Engineering and Archi-tecture, Zhangjiakou.
Hebei Institute of Coal Mining and Civil Engin-eering, Xingtai.
Hebei Institute of Mechanical and Electrical Engineering, Shijiazhuang.
Hebei Institute of Mining and Metallurgy, Tangshan.
Hebei Institute of Technology, Yihao Road, Dingzigu, Tianjin.
Tel: (22) 67355
Hebei School of Water Conservancy, Cangzhou.
North China Institute of Electrical Power and Hydroelectric Power, 12 Qingnian Road, Baoding.

Tel: 4951
North China Institute of Industrial Agricultural Engineering, Xingtai.
North China Institute of Water Conservancy and Hydro-Power, 62 Zhonghua Street, Handan.
Tel: 24860
Shijiazhuang Institute of Technology for Railway Corps, Shijiazhuang.
Hebei Institute of Geology, Zhangjiakou.
Hebei School of Forestry, Yixian.
Zhangjiakou School of Agriculture, District of Xuanhua.
Chengde Medical College, Chengde.
Zhangjiakou Medical College, Zhangjiakou.
Tangshan Coal Medical College, Tangshan.
Hebei College of Chinese Traditional Medicine, Shijiazhuang.
Hebei Teachers College, Hongqing Road, Qiaoxi District, Shijiazhuang.
Tel: (311) 34262
Baoding Teachers School, Baoding.
Chengde Teachers School, Chengde.
Handan Teachers School, Handan.
Hengshui Teachers School, Hengshui.
Lanfang Teachers School, District of Anci.
Shijiazhuang Teachers School, Shijiazhuang.
Tangshan Teachers School, Tangshan.
Zhangjiakou Teachers School, Zhangjiakou.
Hebei Institute of Finance and Trade, Shijiaz-hang.

Heilongjiang (Province)

Daqing Petroleum Institute, Anda County.
Tel: 31133
Harbin Institute of Civil Engineering and Archi-tecture, 144 Xidazhi Street, Nangang District, Harbin.
Tel: (451) 33512
Harbin Institute of Electrical Technology, Da-qing Road, Harbin.
Tel: (451) 55941
Harbin Institute of Shipbuilding Engineering, Wenmiao Jie, 11/F, Nangangqu, Harbin.
Tel: (451) 32571
Heilongjiang Institute of Mining, Jixi.
Heilongjiang Hydraulic Institute, Harbin.
Tel: 61903
Jiamusi Institute of Technology, Jiamusi.
Northeast Institute of Heavy Machinery, Heping Street, Fulaerji District, Qiqihar.
Tel: 83984
Qiqihar Institute of Light Industry, Qiqihar.
Northeast College of Forestry, Harbin.
Tel: (451) 63163
Northeast Agricultural Institute, Gongbin Road, Xianfang District, Harbin.
Tel: (451) 51115
Jiamusi Medical College, Jiamusi.

Heilongjiang College of Traditional Chinese Medicine, Harbin.
Mudanjiang Medical School, Mudanjiang.
Qiqihar School of Medicine, Qiqihar.
Mudanjiang Teachers College, Mudanjiang.
Qiqihar Teachers College, Qiqihar.
Daqing Teachers School, Daqing.
Harbin Teachers School, Harbin.
Hulan Teachers School, Hulan.
Jiamusi Teachers School, Jiamusi.
Tel: 21857
Keshan Teachers School, Keshan.
Suihua Teachers School, Suihua.
Heilongjiang Nong-ken Normal College, Acheng.
Tel: 2546
Heilongjiang Institute of Commerce, Harbin.
Heilongjiang School of Finance, Harbin.
Harbin Monetary School, Harbin.

Henan (Province)

Zhengzhou Institute for Cereal Preservation and Processing, Songshan Road, Zhengzhou.
Tel: (371) 47915
Jiaozuo Mining Institute, Jiaozuo.
Luoyang Institute of Technology, Luoyang.
Zhengzhou Institute of Light Industry, Zhengzhou.
Tel: 32076
Zhengzhou Institute of Technology, 52 Wenhua Road, Zhengzhou.
Tel: (371) 32114
Zhengzhou School of Mechanical and Electrical Engineering for Textile Technology, Zhengzhou.
Henan Agricultural Institute, Zhengzhou.
Baiqan Agricultural School, Hui County.
Yuxi Agricultural School, Xinan County.
Zhengzhou School of Animal Husbandry and Veterinary Medicine, Xinan County.
Henan Medical College, Zhengzhou.
Xinxiang Medical College, Ji County.
Henan College of Traditional Chinese Medicine, Jinshui Road, Zhengzhou.
Tel: (371) 26695
Kaifeng Medical School, Kaifeng.
Luoyang Medical School, Luoyang.
West Henan School of Medicine, District of Yanshi.
Xinxiang Teachers College, Xinxiang.
Xinyang Teachers College, Xinxiang.
Anyang Teachers School, Anyang.
Luoyang Teachers School, Luoyang.
Nanyang Teachers School, Nanyang.
Shangqiu Teachers School, Shangqiu.
Xuchang Teachers School, Xuchang.
Tel: 4853
Zhengzhou Teachers School, Zhengzhou.
Zhoukou Teachers School, Zhoukou.

Henan Institute of Finance and Economics, Zhengzhou.
Zhengzhou Management School for Aviation Industry, Zhengzhou.

Hubei (Province)

Gezhouba Institute of Hydroelectrical Engineering, Yichang.
Tel: 22011
Huazhong Institute of Technology, Wuhan.
Tel: (27) 870152
Hubei Institute of Light Industry, Ma-fang-shan Wuchang, Wuhan.
Wuhan Institute for Building Materials, Wuhan.
Wuhan Institute for Cereal Preservation and Processing, Wuhan.
Wuhan Institute of Chemical Technology, Wuhan.
Tel: 870369
Wuhan Institute of Technology, Wuhan.
Wuhan Institute of Textile Technology, Wuhan.
Wuhan Institute of Urban Construction, Wuhan.
Wuhan Institute of Water Conservancy and Electric Power, Luojia Hill, Wuhan.
Tel: (27) 812212
Wuhan School of Building Construction for Metallurgical Industry, Wuhan.
Wuhan School of River Transport, Wuhan.
Tel: (27) 661491
Wuhan College of Geology, Yuijashan, Wuhan.
Tel: (27) 70481
Hubei Agricultural Machinery Institute, Wuhan.
Hubei Medical College, 39 Donghu Road, Wuhan.
Tel: (27) 811495
Hubei College of Traditional Chinese Medicine, 110 Yunjia Bridge, Wuhan.
Tel: (27) 75694
Wuhan Metallurgical Medical School, Wuhan.
Enshi Medical School, Enshi.
Yichang Medical School, Yichang.
Hubei College of Education, 23 Wuluo Road, Wuchang.
Huangshi Teachers College, Huangshi.
Huazhong Teachers College, Wuhan.
Wuhan Teachers College, Wuhan.
Enshi Teachers School, Enshi.
Huanggang Teachers School, District of Huanggang.
Jingzhou Teachers School, Jingzhou.
Xiaogan Teachers School, Xiaogan.
Tel: 3906
Xianning Teachers School, Xianning.
Yichang Teachers School, Yichang.
Yingchen Teachers School, Xiangfan.
Yunyang Teachers School, Jun County.
Hubei Institute of Finance and Economics, Wuhan.

Zhongnan Institute of Political Science and Law, Wuhan.
Wuhan Institute of Physical Culture, Wuhan.
Hubei Academy of Fine Arts, 38 Huazhoncuan, Wuhan.
Tel: (27) 877201
Zhongnan Institute for Nationalities, Wuhan.

Hunan (Province)

Changsha Transportation College, Changsha.
Changsha Railway Institute, 148 Shaoshan Road, Changsha.
Tel: (731) 35211
Hengyang Institute of Technology, Henyang.
Xiangtan Mining Institute, Xiangtan.
Zhongnan China Institute of Metallurgy, Changsha.
Zhongnan China Institute of Forestry, Zhuzhou.
Tel: 31631
Hunan Agricultural Institute, East Lake, Eastern Suburb, Changsha.
Tel: (731) 24871
Hengyang Medical College, Hengyang.
Hunan College of Traditional Chinese Medicine, 84 Shaoshan Road, Changsha.
Tel: (731) 32275
Hunan Medical College, Bei Zhan Road, Changsa.
Tel: (731) 24411
Hunan Teachers College, Changsha.
Changde Teachers School, Changde.
Chenzhou Teachers School, Chenzhou.
Hengyang Teachers School, Hengyang.
Tel: 25971
Shaoyang Teachers School, Shaoyang.
Xiangtan Teachers School, Xiangtan.
Yiyang Teachers School, Yiyang.
Yueyang Teachers School, Yueyang.
Hunan Institute of Finance and Economics, Changsha.
Hunan School of Commerce, Changsha.

Inner Mongolia (Autonomous Region)

Baotou Institute of Iron and Steel Technology, Baotou.
Inner Mongolia Engineering College, Hohhot.
Tel: (471) 44933. Telex: 85004 itcc cn
Inner Mongolia Institute of Forestry, Hohhot.
Tel: (471) 44665
Inner Mongolia Institute of Agricultural and Animal Husbandry, Hohhot.
Tel: (471) 44746
Zhelimu Animal Husbandry Institute, Tongliao.
Baotou Medical College, Baotou.
Inner Mongolia Medical College, Hohhot.
Medical College of Inner Mongolia Nationality, Hohhot.

Zhelimu Medical College, Tongliao.
Teachers College for Inner Mongolia Nationality, Tongliao.
Baotou Teachers School, Baotou.
Teachers School of Zhaowudameng Mongolian Nationality, Chifeng.
Inner Mongolia Institute of Finance and Economics, Hohhot.

Jiangsu (Province)

China Mining Institute, Xuzhou.
Tel: (516) 88653
East China Institute of Technology, 200 Xiaolingwei, Nanjing.
Tel: (25) 43145
Jiangsu Institute of Chemical Technology, Changzhou.
Jiangsu Institute of Technology, Zhenjiang.
Tel: (511) 24071
Lianyungang Chemical Mining School, Lianyungang.
Nanjing Aeronautical Institute, 29 Yu dao Street, Nanjing.
Tel: (25) 46752. Telex: 34155 nanj cn
Nanjing Chemical Engineering and Energetics, Nanjing.
Nanjing Institute of Chemical Technology, 5 Xinmofan Road, Nanjing.
Nanjing Institute of Civil Engineering and Architecture, Nanjing.
Nanjing Institute of Meteorology, Panchenggi, Pukou District, Nanjing.
Tel: (25) 51343
Nanjing Institute of Posts and Telecommunications, 38 Guandong Road, Sanpailou, Nanjing.
Tel: (25) 33862
Nanjing Institute of Technology, Sipailou, Nanjing.
Tel: (25) 34691. Telex: 34137
Suzhou Institute of Silk Technology, Xiangmen Road, Suzhou.
Tel: (512) 25614
Wuxi Institute of Light Engineering, Wuxi.
Tel: (510) 21243
Zhenjiang Shipbuilding Institute, P.O. Box 414, Zhenjiang.
Tel: 22292
Nanjing School of River Navigation, Nanjing.
Nantong Textile School, Nantong.
Yancheng Technical School, District of Yancheng.
Yangzhou Industrial School, Yangzhou.
Jiangsu Agricultural Institute, Western Suburb, Yangzhou.
Tel: 42521
Suzhou Sericulture School, District of Wuxian.
Nanjing Medical College, Hanzhong Road, Nanjing.

Tel: (25) 42696
Nantong Medical College, 19 Qixiu Road, Nantong.
Tel: (513) 7191
Suzhou Medical College, 48 Renmin Road, Suzhou.
Tel: (512) 25696. Telex: 36302 sitlx cn
Xuzhou Medical College, Xuzhou.
Tel: 24932
Nanjing College of Traditional Chinese Medicine, 282 Nanzhong Road, Nanjing.
Tel: (25) 41337
Nanjing Railway Medical College, 87 Dingjiaqiao Road, Nanjing.
Tel: (25) 31508
Nanjing Institute of Pharmacy, 24 Tongia Xiang, Nanjing.
Tel: (25) 34371
Yangzhou Medical School, Yangzhou.
Zhenjiang Medical School, Zhenjiang.
Nanjing Teachers College of Education, Nanjing.
Xuzhou Teachers College, 57 Heping Road, Xuzhou.
Tel: (516) 88750
Yancheng Teachers College, District of Yancheng.
Yangzhou Teachers College, The Shore of the Slender West Lake, Yangzhou.
Tel: 43011
Suzhou Railway Teachers College, Suzhou.
Huaiyang Teachers School, Huaiyang.
Nantong Teachers School, Nantong.
Suzhou Teachers School, Suzhou.
Zhenjiang Teachers School, Zhenjiang.
Jiangsu Commercial School, Yangzhou.
Nanjing Institute of Food Economics, 14 Hongmiao Lane, Fujian Road, Nanjing.
Tel: (25) 86033
Jiangsu School of Public Security, Nanjing.
Nanjing Institute of Physical Culture, Nanjing.
Nanjing Academy of Arts, 15 Huju Road, Nanjing.
Tel: (25) 31250. Telex: 34136 glynj cn

Jiangxi (Province)

East China Institute of Geology, Nanchang.
Jiangxi Institute of Technology, Nanchang.
Jingdezhen Porcelain Institute, Jingdezhen.
Nanchang Institute of Aircraft Industry, Nanchang.
Jiangxi Medical College, Bayidadao, Nanchang.
Tel: (791) 64936
Jiangxi College of Traditional Chinese Medicine, Nanchang.
Jiangxi Medical College for Metallurgy, Ganzhou.
Gannan Medical School, Ganzhou.
Shangrao Teachers College, N° 1 Maojialing,

Shangrao City.
Tel: 2440
Gannan Teachers School, Ganzhou.
Fuzhou Teachers School, Fuzhou.
Jian Teachers School, Jian.
Jiujiang Teachers School, Jiujiang.
Tel: 3591
Yichun Teachers School, Yichun.
Jiangxi Institute of Finance and Economics, Nanchang.

Jilin (Province)

Changchun College of Geology, 27 Fu Jin Road, Changchun.
Tel: (431) 24781. Telex: 1967
Changchun Institute of Optics and Precision Mechanics, 7 Weixing Road, Changchun.
Tel: (431) 55931
Changchun Institute of Post and Telecommunications, Changchun.
Jilin Institute of Chemical Technology, Jilin.
Jilin Institute of Civil Engineering and Architecture, Changchun.
Jilin Institute of Forestry, Jilin.
Jilin Institute of Technology, Changchun.
Northeast Institute of Electric Power, Changchun Road, Jilin.
Tel: (431) 44186
Jilin Mechanical and Electrical School, Changchun.
Yanbian Agricultural Institute, District of Yanji.
Yanbian Medical College, Yanji.
Changchun College of Traditional Chinese Medicine, Changchun.
Changchun Teachers College, Changchun.
Jilin Teachers College, Jilin.
Siping Teachers College, Siping.
Tonghua Teachers College, Tonghua.
Baicheng Teachers School, Baicheng.
Yanbian Teachers School, Yanji.
Jilin Institute of Finance and Economics, Changchun.
Jilin Physical Culture Institute, Changchun.
Jilin Academy of Arts, Changchun.

Liaoning (Province)

Anshan Institute of Iron and Steel Technology, Zhonghua Road, Tiedong District, Anshan.
Tel: (412) 25931
Dalian Institute of Light Industry, Dalian.
Dalian Institute of Technology, Luanjincum, Ganjingxi District, Dalian.
Tel: 91511. Telex: 86231 dit cn
Dalian Maritime Institute, Lingshuiqiao, Dalian.
Tel: 91611
Dalian Railway Institute, Xishancun, Shahekon

District, Dalian.
Tel: 44323
Fushun Institute of Petroleum, Fushun.
Fuxin Mining Institute, Zhongua Road, Fuxin.
Tel: (418) 4321
Jinzhou Institute of Technology, Jinzhou.
Liaoning Institute of Construction Engineering, Shenyang.
Shenyang Aeronautical Engineering Institute, Huang-He Street, Shenyang.
Shenyang Institute of Chemical Technology, Shenyang.
Northeast Institute of Technology, Wenhua Road, Heping District, Shenyang.
Tel: (24) 483081. Telex: 80033 neit cn
Shenyang Mechanical and Electrical Institute, Shenyang.
Shenyang Metallurgical and Machinery School, Shenyang.
Shenyang School of Gold Prospecting, Shenyang.
Tel: 4141
Shenyang Agricultural Institute, Maguanqiao, Dongling, Shenyang.
Tel: (24) 4479
Dalian Institute of Aquatic Products, Dalian.
Dalian Medical College, 220 Xinghai Street, Dalian.
Tel: 491242
Jinzhou Medical College, 190 Lean Street, Jinzhou.
Tel: (416) 5943
Liaoning College of Traditional Chinese Medicine, Beling Street, Shenyang.
Tel: (24) 62567
Shenyang Institute of Pharmacy, Wenhua Road, Shenhe District, Shenyang.
Tel: (24) 482706
Shenyang School of Pharmacy, Shenyang.
Jinzhou Teachers College, Jinzhou.
Liaoning Teachers College, Huanghe Street, Duanggu District, Liaoning.
Tel: (24) 65302
Shenyang Teachers College, Shenyang.
Tieling Teachers College, Tieling.
Yingkou Teachers College, Yingkou.
Anshan Teachers School, Anshan.
Chaoyang Teachers School, Chaoyang.
Dandong Teachers School, Dandong.
Dalian Institute of Foreign Languages, Dalian.
Liaoning Institute of Finance and Economics, Dalian.
Liaoning School of Commerce, Jinzhou.
Chinese Institute of Police, Shenyang.
Shenyang Institute of Physical Culture, Shenyang.
Shenyang Conservatory of Music, Shenyang.
Lu Xun Academy of Fine Arts, 1 Sanhao Street, Heping District, Shenyang.
Tel: (24) 482635

Ningxia (Hui Autonomous Region)

Ningxia Institute of Technology, Yinchuan.
Ningxia Agricultural College, Yongning County, Ningxia.
Ningxia Medical College, Southern Suburb, Yinchuan.
Tel: (951) 2831
Guyuan Teachers School, District of Guyuan.
Yinchuan Teachers School, Helan.

Qinghai (Province)

Qinghai Institute of Engineering and Agriculture, Xining.
Qinghai Animal Husbandry and Veterinary College, Xining.
Qinghai Medical College, 84 Kun Lun Road, Xining.
Qinghai Educational College, 91 Ba Yi Road, Xining.
Tel: (971) 55137
Qinghai College of Nationalities, 25 Bayi Road, Xining.
Tel: (971) 75340

Shaanxi (Province)

Northwest Institute of Civil Engineering, Xi'an.
Northwest Institute of Forestry, Wugong.
Northwest Institute of Light Industry, West Renmin Road, Xi'anyang.
Tel: (910) 4389
Northwest Institute of Telecommunication Engineering, 2 Taibai Road, Xi'an.
Tel: (29) 55801
Xi'an Institute of Textile Technology, Jin Hua Road, Xi'an.
Tel: (29) 31963
Shaanxi Institute of Mechanical Engineering, Jin Hua Road, Xi'an.
Tel: (29) 31236
Shaanxi Institute of Technology, Hanzhong.
Xi'an Institute of Metallurgy and Construction Engineering, 13 Yan'ta Road, Xi'an.
Tel: (29) 51293
Xi'an Institute of Geology, 4 Yan'ta Road, Xi'an.
Tel: (29) 52991
Xi'an Institute of Highways, Cuihua Road, Xi'an.
Tel: (29) 52927
Xi'an Institute of Petroleum, Xi'an.
Xi'an Institute of Technology, Xi'an.
Xi'an Mining Institute, 14 Yan'ta Road, Xi'an.
Tel: (29) 52931
Xi'an Medical College, Xi'an.
Yanan Medical College, Yanan.
Shaanxi College of Traditional Chinese Medicine, Weiyang Road, Xi'an.
Tel: (910) 2766

Huashan Medical School for Metallurgy, Huaying.
Baoji Teachers College, Baoji.
Hanzhong Teachers College, Hanzhong.
Weinan Teachers School, District of Weinan.
Xianyang Teachers School, Xianyang.
Xi'an Institute of Foreign Languages, Xi'an.
Shaanxi Pedagogical Institute, Xing Shan Si Dong Jie 11, Xiao Zhai, Xi'an.
Shaanxi Institute of Finance and Economics, Cuihua Road, Xi'an.
Tel: (29) 52221
Northwest Institute of Political Science and Law, Changannan Road, Xi'an.
Tel: (29) 52056
Xi'an Institute of Physical Culture, Xi'an.
Xi'an Music Conservatory, Xi'an.
Xi'an Academy of Fine Arts, Xingguosi, Xi'an.
Tel: (29) 52517

Shandong (Province)

East China Petroleum Institute, Dongying.
Tel: 24901
Shandong College of Oceanography, 5 Yushan Road, Qingdao.
Tel: (532) 84361
Shandong Institute of Agricultural Mechanization, Zibo.
Shandong Institute of Building Materials, Zibo.
Shandong Institute of Chemical Technology, Quingdao.
Shandong Institute of Civil Engineering, Jinan.
Shandong Institute of Light Industry, Jinan.
Shandong Institute of Metallurgy, Quingdao.
Shandong Institute of Textile Technology, Quingdao.
Shandong Mining Institute, District of Taian.
Tel: (538) 3310
Shandong Agricultural Institute, District of Taian.
Laiyang Agricultural College, Laiyang.
Tel: 777
Shandong Academy of Medicine, Jing Shi Road 35, Jinan.
Binzhou Medical College, Binzhou.
Changwei Medical College, Weifang.
Qingdao Medical College, 10 Huangtai Road, Qingdao.
Tel: (532) 24523
Taishan Medical College, Taian.
Shandong Institute of Traditional Chinese Medicine, 23 Jingshi Road, Jinan.
Tel: (531) 4694
Heze Medical School, District of Heze.
Jining Medical School, Jining.
Yishui Medical School, District of Yishui.
Liaocheng Teachers Institute, Liaocheng.
Qufu Teachers Institute, Qufu.

Binzhou Teachers School, Binzhou.
Changwei Teachers School, Weifang.
Dezhou Teachers School, Dezhou.
Heze Teachers School, Heze.
Jining Teachers School, Jining.
Linyi Teachers School, Fei County.
Taian Teachers School, Taian.
Yantai Teachers College, Yantai.
Tel: 23567
Shandong Institute of Economics, Jinan.
Tel: (531) 44161
Shandong Institute of Physical Culture, Jinan.
Shandong Academy of Arts, Jinan.

Shanghai (Municipality)

Shanghai Institute of Mechanical Engineering, 516 Jun Gong Road, Shanghai 200093.
Tel: (21) 433040
Shanghai Maritime College, 1550 Pudong Street, Shanghai.
Tel: (21) 84094
Shanghai Railway Institute, Zhennan Road, Shanghai.
Tel: (21) 506344
Shanghai Technical College of Metallurgy, 121 Caobao Road, Shanghai 201103.
Shanghai School of Building Materials, Shanghai.
East China Institute of Chemical Technology, 130 Meilong Road, Shanghai.
Tel: (21) 380811. Telex: 33428 ecict cn
Shanghai School of Medical Apparatus and Instruments, Shanghai.
Shanghai School of Petrochemical Technology, Shanghai.
Shanghai School of Science and Technology, Shanghai.
Shanghai School of Textile Industry, Shanghai.
Shanghai Agricultural Institute, Shanghai.
Shanghai First Medical College, Shanghai.
Shanghai College of Traditional Chinese Medicine, 530 Lingling Road, Shanghai.
Tel: (21) 388400
Shanghai Railways Medical College, Shanghai.
Shanghai Foreign Language Institute, 119 Ti Yu Hui Lu, Shanghai.
Tel: (21) 664900
Shanghai Institute of Finance and Economics, Shanghai.
Shanghai Institute of Foreign Trade, Shanghai.
Tel: (21) 598181. Telex: 33531 sioft can
Shanghai School of Tourism, Shanghai.
Shanghai Customs School, Shanghai.
East China Institute of Political Science and Law, 1575 Wanghangdu Road, Shanghai.
Tel: (21) 520611
Shanghai Institute of Physical Culture, 650 Qingyuanhuan Road, Shanghai.

Tel: (21) 480545

Shanghai Conservatory of Music, 20 Fenyang Road, Shanghai.
Tel: (21) 370137

Shanghai Drama Institute, 630 Huashan Road, Shanghai.
Tel: (21) 521909

Shanxi (Province)

Taiyuan Machinery Institute, Shanglancun, Beixao District, Taiyuan.
Tel: (351) 59411

Taiyuan Institute of Heavy Machinery, Rongliu Road, Taiyuan.
Tel: (351) 66521

Shanxi Medical College, 10 Xinjian South Road, Taiyuan.
Tel: (351) 21511

Datong Medical School, Datong.

Southeast Shanxi Medical School, Changzhi.

Shanxi Teachers College, Linfen.

Taiyuan Teachers College, Taiyuan.
Tel: (351) 2370

Central Shanxi Teachers School, Yuci.

Southeast Shanxi Teachers School, Changzhi.

Xin County Teachers School, Xin County.

Yanbei Teachers School, Shuo County.

Shanxi Institute of Finance and Economics, Taiyuan.

Sichuan (Province)

Chengdu College of Geology, Shilidian, Northeastern Suburb, Chengdu 610059.
Tel: (28) 34712

Chengdu Institute of Meteorology, Chengdu.

Chengdu Institute of Telecommunication Engineering, 4 Jianshe Road, Chengdu.
Tel: (28) 33312. Telex: 60202

China Institute of Mining Technology, Chongqing.

Chongqing Civil Engineering Institute, Shapingba District, Chongqing.
Tel: (811) 661989. Telex: 5120

Chongqing Institute of Post and Telecommunications, Chongqing.

Chongqing Institute of River and Highway Transport, Chongqing.

Sichuan Institute of Building Materials, District of Mianyang.

Sichuan Institute of Chemical Technology, Zigong.

Sichuan Institute of Technology, Chendu, Pi County.

Southwest Institute of Petroleum, 6 Shiyou East Road, Nanchong.
Tel: 2278

Chinese Aviation Pilot School, Guanghan.

Sichuan Agricultural Institute, Yaan.

Southwest Agricultural College, Chongqing.
Tel: (811) 3964

Sichuan Institute of Animal Husbandry and Veterinary Medicine, Rongchang.

Mianyang Agricultural School, Mianyang.

Xichang Agricultural College, Mapinda, Xichang.
Tel: 3334

Chongqing Medical College, Chongqing.

Luzhou Medical College, Luzhou.

Sichuan Medical College, Chengdu.
Tel: (28) 24411

Chengdu College of Traditional Chinese Medicine, 13 Xinlo Road, Chengdu.
Tel: (28) 21611

Nanchong Medical School, Nanchong.

Aba Teachers College, District of Wenchuan.

Chongqing Teachers College, Chongqing.

Liangshan College of Education, Xichang.

Nanchong Teachers College, 10 Renminxi Road, Nanchong.
Tel: 2244

Southwest Teachers College, Chongqing.

Daxian Teachers School, District of Daxian.

Fuling Teachers School, Fuling.

Jianjing Teachers School, District of Yongchuan.

Leshan Teachers School, Leshan.

Mianyang Teachers School, Mianyang.

Neijiang Teachers School, Neijiang.

Sichuan Institute of Foreign Languages, Chongqing.

Sichuan Institute of Finance and Economics, Guanghuachan, Chengdu.
Tel: (28) 23116

Southwest Institute of Political Science and Law, Shapingba, Chongqing.
Tel: (811) 661223

Chengdu Institute of Physical Culture, 2 Tiyuan road, Southern Suburb, Chengdu.
Tel: (28) 54811

Sichuan Conservatory of Music, Chengdu.

Sichuan Institute of Fine Arts, Huangjueping, Jiulongpo District, Chongqing.
Tel: (811) 23423

Southwest Institute for Nationalities, Chengdu.

Tianjin (Province)

China Civil Aviation Institute, Tianjin.
Tel: (22) 247602

Tianjin Institute of Light Industry, 1486 Dagu Nanlu, Tianjin.
Tel: (22) 82965

Tianjin Institute of Science and Technology, Tianjin.

Tianjin Institute of Textile Technology, 89 Cheng Linzhung Road, Hedong District, Tianjin.

Tel: (22) 43251
Tianjin Agricultural Institute, Tianjin.
Tianjin Medical College, 62 Qi Xiang Tai Road, Tianjin.
Tianjin College of Traditional Chinese Medicine, Xihucun, Nankai District, Tianjin.
Tel: (22) 23737
Tianjin Medical School, 22 Qixiangtai Road, Heping District, Tianjin.
Tel: (22) 332691
Tianjin Teachers College, Tianjin.
Tianjin Technical Teachers Institute, Tianjin.
Tianjin Institute of Foreign Languages, 137 Machangdao, Hexi District, Tianjin.
Tel: (22) 397101
Tianjin Institute of Commerce, Tianjin.
Tianjin Institute of Finance and Economics, 25 Zhujiangdao, Hexi District, Tianjin.
Tel: (22) 82657
Tianjin Institute of Foreign Trade, Tianjin.
Tianjin Institute of Physical Culture, Tianjin.
Tianjin Music Conservatory, 5 Shiyijing Road, Hedong District, Tianjin.
Tel: (22) 42882
Tianjin Institute of Fine Arts, Tianjin.

Tibet (Autonomous Region)

Tibet College of Agriculture and Animal Husbandry, District of Linzhi.
Tibet Teachers College, Lhasa.
Tibet Institute of Nationalities, Xianyang.

Xingjiang (Province)
(Uygur Autonomous Region)

Xingjiang August 1st Agricultural College, Zhimancheng, Urumqi.
Tel: (991) 42141
Xingjiang Institute of Petroleum, Urumqi.
Xingjiang Institute of Technology, Youhao Road, Urumqi.
Tel: (991) 41911
Shihezi Agricultural College, Shihezi.
Tel: 2392
Shihezi Medical College, Shihezi.
Xingjiang Medical College, Urumqi.
Kashi Teachers College, Kashi.
Ili Teachers College, Ining.
Hetian Teachers School, District of Hetian.
Xingjiang Institute of Finance and Economics, Urumqi.

Yunnan (Province)

Kunming Institute of Technology, Lianhuanchi, Northern Suburb, Kunming.
Tel: (871) 29021
Yunnan Institute of Technology, Huancheng Donglu, Kunming.
Tel: (871) 29031
Dali Medical College, Dali.
Kunming Medical College, Renmin Road, Kunming.
Tel: (871) 81966
Yunnan College of Traditional Chinese Medicine, Kunming.
Dali Teachers College, Dali Xia-guang, Dali Bai National Autonomous Region.
Kunming Teachers College, Kunming.
Baoshan Teachers School, District of Baoshan.
Kunming Teachers School, Kunming.
Mengzi Teachers School, District of Mengzi.
Qujing Teachers School, District of Qujing.
Simao Teachers School, District of Simao.
Zhaotong Teachers School, District of Zhaotong.
Yunnan Institute of Finance and Trade, Kunming.
Yunnan School of Political Science and Law, Kunming.
Yunnan Academy of Arts, Kunming.
Yunnan Institute of Nationalities, Lianhuachi, Kunming.
Tel: (871) 23298

Zhejiang (Province)

Hangzhou Electronic Engineering Institute, Hangzhou.
Zhejiang Institute of Forestry, District of Lin'an.
Zhejiang Fisheries Institute, District of Putuo.
Tel: 3851
Zhejiang Institute of Silk Textiles, 88 Wenyi Road, Hangzhou.
Tel: (571) 85814
Zhejiang Institute of Technology, Mishi Lane, Hangzhou.
Tel: (571) 88514
Wenzhou Medical College, Yixueyuan Road, Wenzhou.
Tel: 4941
Zhejiang College of Traditional Chinese Medicine, Qhingchun Road, Hangzhou.
Tel: (571) 71568
Jiaxing Teachers School, District of Wuxing.
Lishui Teachers School, District of Lishui.
Ningbo Teachers School, Ningbo.
Shaoxing Teachers School, Shaoxing.
Taizhou Teachers School, Lihai County.
Wenzhou Teachers School, Wenzhou.
Hangzhou Institute of Commerce, Jiao Gong Road, Hangzhou.
Tel: (571) 81024. Telex: 5096
Zhejiang School of Metallurgical Economics, District of Jiande.
Zhejiang Academy of Fine Arts, 218 Nanstan Road, Hangzhou.
Tel: (571) 22634

Chinese SCM (WSCF)
c/o Dr Y.C. Tu, National YMCA, 13, Huch In
Lu, Shanghai.

Ministry of Education
35 Damucanghutong, Xidan, Beijing.
Tel: (1) 662730

National Commission of the People's Republic of China for Unesco
Ministry of Education, 35 Damucanghutong, Xidan, Beijing.
Tel: (1) 662730. Telex: 22014 sedc cn. Cables: unescocom beijing

COLOMBIA
COLOMBIE

UNIVERSITIES AND OTHER UNIVERSITY INSTITUTIONS—
UNIVERSITES ET AUTRES ETABLISSEMENTS UNIVERSITAIRES

Public Institutions— Etablissements publics

Colegio Mayor de Antioquia, Calle 65 Carrera 78
Robledo, Medellín (Antioquia).   *1945*
Tél: 2334740
bactériologie-lab clin, techn-dess arc, tour.
Colegio Mayor de Cundinamarca, Calle 28 No.
6–02, Bogotá.   *1945*
Tél: 2340257
bactériologie-lab clin, dess arc, trav soc.
Escuela de Cadetes de Policia «General Santander», Autopista Sur Calle 42, Bogotá.
Tél: 2381674
Escuela Superior de Administración, Pública,
Diagonal 40 No. 46A–37, Bogotá.   *1958*
Tél: 2699147
P : pol-adm.
Escuela Superior de Administración Pública,
Calle 56 (Bolívia) No 45–34, Medellín (Antioquia).
Tél: 2543780
P : adm municipale.
Instituto Departamental de Bellas Artes "Antonio María Valencia", Avenida 2 Norte No. 7–38,
Cali (Valle).
Tél: 0803850
P : arts plast, dess.
Instituto Universitario de Cundinamarca «ITUC», Diagonal 18 No. 20–29, Fusagasugá
(Cundinamarca).   *1969*
Tél: 0002144
éd, techn agr, techn adm-fin; éd, techn inf,
(Girardot); éd, techn adm (Ubaté).
Instituto Universitario de La Paz, Avenida Santander, Calle 9 No. 10–22, Santander.
Tél: 0021908

P : vét-zoo.
Unidad Central del Valle del Cauca, Carrera 26
No. 30–58, Tuluá (Cauca).
Tél: 0004375
P : éd, adm des aff, comp, dr.
Unidad Universitaria del Sur de Bogotá (Formación a Distancia),
Carrera 7a No. 6–5A, Bogotá.
Tél: 2894063
techn agr, techn res energ, transp, ing.
Universidad de La Amazonia, Avenida Circunvalación, Barrio el Cedral, Florencia
(Caquetá).
Tél: 0002905
éd, comp, zoo.
Universidad de Antioquía, Ciudad Universitaria,
Calle 67 h°–5–108, Medellín.   *1801*
Tél: 2334740
P : éd, anth, biol, commun soc, phy, phil-let, gé
des systèmes, psyc, stat, hist, bactériologie et
lab clin, éco, anglais, math, ch, socio, trav soc,
ch, dr-pol, adm des aff, élec, électro, gé ind,
méc, mét, gé ch, gé sa, méd, dent, ch phar, vét,
zoo, bibl, nutr-diét, inf, tec alim, arts plast, lang
mod.
Universidad del Atlántico, Carrera 43 No. 50–53,
Barranquilla (Atlántico).   *1941*
Tél: 0313513. Cables: uniatlantico
P : éd, arc, dr, éco, adm des aff, comp publ, gé
ch, ch-phar, nutr-diét, pnt, soc, lang.
Universidad de Caldas, Calle 65 No. 26-10,
Apartado aéreo 275, Manizales (Calda).   *1943*
Tél: 0855240
P : éd, agr, phil-let, trav soc, dr, inf, méd, vét-

zoo, arts plastiques, éd mus, géol.
Universidad de Cartagena, Carrera 6 No. 36–100, Cartagena (Bolívar). *1774*
Tél: 0655032
P : dr, méd, ch-phar, dent, gé civ, éco, inf, trav soc, adm des aff, comp.
Universidad del Cauca, Calle 5 No. 4-70, Popayán (Cauca). *1827*
Tél: 0023020. Télex: 5966 uncan co. Cables: unicauca
P : éd, dr-pol, méd, inf, gé civ, électro-télé-commun, comp publ, agr, anth, arts plast, phil, lit-lang espagnol, géo-techn.
Conservatoire : mus.
Universidad de Córdoba, Kilometro 3 via Cereté, Apartado aéreo 354, Montería (Córdoba).
1966
Tél: 0003278. Cables: unicordoba
P : éd, agr, vét-zoo, inf.
Universidad Distrital «Francisco José de Caldas», Carrera 8 No. 40–78, Bogotá. *1950*
Tél: 2457088
P : éd, techn.
Universidad Francisco de Paula Santander, Avenida Gran Colombia 12 E 96, Cúcuta (Norte de Santander). *1962*
Tél: 0040072
P : éd, techn, gé civ, élec, méc, gé ch, adm des aff, comp publ, électro-méc, techn inf, techn mine, gé des systèmes.
E : agr.
Section à Ocaña.
Tél: 0023344
Universidad Industrial de Santander, Ciudad Universitaria, Bucaramanga (Santander).
1948
Tél: 0356576
P : éd, gé civ, élec, gé ind, méc, mét, pét, gé ch, gé des systèmes, méd, physio, lab clin et bactériologie, nutr-diét, inf, ch, arc, serv soc, hist, phy, géol.
Universidad de La Guajira, Calle 26 Salida a Valledupar, Apartado aéreo 172, Riohacha (La Guajira).
Tél: 0073856
P : adm des aff, gé ind, lang mod.
Universidad Nacional de Colombia, Ciudad Universitaria, Bogotá. *1825*
Tél: 2442830. Télex: 42531 incca co. Cables: apartado aero 14490
P : éd, agr, dr-pol, inf, gé agr, arc, chant, cér, géol, gé des systèmes, méd, dent, vét, orchestre, sculp, mus, pnt, art-dess, biol, stat, phar, phy, géol, math, ch, adm des aff, comp, éco, anth, phil-lang, phil, socio, psyc, trav soc, math, gé civ, élec, méc, gé ch, nutr-diét, thér, zoo.
SECCIONAL MANIZALES, Carrera 27 No. 64–60, Apartado aéreo 127, Manizales.

1950
P : gé civ, adm des aff, arc, élec, gé ind, gé ch.
SECCIONAL MEDELLÍN, Carrera 64 por Calle 65, Autopista Norte, Medellín. *1887*
P : arc, ing civ, agr, constr, math app, zoo, éco agr, for, arts, hist, gé agr, mine, ing, géol.
SECCIONAL PALMIRA, Carretera 32 Chapinero, Palmira. *1934*
P : agr, zoo, gé agr.
Universidad de Nariño, Carrera 22 No. 18-109, Pasto (Nariño). *1904*
Tél: 0035652. Cables: unarino
P : éd, dr-soc, éco, gé civ, gé agr, zoo, arts plast.
Universidad de Pamplona, Calle 6 No. 3-23, Pamplona (Norte de Santander). *1960*
Tél: 0082960
P : éd, techn alim.
Universidad Pedagógica Nacional, Calle 72 No. 1186, Bogotá. *1931*
Tél: 2352600. Cables: apartado aero 75144
P : éd.
Universidad Pedagógica y Tecnológica de Colombia, Carretera Central del Norte, Tunja (Boyacá). *1872*
Tél: 0422173. Cables: upetec
P : éd, gé agr, trans, mét, électroméc, éco, inf, adm des aff.
SECCIONAL CHIQUINQUIRÁ, Calle 14 No. 12-37, Chiquinquirá.
P : éd.
SECCIONAL DUITAMA, Carrera 18, Calle 23, Duitama.
P : éd.
SECCIONAL SOGAMOSO, Calle 4 No. 15-134, Sogamoso.
P : comp, gé géol, gé mine, gé ind.
Universidad Popular del César, Calle 15 No. 4-100, Valledupar (El César).
Tél: 0023890
P : éd, adm des aff, comp publ, inf.
Universidad del Quindío, Carrera 15, Calle 12, Armenia (Quindio). *1960*
Tél: 0052181. Télex: 8531 uquin co
P : éd, comp publ, gé civ, méc, élec, méd, gé cio, topog.
Universidad de Sucre, Calle 19 No. 22-58, Sincelejo (Sucre).
Tél: 0021240
P : éd, gé agr, prod agr, inf.
Universidad Surcolombiana, Avenida Pastrana Borrero Carrera 1, Neiva (Huila).
Tél: 0045444
P : éd, adm des aff, comp, gé agr, inf, méd, pét.
Universidad Tecnológica del Chocó »Diego Luis Córdoba», Carrera 2 No. 25-22, Apartado aéreo 22, Quibdó (Chocó).
Tél: 0000735

P : éd, trav soc, techn agr, adm des aff, techn civ, techn pêch, techn mine.

Universidad Tecnológica de Los Llanos Orientales, Apartado aéreo 2621, Km. 11, Via Puerto López, Villavicencio (Meta).
Tél: 0023449
P : éd, gé agr, vét-zoo, inf.

Universidad Tecnológica del Magdalena, San Pedro Alejandrino, Apartado aéreo 731, Santa Marta (Magdalena). *1958*
Tél: 0036150
P : éd, éco agr, gé agr, gé pêch, adm des aff agr.

Universidad Tecnológica de Pereira, La Julita, Apartado aéreo 97, Pereira (Risaralda). *1958*
Tél: 0034944. Cables: universtec
P : éd, gé ind, élec, méc, méd.
I : polytec.

Universidad del Tolima, Barrio Santa Elena, Apartado aéreo 546, Ibagué (Tolima). *1945*
Tél: 0034128
P : éd, gé agr, gé for, vét-zoo, adm des aff, topog, techn arc.

*****Universidad del Valle**, Meléndez San Fernando, Calle 4B No. 36–00, Cali (Valle del Cauca). *1945*
Tél: 0391486. Télex: 51332 uváll co. Cables: univalle
P : éd, sc, hum, éco, arc, trav soc, adm des aff, biol, commun soc, comp publ, inf, stat, phil, physio, gé agr, gé civ, élec, gé ind, méc, gé ch, gé sani, math-phy, méd, dent, psyc, ch, socio, mus, techn de lab clin, phonoaudiologie, topog, ch.

Private Institutions – Etablissements privés

Centro de Investigación y Planeamiento Administrativo, Apartado aéreo 6478, Carrera 43 No. 49-57, Medellín (Antioquia).
Tél: 282-00-88

Colegio de Estudios Superiores de Administración, Diagonal 35 No. 5–41, Bogotá.
Tél: 2851026
P : adm des aff.

Colegio Mayor de Nuestra Señora del Rosario, Calle 14 No. 6-25, Bogotá. *1953*
Tél: 2820088
P : adm des aff, éco, dr, méd, inf, physio, phonoaudiologie, thér, phil-let.

Colegio Odontológico Colombiano, Calle 13 No. 4–38, Bogotá.
Tél: 2421375
P : dent.

Corporación Autónoma Universitaria de Manizales, Antigua Estación del Ferrocarril, Manizales (Caldas).
Tél: 083 61 01
P : dent, éco, physio, gé dis systémes.

Corporación Educativa del Caribe, Carrera 19 No. 28A–109, Sincelejo (Sucre).
Tél: 0021402
P : éd.

Corporación Educativa Mayor del Desarrollo «Simón Bolívar», Carrera 59 No. 59-92, Barranquilla (Catlántico). *1972*
Tél: 0358963
P : éd, dr, éco, socio, trav soc.

Escuela de Administración de Negocios, Calle 72 No. 9-71, Bogotá. *1968*
Tél: 2112111-211
P : adm des aff, gé des systémes.

Escuela Colombiana de Medicina, Transversal 9A bis No. 133–25, Bogotá.
Tél: 2741662

Corporación Tecnológica de Bolívar, Carrera 21 No. 25-92, Cartagena (Bolívar). *1945*
Tél: 0662518
P : éco, élec, gé ind, méc.

Corporación Universidad Piloto de Colombia, Carrera 19 No. 17–33, Alto Magdalena (Santa Marta).
Tél: 0028505
P : gé des systèmes, techn.

Corporación Universidad Piloto de Colombia, Carrera 9 No. 45A-44, Bogotá. *1962*
Tél: 2856450
P : arc, éco, gé des systèmes, comp publ.

Corporación Universitaria Adventista, Carrera 84 No. 33AA–01, Medellín (Antioquia).
Tél: 2507948. Cables: icolvo n
P : éd, adm, des aff.

Corporación Universitaria «Antonio Nariño», Calle 20 Sur No. 13-61, Bogotá. *1976*
Tél: 2724630
P : éd, adm des aff, comp publ, gé ind, électro, gé des systémes "software".

Corporación Universitara Autónoma de Bucaramanga, Calle 48 No. 39-234, Bucaramanga (Santander). *1952*
Tél: 0375111
P : éd, adm-fin, commun soc, comp publ, dr.

Corporación Universitaria Autónoma de Occidente, Calle 9B No. 29A–67, Cali (Valle del Cauca). *1969*
Tél: 0588191
P : éco, élec, méc, gé ind, commun soc-jour.

Corporación Universitara de Boyaca, Calle 19 No. 11-64, Tunja (Boyacá).
Tél: 0425930
P : gé sani, adm des aff, gé des systèmes, rel ind, adm com.

Corporación Universitaria de Ciencias Agro-

pecuarias, Calle 55 No. 13–90, Bogotá.
Tél: 2480893
P : vét, zoo.
Corporación Universitaria de Colombia IDEAS,
Calle 69 No. 7–77, Bogotá.
Tél: 2494508
P : adm inft.
Corporación Universitaria de Ibagué, Calle 14
No. 7-53, Barrio Ambalá (Ibagué).
Tél: 0640616. Cables: coruniversitario
P : adm fin, comp publ, gé ind.
**Corporación Universitaria de la Costa
(UNICOSTA)**, Carreras 54 y 58, Calle 58,
Barranquilla (Atlántico).   *1969*
Tél: 328350
P : éd, adm des aff, arc, dr, éco, gé civ.
Corporación Universitaria Lasallista, Calle 54A
No. 30-01, Medellín (Antioquia).
Tél: 2498891
P : éd, adm, des aff agr, gé alim.
Corporación Universitaria del Meta, Carrera 32
No. 34A–31, Meta (Villavicencio).
Tél: 0026830
P : adm des aff agr.
Corporación Universitaria «Rafael Nunez»,
Carrera 17 No. 25–90, Bolívar (Castagena).
Tél: 0655137
P : éd.
Corporación Universitaria Santa Rosa de Cabal,
Calle 12 No. 13-56, Santa Rosa de Cabal
(Risaralda).
Tél: 0001223
P : adm des aff agr.
Corporación Universitaria del Sinu, Carrera 3
No. 29-26, Montería (Córdoba).
Tél: 0002467
P : éd, dr, adm des aff, comp publ, lang, trav
soc.
**Escuela Colombiana de Ingeniería «Julio
Garavito»**, Autopista del Norte Km 13,
Bogotá.   *1972*
Tél: 6760451
P : gé civ, élec, gé des systèmes.
Escuela de Ingeniería de Antioquia, Calle 25 Sur
No. 42–73 Envigado Zúñiga, Medellín (Anti-
oquia).
Tél: 2764360
P : gé civ, gé géol.
**Fundación Educacional Interamericana «Univer-
sidad Católica de Colombia»**, Diagonal 47 No.
1550, Bogotá.   *1970*
Tél: 2853912
P : arc, dr, éco, gé civ, gé ind, psyc.
Fundación Educativa de Estudios Superiores,
Calle 63 No. 3–45, Bogotá.
Tél: 2359806
**Fundación Escuela de Ciencias de la Salud de la
Sociedad de Cirugía de Bogotá**, Calle 10a No.
18-75, Bogotá.   *1976*

Tél: 2473680
P : inf.
**Fundación Escuela de Medicina «Juan N.
Corpas»**, Avenida Flores de Los Andes, Suba
Km. 3, Bogotá.   *1972*
Tél: 6813637
**Fundación Instituto Universitario de Ciencia y
Tecnología «Konrad Lorenz»**, Calle 77 No. 11-
63, Bogotá.
Tél: 2486790
P : psyc.
Fundación Universidad de América, Avenida de
Los Cerros No. 19-91, Bogotá.   *1952*
Tél: 2815715
P : arc, éco, gé ind, méc, gé ch, pét.
**Fundación Universidad de Bogotá «Jorge Tadeo
Lozano»**, Calle 23 No. 4-47, Bogotá.   *1954*
Tél: 2834610
P : adm des aff, agr, com int, comp publ, ba,
commun soc, éco, ét dipl-pol, gé géog, biol
mar, dess arc décor et publicité, gé alim, dess
ind; arc, com ext, adm tour (Cartagena).
E : ba.
Fundación Universidad Central, Carrera 5 No.
21-38, Bogotá.   *1966*
Tél: 2848249
P : comp publ, éco, adm des aff, publicité, gé
des systèmes.
Fundación Universidad del Norte, Kt. 5 Carretera
a Pto. Colombia, Barranquilla.   *1966*
Tél: 0350722
P : éd, dr, adm des aff, méc, gé civ, inf, méd,
méc, élec, gé des systèmes-inft, gé ind, psyc.
Fundación Universitaria Agraria de Colombia,
Calle 170 No. 50-90, Bogotá.
Tél: 0721630
P : gé civ, alim.
Fundación Universitaria Autónoma de Colombia,
Carrera 5a No. 1143, Bogotá.   *1971*
Tél: 2818624
P : dr, éco, gé des systèmes, gé ind.
Fundación Universitaria Católica de Oriente,
Calle 41 No. 45-201, Ríonegro (Antioquia).
Tél: 2715959
P : adm des aff agr, adm des aff, relig, com ext,
gé ind, gerontologie.
**Fundación Universitaria de García Rovira, Norte
y Gutiérrez**, Ciudad Universitaria, Málaga
(Santander).
Tél: 004753
P : adm des aff agr, gé for, zoo.
Fundación Universitaria «Los Libertadores»,
Carrera 10 Calle 74 No. 65-98, Bogotá.
Tél: 2350688
P : éd, adm tour, com ext.
Fundación Universitaria «Luis Amigo», Trans-
versal 51A No. 67B-134, Medellín (Antioquia).
Tél: 2301804
P : péd rééducative.

Fundación Universitaria de Manizales, Carrera 9 No. 1903, Manizales (Caldas).
Tél: 0841450
P : psyc, dr, éco, comp publ.

fundación Universitaria «María Caño», Calle 52 No. 49-27, Medellín (Antioquia).

Fundación Universitaria Monserrate, Calle 72 No. 11-41, Bogotá. *1948*
Tél: 2174912
P : éd, trav soc.

Fundación Universitaria de Popayan, Calle 5a No. 3-38 Sede Los Robles, Popayan (Cauca).
Tél: 0021920
P : mine, adm agr, écol.

Fundación Universitaria San Martín, Calle 61A No. 14-28, Bogotá.
Tél: 2555919
P : dent.

Instituto de Ciencias de la Salud, Apartado aéreo 054591, Tr. Superior Calle 10, Medellín (Antioquia).
Tél: 2465145
P : méd, dent.

Instituto Universitario de Historia de Colombia, Carrera 9 No. 9-52, Bogotá. *1966*
Tél: 2825316

Institución Universitaria «Sergio Arboledo», Calle 74 No. 14-14, Bogotá.
Tél: 2123981
P : dr, adm des aff, phil-hum.

Pontificia Universidad Javeriana, Carrera 7 No. 40-62, Bogotá. *1623, 1931*
Tél: 2875791
P : éd, arc, dess ind, dr, éco, inf, gé civ, gé ind, électro, méd, phil, phil-let, dent, psyc, serv soc, hist, lit, nutr-diét, math, adm des aff, bactériologie, biol, sc relig, théo et catéchisme, bibl, commun, comp; comp, psyc, adm des aff, gé ind (Cali).

Universidad Autónoma del Caribe, Calle 90 No. 46-112, Barranquilla (Atlántica). *1967*
Tél: 0452605. Cables: uniantonoma
P : adm des aff, arc, commun soc, comp publ, socio, dess tex, adm tour.

Universidad Autónoma Latinoamericana «Unaula», Carrera 55 No. 4951, Medellín (Antioquia). *1966*
Tél: 2311199
P : éd, dr, éco, comp publ, socio.

Universidad Católica de Manizales, Carrera 23 No. 60-63 Zona 4, Manizales (Caldas).
Tél: 60019
P : éd, bactériologie-lab clin, phonoaudiologie, arc, adm tour, promotion soc, publicité.

Universidad Católica Popular de Risaralda, Calle 20 No. 3-65, Pereira (Risaralda).
Tél: 0046524
P : adm des aff, éco ind.

Universidad Cooperativa de Colombia, Avenida Caracas No. 37–63, Bogotá. *1958*
Tél: 2454798
P : éd, adm des aff, éco, socio.
Sections à : Barrancabermeja, Bucaramanga, Medellín, Sta. Marta.

Universidad Escuela de Administración y Finanzas y Tecnologías «EAFIT», Carrera 49 No. 7 Sur, 50 Avenida Las Vegas, Medellín (Antioquia). *1960*
Tél: 2664324
P : adm des aff, comp publ, gé civ, gé prod, gé des systèmes, gé production, géol, méc.

*Universidad Externado de Colombia, Calle 12 No. 1-17 Este, Bogotá. *1886, 1918*
Tél: 2413484
P : éd, éco, dr, trav soc, adm des aff, comp, commun soc, hôtel-tour, fin-rel int.

*Universidad INCCA de Colombia, Carrera 13 No. 24-15, Bogotá. *1955*
Tél: 28-65-200. Télex: 42531 incca co
P : éd, éco agr, éco des aff, dr, psyc, gé ind, gé des systèmes, gé alim, méc.

Universidad La Gran Colombia, Avenida Bolívar 7-46, Bogotá. *1951*
Tél: 2438047
P : éd, arc, comp, dr, éco, gé civ, dr, éco (Armenia).

Universidad de La Sabana, Calle 70 No. 11-79, Bogotá.
Télex: 42574 inald co
P: éd, adm des aff, commun soc, arts plast, ba, psyc, dr.

Universidad de La Salle, Calle 11 No. 1-47, Bogotá. *1964*
Tél: 2830900
P : éd, adm des aff, adm agr, bibl, éco, gé civ, gé alim, élec, gé sani, phil-let, optom, trav soc, arc, comp publ, stat, vét, zoo.

Universidad Libre de Colombia, Carrera 6 No. 8-54, Bogotá. *1923*
Tél: 2869466
P : éd, dr, comp publ, mét, gé ind.
SECCIONAL BARRANQUILLA, Calle 46 No. 48170, Barranquilla. *1956*
Tél: 0315801
P : dr, méd.
SECCIONAL CALI, Diagonal 37A No. 3-29, Cali.
Tél: 0587161
P : adm des aff, comp publ, dr, méd.
SECCIONAL CÚCUTA, Avenida 4a No. 13-50, Cúcuta.
Tél: 0046351
P : éd, comp, dr.
SECCIONAL PEREIRA, Carrera 7a No. 40-03, Pereira.
Tél: 0066024
P : dr, éco.
SECCIONAL SOCORRO, Calle 16 No. 14-08,

Socorro.
Tél: 0072639
P : éd.
Universidad de Los Andes, Carrera 1 E No. 18-A-10, Bogotá.   *1948*
Tél: 2437474. Télex: 42343 unand co
P : arc, adm des aff, éco, math, phy, lang mod, bactériologie, biol, microbiol, psyc, anth, pol, gé civ, élec, méc, gé ind, gé des systèmes, phil-let, dr.
Universidad Mariana, Calle 18 No. 34-104, Pasto (Nariño).   *1967*
Tél: 0033616
P : éd, comp, inf, trav soc.
Universidad de Medellín, Carrera 87 No. 30-65 Los Alpes (Belen), Medellín (Antioquia).
                                                 1950
Tél: 2383906
P : dr, éco ind, adm des aff, comp publ, gé civ, stat.
Universidad Metropolitana, Carrera 42F No. 75B-169, Barranquilla (Atlántico).   *1973*
P : bactériologie, inf, phil-let, physio, méd,

nutr-diét, dent, psyc, trav soc.
*Universidad Pontificia Bolivariana, Calle 52 No. 40-88, Medellín (Antioquia).   *1936*
Tél: 2497199. Télex: 65047 upb co
P : éd, arc-urb, dr, gé ch, élec, méc, électro, socio, trav soc, commun soc, phil-let, phil, théol, dess, méd, adm des aff.
*Universidad de San Buenaventura, Calle 73 No. 10-45, Bogotá.   *1715, 1882, 1964*
Tél: 2354942
P : éd, phil, théo; éd, dr, comp, éco, gé des systèmes, arc (Cali); éd, psyc, socio, gé des systèmes (Medellín).
Universidad Santiago de Cali, Calle 5, Carrera 62, Cali (Valle del Cauca).
Tél: 0515342
P : éd, adm des aff, comp publ, dr.
*Universidad de Santo Tomás, Carrera 9a No. 51-23, Bogotá.   *1580, 1965*
Tél: 2110085
P : éd, gé civ, élec, éco, adm, dr, socio, psyc, phil-sc relig, comp; éco, arc, dent, dr, comp publ (Bucaramanga).

OTHER INSTITUTIONS—AUTRES INSTITUTIONS
Technical Education—Enseignement Technique

Centro Educativo de Computos y Sistemas «CEDESISTEMAS», Calle 54 No. 45-29, Medellín (Antioquia).   *1976*
Tél: 2424680
Centro de Investigaciones y Recreación Dirigida «CIRDI», Carrera 19 No. 75-86, Bogotá. *1972*
Tél: 2110262
Centro Nacional de la Construcción «SENA», Carrera 18A No. 2-18 sur, Bogotá.
Tél: 2463647
Colegio Mayor de Bolívar, Calle de la Factoría 35-95, Cartagena (Bolívar).   *1945*
Tél: 0044060
P : éd, techn-dess arc, sec, trad, ét soc.
Colegio Mayor de Cultura Popular del Cauca, Calle 5 No. 4-33, Popayán.   *1945*
Tél: 0023562
P : dess arc.
Corporación Academia Tecnológica de Colombia, Calle 55 No. 41-10, Medellín (Antioquía)
Tél: 2399089
Corporación de Educación del Norte del Tolima «COREDUCACIÓN», Casa de los Virreyas (Calle el Retiro esq. Calle de las Trampas), Honda.
Tel: 0003266
Corporación Educativa de Administración y Finanzas de Nariño, Carrera 26 No. 14–83, Nariño.

Tel: 0032322
Corporación Educativa Centro Superior de Cali, Calle 14 Norte No. 6-26 y Cra. 6 No. 8-49, Cali.
Tél: 0615816
P : adm des aff, comp gé ind, sec.
Corporación Educativa «ESUMER», Calle 76 No. 80–126, Carretera al Mar, Medellín (Antioquia).   *1964*
Tél: 2344259
Corporación Educativa-Instituto de Educación Empresarial «IDEE», Avenida la Norte No. 3N-27, Cali (Valle del Cauca).
Tél: 0813940
P : techn adm.
Corporación Escuela de Administración de Empresas «EAE», Carrera 34 No. D29-09, Cali (Valle del Cauca).   *1969*
Tél: 0541856
P : adm des aff.
Corporación Tecnológica de Ciencias Empresariales, Calle 36 No. 1712, Bogotá.
P : com.
Corporación de Estudios Tecnológicos Norte del Valle, Calle 10a No. 3-95, Cartago (Valle).
                                                 1971
Tél: 2481223
P : comp, adm agr.
Corporación Institute Colombo-Aléman para la formación Tecnológica, Carrara 52 No. 218–

85, Bogota.
Tél: 6760257
P : com ext, adm des aff ind.
Corporación Tecnológica de Bogotá, Carrera 21 No. 54-85, Bogotá.
Tél: 2481223
Corporación Tecnológica Industrial Colombiana, Calle 13 No. 65B-21, Bogotá.
Tél: 2606477
Corporación Tecnológica de Ciencias Empresariales, Calle 36 No. 17-12, Bogotá.
Tél: 2879421
P : com.
Corporación Tecnológica de Santander, Carrera 30 No. 53-16, Bucaramanga (Santander).
Tél: 0372949
Escuela Colombiana de Mercadotecnia, Calle 56 No. 46-39, Medellín (Antioquia). *1970*
Tél: 2399854
Escuela Nacional del Deporte, Calle 9 No. 34-01, Cali (Valle).
Tél: 0586764
P : phys.
Escuela Tributaria e Tecnologías de Colombia, Calle 62 No. 49-67, Medellín (Antioquia). *1975*
Tél: 2543077
Fundación Centro de Estudios Superiores «María Goretti», Avenida de Las Américas, Pasto (Nariño).
Tél: 0035357
P : techn.
Fundación Educativa de Estudios Superiores, Calle 63 No. 3-45, Bogotá.
Tél: 2359806
Fundación Instituto Tecnológico «CONFENALCO», Cartagena (Bolívar).
Tél: 0620889
Fundación Tecnológica «Antonio de Arevalo», Calle de La Moneda No. 7-122, Bolívar (Cartagena).
Tél: 0647082
Fundación Tecnológico del Área Andina, Calle 71 No. 13-21, Bogotá.
Tél: 2489054
P : adm de la constr, tec alim, mine.
Fundación Tecnológica Politécnico Nacional, Calle 34A No. 76-35, Medellín (Antioquia)
Tél: 2503481
Instituto Central Femenino, Calle 50 No. 41-55, Medellín (Antioquia).

Tél: 2393756
techn éd.
Instituto Superior de Ciencias Sociales y Económico-Familiares «ICSEF», Calle 70 No. 13-12, Bogotá. *1971*
Tél: 2483309
Instituto Superior de Educación Rural «ISER», Carrera 8 No. 8-155, Pamplona (Norte de Santander). *1956*
Tél: 0002597
Instituto Tecnológico «Pascual Bravo», Apartado aéreo 6821, Transversal 73 No. 73A-226, Medellín (Antioquica). *1938, 1950*
Tél: 2345082
Instituto Tecnológico de Administración y Economía, Calle 35 No. 981, Bucaramanga (Santander). *1972*
Tél: 0321885
Instituto Tecnológico Colombiano de Incolda, Avenida Guadalupe No. 1B-71, Cali (Valle).
Tél: 0514322
Instituto Tecnológico de Electrónica y Comunicaciones «ITEC», Transversal 49 No. 105–84, Bogotá.
Tél: 2536040
Politécnico Colombiano «Jaime Isaza Cadavid», Avenida Las Vegas Calle 10 No. 48-85, El Poblado, Medellín (Antioquia). *1964*
Tél: 2665700
Section à : Ríonegro.
Politécnico Grancolombiano, Calle 57 Carrera 3 Este, Bogotá.
Tél: 2126064
Politécnico «Marco Fidel Suárez», Carrera 49 No. 52-29, Bello (Antioquía).
Tél: 2751821
Servicio Nacional de Aprendizaje «SENA», Calle 52 No. 2bis-15, Cali (Valle del Cauca).
Tél: 0467198
P : topog.
Tecnológico «INPI», Calle 67 No. 5-27, Bogotá.
Tél: 2110928
P : éd spéc, thér lang.
Unidades Tecnológicas de Santander, Apartado aéreo 899, Calle 10 No. 28-77, Bucaramanga (Santander). *1963, 1986*
Tél: 0358366

Egalement 60 Institutions d'enseignement professionnel de niveau moyen.

Asociación Colombiana de Universidades

Les universités colombiennes sont des institutions officielles ou privées, autonomes, jouissant de la personnalité juridique, et gouvernées par leurs propres statuts, lesquels sont élaborés en fonction des normes de la Constitution et des lois.

Le Congrès national des universités, réuni à Bogotá au mois de décembre 1957, décida de créer l'Association colombienne des universités comme organisme autonome et permanent, jouissant de la personnalité juridique, et constitué par les universités officielles et privées du

pays légalement reconnues, conformément à l'esprit et aux buts exprimés dans l'acte de fondation.

Publications: ASCUN Boletín informativo (mensuelle); Mundo universitario (trimestrielle).

The universities of Colombia are autonomous bodies, and are either official or private institutions. They are governed by their own statutes, which have been drawn up according to the Constitution and laws of the country. The national congress of universities, which met in Bogotá in December 1957, decided to form the Association of Colombian universities as a permanent autonomous organization which, under the terms of its act of foundation, comprises the official universities and the legally organized private universities.

Publications: ASCUN Boletín informativo (monthly); Mundo universitario (quarterly).

Directeur exécutif: R.P. Alfonso Borrero Cabal, S.J.

Secrétaire général: Jorge Rivadeneira Vargas.

Carrera 10 No. 88-45, Apartado aéreo 012300, Bogotá.

Tél: 2361424

Instituto Colombiano para el Fomento de la Educación Superior (ICFES)

L'Institut colombien pour le développement de l'enseignement supérieur (ICFES) est un établissement public rattaché au Ministère de l'éducation nationale; il assiste le pouvoir exécutif dans l'exercice des fonctions qui, de par la Constitution, lui incombent en matière d'enseignement supérieur.

Ses principales fonctions sont, notamment: d'établir des normes réglementaires en ce qui concerne l'enseignement supérieur, le contrôle et la surveillance des institutions qui composent le système; de promouvoir le développement de l'enseignement dans les domaines de la recherche, des ressources, des services consultatifs et du perfectionnement des enseignants; d'appliquer les accords ou traités internationaux relatifs à la reconnaissance des grades et diplômes d'enseignement supérieur obtenus à l'étranger; d'autoriser la création et la mise sur pied des programmes correspondant aux différents types d'enseignement; et, de façon générale, de veiller au respect des règles régissant l'enseignement supérieur sous tous ses aspects.

The Colombian Institute for the Development of Higher Education (ICFES) is attached to the Ministry of Education which it assists in its work in matters concerning higher education.

Its principal functions are, notably: to establish statutory standards concerning higher education and the control and supervision of the institutions within the system; to promote development in the fields of research, resources, consultative services and the proficiency of academic staff; to apply the international agreements regarding the recognition of degrees and diplomas obtained abroad; to authorize the creation and setting up of the various programmes of study; and, in general, to see that the regulations governing higher education in all its aspects are respected.

Directeur: Galo Burbano (e).

Calle 17 No. 3-40 ó A.A., 6319 Bogotá.

Tél: 281-9311

Federación Universitaria Nacional – FUN
Apartado nacional 7503, Cuan No. 12110, Bogotá, D.E.

Instituto Colombiano de Especialización Técnica en el Exterior – ICETEX
Apartado aéreo 57-35, Bogotá, D.E.
Tél: 286-5666

Servicio Universitario Mundial (WUS)
Apartado aéreo 45057, Bogotá, D.E.
Tél: 446-336

Unión Nacional de Estudiantes Colombianos – UNEC (IUS)
Apartado aéreo 2168, Bogotá, D.E.

Equipos Intelectuales de Colombia (Pax Romana)
c/o P. Eugenio Saldarriaga, Calle 54 No. 38-29, Medellín.

World Union of Jewish Students (WUS)
Correspondant: 89 Chaussee De Vleurgat, 1050 Brussels (Belgium).
Tél: (2) 647-7279. Télex: 2065

*

Ministerio de Educación Nacional
Bogotá, D.E.
Tél: 222-4903. Fax: 222-0324. Télex: 42456 sgmen co

Comisión Nacional Colombiana de Cooperación con la Unesco
Ministerio de Educación Nacional, Bogotá, D.E.
Tél: 222-4691. Fax: 222-0324. Télex: 42456 sgmen co

PEOPLE'S REPUBLIC OF THE CONGO
REPUBLIQUE POPULAIRE DU CONGO

*Université Marien Ngouabi, B.P. 69, Brazzaville. *1971*
Tél: 81 24-36. Télex: 5331 kg
F : let-hum, sc, dr, éco.
I : éd, sa, phys, dév rur, gestion; péd (Loubomo).
E: adm-magistracy, te-c.
Fédération nationale de la Jeunesse estudiantine —FENAJEST (IUS)
B.P. 855, Brazzaville.

Télex: 5210

*

Ministère de l'Enseignement secondaire et supérieur
B.P. 493, Brazzaville.
Tél: 81 24-60
Commission nationale congolaise pour l'Unesco
B.P. 493, Brazzaville.
Tél: 81 19-86

COSTA RICA
COSTA RICA

UNIVERSITIES—UNIVERSITES

Public Institutions—Etablissements publics

*Universidad de Costa Rica, Ciudad Universitaria «Rodrigo Facio», San Pedro de Montes de Oca, San José. *1843, 1940*
Tél: 25-55-55. Télex: 2544 unicori
F : soc, ing-arc, arts-let, sc, sc de sa.
Ce : ét gén.
CENTRO REGIONAL SAN REMÓN, Alajuela.
CENTRO REGIONAL, TURRIALBA, Cartago.
CENTRO REGIONAL GUANACASTE, Liberia.
CENTRO REGIONAL LIMÓN, Limón.
Universidad Estatal a Distancia, Ap. 2 de Plaza González Viquez, San José. *1977*
Tél: 24-16-89. Télex: 3003 uned cr
D : sc nat, soc, éco, éd, hum, math, comp-adm.
CENTRO REGIONAL SAN JOSÉ, San José.
CENTRO REGIONAL SAN ISIDRO DEL GENERAL.
CENTRO REGIONAL DEL SUR, Ciudad Neilly.

CENTRO REGIONAL SIQUIRRES, Limón.
CENTRO REGIONAL PUNTARENAS, Puntarenas.
CENTRO REGIONAL ALAJUELA, Alajuela.
CENTRO REGIONAL SAN CARLOS, Ciudad Quesada.
CENTRO REGIONAL PALMARES, Alajuela.
CENTRO REGIONAL OROTINA, Alajuela.
Universidad Nacional, Apartado 86, Heredia. *1973*
Tél: 37-63-63. Télex: 7550 unavi cr
F : phil-let, soc, géosc-mar, sc, exactes-nat, sc de sa-vét.
Ce : ét gén.
Instituto Tecnológico de Costa Rica, Apartado 159, Cartago. *1971*
Tél: 51-55-33. Télex: 51-53-33
D: ing, inft, agr-for, adm.

Private Institutions—Etablissements privés

*Universidad Autónoma de Centro América, Apartado postal 7637, San José. *1976*

Tél: 23-58-22. Télex: 2907
D: adm des aff, adm publ, comp, banc,

resources hum, gé ind, gé adm, inf, arc ba, dr, éco, soc, pol, rel int, rel publ, dess, phil, géog, hist, hum, éd, méd, mus, jour, théo cath.

Universidad Adventista de Centro América, Caretera a Utuquís, Alajuela.   *1986*

Universidad Internacional de las Américas, Calle 23 entre Avenida Central y la, San José.   *1986* Tél: 33-5304. Fax: 506-223216 F: adm des aff, com int, dr, éd, gé des systèmes,

gé ind, Anglaise, tour.
CENTRO REGIONAL, San Isidro de El General.

Universidad Latinoamericana de Ciencias y Tecnología, Apartado 10235, 1000 San José.
                                               1988

Universidad Panamericana, Calle 23 entre avenida Central y la, Apartado 886, 1002 San José.   *1988*

OTHER INSTITUTIONS—AUTRES INSTITUTIONS

Professional Education—Enseignement professional

Centro Agronómico Tropical de Investigación y Enseñanza, Turrialba.   *1942, 1973* agr-zoo.

Colegio Universitario de Alajuela CUNA, Apartado postal 229, Alajuela.

Colegio Universitario de Cartago CUC, Apartado postal 422, Cartago.

Colegio Universitario de Puntarenas CUP, Puntarenas.   *1980*

Escuela Centroamericana de Ganadería, Apartado postal 7, Atenas, Alajuela.   *1969* élev.

Escuela Superior de Administración de Negocios,

Apartado postal 3510, San José.
adm des aff.

Instituto de Tecnología Administrativa, Apartado postal 1900, San José.   *1980* adm.

Instituto Superior de Administración de Empresas, Apartado postal 31, San Francisco de Dos Ríos, San José.   *1972, 1978* Tél: 21-42-67

Instituto Técnico de Administración de Negocios, Apartado postal 1380, Barrio Escalante, San José.   *1968* Tél: 25-58-78

Asociación Costarricense de Mujeres Universitarias (IFUW)
Apartado 311, San Pedro de Montes de Oca, San José.

Servicio Universitario Mundial (WUS)
Apartado 144, Heredia.
Tél: 35-30-46. Télex: 7562 cidsa cr

Federación de Estudiantes Universitarios de Costa Rica—FEUCR (IUS)
Apartado 30, Ciudad Universitaria Rodrigo Facio, San José.
Télex: 3011 cosuca cr

Juventud Universitaria Católica (Pax Romana)
Apartado 2715, Casa Cural de San Pedro en San Pedro de Montes de Oca, San José.

Movimiento Estudiantil Cristiano de Costa Rica (WSCF)
Edly Hall Reid, Apartado 2773, San José.

Tél: 33-62-05
Jovenes Costarricenses pro Naciones Unidas (ISMUN)
Apartado postal 4699, San José.

World Union of Jewish Students (WUJS)
Correspondant: 89 Chaussee De Vieurgat, 1050 Brussels (Belgium).
Tél: (2) 647-7279. Télex: 20625

*

Ministerio de Educación Pública
Boîte postale 10087, 1000 San José.
Tél: 23-16-66

Comisión Costarricense de Cooperación con la Unesco
Ministerio de Educación Pública, San José.
Tél: 24-43-20. Télex: 2107. Cables: comisión unesco relaciones san josé

COTE D'IVOIRE
COTE D'IVOIRE

UNIVERSITIES—UNIVERSITES

*Université nationale de Côte d'Ivoire, B.P.V. 34, Abidjan. (M. le Recteur). *1964* Tél: 4390-00. Télex: 23469 rectu ci

F : dr, éco, sc, méd, let-hum, phar.
I : dent.

OTHER INSTITUTIONS—AUTRES INSTITUTIONS
Technical Education—Enseignement technique

Institut national supérieur de l'Enseignement technique, B.P.V. 79, Abidjan. (M. le Directeur). *1975*
Tél: 44-42-88. Télex: 2288
E : gé de spécialités.
E (sup.) : ing, comp.
I : techn ind, techn tertiaire.
I (sup.) : comp, inft, sec.

Institut national de la Jeunesse et des Sports, B.P.V. 803, Abidjan 04. *1961*
Tél: 35-52-53
Centre d'Animation et de Formation à l'Action culturelle, B.P.V. 39, Abidjan. *1984*
Tél: 29-20-00
Académie des Sciences et Techniques de la Mer, B.P.V. 158, Abidjan. *1986*

Professional Education—Enseignement professionnel

Ecole nationale d'Administration, B.P.V. 20, Abidjan. *1960*
Tél: 41-52-25
Ecole nationale supérieure agronomique, B.P. 35, Km 8 Route d'Adzopé, Abidjan 08. *1965*
Tél: 37-17-16
Ecole nationale supérieure de Statistique et d'Economie appliquée, B.P. 3, Abidjan 08. *1968*
Tél: 44-08-40
Ecole normale supérieure, B.P. 18, Abidjan 08. *1964*

Ecole supérieure des Postes et Télécommunications, Abidjan 18. *1967*
Tél: 35-67-17
Ecole nationale supérieure des Travaux publics, B.P. 148, Abidjan. *1963, 1967*
Tél: 64-01-00. Télex: 22606 ensipa ci
Institut national des Arts, B.P.V. 39, Abidjan. *1971*
Institut national de la Formation sociale, B.P. 2625, Abidjan 01. *1978*
Tél: 44-16-72

Union nationale des Etudiants et Elèves de Côte d'Ivoire—UNECI
B.P. 8018, Abidjan-Cocody.
Association chrétienne des Elèves et Etudiants protestants de Côte d'Ivoire (WSCF)
B.P. 05, Abidjan 08.

*

Ministère de l'Education nationale chargé de l'Enseignement secondaire et supérieur
B.P. V120, Abidjan 01.
Tél: 32-06-88. Télex: 23377 mineduca abidjan
Commission nationale ivoirienne pour l'Unesco
Ministère de l'Education nationale chargé de l'Enseignement secondaire et supérieur, B.P. V.120, Abidjan 01.
Tél: 32-48-25. Télex: 22151 unesco ci

CUBA
CUBA

UNIVERSITIES—UNIVERSITES

Universidad de Camagüey, Carretera de Circun-
valación, Camagüey.　　　　　　　　*1969*
Tél: 95119. Télex: 31201 univers
F : agr-zoo, hum, techn, sc, sc méd.
I : éco, éd.
*Universidad de La Habana, L y San Lázaro,
Ciudad de La Habana.　　　　　　　*1728*
Tél: 73231. Télex: 511277 esc matematicas uh
F : agr-zoo, hum, techn, sc, sc méd.
I : éco, éd.
*Universidad Central de Las Villas, Carretera de

Camajuane Km. 10, Santa Clara, Las Villas.
　　　　　　　　　　　　　　1949, 1952
Tél: 4581/9. Télex: 41130 univ las villas
F : agr-zoo, hum, techn, sc, sc méd.
I : éco, éd.
*Universidad de Oriente, Avenida Patricio
Lumumba s/n, Santiago de Cuba, Oriente.
　　　　　　　　　　　　　　1947, 1959
Tél: 33011. Télex: 061-145
F : agr-zoo, hum, techn, sc, sc méd.
I : éco, éd.

OTHER INSTITUTIONS—AUTRES INSTITUTIONS

Centro Nacional de Investigaciones Científicas,
Avenida 25, Calle 158, Reparto Cubanacán, La
Habana.
Tél: 219587
Centro Universitario de Holguín, Miró No. 125 e/
Frexes y Aguilera, Holguín.　　　　*1976*
Centro Universitario de Matanzas, Calle Medio
No. 100 e/Zaragoza y Manzaneda, Matanzas.
　　　　　　　　　　　　　　1976
Tél: 2612
Centro Universitario de Pinar del Río, Martí No.
270 esq. a 27 de Noviembre, Pinar del Río.
　　　　　　　　　　　　　　1976
Instituto Superior Agrícola de Ciego de Avila,
Ciego de Avila.　　　　　　　　*1978*
Tél: 25702. Télex: 32146
Instituto Superior de Arte, Calle 120 No. 1110 e/
9na y 13 Cubanacán, Ciudad de La Habana.
　　　　　　　　　　　　　　1976
Instituto Superior de Ciencias Agropecuarias,
Km. 10 Carretera de Manzanillo, Bayamo,
Granma.　　　　　　　　　　　*1976*
**Instituto Superior de Ciencias Agropecuarias de
La Habana**, Quinta de los Molinos-Avenida
Salvador Allende y Luaces, La Habana.　*1976*
**Instituto Superior de Ciencias Médicas de
Camagüey**, Hospital Provincial y Politécnico de
la Salud, Camagüey 1.　　　　　　*1981*
Tél: 8536
**Instituto Superior de Ciencias Médicas de La
Habana**, 146 No. 2504 e/31 y 25 Cubanacán,
Ciudad de La Habana.　　　　　　*1976*
**Instituto Superior de Ciencias Médicas de Villa
Clara**, Arias No. 9 Hospital Provincial e/Doble

Via y Circunvalación, Sta. Clara, Villa Clara.
　　　　　　　　　　　　　　1976
Tél: 27820
**Instituto Superior de Ciencias Médicas de San-
tiago de Cuba**, Avenida de las Américas e/1,
Santiago de Cuba.　　　　　　　*1976*
Tél: 6679
**Instituto Superior de Cultura Física «Manuel
Fajardo»**, Sta. Catalina e/Primelles y Boyeros,
Ciudad de La Habana.　　　　　　*1976*
Tél: 406171
Instituto Superior Minero Metalúrgico de Moa,
Moa, Holguín.　　　　　　　　*1976*
Instituto Superior Pedagógico, Carretera de
Circunvalación, Camagüey.　　　　*1976*
**Instituto Superior Pedagógico de Lenguas
Modernas**, Ciudad Libertad, Marianao,
Ciudad de La Habana.　　　　　　*1976*
**Instituto Superior Pedagógico de la Educación
Técnica y Profesional**, Avenida Vantroi y
Rancho Boyeros, Ciudad La Habana.　*1976*
Instituto Superior Pedagógico de Guantánamo,
Guantánamo.
Instituto Superior Pedagógico de Holguín, Calle
Quinta e/ Maceo y Hospital, Holguín.　*1976*
Instituto Superior Pedagógico de La Habana, La
Habana.
Instituto Superior Pedagógico de Las Villas,
Universidad Central, Carretera de Camaguani
Km. 10, Santa Clara, Villa Clara.　　*1976*
Instituto Superior Pedagógico de Manzanillo,
Veguitas, Manzanillo, Granma.　　　*1976*
Instituto Superior Pedagógico de Matanzas, Calle
Rio e/ Matanzas y Medio, Matanzas.　*1976*

Instituto Superior Pedagógico de Pinar del Río, Colon Rpto. Llamalari (Antigua Sec. Básica «Frank Pais»), Pinar del Río.   *1976*
Instituto Superior Pedagógico de Santiago de Cuba, Avenida Patricio Lumumba s/n, Santiago de Cuba.   *1976*
Instituto Superior Politécnico «José A. Echeverría», CUJAE, Marianao, Ciudad de La

Habana.   *1976*
Tél: 200641. Télex: 511153 ccft cujac
Instituto Superior de Servicio Exterior, 22 e/Ira y 3ra, Miramar, Ciudad de La Habana.   *1976*
Tél: 25097
Instituto Superior Técnico de Cienfuegos, Cienfuegos.
Tél: 21521. Télex: 042141

Federación Estudiantil Universitaria—FEU (IUS)
Calle 23, No. 502 bajos, entre GyH Vedado, La Habana.
Télex: 511843 oclae cu
Movimiento Estudiantil Cristiano de Cuba (WSCF)
Calle 6 no. 273 E/11 y 13 Vedado, Ciudad, Habana 4.

*

Dirección de Organismos Internaccionales
Ministerio de Relaciones Exteriores, Calle 5a, entre G & H, Vedado, La Habana.
Tél: 305031. Télex: 511122
Ministerio de Educación Superior
Vice-Ministerio de Educación Superior, Calle 23 no. 565 Vedado, Ciudad de La Habana.
Tél: 36655. Télex: 511253 prov mined
Comisión Nacional Cubana de la Unesco
Avenida Kohly 151, Nuevo Vedado, La Habana.
Tél: 36161. Cables: concurn habana

CYPRUS
CHYPRE

Higher Technical Institute, Athalassa Area, Nicosia.   *1968*
Tel: 494454
D : *elec, civ eng, mec, mar eng, comp.*
Pedagogical Academy of Cyprus, Nicosia.   *1959*
School of Nursing, Nicosia.   *1955*

Hotel and Catering Institute, P.O. Box 4812, Nicosia.   *1969*
Telex: 2850 xenia cy
Cyprus Forestry College, Prodromos, Limassol.   *1951*
Mediterranean Institute of Management (M.I.M.), P.O. Box 536, Nicosia.   *1976*

Pancyprian Federation of Students and Young Scientists—POFNE (IUS)
Achilleos Kyrou 7/23, P.O. Box 4126, Nicosia.
Telex: 3155 printco cy. Cables: pofne nicosia
United Nations Association of Cyprus (Youth Section) (ISMUN)
P.O. Box 1508, Nicosia.

*

Ministry of Education
Odos Gr. Afxentiou, Cooperation Central Banking Building, Nicosia.
Tel: 2403101. Telex: 5760 mineduc cy
Cyprus National Commission for Unesco
Ministry of Foreign Affairs, Nicosia.
Tel: 40-2493. Fax: 445021. Telex: 2266. Cables: minforeign nicosia

CZECHOSLOVAKIA
TCHECOSLOVAQUIE

UNIVERSITIES AND TECHNICAL UNIVERSITIES – UNIVERSITES ET UNIVERSITES TECHNIQUES

*Univerzita Komenského [U. Komensky], Safárikovo nám 6, Bratislava. (M. le Secrétaire).
1919
Tél: 580-41/5
F : phil, méd, dr, phar, nat, péd, phys; méd (Martin).
Univerzita Palackého [U. Palacky], Krížkovského 10, Olomouc. *1573, 1946*
Tél: 22441
F : méd, phil, nat, péd.
*Univerzita Jana Evangelisty Purkyně, A. Nováka 1, 60177, Brno. *1919*
Tél: 750-371. Cables: bljep brno
F : dr, phil, nat, méd, péd.
*Univerzita Karlova [U. Charles], Ovocný trh 5, Praha 1. *1348*
Tél: 228-441/8
F : dr, méd, méd-péd, hyg, phil, math-phy, nat, péd, phys, jour; méd (Plzeň, Hradec Králové), phar (Hradec Králové).
*Univerzita Pavla Jozefa Safárika, Srobárova 57,

Košice. *1959*
Tél: 226-08
F : méd, nat, péd, dr; phil, péd (Prešově).
*Ceské vysoké učení technické v Praze [E. technique sup. tchèque], Zikova 4, Praha 6. *1707*
Tél: 332
F : méc, gé civ, élec, phy nucl & app.
*Slovenská vysoká škola technická v Bratislave [E. technique sup. slovaque], Gottwaldovo nám. 50, Bratislava. *1938*
Tél: 53740
F : méc, gé civ, élec, ch.
Vysoká škola technická [E. technique sup.], Švermova 9, Košice. *1937, 1952*
Tél: 399-063-075
F : méc, mét, mine, élec.
Vysoké učení technické, Opletalova 6, Brno.
1899
Tél: 25831. Télex: 62536 vutck c
F : méc, gé civ, élec; techn (Gottwaldov).

OTHER INSTITUTIONS – AUTRES INSTITUTIONS
Technical Education – Enseignement technique

Vysoká škola chemicko-technologická v Praze [E. sup. de Chimie et de Technologie], Suchbátarova 5, Praha 6. *1953*
Tél: 332. Télex: 122744 vsch c
F : techn ch, techn-bioch-alim, gé ch, comb-hyd.
Vysoká škola chemicko-technologická [E. sup. de Chimie et de Technologie], Leninovo nám. 656, Pardubice. *1950*
Tél: 25111
Vysoká škola strojní a elektrotechnická [E. sup. des Machines et de l'Electricité], Nejedlého sady 14, Plzeň. *1950*
Tél: 36881. Télex: 154292 tech c

F : méc, élec.
Vysoká škola strojní a textilní [E. sup. des Machines et des Textiles], Hálkova 6, Liberec.
1953
Tél: 25441/5
F : méc, tex.
*Vysoká škola báňská [E. sup. des Mines], Třida, Vitezného února, Ostrava-Poruba. *1849*
Tél: 424111. Télex: 52568 vsbos c
F : mine-géol, mét, méc-mine.
Vysoká škola dopravy a spojov [E. sup. des Transports], Moyzesova 20, Zilina. *1952*
Tél: 234-08
F : trans-éco, méc-élec.

Professional Education—Enseignement professionnel

Vysoká škola zemědělská [E. sup. d'Agriculture], Zemědělská 1, Brno. *1919*
Tél: 604. Télex: 62489 vzs c
F : for, agr, éco.

*Vysoká škola pol'nohospodárska, Nábrežie mládeže, Nitra. *1939, 1946, 1952*
Tél: 23501/5. Télex: 98445
F : éco, agr, méc.

Vysoká škola zemědělská, Kamýcká ul., No. 129, Suchdol, Praha 6. *1906, 1952*
Tél: 32-36-40. Télex: 122323 vszp c
F : éco, agr, méc; éco (Ceské Budějovice).

Vysoká škola lesnícka a dreváska [E. sup. des Forêts et du Bois], Stúrova 4, Zvolen.
1946, 1952
Tél: 635. Télex: 72267 vsld c
F : for, ind du bois.

Vysoká škola veterinární [E. sup. vétérinaire], Palackého 1, Brno. *1918*
Tél: 7110. Télex: 63039

Vysoká škola veterinárska, Komenského 73, Košice. *1949*
Tél: 32111. Télex: 77322 vsuke c

Vysoká škola ekonomická [E. sup. des Sciences économiques], Odbojárov 12, Bratislava. *1952*
Tél: 63067
F : éco-plan, éco-prod, com, adm.

Vysoká škola ekonomická, Nám. A. Zápotockého, Praha 3. *1952*
Tél: 2125111. Télex: 122310 vse c
F : éco-plan, éco-prod, com, adm.

Vysoká škola músických umění [E. sup. de Musique], Jeráskova 3, Bratislava. *1949, 1951*
Tél: 33-23-06
F : mus, théat.

Janáčkova akademie múzických umění [A. de Musique], Komenského nám. 6, Brno. *1947*
Tél: 26842

Akademie múzických umění, Smetanovo nábř 2, Praha 1. *1945, 1951*
Tél: 26-62-62
F : mus, théat, film-télévision.

Vysoká škola výtvarných umění [E. sup. d'Arts plastiques], Hviezdoslavovo nám. 18, Bratislava. *1949*
Tél: 33-24-31

Adademie výtvarných umění [A. d'Arts plastiques], U. Akademie 4, Praha 7. *1896, 1919*
Tél: 37-36-41

Vysoká škola umělecko-prumyslová [E. des Arts appliqués], Nám Krasnoarmějcu, Praha 1.
1946
Tél: 23-19-512

Teacher Training—Formation pédagogique

Pedagogická fakulta v Banské Bystrici, Tajovského 3, Banská Bystrica. *1964*
Tél: 345-45-59

Pedagogická fakulta y Českých Budějovicich, Jeronýmova 10, České Budějovice. *1964*

Pedagogická fakulta v Hradci Králové, Nám. I. Lenina 301, Hradec Králové. *1964*
Tél: 25226

Pedagogická fakulta v Nitře, Lomonosova 1, Nitra. *1964*

Tél: 73-59
Pedagogická fakulta v Ostravě, Dvořákova 7, Ostrava. *1964*
Tél: 245-51

Pedagogická fakulta v Plzni, Veleslavínova 42, Plzeň. *1964*

Pedagogická fakulta v Ústí nad Labem, Ceské mládeze 8, Ústí nad Labem. *1964*
Tél: 264-41

Le Syndicat des Travailleurs de l'Enseignement et de la Science de Tchécoslovaquie
Le Syndicat groupe parmi ses membres les enseignants de tous les degrés, ainsi que les professeurs de l'enseignement supérieur et les travailleurs des institutions éducatives et scientifiques.
The Czechoslovak Trade Union of Educational and Scientific Workers includes among its members the teachers in all types of schools, academic staff, scientists, and other persons employed in educational and learned institutions.
Nám. M. Gorkého 23, 112 82 Praha 1.
Télex: 122410 roh c

Czechoslovak Student Centre—CSC/CSUV (IUS)
Nám. M. Gorkého 24, 11647 Praha 1.
Cestovni Kancelar Mladeze [Youth and Student Travel Bureau]—CKM
Zitna Ulice 12, Praha 2.
Télex: 122299 ckmr c
Ecumenical Council of Churches in Czechoslovakia (WSCF)
Pavelvych open, Vitkova 13, 1500 Praha 5.

*

Czechoslovak Committee for Technical Assistance

Ministry of Foreign Trade (Trida Politických).
Veznu 20, Praha 1.
Télex: 121077 obza c
Ministère de Education, Karmelitska 7, 118 12
Praha 1.

Tél: 53-16-51. Télex: 121053 cms c
Commission tchécoslovaque pour l'Unesco
Valdstejnské nám. 1, Praha 1.
Tél: 53-91-51. Cables: unescoczechoslovak
prague

DENMARK
DANEMARK

UNIVERSITIES AND TECHNICAL UNIVERSITIES—
UNIVERSITES ET UNIVERSITES TECHNIQUES

*Aalborg Universitetscenter, Postbox 159, 9100
Aalborg. *1974*
Tel: (8) 15-91-11. Fax: 98102931. Telex: 69790
aub dk.
F : *arts, techn-nat, soc.*
D : *mec, civ eng.*
*Aarhus Universitet, Ndr. Ringgade 1, 8000
Aarhus C. *1928*
Tel: (6) 13-43-11
F : *med, nat, soc, theo, arts.*
Danmarks Ingeniørakademi København,
Bygning 101A, 2800 Lyngby. *1957*
Tel: (2) 88-22-22. Telex: 37529 dthia dk
F : *ch, mec, civ, elec.*
*Den Polytekniske Lareanstalt, Danmarks
tekniske Højskole[Technical U.], Bygning 101,
2800 Lyngby. *1829*

Tel: (2) 88-22-22. Telex: 37529 dthia dk
F : *sc, ch, mec, civ eng, elec.*
*Københavns Universitet, Nørregade 10, Post-
box 2177, 1017 København K. *1478*
Tel: (33) 91-08-28. Telex: unicop dk
F : *theo, med, arts, soc, nat.*
*Odense Universitet, Campusvej 55, 5230
Odense M. *1966*
Tel: (9) 15-86-00. Telex: 59918 oubibl dk
F : *med, arts, nat.*
S : *eco-bus.*
Roskilde Universitetscenter, Postbox 260, 4000
Roskilde. *1972*
Tel: (2) 75-77-11. Telex: 43158 rubibl dk
D : *arts, nat, soc.*
Ce : *commun, integrated ed, soc.*

OTHER INSTITUTIONS—AUTRES INSTITUTIONS

Technical Education—Enseignement technique

Ingeniørhøjskolen, Aarhus Teknikum, Dalgas
Avenue 2, 8000 Aarhus C.
Tel: (6) 13-62-11
Ingeniørhøjskolen, Esbjerg Teknikum, Ole
Rømersvej 3, 6700 Esbjerg.
Tel: (5) 12-76-66
Ingeniørhøjskolen, Haslev Teknikum, Braabyvej
45, 4690 Haslev.
Tel: (3) 69-14-00
Ingeniørhøjskolen, Helsingør Teknikum, Rasmus
Knudsensvej 50, 3000 Helsingør.
Tel: (2) 21-66-22
Ingeniørhøjskolen, Horsens Teknikum, Chr. M.

Østergaardsvej 4, 8700 Horsens.
Tel: (5) 62-88-11
Ingeniørhøjskolen, Københavns Teknikum,
Prinsesse Charlottesgade 38, 2200 København
N.
Tel: (33) 39-48-11
Ingeniørhøjskolen, Odense Teknikum, Niels
Bohr Allé 1, 5230 Odense M.
Tel: (9) 13-08-27
Ingeniørhøjskolen, Sønderborg Teknikum,
Voldgade 5, 6400 Sønderborg.
Tel: (4) 42-55-50

Professional Education—Enseignement professionnel

Arkitektskolen i Aarhus [S. of Architecture], Nørreport 20, 8000 Aarhus C. *1965*
Tel: (6) 13-08-22

Danmarks Biblioteksskole [S. of Librarianship], Birketinget 6, 2300 København S.
Also department at Aalborg.
Tel: (31) 58-60-66

Danmarks Farmaceutiske Højskole [S. of Pharmacy], Universitetsparken 2, 2100 København Ø. *1892*
Tel: (31) 37-08-50

Handelshøjskolen i Aarhus [Aarhus S. of Economics, Business Administration, and Modern Languages], Fuglesangs Allé 4, 8210 Aarhus V. *1939*
Tel: (6) 15-55-88

Handelshøjskolen i København [Copenhagen S. of Economics, Business Administration, and Modern Languages], Nansensgade 19, 1366 København K. *1917*
Tel: (33) 14-44-14
Also 9 affiliated schools in Aarhus and København.

Rigshospitalets Jordemoderskole, Afdelingen i København [S. of Midwifery], Rigshospitalet, afsnit 5014, Blegdamsveg 9, 2100 København.
Tel: (31) 38-66-33. Telex: 15784 rhblod dk
Also department at Aalborg.

Danmarks Journalisthøjskole [C. of Journalism], Halmstadgade 11, 8200 Aarhus N.
Tel: (6) 16-11-22

Det kongelige danske Kunstakademis, Arkitektskole [A. of Fine Arts, S. of Architecture], Kongens Nytorv 1, 1050 København K. *1754*
Tel: (1) 12-68-60

Det kongelige danske Kunstakademi, Billedkunstkole [A. of Fine Arts, S. of Painting, Sculpture and Graphic Arts], Kongens Nytorv 1, 1050 København K.
Tel: (31) 12-68-60

Nordjysk Musikkonservatorium [North Jutland A. of Music], Ryesgade 52, 9000 Aalborg.

Tel: (8) 12-77-44

Det jyske Musikkonservatorium [Jutland A. of Music], Fuglesangs Allé 26, 8210 Aarhus V. *1927*
Tel: (6) 15-53-80

Det fynske Musikkonservatorium [Funen A. of Music], Islandsgade 2, 5000 Odense.
Tel: (9) 11-06-63

Vestjysk Musikkonservatorium [West Jutland A. of Music], Islandsgade 50, 6700 Esbjerg.
Tel: (5) 12-61-00

Det kongelige danske Musikkonservatorium [A. of Music], Niels Brocks Gade 1, 1574 København V. *1867, 1947*
Tel: (31) 12-42-74

Den Sociale Højskole i Esbjerg, Storegade 182, 6705 Esbjerg Ø.
Tel: (5) 13-35-00

Den Sociale Højskole i København [S. of Social Work], Randersgade 10, 2100 København Ø.
Tel: (31) 42-46-01

Den Sociale Højskole i Odense, Campusvej 55, 5230 Odense M.
Tel: (9) 15-86-00

Den Sociale Højskole i Aarhus, Søndervangen 90, 8260 Viby J.
Tel: (6) 14-23-66

Aarhus Tandlagehøjskole [Dental C.], Vennelyst Boulevard, 8000 Aarhus C. *1958*

København Tandlagehøjskole [Dental C.], Nørre Allé 20, 2200 København N. *1886*
Tel: (31) 37-17-00

Den kongelige Verterinar- og Landbohøjskole [Veterinary and Agricultural U.], Bülowsvej 13, 1870 Frederiksberg C. *1856*
Tel: (1) 35-17-88

Socialpadagogisk Højskole [The Advanced Training S. of Social Pedagogues], Kastelsvej 60, 2100 København Ø.

Also 12 paramedical Schools and 33 Schools of Nursing.

Teacher Training—Enseignement pédagogique

Danmarks Larerhøjskole Emdrupborg [S. of Educational Studies], Emdrupvej 101, 2400 København NV. *1963*
Tel: (1) 69-66-33

Danmarks Højskole for Legemsøvelser [Physical Training Teachers' C.], Nørre Allé 51, 2200

København N.
Tel: (31) 39-25-56

Also 24 Teacher Training Colleges, 15 Schools of Social Pedagogics, and 25 Pre-school Teacher Training Colleges.

Rektorkollegiet/Conference of Danish Rectors
In Denmark, as in many other countries with

self-governing universities, a considerable development of the collaboration between the

universities and other institutions of university rank has become necessary, partly as a result of a demand for it by the Central Government.

Generally speaking, the Conference has no executive powers, but it may, and in certain cases is obliged to, make statements on matters of common interest to the institutions. A Council, consisting of the administrative heads of institutions of university rank, is concerned with administrative and technical matters.

The Secretariat of the Conference of Danish Rectors acts as a secretariat for the Conference and the Council.

Au Danemark, comme dans de nombreux pays où les universités sont autonomes, une intensification considérable de la coopération entre les universités et les autres établissements de rang universitaire est devenue nécessaire, en partie du fait de la pressante demande formulée à ce sujet par le Gouvernement central.

En général, la Conférence ne détient pas de pouvoirs exécutifs, mais elle a la possibilité, et dans certains cas l'obligation, de rédiger des rapports sur des problèmes revêtant pour les établissements un intérêt commun. Un Conseil, composé des chefs administratifs d'établissements de rang universitaire, s'occupe des questions administratives et techniques.

Le Secrétariat de la Conférence des recteurs danois sert de secrétariat pour la Conférence et le Conseil.

Chairman: Prof. Ove Nathan, Rector, University of Copenhagen.
Secretary: Ellen Hansen.
Frederiksholms Kanal 26, 1220 København K.
Tel: (33) 92-53-00. Fax: (33) 92-53-03. Telex: 16243 educ dk

Direktoratet for de videregående uddannelser
The Directorate is the executive unit of the Ministry of Education for relations with institutions of higher education and other institutions of education at the post-secondary level. The Directorate has four units, one dealing with matters concerning the administration of institutions for higher education, one dealing with various questions of education, one with budgeting and planning, and one with long-term planning and development.

The Directorate has established five advisory committees for the following fields: humanities, natural sciences, social sciences, health education and engineering.

La direction est l'organe exécutif du Ministère de l'éducation chargé des relations avec les institutions d'enseignement supérieur et les autres institutions d'enseignement de niveau post-secondaire. Elle comprend quatre divisions, une pour l'administration des institutions d'enseignement supérieur, une pour les problèmes divers de

l'éducation, une pour les questions budgétaires et la planification, et une pour la planification à long terme et le développement.

La Direction a créé cinq comités consultatifs pour les domaines suivants: sciences humaines, sciences naturelles, sciences sociales, enseignement médical et paramédical et formation des ingénieurs.

Frederiksholms Kanal 26, 1220 København K.
Tel: (33) 92-55-00

Statens Teknisk-videnskabelige Forskningsråd/ Danish Technical Research Council.
The purpose of the Council is to advise public authorities and institutions on public support for Danish scientific and industrial research, utilization of the research and the education of scientific personnel. The Council initiates actions on behalf of the government and supports, upon application, research projects, including purchase of special apparatus, further education of scientists, and publication of scientific papers.

Le Conseil danois pour la recherche technique a pour but de conseiller les pouvoirs publics et les institutions sur le soutien que doit apporter le secteur public à la recherche scientifique et industrielle danoise, à l'utilisation de la recherche et à la formation du personnel scientifique. Le Conseil entreprend des actions pour le compte du gouvernement et apporte, sur demande, son soutien aux projets de recherche, notamment pour l'achat d'équipements particuliers, le perfectionnement de la formation des chercheurs et la publication de rapports scientifiques.

Chairman: Erik Nilsson.
Holmens Kanal 7, 1060 København K.
Tel: (31) 11-43-00

Akademikernes Centralorganisation (AC)
The Central Organization of Academics AC is the central body for 21 organizations of graduates from universities and other institutions of higher education and it is concerned with the economic, social and educational interests of all sections of the population, including civil servants, teachers, and graduates in the professions.

There is no special organization for university teachers but the AC has a special committee which co-ordinates action and advises the Board of the AC on negotiations and other matters affecting university teachers and research workers.

L'AC est un organisme central regroupant 21 organisations de diplômés des universités et autres institutions d'enseignement supérieur; il veille aux intérêts, sur les plans économique, social et éducatif, de toutes les catégories de population, notamment les fonctionnaires, les enseignants et les diplômés des professions libérales.

Il n'existe pas d'organisation particulière pour les enseignants universitaires, mais l'AC dispose d'une commission spéciale qui donne ses avis au Conseil et coordonne son action pour les négociations et autres problèmes intéressant les enseignants universitaires et les chercheurs.
Nørre Voldgade 29, 1358 København K.
Tel: (33) 12-85-40

Planlaegningsrådet for forskningen/The Danish Council for Scientific Policy and Planning
Holmens Kanal 7, 1060 København K.
Tel: (31) 11-43-00. Fax: (31) 32-35-01. Telex: 15652 fs
Dansk Magisterforening (IAUPL)
Contact: 18 rue du Docteur Roux, 75015 Paris (France).
Tel: (33-1) 47-83-31-65
Kvindelige Akademikere (IFUW)
Chairman (Internat. Rel.) and Secretary: Mrs. Birgitte Weis Bentzon.
Springbanen 87, 2820 Gentofte.
World University Service
Noerrebrogade 66, Bygning B, 2 sal, 2200 København N.
Tel: (31) 35-87-88. Fax: 15850 wus dk. Cables: wuskomite copenhagen
Danske Studerendes Faellesraad—DSF-
Knabrostraede 3, 1210 København K.
Danmarks Internationale Studenterkomité—DIS
Skindergade 36, 1159 København K.

Scandinavian Student Travel Service— SSTS
51 Studiestrade, 1554 København V.
Academicum Catholicum (Pax Romana)
Jaegersborgvej 38, 2800 København-Lyngby.
Danmarks Kristne Studenterbevaegelse (WSCF)
Kirketjenesten i Danmark, Kløvermarksvej 4, 8200 Aarhus N.
Tel: (6) 16-26-55)
Internationalet Forum (ISMUN)
Knabrostraede 3, 3, 1210 København K.
Jødisk Studenterklub i Danmark (WUJS)
Contact: 89 Chaussee De Vleurgat, 1050, Brussels.
Tél: (2) 647-7279. Télex: 20625

*

Undervisningsministeriet (Ministry of Education)
Frederiksholms Kanal 26, 1220 København K.
Tel: (33) 92-53-00
Ministry of Education, International Relations Division
Nyhavn 38, 1051 København K.
Tel: (31) 92-50-00. Fax: (1) 95-55-47. Telex: 16243
Danish National Commission for Unesco
Vester Voldgade 117, 1552 København V.
Tel: (33) 92-52-16. Fax: (33) 92-54-92. Telex: 112-112
Danish International Developing Agency (DANIDA)
Amaliegade 7, 1256 København K.

DOMINICAN REPUBLIC
REPUBLIQUE DOMINICAINE

UNIVERSITIES—UNIVERSITES

*Universidad Autónoma de Santo Domingo, Ciudad Universitaria, Santo Domingo. (Sr. Secretario General). *1538*
Tél: 533-1694. Télex: 5460182
F : let-hum, sc, éco-soc, dr, ing-arc, méd, agr-vét.

Universidad Católica «Madre y Maestra», Apartado postal 822, Santiago. *1962*
Tél: 583-0441. Télex: 3461032
F : sc-adm, ing, sa.

Universidad «APEC», Apartado postal 59-2, Avenida Máximo Gómez 72, Santo Domingo. *1985*
Tél: 687-3181
F : adm, hum-sc.

Universidad Adventista Dominicana, Apartado postal 770, Sonador, Bonado. *1982*
D : sc, psyc, adm des entrep, théo, éd.

Universidad Católica de Santo Domingo, c/ Santo Domingo 3, La Julia, Santo Domingo. *1984*
F : théo, hum, commun soc, éd.

Universidad Central del Este, Apartado postal 512, Avenida Circunvalación, San Pedro de Macorís. *1971*
Tél: 529-3562
comp, adm des entrep, éco, sec, dr, agr, élec, méc, gé ind, vét, arc, sucre, gé civ, péd, méd, od, phar, nutr.

Universidad Colegio Dominicano de Estudios Profesionales, Prol. Independencia, Km. 9 1/2, Carretera Sánchez, Santo Domingo. *1985*
F : éco-soc, hum, sc-techn, jur, agr-vét, sa.

Universidad Dominicana O&M, Apartado postal 509, Avenida Independencia, Santo Domingo. *1978*

Universidad Eugenio María de Hostos, Avenida Abraham Lincoln 753, Santo Domingo. *1984*
Tél: 532-5881
F : sa, sc-techn, éco-adm, hum-soc.

Universidad Iberomericana, Apartado postal 1600, Avenida Francia 129, Santo Domingo. *1982*
F : arc-art, ét gén, éco, sa, agr.

Universidad Interamericana, Dr. Baez 4, Santo Domingo. *1982*
psyc, commun, rel publ, stat, socio, éd, inf, tour, adm agr, adm, sec, adm des entrep, dr.

Universidad Nacional Evangélica, Avenida Juan Pablo Duarte 110, Santiago. *1986*

Universidad Nacional Pedro Henríquez Ureña, Apartado postal 1423, Carretera Duarte Km. 6, Santo Domingo. *1967*
Tél: 562-6601. Telex: 3264535
F : sc, arc-art, agr, éco-soc, éd, jur-pol, sa, ing-techn.

Universidad Nordestana, Apartado postal 239, San Francisco de Macorís. *1978*
Tél: 588-3239
F : agr, éd, méd, éco-soc, sc.

Universidad Odontológica Dominicana, Prol. 27 de Febrero, Las Caobas, Santo Domingo. *1985*
od.

Universidad Tecnológica del Cibao, Apartado postal 401, Avenida Independencia esq., Juana Saltitopa, La Vega. *1986*
F : soc-hum, sc-techn, sa.

Universidad Tecnológica de Santiago, Apartado postal 21423, Avenida Máximo Gómez 40, Santo Domingo. *1978*
Tél: 582-7156

Universidad Tecnológica del Sur, c/Duarte 46, Azua. *1984*
éd, tec, gé agr, comp, adm, inf.

Universidad Ulises Francisco Espaillat, c/Rafael A. Sánchez 52, Ens. Naco, Apartado postal 22432, Ciudad Santo Domingo. *1986*
F : pol-soc.

Instituto Nacional de Ciencias Exactas, Apartado postal 1796, c/Conde, Edificio Baquero, Santo Domingo. *1974*
gé ind, gé civ, arc, agr.

Instituto Superior de Agricultura, Apartado postal 166, La Herradura, Santiago. *1986*
Tél: 582-6621
agr, adm des entrep, phil, éco.

Instituto Técnico Superior, c/Juan Sánchez Ramírez 23, Gazcue, Apartado postal 711-2, Ciudad Santo Domingo. *1987*
tec, comp, adm des entrep.

Instituto Tecnológico del Cibao Oriental, Cotuí. *1983*
F : agr, sc-hum, ing, formation, permanente.

*Instituto Tecnológico de Santo Domingo, Apartado postal 249, Avenida de Los Próceres, Galá, Santo Domingo. *1973*
Tél: 567-9271. Télex: 4184 intec dr.
F : ing, sc-hum, sa, soc.

Asociación Dominicana de Rectores de Universidades (ADRU)

L'Association dominicaine des recteurs d'université est reconnue par la loi et rassemble les recteurs des universités suivantes: Universidad Católica Madre y Maestra, Universidad Nacional Pedro Henríquez Ureña, Universidad APEC, Instituto Tecnológico de Santo Domingo, Universidad Central del Este, Universidad Nordestana, Universidad Tecnológica del Cibao, Instituto Tecnológico del Cibao Oriental, et Universidad Iberoamericana.

Ses principaux objectifs sont de: développer les relations interuniversitaires afin de favoriser et de développer les activités scientifiques, académiques, sportives, de recherche et d'éducation permanente; faire connaître ses opinions sur les problèmes éducatifs, scientifiques et culturels au sein des organismes représentatifs de la communauté nationale et internationale; et promouvoir les échanges et les relations amicales avec les organisations nationales et internationales s'occupant particulièrement d'enseignement supérieur.

The Dominican Association of University Rectors is recognized in law and consists of the Rectors of the following Universities: Universidad Católica Madre y Maestra, Universidad Nacional Pedro Henriquez Ureña, Universidad APEC, Instituto Tecnológico de Santo Domingo, Universidad Central del Este, Universidad Nordestana, Universidad Tecnológica del Cibao, Instituto Tecnológico del Cibao Oriental, et Universidad Iberoamericana.

Its principal tasks are to: develop inter-university relations in order to encourage and develop scientific, academic, and sport activities, research and lifelong education; to make its opinions known on educational, scientific and cultural matters within the representative bodies of the national and international community; and to promote exchanges and friendship with national and international organizations specially concerned with higher education.

Secrétaire exécutive: Sonia Lizardo.
Calle Luperón Esq. Hostos (altos), Apartado postal 2465, Santo Domingo.
Tél: 689-7465. Télex: 3460809

Consejo Nacional de Educacion Superior (CONES)
President: Altagracia Bautista de Suarez.
Santo Domingo.
Tél: 688-8357

Servicio Universitario Mundial (WUS)
Apartado 2137, Santo Domingo.
Tél: 689-8523

Federación de Estudiantes Dominicanos—FED (IUS)
Apartado 294, Santo Domingo.

Movimiento de Intelectuales Católicos (Pax Romana)
c/o Parroquia Santa Ana, Avenida Borney Morgan, Barrio Gualey, Santo Domingo.

*

Secretaría de Estado de Educación, Bellas Artes y Cultos
Avenida Máximo Gómez, Santo Domingo.
Tél: 688-9779

Comisión Nacional Dominicana de la Unesco
Secretaría de Estado de Educación, Bellas Artes y Cultos, Avenida Máximo Gómez, Santo Domingo.
Tél: 689-9410

ECUADOR
EQUATEUR

UNIVERSITIES AND TECHNICAL UNIVERSITIES –
UNIVERSITES ET UNIVERSITES TECHNIQUES

*Universidad Católica de Cuenca, Calle Bolívar y Benigno Malo, Apartado de Correos 19-A, Cuenca. (Sr. Rector).   *1970*
Tél: 823040. Télex: 48567 ucacue ed
F : dr-soc-pol, péd-psyc, éco, gé com, gé ch, gé agr, méd-sa.

Universidad de Cuenca, Avenida 12 de Abril, Apartado de Correos 168, Cuenca.   *1868*
Tél: 831556
F : dr, ing, phil-let-éd, ch, méd, dent, arc, éco.

*Pontificia Universidad Católica del Ecuador, Avenida 12 de Octubre y Robles, Apartado de Correos 2184, Quito.   *1946*
Tél: 520947
F : éd, dr, éco, hum, ing, théo, inf.

*Universidad Central del Ecuador, Avenida América y Alfredo Pérez Guerrero, Apartado 3291, Quito.   *1826*
Tél: 233080
F : dr, méd, ing, phil-let-éd, éco, adm, agr, vét-zoo, ch-phar, dent, arc-urb, ba, psyc.

*Universidad Católica de Santiago de Guayaquil, Avenida Carlos Julio Arosemena, Apartado de Correos 4671, Guayaquil.   *1962*
Tél: 202130
F : dr-soc, arc, ing civ, phil-let-éd, éco, méd, tec, techn.

*Universidad de Guayaquil, Calle Chile entre Chiriboga y Luzaranga, Apartado de Correos 471, Guayaquil.   *1867*
Tél: 324239. Télex: 43179 uguaye ed
F : dr-soc, méd, math, arc, éco, ch, nat, gé ch, phil-let-éd, vét-zoo, psyc, commun soc.

Universidad Laica «Eloy Alfaro» de Manabí, Vía San Mateo, Casilla 2732, Manta.
Tél: 610283

Universidad Laica «Vicente Rocafuerte», Avenida de las Américas, Apartado de Correos 1133, Guayaquil.   *1963, 1966*
Tél: 392121
F : arc, éd, éco, gé civ, dr-soc, adm.
Sections à Manta, et Portoviejo.

*Universidad Nacional de Loja, Calle Bernardo Valdivieso, Apartado de Correos Letra "S", Loja.   *1895, 1943*
Tél: 962684. Télex: 44535 unloja ed
F : phil-let-éd, dr-pol-soc, agr, vét, méd.

*Universidad Técnica de Ambato, Avenida Colombia y Chile, Apartado de Correos 334, Ambato.   *1969*
Tél: 823430
F : adm-gestion, comp, ing, éd.

Universidad Técnica de Babahoyo, Vía Flores, Apartado de Correos 66, Babahoyo.   *1970*
Tél: 730649
F : éd, ing.

Universidad Técnica de Esmeraldas, Avenida Nuevo Horizonte, Apartado de Correos 179, Esmeraldas.   *1970*
Tél: 713700
F : agr, éd, adm, socio-trav soc.

Universidad Técnica Particular de Loja, Apartado de Correos 608, Loja.   *1971*
Tél: 961824. Télex: 44533 unitel ed.
F : éco, ind agr-zoo, gé civ, éd.

Universidad Técnica de Machala, Calle Tarqui entre Sucre y 9 de Octubre, Apartado de Correos 466, Machala.   *1969*
Tél: 921452
F : gé agr-vét, ch, socio, adm-comp, gé civ.

Universidad Técnica de Manabí, Ciudadela Universitaria, Apartado de Correos 82, Portoviejo, Prov. de Manabí.   *1952*
Tél: 652677
F : math-phy-ch, gé agr (2), vét, soc-éd, sa-inf, adm-éco.

Universidad Técnica del Norte, Avenida Pérez Guerrero y Olmedo, Casilla 199, Ibarra.
Tél: 715430

Universidad Tecnológica Equinoccial, Rumipamba y Borgeois 210, Casilla 2764, Quito.
Tél: 453779

Universidad Técnica Estatal de Quevedo, Casilla 74, Quevedo, Los Ríos.
Tél: 715430

*Escuela Politécnica Nacional, Calle Isabella Católica y Vintimilla, Apartado de Correos 2759, Quito.   *1869*
Tél: 237914
F : élec, ch, méc, gé civ, géol-mine-pét, gé ind.

*Escuela Superior Politécnica del Chimborazo, Apartado de Correos 4703, Ríobamba.   *1969*
Tél: 961977
F : gé mét-méc, gé agr, nutr-diet, gé zoo, ch,

adm des aff.

Escuela Superior Politécnica del Litoral, Calle Rocafuerte y Loja, Apartado de Correos 5863, Guayaquil. *1958*

Tél: 308809
D : élec, méc, nav, géol-mine-pét.
I : phy, math, ch, ét gén.
E : inft, pêch.

Consejo Nacional de Universidades y Escuelas Politécnicas (CONUEP)

Le Conseil national des universités et écoles polytechniques (CONUEP) a été créé en 1982 en vertu de la loi sur les universités et les écoles polytechniques.

Il a pour fonctions d'orienter et de coordonner les activités académiques des établissements d'enseignement supérieur; de faire rapport au Congrès national sur les projets de création d'universités et d'écoles polytechniques nouvelles; d'approuver la création de nouveaux services et locaux dans les universités et les écoles polytechniques; de promouvoir la recherche scientifique et technologique et d'assurer à cet effet la gestion du fonds universitaire; d'établir des normes relatives au classement par ordre hiérarchique des enseignants, aux enseignements de post-graduation, et aux équivalences de grades et titres; de répartir les crédits destinés à l'enseignement supérieur; et d'approuver les statuts des universités et des écoles polytechniques. Vingt-et-une universités sont actuellement membres du CONUEP.

Le CONUEP a pour vocation d'affirmer l'autonomie universitaire et la liberté de l'enseignement, et de coordonner les programmes d'enseignement et de recherche. Y sont individuellement représentées, outre le Ministère de l'Education et le Conseil national de Développement, toutes les universités et écoles polytechniques en la personne de leur recteur, ainsi que par des représentants des enseignants, des étudiants et du personnel universitaire non enseignant.

Le Conseil se réunit régulièrement chaque mois. Il a, pour le bon déroulement de ses activités, constitué les Commissions de travail suivantes: affaires académiques; affaires économiques; affaires administratives et relevant du domaine de la planification; recherche scientifique et technologique. Ces commissions élaborent des propositions qui sont soumises au Conseil et qui sont, après approbation, transformées en résolutions et en normes applicables à l'ensemble des universités et écoles polytechniques.

Le Conseil élit tous les deux ans un Président parmi les recteurs des universités et écoles polytechniques. Celui-ci dirige les réunions du Conseil, re présente les institutions membres du point de vue juridique et organise l'ensemble des activités du Conseil. Il préside également le Comité directeur qui se compose des présidents des commissions. Le financement du CONUEP est assuré dans le budget général de l'Etat.

CONUEP dispose, pour l'assister, d'un Secrétariat permanent dirigé par un Secrétaire général élu tous les deux ans et qui doit obligatoirement enseigner dans une université ou une école polytechnique. Le Secrétariat général est chargé de transmettre et d'exécuter les résolutions du Conseil el comporte actuellement les departements suivantes: 1) la Planification, chargé de coordonner les actions de caractère interuniversitaire dans le domaine académique; 2) les finances, qui gère les ressources du Conseil et collabore à la répartition des fonds destinés à l'enseignement supérieur; 3) les Projets, chargé de la gestion et du suivi des projets de recherche scientifique et technologique réalisés dans les universités et les écoles polytechniques. Il assure également la coordination des séminaires, conférences et symposiums; 4) le Service-conseil juridique définit, entre autres, les critères servant de base à l'élaboration des Statuts de chacune des universités et des écoles polytechniques, et se prononce sur les normes édictées par la Conseil; 5) le Service de coordination de l'information et de la culture s'occupe de la publication du Bulletin du Conseil et des autres instruments de diffusion.

The National Council of Universities and Polytechnics (CONUEP) was created in 1982, by the law on universities and polytechnics. Its functions are to guide and co-ordinate all activities of the institutions of higher education; to inform the National Congress of the creation of new universities and polytechnics; to approve the creation of new services and facilities within the universities and polytechnics; to promote scientific and technological research and to manage university resources for this purpose; to establish norms concerning the hierarchy of academic staff, postgraduate studies, and the equivalence of diplomas and degrees; to distribute funds for higher education; and to approve university and polytechnic statutes. Twenty-one universities are members of CONUEP.

The purpose of CONUEP is to enhance university autonomy and academic freedom and to coordinate study and research programmes. It consists of a representative of the Ministry of

Education, a member of the National Development Council, the rectors of every university and polytechnic, and of representatives of the academic staff, student bodies and non-academic staff.

The Council meets every month. It has constituted the following commissions to ensure its functioning: academic affairs; economic affairs; administration and planification; scientific and technological research. These commissions make proposals that are submitted to the Council. If approved, they become resolutions and norms that are applied to all the universities and polytechnics.

Every two years, the Council elects a President among the rectors of the universities and polytechnics. He chairs the meetings of the Council, is the legal representative of the member institutions and organizes the activities of the Council. He is also the head of the Administrative Board, which is made up of the presidents of the Commissions. CONUEP's financial resources are part of the State budget.

CONUEP also has a permanent secretariat headed by a Secretary-General who is elected every two years and who must teach in a university or a polytechnic. The Secretariat transmits and carriers out the resolutions of the Council and is made up of the following departments: 1) Planification, which co-ordinates interuniversity activities in the academic field; 2) Finance, which administrates the Council's resources and distributes funds for higher education; 3) Projects, which is responsible for the management and follow-up of scientific and technological research projects that are carried out in the universities and polytechnics. It also co-ordinates seminars, conferences and symposia; 4) Legal Advice Service, which establishes the criteria on which the statutes of each university and polytechnic are based and gives its opinion on the norms set up by the Council; 5) Information and Cultural Coordination Service, which publishes the Council's Bulletin and other documents.

Secrétaire général: Iván Carvajal Aguirre.
9 de Octubre 624 y Jerónimo Carrión, Quito.
Tél: 569-898. Télex: 21442

Servicio Universitario Mundial (WUS)
Casilla 8921, Quito.

Federación de Estudiantes Universitarios del Ecuador—FEUE (IUS)
Universidad de Guayaquil, Apartado 171, Guayaquil.

Juventud Universitaria Católica del Ecuador (Pax Romana)
Apartado postal 2393, Quito.

Coordinadora Ecuménica de Pastoral Juvenil (CEPAJ) (WSCF)
Pasaje Farget 155 y Santa Prisca, Oficina 410, Quito.
Tél: 570580

*

Comisión de Cooperación Técnica
Dirección General de Relaciones Culturales, Ministerio de Relaciones Exteriores, Quito.
Télex: 43768 minext ed

Ministerio de Educación Pública
Mejia 322, Quito.
Tél: 21-62-24. Télex: 21267 minedu ed

Comisión Nacional Ecuatoriana de la Unesco
Calle Buenos Aires 136, Quito.
Tél: 540701. Cables: comiunesco quito

ARAB REPUBLIC OF EGYPT
REPUBLIQUE ARABE D'EGYPTE

UNIVERSITIES – UNIVERSITES

*Ain Shams University, Kasr-el-Zaafaran, Abbassia, Cairo. (The Secretary-General).
1950
Tel: 820230. Telex: 94070 ushms un
F : *arts, sc, med, law, agr, com, eng, lang, ed.*
I : *nurs, env res, childhood st.*
C : *for women.*

*Al-Azhar University, Al-Azhar District, Cairo.
1970, 1961
Tel: 904051
F : *Arab lang, relig, law, Isl relig, Isl Daowa (call), Isl st, lang-translation, com, sc, med, dent, phar, eng, agr, ed; Isl cult (for girls); Isl lang, Isl law (Assiut); Arab lang, Isl relig (Mansoura); Arab lang; Isl relig (Zagazig); Arab lang; Isl relig (Menoufia); law, Isl relig (Tanta); Arab lang; law (El-Behera).*

*Alexandria University, 22 Al-Gueish Avenue, Shattby, Alexandria. *1942*
Tel: 71675. Telex: 54467 univy un
F : *agr, arts, eng, law, med, dent, ed, sc, phar, tour & hotels, com; vet (Edfina); ed (Daman-hour).*
I : *publ heal, nurs, med res, grad st & res.*

*Assiut University, Assiut. *1957*
Tel: 3000. Telex: 92863 asunv un
F : *sc, med, eng, agr, phar, vet, com, law, ed, phys (for men); ed, arts, sc, com, (Sohag); ed, arts, sc (Kena); ed, sc (Aswan).*
I : *nurs.*

*Cairo University, Orman, Giza, Cairo.
1908, 1925
Tel: 727326. Telex: 94372 uncai un
F : *agr, arts, com, law, eng, sc, med, dent, urb plan, phar, mass commun, vet, eco-pol, Dar al-Ulum (Arab st), archae; com, law, vet, sc, arts (Beni Sweif); eng, agr, ed, soc (Fayoum).*
I : *stat & res, African st & res, cancer res, nurs, physio, urb plan, tumours; ed st (Fayoum).*

*University of Helwan, 96 Ahmed Oraby Street, El-Mohandessin, Cairo. *1975*
Tel: 3444055
F : *com-bus adm, appl arts, fa, agr, ed, sc, art ed, mus, soc serv, hom eco, tour & hotels, phys (for men), phys (for women); eng-techn (Helwan); eng-techn (Mattariya); fa, phys (for men), phys (for women) (Alexandria).*

*Mansoura University, Mansoura. *1972*
Tel: 347054
F : *sc, ed, med, phar, law, com, dent, eng, agr, arts; ed, sc (Damiette).*

*Menoufia University, Shebin Al-Kom. *1976*
Tel: 322170. Telex: 23832 muske un
F : *sc, law com, agr, eng-techn, ed, med, arts; electro (Menouf).*

*Minya University, Minya. *1976*
Tel: 324420. Telex: 24000 mnunv un
F : *agr, arts, ed, sc, eng-techn, phys (for men), med, fa, Arab st.*
I : *liver st & res.*

Suez Canal University, Al Ismailia. *1976*
Tel: 24009
F : *med, vet, sc, agr, pet-met, ed; com, eng-techn (Port Said); ed (El-Arish); ed (Suez).*

*Tanta University, Tanta. *1972*
Tel: 327928. Telex: 23605 untna un
F : *arts, law, med, phar, dent, sc, eng, phys (for men), com, ed; ed, agr (Kafr Al Sheikh).*
I : *nurs.*

*Zagazig University, Zagazig. *1974*
Tel: 747875. Telex: 92860 zu un
F : *com, ed, agr, vet, arts, law, sc, med, phar phys (for men), phys (for women), eng; com, sc, arts, vet, agr, ed, med (Banha); eng (Shou-bra).*
I : *nurs, efficiency productivity.*

*The American University in Cairo, 113 Kasr-Al Eini Street, Cairo. (The President). *1919*
Tel: 3542964. Telex: 92224 aucai un
F : *arts-sc.*
D : *eco-pol, mass commun, English & comparative lit, socio-anth-psyc, mater eng-phys sc.*
Ce : *Middle East mangt st, soc res, Arabic st, comp.*
I : *English lang.*

OTHER INSTITUTIONS—AUTRES INSTITUTIONS

Technical Education—Enseignement technique

Institute of Automotives, Wadi Hoaf, Cairo.
Chemical Institute, Shoubra, Cairo.
Institute of Construction, Helwan.
Institute of Electronics, Benha.
Institute of Industrial Studies, Aswan.
Institute of Industrial Studies, Sahaffa Street, Cairo.
Institute of Industrial Studies, Kemb Shizar, Alexandria.
Institute of Industrial Studies, Kewesna.
Institute of Industrial Studies, Mattariyah.
Institute of Industrial Studies, Nagh-Hamady.

Institute of Industrial Studies, Port Said.
Institute of Industrial Studies, Zagazig.
Institute of Irrigation and Surveying, Assiut.
Institute of Irrigation and Surveying, Gizah, Cairo.
Optics Institute, Mounirah, Cairo.
Tel: 847642
Television Technology Institute, Dar El-Salam, Cairo.
Wool Textile and Spinning Institute, Imbaba, Cairo.

Professional Education—Enseignement professionnel

Higher Institute of Co-operatives and Agricultural Guidance, Assiut.
Higher Institute of Agricultural Co-operative Studies, Cairo.
Higher Institute of Cinema, Pyramids Road, Gizah, Cairo.
Tel: 850291
Commercial Technical Institute, Abbassia.
Institute of Commercial Studies, Alexandria.
Institute of Commercial Studies, Assiut.
Institute of Commercial Studies, Aswan.
Institute of Commercial Studies, Benha.
Institute of Commercial Studies, Beni Sweif.
Institute of Commercial Studies, Damanhour.
Institute of Commercial Studies, Mansoura.
Institute of Commercial Studies, Mattariyah.
Institute of Commercial Studies, Port Said.
Institute of Commercial Studies, Roda.
Institute of Commercial Studies, Shebin Al-Kom.
Institute of Commercial Studies, Shoubra.
Institute of Commercial Studies, Sohag.
Institute of Commercial Studies, Tanta.
Institute of Commercial Studies, Zagazig.
Higher Institute of Co-operative and Administrative Studies, Mounira, Cairo.
Tel: 20544 hicom un
Higher Institute of Dramatic Arts, 15 El Maahad

El Swissry Street, Zamalek, Cairo.
Tel: 853233
Institute for Hotel Service, Cairo.
Institute of Secretarial Studies, Coptic Girls' College, Cairo.
Institute of Secretarial Studies, Ramsis Girls' College, Cairo.
Institute of Managerial and Secretarial Studies, Garden City, Cairo.
Branch at Heliopolis.
Institute for Medical Assistants, Alexandria.
Institute for Medical Assistants, Assiut.
Institute for Medical Assistants, Imbaba, Cairo.
Institute for Medical Assistants, Mansoura.
Institute for Medical Assistants, Tanta.
Institute for Medical Assistants, Zagazig.
Higher Institute of Social Service, Alexandria.
Intermediate Institute of Social Service, Alexandria.
Higher Institute of Social Service, Aswan.
Intermediate Institute of Social Service, Aswan.
Intermediate Institute of Social Service, Garden City, Cairo.
Higher Institute of Social Service, Kafr Al Sheikh.
Branch at Damanhour.
Higher Institute of Social Service, Cairo.

Supreme Council of Universities

The Supreme Council of Universities is responsible for the general policy of university education and scientific research in universities.

It supervises the academic work of the universities in the light of the nation's needs and of the national, social, economic, cultural and scientific objectives of the State.

Throughout the field of higher education the Council co-ordinates university studies and academic degrees, teaching in the corresponding faculties, institutes and departments of the universities, and university teaching posts.

One of its functions is to determine the fields of specialization of professorships and to create new departments as well to decide on the equivalence

of foreign degrees. The Council sets up committees of specialized university professors from Egypt or abroad, or suitably qualified persons to assess the academic work of the candidates for appointments as assistant professors or professors. These committees are established on the decision of the Minister of Higher Education.

The Council determines the numbers of the students to be admitted to the different faculties of each of the universities and lays down the regulations for admission. It sets up the university by-laws as well as the faculty regulations and gives comments on the government grants given annually to each of the universities. In addition, it deals with all requests made to it by the Minister of Higher Education or by any of the University Councils.

The Supreme Council of Universities is presided over by the Minister of Higher Education and its members are: the Presidents of the universities; the vice-presidents; one of the deans as representative of each university elected annually by its council; not more than five members well-versed in matters concerning university teaching and public affairs who are nominated by the Minister of Higher Education for a two-year period of office which is renewable; and the Secretary of the Supreme Council.

Le Conseil suprême des Universités fixe la politique générale de l'enseignement universitaire et de la recherche scientifique dans les universités.

Il veille aux travaux scientifiques des universités, en tenant compte des besoins du pays et des objectifs que l'Etat se propose d'atteindre sur le plan national, social, économique, culturel et scientifique.

Le Conseil coordonne, pour l'ensemble de l'enseignement supérieur des études et les grades universitaires, l'enseignement effectué dans les facultés, les instituts ou les sections similaires des universités, les postes d'enseignement des universités.

Il s'occupe de déterminer les domaines de spécialisation des départements, d'en créer de nouveaux, et d'établir l'équivalence des diplômes étrangers. En ce qui concerne la nomination aux postes de maître de conférences ou de professeur, le Conseil forme des comités pour l'appréciation des travaux académiques des candidats. Ces

comités se composent de professeurs spécialisés des universités égyptiennes ou étrangères ou d'autres personnalités compétentes. Ces comités sont formés par décision du Ministre de l'Enseignement supérieur.

Le Conseil détermine le nombre d'étudiants qui seront admis dans les différentes facultés de chacune des universités et fixe les conditions d'admission. Il établit les règlements des universités, ainsi que les règlements en vigueur à l'intérieur des facultés, et formule des observations sur les crédits que le gouvernement octroie chaque année à chacune des universités. Il répond en outre à toute demande qui lui est adressée par le Ministre de l'Enseignement supérieur ou par l'un des Conseils universitaires.

Le Conseil supérieur des Universités est présidé par le Ministre de l'Enseignement supérieur. Ses membres sont le président et le vice-président de chaque université et un des doyens élu comme représentant par le Conseil de celle ci; cinq membres au plus, choisis parmi les personnalités compétentes dans les questions de l'enseignement universitaire et les affaires publiques, et qui sont nommés par décret du Ministre de l'Enseignement supérieur pour deux ans renouvelables; et le secrétaire du Conseil supérieur des Universités.

President: The Minister of Higher Education.
Secretary-General: Prof. Dr. El-Sayed Hassan Hassanein.
Tel: 726131; 728877. Telex: 92312 frcu un

Egyptian Association of University Women (IFUW)
26 Saleh Salem, Alexandria.
General Union of Students of the Arab Republic of Egypt—GUSARE (IUS)
Ecumenical Youth Committee (WSCF)
Amba Rueis Building, Ramses Street, Abbasia, Cairo.

*

Ministry of Higher Education
Cairo.
Tel: 3549479. Telex: 92176 national
Egyptian National Commission for Unesco
17 Shareh Ismail Abu El Footoh, Dokki, Cairo.
Tel: 716659. Cables: unescedu cairo

EL SALVADOR
EL SALVADOR

UNIVERSITIES—UNIVERSITES

Universidad «Albert Einstein», Urb. Lomas de San Francisco, Calle Circunvalación, Block L, Lote No. 6, San Salvador. *1977*
Tél: 24-3068
F : ing-arc.

Universidad Americana, Calle No. 3 Col. La Mascota, San Salvador. *1982*
Tél: 23-9691
F : sc-hum.

Universidad Autónoma de Santa Ana, 23 Avenida Sur y 9a/11a Calle Ote., Santa Ana. *1981*
Tél: 41-2914
F : éco, sa, jur.

Universidad Cap. General Gerardo Barrios, 4a Calle Pte. 207, San Miguel. *1982*
Tél: 61-0152
F : ing-arc, éco, sc-hum, jur-soc, agr.

Universidad Católica de Occidente, A.P. 1836, Santa Ana. *1982*
Tél: 41-3217
F : sc-hum.

Universidad Centroamericana «José Simeón Cañas», Autopista Sur, Jardines de Guadalupe, San Salvador. *1965*
Tél: 24-0011. Télex: 30018 proca
F : ing, éco, hum-nat.

Universidad Cristiana de las Asambleas de Dios, 27 Calle Ote. 134, San Salvador. *1983*
Tél: 25-5046
F : sc-hum.

Universidad Don Bosco, 3a Avenida Norte 1403, San Salvador. *1983*
Tél: 25-8878
F : ing, sc-hum.

Universidad Dr. José Matias Delgado, 85 Avenida Norte y Pje. Arrué, 916 Col. Escalón, San Salvador. *1977*
Tél: 23-4061. Télex: 20386 unidel sal
F : éco, jur-soc, cult gén-ba.
E : comp, banc, adm publ.

Universidad de Educación Integral, Avenida España 321, Edificio España, San Salvador.

*****Universidad de El Salvador**, Ciudad Universitaria, San Salvador. *1841, 1847*
Tél: 25-9427. Télex: 20794
F : ing-arc, éco, sc-hum, jur-soc, méd, ch-phar, dent, agr.

Universidad Evangélica de El Salvador, 63 Avenida Sur y Pje. 1 No. 138, San Salvador. *1981*

Tél: 23-6354
F : ing-arc, sc-hum, dent, agr, méd.

Universidad Francisco Gavidia, Alameda Roosevelt 2937, San Salvador. *1981*
Tél: 24-5962
F : soc, éco.

Universidad de La Paz, 9a Calle Ote. y 2a Avenida Norte 618, Edif. San Francisco, San Salvador.
Tél: 22-5980

Universidad Las Américas de El Salvador, 3a Calle Ote. 111, San Salvador. *1982*
Tél: 21-7647
F : éco, jur-soc.

Universidad Leonardo Da Vinci, Avenida Roosevelt 2139, San Salvador. *1981*
Tél: 23-6034
F : éco.

Universidad Modular Abierta, 3a Calle Pte. 1126, San Salvador. *1982*
Tél: 21-9697
F : éco, sc-hum.

Universidad Nueva San Salvador, 49 Avenida Sur 725, Col. Flor Blanca, San Salvador. *1981*
Tél: 23-0920
F : ing-arc, éco, sc-hum, jur-soc, sc, sa, dent.

Universidad Occidental de El Salvador, 6a Avenida Sur 52, Apartado postal 270, Santa Ana. *1981*
Tél: 41-0222
F : ing, éco, sc-hum.

Universidad de Oriente, Avenida Gerardo Barrios y 8a Calle Pte. 102, San Miguel. *1982*
Tél: 61-0542
F : ing-arc-agr, sc-hum, jur-éco, sa.

Universidad Pedagógica, 7a Avenida Norte 411, San Salvador. *1982*
Tél: 22-5052
F : sc-hum.

Universidad Politécnica de El Salvador, 19 Calle Pte. 320, San Salvador. *1979*
Tél: 26-4153
F : éco, ing-arc.

Universidad Salvadoreña, Calle San Antonio Abad y Avenida Alvaredo 164, Colonia Buenos Aires, San Salvador. *1982*
Tél: 25-8861
F : ing, éco.

Universidad Salvadoreña Alberto Masferrer, 3a

Calle Pte. 1040, San Salvador. *1980*
Tél: 22-8006
F : ing-arc, éco, jur-soc, sa, agr.
Universidad Salvadoreña «Berry», 27 Avenida
Norte 1138, San Salvador. *1983*
Tél: 25-0854
F : éco.
Universidad Salvadoreña «Isaac Newton», 1a
Avenida Norte 838, San Salvador. *1982*
Tél: 21-9054
F : sc-hum, éco, ing-arc.
Universidad Santaneca de Ciencia y Tecnología,
2a Planta, Plaza de Vidrio entre 7a y 9a Calle
Pte. Santa Ana. *1982*
Tél: 41-2399
F : sc-hum, éco, ing-arc.

Universidad de Sonsonate, 2a Avenida Norte 66,
Sonsonate. *1982*
Tél: 51-0674
F : ing-nat, éco-soc.
Universidad Técnica Latinoamericana, 2a Calle
Ote. 3-2, Santa Tecla. *1981*
Tél: 28-1166
F : ing, éco, sc anim.
Universidad Tecnológica, Calle Rubén Darío
1215, Edificio Chaín, San Salvador. *1981*
Tél: 22-1173
F : ing-arc, éco, hum-nat.
Universidad del Vendedor Salvadoreño, Boule-
vard de los Héroes 1421, San Salvador.
Tél: 26-0518

OTHER INSTITUTIONS — AUTRES INSTITUTIONS

Technical Education — Enseignement technique

Instituto Tecnológico Centroamericano, Km. 11,
Carretera a Nueva, San Salvador.
Tél: 28-06019
adm des aff, com, alim, gé agr, gé arc, gé civ,
élec, gé ind, méc, éd, adm publ.
Instituto Tecnológico de Chalatenango, Final C.
Morazán, Bo. El Calvario, Chalatenango.
Tél: 35-2126
agr-ind, adm des aff, sa, hyg dent, gé agr, éd.
**Instituto Tecnológico General Francisco Menén-
dez**, 29 C.O. y 20 Avenida Norte, San Salvador.
Tél: 26-4611
tour, trav soc, gé arc, gé électro, gé ind, méc,
éd.
Instituto Tecnológico de San Miguel, Final 7a
Avenida Sur, Bo. San Nicolás, San Miguel.
Tél: 61-316
aquaculture, adm des aff, agro-ind, hôtel-tour,
trav soc, gé civ, élec, gé ind, méc, éd, adm publ.
Instituto Tecnológico de San Vicente, 6a Calle
Ote.y 9a Avenida Sur, San Vicente.
Tél: 33-0250

adm des aff, prod agr, trav soc, éd.
Instituto Tecnológico de Santa Ana, Avenida
Santa Ana California y 31 Calle Pte., Santa
Ana.
Tél: 41-1132
adm des aff, trav soc, gé civ, élec-électro, gé
ind, méc, gé tex, éd, adm publ.
Instituto Tecnológico de Sonsonate, 25 Calle Pte.
y Final Avenida Morazán, Sonsonate.
Tél: 51-0636
adm des aff, prod pêch, sa, éd, entretien ind,
adm publ.
Instituto Tecnológico de Usulután, Final 7a Calle
Ote. y Avenida El Molino, Usulután.
Tél: 62-0406
prod agr, trav soc, gé civ-const.
Instituto Tecnológico de Zacatecoluca, Calle El
Volcán, Zacatecoluca.
Tél: 34-0292
adm des aff, prod agr, sa, trav soc, éd, adm
publ.

**Asociación de Mujeres Universitarias de El
Salvador** (IFUW)
Apartado postal 1293, San Salvador.
Servicio Universitario Mundial (WUS)
Apartado postal 1703, Universidad de El Salva-
dor, San Salvador.
Tél: 25-94-27. Télex: 0373-20794
Intelectuales Católicos de El Salvador (Pax
Romana)
c/o Universidad Centroamericana de El
Salvador, Dpto. de Economía, Jardines de

Guadalupe, San Salvador.
**Acción Católica Universitaria Salvadoreña —
ACUS** (Pax Romana)
Apartado postal 1112, San Salvador.
**Asociación General de Estudiantes Universitarios
Salvadoreños — AGEUS** (IUS)
Ciudad Universitaria Rodrigo Facio, San José.
Télex: 3011 cosuca cr (att. ageus). Cables:
cosuca san josé

*

Ministerio de Educación
6a Calle Oriente 435, San Salvador.
Tél: 22-7801
Comisión Nacional Salvadoreña de Cooperación con la Unesco

Ministerio de Educación, Oficina de Relaciones Internacionales, Apartado postal 1175, San Salvador.
Tél: 22-6889

ETHIOPIA
ETHIOPIE

UNIVERSITIES—UNIVERSITES

*Addis Ababa University, P.O. Box 1176, Addis Ababa. (The President).   *1950, 1961*
Tel: 110844. Telex: 21205 aauniv addis
  BAHIR DAR TEACHERS' COLLEGE, P.O. Box 79, Bahir Dar.   *1971*
  COLLEGE OF SOCIAL SCIENCES, Sidist Kilo Campus, P.O. Box 1176, Addis Ababa.
                                              1951, 1978
  FACULTY OF EDUCATION, Sidist Kilo Campus, P.O. Box 1176, Addis Ababa.
                                                    1962
  FACULTY OF LAW, Sidist Kilo Campus, P.O. Box 1176, Addis Ababa.   *1963*
  FACULTY OF MEDICINE, Black Lion Hospital Compound, P.O. Box 1176, Addis Ababa.
                                                    1965
  FACULTY OF SCIENCE, Arat Kilo Campus, P.O. Box 1176, Addis Ababa.   *1951*
  FACULTY OF TECHNOLOGY, Northern Campus, Amist Kilo Campus, P.O. Box 385, Addis Ababa.   *1953*
  Southern Campus, P.O. Box 518, Addis Ababa.   *1954*

  FACULTY OF VETERINARY MEDICINE, P.O. Box 32, Debre Zeit.   *1979*
  GONDAR COLLEGE OF MEDICAL SCIENCES, P.O. Box 196, Gondar.   *1954, 1979*
  INSTITUTE OF LANGUAGE STUDIES, Sidist Kilo Campus, P.O. Box 1176, Addis Ababa.
                                              1951, 1978
  JUNIOR COLLEGE OF AGRICULTURE, P.O. Box 5, Awassa.   *1976*
  SCHOOL OF GRADUATE STUDIES, Amist Kilo Campus, P.O. Box 1176, Addis Ababa.
                                                    1978
  SCHOOL OF PHARMACY, Amist Kilo Campus, P.O. Box 1176, Addis Ababa.   *1961*
*Asmara University, P.O. Box 1220, Asmara.
                                                    1958
Tel: (4) 113600. Telex: 42091 asmuniv et
F : *sc.*
C : *soc.*
I : *lang st.*
Alemaya University of Agriculture, Alemaya, P.O. Box 138, Dire Dawa, Harer.   *1954, 1985*
Tel: 111400

OTHER INSTITUTIONS—AUTRES INSTITUTIONS

Ambo Junior College of Agriculture, P.O. Box 19, Ambo.   *1931*
Tel: 59
Arba Minch Institute of Water Technology, P.O. Box 21, Arba Minch.   *1986*
College of Urban Planning, P.O. Box 1023, Addis Ababa.   *1968*
Tel: 117519
Debre Zeit Institute for Animal Health Assistants, P.O. Box 34, Debre Zeit.   *1963*
Kotebe College of Teacher Education, P.O. Box 5534, Addis Ababa.   *1969*
Junior College of Commerce, P.O. Box 3131,

Addis Ababa.   *1943, 1978*
Tel: 448020
Jimma Junior College of Agriculture, P.O. Box 307, Jimma.   *1952*
Tel: 110102
Jimma Health Science Institute, P.O. Box 378, Jimma.   *1983*
Polytechnic Institute, P.O. Box 26, Bahir Dar.
                                                    1963
Tel: 200277
Wondo Genet Forest Resource Institute, P.O. Box 1034, Wondo Genet, Shashamene.   *1978*
Tel: (6) 100522

Revolutionary Ethiopia Youth Association—
REYA (IUS)
P.O. Box 5729, Addis Ababa.
Telex: 21475
Kessate Berhan Association (Pax Romana)
Faculty of Education, Addis Ababa University,
P.O. Box 1176, Addis Ababa.

Commission for Higher Education
Addis Ababa.
Tel: 126888. Telex: 21452 cohed et
Ethiopian National Agency for Unesco
P.O. Box 2996, Addis Ababa.
Tel: 118219. Telex: 21435 moe

*

FIJI
FIDJI

UNIVERSITIES—UNIVERSITES

University of the South Pacific, P.O. Box 1168,
Suva.   *1970*
Tel: 313900. Telex: 2276 usp fj
S : *ed, nat resources, soc & eco dev, agr.*
Alafua Campus, P.O. Box 890, Alafua,
Western Samoa.
S: *agr*
University Centre, Tonga, p. 577
University Centre, Raratong,Cook Island.*1970*

University Centre, Tarawa, Kiribati.   *1970*
University Centre, Nauru. ·   *1970*
University Centre, Honiara, Solomon Islands,
p. 387.   *1970*
University Centre, Funafuti, Tuvalu.   *1970*
University Centre, Port Villa, Vanuatu. *1970*
University Centre, Apia, Western Samoa,
p. 577.   *1970*

Technical Education—Enseignement technique

The Fiji Institute of Technology, Suva.   *1963*
Tel: 381044
S : *bui-civ eng, mar st, food-fash, bus st, gen st,*

printing, mec.
Western Division Technical Centre, BA.   *1978*

Professional Education— Enseignement professionnel

The Fiji School of Agriculture, Koronivia. *1954*
The Fiji School of Medicine, Tamavua, Suva.
        1883

The Fiji School of Nursing, Tamavua, Suva.

Teacher Training—Formation pédagogique

Corpus Christi Training College, Suva.   *1958*
Fulton College.   *1942*

Lautoka Teachers' College, Lautoka.   *1977*

World University Service (WUS)
Contact: The Secretary, University of the South
Pacific, Student's Association, P.O. Box 1168,
Suva.
Tel: 27474. Telex: 2276 fj
University of the South Pacific Students' Associa-
tion—USPSA (IUS)
P.O. Box 1168, Suva.

Telex: 2276 uspsa
Association of Fiji Women Graduates (IFUW)
P.O. Box 13495, Suva.

*

Ministry of Education and Youth
Suva.
Tel: 314477

FINLAND
FINLANDE

UNIVERSITIES AND UNIVERSITY INSTITUTIONS—
UNIVERSITES ET INSTITUTIONS UNIVERSAIRES

*Helsingin yliopisto [U. of Helsinki], Hallitus-katu 8, 00100 Helsinki 10.   *1640*
Tel: 10-1911. Fax: 0-656591. Telex: 124690 unih sf
F : *theo, law, med, pol, agr-for, hum, math-sc, ed, publ heal, dent, psyc, phar.*
*Joensuun yliopisto [U. of Joensuu], PL 111, 80101 Joensuu.   *1969, 1984*
Tel: 73-1511. Fax: 73-260114. Telex: 46223 joy sf
F : *hum, math, sc, ed, soc, for, theo (orthodox), psyc.*
*Jyväskylän yliopisto [U. of Jyväskylä], Semina-arinkatu 15, 40100 Jyväskylä.   *1934, 1966*
Tel: 41-291211. Telex: 28219 jyk sf
F : *hum, ed, math-sc, phys, soc, publ heal, eco, psyc.*
*Kuopion yliopisto [U. of Kuopio], PL 6, 70211 Kuopio.   *1966, 1984*
Tel: 71-162211. Telex: 42218 kuy sf
D : *med, math-phy-ch, biol, env hyg, publ heal, soc, dent, phar.*
Lapin korkeakoulu [U. of Lapland], PL 63, 96101 Rovaniemi.   *1979*
Tel: 60-3241. Telex: 37130 lapko sf
F : *ed, law, soc.*
*Oulun yliopisto [U. of Oulu], PL 191, 90101 Oulu.   *1958*
Tel: 81-222700. Telex: 32375 oylin sf
F : *hum, sc, med, techn, ed, soc, publ heal, arc.*
*Tampereen yliopisto [U. of Tampere], PL 607, 33101 Tampere.   *1925, 1966*
Tel: 31-156111. Telex: 22263 tayk sf
F : *soc, hum, eco-adm, med, ed.*
*Turun yliopisto [U. of Turku], Yliopistonmäki, 20500 Turku.   *1920*
Tel: 21-645111. Telex: 62123 tyk sf
F : *math-sc, hum, med, soc, law, ed, psyc, publ heal, dent.*
Vaasan korkeakoulu [U. of Vaasa], Raas-tuvankatu 31, 65100 Vaasa.   *1968, 1980*
Tel: 61-122511. Telex: 74262 vkk sf
D : *eco, hum, soc.*
*Åbo Akademi [Swedish U. of Turku, Åbo A.], Domkyrkotorget 3, 20500 Åbo. (The Secretar-iat).   *1917*
Tel: 21-654311. Telex: 62301 aabib sf

F : *hum, math-sc, tec, ch, theo, eco-pol, ed, psyc, phar.*
*Teknillinen korkeakoulu [Helsinki U. of Tech-nology], Otakaari 1, 02150 Espoo 15.
1849, 1908
Tel: 0-460144. Telex: 125161 tkk sf
D : *phy, civ eng, mec, elec, ch, for prod, mine-met, surv, arc, prod eco, infor techn.*
Lappeenrannan teknillinen korkeakoulu [Lap-peenranta U. of Technology], PL 20, 53851 Lappeenranta.   .   *1966, 1969*
Tel: 53-27570. Telex: 58290 ltkk sf
D : *mec, energ, prod eco, ch techn.*
*Tampereen teknillinen korkeakoulu [Tampere U. of Technology], PL 527, 33101 Tampere.
1965
Tel: 31-162111. Telex: ttktr sf
D : *elec, mec, civ eng, arc, infor techn.*
Helsingin kauppakorkeakoulu [Helsinki S. of Economics and Business Administration], Runeberginkatu 14-16, 00100 Helsinki.   *1911*
Tel: 0-43131. Telex: 122220 econ sf
Svenska Handelshögskolan [Swedish S. of Econ-omics and Business Administration], Arkadia-gatan 22, 00100 Helsingfors.   *1909, 1927*
Tel: 0-440291
Turun kauppakorkeakoulu [Turku S. of Econ-omics and Business and Administration], Rehtoripellontie 5, 20500 Turku.   *1950*
Tel: 21-512333. Telex: 62310 tkkk sf
Eläinlääketieteellinen korkeakoulu [C. of Veter-inary Medicine], Hämeentie 57, 00550 Helsinki.   *1945*
Tel: 90-711411. Telex: 123203 elkk sf
Sibelius-Akatemia [Sibelius A.], Töölönkatu 28, 00260 Helsinki.   *1882*
Tel: 0-408166
mus.
Taideteollinen korkeakoulu [U. of Industrial Arts], Hämeentie 135, 00560 Helsinki.
1842, 1973
Tel: 0-75631
D : *art ed, vis commun, prod-env des.*
Teatterikorkeakoulu [Theatre A.], Ehrensvärd-intie 31-35, 00150 Helsinki.   *1981*
Tel: 0-642822

Suomen Korkeakoulujen Rehtorien Neuvosto

The Finnish Council of University Rectors is open to the Rectors of universities and institutions of university rank. The Vice-Rectors are deputy members. The Rectors elect from among themselves for a one-year term a President, a Vice-President and an Executive Committee; they may be re-elected. The Council also has a Secretary-General.

The task of the Council is to deal with fundamental and other important questions of common concern to the Universities. The Council may in these matters make recommendations and declarations and render opinions. It may also undertake other tasks entrusted to it by the Universities or by the State.

The Rectors meet regularly 5 or 6 times a year at different Universities; the Executive Committee convenes more often. Occasionally, the Council also organizes meetings at which a larger number of representatives of Universities, various national organizations and social institutions are invited to discuss subjects of current interest related to the Universities.

Le Conseil finlandais des Recteurs d'université est un organisme auquel peuvent adhérer les recteurs des universités et institutions de rang universitaire. Les vice-recteurs des institutions sont membres suppléants. Les recteurs élisent en leur sein, pour un an, un président, un vice-président et un comité exécutif, qui sont rééligibles. Le Conseil a également un Secrétaire général.

Le Conseil a pour tâche de s'occuper de questions fondamentales et d'autres problèmes importants, qui revêtent pour les universités un intérêt commun. Le Conseil peut en la matière formuler des recommandations, faire des déclarations et exprimer des avis. Il peut également entreprendre d'autres tâches, à la demande des universités ou de l'Etat.

Les recteurs se réunissent régulièrement cinq ou six fois par an dans des universités différentes; le Comité exécutif, pour sa part, se réunit plus fréquemment. De temps à autre le Conseil organise également des réunions auxquelles il invite un grand nombre de représentants des universités, de diverses organisations nationales et d'institutions sociales, afin de débattre de questions d'actualité concernant les universités.

Secretary-General: Prof. Mikael Hidén.

University of Helsinki, Hallituskatu 8, 00100 Helsinki 10.

Tel: 19-12-335

Korkeakoulujen ja opetusalan henkilökuntaliitto Högskolornas och undervisningssektorns personalförbund KHL ry (Union of University College and Teaching Personnel)
Ratamestarinkatu 11, 00520 Helsinki.

Helsingin yliopiston henkilökuntayhdistys r.v. (Association of the Personnel of the University of Helsinki)
Meritullinkatu 24B 31, 00170 Helsinki 17.

Association of University Professors in Finland (IAULP)
Contact: 18, rue de Docteur Roux, 75015 Paris.
Tel: 47-83-31-65

Suomen Akateemisten Naisten Liitto-Finlands Kvinnliga Akademikers Forbund (IFUW)
Frederikinkatu 41A8, 00120 Helsinki 26.

Suomen Ylioppilaskuntien Liittoo—SYL (IUS)
Mannerheimintie 5, C 00100 Helsinki.
Tel: 124888 (att. syl)

Catholic Student Association in Finland (Pax Romana)
PL134, 00141 Helsinki 14.

Student Christian Federation (WSCF)
Siltasaarenkatu 11 C 45, 00530 Helsinki.
Tel: 719286

Orthodox Student Association (WSCF)
Unionkatu 39, 00170 Helsinki.

United Nations Student Association of Finland (ISMUN)
Mannerheimintie 5C 7krs, Box 93, Helsinki.

*

Ulkoasiainministerio (Foreign Office)
Helsinki.
Tel: 13-41-51

Opetusministerio (Ministry of Education)
P.L. 293, 00171 Helsinki.
Tel: 13-41-71

Finnish National Commission for Unesco
Ministry of Education, Meritullinkatu 10, 00170 Helsinki.
Tel: 13-41-71. Fax: 0-6121335. Telex: 122079 mined sf

FRANCE
FRANCE

UNIVERSITIES AND POLYTECHNIC INSTITUTES— UNIVERSITES ET INSTITUTS POLYTECHNIQUES

Public Establishments—Etablissements publics

Université de Provence (Aix-Marseille I), 1, place Victor Hugo, 13331 Marseille Cedex 3.
1413, 1970
Tél: 91 95 90 71. Fax: 91 50 13 00. Télex: 40 20 14 amiup
Ut : hist, lang-lit-civ anglo-am, lang-civ orntl-slav, lang-lit-civ romanes-Am latine, lang-lit-civ ger, let, arts-let-expression, psyc, soc-ethn, phil, math, phy, ch, nat, rech médit, obs.
I : systèmes thermiques ind (IUSTI).

Université d'Aix-Marseille (Aix-Marseille II), 58, bld. Charles-Livon, 13007 Marseille.
1413, 1970
Tél: 91 52 90 34
F : dent, méd, phar; éco (Aix).
Ut : méd trop; sc (Luminy); sc exactes-nat, phys-sport; géog (Aix).
I : techn (Aix).

*Université de Droit, d'Economie, et des Sciences (Aix-Marseille III), 3, avenue Robert Schuman, 13621 Aix-en-Provence. *1431, 1973*
Tél: 42 20 19 05. Télex: 42 07 27 udesam
F : dr-pol, éco app.
Ut : rech jur; prop sc, rech scq et tec, formation prof-scq-tec, formation des maîtres scq (IUSPIM) (Marseille).
I : sc pour l'ing, dr des aff, crim, ét françaises pour étr, adm des entreprises, pol; techn (Marseille).
E : phy.

Université de Picardie, Rue Salomon Mahlangu, 80025 Amiens Cedex. *1964, 1970*
Tél: 22 95 13 14
Ut : dr, méd, phar, sc exactes-nat, let, lang-cult étr, phil-hum, hist géog, éco-gestion, math; sc-tec (St. Quentin).
I : techn.

Université d'Angers, 30, rue des Arènes, B.P. 3532, 49035 Angers Cedex. *1970*
Tél: 41 88 58 43
Ut : dr-éco, let-hum, méd-phar, sc exactes-nat, sc-tec (rech).
I : techn.

Université d'Avignon, 35, avenue Joseph Vernet, 84000 Avignon. *1972*

Tél: 90 82 68 10. Télex: 43 25 26 uniavi
Ut : let-hum, sc exactes-nat.

Université de Franche-Comté, 30 avenue de l'Observatoire, 25030 Besançon Cedex.
1423, 1829, 1970
Tél: 81 50 81 21
Ut : let-hum, sc méd-phar, éco-jur, sc exactes-nat, rech biol-méd, phys-sport, obs.
E : méc-microtec.
I : techn, ch; techn (Belfort).

*Université de Bordeaux I, 351, cours de la Libération, 33405 Talence Cedex.
1423, 1970
Tél: 56 80 84 50. Fax: 56 80 08 37
Ut : sc, math-inft, phy, ch, biol, sc jur, éco, éco approfondies, aménagement territoire-dév rég, ét rechs géol d'Aquitaine (rech); obs (Floirac).
I : sc et tec des alim (ISTAB), pol, gestion; techn (Gradignan).
E : électro-radioélec, ch.

Université de Bordeaux II, 146, rue Léo-Saignat, 33076 Bordeaux Cedex. *1423, 1970*
Tél: 56 90 91 24. Télex: 57 22 37 unibxii
Ut : sc méd (3), sc phar, od, méd-hyg trop, biol-physiopathologie des facteurs d'ambiance, psychiatrie, soc-psyc, bioch-biol cellulaire.
I : phys-sport, sc hum app, œnologie.
D : inf, lang vivantes, commun audiovis, santé-dév.

Université de Bordeaux III, Esplanade Michel de Montaigne, Domaine Universitaire, 33405 Talence Cedex. *1423, 1970*
Tél: 56 84 50 50
Ut : let-arts, phil, hist, géog-ét rég, lang-lit pays anglophones, lang-lit ger scand, lang-lit-civ étr (2), ét ibériques, tec d'expression-commun, rech homme & env.
I : techn (Gradignan).

*Université de Bretagne Occidentale (Brest), Rue des Archives, B.P. 137, 29269 Brest Cedex.
1970
Tél: 98 03 24 83
Ut : méd, sc-tec, let-soc, dr-éco, od.
I : techn; techn (Quimper); techn (Lorient).

Université de Caen, Esplanade de la Paix, 14032

Caen Cedex. *1970*
Tél: 31 45 55 00
Ut : dr-pol, éco-gestion, méd, phar, sc de l'homme, sc vie et comportement, sc terre-aménagement rég, lang étr, hist, sc, adm des aff, sc alim-nutr, phys-sport.
I : techn, sc, matière-rayonnement.
Université de Savoie Chambery, Jacob Belle-combette B.P. 1104, 73011 Chambéry Cedex.
1970
Tél: 79 69 27 18. Fax: 79 62 79 73
Ut : sc exactes-nat, let-hum-soc, dr, lang étr, adm gén, éco & soc.
E (sup): gé de l'env et de la const (ESIGEC).
I : techn (Annecy).
Université de Clermont-Ferrand I, 49, boulevard Gergovia, B.P. 32, 63001 Clermont-Ferrand.
1854, 1970, 1976
Tél: 73 35 55 20. Fax: 73 35 55 18
Ut : od, méd, phar, jur-pol, éco-gestion, soc.
I : techn.
Université de Clermont-Ferrand II, 34, avenue Carnot, B.P. 185, 63006 Clermont-Ferrand Cedex. *1854, 1970, 1976*
Tél: 73 92 97 32
Ut : sc exactes-nat, sc exactes-nat (rech), let-hum, techn, phys-sport, obs.
I : techn (Montluçon).
E : ch.
Ce : sc-tec (CUST) (Aubière).
Université de Technologie de Compiègne (voire p. 142)
Université de Corse, 7, Avenue Jean Nicoli, B.P. 24, 20250 Corte. *1975*
Tél: 95 46 10 45
Ut : let-hum, dr, éco, sc.
D : ét Corse.
I : techn, adm des entrep.
Université de Bourgogne, Campus Universitaire de Montmuzard, B.P. 138, 21004 Dijon Cedex.
1722, 1970
Tél: 80 39 50 00
Ut : méd, phar-biol, dr-pol, éco-gestion, let-phil, rel int, lang-lit-civ étr, hum, nutr (rech), sc, phys-sport, sc vie & env, math-inft-phy-ch.
I : sc terre; techn; techn (Le Creusot).
E : biol app à la nutr & alim.
Ce : ét rég, adm gén.
Université Joseph Fourier (Grenoble I), Domaine Universitaire Saint-Martin-d'Hères, B.P. 68, 38402 Saint-Martin-d'Hères (B.P. 53, Centre de Tri, 38041 Grenoble Cedex.) *1339, 1970*
Tél: 76 51 46 00. Fax: 76 52 48 48
Ut : biol, méd (2), phar, géog, math-inft, méc, phy, ch, sc terre, phys-sports.
E : techn.
I : sc nucl, techn, sc-tec (ISTG).
Université des Sciences sociales (Grenoble II), Domaine Universitaire, Saint-Martin-d'Hères

47x, 38040 Grenoble Cedex. *1339, 1970*
Tél: 76 82 54 00. Télex: 98 09 10 unisog
Ut : psyc-sc de l'éd, dr, éco, hist-hist des arts, phil-socio, urb & aménagement, inft & math-soc.
I : techn, adm des entrep, rech éco-plan, com, pol.
Université Stendahl (Grenoble III), Domaine Universitaire Saint-Martin-d'Hères 25x, 38040 Grenoble Cedex. *1339, 1970*
Tél: 76 44 82 18
Ut : let, lang vivantes, et anc.
Université du Havre, 25, rue Philippe Lebon, B.P. 1123, 76063 Le Havre Cedex.
Tél: 35-22-92-50
Ut: éco, sc exactes et nat.
I : techn.
Université des Sciences et Techniques de Lille-Flandres Artois (Lille I), Domaine Universitaire scientifique, 59655 Villeneuved'Ascq.
1560, 1970
Tél: 20-43-43-43. Fax: 20-43-39-95. Télex: 136339 ustl
Ut : éco-soc, math pures-app, inft électro-électrotec-automatique, phy, ch, biol, sc terre, géog-aménagement spatial (Lille); sc exactes-nat (Calais).
I : techn, préparation aux aff (Lille); techn (Béthune); techn (Calais, Dunkerque).
E : ing (EUDIL), ch; ing sc agr-alim (IAAL) (Lille).
Université de Droit et de la Santé (Lille II), 42, rue Paul Duez, 59653 Lille. *1560, 1970*
Tél: 20-52-56-29
Ut : méd (3), phar, od, jur-pol-soc.
I : phys-sport (Ronchin); sc du trav, techn (Villeneuve d'Ascq).
Université des Sciences humaines, des Lettres et des Arts (Lille III), Domaine universitaire littéraire et artistique de Villeneuve d'Ascq, Pont de Bois, B.P. 149, 59653 Villeneuve-d'Ascq Cedex. *1560, 1970*
Tél: 20-91-92-02
Ut : phil, lang-lit-civ anglophones, ling française-sc des lit, hist art-arché, math-éco-soc, lang anc, psyc-soc, ét romanes-sémitiques-slaves-hongroises, ét ger, tec réadaptation.
I : techn.
Université de Limoges, 13, rue de Genève, 87065 Limoges Cedex. *1646, 1970*
Tél: 55-45-76-01
Ut : sc méd-phar, jur-éco, let-hum, sc exactes-nat.
I : techn.
Université Claude-Bernard (Lyon I), 43, boulevard du 11 novembre 1918, 69622 Villeurbarne Cedex. *1809, 1970*
Tél: 78-89-81-24. Télex: 330208 ucbl
Ut : math, phy, ch-bioch, sc nature, sc physio-

logiques, phy nucl, méd (4), phar, biol hum, tec
réadaptation, méc, od, phys-sport, obs.
I : techn (2), météo.

Université Lumière (Lyon II), 86, rue Pasteur,
69365 Lyon Cedex 2.   *1809, 1970*
Tél: 78-69-24-45. Fax: 78-69-24-45-240
Ut : jur, psyc-soc, let-civ monde médit, sc du
langage, let-civ class et mod, let-civ étr, hist-
géog.
I : pol, formation aux pratiques psyc-socio-éd.
D : éco-gestion.

Université Jean Moulin (Lyon III), 1, rue de
l'Université, B.P. 638, 69339 Lyon Cedex 02.
                                        1809, 1973
Tél: 72-72-20-20. Télex: 380311 lyon 111
Ut : dr, phil, let-civ, lang.
I : adm des entrep, ét du trav-sécurité sociale.

Université du Maine Le Mans, B.P. 535, Route de
Laval, 72017 Le Mans Cedex.   *1970*
Tél: 43-24-70-37
Ut : sc, let-hum, jur-éco-soc, sc exactes-nat.
I : techn.

Université de Metz, Ile du Saulcy, B.P. 794, 57012
Metz Cedex.   *1970*
Tél: 87-30-26-63. Fax: 87-30-24-44. Télex:
930462 univmtz
Ut : let-hum, sc exactes-nat, jur-éco-soc.
I : techn.

Université de Montpellier I, 5, boulevard Henri
IV, B.P. 1017, 34006 Montpellier Cedex.
                                        1220, 1970
Tél: 67-41-20-90. Télex: 490283 unimont
Ut : dr-soc, adm-éco-soc, gestion-dr, de l'entre-
priser soc-jur-éco (rech), méd, phar, alimbiol
(rech), phar ind, od, phys-sport, rech matér
alim-biol.

**Université des Sciences et Techniques du Langue-
doc (Montpellier II)**, Place Eugène-Bataillon,
34060 Montpellier Cedex.   *1220, 1970*
Tél: 67-63-91-44
Ut : sc de la vie, sc terre, formation gén,
formation des maîtres, formation sc fond,
math, phy, ch.
I : techn, sc de l'ing (ISIM), adm des aff; techn
(Nîmes).
E : ch.

Université Paul Valéry (Montpellier III), Route
de Mende, B.P. 5043, 34032 Montpellier
Cedex.   *1220, 1970*
Tél: 67-63-91-10
Ut : let-phil-art, lang-lit-civ médit, cultures-civ,
lang-lit-civ anglo-am-ger-slaves, lang-civ class-
iques, géog, soc-ethn, psyc, math app aux sc de
l'homme, éco app aux sc hum, ing, psychopéd
méd-socio.

Université de Haute-Alsace, 2, rue des Frères
Lumière, 68093 Mulhouse Cedex.   *1970, 1975*
Tél: 89-43-43-53
Ut : sc exactes-app, let-hum.

E : ch, industries, tex.
I : techn.

Université de Nancy I, 24-30, Rue Lionnois, B.P.
3137, 54013 Nancy Cedex.   *1572, 1970*
Tél: 83-32-81-81. Télex: 960646 nancyun
Ut : méd (2), phar-biol, sc biol, dent, sc
matière, sc math, sc terre-mét-ch minér, phy-
ch-biol, alim-nutr, phys.
E (sup) : sc et techn des ind du bois (ESSTIB)
(Epinal).
I : sc ing, techn.

Université de Nancy II, 25 rue Baron Louis, B.P.
454, 54001 Nancy Cedex.   *1572, 1970*
Tél: 83-37-12-97
Ut : jur-éco, let, lang-lit étr, math-inft, hist-
géog, phil-soc-psyc-péd, ling app, rech rég,
connaissance de l'homme.
I : com, techn, dr du trav, adm-pol.
Ce : télé-ensg européen universitaire.

Université de Nantes, 1, quai de Tourville, B.P.
1026, 44035 Nantes Cedex.   *1962, 1970*
Tél: 40-89-73-16. Fax: 40-89-67-98. Télex:
750579 univnan
Ut : méd-tec méd, phar, od, jur, éco, let-hum,
hist-socio, lang, géog, math, phy, ch, gé ind, sc
de la nature.
I : électro (IRESTE), thermique énerg-matér
(ISTEM), adm des entrep, techn; techn (Saint-
Nazaire).
E : méc, élec, therm, matériaux.

Université de Nice, Parc Valrose, 06034 Nice
Cedex.   *1965, 1970*
Tél: 93-52-98-98. Télex: 970281 uninice
Ut : méd, dr-éco, let-hum, dr de la paix et du
dév, sc-tec, math-sc phy, obs, od, phys.
E (sup) : inft (ESSI).
I : adm des entrep, poly, techn.

Université d'Orléans, Château de la Source,
Orléans 2, 45046 Orléans Cedex.   *1962, 1970*
Tél: 38-17-17-1
Télex: 783388 univorl
Ut : dr-éco, let-hum, sc fond-app, sc tec
avancées.
E (sup) : energ-matériaux (ESEM).
I : techn; techn (Bourges).
Ce : ét ligériennes.

*Université Panthéon-Sorbonne (Paris I), 12,
place du Panthéon, 75231 Paris Cedex 05.
                                        XIles., 1970
Tél: 46-34-97-00
Ut : éco-gestion, pol, éco-gestion, analyse-pol
éco, trav-ét soc, dr des aff, adm publ-dr publ, ét
eur-int & comparatives, art-arché, arts plast-sc
de l'art, géog, hist, philesthétique.
I : adm des entrep, ét du dév éco-soc, soc-trav,
démographie.

***Université de Droit, d'Economie et de Sciences
sociales (Paris II)**, 12, place du Panthéon, 75231
Paris Cedex 05.   *XIles., 1970*

Tél: 46-34-97-00

Ut : éco, ét pén-crim, hist-socio institutions et économie, dr des aff, adm publ, pol, ét eur-int-comparées, dr privé gén, dr publ-adm publ.

I : presse, hautes ét int, dr des aff, crim, dr comparé, ét judiciaires, dr romain; image et commun (IMAC) (St. Denis).

D : psyc soc-socio jur, lang mod-civ, inft, dr du trav.

Université de la Sorbonne-Nouvelle (Paris III), 17, rue de la Sorbonne, 75231 Paris Cedex 05. *Xlles., 1970*

Tél: 40-46-22-11

Ut : théât, lit gén & comparée, lang-lit anglo-phones, lang-civ Am latine, ét françaises pour l'étr, lang-civ Orient-Afrique Nord, italien-roumain, ét ibériques, ling-lit, ling gén-app.

E : interp-trad.

D : sc jur-éco-pol, cinéma, expression & commun, phys.

Université de Paris-Sorbonne (Paris IV), 1, rue Victor-Cousin, 75230 Paris Cedex 05. *Xlles., 1970*

Tél: 40-46-22-11

Ut : arché art, lang française, grec, latin, anglais, hist, géog, phil, ét ger, ét slavistique, italien-roumain, ét ibériques et latino-américaines, mus-musicologie, civ Occident mod (rech).

I : sc hum app, lit française.

Ce : ét lit-sc app.

D : inft, ét médié, islamologie, sc des relig, civ française, civ antiquités class, lang étr app.

Université René Descartes (Paris V), 12, rue de l'Ecole de Médecine, 75270 Paris Cedex 06. *Xlles., 1970*

Tél: 40-46-16-16

Ut : soc, psyc, ling gén-app, sc éd, math-logique-inft, méd (3), bioméd (rech), méd-biol, méd légale-dr méd-déontologie méd, od, phar-biol, mécanismes d'action des médicaments et des toxiques (rech), biol hum (rech), phys-sport, dr.

I : psyc, techn.

*Université Pierre-et-Marie Curie (Paris VI), 4, place Jussieu, 75230 Paris Cedex 05. *Xlles., 1970*

Tél: 43-36-25-25

Ut : math, analyse, méc, inft-stat, app de la phy, optique-phy atom moléculaires, phy des milieux condensés, phy théor, ch phy, ch org, ch inorg, bioch, physiologie animale, zoo, sc terre, méd (3), stom, génétique.

E : ch, sc-techn.

I : sc-techn (IST), phy du globe, stat, program-mation, biol végétale.

D : lang vivantes, géog, phys.

*Université de Paris VII, 2, place Jussieu, 75251 Paris Cedex 05. *Xlles., 1970*

Tél: 43-36-25-25. Télex: 270075 pariset

Ut : méd (2), hématologie, math, phy, ch, soc, phy de la terre, bioch, biol-génétique, didac-tique des disciplines scq, sc textes et documents (grec, latin, français), lang-civ d'Asie orntl, géog-sc de la société, sc hum clin, anth-ethnologie-sc des relig, dent.

I : anglais.

D : ling (rech), ét env, audio-visuel, sc terre, socio, inft gén, lang étr pour non spécialistes, formation perm, phys-sport.

Université de Vincennes-Saint-Denis (Paris VIII), 2, rue de la Liberté, 93526 Saint-Denis Cedex 02. *Xlles., 1970*

Tél: 48-21-63-64

Ut : allemand, arts, éco pol, ét lit, ét slaves-orntl-asiatiques, géog, urb, ét hist-socio, inft-ling, psyc-éd, phil-psycanalyse, sc jur-pol, soc, ét pays anglophones, lang romanes, éd.

*Université de Paris-Dauphine (Paris IX), Place du Maréchal de Lattre-de-Tassigny, 75776 Paris Cedex 16. *Xlles., 1970*

Tél: 45-05-14-10. Télex: 649322 upd

Ut : gestion-éco app, gestion, éco app, sc organisations, inft de gestion, math de la décision.

Université de Paris-Nanterre (Paris X), 200, avenue de la République, 92001 Nanterre Cedex. *Xlles., 1970*

Tél: 40-97-72-00. Télex: 63-08-98 upxnant

Ut : ét anglo-am, lang ger-slaves app, lang romanes, géog, hist, let anc-mod-ling, phil-hist de l'art-arché-math, psyc de l'éd, soc, éco, sc jur-pol, phys-sport, adm-dr publ.

I : techn (Ville d'Avray).

Université de Paris-Sud (Paris XI), Centre Scien-tifique, 15, rue Georges-Clémenceau, 91405 Orsay Cedex. *Xlles., 1970*

Tél: 69-41-67-50

Ut : math-phy, ch, biol-géog (orientation et formation), sc exactes-nat, ch (rech), accélér-ateur linéaire; sc jur-éco (Sceaux); méd, scq-méd; phar-biol, ch thérapeutique, hyg-protec-tion de l'homme (rech) (Châtenay-Malabry); phys (Bures-sur-Yvette).

I : techn (Saclay-Orsay); techn (Cachan); techn (Sceaux); phy nucl, optique théor et appl.

E : élec.

Formation : ing (FIUPSO).

*Université de Paris-Val-de-Marne (Paris XII), Avenue du Général de Gaulle, 94010 Créteil Cedex. *Xlles., 1970*

Tél: 48-98-91-44. Télex: 211752 upvm

Ut : méd, let-hum, sc adm-éco; dr-soc, éco (La Varenne St. Hilaire).

I : techn, urb.

Université Paris-Nord (Paris XIII), Avenue Jean-Baptiste Clément, 93430 Villetaneuse. *Xlles., 1970*

Tél: 49-40-30-00. Télex: 610670 usinor
Ut : éco-gestion, let-hum, scq-polytec, sc de
l'expression et de la commun, dr-pol.
Ce : sc-poly (CSP), méd-biol; méd (Bobigny);
sc-poly (Saint-Denis).
I : techn; techn (Saint-Denis).
Université de Pau et des Pays de l'Adour, Villa
Lawrence, 68, rue Montpensier, B.P. 576,
64010 Pau Cedex.   *1970*
Tél: 59-32-56-47
Ut : let-hum, sc exactes-nat, dr-éco.
I : rech scq; techn, jur-éco (Bayonne).
Université de Perpignan, Avenue de Villeneuve,
66025 Perpignan Cedex.   *1970*
Tél: 68-510051. Fax: 68-67122. Télex: 505005
Ut : hum-soc, sc exactes-nat, dr-éco.
I : techn.
*Université de Poitiers, 15, rue de Blossac, 86034
Poitiers Cedex.   *1431, 1970*
Tél: 49-88-26-32
Ut : jur-soc, éco-gestion, sc exactes-nat, sc
fond-app, lang-lit, hum, méd, phar, phys-sport.
I : techn, sc-tec; techn (La Rochelle).
E : méc-aéro (ISTP).
Ce : ét aérodynamiques-thermiques, ét civ
médié.
*Université de Reims Champagne-Ardennes, 23,
rue Boulard, 51100 Reims.   *1967, 1970*
Tél: 26-05-30-00
Ut : let-hum, méd, od, phar, sc (ISIP), dr-éco.
I : techn; techn (Troyes).
Université de Rennes (Rennes I), 2, rue du
Thabor, 35014 Rennes Cedex.   *1461, 1970*
Tél: 99-36-28-54
Ut : jur, éco-éco app à la gestion, physico-ch-
biol fond app, clin-thér méd, médicament, sa
dans la collectivité (rech), od, math-inft, struc-
tures-propriétés de la matière, sc vie-env, phil.
I : gestion, techn; techn (Lannion).
E (sup) : ch, sc app-techn (ENSSAT) (Lan-
nion).
Université de Haute-Bretagne (Rennes II), 6,
avenue Gaston Berger, 35043 Rennes Cedex.
                                       1461, 1970
Tél: 99-33-52-52
Ut : lang-lit-civ étr, anglais, géog-aménage-
ment de l'espace, sc hist-pol, arts, lit, psyc-
socio-sc éd, lang-sc culture (rech), phys-sport,
sc-tec.
I : armoricain de rech hist; techn (Vannes).
Université de Rouen-Haute-Normandie, Rue
Thomas Becket, 76134 Mont-Saint-Aignan.
                                       1967, 1970
Tél: 35-14-60-60. Télex: 770127 univrou
Ut : dr-éco, let-hum, sc-tec, sc comportement
et de l'éd; méd-phar (St. Etienne du Rouvray);
sc-tec (Le Havre).
I : techn (Rouen); techn (Le Havre).
D : aff int.

*Université Jean-Monnet, 34, rue Francis-
Baulier, 42023 Saint-Etienne Cedex.   *1970*
Tél: 77-25-22-02. Télex: 300816 unistet
Ut : dr-éco, méd, sc, let-hum, lang.
I : techn.
Université Louis Pasteur (Strasbourg I), 4, rue
Blaise Pascal, 67070 Strasbourg Cedex.
                                       1537, 1970
Tél: 88-41-60-00. Fax: 88-60-75-50. Télex:
870260 ulp
Ut : sc méd, sc bioméd (rech), sc phar, od,
math, phy-ch (rech), sc matière, sc vie-terre, sc
comportement-env, géog, éco, obs.
I : phy du globe.
E : application des hauts polymères, phy.
E (sup) : bio techn (ESBS).
Université des Sciences humaines (Strasbourg II),
22, rue Descartes, 67084 Strasbourg Cedex.
                                       1437, 1970
Tél: 88-41-73-00
Ut : lang class, lang-lit-civ étr, let mod, phil, sc
hist, soc, théo prot, théo cath, phys-sport.
Ce : phill romane.
Université Robert Schuman (Strasbourg III),
Place d'Athènes, 67084 Strasbourg Cedex.
                                       1437, 1970
Tél: 88-41-42-00
Ut : dr-pol, jur-pol-soc (rech), rech app et
techn.
I : trav, ét pol, éco app aux aff, com, ét eur,
techn.
Ce : ét int et propriété ind, jour.
Université de Toulon et du Var, Avenue de
l'Université, 83130 La Garde.   *1970*
Tél: 94-75-90-50
Ut : sc-tec, dr-éco.
I : techn.
Université des Sciences sociales (Toulouse I),
Place Anatole France, 31042 Toulouse Cedex.
                                       1229, 1970
Tél: 61-63-35-00
Ut : rech sur l'organisation des sociétés, dr 1er
cycle), dr (2e & 3e cycles), adm-éco-soc, éco,
inft, ét sp.
I : préparation aux aff, pol; techn (Rodez).
Université de Toulouse-le-Mirail (Toulouse II), 5,
allée Antonio Machado, 31058 Toulouse
Cedex.   *1229, 1970*
Tél: 61-41-11-05
Ut : ét phil-pol, sc comportement-éd, soc, lang-
lit-civ étr, let-lang anc, hist-arché-hist de l'art,
géog, éco-gestion, let mod, math-inft-stat, ét
hispaniques-hispano-am.
I : rech interdisciplinaire, techn.
Université Paul Sabatier (Toulouse III), 118,
route de Narbonne, 31062 Toulouse Cedex.
                                       1229, 1970
Tél: 61-55-66-11
Ut: math-inft-gestion, phy-ch automatique,

nat, dent, lang vivantes, sc phar, tec de réadaptation; sc méd (Purpan); sc méd (Rangueil); obs (2), phys-sport.
I : techn.
Université François Rabelais Tours, 3, rue des Tanneurs, 37041 Tours Cedex. *1962, 1970*
Tél: 47-38-56-00
Ut : méd, phar, sc exactes-nat, lang-lit-civ des pays anglophones, lang-lit-civ class et mod, sc de l'homme, dr-éco aménagement-géog-inft.
I : techn.
Ce : ét de la Renaissance.
Université de Valenciennes et du Hainaut-Cambrésis, Le Mont-Houy, 59326 Valenciennes Cedex. *1970*
Tél: 27-42-41-00. Télex: 810270 uni vhc
Ut : sc exactes-nat, let-hum-arts, dr-écogestion.
E : méc-énerg.
I : techn.

Institut National Polytechnique de Grenoble, 46, avenue Félix-Viallet, 38031 Grenoble Cedex. *1961, 1970*
Tél: 83-57-48-48
E : électro-radioélec; électroch-mét, élec, hyd, math app-inft, matériaux cellulosiques et processus papeterie (St.-Martin-d'Hères).
Institut National Polytechnique de Lorraine, Porte de la Craffe, B.P. 3308, 54014 Nancy Cedex. *1872, 1970*
Tél: 83-57-48-48
E : agr-ind-alim, géol app, ind mét-mine, ind ch, élec-méc.
Institut National Polytechnique de Toulouse, Place des Hauts-Murats, 31006 Toulouse Cedex. *1906, 1970*
Tél: 61-52-21-37
E : agr, électro tec, ch.
I : gé ch.

Private Establishments—Etablissements privés

***Université Catholique de l'Ouest**, 3, place André Leroy, B.P. 808, 49005 Angers Cedex. *1875*
Tél: 41-88-33-12
F : théo, let, sc.
E : ch.
Ce : ét françaises.
***Fédération Universitaire et Polytechnique de Lille**, 60, boulevard Vauban, 59046 Lille Cedex. *1873, 1974*
Tél: 20-30-88-27
F : théo, dr-éco, soc, méd-phar, let-hum, sc.
I : polytec, ét relig, mus liturgique, éco d'entreprise, scq-gestion, scq de haute direction, comp, cult francaises contemporaines, électro, agr, tec.
E : com, sec, inf, obst, masso-kinésithérpédicurie, trad-interp, lang étr, serv soc, ét ind, jour, péd, ing.
***Facultés Catholiques de Lyon**, 25-29 rue du Plat, 69288 Lyon Cedex 02. *1875*
Tél: 72-32-50-12
F : phil, dr-éco, théo, let-hum, sc, dr can.
I : lang & cult français, phil (rech), ét fam, péd,

soc app, théo, socio.
E : bioch-biol.
***Institut Catholique de Paris**, 21, rue d'Assas, 75270 Paris Cedex 06. *1875*
Tél: 42-22-41-80
D : théo.
F : dr can, phil, let, théo, sc.
I : soc, mus liturgique, pastorale catéchétique, ét relig, liturgie, ét œcuméniques, sc & théo des relig, péd, lang-cult françaises, interp-trad, électro, géol, phys; agr (Beauvais).
E : lang orntl anc, éco-com, psyc, psy-chopéd, bibl-doc, ch organique-minérale, phys (féminine), psyc-practiciens.
Ce : ibéro-am, hist relig (rech), jur-éco, péd.
Institut Catholique de Toulouse, 31, rue de la Fonderie, 31068 Toulouse Cedex. *1877*
Tél: 61-52-62-35
F : théo, dr can, phil, let.
I : ét relig et pastorales, péd.
E : sc; agr (Purpan); éd jeunes enfants, sec.
C : péd, ét soc, relig.

SPECIALIZED PUBLIC INSTITUTIONS*—
ETABLISSEMENTS PUBLICS SPECIALISES*

Collège de France, 11, place Marcelin Berthelot, 75005 Paris. *1530*
Tél: 43-29-12-11
Conservatoire national des Arts et Métiers, 292, rue Saint-Martin, 75141 Paris Cedex 03. *1794*
Tél: 42-27-20-00

***Ecole centrale des Arts et Manufactures**, Grande Voie des Vignes, 92290 Châtenay-Malabry. *1829*
Tél: 46-83-64-64. Télex: 250659 ecparis f
Ecole nationale des Chartes, 19, rue de la Sorbonne, 75005 Paris. *1821*

Tél: 46-33-41-82

Ecole nationale supérieure d'Arts et Métiers, 151, boulevard de l'Hôpital, 75640 Paris Cedex 13. *1912*
Tél: 43-36-49-55. Télex: 220064 etrav ext 379 f

Ecole des hautes Etudes en Sciences sociales, 54 boulevard Raspail, 75006 Paris.
Tél: 45-44-39-79

Ecole pratique des hautes Etudes, Palais de la Sorbonne, 46, rue Saint-Jacques, 75005 Paris.
1868
Tél: 43-54-83-57

*Institut d'Etudes politiques, 27, rue Saint-Guillaume, 75341 Paris Cedex 07.
Tél: 45-49-50-50

Institut national des Langues et Civilisations orientales, 2, rue de Lille, 75007 Paris. *1971*
Tél: 42-60-34-58

Muséum national d'Histoire naturelle, Jardin des Plantes, 57, rue Cuvier, 75005 Paris. *1635*
Tél: 43-36-14-41

Observatoire de Paris, avenue Denfert-Rochereau, 75014 Paris.
Tél: 40-51-22-21. Télex: 270776 obs

Palais de la Découverte, Avenue Franklin Roosevelt, 75008 Paris.
Tél: 43-59-16-65

* "Les Grands Etablissements"

OTHER INSTITUTIONS—AUTRES INSTITUTIONS

Public Establishments (1)—Etablissements publics (1)

Schools of Engineering—Ecoles d'Ingénieurs

Ecole nationale de l'Aviation civile, 7, avenue Edouard Belin, B.P. 4005, 31055 Toulouse Cedex. *1948*
Tél: 61-55-79-99. Télex: 530452 enactse

Ecole nationale supérieure de l'Aéronautique et de l'Espace, 10, avenue Edouard-Belin, B.P. 4032, 31055 Toulouse Cedex. *1909*
Tél: 61-33-48-48. Télex: 531642 supaero f

Ecole nationale supérieure d'Ingénieurs de Constructions aéronautiques, 49 avenue Léon-Blum, 31056 Toulouse Cedex. *1948*
Tél: 61-48-63-11. Télex: 531620 ceat f

Ecole nationale supérieure d'Arts et Métiers, 2, cours des Arts-et-Métiers, 13617 Aix-en-Provence. *1843*
Tél: 42-38-13-02. Fax: 42-38-66-64

Ecole nationale supérieure d'Arts et Métiers, 2, boulevard du Roncerey, 49000 Angers.
Tél: 41-88-54-25

Ecole nationale supérieure d'Arts et Métiers, 3-5, rue de La Rochefoucauld, 51006 Châlons-sur-Marne. *1806*
Tél: 26-65-15-55

Ecole nationale supérieure d'Arts et Métiers, 71250 Cluny.
Tél: 85-59-02-25

Ecole nationale supérieure d'Arts et Métiers, 8, boulevard Louis XIV, 59046 Lille Cedex.
Tél: 20-53-11-00. Fax: 20-53-55-93

Ecole nationale supérieure des Arts et Industries, 24, boulevard de la Victoire, 67084 Strasbourg Cedex. *1875*
Tél: 88-35-55-05

Ecole nationale supérieure d'Arts et Métiers, Esplanade de l'Université, 33405 Talence.
1806
Tél: 56-80-76-50. Fax: 56-37-90-34

Ecole centrale de Lyon, 36, avenue Guy Collonghue, 69130 Ecully. *1857*
Tél: 78-33-81-27. Télex: 310856 ece ly ing

Ecole nationale supérieure de Céramique industrielle, 47 rue Albert Thomas, 87065 Limoges Cedex. *1893*
Tél: 55-79-34-80

Ecole nationale d'Ingénieurs de Belfort, 8, rue Anatole-France, 90016 Belfort Cedex. *1962*
Tél: 84-21-37-00. Télex: 361526 emi bel

Ecole nationale d'Ingénieurs de Brest (Constructions électroniques), Avenue Victor le Gorgeu, 29283 Brest Cedex. *1961*
Tél: 98-03-30-31

Ecole nationale d'Ingénieurs de Metz, Ile du Saulcy, 57045 Metz. *1962*
Tél: 87-32-53-05. Fax: 87-30-39-89. Télex: 860217 enimetz

Ecole nationale d'Ingénieurs de Saint-Etienne, 56, rue Jean Parot, 42023 Saint-Etienne Cedex.

---

(1) Many of the institutions listed in this section also fall within the framework of one of the universities.

(1) Nombre des établissements répertoriés dans cette section fonctionnent également dans le cadre d'une université.

1961
Tél: 77-25-71-40. Télex: 307125 enise
Ecole nationale d'Ingénieurs de Tarbes, Chemin
d'Azereix, B.P. 311, 65013 Tarbes Cedex. *1963*
Tél: 62-93-98-21
**Ecole nationale supérieure de Chimie et de
Physique de Bordeaux**, 351, cours de la Libér-
ation, 33405 Talence. *1891*
Tél: 56-80-78-93
**Ecole nationale supérieure de Chimie de
Clermont-Ferrand**, Ensemble scientifique des
Cézeux, 24, avenue des Landais, B.P. 71, 63170
Aubière. *1908*
Tél: 73-26-41-10
Ecole nationale supérieure de Chimie de Lille,
Centre Universitaire scientifique, B.P. 40,
59652 Villeneuve-d'Ascq, Cedex. *1894*
Tél: 20-91-00-95. Fax: 20-47-05-99
**Ecole nationale supérieure de Chimie de Mont-
pellier**, 8, rue de l'Ecole normale, 34075 Mont-
pellier Cedex. *1908*
Tél: 67-63-52-73
**Ecole nationale supérieure d'Ingénieurs de
Chimie de Mulhouse**, 3, rue Alfred-Werner,
68013 Mulhouse Cedex. *1822*
Tél: 89-42-70-20
**Ecole nationale supérieure des Industries chim-
iques de Nancy**, 1, rue de Grandville, 54042
Nancy.
Tél: 83-35-21-21. Télex: 961316 f
Ecole nationale supérieure de Chimie de Paris, 11,
rue Pierre-et-Marie-Curie, 75231 Paris Cedex
05.
Tél: 43-36-25-25
Ecole nationale supérieure de Chimie de Rennes,
Avenue du Général Leclerc, 35000 Rennes-
Beaulieu. *1919*
Tél: 99-36-29-95
**Ecole nationale supérieure d'Ingénieurs de Génie
chimique de Toulouse**, Chemin de la Loge,
31078 Toulouse Cedex.
Tél: 61-52-92-41
**Ecole nationale supérieure de Chimie de Tou-
louse**, 118, route de Narbonne, 31077 Toulouse
Cedex.
Tél: 61-53-14-21
**Ecole nationale supérieure de l'Electronique et de
ses Applications**, Impasse des Chênes-
Pourpres, 95000 Cergy. *1952*
Tél: 30-30-92-44
**Ecole nationale supérieure d'Electronique et de
Radioélectricité de Bordeaux**, Faculté des
Sciences, 351, cours de la Libération, 33405
Talence Cedex. *1920*
Tél: 56-80-84-50. Fax: 56-37-20-23
**Ecole nationale supérieure d'Ingénieurs-électric-
iens de Grenoble**, Domaine Universitaire, B.P.
46, 38402 Saint-Martin-d'Hères.
Tél: 76-82-62-00. Télex: 320245 public x greno f

**Ecole nationale supérieure d'Electrochimie et
d'Electrométallurgie de Grenoble**, Domaine
Universitaire, 38403 Saint-Martin-d'Hères.
Tél: 76-82-65-00
**Ecole nationale supérieure d'Electronique et de
Radioélectricité de Grenoble**, 23, rue des
Martyrs, 38031 Grenoble.
Tél: 76-87-69-76
**Ecole nationale supérieure d'Electricité et de
Mécanique de Nancy**, 2, rue de la Citadelle,
B.P. 850, 54011 Nancy Cedex.
Tél: 82-32-39-01. Télex: 961316 ensem
**Ecole nationale supérieure d'Electrotechnique,
d'Electronique, et d'Informatique et d'Hydrau-
lique de Toulouse**, 2, rue Charles Camichel,
31071 Toulouse Cedex.
Tél: 61-58-82-00. Télex: 530161 f
Institut français du Froid industriel, Conserva-
toire nationale des Arts et Métiers, 292, rue
Saint-Martin, 75141 Paris Cedex 03. *1942*
Tél: 40-27-20-00
Ecole nationale des Sciences géographiques, Insti-
tut géographique national, 2, avenue Pasteur,
94160 Saint-Mandé. *1941*
Tél: 43-74-12-15
**Ecole nationale supérieure de Géologie et de
Prospection minière de Nancy**, 94, avenue de
Lattre-de-Tassigny, B.P. 452, 54001 Nancy
Cedex.
Tél: 83-32-85-86
Ecole supérieure de Géomètres et Topographes,
(Conservatoire national des Arts et Métiers),
18, allée Jean Rostand, 91000 Evry.
Tél: 60-77-97-40
**Ecole d'Application des Hauts Polymères de
l'Université de Strasbourg I**, 4, rue Boussing-
ault, 67000 Strasbourg. *1965*
Tél: 88-41-65-00
**Ecole nationale supérieure d'Hydraulique et de
Mécanique de Grenoble**, Domaine Universit-
aire, B.P. 53, 38400 Saint-Martin-d'Hères.
Tél: 76-82-50-00. Télex: 980668 hymegre
Institut industriel du Nord de la France, Domaine
Universitaire scientifique de Lille, B.P. 48,
59651 Villeneuve-d'Ascq.
Tél: 20-91-01-15
**Ecole nationale supérieure des Techniques indus-
trielles et des Mines d'Alès,** 6, avenue de
Clavières, 30107 Alès Cedex. *1843*
Tél: 27-87-16-14. Télex: 490623 f
**Ecole nationale des Techniques industrielles et des
Mines de Douai**, 941, rue Charles Bourseul,
59508 Douai Cedex. *1878*
Tél: 27-87-16-14. Fax: 27-88-30-36. Télex:
820795 drinpdc f
**Centre d'Etudes supérieures des Techniques
industrielles**, 3, rue Ferdinand Hainaut, 93407
Saint-Ouen. *1956*
Tél: 40-11-43-85

Institut d'Informatique d'Entreprise (Conservatoire national des Arts et Métiers), 18, allée Jean-Rostand, 91002 Evry Cedex.
Tél: 60-77-97-40

Ecole nationale supérieure d'Informatique et de Mathématiques appliquées de Grenoble (Institut national polytechnique), Domaine Universitaire, B.P. 68, 38400 Saint-Martin-d'Hères.
Tél: 76-51-46-00. Fax: 76-51-33-79

Ecole des Ingénieurs de la Ville de Paris, 57, boulevard St. Germain, 75006 Paris.
Tél: 46-34-21-99

Institut supérieur des Matériaux et de la Construction Mécanique (Ecole de spécialisation), 3, rue Fernand Hainaut, 93407 Saint-Ouen Cedex.   *1948*
Tél: 46-06-40-85. Télex: 281125 ismcm f

Institut des Sciences de la Matière et du Rayonnement, 5, avenue d'Edimbourg, 14032 Caen Cedex.
Tél: 31-93-37-14

Ecole nationale supérieure de Mécanique et des Microtechniques, La Boutoie, Route de Gray, 25030 Besançon.   *1927*
Tél: 81-50-36-55

Ecole nationale supérieure de Mécanique, 1, rue de la Noë, 44072 Nantes Cedex.   *1919*
Tél: 40-37-16-00. Télex: 711716 ensiminte f

Ecole nationale supérieure de Mécanique et d'Aérotechnique de Poitiers, Rue Guillaume VII, 86034 Poitiers.   *1948*
Tél: 49-88-32-17

Ecole nationale d'Ingénieurs de Mécanique et d'Energétique, Le Mont-Houy, 59326 Valenciennes Cedex.
Tél: 27-41-14-20

Ecole nationale de la Météorologie, avenue Gustave Cariolis, 31057 Toulouse Cédex.
Tél: 61-07-90-90. Fax: 61-07-96-30. Télex: 521990 mto jd f.

Ecole supérior de Métrologie, 941 rue Charles Bourseul, 59508 Douai Cedex
Tél: 27-87-16-14

Ecole nationale supérieure des Mines de Nancy, Parc de Saurupt, 54042 Nancy Cedex.
Tél: 83-57-42-32. Télex: 850661 emin

Ecole nationale supérieure des Mines de Paris, 60, boulevard Saint-Michel, 75006 Paris.   *1783*
Tél: 43-29-21-05. Fax: 64-22-39. Télex: 694736 minefon

Ecole nationale supérieure des Mines de Paris, 35, rue St. Honoré, 77305 Fontainebleau.

Ecole nationale supérieure des Mines, 158, cours Fauriel, 42023 Saint-Etienne.   *1816*
Tél: 77-42-01-23. Télex: 300923 emse

Institut national des Sciences et Techniques nucléaires, B.P. 6, 91190 Gif-sur-Yvette.
                                                      1956
Tél: 69-08-24-19

Ecole nationale supérieure du Pétrole et des Moteurs, 4, avenue de Bois-Préau, B.P. 311, 92502 Rueil-Malmaison Cedex.   *1925*
Tél: 47-49-02-14. Fax: 47-49-04-11. Télex: 203050 ifp af

Ecole supérieure d'Ingénierie de Pétroléochimie et de Synthèse organique industrielle d'Aix Marseille III, Domaine Universitaire de St. Jérôme, Rue Henri-Poincaré, 13397 Marseille Cedex 4.   *1959*
Tél: 91-98-33-89

Ecole nationale supérieure de Physique, Domaine Universitaire, B.P. 46, 38402 Saint-Martin-d'Héres Cedex.
Tél: 76-82-62-00

Ecole nationale supérieure de Physique de Marseille, Domaine Universitaire de St. Jérôme, avenue de l'Escadrille, 13397 Marseille Cedex 4.   *1959*
Tél: 91-98-90-10. Télex: 402876 facse j f

Ecole supérieure de Physique et Chimie industrielles de la Ville de Paris, 10, rue Vauquelin, 75231 Paris Cedex 05.   *1882*
Tél: 43-37-77-00

Ecole nationale supérieure de Physique de Strasbourg, 7, rue de l'Université, 67000 Strasbourg.
Tél: 88-35-51-50. Télex: 870260 ulp f

Institut de Physique du Globe de l'Université de Strasbourg I, 5, rue René Descartes, 67084 Strasbourg.   *1919*
Tél: 88-41-63-00. Télex: 870260 ulp f

Ecole polytechnique, Route de Saclay, 91128 Palaiseau Cedex.   *1794*
Tél: 69-41-82-00. Fax: 69-41-33-92. Télex: 691596 ecolex f

Ecole nationale des Ponts et Chaussées, 28, rue des Saints-Pères, 75007 Paris.   *1747*
Tél: 42-60-34-13. Fax: 42-60-34-13-1700. Télex: 216278 f

Institut national des Sciences appliquées de Lyon, 20, avenue Albert-Einstein, 69621 Villeurbanne Cedex.   *1957*
Tél: 78-94-81-25. Télex: 380856 insalyn f

Institut national des Sciences appliquées de Rennes, 20, avenue des Buttes-de-Coësmes, 35031 Rennes Cedex.   *1966*
Tél: 99-28-64-00

Institut national des Sciences appliquées de Rouen, place Emile Blondel, B.P. 8, 76130 Mont-Saint-Aignan.
Tél: 35-71-29-72

Institut national des Sciences appliquées, Avenue de Rangueil, 31077 Toulouse Cedex.   *1963*
Tél: 61-55-95-26

Université de Technologie de Compiègne, Rue Roger Couttolenc, B.P. 233, 60206 Compiègne Cedex.
Tél: 44-20-99-77. Fax: 44-86-43-90 sc appl.

Ecole nationale supérieure de Techniques avancées, 32, boulevard Victor, 75015 Paris.
1969
Tél: 45-52-43-21 (Ext. 4401)

Ecole nationale supérieure des Télécommunications de Bretagne, B.P. 856, 29279 Brest Cedex.
Tél: 98-00-11-11. Télex: 940729 f

Institut national des Télécommunications, Ilot des Epinettes, 91011 Evry.
Tél: 60-77-94-11. Télex: 200914 direnseg f

Ecole nationale supérieure des Télécommunications, 46, rue Barrault, 75013 Paris.   *1878*
Tél: 45-81-77-77. Télex: 200180 suptlcm

Ecole nationale supérieure des Industries textiles, 11, rue A.-Werner, 68093 Mulhouse Cedex.

1861
Tél: 89-42-46-22

Ecole nationale supérieure des Arts et Industries textiles de Roubaix, 2, place des Martyrs de la Résistance, 59070 Roubaix Cedex 01.   *1885*
Tél: 20-70-94-82

Ecole technique supérieure des Travaux maritimes, Rue Maurice-Audin, 69120 Vaulx-en-Velin.
Tél: 78-80-82-69

Ecole nationale des Travaux publics de l'Etat, Rue Maurice Audin, B.P. 4, 69120 Vaulx-en-Velin.   *1891, 1953*
Tél: 72-04-70-70. Télex: 370511 entpe f

Schools of Agriculture and Food Technology— Ecoles agronomiques et des Industries alimèntaires

Ecole supérieure de Formation agricole, 44, rue Rabelais, 49044 Angers Cedex.
Tél: 41-88-58-12

Ecole nationale de Formation agronomique, Route de Narbonne, B.P. 87 31326 Castenet Tolosan Cedex.
Tél: 61-73-04-25

Ecole nationale d'Ingénieurs des Travaux agricoles (option Horticulture), 2, rue Le Nôtre, 49045 Angers Cedex.
Tél: 41-48-36-24

Ecole nationale d'Ingénieurs des Travaux agricoles de Bordeaux, 1, cours du Général de Gaulle, 33170 Gradignan.   *1962*
Tél: 56-04-03-03

Ecole nationale d'Ingénieurs des Travaux agricoles de Dijon, 2 boulevard Olivier de Serres, 21812 Quetigny.
Tél: 80-46-30-01

Ecole nationale d'Ingénieurs de Travaux agricoles de Marmilhet, 63370 Lempdes-Clermont-Ferrand.
Tél: 73-92-52-36

Ecole nationale supérieure des Industries agricoles et alimentaires, 1, Avenue des Olympiades, 91305 Massy Cedex.   *1893*
Tél: 69-20-05-23. Télex: 602174 ensia

Ecole nationale supérieure d'Agronomie et des Industries alimentaires de Nancy, 2, avenue de la Forêt de la Haye, 54800 Vandoeuvre-les-Nancy 54500.
Tél: 73-92-52-36

Ecole nationale d'Ingénieurs des Techniques des Industries agricoles et alimentaires, Chemin de la Geraudière, 44072 Nantes Cedex 03 44072.
Tél: 40-40-03-00

Ecole nationale supérieure des Sciences agronomiques appliquées, 26, boulevard Docteur Petit-

jean, B.P. 588, 21016 Dijon Cedex. *1920, 1966*
Tél: 80-66-54-12

Ecole supérieure d'Agronomie tropicale dépendant du Centre national d'Etudes agronomiques des Régions chaudes, avenue du Val-de-Montjenaud, 34033 Montpellier Cedex.
Tél: 67-54-55-33

Ecole nationale supérieure d'agronomie, 9, place Viala, 34060 Montpellier Cedex.   *1872*
Tél: 67-61-22-00. Fax: 67-61-25-80. Télex: 490818 f

*Institut national agronomique Paris-Grignon, 16, rue Claude-Bernard, 75005 Paris.
Tél: 45-70-15-50. Télex: 250985 inapng f

Ecole nationale supérieure agronomique, 65, rue de Saint-Brieuc, 35042 Rennes Cedex.   *1826*
Tél: 99-59-02-40

Ecole nationale supérieure agronomique, 145, avenue de Muret, 31076 Toulouse Cedex.
Tél: 61-42-83-98. Cables: ensagro toulouse

Ecole nationale supérieure agronomique féminine de Rennes, 65, rue de Saint-Brieuc, 35042 Rennes Cedex.   *1964*
Tél: 99-59-12-44

Ecole nationale du Génie rural, des Eaux et des Forêts, 14 rue Girardet, 54042 Nancy Cedex.
Tél: 83-35-10-20

Ecole nationale du Génie rural, des Eaux et Forêts, 19, avenue du Maine, 75732 Paris Cedex 15.   *1874*
Tél: 45-49-88-00. Télex: 200574 engref f

Ecole nationale d'Ingénieurs des Travaux des Eaux et Forêts, Domaine des Barres, 45290 Nogent-sur-Vernisson.   *1884*
Tél: 38-97-60-20

Institut d'Etudes supérieures d'Industries et d'Economie laitières, 16, rue Claude-Bernard, 75231 Paris Cedex 05.

Tél: 47-07-16-45
Ecole nationale d'Ingénieurs des Travaux ruraux et des Techniques sanitaires, 1, quai Koch, B.P. 1039F, 67070 Strasbourg Cedex.   *1960*
Tél: 88-35-67-72. Télex: 890942 entrts
Ecole nationale des Haras, Le Pin au Haras, 61310 Exmes.   *1892*
Tél: 33-67-92-79
Ecole nationale supérieure d'Horticulture, 4, rue Hardy, 78000 Versailles.   *1873*
Tél: 39-50-60-87
Institut d'Œnologie, Domaine Universitaire, 351, cours de la Libération, 33405 Talence Cedex.   *1957*
Tél: 56-80-77-91

Institut national de Promotion supérieure agricole, Rue des Champs Prévois, 21100 Dijon.
Tél: 80-66-72-27
Ecole nationale supérieure de Biologie appliquée à la Nutrition et à l'Alimentation Dijon, Campus Universitaire Montmuzard, 21100 Dijon.
Tél: 80-65-14-12. Télex: 350188 dijuniv f
Institut scientifique et technique de l'Alimentation, 292, rue Saint-Martin, 75003 Paris.
Tél: 48-87-37-38
Institut d'Elevage et de Médecine vétérinaire des Pays tropicaux, 10, rue Pierre-Curie, 94704 Maisons-Alfort.   *1920*
Tél: 43-68-88-73

Schools of Education—Ecoles normales supérieures

Ecole normale supérieure, 45, rue d'Ulm, 75230 Paris Cedex 05.   *1794*
Tél: 43-29-12-25
Ecole normale supérieure, 48, boulevard Jourdan, 75690 Paris Cedex 14 (Lettres)
Tél: 45-89-08-33
1, rue Maurice Arnoux, 92120 Montrouge (Sciences).   *1881*
Tél: 46-57-12-86
Ecole normale supérieure de Fontenay-aux-Roses, 31, av. Lombart, 92260 Fontenay-aux-Roses.   *1887*

Tél: 47-02-60-50
Ecole normale supérieure de Saint-Cloud, Avenue de la Grille d'Honneur, Parc de Saint-Cloud, 92211 Saint-Cloud.   *1882, 1945*
Tél: 47-71-91-11. Fax: 46-02-39-11
Ecole normale supérieure, 61, avenue du Président-Wilson, 94230 Cachan.   *1912*
Tél: 46-64-15-51. Fax: 47-40-20-74. Télex: 250948 enset f
Ecole normale supérieure de Lyon, 46, allée d'Italie, 69364 Lyon Cedex.
Tél: 72-73-48-25

Schools of Commerce and Business Administration— Ecoles de Commerce et de Gestion

Institut d'Administration des Entreprises, 29, avenue Robert-Schuman, 13617 Aix-en-Provence Cedex.   *1955*
Tél: 42-59-09-47
Institut d'Administration des Entreprises, Domaine Universitaire de Saint-Martin d'Hères, 47x, 38040 Grenoble Cedex.   *1956*
Tél: 76-54-81-78
Institut d'Administration et de Gestion des Entreprises, 15, quai Claude Bernard, 69007 Lyon Cedex 1.   *1936*
Tél: 78-69-24-93
Institut d'Administration des Entreprises, Avenue Emile-Henriot, 06005 Nice.   *1966*
Tél: 93-87-14-51
Institut d'Administration des Entreprises, 162, rue St. Charles, 75740 Paris Cedex 15.   *1956*
Tél: 45-54-97-24
Institut d'Administration des Entreprises, 43, place Charles de Gaulle, 86022 Poitiers Cedex.   *1956*
Tél: 49-88-27-54

Ecole nationale d'Assurances, 292, rue Saint-Martin, 75003 Paris.   *1946*
Tél: 42-71-24-14
Institut technique de Banque, 292, rue Saint-Martin, 75141 Paris Cedex 03.   *1950*
Tél: 48-87-64-40
Institut d'Etudes commerciales, Domaine Universitaire de Saint-Martin d'Hères, 47x, 38400 Grenoble Cédex.   *1912, 1956*
Tél: 76-54-81-78. Télex: 980910 unisog f
Institut commercial de Nancy, 4, rue de la Ravinelle, 54000 Nancy.   *1905*
Tél: 83-35-22-52
Institut européen d'Etudes commerciales supérieures, 3, avenue d'Alsace, 67000 Strasbourg.   *1919, 1956*
Tél: 88-36-56-77
Institut de Techniques Comptables, Domaine universitaire Littéraire et Juridique, sac postal 19, 59650 Villeneuve-d'Ascq.
Tél: 20-91-10-26

Institut d'Economie appliquée aux Affaires, 61, avenue des Vosges, 67000 Strasbourg.
Tél: 88-35-03-82

Institut d'Economie régionale et de Droit de l'Aménagement du Territoire, 42, rue Paul-Daez, 59000 Lille.
Tél: 20-53-16-29

Institut national des Techniques économiques et comptables, 292, rue Saint-Martin, 75141 Paris Cedex 3.
Tél: 42-71-24-14

Institut d'Etudes économiques et juridiques appliquées à la Construction et à l'Habitation, 2, cours des Arts-et-Métiers, Alx-en-Provence.
Tél: 42-38-13-02

Institut d'Etudes du Développement économique et social, 58, boulevard Arago, 75013 Paris.
1957
Tél: 43-36-23-55

Institut de Recherche économique et de Planification, Domaine Universitaire, 47x, 38400 St-Martin-d'Hères.
1969
Tél: 76-54-81-78

Institut technique de Prévision économique et sociale, 292, rue Saint-Martin, 75141 Paris Cedex 03.
Tél: 42-71-24-14

Institut de Science financière et d'Assurances de l'Université Claude Bernard, 43, boulevard du 11 novembre 1918, 69622 Villeurbanne Cedex.
1930
Tél: 78-89-73-38

Centre régional de Formation des Personnels Communaux, 249, rue Pierre Brossolette Esquerdes, 62380 Lumbres.

Institut régional de Gestion, 35, place Pey-Berland, 33076 Bordeaux Cedex.
1956
Tél: 56-52-9-88

Institut de Gestion de Rennes, 9, rue Jean-Macé, 35000 Rennes.
1955
Tél: 99-36-24-57

Institut de Préparation aux Affaires, 4, boulevard Gabriel, 21000 Dijon.
1963
Tél: 80-65-35-66

Institut de Préparation aux Affaires, 1 *bis*, rue Georges-Lefèvre, 59000 Lille.
Tél: 20-52-32-56

Institut de Préparation aux Affaires, Place Eugène-Bataillon, 34060 Montpellier Cedex.
Tél: 67-63-91-44

Institut de Préparation aux Affaires, 2, rue Albert-Lautman, 31070 Toulouse Cedex.
Tél: 61-21-55-18

Institut de Statistique, 4, place Jussieu, 75230 Paris Cedex 05.
1922
Tél: 43-36-25-25

Ecole nationale de la Statistique et de l'Administration économique, 3, avenue Pierre Larousse, 92241 Malakoff Cedex.
1942
Tél: 45-40-10-11

Institut d'Etudes supérieures des Techniques de l'organisation, Conservatoire national des Arts et Métiers, 292, rue Saint-Martin, 75141 Paris Cedex 03.
1956
Tél: 42-71-24-14

Schools of Political Science and Public Service—
Ecoles d'Etudes politiques et de la Fonction publique

Centre de Préparation à l'Administration générale, 25, rue Gaston-de-Saporta, 13625 Aix-en-Provence Cedex.
Tél: 42-59-01-15

Institut de Préparation à l'Administration générale, U.E.R. de Droit, Esplanade de la Paix, 14032 Caen.
Tél: 31-93-11-78

Institut de Préparation à l'Administration générale, 36, bd Côte-Blatin, 63000 Clermont-Ferrand Cedex.
Tél: 73-35-22-88

Institut de Préparation à l'Administration générale, Avenue du Général de Gaulle, 94010 Créteil Cedex.
Tél: 48-98-91-44

Institut de Préparation à l'Administration générale, 4, boulevard Gabriel, 21000 Dijon.

Tél: 80-39-55-00

Centre de Préparation à l'Administration générale, I.E.P., Domaine Universitaire de Saint-Martin d'Hères, B.P. 17, 38402 Grenoble Cedex.
Tél: 76-54-13-54

Institut de Préparation à l'Administration générale, Rue de Lille, B.P. 19, 59650 Villeneuve d'Ascq Cedex.
Tél: 20-91-10-26

Centre de Préparation à l'Administration générale, I.E.P., 1, rue Raulin, 69007 Lyon.
Tél: 78-72-85-63

Institut de Préparation à l'Administration générale, UER de Droit, 39, rue de l'Université, 34060 Montpellier Cedex.
Tél: 67-60-50-66

Institut de Préparation à l'Administration

générale, 4, rue de la Ravinelle, 54000 Nancy.
Tél: 82-32-05-10

Institut de Préparation à l'Administration générale, 4, rue Danton, 75270 Paris Cedex 06.
Tél: 43-26-94-81

Centre de Préparation à l'Administration générale, 10, rue de l'Université, 86000 Poitiers.
Tél: 49-41-66-38

Institut de Préparation à l'Administration générale, 4, place St. Mélaine, 35000 Rennes.
Tél: 99-38-77-33

Institut de Préparation à l'Administration générale, 9, place de l'Université, 67084 Strasbourg Cedex.
Tél: 88-35-59-40

Centre de Préparation à l'Administration générale, I.E.P., Allée Ausone, B.P. 101, 33405 Talence Cedex.
Tél: 56-80-60-57

Centre de Préparation à l'Administration générale, I.E.P.,*2ter*, rue des Puits-Creusés, 31000 Toulouse.
Tél: 61-21-93-10

Institut national d'Administration publique, 2, avenue de l'Observatoire, 75006 Paris   *1966*
Tél: 43-20-12-60. Cables: insintap

Ecole nationale d'Administration, 13, rue de l'Université, 75007 Paris.   *1945*
Tél: 42-61-55-35

Institut d'Etudes administratives et politiques, 4, rue de la Ravinelle, 54001 Nancy.   *1955*
Tél: 83-35-91-13

Institut régional d'Administration, quai des Martyrs de la Libération, B.P. 208, 20200 Bastia (Corse).
Tél: 95-32-22-00. Télex: 40370

Institut régional d'Administration, 49, rue Jean-Jaurès, B.P. 213, 59018 Lille.
Tél: 20-52-02-02. Fax: 20-85-07-13

Institut régional d'Administration, 15, avenue de Lyon, 57000 Metz.
Tél: 87-75-44-11

Institut régional d'Administration, 6, route de la Jonelière, 44300 Nantes.
Tél: 40-74-34-77. Cables: I.R.A. nantes

Institut régional d'Administration, 1, avenue Dutrievoz, B.P. 2016, 69616 Villeurbanne Cedex.   *1970*
Tél: 78-89-89-41

Ecole nationale du Cadastre, 76, chemin du Calquet, 31081 Toulouse Cedex.
Tél: 61-49-30-87

Ecole nationale de la Concurrence et de la Con-

sommation, 6, rue Saint-Maur, 75011 Paris.
Tél: 43-79-41-10

Institut de Démographie, Esplanade de la Paix, 14032 Caen Cedex.   *1954*
Tél: 31-94-59-10

Institut de Démographie, 13, place Carnot, 54000 Nancy.   *1954*
Tél: 28-52-21-00. Cables: idun-université nancy

Institut de Démographie, 22, rue Vauquelin, 75005 Paris.   *1957*
Tél: 43-37-48-11

Institut national des Techniques de la Documentation, 292, rue Saint-Martin, 75141 Paris Cedex.   *1950*
Tél: 48-87-64-40

Ecole nationale des Douanes, 86 Boulevard Orléans 76037 Rouen.   *1947*
Tél: 46-24-94-97. Fax: 35-62-08-55-434

Ecole nationale des Impôts, 1, rue Ledru, 63033 Clermont-Ferrand Cedex.   *1951*
Tél: 73-93-88-44

Ecole nationale de la Magistrature, 8, rue Chanoinesse, 75004 Paris.
Tél: 43-26-22-11

Ecole nationale supérieure de Police, 8, avenue Gambetta, 69450 St. Cyr-au-Mont d'Or.   *1941*
Tél: 78-64-02-88

Institut d'Etudes politiques, 25, rue Gaston-de-Saporta, Place de l'Université, 13625 Aix-en-Provence Cedex.   *1956*
Tél: 42-21-06-72

Institut d'Etudes politiques, 1, rue Raulin, 69365 Lyon Cedex 2.   *1948*
Tél: 78-72-85-63

Institut d'Etudes politiques, Domaine Universitaire, B.P. 45, 38402 St-Martin-d'Hères Cedex.   *1946*
Tél: 76-54-13-54

Institut d'Etudes politiques, 9, place de l'Université, 67084 Strasbourg Cedex.   *1945*
Tél: 88-35-59-40

Institut d'Etudes politiques, Domaine Universitaire, Allée Ausone, B.P. 101, 33405 Talence-Pessac Cedex.   *1948*
Tél: 56-80-60-57

Institut d'Etudes politiques, 2 *ter*, rue des Puits-Creusés, 31000 Toulouse.   *1947*
Tél: 61-21-93-10

Ecole nationale des Services du Trésor, Bois de la Grange, Noisiel, 77420 Champs-sur-Marne Cedex.
Tél: 60-05-92-04

Schools of Architecture and Fine Arts—Ecoles d'Architecture et des Beaux-Arts

Ecole d'Architecture de Bordeaux, Domaine de Raba, Cours de la Libération, 33405 Talence Cedex.
Tél: 56-80-65-44. Fax: 56-37-03-23
Antenne Pédagogique d'Architecture, B.P. 47, 95000 Cergy Cedex.
Ecole d'Architecture de Clermont-Ferrand, 71, boulevard Côte-Blatin, 63000 Clermont-Ferrand.   *1968*
Tél: 73-93-18-55
Ecole d'Architecture de Grenoble, 10, Galerie des Baladins, 38000 Grenoble.   *1927, 1968*
Tél: 76-23-31-72. Télex: 308658 cratere
Ecole d'Architecture de Lille, Rue Verte, quartier de l'Hôtel de Ville, 59650 Villeneuve d'Ascq.   *1775*
Tél: 20-91-26-41
Ecole d'Architecture de Lyon, 27, rue de Villeneuve, 69130 Ecully.
Tél: 17-33-01-14
Ecole d'Architecture de Marseille-Luminy, Domaine de Luminy, 70 Route Leon Lachamps, 13288 Marseille-Luminy Cedex 2.
1752
Tél: 91-26-80-80
Ecole d'Architecture du Languedoc-Roussillon, 179, rue de l'Espérance, .Plan des Quatre-Seigneurs, 34000 Montpellier.
Tél: 67-63-34-30
Ecole d'Architecture de Nancy, Parc de Rémincourt, 54600 Villers-les-Nancy.
Tél: 83-27-10-77. Fax: 83-27-39-74
Ecole d'Architecture de Nantes, 'La Mulotière', Rue Massenet, 44300 Nantes.   *1946*
Tél: 40-76-07-33
Ecole d'Architecture de Paris-Belleville, 7880, rue Rebeval, 75019 Paris.   *1648*
Tél: 42-41-33-60
Ecole d'Architecture de Paris-Conflans, 11, rue du Séminaire de Conflans, 94220 Charenton-le-Pont.
Tél: 43-68-00-55
Ecole d'Architecture de Paris-la-Défense, 158 rue Salvador Allende, 92023 Nanterre Cedex.
Tél: 47-76-01-05
Ecole d'Architecture de Paris-la-Seine, 14, rue Bonaparte, 75006 Paris.
Tél: 42-72-81-11
Ecole d'Architecture de Paris-la-Villette, 144, rue de Flandre, 75019 Paris.
Tél: 42-08-79-70
Ecole d'Archtecture de Paris-Tolbiac, 5, rue du Javelot, 75645 Paris Cedex 13.
Tél: 45-84-11-13
Ecole d'Architecture de Paris-Villemin, 11, quai Malaquais, 75272 Paris Cedex 06.
Tél: 42-60-34-57
Ecole d'Architecture de Rennes, 34, rue Hoche, 35000 Rennes.
Tél: 99-63-21-77
Ecole d'Architecture de Normandie, 27 rue Lucien Fromage, 76160 Darnetal.
Tél: 35-08-07-78
Ecole d'Architecture de Saint-Etienne, 1, rue du Buisson, 42000 Saint-Etienne.
Tél: 77-32-69-31
Ecole d'Architecture de Strasbourg, Palais du Rhin, 3, Place de la République 67000 Strasbourg.
Tél: 88-32-25-35. Télex: 870961 strarch
Ecole d'Architecture de Toulouse, Chemin du Mirail, 31300 Toulouse-le-Mirail.
Tél: 61-40-47-28
Ecole d'Architecture de Versailles, 2, avenue de Paris, 78000 Versailles.
Tél: 49-51-52-51

Ecole nationale supérieure des Arts appliqués et des Métiers d'Art, 63, rue Olivier-de-Serres, 75015 Paris.
Tél: 45-33-72-06
Ecole nationale supérieure des Arts décoratifs, 31, rue d'Ulm, 75005 Paris.   *1766*
Tél: 43-29-86-79
Ecole municipale des Arts décoratifs, 1, rue de l'Académie, 67000 Strasbourg.
Tél: 88-35-38-58
Conservatoire national supérieur d'Art dramatique, 2 *bis*, rue du Conservatoire, 75009 Paris.
Tél: 47-70-45-79

Ecole nationale des Beaux-Arts et des Arts appliqués à l'Industrie de Bourges, 7, rue Edouard Branly, 18000 Bourges.   *1824*
Tél: 48-70-11-45
Ecole nationale des Beaux-Arts, 3, rue Michelet, 21000 Dijon.   *1766*
Tél: 80-30-21-27
Ecole nationale des Beaux-Arts, 10, rue Neyret, 69001 Lyon.
Tél: 78-28-13-67
Ecole nationale des Beaux-Arts, 1, avenue Boffrand, 54000 Nancy.   *1702*
Tél: 83-40-16-25
Ecole nationale supérieure des Beaux-Arts, 17, quai Malaquais, 75272 Paris Cedex 06.
Tél: 42-60-34-57
Ecole régionale des Beaux-Arts, 30, rue Hoche, 35000 Rennes.   *1881*
Tél: 99-28-55-78

Ecole des Beaux-Arts et des Arts appliqués, 5, quai de la Daurade, 31000 Toulouse.
Tél: 61-23-25-45

Institut des hautes Etudes cinématographiques, 4, avenue de l'Europe, 94360 Brie-sur-Marne.
1943
Tél: 48-81-39-33
Ecole nationale Louis Lumière, 8, rue Rollin, 75005 Paris.   *1926*
Tél: 43-54-10-17

Ecole du Louvre, 34, quai du Louvre, 75041 Paris, Cedex 01.   *1882*
Tél: 42-60-25-50

Ecole nationale de Musique et d'Art dramatique, 5, rue de l'Ecole de Droit, 21000 Dijon.
Tél: 80-32-83-19
Conservatoire national supérieur de Musique, 14, rue de Madrid, 75008 Paris.   *1795*
Tél: 42-93-15-20

Institutes of Physical Education—Instituts d'Education physique

Institut national du Sport et de l'Education physique, 11, avenue du Tremblay, 75012 Paris.   *1933*
Tél: 48-08-41-20
Institut régional d'Education physique, place St.-Jacques, 25030 Besançon Cedex.
Institut régional d'Education physique et sportive, 3, place de la Victoire, 33076 Bordeaux Cedex.   *1928*
Tél: 56-91-34-24
Institut régional d'Education physique, Campus II, Boulevard Maréchal-Juin, 14032 Caen Cedex.
Institut régional d'Education physique et sportive, Rue Paul Doumer, 63000 Clermont-Ferrand.   *1929*
Tél: 73-93-93-17
Centre régional d'Education physique, Rue des Marettes, 35802 Dinard.
Tél: 99-46-16-23
Centre régional d'Education physique et sportive, Château de Mirande, rue Pierre de Coubertin, 21000 Dijon Cédex.
Tél: 80-65-46-12
Institut régional d'Education physique et Cadres sportifs, Domaine Universitaire, 38400 St-Martin-d'Hères.
Tél: 76-54-45-81
Institut régional d'Education physique et sportive, 9, chemin Latéral, 59790 Ronchin.
1928
Tél: 20-52-52-35
Institut régional d'Education physique, 15, boulevard du 11 novembre 1918, 69621 Villeurbanne.
Tél: 78-89-17-53
Unité d'Enseignement et de Recherche en Education physique et sportive, 70, route Léon-Lachamp, 13288 Marseille Cedex 2.
Tél: 91-26-92-61
Centre régional d'Education physique et sportive, 3, impasse Barnabé, 34000 Montpellier.
Tél: 67-54-16-12
Centre régional d'Education physique et sportive, 1, avenue Foch, 54311 Essey-les-Nancy. *1929*
Tél: 83-27-58-51
Institut régional d'Education physique, 200, avenue de la République, 92001 Nanterre Cedex.
Institut régional d'Education physique, 1, rue Lacretelle, 75015 Paris.   *1928*
Tél: 48-28-55-62
Centre régional d'Education physique et sportive, Château de Boivre, Vouneuil-sous-Biard, 86000 Poitiers.
Tél: 49-53-31-24
Centre régional d'Education physique et sportive, Rue des Marettes, 35802 Rennes Cedex.
Tél: 99-46-16-25
Centre régional d'Education physique et sportive, 4, allée du Sommerhof, 67035 Strasbourg Cedex 3.
Tél: 88-30-38-64
Institut régional d'Education physique et sportive, 118, rte de Narbonne, 31077 Toulouse Cedex.   *1929*
Tél: 61-52-98-44

Schools of Veterinary Science—Ecoles vétérinaires

Ecole nationale vétérinaire d'Alfort, 7, avenue du Général de Gaulle, 94704 Maisons-Alfort Cedex.   *1765*
Tél: 43-96-71-00. Télex: 213863 ecalfort f
Ecole nationale vétérinaire de Lyon, Route de Sain Bel, 69260 Charbonnières les Bains.
Tél: 78-87-00-84. Télex: 375647 envl f
Ecole nationale vétérinaire de Nantes, Routes de Gachet, 44026 Nantes Cedex.
Tél: 40-30-08-40. Télex: 701457 envntes f

Ecole nationale vétérinaire de Toulouse, 23, chemin des Capelles, 31076 Toulouse Cedex. *1829, 1964*
Tél: 61-49-11-40. Télex: 530724 envtlse f

Other Specialized Institutions—Autres Etablissements spécialisés

Ecole normale nationale d'Apprentissage de Lyon, 4, rue Alfred de Musset, 69100 Villeurbanne.
Tél: 78-68-52-15

Ecole normale nationale d'Apprentissage de Nantes, 23, rue du Recteur Schmitt, 44072 Nantes.
Tél: 40-74-25-10

Ecole normale nationale d'Apprentissage, 26, avenue Léon Jouhaux, 92160 Antony.
Tél: 46-66-42-50

Ecole normale nationale d'Apprentissage, 118, rte de Narbonne, 31077 Toulouse.
Tél: 61-52-76-07

Ecole normale nationale d'Apprentissage Paris Nord, Place du 8 mai 1945, 93206 Saint-Denis. *1946*
Tél: 48-22-06-60. Télex: 614907 ennia f

Ecole normale nationale d'Apprentissage de Lille, 365, rue Jules Guesde, 59650 Villeneuve-d'Ascq.
Tél: 20-91-14-64

Ecole nationale supérieure des Sciences de l'Information et des Bibliothèques, 17-21, boulevard du 11 novembre 1918, 69621 Villeurbanne.
Tél: 78-89-64-45

Centre régional de formation professionnelle des Bibliothécaires, 6, place de la Republique, 67070 Strasbourg Cedex.

Institut de Droit canonique, Palais Universitaire, 67000 Strasbourg. *1920*
Tél: 88-35-59-40

Institut de Droit comparé, 28, rue Saint-Guillaume, 75007 Paris. *1931*
Tél: 42-22-35-93

Institut d'Etudes Judiciaires, Domaine Universitaire Littéraire et Juridique, sac postal 19, 59650 Villeneuve-d'Ascq.
Tél: 20-91-10-26

Ecole nationale de la Magistrature, 9, rue du Maréchal-Joffre, 33080 Bordeaux Cedex.
Tél: 56-52-05-50. Fax: 56-81-82-63

Centre européen universitaire de Nancy, 15, place Carnot, 54042 Nancy Cedex. *1950*
Tél: 83-36-52-84

Centre de Documentation et de Recherches européennes, comparatives et internationales, 9, rue J.-Macé, 35000 Rennes.
Tél: 99-38-03-01

Institut des hautes Etudes européennes, 5, rue

Schiller, 67000 Strasbourg Cedex. *1953*
Tél: 88-35-02-69

Institut d'Etudes françaises de Touraine, 1, rue de la Grandière, 37000 Tours Cedex. *1912*
Tél: 47-05-76-83

Ecole française d'Extrême-Orient, 22, avenue du Président Wilson, 75116 Paris.

Institut d'Etudes internationales et des Pays en voie de développement, Place Anatole-France, 31070 Toulouse Cedex.
Tél: 61-23-01-45

Ecole supérieure d'Interprètes et de Traducteurs de l'Université de Paris Sorbonne Nouvelle, Place du Maréchal-de-Lattre de-Tassigny, 75116 Paris. *1957*
Tél: 45-05-14-10

Institut des Professeurs de Français à l'Etranger, 46, rue Saint-Jacques, 75005 Paris. *1920*
Tél: 43-29-12-13

Institut français de Presse, 83 *bis*, rue Notre-Dame-des-Champs, 75006 Paris. *1951*
Tél: 45-20-12-24

Ecole nationale de la Marine marchande du Havre, 66, route du Cap, 76310 Sainte-Adresse.
Tél: 35-46-24-63

Ecole nationale de la Marine marchande, 95, traverse Prat, 13008 Marseille.
Tél: 91-73-02-98. Télex: 420048 enmm ma f

Ecole nationale de la Marine marchande, 38, rue Joseph-Blanchart, 44100 Nantes.
Tél: 40-73-64-80

Ecole nationale de la Marine marchande, Rue Pierre-Loti, 22500 Paimpol.
Tél: 96-20-80-27

Ecole nationale de la Marine marchande, Rue de la Victoire, 35400 Saint-Malo.
Tél: 99-40-83-46

Institut de Médecine légale et sociale, Place Théo Varlet, 59000 Lille.
Tél: 20-56-60-79

Ecole nationale de la Santé publique, Avenue du Professeur Léon Bernard, 35043 Rennes Cedex. *1945*
Tél: 99-59-29-36. Télex: 741465 ensp f

Unité des Sciences odontologiques, Bâtiment Universitaire de la Buire, rue Guillaume Paradin, 69008 Lyon. *1899, 1973*
Tél: 78-74-88-59

Institut de Psychologie, Ensemble Universitaire, 69500 Bron-Parilly.   *1984*
Tél: 78-00-60-10

Institut de Psychologie appliquée, 34, avenue Carnot, 63006 Clermont-Ferrand Cedex.   *1947*
Tél: 73-92-97-32

Institut de Psychopédagogie médicosociale "Mas Prunet", Route de Lavérune, 34000 Montpellier.
Tél: 67-42-46-03

Institut de Psychologie, 1, rue Goethe, 67000 Strasbourg.   *1900*
Tél: 88-35-59-40

Institut de Psychologie, 4, rue Albert-Lautman, 31070 Toulouse Cedex.   *1959*
Tél: 61-22-08-31

Institut de préparation aux fonctions sociales et éducatives spécialisées, 8, rue Joliot Curie, 51100 Reims.
Tél: 26-06-22-88

Institut de Formation d'Educateurs spécialisés de l'Enfance et de l'Adolescence inadaptées, Le Château Peynier, 13790 Rousset.

Centre de Formation de Conseillers d'Orientation, 3 *bis*, rue Bart, 59000 Lille.
Tél: 20-57-09-29

Institut national d'Etude du Travail et d'Orientation professionnelle, 41, rue Gay-Lussac, 75005 Paris.   *1928*
Tél: 43-29-12-23

Institut national du Travail, Marcy l'Etoile, 69260 Charbonnières-les-Bains.
Tél: 78-87-02-44. Fax: 78870118. Télex: 370820 intlyon f

Institut Universitaire de Formation continue, La Bouloie, Route de Gray, 25030 Besançon Cedex.   *1973*
Tél: 81-50-32-66

Service Universitaire de Formation continue de Bourgogne, 6, boulevard Gabriel, B.P. 138, 21000 Dijon, Cedex.   *1958*
Tél: 80-65-43-98

Centre Universitaire d'Education et de Formation des Adultes, Domaine Universitaire, 38400 St-Martin-d'Hères.   *1951, 1969*
Tél: 76-54-51-63

Centre Université Economie d'Education permanente, 104, rue Jeanne d'Arc, 59000 Lille.
Tél: 20-52-54-24

Centre Universitaire de Formation et d'Education permanente, 10, rue de l'Université, 86022 Poitiers.   *1959*
Tél: 49-41-02-06

Centre départemental d'Education ouvrière du Nord de la France, sac postal 19, 59650 Villeneuve-d'Ascq.   *1954*

Institut de Promotion supérieure du Travail, 3, place Victor-Hugo, 13331 Marseille Cedex 3.
                                              1953-7
Tél: 91-95-90-71

Institut de Promotion supérieure du Travail, 39, avenue de la Forêt-Noire, 67000 Strasbourg.
Tél: 88-61-25-21

Institut de Promotion supérieure du Travail, 39, allée Jules-Guesde, 31000 Toulouse.
Tél: 61-52-69-70

Institut des Sciences sociales du Travail (Centre de Formation supérieure), 37, avenue du Président F. Roosevelt, 92330 Sceaux.   *1951*
Tél: 47-02-53-73

Institut des Sciences du Travail, sac postal 19, 59650 Villeneuve-d'Ascq.   *1950*
Tél: 20-91-10-26

Institut national de Formation des Cadres supérieurs de la Vente, 292, rue Saint-Martin, 75141 Paris Cedex 03.   *1957*
Tél: 42-71-24-14

Institut d'Etudes du Travail et de la Sécurité sociale, 1, rue de l'Université, 69224 Lyon Cedex 7.
Tél: 78-69-24-93˙

Centre national d'Etudes supérieures de la Sécurité sociale, 27 rue des Docteurs Charcot, 42031 St. Etienne Cedex.
Tél: 77-57-72-74. Télex: 307102 cness

Office de la Recherche scientifique et technique d'Outre-Mer, 213 rue Lafayette, 75010, Paris.
Tél: 42-25-31-52.   Télex: 214627   orstom.
Cables: orstom-paris

Private Establishments—Etablissements privés

Schools of Engineering—Ecoles d'Ingénieurs

Ecole superieure des Techniques aerospatiales, Bâtiment 502 *bis*, Complexe scientifique d'Orsay, 91405 Orsay.   *1930*
Tél: 69-28-68-57

Ecole supérieure des Techniques aéronautiques et de Construction automobile, 3, rue Pablo

Neruda, 92300 Levallois Perret.   *1925*
Tél: 47-31-81-00

Institut Catholique d'Arts et Métiers de Lille, 6, rue Auber, 59046 Lille Cedex.   *1898*
Tél: 20-93-58-55

Ecole Catholique d'Arts et Métiers de Lyon, 40 montée Saint-Barthélemy, 69321 Lyon Cedex 05. *1900*
Tél: 78-37-81-81

Centre associé Mosellan au Conservatoire national des Arts et Métiers, 7, rue Androuin-Roucel, 57000 Metz.
Tél: 87-74-17-14

Institut supérieur du Béton armé, 28, rue des Electriciens, 1375 Marseille Cedex 12. *1952*
Tél: 91-49-91-40

Ecole supérieure du Bois, 6-8, avenue de Saint Mandé, 75012 Paris. *1934*
Tél: 46-28-09-33

Ecole supérieure des Industries du Caoutchouc, 60 rue Auber, 94408 Vitry-sur-Seine Cedex. *1942*
Tél: 46-71-91-22

Ecole technique supérieure priveé de Chimie de l'Ouest, 60, rue Michelet, 49005 Angers, Cedex. *1950*
Tél: 41-88-98-33

Institut de Chimie et de Physique industrielles, 31, place Bellecour, 69288 Lyon Cedex 1. *1919*
Tél: 78-37-52-86

Ecole supérieure de Chimie de Marseille, Centre Saint-Jérôme, avenue de l'Escadrille Normandie-Nieman, 13397 Marseille Cedex. *1909*
Tél: 91-98-39-01

Ecole supérieure de Chimie organique et minérale, 12, rue Cassette, 75006 Paris.
Tél: 45-48-87-43

Ecole supérieure de Chimie industrielle de Lyon, 43, boulevard du 11 Novembre 1918, B.P. 2977, 69616 Villeurbanne Cedex. *1883*
Tél: 78-89-66-56

Lycée technique du Bâtiment, 7, rue St-Lambert, 75015 Paris. *1957*
Tél: 45-54-92-32

Ecole supérieure d'Application des Corps gras, Rue Monge, Parc industriel de Pessac, 33600 Pessac. *1952*
Tél: 56-36-00-44

Ecole supérieure du Cuir, des Peintures, des Encres et des Adhésifs, 181, avenue Jean-Jaurès, 69342 Lyon Cedex 7.
Tél: 78-72-28-31

Institut des Techniques économiques et comptables de Lorraine, 46, cours Léopold, 54000 Nancy.
Tél: 83-36-04-25

Ecole supérieure d'Electricité, Antenne de Rennes, Avenue de la Boulais, 35510 Cesson Sevigne.
Tél: 99-00-21-00

Ecole supérieure d'Electricité, Plateau du Moulon, 91190 Gif-sur-Yvette. *1894*
Tél: 69-41-80-40

Ecole d'Electricité et de Mécanique industrielles (Ecole Violet), 115, avenue E. Zola, 75739 Paris Cedex 15. *1902*
Tél: 45-77-30-84

Ecole supérieure d'Electronique de l'Ouest, 4, rue Merlet-de-la-Boulaye, 49024 Angers Cedex. *1956*
Tél: 41-88-92-25

Institut supérieur d'Electronique du Nord, 41, blvd. Vauban, 59046 Lille Cedex.
Tél: 20-30-62-20. Télex: 120360

Institut supérieur d'Electronique de Paris, 21, rue d'Assas, 75270 Paris Cedex 06. *1955*
Tél: 45-48-24-87

Ecole supérieure de Fonderie, 278-280, avenue Aristide-Briand, 92220 Bagneux. *1923*
Tél: 46-64-54-50

Centre d'Etudes supérieures industrielles, 297, rue de Vaugirard, 75015 Paris.
Tél: 42-50-11-51
(Aussi 3 centres région parisienne et en province: Aix, Arras, Balma, Blanquefort, Bordeaux, Ecully, Evry, Le Mans, Lyon, Nantes, Orléans, Rennes, Rouen, Strasbourg, Toulouse, Vandeouvre)

Ecole des hautes Etudes industrielles, 13, rue de Toul, 59046 Lille Cedex.
Tél: 78-33-18-73

Ecole des Etudes et Recherches en Informatique et Electronique, Parc scientifique Georges Besse, 30000 Nîmes.
Tél: 66-29-05-05

Ecole supérieure d'Informatique, Electronique Automatique, 9, rue Vésale, 75005 Paris.
Tél: 43-37-78-43

Ecole française d'Electronique et d'Informatique, 110, rue Amyot, 75005 Paris. *1936*
Tél: 47-07-05-95

Ecole supérieure d'Ingénieurs de Marseille, 28, rue des Electriciens, 13375 Marseille Cedex 12. *1891*
Tél: 91-49-91-40

Ecole supérieure d'Ingénieurs en Electrotechnique et en Electronique, B.P. 99, Cité Descartes, 93160 Noisy. *1904*
Tél: 45-92-65-00. Télex: 231586 esiee f

Ecole supérieure d'Ingénieurs en Génie électrique (Ecole Charliat), 58, rue Méridienne, 76100 Rouen. *1901*

Ecole d'Ingénieurat de Tours, l'Auberdière, 37200 Tours.
Tél: 47-38-58-00

Ecole spéciale de Mécanique et d'Electricité, 4, rue Blaise-Desgoffe, 75006 Paris.   *1905*
Tél: 45-48-03-70

Ecole nationale supérieure de Meunerie et des Industries céréalières, 16, rue Nicolas-Fortin, 75013 Paris.   *1924*
Tél: 43-37-42-47

Ecole supérieure d'Optique, B.P. 43, 91406 Orsay Cedex.   *1920*
Tél: 69-41-68-14. Télex: 692166 f

Lyceé technique privé d'Optométrie, 134, route de Chartres, 91440 Bures-sur-Yvette.   *1917*
Tél: 69-07-67-37

Ecole d'Optique-Lunetterie, 14, rue Nicolas Leblanc, 59000 Lille.
Tél: 20-57-38-52

Ecole française d'Ingénieurs des Industries papetieres et graphiques, B.P. 3, Domaine Universitaire, 38400 Saint-Martin-d'Hères.
Tél: 76-42-01-27

Ecole polytechnique féminine, 3 *bis*, rue Lakanal, 92330 Sceaux.   *1925*

Ecole supérieure de Soudage et de ses applications, 32, boulevard de la Chapelle, 75880 Paris Cedex.   *1930*
Tél: 42-03-94-05

Ecole supérieure des techniques industrielles et des textiles, 1, alleé Lakanal, B.P. 209, 59654 Villeneuve-d'Asq Cedex.
Tél: 20-91-35-21. Télex: 120369 gefirn f

Institut textile de France, 35, rue des Abondances, 92100 Boulogne-sur-Seine Cedex.   *1948*
Tél: 48-25-18-90

Ecole supérieure des Industries textiles d'Epinal, 86, rue d'Alsace, 88000 Epinal.   *1905*
Tél: 29-35-50-52

Ecole supérieure des Industries textiles de Lyon, 43, cours Général-Giraud, 69283 Lyon Cedex 01.   *1884, 1942*
Tél: 78-27-07-00

Ecole spéciale des Travaux publics, du Bâtiment et de l'industrie, 57, boulevard Saint-Germain, 75240 Paris Cedex 05.
Tél: 46-34-21-99. Fax: 43-26-90-39. Télex: 203385 eyrotp f

Schools of Agriculture—Ecoles agronomiques

Ecole supérieure d'Agriculture, 24, rue Auguste-Fonteneau, 49007 Angers Cedex.
Tél: 41-88-58-12

Institut supérieur agricole de Beauvais, rue Pierre Waguet, B.P. 313, 60026 Beauvais Cedex.
Tél: 44-45-82-63

Ecole supérieure d'Ingénieurs et Techniciens pour l'Agriculture, B.P. 201, 27100 Val De Reuil.   *1919*
Tél: 32-59-14-59

Institut supérieur d'Agriculture, 13, rue de Toul, 59046 Lille Cedex.
Tél: 20-30-83-14. Télex: 120369 f

Institut supérieur d'Agriculture Rhône-Alpes, 31, place Bellecour, 69288 Lyon, Cedex 02.
Tél: 78-42-10-78

Ecole supérieure d'Agriculture de Purpan-Toulouse, 75, voie du Toec, 31076 Toulouse Cedex.
Tél: 61-49-23-11

Schools of Commerce and Business Administration— Ecoles de Commerce et de Gestion

Académie commerciale internationale, 43 rue de Tocqueville, 75017 Paris.
Tél: 47-54-65-00. Télex: 641468 accipex

Institut européen d'Administration des Affaires, Boulevard de Constance, 77305 Fontainebleau Cedex.   *1958*
Tél: 60-72-40-00

Ecole européenne des Affaires, 108, boulevard Malesherbes, 75017 Paris.
Tél: 47-54-65-00

Ecole du Chef d'Entreprise et des Cadres supérieurs, 24, rue Hamelin, 75116 Paris.   *1944*

Tél: 45-53-31-59

Ecole supérieure de Commerce international, Avenue de Valvins, 77210 Avon-Fontainebleau.
Tél: 64-22-49-50. Télex: 600767 melu f

Ecole supérieure de Commerce de Lyon, Avenue Guy de Collongue, 69132 Ecully.   *1872*
Tél: 78-33-81-22. Télex: 900486 esclyon f

Ecole supérieure de Commerce du Centre, 1, rue Léo-Delibes, 37005 Tours Cedex.
Tél: 47-27-42-43. Télex: 750020 chamsotours

Ecole supérieure de Commerce et d'Administra-

tion des Entreprises, 18, place Saint-Michel, 80038 Amiens Cedex. *1942*
Tél: 22-91-57-02

Ecole supérieure des Sciences commerciales, 1, rue Lakanal, 49016 Angers, Cedex.
Tél: 41-48-30-55

Ecole supérieure de Commerce et d'Administration des Entreprises de Bretagne, 2, avenue de Provence, B.P. 214, 29272 Brest Cedex. *1962*
Tél: 98-03-25-01

Ecole supérieure de Commerce de Clermont-Ferrand, 4, boulevard Trudaine, 63037 Clermont-Ferrand. *1919*
Tél: 73-92-39-71. Telex: 990753 escclfd

Ecole supérieure de Commerce et d'Administration des Entreprises de Bourgogne et de Franche-Comté, 29, rue Sambin, 21000 Dijon. *1899*
Tél: 80-72-12-40

Ecole supérieure de Commerce et d'Administration des Entreprises, 7, rue Hoche, 3800 Grenoble.
Tél: 76-43-02-12

Ecole des hautes Etudes commerciales, 1, rue de la Libération, 78530 Jouy-en-Josas.
Tél: 39-56-70-00

Ecole supérieure de Commerce et d'Administration des Entreprises, 1, rue Emile-Zola, 76000 Le Havre. *1871*
Tél: 35-21-12-18

Ecole supérieure de Commerce et d'Administration des Entreprises, Avenue Gaston-Berger, 59045 Lille Cedex. *1947*
Tél: 20-52-67-19

Ecole de hautes Etudes commerciales du Nord, 1 Rue du Port, 59058 Lille Cedex.
Tél: 20-54-25-34. Fax: 20308306. Télex: 120369 gefirn

Ecole supérieure de Commerce de Lyon, 23, Avenue Guy de Collongue, B.P. 174, 69132 Ecully, Cedex.
Tél: 78-33-81-22. Télex: 900486 esellyon

Ecole supérieure de Commerce et d'Administration des Entreprises, Domaine Universitaire de Luminy, Case 911, 13288 Marseille Cedex. *1872*
Tél: 91-41-01-60

Ecole supérieure de Commerce de Rouen, Boulevard André-Siegfried, B.P. 34, 76130 Mont-Saint-Aignan. *1871*
Tél: 35-74-03-00. Télex: 770036 rehano f

Ecole supérieure de Commerce et d'Administration des Entreprises, 2300, avenue des Moulins, 34030 Montpellier Cedex. *1897*
Tél: 67-40-42-43. Télex: 49-00-31 chamco

Groupe Ecole de Commerce de Nantes, 8, route de la Jonelière, 44003 Nantes Cedex. *1900*
Tél: 40-29-44-55

Ecole supérieure de Commerce du Ceram, Sophia Antipolis, B.P. 20, 06561 Valbonne Cedex.

Tél: 93-95-45-45. Fax: 93654401.

Ecole supérieure de Commerce de Paris, 79, avenue de la République, 75543 Paris, Cedex 11.
Tél: 45-55-39-08

Institut de Commerce international, 5, avenue Pierre Ier de Serbie, 75116 Paris.
Tél: 45-05-30-00. Télex: 611934 cfcep f

Ecole supérieure de Commerce et d'Administration des Entreprises, 74, allée de Morlaas, 64000 Pau.
Tél: 59-02-88-51

Ecole supérieure de Commerce et d'Administration des Entreprises, 11, rue de l'Ancienne Comédie, 86001 Poitiers Cedex. *1961*
Tél: 49-88-25-75. Télex: 793294 escpoit

Ecole supérieure de Commerce de Reims, B.P. 302, 51061 Reims Cedex. *1929*
Tél: 26-08-06-04. Télex: 890917 f

Ecole Franco-Allemande de Commerce et d'Industrie, 12, Cours St. Eloi, 75012 Paris.
Tél: 43-44-06-53

Ecole supérieure de Commerce et d'Administration des Entreprises, Domaine de Raba, Cours de la Libération, 33405 Talence, Cedex. *1874*
Tél: 56-80-70-50

Ecole supérieure de Commerce de Toulouse, 20, Boulevard Lascrosses, 31068 Toulouse Cedex. *1903*
Tél: 61-29-49-49. Télex: 531877 f

Ecole supérieure de Commerce du Centre, 1 rue Loe Delibes, 37005 Tours, Cedex.
Tél: 47-27-42-43

Institut libre des hautes Etudes économiques et commerciales, 35, cours Xavier Arnozan, 33000 Bordeaux.
Tél: 56-44-95-97˙

Ecole supérieure des Sciences économiques et commerciales, Avenue de la Grande Ecole, B.P. 105, 95001 Cergy-Pontoise Cedex.
Tél: 30-30-40-57. Télex: 607789 essec

Institut d'Economie d'Entreprise et de Formation sociale pour Ingénieurs, 41, rue du Port, 59046 Lille Cedex.
Tél: 20-30-83-14. Télex: 120369. Cables: gefirn

Institut d'Economie scientifique et de Gestion, 1 rue François Baës, 59800 Lille.
Tél: 20-54-58-92

Institut d'Expertise-comptable, 60, boulevard Vauban, 59000 Lille.
Tél: 20-93-61-70

Institut supérieur des Sciences techniques et d'Economie commerciale, 24, rue Hamelin, 75016 Paris.
Tél: 47-27-88-70

Institut français de Gestion, 31320 Castenet Tolosan.

Tél: 61-53-59-27

Institut de Gestion internationale agroalimentaire (Ecole supérieure privée), 56 Campus, Avenue du Parc, 95033 Cergy-Pontoise Cedex.
Tél: 30-73-28-88. Télex: 697789

Institut supérieur de Gestion, 8, rue de Lota, 75116 Paris.
Tél: 47-81-21-14

Centre Parisien de Management, 108, boulevard Malesherbes, 75017 Paris.   *1973*
Tél: 47-66-51-34

Centre d'Enseignement du Management, 3, rue Cassette, 75006 Paris.
Tél: 45-44-38-80

Institut français de Gestion, 31320 Castenet Tolosan.

Tél: 61-53-59-27

Institut de Gestion international agroalimentaire (Ecole supérieure privée), 56 Campus, Avenue du Parc, 95033 Cergy-Pontoise Cedex.
Tél: 30-73-28-88. Télex: 697789 f

Institut supérieur de Gestion, 45, rue Spontini, 75016 Paris.
Tél: 47-81-21-14

Centre Parisien de Management, 108, boulevard Malesherbes, 75017 Paris.   *1973*
Tél: 47-66-51-34

Centre d'Enseignement du Management, Collège des Sciences sociales et économiques, 3, rue Cassette, 75006 Paris.
Tél: 45-44-38-80

Schools of Notarial and Legal Studies—Ecoles de Notariat et d'Etudes juridiques

Institut de Droit appliqué, 143, avenue de Versailles, 75016 Paris.   *1946*
Tél: 45-25-56-74

Faculté libre internationale de Droit rural et des Sciences sociales agraires, 3191, route de Mende, 34000 Montpellier.

Institut des hautes Etudes de Droit rural et d'Economie agricole, 11, rue Ernest Lacoste, 75012 Paris.   *1950*
Tél: 46-28-38-96

Ecole privée de Législation professionnelle, 44, rue Etienne Marcel, 75002 Paris.   *1905*
Tél: 42-36-32-14

Ecole de Notariat, 3, place Louis-Dewailly, 80000 Amiens.
Tél: 22-91-38-40

Ecole de Notariat, 11, rue Chevreuil, 49000 Angers.   *1892*
Tél: 41-88-72-12

Ecole de Notariat de Clermont-Ferrand, Rue de la Rotande, 63000 Clermont-Ferrand.   *1913*
Tél: 73-93-81-31

Ecole de Notariat, 3, rue du Lycée, 21000 Dijon.
                                                                        1908
Tél: 80-67-15-71

Ecole de Notariat, 15, quai Claude-Bernard, 69007 Lyon.   *1902*
Tél: 78-72-80-33

Ecole de Notariat, 72, Blvd. Périer, 13008 Marseille.   *1902*
Tél: 91-33-67-13

Ecole de Notariat, Avenue des Apothicaires, 34000 Montpellier.
Tél: 67-63-22-25

Ecole de Notariat, 119 *bis*, rue de Coulmiers, 44000 Nantes.   *1905*
Tél: 40-74-08-76

Ecole de Notariat de Paris, 9, rue Villaret-de-Joyeuse, 75017 Paris.   *1897*
Tél: 47-54-01-92

Ecole de Notariat, 15 *bis*, rue Poullain-Duparc, 35000 Rennes.   *1892*
Tél: 99-30-36-45

Ecole de Notariat, 39, rue du Champ-aux-Oiseaux, 76000 Rouen.   *1893*
Tél: 35-70-50-41

Ecole de Notariat, 2, rue des Juifs, 67000 Strasbourg.
Tél: 88-32-10-55

Ecole de Notariat, 2, rue Albert-Lautman, 31000 Toulouse.   *1898*
Tél: 61-23-01-45

Ecole de Notariat, 32, rue de Richelieu, 37000 Tours.
Tél: 47-05-60-20

Other Specialized Institutions—Autres Etablissements spécialisés

Institut des Actuaires français, 243, rue St. Honoré, 75001 Paris.
Tél: 48-78-46-72

Ecole d'Anthropologie, 1, place d'Iéna, 75116 Paris.   *1876*
Tél: 47-93-09-84

Ecole supérieure technique de Biologie appliquée, 56, rue Planchat, 75020 Paris.
Tél: 43-71-47-40

Ecole dentaire de Paris (Société de l'Ecole et du Dispensaire dentaires de Paris), 45, rue de la

Tour-d'Auvergne et 5*bis*, Cité Charles Godon, 75009 Paris. *1880*
Tél: (1) 48-78-74-86; (2) 45-26-73-94

Institut international supérieur de Formation des Cadres de Santé, 162, avenue Lacassagne, 69424 Lyon Cedex 03. *1965*
Tél: 78-54-54-12

Ecole de Formation d'Educateurs spécialisés de l'Enfance et de l'Adolescence inadaptées, 21000 Dijon.

Institut océanographique, 195, rue Saint-Jacques, 75005 Paris. *1906*
Tél: 43-25-63-10

Centre d'Etudes préparatoires aux Organisations internationales, 16, rue Miollis, 75015 Paris.
Tél: 45-66-97-58

Institut de Psychanalyse, 187, rue Saint-Jacques, 75005 Paris.
Tél: 46-33-32-90

Ecole de Psychologues practiciens, 21, rue d'Assas, 75270 Paris Cedex 06.
Tél: 45-48-17-75

Ecole de Formation Psycho-Pédagogique, 22, rue Cassette, 75005 Paris. *1946*
Tél: 45-48-80-46

Institut européen des hautes Etudes internationales, Palais de Marbre, 9, avenue de Fabron, 06200 Nice.
Tél: 93-86-39-12

Ecole internationale de Langue et de Civilisation françaises—Alliance française, 101, boulevard Raspail, 75270 Paris cedex 06. *1914*
Tél: 45-44-38-28. Télex: 204941 allfran f.
Cables: allfran

Ecole supérieure de Journalisme, 50, Rue Gauthier de Chatillon, 59000 Lille.
Tél: 20-54-48-21. Télex: 120388 esjull

Ecole supérieure de Journalisme, 4, place St-Germain-des-Prés, 75006 Paris.
Tél: 42-22-68-06

Fondation des Journalistes de demain, 6, rue Ancelle, 92525 Neuilly-sur-Seine Cedex.
Tél: 46-24-01-23

Ecole française libre des Attachés de Presse, 61, rue Pierre-Charron, 75008 Paris.
Tél: 43-59-07-79

Centre de Formation et de Perfectionnement des Journalistes, 33, rue du Louvre, 75002 Paris.
1946
Tél: 45-08-86-71. Télex: 240586 cfpj je f

Ecole libre de Marketing et de Publicité, 61, rue Pierre Charron, 75008 Paris.
Tél: 43-59-07-79

Institut supérieur international du Parfum, de la Cosmétique et de l'Aromatique alimentaire, 18, rue Mansart, 78010 Versailles.

Tél: 39-54-82-85

Institut libre d'Etudes supérieures de la Côte-d'Azur, 37, rue d'Antibes, 06400 Cannes.
Tél: 93-43-43-82

Institut libre d'Etudes des Relations internationales, 12, rue des Saints-Pères, 75006 Paris. *1948*
Tél: 42-96-51-48

Ecole supérieure des Professions immobilières, 2, impasse du Mont Tonnerre, 75015 Paris. *1954*
Tél: 47-83-48-75

Ecole nouvelle d'Organisation économique et sociale, 62, rue de Miromesnil, 75008 Paris.
1937
Tél: 45-22-53-86

Institut polytechnique des Sciences appliquées, 12, rue Béranger, 75003 Paris.
Tél: 42-72-95-03

Collège des Sciences sociales et économiques, 14, rue Monsieur-le-Prince, 75006 Paris.
Tél: 43-29-70-50

Institut de Sciences sociales appliquées, 29, rue du Plat, 69005 Lyon. *1948*
Tél: 78-42-10-30

Institut de Sociologie, 25, rue du Plat, 69005 Lyon.
Tél: 78-42-10-30

Institut d'Etudes sociales, 21, rue d'Assas, 75006 Paris. *1924*
Tél: 42-22-41-80

Ecole Libre des hautes Etudes sociales (Ecole des hautes Etudes internationales, Ecole supérieure de Journalisme), 4, place St-Germain-des-Prés, 75006 Paris. *1889*
Tél: 42-22-68-06

Ecole pratique de Service social, 139, boulevard du Montparnasse, 75006 Paris. *1913*
Tél: 43-22-44-97

Ecole nationale de Service social de la Sécurité sociale, 53*bis*, rue Boussingault, 75013 Paris.
1947
Tél: 45-89-62-49

Ecole technique des Surintendantes d'Usines et de Services sociaux, 8 villa du Parc Montsouris, 75014 Paris. *1917*
Tél: 45-65-00-70

Ecole de Secrétariat bilingue et trilingue, 60, boulevard Vauban, 59046 Lille Cedex. *1961*
Tél: 20-30-88-27

Ecole supérieure de Traducteurs, Interprètes, et Cadres du Commerce extérieur, 60, boulevard Vauban, 59046 Lille, Cedex. *1961*
Tél: 20-30-88-27

Institut supérieur d'Interprétariat et de Traduction, 21, rue d'Assas, 75270 Paris Cedex 06.
1957
Tél: 42-22-33-16

Conférence des Recteurs français

La Conférence est une Association créée en 1967; elle remplace le Comité des Recteurs fondé en 1950. Pour être membre de la Conférence, il faut assumer les fonctions de Recteur, Chancelier des Universités, dans une Académie. Les Recteurs des vingt-sept Académies entre lesquelles est divisé le territoire français font effectivement partie de l'Association.

Celle-ci a pour objet: d'établir des rapports personnels et permanents entre ses membres; de favoriser l'examen des problèmes professionnels liés à l'exercice de leurs fonctions; et d'établir et maintenir des relations avec les instances nationales et internationales préoccupées des problèmes d'éducation, de science et de culture. A ce dernier titre, la Conférence des Recteurs français s'intéresse activement au rapprochement international des universités et à leur coopération.

Le bureau de la Conférence est composé: d'un Président d'Honneur qui est de droit le Recteur de l'Académie de Paris; d'un Président, d'un Vice-Président et d'un Secrétaire-Trésorier, qui sont élus annuellement par les membres de l'Association. Le Président réunit la Conférence chaque fois qu'il est nécessaire et au moins une fois par trimestre. Il la représente près toutes instances nationales et internationales et il est notamment son porte-parole dans les relations avec les Associations universitaires internationales.

The French Rectors' Conference, founded in 1967, replaces the Committee of Rectors (Comité des Recteurs) established in 1950. Its members are the Rectors (University Chancellors) of the 27 Academies into which France is divided.

The purposes of the Conference are: to establish permanent and personal links between its members; to encourage study of their professional problems; and to establish and maintain contact with national and international bodies concerned with problems of education, science and culture. The Conference is thus actively engaged in promoting international university relations and co-operation.

The officers of the Conference are: the Honorary President, ex officio the Rector of the Academy of Paris; and a President, Vice-President, and Secretary-Treasurer, who are elected annually by the members. The President convenes the Conference at least four times a year. He represents the Conference in its relations with national and international bodies and is its spokesman in contacts with international university associations.

47, rue des Ecoles, 75005 Paris.

Tél: 43-29-12-13

Conférence des Présidents d'Université

Créée par décret du 24 février 1971, la Conférence regroupe tous les présidents des universités françaises et des autres établissements publics à caractère scientifique et culturel. Elle compte 77 membres. Elle répond à un double besoin: d'une part, elle joue un rôle consultatif, émettant des vœux et des avis sur les questions qui lui sont soumises par le Ministre de l'Education Nationale et éclairant celui-ci sur les besoins communs aux institutions; d'autre part, elle fonctionne comme une association d'étude animée par ses seuls membres; elle permet aux responsables des nouvelles universités de débattre des problèmes qui les intéressent toutes. Dans le premier cas, la Conférence se réunit à l'initiative et sous la présidence du Ministre; dans le second cas, elle est libre de fixer ses conditions de travail, son ordre du jour et la date de ses réunions.

La Conférence des Présidents comprend une commission permanente composée de 16 membres élus chaque année. Cette commission est chargée de préparer les débats des séances plénières qui ont lieu tous les mois. Six autres commissions fonctionnent au sein de la Conférence. Elles s'occupent des domaines suivants: pédagogie et formation permanente, recherche, moyens et personnels, vie de l'étudiant, relations extérieures, règlements et législation. Les Présidents de ces commissions siègent tous à la Commission permanente.

Established by a decree of 24 February 1971, the Conference comprises all the Presidents of the French universities and of other public establishments of an academic, scientific and cultural nature. It has 77 members. It meets two principal needs: on the one hand, it has a consultative role, formulating recommendations and opinions on questions submitted to it by the Minister of Education and advising him on common institutional needs; and on the other hand, it plays the part of a study and research association for its own members; it enables those responsible for the new universities to discuss problems of common interest. In its first role, the Conference meets on the initiative and under the presidency of the Minister; in its second, it decides independently on its working methods, its agenda and the date of its meetings.

The Conference has a permanent commission composed of 16 members elected annually. This commission is responsible for preparing the work of the plenary sessions, held every month. Six other commissions exist within the Conference. They deal with the following matters: teaching and lifelong education, research, resources and staff, student life, external relations, regulations and legislation. The presidents of these commissions are members of the permanent commission.

Président: Lionel Jospin, Ministre de l'Education Nationale.

Vice-Présidents: Daniel Laurent, Université de Paris XII-Créteil; Jean-Jacques Conté, Université de Toulouse III; Jean-Paul Jacqué, Université de Strasbourg III.

Président de la Commission des Relations extérieures: Michel Cousin, Université de Lyon II.

Secrétaires: Mlle Maryvonne Jabot; Mlle Claudine Briard.

Université René Descartes, 12, rue de l'Ecole de Médecine, 75270 Paris Cedex 06.

Tél: 43-54-50-49

L'Union des Etablissements d'Enseignement supérieur Catholique (UDESCA)

L'Union a été créée le 5 décembre 1973 par son Assemblée Générale Constituante. Ses membres fondateurs sont les cinq établissements suivants: l'Université Catholique de l'Ouest (Angers), la Fédération Universitaire et Polytechnique de Lille, les Facultés Catholiques de Lyon, l'Institut Catholique de Paris, l'Institut Catholique de Toulouse, plus la Fédération des Ecoles Supérieures d'Ingénieurs et de Cadres (F.E.S.I.C.).

Son but est d'assurer la coordination des établissements d'enseignement supérieur catholique et la convergence de leurs efforts marqués par le souci d'une présence chrétienne dans le monde universitaire face aux grands problèmes de la société contemporaine.

L'Asemblée de l'UDESCA, qui se réunit deux fois par an, comprend des représentants élus des professeurs et des étudiants des différents ensembles universitaires. Son Conseil est composé, avec les recteurs et le représentant de la F.E.S.I.C., des représentants élus des Facultés de théologie, de droit canonique et sciences religieuses, des Facultés et Instituts de philosophie, et des Facultés profanes.

Conscients de leur unité dans la diversité, les organismes constitutifs de l'UDESCA entendent contribuer ensemble d'une façon originale au service national de l'enseignement supérieur.

The Union of Catholic institutions of higher education (UDESCA) was established on 5 December 1973 by a Constituent General Assembly. The five founder members are: Université Catholique de l'Ouest, Angers; Fédération Universitaire et Polytechnique de Lille; Facultés Catholiques de Lyon; Institut Catholique de Paris; Institut Catholique de Toulouse; and Fédération des Ecoles supérieures d'Ingénieurs et de Cadres (F.E.S.I.C.).

Its aim is to ensure the co-ordination of Catholic institutions of higher education and the concentration of their efforts and concern for a Christian presence in the university world as it faces the major problems of contemporary society.

The Assembly of the Union meets twice a year and comprises representatives elected by the academic staff and the students of the various institutions. Its Council comprises the rectors and a representative of the Fédération des Ecoles supérieures d'Ingénieurs et de Cadres, and elected representatives of the faculties of theology, of canon law and religious sciences, of the faculties and institutes of philosophy, and of the lay faculties.

Conscious of their unity in the midst of diversity, the constituent members of UDESCA seek together to make an original contribution to higher education nationally.

Président: Mgr Gérard Defois, Recteur, Institut Catholique de Lyon.

Vice-Président: Mgr Paul Guiberteau, Recteur, Institut Catholique de Paris.

Tél: 45-48-61-42

Office National d'Information sur les Enseignements et les Professions (O.N.I.S.E.P.)

Créé en 1970, l'O.N.I.S.E.P. est un Etablissement public national placé sous la tutelle du Ministre de l'Education Nationale administré par un Directeur nommé par décret en Conseil des Ministres, et un Conseil d'Administration de 55 membres réélus tous les trois ans comprenant: des représentants des services publics, du patronat, des chambres syndicales du Commerce et de l'Industrie, des métiers, de l'agriculture, des organisations syndicales de salariés, d'exploitants agricoles, des associations de parents d'élèves, des représentants des enseignants et établissements publics à caractère culturel et scientifique, des Centres d'Information et d'Orientation, des étudiants, des représentants du personnel et trois personnalités choisies par le Ministre de l'Education Nationale en raison de leurs compétences.

En liaison avec les universités, les administrations, les professions et organismes intéressés, l'O.N.I.S.E.P. a pour mission: a) d'élaborer et de mettre à la disposition des utilisateurs la documentation nécessaire à l'information et à l'orientation par une meilleure connaissance des moyens d'éducation et des activités profesionnelles; b) de contribuer aux études et recherches relatives aux méthodes et aux moyens propres à développer cette documentation; c) de faire des études et de susciter des recherches tendant à améliorer la connaissance des activités professionnelles et de leur évolution; d) de contribuer à la définition des orientations générales de la politique de formation du personnel chargé de l'information sur les enseignements et les professions; e) de participer à la formation du personnel d'information et d'orientation.

L'O.N.I.S.E.P. est structuré en Services Cen-

traux élaborant une documentation nationale écrite, télématique et audiovisuelle, et 28 Délégations Régionales, une par académie, placées sous la tutelle du Recteur, produisant des informations régionales sur support papier, informatique ou télématique, souvent en collaboration avec des partenaires sociaux, pour aider à la mise en oeuvre de la politique générale d'insertion sociale et professionnelle des jeunes.

Publications: Chaque année plus de 200 titres, totalisant 10 millions d'exemplaires, sont publiés par l'O.N.I.S.E.P. et diffusés gratuitement à 90%. Par catégories on peut distinguer: *Les brochures systématiques* (l'entrée en 6ème, Après la 5ème, Après la 3ème, Après la 2nde, Après le baccalauréat) sont distribuées chaque année individuellement à tous les élèves de l'enseignement secondaire. *les collections* offrant une information plus large sur les formations, les métiers et les débouchés comprenant trois séries: a) Bac pas bac, que faire après. Cette brochure remise à jour chaque année recouvre tous les secteurs de la vie professionnelle ouverts aux jeunes; b) les Cahiers de l'ONISEP présentent, sous forme de monographie, métiers et formations regroupés par secteurs en s'attachant plus particulièrement aux formations d'employés qualifiés et de techniciens; c) la revue "Avenirs" qui traite des formations supérieures accessibles après le baccalauréat et de leurs débouchés. *Des guides, répertoires, fiches, revues*, destinés au public ou aux informateurs spécialisés sur les concours administratifs, la formation continue, l'enseignement supérieur, les problèmes d'insertion sociale des personnes handicapées ou encore l'évolution de l'emploi et son articulation avec la formation.

Toutes ces brochures sont en consultation dans les Centres d'Information et d'Orientation (C.I.O), les cellules d'accueil d'information des universités, en vente en librairie ou par correspondance.

L'Office utilise par ailleurs largement la communication audiovisuelle (Films, diaporamas, émissions de télévision mais aussi radios nationales ou locales) plus à même de séduire les adolescents, et développe, grâce à la collaboration des Délégations Régionales, l'information télématique permettant aux usagers de n'importe quel point de France, à partir d'un minitel, d'avoir accès aux fichiers de l'Office.

Established in 1970, the National Office for Information on Education and the Professions is a public body under the jurisdiction of the Minister of Education and is administered by a Director, appointed by decision of the Council of Ministers, and by an Administrative Board of 55 members re-elected every three years and representatives from public services, of employers, or Chambers of Commerce and Industry, professional organizations, agriculture, employees' unions, farmers, pupils' parents associations, academic staff and public cultural and scientific institutions, Centres of Information and Guidance, and three personalities chosen by the Minister of Education for their competence in higher education affairs.

In co-operation with the universities, the public authorities, the professions and other interested bodies, the Office is responsible for: a) preparing, and making available to teachers, parents, students and pupils, documentation giving information and guidance which will contribute to a better understanding of educational opportunities and of the different professions and careers; b) contributing to study and research into methods of developing this documentation; c) making studies and stimulating research likely to lead to a better understanding of different professions and careers and their evolution; d) contributing to the definition of general policy objectives for the training of personnel responsible for providing information about education and the professions; e) participating in the training of information and guidance personnel.

The Office's central service is responsible for the production of documentation at the national level in written form, as well as by telematic and audiovisual means. Twenty-eight regional centres under the jurisdiction of the Rector of each academic district produce regional information, written or on computer, often in collaboration with other contributors to help implement general policy for the social and professional integration of young people.

Publications: Each year more than 200 titles with a total of 10m copies are published by O.N.I.S.E.P. and 90% are distributed free of charge. By categories may be mentioned: Regular pamphlets (secondary education and after the "baccalauréat" distributed individually each year to all secondary pupils: Collections giving fuller information on courses, professions and career prospects in three series: a) "Bac pas bac". This leaflet, up-dated each year, covers all sectors of professional life open to young people; b) "Les Cahiers de l'ONISEP", presented in monograph form, describe careers and courses grouped into areas, placing special emphasis on the training of qualified employees and technicians; c) the journal "Avenirs" which deals with further training and prospects available following the "baccalauréat". Guides, handbooks, index cards, and reviews intended for the public or advisers specialized in the administrative competitive examination, lifelong education, higher education, the problems of the social integration of the handicapped, or the current trend of employment and its links with training.

All these brochures may be consulted in the Centres of Information and Guidance, university reception offices, and are on sale in bookshops or by correspondence.

In addition, the Office uses extensive audio-visual means of communication (films, "diaporamas", and national and local radio) which are suited to attract adolescents, and to develop, thanks to the cooperation of regional delegations, telematic information which allows the user from any part of France to have access through the "minitel" system to the Office's files.
Directeur de l'ONISEP: Pierre Mondon.
50, rue Albert, 75013 Paris.
Tél: 45-83-32-21

Centre National des Oeuvres Universitaires et Scolaires

Constitué par une loi en 1955 en établissement public à caractère administratif, le Centre est doté de la personnalité civile et de l'autonomie financière. Il est soumis à la tutelle du Ministère de l'Education Nationale et administré par un conseil d'administration qui définit la politique générale des oeuvres et répartit les subventions et aides diverses entre les CROUS (Centres Régionaux des Oeuvres Universitaires et Scolaires).

Le Centre National a pour mission de favoriser l'amélioration des conditions de vie et de travail des étudiants ou élèves de classes préparatoires et des sections BTS, qu'ils soient français ou étrangers, boursiers ou non boursiers. A cet effet, il oriente, coordonne et contrôle l'action des 28 Centres Régionaux (1 par académie) et des 12 Centres Locaux implantés dans les villes universitaires moins importantes.

Diverse dans ses aspects, l'action des Oeuvres Universitaires se manifeste dans différents domaines: Les résidences universitaires, où les responsables s'efforcent de faire régner les meilleures conditions de vie et de travail sans négliger l'action culturelle que justifient ces collectivités de jeunes; elles offrent, en 1986, 102 537 lits. Les Centres Régionaux disposent aussi de 9371 places réservées dans les habitations à loyers modérés (HLM) et de 2806 lits dans des foyers agréés. Enfin, dans chaque CROUS, un service du logement en ville aide les étudiants à trouver place chez des particuliers propriétaires de chambres ou d'appartements. Les 169 restaurants universitaires offrent plus de 163 000 places. Les étudiants peuvent y trouver, pour un prix modique, 3 types de restauration, et des cafétérias, brasseries, grills, proposent en outre des boissons et des préparations diverses à consommer sur place ou à emporter.

Un Fonds de Solidarité Universitaire (FSU) a été créé pour permettre l'attribution de prêts ou de dons à des étudiants momentanément gênés. Chaque cas est étudié par une assistante sociale, puis par une commission d'attribution. Un service de Liaison Etudiants-Entreprises (SLEE) est chargé d'organiser et de préparer des stages favorisant la formation humaine et professionnelle des étudiants, en même temps qu'il leur propose des emplois temporaires.

Le Centre National et les Centres Régionaux sont chargés, par le Ministère des Affaires Etrangères et par le Ministère de la Coopération, de l'accueil en France de nombreux étudiants étrangers, boursiers du gouvernement français.

Les services d'accueil du Centre National et des Centres Régionaux et Locaux facilitent les démarches de ces étudiants auprès des administrations françaises, assurent leur placement dans les Universités et Ecoles, suivent leurs études et favorisent leur insertion et leur séjour dans la société française.

Depuis quelques années, des personnalités de pays voisins, qui s'occupent des services sociaux en faveur des étudiants, sont invités à participer à des travaux d'étude sur les divers systèmes d'aide aux étudiants. Le Centre National, avec l'aide des Centres Régionaux, organise des rencontres internationales afin de favoriser les échanges entre étudiants français et étrangers. Ces échanges sont particulièrement riches entre la France et la République Fédérale d'Allemagne.

Founded by law in 1955 as a public establishment, the National Centre of the Student Social and Welfare Service enjoys civil status and financial autonomy. It is supported by the Ministry of Education and administered by a Council which defines the general policy of its work and allocates the subventions and various contributions to the Regional Centres (CROUS).

The Centre seeks to improve the living and working conditions of students or pupils of preparatory classes and professional degree (BTS) sections, whether they are French or foreign, or whether or not they are scholarship holders. To this end, it guides, co-ordinates and supervises the 28 Regional Centres (1 for each academic district) and the 12 local Centres in other areas.

With its varying aspects, the work of the Welfare Service is expressed in different areas: University residences, where those in charge endeavour to create the best living and working conditions and to promote cultural activities best suited to a group of young people. In 1986, the residences offer 102,537 beds. The Regional Centres also have at their disposal 9371 places reserved in apartments at moderate rents and 2806 beds in hostels. Furthermore, in each Centre, a housing service is available to help students find accommodation in private rooms or apartments. 169 university restaurants cater for 163,000 places where students

may find, at modest prices, three types of meals, and cafeterias, "brasseries", and grills offer drinks and snack meals to consume on the premises or take away.

A "Fund for University Solidarity" has been created for the allocation of loans or donations to students in temporary financial difficulty. A "Student-Industry Liaison Service" organizes and prepares courses for the social and vocational training of students, and at the same time offers temporary employment.

The National Centre and Regional Centres are requested by the Ministries of Foreign Affairs and Co-operation to be in charge of welcoming many foreign students with French Government scholarships. Such orientation services assist them over their initial administrative problems, ensure their entry to the universities and "grandes écoles", follow their studies and encourage their integration into French society.

For some years, representatives from neighbouring countries who are responsible for student welfare services, have been invited to participate in making studies of different student aid systems. The National Centre, assisted by the Regional Centres, organizes international meetings with the object of encouraging student exchanges, notably between France and the Federal Republic of Germany.

Directeur: Albert Prévos.

69, quai d'Orsay, 75007 Paris.

Tél: 47-05-31-10. Télex: 203048 cnous

Fondation Santé des Etudiants de France (Fondation S.E.F.)

La Fondation prend en charge, pour des traitements exclusivement médicaux, 1600 jeunes malades -étudiants, grands scolaires et jeunes travailleurs- atteints d'affections physiques, de handicaps moteurs ou de troubles psychiques.

Son objectif de réadaptation, de réinsertion scolaire ou professionnelle est le fruit de la collaboration, au sein des treize établissements, d'équipes de soins pluridisciplinaires et de professeurs de l'enseignement supérieur et secondaire mis à leur disposition par le service public de l'Education Nationale: son but consiste donc à éviter que les jeunes malades ne subissent pas, du fair de leurs soins, de retard dans leur cursus scolaire, ou bénéficient d'une réorientation lorsque le handicap créé par la maladie l'oblige.

Les Centres médicaux situés en Région Parisienne (8) ou dans de grandes villes de Province (5) bénéficient de la proximité de toutes les universités, et leur enseignement secondaire, spécifiquement adapté aux soins et aux handicaps, est assuré par 290 professeurs en liaison étroite avec les lycées généraux. Les établisse-

ments sont ouverts à des étudiants ou élèves français et étrangers.

Les soins qui y sont dispensés concernent: les maladies pulmonaires (asthme, bronchopathie, tuberculose); rénales (hémodialyse, transplantation); hématologiques (tumeurs, greffe de moëlle); hépatiques, métaboliques ou infectieuses (SIDA); les handicaps moteurs traumatiques, neurologiques, orthopédiques; les troubles psychiques.

Les demandes de renseignement et d'admission sont à adresser à la Direction Générale de la Fondation S.E.F. qui assurera la liaison avec les différents établissements.

The Foundation (S.E.F.) is responsible for the medical treatment of 1600 young patients—university or high school students and young workers suffering from physical diseases, motor disabilities, or mental disorders. Reabilitation and reinsertion into school or professional life is carried out through the co-operation, within the 13 establishments, of multidisciplinary nursing teams with university professors or secondary school teachers placed at their disposal by the national education's public service.

The Foundation's aim is to avoid young patients getting behind in their studies, due to medical treatment, and for them to benefit from a reorientation made necessary by illness. The medical centres situated in the Paris area (8) or in the main provincial cities (5) are located in the vicinity of all major universities, and the secondary school tuition, specifically adapted for those under medical treatment and the handicapped is assured by 290 teachers working closely with neighbouring schools.

The treatment available covers; chest diseases (asthma, bronchial diseases, tuberculosis); kidney diseases (helodialysis, transplants); blood diseases (tumours, marrow grafting); hepatic, matabolic or infectious diseases (AIDS); motor disabilities of traumatic, neurolgic or orthopaedic origin; and metal illnesses.

Inquiries for information and admission should be addressed to the headquarters of the Foundation S.E.F., who will get in touch with the various establishments.

Président: C.A. Colliard, Doyen honoraire de la Faculté de Droit de Grenoble.

Directeur général: Edouard Laporte.

Directeur médical et scientifique: Dr C. Ciancioni.

8, rue Emile-Deutsch-de-la-Meurthe, Boîte postale 147, 75664 Paris Cedex 14.

Tél: 45-89-43-39

Syndicat national de l'Enseignement supérieur (Fédération de l'Education Nationale)

78, rue du Faubourg-Saint-Denis, 75010 Paris.

Tél: 47-70-90-35

Fédération nationale des Syndicats autonomes de l'Enseignement supérieur (IAUPL)
18, rue du Docteur Roux, 75015 Paris.
Tél: 47-83-31-65

Association française des Femmes diplômées des Universités (IFUW)
Reid Hall, 4, rue de Chevreuse, 75006 Paris.
Tél: 43-20-01-32

Entr'aide universitaire française (WUS)
40, rue Rouelle, 75015 Paris.
Tél: 45-77-24-90. Télex: 200145 umpesix f

Union nationale des Etudiants de France (UNEF) (IUS)
52, rue Edouard Pailleron, 75019 Paris.
Tél: 45-26-20-65

Union nationale des Etudiants de France (Indépendante et Démocratique) (U.N.E.F.)
Président: Jean-Christophe Cambadelis.
55, boulevard de Strasbourg, 75010 Paris.
Tél: 45-23-45-50

Conférence des Grandes Ecoles
Président: Daniel Gourisse. 60,
Boulevard St. Michel, 75272 Paris Cedex 06.

Confédération nationale des Etudiants de France
120, rue Notre-Dame des Champs, 75006 Paris.
Tél: 43-54-74-88

Mutuelle nationale des Etudiants de France
37, boulevard St. Michel, 75006 Paris.
Tél: 42-43-31-41

Centre catholique des Intellectuels français (Pax Romana)
61, rue Madame, 75006 Paris.
Tél: 45-48-04-44

«Mission Etudiante» (Pax Romana)
7, rue Vauquelin, 75005 Paris.
Tél: 43-36-21-87

Fédération française des Associations chrétiennes d'Etudiants (WSCF)
26, rue Vauban, 91570 Bièvres.
Tél: 60-19-14-91

Union des Etudiants juifs de France (WUJS)
Correspondant: 89, chaussee de Vleurgat, 1050 Brussels.
Tél: (2) 647-7279. Télex: 20625

*

Ministère des Affaires étrangères, Direction générale des Affaires culturelles et techniques
37, quai d'Orsay, 75007 Paris.
Tél: 40-66-66-99

Ministère de l'Education nationale, Direction de l'Enseignement supérieur
61-65, rue Dutot, 75015 Paris.
Tél: 45-39-25-75

Commission de la République française pour l'Education, la Science et la Culture
42, avenue Raymond Poincaré, 75116 Paris.
Tél: 40-66-66-21

FRENCH POLYNESIA
POLYNESIE FRANÇAISE

Université du Pacifique, B.P. 4635, Papeete, Tahiti.   *1987*
Tél: 689-42-16-80

dr, sc, techn.
Centre Universitaire, Nouméa, p. 309

GABON
GABON

*Université Omar Bongo, B.P. 13131, Boulevard Léon M'ba, Libreville.   *1971, 1978*
Tél: 73-20-33. Télex: 5336 ung
F : dr-éco, let-hum, méd-sa.
  ECOLE DE MAGISTRATURE, B.P. 46, Libreville.   *1971*
  ECOLE NATIONALE D'ADMINISTRATION, B.P. 86, Libreville.
  ECOLE NORMALE SUPÉRIEURE, B.P. 16030, Libreville.
  Tél: 73-31-61
  ECOLE NORMALE SUPÉRIEURE DE L'ENSEIGNEMENT TECHNIQUE, B.P. 3989, Libreville.

Tél: 73-29-88
INSTITUT NATIONAL D'ETUDES FORESTIÈRES DU CAP ESTÉRIAS, Libreville.
INSTITUT NATIONAL DES SCIENCES DE GESTION, B.P. 190, Libreville.   *1973*
Tél: 73-28-45
ECOLE NATIONAL DE SECRÉTARIAT, B.P. 17014, Libreville.
Tél: 76-18-22
Université des Sciences et Techniques de Masuku, B.P. 901.903, Franceville.   *1986*
F: sc.
E: ing.

Ministère de l'Education nationale
Libreville.
Tél: 72-20-49. Télex: 5501 mineduc
Commission nationale gabonaise pour l'Unesco

Ministère de l'Education nationale, B.P. 264, Libreville.
Tél: 72-20-49. Télex: 5501

THE GAMBIA
LA GAMBIE

Gambia College, Brikama.   *1978*
D: *agr, ed, nurs, publ heal.*
Tel: 714

National Union of Gambian Students—NUGS (IUS)
P.O. Box 132, Banjul
Student Christian Movement of Gambia (WSCF)
P.O. Box 2261, Serrekunda.

       *

Ministry of Education, Youth, Sports and Culture
Banjul.
Gambia National Commission for Unesco
Ministry of Education, Youth, Sports and Culture, Banjul.
Tel: 28-231 (Ext. 139). Telex: 2204. Cables: unesco commission mined banjul

GERMAN DEMOCRATIC REPUBLIC
REPUBLIQUE DEMOCRATIQUE ALLEMANDE

UNIVERSITIES AND TECHNICAL UNIVERSITIES(1) —
UNIVERSITES ET UNIVERSITES TECHNIQUES (2)

*Humboldt-Universität zu Berlin, Unter den Linden 6, 1086 Berlin. (Universitäts-Sekretariat). *1809*
Tel: 20930. Telex: 112823 unibn dd
Sect : *phil, hist, law, crim, phill, math, rehabilitation-commun, Asian st, hort, plant prod, food, phy, ch, biol, electro, psyc, med, geog, agr, zoo-vet, eco, ed, phys, theo, for lang, aesthetics-arts, Ger st, slavonic st, English & Am st, romance st.*
I : *lib, socio.*
Ce : *comp.*

*Ernst-Moritz-Arndt-Universität Greifswald, Domstrasse 11, 2200 Greifswald. *1456*
Tel: 630. Telex: 318336 unig dd
Sect : *phil, hist, arts-mus, phill, math, phy-electro, ch, North Eur st, biol, ed, med, phar, geog, geol, phys, theo.*

*Martin-Luther-Universität Halle-Wittenberg, Universitätsplatz 10, 4010 Halle/Saale. *1502*
Tel: 8320. Telex: 4353 unihal dd
Sect : *phil, hist-pol, law, arts, phill, math, phy, dent, ch, biosc, med, phar, geog, agr, eco, ed, phys, theo, Ger lang-lit, mod lang-lit, for lang, classical-orntl st.*

*Friedrich-Schiller-Universität Jena, Goetheallee 1, 6900 Jena. *1558*
Tel: 820. telex: 5886134 uni dd
Sect : *phil, hist, law, lit art, phill, math, phy, ch, instrument techn, biol, techn, eco, med-dent, ed, phys, psyc, theo, archae, lang-phill.*
I : *hist of med-nat, lang.*

*Karl-Marx-Universität Leipzig, Karl-Marx-Platz 10, 7010 Leipzig. *1409*
Tel: 7190. Telex: 51350 uni dd
Sect : *phil, hist, law, cult-arts, phill, math, phy, ch, Middle East & African st, for lang, biol, psyc, med, agr, zoo-vet, eco, ed, phys, theo, jour, scientific communism, ling, dent.*

I : *phys, int st, trop agr-vet, ped, interp.*

*Wilhelm-Pieck-Universität Rostock, Universitätsplatz 1, 2500 Rostock. *1419*
Tel: 3690. Telex: 31140 unir dd
Sect : *phil, hist, phill, math, phy, ch, biol, infor, land dev-plant prod, mar techn, Latin Am st, electro, med-dent, agr, zoo, ped-psyc, phys, theo, bus adm, ling-lit.*
I : *eco mangt, ind.*

*Technische Universität Dresden, Mommsenstrasse 13, 8027 Dresden. *1928*
Tel: 463-4312 Telex: 2278 teuni dd
F : *soc, nat-math, elec-electro, mec, civ eng-hyd-for.*
D : *phil-hum, ped, mangt, phy, ch, math, comp, infor, electro, elec, energ, mec, prod eng, processing techn, atm, civ eng, arc, surv, hyd eng, for, labour st, appl ling.*
I : *phys, eco, prof retraining, law.*

*Technische Universität Karl-Marx-Stadt, Strasse der Nationen 62, 9010 Karl-Marx-Stadt. *1953*
Tel: 6680. Telex: 75061 th dd
Sect : *phil, math, infor, phy-electro, comp, machine eng, metal techn, atm, tex-leather, ch-mater, eco, ped, lang, processing techn.*

*Technische Hochschule «Otto von Guericke», Boleslaw-Bierut-Platz 5, 3040 Magdeburg. *1953*
Tel: 5920. Telex: 8214 thoug dd
Sect : *phil, math, phy, eco, comp, mec, met, thermal-hyd eng, atm-elec, ch equipment.*

*Technische Hochschule «Carl Schorlemmer» Leuna-Merseburg, Otto-Neuschke-Strasse, 4200 Merseburg. *1954*
Tel: 460. Telex: 471320 thim dd
Sect : *phil, math, ch, ch eng, phy, eco, mater, eng, process techn.*
I : *ind eco, eco.*

---

(1) Including institutions of full university status. Within the broad range of disciplines indicated, each institution comprises numerous subject *sections* which constitute the structural basis for interdisciplinary teaching and research.

(1) Y compris les institutions ayant rang d'université. Dans le large éventail des disciplines indiquées, chaque institution comporte de nombreuses *sections* qui constituent la base structurelle d'un enseignement et d'une recherche interdisciplinaires.

*Bergakademie Freiberg [A. des Mines], Akademiestrasse 6, 9200 Freiberg/Sa. *1765*
Tel: 510. Telex: 785035 baf dd
Sect : *phil, math, phy, mine-geol, ind eco, geosc, mec-energ, met-mater, process & silicate eng.*
I : *ind eng, eng.*

*Hochschule für Architektur und Bauwesen Weimar [S. of Architecture and Building], Geschwister-Scholl-Strasse 8, 53 Weimar. *1860*
Tel: 730. Telex: 618950 habw dd
Sect : *phil, math, app tec sc, arc, civ eng, mater, comp, urb plan.*

Technische Hochschule Leipzig, Karl-Liebknecht-Strasse 132, 7030 Leipzig. *1977*
Tel: 39280. Telex: 51552 tehael dd
Sect : *phil, math-comp, nat, poly-graphic arts, atm-cyb, bui, mangt, const, elec systems.*
I : *eco.*

*Technische Hochschule Ilmenau, Ehrenberg, Block G, 6300 Ilmenau. *1953*

Tel: 740. Telex: 62345 thits dd
Sect : *phil, phy-electro, math-comp-cyb, tec & biomed cyb, elec, infor-theor elec, const.*
I : *infor-jur-patents, ind.*

*Hochschule für Ökonomie «Bruno Leuschner», Hermann-Duncker-Strasse 8, 1157 Berlin. *1950*
Tel: 5040. Telex: 112850 oekon dd
Sect : *phil, eco, infor bus adm.*

Akademie für Staats- und Rechtswissenschaft der DDR [A. of Political Science and Law], August-Bebel-Strasse 89, 1502 Potsdam-Babelsberg. *1948*
Tel: 76701. Telex: 15508 asr dd

Hochschule für Verkehrswesen «Friedrich List» [C. of Transport and Communications], Friedrich-List-Platz 1, 8010 Dresden. *1952*
Tel: 4620. Telex: 2444 hfv dd
Sect : *phil, math, app phy, trans, comp-nat, vehicle techn, eco.*

OTHER INSTITUTIONS – AUTRES INSTITUTIONS

Hochschule für Grafik und Buchkunst Leipzig [C. of Graphic Arts and Book Design], Dimitroffstrasse 11, 7010 Leipzig. *1764*
Tel: 391-32-11

Hochschule für industrielle Formgestaltung Halle [C. of Industrial Design], Burg Giebichenstein Neuwerk 7, 4000 Halle. *1915*
Tel: 8500. Telex: 4510 hifah dd

Kunsthochschule Berlin [C. of Fine and Applied Arts], Nr. 20 Strasse 203, 1120 Berlin-Weissensee. *1947*
Tel: 56-54-061

Hochschule für bildende Künste [C. of Fine Arts], Günzstrasse 34, 8019 Dresden. *1764*
Tel: 45-90-112

Hochschule für Film und Fernsehen der DDR, Karl-Marx-Strasse 33–34, Potsdam-Babelsberg, 1502 Babelsberg. *1954*
Tel: 78981. Telex: 15547 hff dd

Hochschule für Musik «Hanns Eisler», Otto-Grotewohl-Strasse 19, 1080 Berlin. *1950*
Tel: 22-02-626

Hochschule für Musik Dresden «Carl Maria von Weber», Blochmannstrasse 2–4, 8010 Dresden. *1856*
Tel: 45-90-213

Hochschule für Musik «Felix-Mendelssohn-Bartholdy», Grassistrasse 8, 7010 Leipzig. *1843*
Tel: 31-14-02

Hochschule für Musik «Franz Liszt», Platz der Demokratie 2–3, 5300 Weimar. *1872*
Tel: 5241

Hochschule für Schauspielkunst «Ernst Busch», Schnellerstrasse 104, 1190 Berlin. *1981*

Theaterhochschule «Hans Otto», Schwägrichenstrasse 3, 7010 Leipzig. *1947*
Tel: 32-51-34

Institut für Literatur «Johannes R. Becher» Leipzig, Karl-Tauchwitz-Strasse 8, 7020 Leipzig. *1955*
Tel: 31-03-86

Medizinische Akademie «Carl Gustav Carus», Fetscher Strasse 74, 8019 Dresden. *1954*
Tel: 4580. Telex: 2359 medak dd

Medizinische Akademie Erfurt, Nordhäuser Strasse 74, 5010 Erfurt. *1954*
Tel: 500. Telex: 61384 medak dd

Medizinische Akademie Magdeburg, Leipziger Strasse 44, 3090 Magdeburg. *1954*
Tel: 670. Telex: 8239 medak dd

Hochschule für Landwirtschaft und Nahrungsgüterwirtschaft Bernburg [C. of Agriculture and Food Technology], Mitschurinstrasse 28, 4351 Bernburg, Saale. *1961*
Tel: 8231. Telex: 48338 hfbb dd

Hochschule für Landwirtschaftliche Produktionsgenossenschaften Meissen [C. for Agricultural Co-operatives], Freiheit 13, 8250 Meissen. *1953*
Tel: 8121. Telex: 277215 lpghs dd

Handelshochschule Leipzig [C. of Commerce], Markgrafenstrasse 2, 7010 Leipzig. *1969*
Tel: 7481. Telex: 51390 cewa dd

Ingenieurhochschule Wartenberg [C. of Engineering], Dorfstrasse 10, 1127 Berlin. *1969*
Tel: 48150. Telex: 114792 ihs dd

Ingenieurhochschule Cottbus, Karl-Marx-Strasse 17, 7500 Cottbus. *1969*

Tel: 690. Telex: 17472 ihscs dd
Ingenieurhochschule Köthen, Bernburger Strasse
52/57, 4370 Köthen.   *1969*
Tel: 670. Telex: 47720 ingsch dd
Ingenieurhochschule Mittweida, Platz der DSF
17, 9250 Mittweida.   *1969*
Tel: 580. Telex: 77520 ihsmit dd
Ingenieurhochschule Zwickau, Dr. Friedrichring

2a, 9541 Zwickau.   *1969*
Tel: 8230. Telex: 77038 ihzrz dd
Ingenieurhochschule für Seefahrt Warnemünde-
Wustrow, Richard-Wagner-Strasse 31, 2530
Warnemünde.   *1969*
Tel: 570. Telex: 31338 ihswm dd
mar eng.

Teacher Training — Formation pédagogique

Deutsche Hochschule für Körperkultur [German
C. of Physical Education], Friedrich-Ludwig-
Jahn-Allee 59, 7010 Leipzig.   *1950*
Tel: 4970. Telex: 512275 dhfk dd
Pädagogische Hochschule «Karl Friedrich
Wilhelm Wander», [C. of Education], Wigard-
strasse 17, 8060 Dresden.   *1952*
Tel: 59900
Pädagogische Hochschule «Dr Theodor Neu-
bauer», Nordhäuser Strasse 63, 5000 Erfurt.
                                                       1953
Tel: 5360. Telex: 618784 phcb
Pädagogische Hochschule «Liselotte Herrmann»,
Goldberger Strasse 12, 2600 Güstrow.   *1949*
Tel: 360. Telex: 328587 phgue
Pädagogische Hochschule «N.K. Krupskaja»,
Kröllwitzer Strasse 44, 4020 Halle.   *1950*
Tel: 30288

Pädagogische Hochschule «Wolfgang Ratke»,
Lohmann-Strasse 23, 4370 Köthen.   *1950*
Tel: 690
Pädagogische Hochschule «Clara Zetkin», Karl-
Heine Strasse 22b, 7031 Leipzig.   *1953*
Tel: 49770
Pädagogische Hochschule «Erich Weinert»,
Brandenburger Strasse 9, 3040 Magdeburg.
                                                       1951
Tel: 33666
Pädagogische Hochschule «Karl Lieb-knecht»,
Am Neuen Palais, 1500 Potsdam.   *1948*
Tel: 9100
Pädagogische Institut «Ernst Schneller», Am
Scheffelberg 39, 9500 Zwickau.   *1965*
Tel: 7480. Telex: 77051 phzwi dd

Hoch- und Fachschulrat der Deutschen Demo-
kratischen Republik
   The Council for Higher and Specialized
Education of the German Democratic Republic
advises the Minister for Higher and Specialized
Education on basic questions affecting the development of higher and specialized education. It
is particularly engaged in advising on long-term
planning of higher education; fixing principles
governing the aims and the content of socialist
education at university and post-graduate level
and in the field of further education; formulating
priorities for research at universities or other
institutions of higher education; establishing
principles for the co-operation in research work
between universities and other scientific institutions in the German Democratic Republic, and
for international co-operation between universities and institutions of higher education in the
German Democratic Republic and those of other
countries and international organizations.
   The Council is made up of members of universities and other institutions of higher and specialized education and of representatives from all
spheres of the society of the German Democratic
Republic: rectors, professors, lecturers,

students, ministers, representatives of the socialist economy and representatives of social
organizations.
   Le Conseil de l'enseignement supérieur et tech-
nique de la République démocratique allemande
fournit un avis consultatif au Ministre de
l'Enseignement supérieur et technique sur les
problèmes fondamentaux du développement de
l'enseignement supérieur et technique. Il s'occupe
avant tout de la planification à long terme de
l'enseignement supérieur et technique et formule
des règles pour les objectifs et le contenu de
l'enseignement socialiste aux niveaux universit-
aire, postgradué, et de l'éducation permanente; il
élabore les principes régissant la coopération entre
les universités et les autres établissements scien-
tifiques en matière de recherche ainsi que ceux
devant régir la coopération entre les universités et
les institutions d'enseignement supérieur de la
République démocratique allemande et les établis-
sements d'autres pays ou les organisations inter-
nationales.
   Le Conseil est composé de représentants des
universités, des autres établissements de l'en-
seignement supérieur et technique ainsi que des
divers domaines de la vie sociale de la RDA:

recteurs, professeurs, assistants, étudiants, ministres, représentants de l'économie socialiste, représentants des organisations sociales.
President: Prof. Hans-Joachim Böhme, Minister of Higher and Specialized Education.
Secretary: Günter Jähnigen.
Secretary for International Co-operation: Prof. Dr. Manfred Nast, Central Institute of Higher Education,
Aristotelessteig 4, 1157 Berlin.
Tel: 525-28-65

Komitee für Angelegenheiten ausländischer Studierender in der DDR (Committee for Affairs of Foreign Students in the GDR—Comité chargé des affaires des étudiants étrangers en RDA)
Marx-Engels-Platz 2, 1020 Berlin.
Tel: 5098911

Gewerkschaft Wissenschaft im Freien Deutschen Gewerkschaftsbund (Union of Scientific Workers in the Confederation of Free German Trade Unions—Syndicat des Travailleurs scientifiques au sein de la Confédération des syndicats libres allemands)
Am Köllnischen Park 2, 1020 Berlin.
Tel: 27010

Forschungsrat der Deutschen Demokratischen Republik (Research Council of the GDR—Conseil de recherche de la RDA)
Köpenicker Strasse 80/82, 1020 Berlin.
Tel: 65760

Deutsche Akademie der Wissenschaften zu Berlin (The German Academy of Science in Berlin—Académie allemande des Sciences à Berlin)
Tel: 2070641
Otto-Nuschke-Strasse 22/23, 1080 Berlin.

Deutsche Akademie der Landwirtschaftwissenschaften (The German Academy of Agricultural Sciences of Berlin—Académie allemande des Sciences agricoles de Berlin)
Krausenstrasse 38/39, 1980 Berlin.

Tel: 2000461

Freie Deutsche Jugend, Studentenabteilung—FDJ (Free German Youth Student Section—Jeunesse Libre Allemande, Section des Etudiants) (IUS)
Unter den Linden 36/38, 1080 Berlin.
Tel: 22310. Telex: 114846 zfdj

Evangelische Studentengemeinde in der DDR (WSCF)
Immanuelkirchstrasse 1A, 1055 Berlin.
Tel: 437-26-42

*

Nationale Äquivalenzkommission der Deutschen Demokratischen Republik
Marx-Engels-Platz 2, 1020 Berlin.
Tel: 230

Ministerium für das Hoch- und Fachschulwesen (Ministry for Higher and Specialized Education —Ministère de l'Enseignement supérieur et technique)
Marx-Engels-Platz 2, 1020 Berlin.
Tel: 209. Telex: 114 590 gbmfh dd

Ministerium für Wissenschaft und Technik (Ministry for Science and Technology—Ministère de la Recherche et de la Technique)
Köpenicker Strasse 80/82, 1020 Berlin.
Tel: 65760. Telex: 113071 mwt dd

Ministerium für Auswärtige Angelegenheiten, Kulturabteilung (Ministry for Foreign Affairs, Department for Cultural Affairs—Ministère des Affaires étrangères, Direction des Affaires culturelles)
Marx-Engels-Platz 2, 1020 Berlin.
Tel: 230. Telex: 114621 aumi dd

Commission of the German Democratic Republic for Unesco
Ministry of Foreign Affairs, Marx-Engels-Platz 2, 1020 Berlin.
Tel: 589-28-17. Telex: 114621 aumi dd. Cables: unescom ddr berlin

FEDERAL REPUBLIC OF GERMANY
REPUBLIQUE FEDERALE D'ALLEMAGNE

UNIVERSITIES AND UNIVERSITY INSTITUTIONS—
UNIVERSITES ET ETABLISSEMENTS UNIVERSITAIRES

*Rheinisch-Westfälische Technische Hochschule Aachen, Templergraben 55, 5100 Aachen.
1870
Tel: (241) 801. Telex: 832704 thac d
F/D : *math-phy, ch-biol, arc, civ eng, mec, mine-geosc-met, elec, phil-hist, sc, eco, med, ped.*

*Universität Augsburg, Universitätsstrasse 2, 8900 Augsburg.
1970
Tel: (821) 598-1. Telex: 53830 uniaug d
F : *cath theo, eco-soc, law, ed, phil, math-geog.*
Ce : *phys, lang.*
Ut : *continuing ed.*

*Universität Bamberg, Kapuzinerstrasse 16, 8600 Bamberg.
1972
Tel: (95-1) 402-1
F : *cath theo, ped-phil-psyc, lang-lit, hist-geosc, soc-eco.*
D : *soc w.*

*Universität Bayreuth, Universitätsstrasse 30, 8580 Bayreuth.
1972
Tel: (192-1) 608-1. Teletex: 921824=ubt
F : *math-phy, biol-ch-geosc, law-eco, lang-lit, hum.*

*Freie Universität Berlin, Altensteinstrasse 40, 1000 Berlin 33.
1948
Tel: (30) 838-1. telex: 184019 fubln d. Teletex: 308622 = fuphysk
D : *med-med ecol, dent, vet, phil-soc, commun, law, eco, ed-ped, hist, class sc, Ger lang, mod lang, math, phy, ch, biol, phar geosc.*

*Technische Universität Berlin, Strasse des 17. Juni 135, 1000 Berlin 12.
1879
Tel: (30) 314-1. Fax: (30) 314-23222. Telex: 184262 tubln d. Teletex: 308621 = tupress
D : *commun-hist, soc-plan, math, phy, synthetic & analytic ch, phy ch-app ch, civ eng-surv, arc, phy eng, process & ch eng, const, prod, trans, food & biotechn, rur plan, agr, mine-geosc, mater sc, eco, elec, comp, env techn, ed-ped.*

Universität Bielefeld, Universitätsstrasse 25, 4800 Bielefeld 1.
1967
Tel: (521) 106-1. Telex: 932362 unibi
F : *biol, ch, hist-phil, ling-lit, math, ped, phy, psyc-phys, law, socio, eco, theo-geog-fa & mus.*

*Ruhr-Universität Bochum, Universitätsstrasse 150, 4630 Bochum 1.
1961

Tel: 700-1. Telex: 825860
F : *prot theo, cath theo, phil-ped-jour, hist, phill, law, eco, soc, East Asian st, phys, psyc, mec, civ eng, elec, math, phy-astr, geosc, ch, biol, nat med, theor & clin med.*

*Rheinische Friedrich-Wilhelms-Universität Bonn, Regina-Pacis-Weg 3, 5300 Bonn 1. *1818*
Tel: (228) 731. Telex: 886657 unibo d
F : *prot theo, cath theo, law-pol, med, phil, hum, math-nat, agr, ped.*

*Technische Universität Carolo-Wilhelmina zu Braunschweig, Pockelsstrasse 14, 3300 Braunschweig.
1745, 1968
Tel: (531) 391-0. Fax: (531) 391-4587. Telex: 952526 tubsw d
D : *math-comp-eco, phy-geosc, ch-phar-biosc, arc, civ eng-surv, mec, elec, phil-soc, ed.*

*Universität Bremen, Bibliotheksstrasse, 2800 Bremen 33.
1971
Tel: (421) 2181. Telex: 245811 unibr d
D : *pol, phy-elec, biol-ch, math-comp, law, eco, soc ped-psyc-phys, lang-Ger lang-fa-mus.*

Technische Universität Clausthal, Adolf Römer-Strasse 2a, 3392 Clausthal-Zellerfeld.
1775, 1968
Tel: (5323) 72-1. Telex: 953828 tuclx d
D : *math-comp, ch, phy, geosc, mine-eng, met mater sc, mec-process & ch eng.*

*Technische Hochschule Darmstadt, Karolinenplatz 5, 6100 Darmstadt.
1836
Tel: (6151) 161. Telex: 419579 thd d
D : *law-eco, soc-hist, ed-psyc, math, phy, mec, phy ch-ch techn, inorg & nucl ch, org & macromolecule ch, biol, geosc-geog, surv, water & trans sc, civ eng, arc, mec, elec energy, elec commun techn, control theory-data proc, comp & infor sc.*

*Universität Dortmund, August-Schmidt-Strasse 4, 4600 Dortmund 50 (Eichlinghofen).
1965
Tel: (231) 755-1. Telex: 822465 unido d
D : *math, phy, ch, comp, stat, ch eng, mec, elec, reg plan, civ eng, eco-soc, ed-biol, spe ed, soc-phil-theo, lang-lit-jour-hist, mus-des-phys-geog.*
I : *env, robotics.*
Ce : *higher ed didactics.*

*Heinrich-Heine-Universität Düsseldorf, Univer-

sitätsstrasse 1, 4000 Düsseldorf 1.
1907, 1923, 1965
Tel: (211) 31-11. Fax: (211) 311-4876. Telex: 8587348 uuni d

F : *phil, math-nat, med.*

*Universität-Gesamthochschule-Duisburg, Lotharstrasse 65, 4100 Duisburg. *1972*
Tel: (203) 3790. Fax: (203) 370435. Telex: 855793 unidu d

D : *phil-relig-soc, ed-psyc-phys, lang-lit, fa & mus ed, eco, biol-ch-geog, mec, met, elec, phytechn, math.*

*Katholische Universität Eichstätt, Ostenstrasse 26, 8078 Eichstätt. *1972*
Tel: (8421) 201. Telex: 55941 lraed

F : *cath theo, phil-ped, lang-lit, hist-soc, mathgeog.*

D : *relig ped-ecl ed, soc work.*

*Friedrich-Alexander-Universität Erlangen-Nürnberg, Schlossplatz 4, 8520 Erlangen. *1743*
Tel: (9131) 851. Fax: (9131) 8104-50. Telex: 629830 unier d

F : *theo, law, med, phil-hist-soc, lang-lit, math-phy, biol-ch, geosc, eco-soc, techn sc, ed.*

*Universität-Gesamthochschule-Essen, Universitätsstrasse 2, 4300 Essen 1. *1972*
Tel: (201) 183-1. Fax: (201) 723-2266. Telex: 8579091 unie d

D : *phil-relig-soc, ed, lit-lang, des-fa ed, eco, math, phy, ch, arc-biosc-geosc, civ eng, surv, mec, energ-elec-process & ch eng, med.*

Nordische Universität, Speicherlinie 34a, 2390 Flensburg. *1985*
Tel: (461) 35052

F : *eco; agr, eng* (in process of development).

Pädagogische Hochschule Flensburg, Mürwicker Strasse 77, 2390 Flensburg. *1946, 1973*
Tel: (461) 35052

I : *ped* (and 23 disciplines including didactics for primary and secondary teacher ed).

Johann Wolfgang Goethe-Universität Frankfurt am Main, Senckenberganlage 31, 6000 Frankfurt Main 11. *1901, 1914*
Tel: (69) 798-1. Telex: 413932 unif d

D : *law, eco, soc, ed, psyc, relig, phil, hist, class phill-fa, mod lang, East Eur & extra-Eur lang & hum, math, phy, ch, bioch-phar-food ch, biol, geosc, geog, med, infor, phys.*

C : *env res, North Am st.*

*Albert-Ludwigs-Universität Freiburg im Breisgau, Heinrich-von-Stephan-Strasse 25, 7800 Freiburg/Br. *1457*
Tel: (761) 2031. Telex: 772740 uf d

F : *theo, law, eco, med, phil-ed-psyc-archae-hist of art-mus-phys, class phill-orntl st-ling-slav lang-rom lang, Ger lang-ethn-English lang, hist-pol-socio, math, phy, ch-phar, biol, geosc-for.*

*Justus-Liebig-Universität Giessen, Ludwigstrasse 23, 6300 Giessen 11.

1607, 1946, 1957
Tel: (641) 702-1. Telex: 482956. Teletex: 6419006 = klingi

D : *law, eco, soc, ed, art ped-mus-phys, psyc, relig, hist, Ger lang, English lang, medit & East Eur lang & cult, math, phy, ch, biol, agr, vet-anim sc, nutr sc, food sc-hom eco, geosc-geog, med.*

*Georg-August-Universität Göttingen, Wilhelmsplatz 1, 3400 Göttingen. *1736*
Tel: (531) 394311. Telex: 96703 unigoe d

D : *theo, law, med, hist-phill, math, phy, ch, geosc, biol, for, agr, eco, soc, ed.*

*Fernuniversität-Gesamthochschule-Hagen, Feithstrasse 152, Postfach 940, 5800 Hagen. *1974*
Tel: (2331) 804-1. Telex: 823137 feuni d

D : *elec, ed-soc, math-infor sc, law, eco.*

Ce : *dev of distance st, distance st res.*

*Universität Hamburg, Edmund-Siemers-Allee 1, 2000 Hamburg 13. *1919*
Tel: (40) 4123-4475. Telex: 214732 unihh d

D : *prot theo, law, eco, med, phil-soc, ed, lang, hist, hist of civilizations-hum, orntl st, math, phy, ch, biol, geogsc, pysc, comp-infor sc, phys, nav const.*

Technische Universität Hamburg-Harburg, Schlossmühlendamm 30, 2100 Hamburg 90.
1978
Tel: (40) 77181. Teletex: 403696 = tuhh

D : *mec, process eng-ch techn, elec, civ eng, env techn, mar techn-bio techn, urb.*

Medizinische Hochschule Hannover, Konstanty-Gutschow-Strasse 8, 3000 Hannover 61 (Kleefeld). *1963*
Tel: (511) 5321. Telex: 922044 mhhk d

Ce : *med, bioch, dent, phar, publ heal, biometry-med informatics-med techn.*

*Universität Hannover, Welfengarten 1, 3000 Hannover 1. *1831, 1847, 1879, 1968*
Tel: (511) 762-0. Fax: (511) 762-2768. Telex: 923868 unihn d

D : *math, phy, ch, geosc, biol, arc, civ eng-surv, mec, elec, hort, env, lit-lang, ed, hist-phil-soc, law, eco.*

Tierärztliche Hochschule Hannover [Hanover S. of Veterinary Medicine], Bischofsholer Damm 15, 3000 Hannover 1. *1778*
Tel: (511) 856-1. Telex: 922034 tiho d

vet, biomed techn, biol-bioch.

*Ruprecht-Karls-Universität Heidelberg, Grabengasse 1, 6900 Heidelberg 1. *1386, 1803*
Tel: (6221) 541. Fax: (6221) 161693. Telex: 461515 unihd d

F : *theo, law, nat med, theor med, clin med, phil-hist, orntl st-class st, mod lang-lit, eco, soc & behavioural sc, math, ch, phar, phy-astr, biol, geosc.*

Hochschule für Jüdische Studien Heidelberg, Friedrichstrasse 9, 6900 Heidelberg. *1979*

Tel: (6221) 22576
judaic st.
Hochschule Hildesheim, Marienburger Platz 22, 3200 Hildesheim. *1978*
Tel: (5121) 883-0
D : *ed-soc, hum, lang-techn, math-infor-nat.*
*Universität Hohenheim, Schloss 1, 7000 Stuttgart 70 (Hohenheim).
1818, 1847, 1904, 1922, 1967
Tel: (711) 459-0. Telex: 7022959 uniho d
F : *nat, biol, agr, eco-soc.*
Universität Kaiserslautern, Erwin-Schrödinger-Strasse, 6750 Kaiserslautern. *1970, 1975*
Tel: (631) 205-1. Telex: 45627 unikl d. Teletex: 631938 = rhrk
D : *math, phy, ch, biol, comp, mec, elec, arc-reg plan-env plan-civ eng, soc.*
*Universität Fridericiana Karlsruhe (T.H.), Kaiserstrasse 12, 7500 Karlsruhe.
1825, 1865, 1967
Tel: (721) 6080. Fax: (721) 608-4290. Telex: 7826521. Teletex: 731304 = hiunika
F : *math, phy, ch, biosc-geosc, hum-soc, arc, civ eng-surv, ch eng, elec, comp, eco.*
*Universität Gesamthochschule-Kassel, Mönchebergstrasse 19, 3500 Kassel 1. *1970, 1972*
Tel: (561) 804-1. Telex: 99572 ghkks d
D : *ed-hum, prof ed-techn, psyc-phys-mus, soc work, soc, app soc-law, eco, English lang-romance lang, Ger lang, arc, city plan-env plan, civ eng, mec, elec, math, phy, biol-ch, agr, int agr eco, fa, vis commun, prod des.*
*Christian-Albrechts-Universität zu Kiel, Olshausenstrasse 40-60, 2300 Kiel.
1665, 1773
Tel: (431) 8801. Telex: 292656 cauki d. Teletex: 43119 = cau
F : *theo, law, eco-soc, med, phil, math-nat, agr.*
Pädagogische Hochschule Kiel, Olshausenstrasse 75, 2300 Kiel. *1926, 1967*
Tel: (431) 54331
I : *ped, psyc, phil, socio* (also 17 disciplines including didactics for primary and secondary teacher ed).
Wissenschaftliche Hochschule für Unternehmensführung, Zwickauer Str. 23, 5400 Koblenz. *1984*
Tel: 261-51081. Telex: 862843 ihaka d
eco, bus adm-mangt.
Universität zu Köln, Albertus-Magnus Platz, 5000 Köln 41 (Lindenthal). *1388, 1919*
Tel: (221) 470-1. Fax: (221) 446193. Telex: 8882291 unik d
F : *eco-soc, law, med, phil, math-nat, ed, spe ed.*
Deutsche Sporthochschule Köln, Carl-Diem-Weg 2, 5000 Köln 41 (Müngersdorf). *1920, 1947*
Tel: (221) 4982-1
D : *ed-hum-soc, med-nat, phy.*
*Universität Konstanz, Universitätsstrasse 10,

7750 Konstanz. *1964*
Tel: (7531) 881. Fax: (7531) 88-3688. Telex: 733359 univ d
F : *math, phy, ch, biol, soc, eco-stat, law, phil.*
Medizinische Universität Lübeck, Ratzeburger Allee 160, 2400 Lübeck 1. *1973*
Tel: (451) 5001. Telex: 26492 mhl d
F : *preclin & nat med, clin med.*
Hochschule Lüneburg, Wilschenbrucher Weg 84, 2120 Lüneburg. *1978*
Tel: (4131) 714-1. Telex: 2182112
D : *ed, eco-soc.*
Johannes Gutenberg-Universität Mainz, Saarstrasse 21, 6500 Mainz. *1447, 1946*
Tel: (6131) 391. Telex: 4187155 phmz d
D : *cath theo, prot theo, law-eco, med, phil-ped, soc, phil I-III, hist, math, phy,ch, phar, biol, geosc, app lang, fa ed, mus ed, phys.*
*Universität Mannheim, Schloss 6800 Mannheim 1. *1907, 1946, 1967*
Tel: (621) 292-0. Telex: 462588 unima d. Teletex: 6211786 = rum
F : *law, bus adm, eco-stat, soc, phil-psyc-ed, lang-lit, hist-geog, math-comp.*
*Philipps-Universität Marburg, Biegenstrasse 10, 3550 Marburg/Lahn. *1527, 1653*
Tel: (6421) Telex: 482372. Teletex: 6421919 = unimar
D : *law, eco, soc-phil, psyc, prot theo, hist, class st, gen Ger ling & phill, mod Ger lit & fa, mod lang & lit, extra-Eur lang & cult, math, phy, ch, ch, phar-food ch, biol, geosc, geog, med, ed.*
*Ludwig-Maximilians-Universität München, Geschwister-Scholl-Platz 1, 8000 München 22.
1472
Tel: (89) 2180-1. Fax: (89) 2604212. Telex: 529860 univm d
F : *cath theo, prot theo, law, bus adm, eco, for, med, vet, phil-fa, phil-phil of sc-stat, psyc-ped, class st-hum, lang-lit, soc, math, phy, ch-phar, biol, geosc.*
*Technische Universität München, Arcisstrasse 21, 8000 München 2. *1827, 1868, 1970*
Tel: (89) 2105-1. Telex: 522854 tumue d. Teletex: 898174 = tumgar
F : *math-comp, phy, ch-biol-geosc, eco-soc, civ eng-surv, arc, mec, elec-comp, agr-hort, brewery & food techn-milk prod, med.*
*Westfälische Wilhelms-Universität Münster, Schlossplatz 2, 4400 Münster/ Westf.
1780, 1902
Tel: (251) 83-1. Fax: (251) 83-2090. Telex: 892529 unims d
D : *prot theo, cath theo, law, eco-soc, med, phil, psyc, ed, soc, hist, Ger lang, English lang, romance lang-slav, class & extra Eur lang & cult, math, phy, ch, biol, geosc, phys, tec-nat.*
Universität Oldenburg, Ammerländer Heerstrasse 67-99, 2900 Oldenburg. *1971*

Tel: (441) 798-0. Fax: (441) 798-3000. Telex: 25655 unol d

D : *ped, commun-aesthetics, soc, eco-law, phil-psyc-phys, math-comp, bio, phy, ch.*

Universität Osnabrück, Neuer Graben-Schloss, 4500 Osnabrück.   *1970*
Tel: (541) 6081. Telex: 944850 unios d

D : *law, eco, soc, ed-phys, hum-geosc, lang-lit, psyc, math infor, phy, biol-ch, cath theo, ed, lang-fa-mus.*

*Universität-Gesamthochschule-Paderborn, Warburger Strasse 100, 4790 Paderborn.
Tel: (5241) 60-1. Telex: 936776 unipb d

D : *hist-geog-relig-soc, ed-psyc-phys, lang-lit, fa-mus-des, eco, phy, art-env plan, civ eng, agr, mec, ch-ch techn, elec, commun techn, elec energy, math-comp.*

*Universität Passau, Neuburger Strasse 18, 8390 Passau.   *1973*
Tel: (851) 5090

F : *cath theo, law, eco, phil, math-comp.*

*Universität Regensburg, Universitätsstrasse 31, 8400 Regensburg.   *1962, 1967*
Tel: (941) 9431. Telex: 65658 unir d

F : *cath theo, law, eco, med, phil-phys-fa, psyc-ped, hist-soc-geog, lang-lit, math, phy, biol-preclin med, ch-phar.*

Erziehungswissenschaftliche Hochschule Rheinland-Pfalz, Grosse Bleiche 60–62, 6500 Mainz.
                                                        1969
Tel: (6131) 234651

D : *ed, phill, nat.*

*Universität des Saarlandes, Am Stadtwald, 6600 Saarbrücken.   *1947*
Tel: (681) 302-1. Fax: (681) 302-3900. Telex: 4428851. Teletex: 6817533 = unis

D : *law, eco, theor med, clin med, hist, soc-env sc, fa-class st, mod lang & lit, math, app math-comp, phy, app phy, inorg ch-phys ch, org ch-phar ch, analytical & biol ch, biol.*

*Universität - Gesamthochschule - Siegen, Hölderlinstrasse 3, 5900 Siegen.   *1972*
Tel: (271) 740-1. Telex: 872337 ghsgnd

D : *soc-phil-theo-hist-geog, ped-psyc-phys, lang-lit, fa & mus ed, eco, math, phy, ch-biol, arc-city plan, civ eng, mec, elec.*

Hochschule für Verwaltungswissenschaften Speyer, Freiherr-com-Stein-Strasse 2, 6720

Speyer.   *1947, 1950*
Tel: (6232) 910-1

adm sc.

*Universität Stuttgart, Keplerstrasse 7, 7000 Stuttgart 1.   *1829, 1890, 1967*
Tel: (711) 20731. Fax: (711) 121-3500. Telex: 721703 unis d

F : *arc-city plan, civ eng-surv, ch, elec, energ techn, prod techn, geosc-biosc, hist-soc-eco, aviation & space techn, math-comp, phil, phy, process & ch eng.*

Universität Trier, Postfach 3825, 5500 Trier.
                                                1970, 1975
Tel: (651) 201-1. Telex: 472680 unitr d

D : *ped, phil, psyc, lang-lit, geog-geosc-hist-pol-class archae, arts hist, eco, law.*

*Eberhard-Karls-Universität Tübingen, Wilhelmstrasse 7, 7400 Tübingen 1.   *1477*
Tel: (7071) 291. Fax: (7071) 29-5092. Telex: 7262867 utna d. Teletex: 7071913 hutioc

F : *prot theo, cath theo, law, eco, theor med, clin med, phil, soc-eco, mod lang, hist, hum, math, phy, ch-phar, biol, geosc.*

Universität Ulm, Oberer Eselsberg, 7900 Ulm/Donau.   *1967*
Tel: (731) 1761-1. Telex: 712567 uniul d. Teletex: 731103 = pathe

F : *nat-math, med-dent.*

Universität Witten-Herdecke, Ruhrstrasse 70, 5810 Witten/Ruhr.   *1982*
Tel: (2302) 57062

F : *med, dent, eco, orntl st, mus ther.*

*Bayerische Julius-Maximilians-Universität Würzburg, Sanderring 2, 8700 Würzburg.
                                                1582, 1945
Tel: (931) 31-1. Telex: 068671 uniwbg d. Teletex: 9318152 = uniwbg

F : *cath theo, law, med, class st-hum, mod lang-hist-hist of art, phil-ed-soc, biol, ch-phar, geosc, math, phy-astr, eco.*

*Bergische Universität-Gesamthochschule-Wuppertal, Gaussstrasse 20, 5600 Wuppertal 1.
                                                        1972
Tel: (202) 439-1. Telex: 8592262 bugw d

D : *soc, hist-phil-theo, ed, lang-lit, des-fa & mus ed, printing techn, eco, math, phy, ch-biol, arc, civ eng, mec, elec, safety techn.*

SCHOOLS OF EDUCATION—
ECOLES PEDAGOGIQUES SUPERIEURES

Pädagogische Hochschule Freiburg im Breisgau, Kunzenweg 21, 7800 Freiburg/Br.   *1962*
Tel: (761) 682-1

Pädagogische Hochschule Heidelberg, Keplerstrasse 87, 6900 Heidelberg 1.   *1962*

Tel: (6221) 4770

Pädagogische Hochschule Karlsruhe, Bismarckstrasse 10, 7500 Karlsruhe 1.   *1768, 1962*
Tel: (721) 23991

Pädagogische   Hochschule   Ludwigsburg,

Reuteallee 46, 7140 Ludwigsburg.   *1962*
Tel: (7141) 140
Pädagogische Hochschule Schwäbisch Gmünd,
Oberbettringer Strasse 200, 7070 Schwäbisch
Gmünd.   *1951, 1958*

Tel: (7171) 606-346
Pädagogische Hochschule Weingarten, Kirch-
latz 2, 7987 Weingarten.   *1949, 1958*
Tel: (751) 44081

PROFESSIONAL EDUCATION— ENSEIGNEMENT PROFESSIONNEL

The undermentioned institutions offer courses in the following fields:
arc, civ eng, clothing techn, mine, prod process techn (incl. plant eng & nav eng), ch eng, printing & reprod techn, elec, nutr & hom techn, precision mec, hort, wood techn, met, interior decor, cer & glass techn, plast techn, agr, env conservation & mangt, food techn, mec (incl. auto eng, nucl eng, aero eng), metal const eng, phy eng, prod techn, ship bui, steel const eng, heal techn-bioeng, tex techn, process & ch eng, surv-cartog, utility supply eng, vini-culture, mater techn, ind eng, navigation-nautics, food-nutr-hom eco, ind des-interior decor, lib & doc sc, fin, for, comp, math, law adm, relig ed, soc work-soc ped, transl-interp, adm, voc guidance, eco-bus adm.
An institution may not offer courses in all these fields and some institutions have also courses in other specialized subjects.

Fachhochschule Aachen, Kurbrunnenstrasse 22, 5100 Aachen.
Tel: (241) 66075. Teletex: 2414015 = fhac
Fachhochschule Aalen, Beethovenstrasse 1, 7080 Aalen/Württ.
Tel: (7361) 5760
Fachhochschule Augsburg, Baumgartnerstrasse 16, 8900 Augsburg.
Tel: (821) 5586-1
Technische Fachhochschule Berlin, Luxemburger Strasse 10, 1000 Berlin 65.
Tel: (30) 4504-1
Fachhochschule für Wirtschaft Berlin, Badensche Strasse 50–51, 1000 Berlin 62.
Tel: (30) 7833804
Fachhochschule für Sozialarbeit und Sozialpädagogik Berlin, Karl-Schrader-Strasse 6, 1000 Berlin 30.
Tel: (30) 2105-1
Evangelische Fachhochschule Berlin, Reinerzstrasse 40/41, 1000 Berlin 33.
Tel: (30) 8264051
Fachhochschule der Deutschen Bundespost Berlin, Ringbahnstrasse 103, 1000 Berlin 42.
Tel: (30) 758-4700. Fax: (30) 7522070. Telex: 183660 fhbln d. Teletex: 302010 = dbpfh
Fachhochschule Biberach an der Riss, Karlstrasse 9/11, 7950 Biberach (Riss).

Tel: (7351) 7991
Fachhochschule Bielefeld, Kurt-Schumacher-Strasse 6, 4800 Bielefeld 1.
Tel: (521) 1061
Fachhochschule Bochum, Universitätsstrasse 150, 4630 Bochum.
Tel: (234) 700-7831. Telex: 825860
Fachhochschule Bergbau Bochum, Herner Strasse 45, 4630 Bochum.
Tel: (234) 625-381. Telex: 825701 wbk d
Fachhochschule f. d. öffentl. Bibliothekswesen Bonn, Wittelsbacherring 9, 5300 Bonn.
Fachhochschule Braunschweig-Wolfenbüttel, Salzdahlumer Strasse 46–48, 3340 Wolfenbüttel.
Tel: (5331) 3010
Hochschule für gestaltende Kunst und Musik Bremen, Am Wandrahm 23, 2800 Bremen 1.
Tel: (421) 310051
Hochschule Bremen, Langemarckstrasse 116, 2800 Bremen 1.
Tel: (421) 5905-1
Hochschule Bremerhaven, Columbusstrasse 2, 2850 Bremerhaven.
Fachhochschule Coburg, Friedrich-Streib Strasse 2, 8630 Coburg.
Tel: (471) 48230
Fachhochschule Darmstadt, Schöfferstrasse 3, 6100 Darmstadt.
Tel: (6151) 125162
Evangelische Fachhochschule Darmstadt, Zweifalltorweg 12, 6100 Darmstadt.
Tel: (6151) 8798-0
Fachhochschule der Deutschen Bundespost Dieburg, Max-Planck-Strasse 2, 6110 Dieburg.
Tel: (6071) 28-1. Telex: 4191840 fhdi d. Teletex: 6071911 = dbpfh
Fachhochschule Dortmund, Sonnenstrasse 96, 4600 Dortmund 1.
Tel: (231) 1391-0. Teletex: 231377 = fhdo
Fachhochschule Düsseldorf, Universitätsstrasse, Gebäude 23.31/32, 4000 Düsseldorf 1.
Tel: (211) 3111-3355
Fachhochschule für Technik Esslingen, Kanalstrasse 33, 7300 Esslingen.
Tel: (711) 3511-1
Fachhochschule für Sozialwesen Esslingen, Flandernstrasse 101, 7300 Esslingen.

172   FED. REP. OF GERMANY—REP. FED. D'ALLEMAGNE

Tel: (711) 394-1
Fachhochschule Flensburg, Kanzleistrasse 91/93, 2390 Flensburg.
Tel: (461) 8051
Fachhochschule Frankfurt, Nibelungenplatz 1, 6000 Frankfurt/Main 1.
Tel: (611) 1533-1
Katholische Fachhochschule für Sozialwesen und Religions-Pädagogik, Wölflinstrasse 4, 7800 Freiburg.
Tel: 761) 42241
Fachhochschule für Sozialwesen, Religions-Pädagogik und Gemeindediakonie in Freiburg, Bugginger Strasse 38, 7800 Freiburg-Weingarten.
Tel: (761) 42241
Fachhochschule Fulda, Marquardstrasse 35, 6400 Fulda.
Tel: (661) 77081. Fax: (661) 68513. Teletex: 6619714 = fhfdai
Fachhochschule Furtwangen (Schwarzwald), Gerwigstrasse 11, 7743 Furtwangen 1.
Tel: (7723) 6561. Teletex: 772315 = fhf
Fachhochschule Giessen-Friedberg, Wiesenstrasse 14, 6300 Giessen 1.
Tel: (641) 3091
Fachhochschule Hamburg, Winterhuder Weg 29, 2800 Hamburg 76.
Tel: (40) 29188-1
Evangelische Fachhochschule für Sozialpädagogik der Diakonenanstalt des Rauhen Hauses Hamburg, Horner Weg 170, 2000 Hamburg 74.
Tel: (40) 65591-180
Fachhochschule Hannover, Ricklinger Stadtweg 120, 3000 Hannover 91.
Tel: (511) 444201
Evangelische Fachhochschule Hannover, Blumhardtstrasse 2, 3000 Hannover 69.
Tel: (511) 53010
Fachhochschule der Stiftung Rehabilitation Heidelberg, Bonhoefferstrasse, 6900 Heidelberg 1.
Tel: (6221) 882258
Fachhochschule Heilbronn, Max-Planck-Strasse 39, 7100 Heilbronn.
Tel: (7131) 51061
Fachhochschule Hildesheim/Holzminden, Hohnsen 3, 3200 Hildesheim.
Tel: (5121) 81012
Fachhochschule Iserlohn, Frauenstuhlweg 31, 5860 Iserlohn.
Naturwissenschaftlich-Technische Akademie Prof. Dr. Grübler, Seidenstrasse 16, 7972 Isny.
Tel: (7562) 2427
Fachhochschule Karlsruhe, Moltkestrasse 4, 7500 Karlsruhe 1.
Tel: (721) 169-1
Fachhochschule Kempten, Immenstädter Strasse 69, 8960 Kempten/Allgäu.

Tel: (831) 2523-0
Fachhochschule Kiel, Breiter Weg 10, 2300 Kiel.
Tel: (431) 561044
Fachhochschule Köln, Reitweg 1, 5000 Köln 21 (Deutz).
Tel: (221) 8275-1. Telex: 887330 fhsk d
Fachhochschule für Bibliotheks- und Dokumentationswesen in Köln, Claudiusstrasse 1, 5000 Köln 41.
Rheinische Fachhochschule Köln, Hohenstaufenring 16/18, 5000 Köln 1.
Tel: (221) 203020. Telex: 8882425 vfhs d
Fachhochschule Konstanz, Brauneggerstrasse 55, 7750 Konstanz.
Tel: (7531) 2060
Institut für Kommunikationsdesign a. d. FH Konstanz (Staatlich anerkannte Fachhochschule), Seestrasse 33, 7750 Konstanz.
Fachhochschule Landshut, Am Lurzenhof 4, 8300 Landshut.
Tel: (871) 51311
Fachhochschule Lippe, Liebigstrasse 87, 4920 Lemgo 1.
Tel: (5621) 702-1. Telex: 935411 fhl d
Fachhochschule Lübeck, Stephensonstrasse 3, 2400 Lübeck 1.
Tel: (451) 500-5001
Fachhochschule Evangelische für Sozialwesen, Maxstrasse 29, 6700 Ludwigshafen.
Tel: (621) 518008
Katholische Fachhochschule für Sozialarbeit, Sozialpädagogik und Religionspädagogik/Kirchl. Bildungsarbeit, Saarstrasse 2, 6500 Mainz.1
Tel: (6131) 37031
Fachhochschule für Technik Mannheim, Speyerer Strasse 4, 6800 Mannheim 1.
Tel: (621) 2926-398
Fachhochschule für Sozialwesen Mannheim, Pettenkoferstrasse 24–26, 6800 Mannheim.
Tel: (621) 333033
Städt Fachhochschule für Gestaltung Mannheim, E3, 16, 6800 Mannheim 1.
Tel: (1621) 293-2774
Fachhochschule München, Lothstrasse 34, 8000 München 2.
Tel: (89) 12071. Teletex: 898147 = fhm
Katholische Stiftungsfachhochschule, Preysingstrasse 83, 8000 München 80.
Tel: (89) 4156-271
Fachhochschule Münster, Hüfferstrasse 27, 4400 Münster/Westf.
Tel: (251) 13-4283. Telex: 892529 unism d
Fachhochschule Niederrhein, Reinarzstrasse 49, 4150 Krefeld 1.
Tel: (211) 82232
Fachhochschule Nordostniedersachsen, Munstermannskamp 1, 2120 Lüneburg.
Tel: (4131) 706-0

Katholische Fachhochschule Nordrhein-Westfalen, Wörthstrasse 10, 5000 Köln 1.
Tel: (221) 733031
Georg-Simon-Ohm-Fachhochschule Nürnberg, Kesslerplatz 12, 8500 Nürnberg 21.
Tel: (911) 5880-1
Evangelische Stiftungsfachhochschule Nürnberg (Fachhochschule der Evangelischen Erziehungsstiftung Nürnberg), Burgschmietstrasse 10, 8500 Nürnberg 90.
Tel: (911) 331019
Fachhochschule für Kunsttherapie d. Freien Kunstschule Nürtingen, Villa Melchior, Neckarstrasse 13 a, 7440 Nürtingen.
Fachhochschule Nürtingen, Neckarsteige 10, 7440 Nürtingen.
Tel: (7022) 701-2347
European Business School, Schloss Reichartshausen, 6227 Oestrich-Winkel.
Tel: (6723) 5065
Fachhochschule Offenburg, Badstrasse 24, 7600 Offenburg.
Tel: (781) 2050
Fachhochschule Oldenburg, Ofener Strasse 16, 2900 Oldenburg i.O.
Tel: (441) 71086
Fachhochschule Osnabrück, Albrechtsstrasse 30, 4500 Osnabrück.
Tel: (541) 608-1
Katholische Fachhochschule Norddeutschland, Detmarstrasse 2, 4500 Osnabrück/Driverstrasse 23, 2848 Vechta.
Tel: (541) 27378
Fachhochschule Ostfriesland, Constantiaplatz 4, 2970 Emden.
Tel: (4921) 807-0
Freie Kunst-Studienstätte, Am Wiestebruch 66–68, 2802 Ottersberg 1.
Fachhochschule für Gestaltung Pforzheim, Holzgartenstrasse 36, 7530 Pforzheim.
Tel: (7231) 63258
Fachhochschule für Wirtschaft Pforzheim, Tiefenbronner Strasse 65, 7530 Pforzheim.
Tel: (7231) 64041
Fachhochschule Ravensburg Weingarten, Doggenriedstrasse, Postfach 1261, 7987 Weingarten.
Tel: (751) 501-341
Fachhochschule Regensburg, Prüfeningerstrasse 58, 8400 Regensburg.
Tel: (941) 23091
Hochschule für Berufstätige, Adolf-Steckel-Strasse 17, 2370 Rendsburg.
Fachhochschule für Technik und Wirtschaft Reutlingen, Pestalozzistrasse 73, 7410 Reutlingen.
Tel: 7121) 271-1
Evangelische Fachhochschule für Sozialwesen, Ringelbachstrasse 221, 7410 Reutlingen.

Tel: (7121) 29108
Fachhochschule des Landes Rheinland-Pfalz, Seppel-Glückert-Passage 10, 6500 Mainz.
Tel: (6131) 234614
Evangelische Fachhochschule Rheinland-Westfalen-Lippe, Immanuel-Kant-Strasse 18-20, 4630 Bochum 1.
Tel: (234) 55911
Fachhochschule Rosenheim, Marienberger Strasse 26, 8200 Rosenheim.
Tel: (8031) 805-0
Fachhochschule des Saarlandes, Goebenstrasse 40, 6600 Saarbrücken 1.
Tel: (681) 54084
Katholische Fachhochschule für Sozialwesen, Rastpfuhl 12a, 6600 Saarbrücken.
Tel: (681) 72031
Fachhochschule für Gestaltung Schwäbisch Gmünd, Rektor-Klaus-Strasse 100, 7070 Schwäbisch Gmünd.
Tel: (7121) 602500
Fachhochschule für Technik Sigmaringen, Anton-Günter-Strasse 41, 7480 Sigmaringen.
Tel: (7571) 4076
Fachhochschule für Bibliothekswesen Stuttgart, Feuerbacher Heide 38–42, 7000 Stuttgart 1.
Tel: (711) 221083
Fachhochschule für Druck Stuttgart, Nobelstrasse 10, 7000 Stuttgart 80 (Vaihingen).
Tel: (711) 6852805
Fachhochschule für Technik Stuttgart, Willi-Bleicher-Strasse 29, 7000 Stuttgart.
Tel: (711) 121-2660
Merz-Akademie, Gänsheidestrasse 119, 7000 Stuttgart 1.
Fachhochschule Ulm, Prittwitzstrasse 10, 7900 Ulm/Donau.
Tel: (731) 61301
Fachhochschule Wedel (PTL Wedel Prof. Dr. H. Harms), Feldstrasse 143, 2000 Wedel (Holstein).
Tel: (4103) 82008
Fachhochschule Weihenstephan, 8050 Freising 12.
Tel: (8161) 71-3339
Fachhochschule Wiesbaden, Kurt-Schumacher-Ring 18, 6200 Wiesbaden.
Tel: (121) 4940
Fachhochschule Fresenius Wiesbaden, Dambachtal 20, 6200 Wiesbaden.
Tel: (6121) 522054
Fachhochschule Wilhelmshaven, Friedrich-Paffrath-Strasse 101, 2940 Wilhelmshaven.
Tel: (4421) 8677
Fachhochschule Würzberg-Schweinfurt, Sanderring 8, 8700, Würzburg.
Tel: (931) 13048

SCHOOLS OF FINE ARTS AND MUSIC—
ECOLES SUPERIEURES DES BEAUX-ARTS ET DE MUSIQUE

Hochschule der Künste Berlin [C. of Arts], Ernst-Reuter-Platz 10, 1000 Berlin 10. *1969* Tel: (30) 3185-0. Telex: 17308066. teletex: 308066 hdkbln

Hochschule für bildende Künste Braunschweig [C. of Fine Arts], Johannes-Selenka-Platz 1, 3300 Braunschweig. *1963* Tel: (531) 391-0

Staatliche Kunstakademie Düsseldorf (Hochschule für bildende Künste), Eiskellerstrasse 1, 4000 Düsseldorf. *1773* Tel: (211) 329334

Staatliche Hochschule für bildende Künste (Städelschule) Frankfurt am Main, Dürerstrasse 10, 6000 Frankfurt 70. *1942* Tel: (69) 621091

Hochschule für bildende Künste Hamburg, Lerchenfeld 2, 2000 Hamburg, 76. *1954* Tel: (40) 29188

Staatliche Akademie der bildenden Künste Karlsruhe, Reinhold-Frank-Strasse 81/83, 7500 Karlsruhe 1. *1854* Tel: (721) 843038

Akademie der bildenden Künste München, Akademiestrasse 2, 8000 München 40. *1770* Tel: (89) 3852-0

Kunstakademie Münster, Scheibenstrasse 109, 4400 Münster.

Akademie der bildenden Künste in Nürnberg, Bingstrasse 60, 8500 Nürnberg. *1662* Tel: (911) 40-5061

Hochschule für Gestaltung Offenbach, Schlossstrasse 31, 6050 Offenbach/m. Tel: (69) 812041

Staatliche Akademie der bildenden Künste Stuttgart, Am Weissenhof 1, 7000 Stuttgart 1. *1761* Tel: (711) 251061

Hochschule für Musik und darstellende Kunst Frankfurt, Eschersheimer Landstrasse 29–39, 6000 Frankfurt/Main 1. *1938* Tel: (611) 550826

Staatliche Hochschule für Musik Freiburg, Schwarzwaldstrasse 41, 7800 Freiburg/Br. *1946* Tel: (761) 36032

Hochschule für Musik und darstellende Kunst Hamburg, Harvestehuder Weg 12, 2000 Hamburg 13. *1950* Tel: (40) 441951

Hochschule für Musik und Theater Hannover, Emmichplatz 1, 3000 Hannover. *1957* Tel: (511) 3100-223. Fax: (511) 661298

Staatliche Hochschule für Musik Heidelberg-Mannheim, L15, 16, 6800 Mannheim 1. *1971* Tel: (621) 292-3511

Staatliche Hochschule für Musik Karlsruhe, Weberstrasse 8, 7500 Karlsruhe 1. *1929* Tel: (721) 135-3294

Hochschule für Musik Köln, Dagobertstr. 38, 5000 Köln 1.

Musikhochschule Lübeck, Gr. Petersgrube 17-29, 2400 Lübeck 1. *1933* Tel: (451) 32082

Hochschule für Musik in München, Arcisstrasse 12, 8000 München 2. *1924*

Staatliche Hochschule für Musik Rheinland, Dagobertstrasse 38, 5000 Köln 1. *1925* Tel: (221) 124033

Musikhochschule des Saarlandes, Bismarckstrasse 1, 6600 Saarbrücken 3. *1957* Tel: (681) 62408

Staatliche Hochschule für Musik und darstellende Kunst Stuttgart, Urbanplatz 2, 7000 Stuttgart 1. *1922* Tel: (711) 21248-40

Staatliche Hochschule für Musik Trossingen, Schultheiss-Koch-Platz 3, 7218 Trossingen 1. Tel: (7425) 6057

Staatliche Hochschule für Musik Westfalen Lippe, Nordwestdeutsche Musikakademie Detmold, Allee 22, 4930 Detmold. *1946* Tel: (5231) 26945

Robert-Schumann-Hochschule Dusseldorf, Fischerstrasse 110, 4000 Düsseldorf.

Staatliche Hochschule für Musik Ruhr (Folkwang Hochschule), Abtei, 4300 Essen 16. Tel: (201) 49921

Hochschule für Musik Würzburg, Hofstallstrasse 6/8, 8700 Würzburg. Tel: (931) 50641

THEOLOGICAL SCHOOLS—
ECOLES D'ENSEIGNEMENT SUPERIEUR THEOLOGIQUE

Philosophisch-Theologische Hochschule der Selesianer Don Boscos, Don-Bosco-Strasse 1, 8174 Benediktbeuren. Tel: (8857) 88-215

Kirchliche Hochschule Berlin, Teltower Damm 120-122, 1000 Berlin 37. Tel: (30) 8151067

Kirchliche Hochschule Bethel, Remterweg 45,

4800 Bielefeld 13 (Bethel).
Philosophisch-Theologische Hochschule St. Georgen, Offenbacher Landstrasse 224, 6000 Frankfurt/Main 70.
Tel: (69) 6061-1
Philosophisch-Theologische Hochschule (Päpstlich Theologische Fakultät), Domplatz 2, 6400 Fulda.
Philosophisch-Theologische Hochschule der Redemptoristen, Waldstrasse 9, 5205 Hennef/Sieg.
Philosophisch-Theologische Hochschule der Franziskaner und Kapuziner, Hörster Platz 5, 4400 Münster.
Hochschule für Philosophie (Philosophische Fakultät S.J.), Kaulbachstrasse 33, 8000 München 22.
Tel: (89) 2386-312

Augustana-Hochschule Neuendettelsau, Waldstrasse 11, Postfach 20, 8806 Neuendettelsau.
Tel: (9874) 744
Lutherische Theologische Hochschule Oberursel, Altkönigstrasse 150, 6370 Oberursel (Taunus).
Theologische Fakultät Paderborn, Kamp 6, 4790 Paderborn.
Philosophisch-Theologische Hochschule SVD St. Augustin, Arnold-Janssen-Strasse 30, 5205 St. Augustin 1.
Theologische Fakultät Trier, Jesuitenstrasse 13, 5500 Trier.
Theologische Hochschule der Pallotiner, Pallottistrassse 3, 5414 Vallendar.
Tel: (261) 6402-1
Kirchliche Hochschule Wuppertal, Missionsstrasse 9b, 5600 Wuppertal 2 (Barmen).
Tel: (202) 85005

OTHER INSTITUTIONS—AUTRES INSTITUTIONS

Hochschule für Wirtschaft und Politik, Von-Melle-Park 9, 2000 Hamburg 13.   *1966*
Tel: (40) 41232198
Universität der Bundeswehr (Armed Forces) Hamburg, Holstenhofweg 85, 2000 Hamburg 70.
Tel: (40) 65141-1. Telex: 214952 bw d
Universität der Bundeswehr (Armed Forces)

München, Werner-Heisenberg-Weg 39, 8014 Neubiberg.
Tel: (89) 6004-1. Fax: (89) 6019137. Telex: 5215800
Hochschule für Fernsehen und Film München, Ohmstrasse 11, 8000 München 40.
                                             1966
Tel: (89) 2380400

Westdeutsche Rektorenkonferenz (WRK)
The West German Rectors Conference, founded in 1949, is the central representative body of all universities and other institutions of higher education (*Hochschulen*) in the Federal Republic of Germany. More specifically, the WRK represents—through their respective rectors or presidents—the following types of institutions: 1) Universities and other institutions of university standing (*Universitäten, Technische Hochschulen, Pädagogische Hochschulen, Gesamthochschulen*) as institutions entitled to award doctorates; 2) Schools of Education in the *Land* Baden-Württemberg; 3) *Fachhochschulen*; 4) Schools of Fine Art and Music; 5) Theological Schools—*Philosophisch-theologische Hochschulen* (cath.), and *Kirchliche Hochschulen* (prot.); 6) Other institutions (e.g., of the Armed Forces).
Although membership is voluntary, all public and many other institutions of the tertiary sector are members. The 190 member institutions (1988) represent more than 95% of the total student enrolment.
In the Plenary Meeting, the highest organ of the Conference, members of Group 1, have one

vote each, members of the other groups are represented according to a differentiated system of votes. The Executive Board (*Präsidium*) consists of the President and five Vice-Presidents. A further organ of the WRK is the *Senat* (26 members).
The purpose of the Rectors Conference is to deal in the general context of higher education policy with all questions of research, teaching, and training—including administrative matters—that are of common interest to its members. Particular aims of the WRK activities are: to arrive at joint solutions of problems concerning all members; to inform the public about the tasks and the needs of the institutions of higher education and their special working conditions; to advise, through recommendations, those who are responsible for political decisions in the legislative and the executive branches of government at the federal level and in the 11 federal states (*Länder*); to observe closely developments regarding higher education policy and to report to its members accordingly; to co-operate with public authorities, science organizations, and academic associations; to represent its members in international and supranational organizations

and establishments; and to promote co-operation with Rectors Conferences or corresponding bodies of other countries.

For reference purposes a collection of material on university reform and related subjects—unique of its kind—is available at the WRK library (1986: 42,000 books, more than 640 periodicals).

Of the numerous WRK publications, the *'Dokumente zur Hochschulreform'*, a comprehensive documentation on study and examination regulations (*Rahmenordnungen für Diplomprüfungen* and *Prüfungs-und-Studienordnungen . . .*), a survey of courses of studies and admission restrictions (*Übersicht über Studienmöglichkeiten . . .*), the Annual Reports (*Arbeitsberichte*), a Survey of Cooperation Agreements between German and Foreign Higher Education Institutions, and the bibliographies, merit special attention.

Fondée en 1949, La Conférence des Recteurs de la République fédérale d'Allemagne, est le principal organisme représentatif de toutes les universités et des autres institutions d'enseignement supérieur (Hochschulen) de la République fédérale d'Allemagne. Pour être plus précis la WRK représente ainsi, par l'intermédiaire de leurs recteurs ou de leurs présidents respectifs, les types d'institution indiqués ci-après: 1) Universités et autres institutions de niveau universitaire (Universitäten, Technische Hochschulen, Pädagogische Hochschulen, Gesamthochschulen) en tant qu'institutions habilitées à conférer des doctorats; 2) Ecoles supérieures de pédagogie du "Land" de Bade-Würtemberg; 3) "Fachhochschulen"; 4) Ecoles des Beaux-Arts et de Musique; 5) "Philosophisch-theologische Hochschulen" (cath.), et "Kirchliche Hochschulen" (prot.); 6) Autres institutions (p.e. des forces armées).

Bien que l'adhésion soit volontaire, toutes les institutions publiques et beaucoup d'autres institutions d'enseignement supérieur du secteur tertiaire sont membres de la Conférence. Les 190 institutions membres (1988) représentent plus de 95% de l'ensemble des étudiants inscrits.

A l'Assemblée plénière, qui est l'organe suprême de la Conférence, les membres du premier groupe disposent chacun d'une voix, les membres des autres groupes étant représentés selon un système de voix différencié. Le Conseil Exécutif (Präsidium) se compose du Président et de cinq Vice-Présidents. La WRK compte également un organe supplémentaire, le "Senat" (26 membres).

La Conférence des recteurs s'occupe, dans le cadre général de la politique de l'enseignement supérieur, de tous les problèmes de recherche, d'enseignement et de formation—y compris des questions administratives—qui intéressent l'ensemble de ses membres. Ses activités sont particulièrement axées sur les objectifs suivants: parvenir à des solutions communes sur les problèmes qui concernent tous ses membres; informer le public des tâches et des besoins des institutions d'enseignement supérieur et de leurs conditions de travail spécifiques; conseiller, en formulant des recommandations, les responsables au niveau tant législatif qu'exécutif des décisions politiques qui sont prises à l'échelon tant du gouvernement fédéral que des onze Etats fédéraux (Länder), suivre de près l'évolution de la politique et en informer ses membres; coopérer avec les autorités publiques, les organismes scientifiques et les associations académiques; représenter ses membres auprès des organisations et des établissements internationaux ou supranationaux, et promouvoir la coopération avec les Conférences de recteurs ou organismes analogues des autres pays.

La bibliothèque de la WRK (1986: 42.000 volumes, plus de 640 périodiques) contient, à usage de référence, une collection—unique en son genre—de documents sur la réforme universitaire et les sujets s'y rapportant.

Parmi les nombreuses publications de la WRK, il convient de citer tout particulièrement les "Dokumente zur Hochschulreform", une documentation détaillée sur les études et les réglementations en matière d'examens (Rahmenordnungen für Diplomprüfungen et Prüfungs- und Studienordnungen . . .), un aperçu des enseignements et des restrictions en matière d'accès aux études (Übersicht über Studienmöglichkeiten . . .), les Rapports annuels (Arbeitsberichte), un "Survey of Cooperation Agreements between German and Foreign Higher Education Institutions", et les bibliographies.

President: Prof. Dr. rer. nat. Dr. jur. h.c. Hinrich Seidel.

Secretary-General: Dr. jur. Christian Bode.

Ahrstrasse 39, D-5300 Bonn 2 (Bad Godesberg).

Tel: (228) 376911

Teletex: 228342 = wrk

Deutscher Hochschulverband

The Association of University Teachers continues the tradition of the Association of German institutions of higher education (Verband der Deutschen Hochschulen) which was disbanded in 1934. The Association is concerned with all matters involving relations between university teachers and the State and society. Membership of the Association is open to the academic staffs of all institutions of higher education in the Federal Republic of Germany and West Berlin endowed with rectorial status and the right to

confer doctorates. Official publication: Mitteilungen des Hochschulverbandes.

L'Association des professeurs d'enseignement supérieur continue la tradition de l'Association des établissements allemands d'enseignement supérieur (Verband der Deutschen Hochschulen) dissoute en 1934. La tâche de la Hochschulverband est de se consacrer à toutes les questions touchant les professeurs vis-à-vis de l'Etat et de la société. Peuvent devenir membres de l'Association les corps enseignants de tous les établissements scientifiques d'enseignement supérieur de la République fédérale d'Allemagne et de Berlin-Ouest, ayant un statut rectoral et le droit de conférer le doctorat.

Organe officiel: Mitteilungen des Hochschulverbandes.

President: Prof. Dr. Hartmut Schiedermair.
Secretary: Dr. Gerth Dorff.
Rheinallee 18, 5300 Bonn 2.
Tel: (228) 364002

Studienstiftung des Deutschen Volkes

The German National Scholarship Foundation, founded in 1925, suspended its activities in 1933 and resumed them in 1948. The financial resources put at its disposal (by the Federal Republic, the *Länder*, the towns, the cantons, the Association of Donors for the Advancement of German Learning and by private donations) have already enabled nearly 18,000 men and women students from West Germany or West Berlin to pursue their studies in a German or foreign university, in an institution of higher technical education, or in a school of fine arts. All teaching staff in higher and secondary educational establishments may put forward candidates. In each institution of higher education a member of staff is responsible for relations with the Foundation.

La Fondation nationale allemande pour les bourses d'études, fondée en 1925, a interrompu ses activités en 1933 pour les reprendre en 1948. Les moyens financiers mis à sa disposition (par la République fédérale, les «Länder», les villes, les cantons, la Société des donateurs pour la science allemande, et les dons privés) ont déjà permis à environ 18.000 étudiants et étudiantes de l'Allemagne occidentale et du secteur ouest de Berlin de poursuivre leurs études, soit dans une université allemande ou étrangère, soit dans un établissement d'enseignement supérieur technique ou dans une école des beaux-arts. Tous les professeurs de l'enseignement supérieur et de l'enseignement secondaire peuvent présenter leurs candidats. Dans chaque établissement d'enseignement supérieur, un chargé de cours est responsable des rapports avec la Fondation.

President: Professor Dr. Manfred Eigen.
Secretary-General: Dr. Hartmut Rahn.
Mirbachstrasse 7, 5300 Bonn 2.

Deutscher Akademischer Austauschdienst e.V.

The German Academic Exchange Service (DAAD) was founded in 1925 at the initiative of the University of Heidelberg. When re-established in 1950, the German Academic Exchange Service began with five employees. The increase in its tasks and the extension of its range of activities are reflected in the increase in the number of employees to 321 (1987) and the growth in its annual budget from 1.8 million DM (1955) to 186.4 million DM (1987).

It is an academic institution for the advancement of international university relations. It is governed by private law and is mainly financed from public funds. The DAAD carries out the tasks inherent in foreign cultural and educational policy and educational assistance to developing countries on behalf of the Federal Government, the *Länder*, and its member universities.

The legal status of the German Academic Exchange Service is that of a registered society. Its members consist of the universities represented on the West German Rectors Conference and their student bodies.

The head office of DAAD in Bonn-Bad Godesberg is directed by the Secretary-General. The German Academic Exchange Service maintains branches in London, Paris, New Delhi, Cairo, New York, Rio de Janeiro, Nairobi, Tokyo, and San José. In 1964 the DAAD established a Berlin office, responsible for the welfare of foreign scholars and students attending universities and research institutes in Berlin and for administering the Artists in Berlin Programme (Berliner Künstler-Programm).

The main activities of DAAD are: to provide information about higher education; to award scholarships and fellowships to German and foreign students, research workers and academic staff in all fields of study so that they may continue their studies, attend language courses, or make visits to carry out research or specialized study; to organize information tours; to recruit German lecturers for foreign universities; and to organize practical training courses for engineers in collaboration with the International Association for the Exchange of Students for Technical Experience (IAESTE).

L'Office Allemand d'Echanges Universitaires (DAAD) a été créé en 1925 à l'initiative de l'Université d'Heidelberg. Prenant un nouveau départ en 1950, il ne comptait alors que cinq collaborateurs. L'augmentation de ses effectifs (321 en 1987) et de son budget annuel (qui est

passé de 1.800.000 DM en 1955 à 186.400.000 DM en 1987) mettent en évidence l'accroissement des tâches qui lui incombent et l'extension de son rayon d'action.

C'est un organisme universitaire dont le but est de promouvoir les relations internationales entre établissements d'enseignement supérieur. C'est une institution de droit privé, financée essentiellement par des fonds publics. Le DAAD se charge, pour l'Etat fédéral, les "Länder" et les universités, de la politique culturelle et scientifique à l'étranger et de l'aide à la formation dans les pays en voie de développement.

L'Office Allemand d'Echanges Universitaires a la forme juridique d'une association déclarée d'intérêt public. Les universités représentées au sein de la Conférence des Recteurs de l'Allemagne de l'Ouest, ainsi que leurs organes étudiants, en sont membres.

Le siège social du DAAD, à Bonn-Bad Godesberg, est dirigé par un secrétaire général. D'autres bureaux se trouvent à Londres, Paris, New Delhi, Le Caire, New York, Rio de Janeiro, Nairobi, Tokyo, and San José. En 1964 un bureau a été créé à Berlin à l'intention des chercheurs et étudiants fréquentant les universités et instituts de recherche de Berlin et pour l'organisation du Programme étrangers à Berlin d'Artistes (Berliner Künstler-Programm).

Les principales activités du DAAD sont les suivantes: fournir des informations sur les études supérieures; accorder des bourses destinées aux étudiants, chercheurs et enseignants allemands et étrangers de toutes disciplines pour leur permettre de poursuivre des études, de suivre des cours de langue, et d'effectuer des séjours de recherche ou de spécialisation, organiser des voyages d'information; recruter des lecteurs allemands pour les universités étrangères, organiser des stages d'ingénieurs, en collaboration avec l'Association internationale pour l'échange d'étudiants en vue de l'acquisition d'une expérience technique (IAESTE).

President: Prof. Dr. Th. Berchem.
Secretary-General: Dr. Karl Roeloffs.
Kennedy-Allee 50, 5300 Bonn-Bad Godesberg.
  Tel: (228) 8821. Telex: 885515 daad d

Its main purpose is to provide information and make recommendations concerning the verification and evaluation of foreign school and university qualifications held by German and foreign nationals wishing to pursue their studies or to obtain professional employment in the Federal Republic. About 20,000 requests are dealt with each year.

The Office has a large reference library devoted to educational systems, qualifications and legislation in all parts of the world. A related documentation centre handles a wide range of material and notably keeps up to date information on matters such as secondary school certificates; education in socialist countries; and systems of higher education.

Les origines de l'Office central de l'enseignement à l'étranger remontent à 1904. Rouvert à Göttingen en 1946, il devint partie intégrante de la Conférence permanente des Ministres de l'éducation des "Länder" en 1958. Ses services sont utilisés en particulier par certains ministères fédéraux ou des "Länder" et par les universités et les autres établissements d'enseignement supérieur.

Son principal objet est de fournir des informations et de formuler des recommandations concernant la vérification et l'évaluation de titres scolaires ou universitaires étrangers dont sont titulaires des citoyens allemands ou étrangers souhaitant poursuivre leurs études ou exercer une profession dans la République fédérale d'Allemagne. A l'heure actuelle, il est saisi d'environ 20.000 demandes par an.

L'Office dispose d'une vaste bibliothèque de référence consacrée aux systèmes d'enseignement, aux titres et diplômes et à la législation de l'éducation dans toutes les parties du monde. Un Centre de documentation qui lui est rattaché recueille et analyse un vaste ensemble documentaire et, notamment, tient à jour des informations sur des questions telles que les diplômes de fin d'études secondaires, l'enseignement dans les pays socialistes, les systèmes d'enseignement supérieur étranger.

Head: Dr. Günter Reuhl.
Nassestrasse 8, 5300 Bonn 1.
  Tel: (228) 501-0

Zentralstelle für ausländisches Bildungswesen

The Central Office for Foreign Education traces its origins to 1904. Re-established in Göttingen in 1946, it became an integral part of the Standing Conference of Ministers of Education of the *Länder* in 1958. The services of the Office are used notably by Ministries of the *Länder* Federal Republic and by universities and other institutions of higher education.

Stifterverband für die Deutsche Wissenschaft

The Donors' Association for the Promotion of Sciences and Humanities in Germany was founded in 1921 and re-established in 1949 on the initiative of German industrial associations, with a view to assisting research, teaching and science education.

L'Association des donateurs pour l'avancement des sciences et des lettres en Allemagne fut fondée

en 1921 et recréée en 1949 par une initiative des associations de l'industrie allemande, en vue de l'aide à la recherche, à l'enseignement et à l'éducation scientifique.
President: Dr. K. Liesen.
Secretary-General: Dr. H. Niemeyer.
Postfach 23 03 60, 4300 Essen 1.
Tel: (201) 711051. Telex: 857544 svesn d

Deutsches Studentenwerk e.V.

The German Student Welfare Service, re-established in 1921, is the joint organization of 50 local student welfare services at universities in the Federal Republic.

Its broad objectives are financial assistance for students by enforcement of the *Bundesausbildungsförderungsgesetz* and by the building and service of students' hostels and refectories. The *Deutsches Studentenwerk* advises local welfare services within the terms of their objectives; for example special training seminars are arranged for the staffs of the local services. It develops programmes for the students' welfare and represents the common interests of local services and students in their relations with the public and administrative authorities of the Federal Republic.

Le Centre allemand des oeuvres universitaires, rétabli en 1921, est l'organisation centrale regroupant cinquante oeuvres locales d'étudiants existant dans les universités de la République fédérale.

Ces oeuvres ont pour objectifs principaux d'octroyer une aide financière aux étudiants en application du "Bundesausbildungsförderungsgesetz" (loi fédérale sur l'aide à la formation), et de construire et d'administrer des résidences et restaurants universitaires. Le "Deutsches Studentenwerk" conseille les oeuvres locales dans le cadre de leurs objectifs propres; des séminaires spéciaux de formation sont, par exemple, organisés à l'intention des personnels des oeuvres locales. Il élabore des programmes d'assistance sociale aux étudiants et représente les intérêts communs des oeuvres locales et des étudiants auprès du public et de l'administration de la République fédérale.
President: Prof. Dr. Albert von Mutiur.
Secretary-General: Horst Bachmann.
Weberstrasse 55, 5300 Bonn 1.
Tel: (228) 2690623

Alexander von Humboldt-Stiftung

The Alexander von Humboldt Foundation, founded in 1860, re-established 1953, has approximately 500 research fellowships per annum which are awarded to highly qualified foreign research-workers (up to 40 years of age).

Post-doctorals of all nationalities and disciplines may apply. The Humboldt fellowships are granted for pursuing research projects of choice at an advanced level at research institutes in the Federal Republic of Germany including West Berlin. Selection is based only on scientific qualification. Scholarship allowance: between DM 2,700 and 3,500 net per month; family allowances; travel expenses; additional grants for German language courses (2 to 6 months). Duration of scholarship: 6 to 12 months, with the possibility of extension up to a maximum period of 24 months. Selection meetings take place usually in March, July and November. No closing dates for applications.

Research Awards are accorded to distinguished Senior U.S. Scientists (including scientists from fields of engineering and medicine) and to humanities scholars of all nations and all internationally renowned. Requirements for nomination: Full/Associate Professor or equivalent position, and research work which received international recognition. Value of the Humboldt Research Award: between DM 25,000 and DM 120,000 net, travel expenses, health insurance. No age limit. Award winners are invited to work with German research colleagues for several months in Germany. Nomination through eminent German scholars. For some years there have been Research Awards for Scientific co-operation with France, Japan, Belgium and Sweden. The aim is to promote scientific co-operation between the federal Republic of Germany and these countries.

Research fellowships are also accorded to young German scholars, from all fields of study, for a period of 1 to 4 years.

La Fondation Alexander von Humboldt, fondée en 1860, recréée en 1953, offre environ 500 bourses de recherche par an à des chercheurs étrangers hautement qualifiés (limite d'âge: 40 ans maximum). Les post-doctorants de tous les pays et de toutes les disciplines peuvent poser leur candidature. Les bourses sont accordées pour poursuivre les recherches de leur choix au niveau avancé dans les instituts de recherche de la République fédérale d'Allemagne y compris Berlin-Ouest. La sélection s'opère uniquement en fonction de la qualification scientifique. Montant des bourses: de 2.700 à 3.500 DM net par mois; allocations familiales; frais de voyage; bourses supplémentaires pour des cours de langue allemande (2 à 4 mois). Durée des bourses: de 6 à 12 mois, avec possibilité de prolongation jusqu'à 24 mois maximum. Les réunions du comité de sélection ont normalement lieu en mars, juillet et novembre. Il n'y a pas de date limite pour les demandes.

Des prix de recherche sont accordés à des

chercheurs américains éminents en sciences naturelles (médecins et ingénieurs inclus) et à des chercheurs en sciences humaines de renommée internationale de toutes les nations. Les conditions de nomination sont les suivantes: avoir un poste de professeur titulaire ou associé ou une position équivalente, et effectuer des travaux de recherche reconnus au niveau international. Montant du prix de recherche: de 25.000 DM à 120.000 DM net, plus les frais de voyage et l'assurance maladie. Il n'y a pas de limite d'âge. Les lauréats sont invités à poursuivre leurs recherches avec leurs collègues allemands pendant plusieurs mois en Allemagne. La nominations est faite par des chercheurs allemands réputés. Il existe, depuis plusieurs années, des prix Alexander von Humboldt pour la coopération scientifique entre la République fédérale d'Allemagne et la France, le Japon, la Belgique et la Suède. Ils ont pour but de promouvoir la coopération scientifique avec ces divers pays.

Des bourses de recherche sont aussi accordées à de jeunes chercheurs allemands de toutes les disciplines, pour une période comprise entre une et quatre années.

President: Prof. Dr. Wolfgang Paul.
Secretary-General: Dr. Heinrich Pfeiffer.
Jean-Paul-Strasse 10-12, D-5300 Bonn 2.
   Tel: (228) 833-0. Telex: 88627 avhs d

Deutsche Forschungsgemeinschaft (DFG)

The *Deutsche Forschungsgemeinschaft*, the central organization for the promotion of basic research, was founded in 1920 and re-established in 1949. Its members are 51 universities, 5 academies and 16 scientific institutions and organizations.

The objects and activities of the DFG are to provide financial assistance for research projects; to encourage co-operation among research workers; to advise government and public authorities on scientific matters; to promote German co-operation in international scientific affairs and to give encouragement to young scientists.

La "Deutsche Forschungsgemeinshaft" l'organisation centrale pour la promotion de la recherche fondamentale, fut fondée en 1920 et recréée en 1949. Elle comporte comme membres: 51 universités, 5 académies, ainsi que 16 institutions et organisations scientifiques.

Les buts et les domaines d'activité de la DFG sont: de soutenir financièrement l'exécution de projets de recherche; de promouvoir la coopération entre les chercheurs; de conseiller le gouvernement et les autorités publiques en matière d'affaires scientifiques; de représenter les intérêts des hommes de science allemands tant dans le pays

qu'à l'étranger; d'encourager les jeunes chercheurs.
President: Prof. Hubert Markl.
Secretary-General: Burkhart Müller.
Kennedyallee 40, 5300 Bonn 2.
   Tel: (228) 885-1. Telex: 172283

Max-Planck-Gesellschaft zur Förderung der Wissenschaften e.V.

The Max Planck Society for the Advancement of Science, founded in 1948, succeeded the Kaiser-Wilhelm-Gesellschaft zur Förderung der Wissenschaften, founded in 1911. It is composed of 60 research institutes and units, each pursuing independent scientific work (fundamental research) and specializing mainly in the fields of natural science and the humanities.

La Société Max Planck pour le développement de la science, fondée en 1948, succède à la Kaiser-Wilhelm-Gesellschaft zur Förderung der Wissenschaften, fondée en 1911; elle comprend 60 instituts et groupes de recherche qui sont indépendants dans leurs activités scientifiques (recherche fondamentale) et principalement spécialisés dans le domaine des sciences naturelles et des lettres.

President: Prof. Dr. Heinz A. Staab.
Secretary-General: Wolfgang Hasenclever.
Residenzstrasse la, Postfach 647, 8000 München 1.
   Tel: (89) 21081. Telex: 522203

Wissenschaftsrat

The Science Council, founded in 1957, makes recommendations to the federal and *Länder* governments on the development of universities and research. The Council has 39 members. The decisions of the General Assembly are prepared by the Scientific Commission and the Administrative Commission. The members of the Scientific Commission are appointed by the President of the Federal Republic. Each of the *Länder* is represented on the Administrative Commission by a minister or a senator, and the Federal Government by six secretaries of state.

Le Conseil scientifique, fondé en 1957, adresse au gouvernement fédéral et aux gouvernements des «Länder» des recommandations sur le développement des universités et de la recherche. Le Conseil comprend 39 membres. Les décisions de l'Assemblée générale sont préparées par la Commission Scientifique et par la Commission Administrative. Les membres de la Commission Scientifique sont nommés par le Président de la République fédérale. Dans la Commission Administrative, les «Länder» sont représentés par un ministre ou un sénateur et le gouvernement fédéral par six secrétaires d'Etat.

President: Prof. Dr. Kurt Kochsiek.
Secretary-General: Ministerialdirektor Dr. Peter Kreyenberg.
Marienburger Strasse 8, 5000 Köln 51.
Tel: (221) 37760

Deutsche Stiftung für internationale Entwicklung (DSE)

The German Foundation for International Development, established in 1959 by the parliamentary parties of the German Federal Parliament together with the German Bundestag, is an integral part of the development assistance programme of the Federal Republic of Germany. Working in close co-operation with the Federal Government and with numerous partners at home and abroad, especially with the organizations of the UN, it concentrates its programmes on the following focal points of national and international development policy:
— International exchange of views with and transfer of professional knowledge to specialists and managerial personnel from developing countries within the framework of international and bilateral seminars.
— Training and advanced training programmes for specialists and managerial personnel in the fields of public administration, crafts and industrial trades, agriculture, and forestry.
— Technical preparation and language briefing in short courses and three-month seminars for German specialists taking up assignments in developing countries.
— Collaboration in the formulation and further elaboration of German development policy through the organization of international and German conferences and meetings of experts in selected professional fields.
— Co-ordination of documentation in the field of developing countries/development assistance through the DSE Documentation Centre and co-operation in the establishment of a national documentation and information network within an international framework.
— Public relations work in Germany and abroad on the aims of the German Foundation for International Development and German development policy.

The Board of Trustees of the Foundation is composed of representatives of political and academic life, management and labour, federal ministries and governments of the *Länder*. Many of the Foundation's activities are carried out in close co-operation with universities and other institutions of higher education. The Foundation's operations are decentralized in six divisions and the Development Policy forum. They are located in Berlin, Bonn, Bad Honnef, Mannheim, and Feldafing.

La Fondation Allemande pour le Développement International, créée en 1959 par les efforts conjugués des groupes parlementaires du Bundestag et du Gouvernement fédéral, constitue une partie essentielle du programme d'aide au développement poursuivi par la République fédérale d'Allemagne. Ses programmes, réalisés en étroite coopération avec le Gouvernement fédéral et de nombreux partenaires nationaux et étrangers, spécialement avec les organisations de l'ONU, se concentrent sur les points capitaux de la politique nationale et internationale d'aide au développement et comprennent les tâches suivantes:
— *Echange des expériences à l'échelon international et transfert de connaissances techniques aux cadres des pays en développement par des séminaires internationaux et bilatéraux.*
— *Réalisation de programmes de formation et de perfectionnement professionnels à l'intention d'experts et de cadres originaires des pays en développement, et portant sur l'administration publique, l'artisanat et l'industrie ainsi que sur l'agriculture et la sylviculture.*
— *Préparation technique générale et linguistique d'experts allemands se destinant à une mission dans un pays en développement.*
— *Coopération à l'élaboration de conceptions dans le domaine de la politique d'aide au développement par l'organisation de conférences internationales et allemandes ainsi que de discussions d'experts dans des domaines spéciaux.*
— *Coordination de la documentation, grâce au Centre de documentation, dans le domaine pays en développement/aide au développement, et collaboration à l'organisation d'un réseau national de documentation et d'information dans un cadre international.*
— *Information du public allemand et étranger sur les objectifs de la Fondation Allemande pour le Développement International et de la politique allemande d'aide au développement.*

Le Conseil d'Administration de la Fondation est composé de représentants des milieux politiques, économiques et scientifiques ainsi que de divers ministères fédéraux et des gouvernements des différents «Länder». Dans la conduite de beaucoup de ses activités la Fondation collabore étroitement avec des universités et autres institutions d'enseignement supérieur. Les activités de la Fondation sont réparties entre six centres spécialisés et le Forum de la Politique du Développement situés à Berlin, Bonn, Bad Honnef, Mannheim, et Feldafing.

Director-General (Acting): Peter Sötje.
Rauchstrasse 25, 1000 Berlin 30.
Tel: (30) 2606-365. Telex: 181615 dseb d

Deutsche Akademikerinnenbunde e.V. (IFUW)
Secretary: Pferdmengestrasse 11, 5000 Köln 51.
World University Service (WUS)
Goebenstrasse 35, 6200 Wiesbaden.
Tel: (6121) 446648
Vereinigte Deutsche Studentenschaften— VDS
Georgstrasse 25–27, 5300 Bonn.
Tel: (228) 223075
German Student Travel Service—GSTS
30 Dietkirchenstrasse, 5300 Bonn.
**ARTU Studentischer Austausch-und Reisedienst
GmbH**
Hardenbergstrasse 9, 1000 Berlin 12.
Telex: 184670 artu d
**Cartellverband der Katholischen Deutschen
Studentenverbindungen** (Pax Romana)
Vogelweideplatz 11/11, 8000 München 80.
**Katholischer   Akademikerverband   (Pax
Romana).**
Venusbergweg 1, 5300 Bonn.
Tel: (228) 217942
Evangelische Studentengemeinde (WSCF)
Kniebisstrasse 29, 7000 Stuttgart 51.
Tel: (711) 281034

I.A.K. (ISMUN)
Contact: 18, rue de Docteur Roux, 75015 Paris
(France).
Tel: (33-1) 47-83-31-65
J.S.V.D. (WUJS)
Contact: 89, Chaussee De Vleurgat, 1050
Brussels (Belgium).
Tel: (2) 647-7279. Telex: 20625

*

Auswärtiges Amt (Foreign Ministry—Ministère
des Affaires étrangères)
Kulturabteilung, Koblenzerstrasse 103, 5300
Bonn.
Tel: (228) 170. Telex: 886591 aabn d. Teletex:
2283835 = aabonn
**Ständige Konferenz der Kultusminister der
Länder in der Bundesrepublik Deutschland**
Nassestrasse 11, 5300 Bonn.
Tel: (228) 5010
German Commission for Unesco
15 Colmantstrasse, 5300 Bonn 1.
Tel: (228) 631591. Telex: 886326 duk d. Cables:
germunescu bonn

GHANA
GHANA

*University of Ghana, P.O. Box 25, Legon,
Accra. (The Registrar).   *1948, 1961*
Tel: 75381. Cables: university legon
F : *agr, arts, law, sc, soc, med.*
  INSTITUTE OF AFRICAN STUDIES, P.O. Box
  75, Legon, Accra.   *1961*
  INSTITUTE OF STATISTICAL, SOCIAL AND
  ECONOMIC RESEARCH, P.O. Box 74,
  Legon, Accra.   *1962*
  INSTITUTE OF ADULT EDUCATION, P.O. Box,
  Legon, Accra.   *1948*
  SCHOOL OF COMMUNICATION STUDIES, P.O.
  Box 53, Legon, Accra.   *1972*
  NOGUCHI   MEMORIAL   INSTITUTE   FOR
  MEDICAL RESEARCH.   *1979*
  REGIONAL   INSTITUTE   FOR   POPULATION
  STUDIES, P.O. Box 96, Legon, Accra.
                                  1972
  SCHOOL OF ADMINISTRATION, P.O. Box 78,
  Legon, Accra.   *1962*
  UNIVERSITY OF GHANA MEDICAL SCHOOL,
  P.O. Box 4236, Accra.   *1964*

  SCHOOL OF PERFORMING ARTS.   *1978*
  GHANA DRAMA STUDIO
*University of Science and Technology, Univer-
sity Post Office, Kumasi.   *1952, 1961*
Tel: 5351. Cables: kumasitech, kumasi
F : *agr, env & dev st, phar, sc, art, soc.*
  COLLEGE OF ART.
  SCHOOL OF ENGINEERING
  SCHOOL OF MEDICAL SCIENCES.   *1975*
  INSTITUTE OF MINING AND MINERAL ENGIN-
  EERING.   *1976*
  S : *mine* (Tarkwa, Kumasi).
  BOADI DAIRY/BEEF CATTLE DEVELOPMENT
  PROJECT.
  HOUSING IMPROVEMENT RESEARCH PRO-
  JECT.   *1963*
  INSTITUTE OF RENEWABLE NATURAL RE-
  SOURCES.   *1982*
  Bureau : *integrated rur dev.*
  Ce : *land adm res, cult st.*
  I : *tec ed.*
*University of Cape Coast, University Post

Office, Cape Coast. *1962, 1971*
Tel: 2440-9. Cables: university, cape coast
F : *arts, sc, agr, ed.*
   CENTRE FOR DEVELOPMENT STUDIES.
1967
   INSTITUTE OF EDUCATION.
   SCHOOL OF AGRICULTURE.
   INSTITUTE OF EDUCATIONAL PLANNING AND
      ADMINISTRATION. *1975*
Ghana Academy of Arts and Sciences, Achimota,
Accra. *1963, 1968*

Tel: 777651
Ghana Institute of Management and Public
Administration, P.O. Box 50, Achimota,
Accra. *1962*
Tel: 77625
Ghana Atomic Energy Commission, P.O. Box 80,
Legon, Accra. *1965*
Council for Scientific and Industrial Research,
P.O. Box M. 32, Accra. *1968*
Tel: 77651

Higher Education Secretariat,
P.O. Box M. 28, Accra.
Tel: 65461
Ghanaian Association of University Women
(IFUW)
P.O. Box 9582, Kotoka Airport, Accra.
National Union of Ghana Students—NUGS
(IUS)
P.O. Box 157, Legon, Accra.
Tel: 2132 scale (attn. nugs)
ICMIC Ghana Federation Accra (Pax Romana)
c/o Rev. Dr. P. Ryan, University of Ghana,
Legon.
Student Christian Movement of Ghana (WSCF)
Accra Community Centre, P.O. Box 339,

Accra.
Tel: 63763
United Nations Student and Youth Association of
Ghana (ISMUN)
Kwame Nkrumah Conference Centre, P.O.
Box 2329, Accra.
                                              *
Ministry of Education and Culture
P.O.B. M44, Accra.
Tel: 665421
Ghana National Commission for Unesco
Ministry of Education and Culture, P.O.B.
M44, Accra.
Tel: 665421. Cables: alled accra

GREECE
GRECE

UNIVERSITIES AND TECHNICAL UNIVERSITIES—
UNIVERSITES ET UNIVERSITES TECHNIQUES

*Ethnikon kai Kapodistriakon Panepistimion
Athinon [National and Capodistrian U. of
Athens], odos Panepistimiou 30, Athinai
10679. (The Secretary-General). *1837*
Tel: (1) 36-14-301. Telex: 223815 univ gr
S : *theo, eco-pol, law, phil, sc, heal sc.*
D : *ed.*
*Ethnikon Metsovion Polytechnion Athinon
[National Technical U. of Athens], odos 28
Octovriou 42, Athinai 10682. *1887*
Tel: (1) 36-16-922. Telex: 222500 hvla gr
D : *civ eng, mec, elec, arc, ch, rur eng-surv,
mine-met, nav mec, gen.*
Panepistimion Kritis [U. of Crete], Rethymnon,
Chania. *1974*

Tel: (831) 240-69. Telex: 291145 pakr gr
S : *phil; heal sc, sc* (Eracleion).
D : *ed.*
Polytechneion Kritis [Technical U. of Crete],
P.O. Box 49, Chania 73101; odos Zaimi 2,
Athinai 10693. *1977*
Tel: (1) 36-04-087 (Athens); (821) 58-089
(Chania). Telex: 223029 tuc gr (Athens);
291211 tuc gr (Chania)
D : *mec, ch, eng, elec, electro, prod & adm eng,
mineral resources, gen.*
Panepistimion Ioanninon [U. of Ioannina],
Ioannina. *1970*
Tel: (651) 25915. Telex: 322160 pnps gr
S : *sc.*

D : *phil, med, ed.*

*Panepistimion Patron [U. of Patras], Patrai 26110. *1964*
Tel: (61) 991-822. Telex: 312447 unpa gr
S : *eng, sc, heal sc.*
D : *ed.*

*Aristoteleion Panepistimion Thessalonikis [Aristoteleion U. of Thessaloniki], odos Panepistimion poli, Thessaloniki 54006. *1925*

Tel: (31) 9911. Telex: 412181 auth gr
S : *law-eco, phil, heal sc, sc, geotec, theo, eng.*
D : *ed.*

Democrition Panepistimion Thrakis [Democritus U. of Thrace], Komotini 69100. *1974*
Tel: (531) 26-111
S : *polytec.*
D : *law, med, ed.*

OTHER INSTITUTIONS—AUTRES INSTITUTIONS

Professional Education—Enseignement professionnel

Anotati Geoponiki Scholi Athinon [Agricultural C. of Athens], Votanikos, Athinai 301. *1920*
Tel: (1) 34-61-944

Anotati Scholi Iconomikon kai Emporikon Epistimon [Athens S. of Economics and Business Science], odos 28 Oktovriou 76, Athinai 104. *1920*
Tel: (1) 82-11-124

Anotati Scholi Kalon Technon [S. of Fine Arts], odos Patission 42, Athinai 10682. *1910*
Tel: (1) 36-16-930

Panteios Anotati Scholi Politicon Epistimon

[Panteios S. of Political Science], Leoforos Sygrou, Athinai 17671. *1937*
Tel: (1) 92-23-227

*Anotati Viomichaniki Scholi Pireos [Piraeus S. of Industrial Business Studies], odos Karaoli kai Dimitriou 40, Piraeus. *1948*
Tel: 41-73-159

*Anotati Viomichaniki Scholi Thessalonikis [Graduate Industrial S. of Thessaloniki], odos Tsimiski 45, Thessaloniki 54623. *1948*
Tel: (31) 279-339

Hellenic Association of University Women (IFUW)
odos Voulis 449, Athinai 10557.

Fititiki Katholike Hestia «O Vissarion» (Pax Romana)
odos Michael Voda 28, Athinai.

Greek Christian Socialist Youth Organization EXON (WSCF)
Solonos 126, Athinai 145.
Tel: 360-00-82

Christianikos Omilos Phititon Epistimonon (Student and Scientist Christian Association) (WSCF)
odos Souliou 3, Athinai 142.
Tel: 362-12-78

Jewish Youth of Athens (WUJS)
Contact: 89 Chaussee de Vleurgat, 1050 Brussels (Belgium).
Tel: (2) 647-7279. Telex: 20625

*

Centre interuniversitaire pour la Reconnaissance des Titres d'Etudes obtenus à l'Etranger (D.I.K.A.T.S.A.)
Leoforos Sygrou 112, Athinai 11741.
Tel: (1) 922 2533

Ipourgion Exoterikon (Ministry of Foreign Affairs), Ahademias n°. 1, Athinai.
Tel: (1) 3610581

Ipourgion Pedias, Diefthinsis Anotatis Ekpedefseos (Ministry of National Education, Division of Higher Education), Mitropoleos n°. 15, Athinai.
Tel: (1) 3236567

Greek National Commission for Unesco
odos Akadimias 3, 106.71 Athinai.
Tel: 36-10-581 (ext. 505). Telex: 218213-216593 ypex gr. Cables: grecunesco athens

GUADELOUPE
GUADELOUPE

Université des Antilles-Guyane (1), Bld. Légitimus, B.P. 771, 97173 Pointe-à-Pitre Cedex.
1970

Tél: 82-38-22. Télex: 919739
Ut : dr-éco (I. Henri-Vizioz), sc exactes-nat.
(Campus Universitaire de Fouillole).

Association générale des Etudiants Guadeloupéens—AGEG (IUS)

GUATEMALA
GUATEMALA

Universidad Francisco Marroquín, 6A Avenida 0-28, Zona 10, Guatemala, C.A. (Sr. Secretario general). *1971*
Tél: 313888. Cables: ufma
E : éco-adm des aff, dr, arc, psyc, méd, soc, gé des systèmes, inft, dent, éd.
D : théo.
Universidad «Mariano Gálvez», 3a Avenida 9-00, Zona 2 Int. El Zapote, Guatemala. *1966*
Tel: 534271
E : dr-soc, éco, gé civ, adm des aff.
D : éd, art app, gestion, ét paraméd.
Universidad Rafael Landívar, Campus Vista Hermosa III, Zona 16, Guatemala. *1961*
Tél: 692151. Cables: uniland
F : dr-soc, éco, hum, ing, éd; hum (Quezalten-

ango).
E : serv soc rur (Quezaltenango), éd; éd (Jalapa); ét fond.
*Universidad de San Carlos de Guatemala, Ciudad Universitaria, Zona 12, Guatemala 12.
1562, 1676
Tél: 763087
F : méd, dent, éco, dr-soc, ch-phar, arc, hum, agr, ing, vét-zoo.
Ce : ét occidentales.
Universidad del Valle de Guatemala, 11 Calle 0-00 Zona 15, Vista Hermosa II, Guatemala.
1966
Tél: 692563
E : sc-hum, soc, éd.

Associación de Estudiantes Universitarios—AEU (IUS)
Universidad de San Carlos, Zona 12, Guatemala.

*

Ministerio de Educación

Palacio Nacional, Guatemala.
Tél: 27212
Comisión Guatemalteca de Cooperación con la Unesco
3a Avenida 13-30, Zona 1, Apartado postal 244, Guatemala 1.
Tél: 86171. Cables: guateunesco guatemala c-a

---

(1) See also Martinique, p. 282.
(1) Voir aussi Martinique, p. 282.

GUINEA
GUINEE

Université de Conakry, B.P. 1147, Conakry.
Tél: 46-16-65
F : soc, adm, sc de la nature, méd, phar, ch, électro, méc, gé civ, sc-tec; adm, sc de la nature (Donka).
I : agr (Foulaya-Kinda); géol-mine (Boké).
E : adm.
Université de Kankan, B.P. 203, Kankan.
Tél: 20-93
F : soc, sc exactes et de la nature.
Institut des Sciences agro-zootehniques «Valéry Giscard D'Estaing», Faranah.
                                              1978
Tél: 81-08-59

Ecole nationale d'Agriculture de Macenta, Macenta.
Ecole nationale d'Agriculture de Tolo, B.P. 29, Mamou.   *1959*
Ecole nationale forestière de Sérédou, Macenta.
                                              1971
Ecole nationale des Postes et Télécommunications, Conakry.   *1970*
Ecole nationale de la Santé, Kindia.   *1966*
Ecole nationale de la Santé, Labé.
Ecole nationale vétérinaire, Mamou.   *1972*
Ecole normale supérieure de Manéah, Coyah.
Ecole normale d'Enseignement technique, B.P. 592, Conakry.

Secrétariat d'Etat à l'Enseignement et à la Recherche scientifique
Conakry.
Tél: 44-38-04

Commission nationale guinéenne pour l'Unesco
Ministère de la Culture et de l'Information, Conakry.
Tél: 44-49-57. Télex: 22331 ndec ge

GUYANA
GUYANE

*University of Guyana, P.O. Box 10 1110, Georgetown. (The Vice-Chancellor).   *1963*
Tel: (2) 54841

F : *agr, arts, nat, soc, ed, techn, heal sc.*
I : *adult & continuing ed, dev st.*

Student Council of the Progressive Youth Organization—PYO (IUS)
41 Robb Street, Lacytown, Georgetown.
Guyana Assembly of Youth (GAY) (ISMUN)
Lot 62, Chalmers Place, Stabroek, P.O. Box 21, Georgetown.

                    *

Ministry of Education, Social Development and Culture
26 Brickdam, Georgetown.
Tel: (2) 63094
Guyana National Commission for Unesco
"Dargan House", 90 Robb and Oronoque Streets, P.O. Box 1014, Georgetown.
Tel: 54-306. Cables: mined geogetown

HAITI
HAÏTI

UNIVERSITIES—UNIVERSITES

Université d'Etat d'Haïti, 25-35 rue Bonne Foi, B.P. 2279, Port-au-Prince. (M. le Secrétaire général).   *1920, 1944*
Tél: 2-3210
F : dr-éco, dent, sc, méd-phar, agr-vét, hum,
ethn.
E : péd, phar.
I : adm-gestion-ét int, ét & rech africaines.
Ce : ling appl.

OTHER INSTITUTIONS—AUTRES INSTITUTIONS

Public Establishments—Etablissements publics

Ecole de Droit Cap-Haïtien, Rue 22J.   *1867, 1976*
Tél: 32-1121
Ecole de Droit des Cayes.   *1894, 1976*
Ecole de Droit des Gonaïves.   *1922, 1976*
Ecole de Droit de Jacmel.
Ecole d'Infirmières Notre-Dame de la Sagesse, Rue 17K, Cap-Haïtien.   *1952*

Tél: 32-0910
Ecole d'Infirmières des Cayes, 1 Rue Mgr Maurice.
Tél: 56-0001
Ecole nationale d'Infirmières Simone O. Duvalier, 131 rue Mgr Guilloux, Port-au-Prince.
Tél: 2-1125

Private Establishments—Etablissements privés

Ecole des hautes Etudes économiques et commerciales, Port-au-Prince.   *1961, 1976*
Tél: 5-4581
Institut international d'Etudes universitaires, c/o Fondation haïtienne de Développement, 104, avenue Christophe, Port-au-Prince.
Tél: 5-2055
Institut Polytechnique, d'Haïti, 26 avenue Ducoste, Port-au-Prince.
Tél: 2-6165
Institut supérieur des Sciences économiques et politiques, 180 Palue, Port-au-Prince.

Tél: 2-6159
Institut supérieur technique d'Haïti, 22 avenue du Chili, P.O. Box 992, Port-au-Prince.
                                            1962, 1976
Tél: 2-4587
Institut de Technologie électronique d'Haïti, Port-au-Prince.
Tél: 2-2932
Institut universitaire Roi Henri Christophe, B.P. 98, Cap-Haïtien.
Tél: 32-1316

Entr'aide universitaire mondiale (WUS)
Secrétaire: Guy Dallemand.
P.O. Box 15000, Petionville.
Tél: 2-0765. Télex: 0203/0001 ppbooth

*

Ministère de l'Education natïon nationale

5, avenue Marie-Jeanne, Port-au-Prince.
Tél: 2-1757
Commission nationale haïtienne de Coopération avec l'Unesco
Ministère de l'Education nationale, 5, avenue Marie-Jeanne, Port-au-Prince.
Tél: 20-747. Cables: commission haitienne unesco mineduc port au prince

HOLY SEE
SAINT-SIEGE

UNIVERSITIES—UNIVERSITES

*Pontificia Universitas Gregoriana, Piazza della Pilotta 4, 00187 Roma.   *1552*
Tél: (6) 67011
F : théo, dr can, phil, hist ecl, missiologie, soc.
I : théo spirituelle, sc relig, psyc.
E : lit latine.
Pontificia Universitas Lateranensis, Piazza San Giovanni in Laterano 4, 00184 Roma.
1773, 1959
Tél: (6) 698-6401
F : théo, phil, dr can & civ.
I : patrologie, théo morale, sc relig, théo vie relig, pastorale, ét mariage & famille.
Pontificia Universitas Urbaniana, Via Urbano VIII 16, 00165 Roma.   *1627, 1962*

Tél: (6) 655-992
F : théo, phil, missiologie, dr can.
I : ét athéisme, catéchèse missionnaire.
*Pontificia Universitas S. Thomae Aquinatis in Urbe, Largo Angelicum 1, 00184 Roma.
1580, 1909, 1963
Tél: (6) 670-21
F : théo, dr can, phil, soc.
I : théo spirituelle, sc relig.
Pontificia Universitas Salesiana, Piazza del l'Ateneo Salesiano 1, 00139 Roma. *1940, 1973*
Tél: (6) 813-2041
F : théo, dr can, phil, éd.
I : lit latine.

OTHER INSTITUTIONS—AUTRES INSTITUTIONS

Pontificium Institutum Biblicum, Via della Pilotta 25, 00187 Roma.   *1909*
Tél: (6) 679-6453
F : sc bibliques, ét orntl ancien.
Pontificium Institutum Studiorum Orientalium, Piazza di Santa Maria Maggiore 7, 00185 Roma.   *1917*
Tél: (6) 731-2254
F : sc eccl orntl, dr can orntl.
Pontificium Athenaeum Anselmianum, Piazza dei Cavalieri di Malta 5, 00153 Roma. *1687, 1867*
Tél: (6) 578-2274
F : théo, phil, liturgie.
I : ét monastiques.
Pontificium Athenaeum Antonianum, Via Merulana 124, 00185 Roma.   *1933*
Tél: (6) 757-4551
F : théo, dr can, phil.
I : biblique, théo spirituelle, ét pastorale, sc péd, théo.
Pontificium Institutum Musicae Sacrae, Piazza Sant'Agostino 20-A, 00186 Roma.
1911, 1931
Tél: (6) 62-0173
Pontificium Institutum Archaeologiae Chris-

tianae, Via Napoleone III 1, 00185 Roma. *1925*
Tél: (6) 73-5824
Pontificia Facultas Theologica S. Bonaventurae, Via del Serafico 1, 00142 Roma.
1587, 1905, 1955
Tél: (6) 59-11651
Pontificia Facultas Theologica SS. «Teresianum», Piazza San Pancrazio 5A, 00152 Roma.   *1935*
Tél: (6) 582-362
F : théo.
I : théo spirituelle.
Pontificia Facultas Theologica «Marianum», Viale Trenta Aprile 6, 00153 Roma.
1866, 1955
Tél: (6) 58-90-441
F : théo.
I : ét mariologiques.
Pontificium Institutum Studiorum Arabicorum et Islamisticae, Piazza S. Apollinare 49, 00186 Roma.   *1960*
Tél: (6) 656-1131
Pontificia Facultas Scientiarum Educationis «Auxilium», Via Cremolino 141, 00166 Roma.
1966
Tél: (6) 69-62040

Congregatio pro Institutione Catholica

La Congrégation pour l'Education Catholique remonte à la Constitution Immensa (22 janvier 1588) du Pape Sixte V, laquelle érigea la Congregatio pro Universitate studii romani destinée à promouvoir et diriger les études de l'Université de Rome et d'autres célèbres Universités comme celles de Bologne, Paris, Salamanque. Le 28 août 1824 le Pape Léon XII créa la Congregatio Studiorum (Constitution Quod divina Sapientia), pour les écoles de tous degrés de l'Etat Pontifical. En 1870, ce Dicastère reçut autorité sur toutes les Universités Catholiques. Le Droit Canon considère comme «Universités Catholiques», au sens strict du mot, les établissements qui appartiennent à une personne ecclésiastique morale, et par conséquent dépendent de la Hiérarchie de l'Eglise Catholique.

Par Motu-Proprio du 4 novembre 1915, le Pape Benoît XV constitua la Sacra Congregatio de Seminariis et studiorum Universitatibus, en fusionnant la Congregatio studiorum avec le Bureau des Séminaires qui existait au sein de la Sacrée Congrégation Consistoriale. La Constitution Regimini Ecclesiae universae du 15 août 1967 a changé le titre de la Congrégation des Séminaires et Universités en celui de «Sacrée Congrégation pour l'Education Catholique» (Sacra Congregatio pro Institutione Catholica). En vertu de cette même Constitution, la Congrégation garde ses attributions précédentes quant aux sémi-naires et maisons d'études pour la formation du clergé, étend sa compétence aux écoles catholiques de niveau primaire et secondaire dépendantes de l'autorité ecclésiastique; mais il lui appartient aussi de promouvoir et d'assister toutes les universités, facultés, instituts et écoles supérieures d'études ecclésiastiques ou civiles, ainsi que les organisations et associations ayant une finalité d'enseignement supérieur ou de recherche, en tant que ces institutions se rattachent à l'Eglise Catholique.

The Congregation for Catholic Education dates back to 1588 and the Constitution Immensa of Pope Sixtus V, which established the Congregatio pro Universitate studii romani, to promote and direct studies at the University of Rome and other distinguished universities, such as Bologna, Paris and Salamanca. In 1824 Pope Leo XII created the Congregatio studiorum by the Constitution Quod divina Sapientia for Schools of the Pontifical State at all levels. In 1870 the Congregation was given authority over all Catholic universities. Under Canon law "Catholic Universities", in the strict sense of the term, are those institutions which belong to a member of the Church or to an ecclesiastic body, and therefore fall within the jurisdiction of the hierarchy of the Catholic Church.

By Motu-Proprio of November 1915, Pope Benedict XV founded the Sacra Congregatio de Seminariis et studiorum Universitatibus, thus joining the Congregatio studiorum with the Office of Seminaries which existed within the Sacred Consistorial Congregation. By the Constitution Regimini Ecclesiae universae of August 1967, the title of Sacra Congregatio pro Institutione Catholica was adopted. Under this Constitution, the attributions of the Congregation with regard to the seminaries and institutions for training the clergy remain unchanged and its authority is extended to cover primary and secondary catholic schools responsible to the Ecclesiastical Authorities. Its function is also to develop and assist all universities, faculties, institutes and colleges of sacred or profane studies, as well as organizations and associations concerned with higher education or scientific research, in so far as they are attached to the Catholic Church.

Préfet: S.E.M. le Cardinal Baum.
Piazza Pio XII 3, 00193 Roma.
   Tél: (6) 69841-58

HONDURAS
HONDURAS

*Universidad Nacional Autónoma de Honduras, Ciudad Universitaria, Boulevard Suyapa, Tegucigalpa, D.C. (Sr. Secretario General).
                                                        1845
Tél: 32-2208. Télex: 1289 unah ho
F : dr-sco, éco-adm des aff, ing, méd, ch-phar, dent, psyc, péd-trav soc.
E : inf.
D : phy, math, biol.
Ce : ét gén.
    CENTRO UNIVERSITARIO REGIONAL DEL NORTE, San Pedro Sula, Cortes.
    ét gén, éco, adm des aff, péd.
    CENTRO UNIVERSITARIO REGIONAL LITORAL ATLÁNTICO, La Ceiba, Atlántida.

gé agr-for.
Universidad de San Pedro Sula, 18 Avenida, 6 calle, N.O., San Pedro Sula, Cortés.
Universidad Privada José Cecilio del Valle. Barrio Buenos Aires, calle la Fuente 603, Tegucigalpa, D.C.
Tel: 22-0575
Escuela Agrícola Panamericana, El Zamorano, Francisco Morazán.   1942
Tél: 332717. Télex: 3111 1567
Escuela Superior del Profesorado «Francisco Morazán», Boulevard Miraflores, Tegucigalpa, D.C.   1957
Tel: 32-7417
D : nat, éd, soc, math, lang-let, sc dom, phys.

Servicio Universitario Mundial (WUS)
Correspondant: Manuel Chavez Borjas.
Apartado postal 62-A, Comayaguela.
Federación de Estudiantes Universitarios de Honduras – FEUH (IUS)
Apartado postal 1260, Tegucigalpa, D.C.
Juventud Universitaria Católica (Pax Romana)
Barrio Buenos Aires, 7a Avenida 521, Tegucigalpa.

*

Ministerio de Educación Pública
la Calle, entre 2a, 3a y 4a Avenidas Comayagüela, D.C.,
Tél: 22-7497
Comisión Nacional Hondureña de Cooperación con la Unesco
Ministerio de Educación Pública, la Calle, entre 2a, 3a y 4a Avenidas, Comayagüela, D.C.
Tél: 22-7497. Cables: mineducacion tegucigalpa.

HONG KONG
HONG-KONG

UNIVERSITIES—UNIVERSITES

*University of Hong Kong, Pokfulam Road, Hong Kong. (The Registrar).   1911
Tel: 5-859 2111. Fax: (852) 5-479907. Telex: 71919 cereb hx
F : arts, sc, eng, med, soc, dent.
S : ed, law, arc.
D : extramural st.
Ce : Asian st, comp, lang, media resources, urb st & plan.
Ut : radioisotope, electro serv, anim lab, med illustration.
*The Chinese University of Hong Kong, Shatin,

New Territories, Hong Kong.   1963
Tel: (695) 2111. Fax: 852-0-(695) 4234. Telex: 50301 cuhk hx
F : arts, sc, soc, bus adm, med.
S : grad.
I : Chinese st, sc-techn, soc st.
D : extramural st.
Ce : Chinese lang, comp serv.
Hong Kong University of Science and Technology, Tai Po Tsai. (Planned).
Tel: 5-251726. Fax: 5-8450227

OTHER INSTITUTIONS—AUTRES INSTITUTIONS

Technical Education—Enseignement technique

Chai Wan Technical Institute, Shing Tai Road, Chai Wan. *1987*
D : *appl sc, com st, comp, elec, gen st, mec.*

City Polytechnic of Hong Kong, Argyle Centre, Tower II, 700, Nathan Road, Kowloon, Hong Kong. *1984*
Tel: 3-984321. Fax: 3-970275. Telex: 39369

Hong Kong Polytechnic, Yuk Choi Road, Hung Hom, Kowloon, Hong Kong. *1972*
Tel: 3-638344
D : *app sc, acc, institutional mangt st, bui-surv, bus-mangt, civ eng, des, elec, electro, lang, math, mec-marine eng, nautical st, prod-ind eng, bui serv eng.*
I : *med & heal care, tex-clothing.*
S : *soc w, des.*
Ce : *env st, comp, land & eng surv.*

Haking Wong Technical Institute, 702, Lai Chi Kok Road, Cheung Sha Wan, Kowloon, Hong Kong. *1977*
Tel: 3-615161
D : *const, elec, mec, hotel-tour, marine-fabrication.*

Kwai Chung Technical Institute, 20, Hing Shing Road, Kwai Chung, New Territories, Hong Kong. *1975*
Tel: 0-246221
D : *com, elec, const, mec, tex & clothing ind.*

Kwun Tong Technical Institute, 25, Hiu Ming Street, Kwun Tong, Kowloon, Hong Kong. *1975*
Tel: 3-414331
D : *clothing ind, elec, mec, printing, tex ind.*

Lee Wai Lee Technical Institute, 30, Renfrew Road, Kowloon, Hong Kong. *1979*
Tel: 3-383611
D : *con, des, gen st, ind techn, mec.*

Morrison Hill Technical Institute, 6, Oi Kwan Road, Wan Chai, Hong Kong. *1970*
Tel: 5-745321
D : *com, const, elec, mec, gen st.*

Sha Tin Technical Institute, 21 Yuen Wo Road, Sha Tin, New Territories, Hong Kong. *1986*
Tel: 0-6957439
D : *com, comp, mec, des, elec, gen st.*

Tuen Mun Technical Institute, Tsing Wun Road, Tuen Mun, New Territories, Hong Kong. *1986*
D : *com, const, elec, gen st, mec.*

Teacher Training—Formation pédagogique

Grantham College of Education, 42, Gascoigne Road, Kowloon, Hong Kong. *1951*

Northcote College of Education, 21, Sassoon Road, Pokfulam, Hong Kong. *1939*

The Hong Kong Technical Teachers' College, 373, Queen's Road East, Hong Kong. *1974*

Sir Robert Black College of Education, 6, Caldecott Road, Piper's Hill, Kowloon, Hong Kong. *1960*

Professional Education—Enseignement professionnel

Hong Kong Adventist College, Clear Water Bay Road, Kowloon, Hong Kong. *1981*
Tel: 3-7191667
D : *arts-sc, bus-comp, religion.*

Hong Kong Baptist College, 224, Waterloo Road, Kowloon, Hong Kong. *1983*
Tel: 3-397333. Telex: 48969
F : *arts, soc, bus, nat, eng.*

Lingnan College, 15, Stubbs Road, Hong Kong. *1978*
Tel: 5-722226
F : *arts, bus, mus, soc.*

Shue Yan College, Wai Tsui Crescent, Braemar Hill Road, North Point, Hong Kong. *1976*
Tel: 5-722676
D : *Chinese lang & lit, English lang & lit, hist, jour, acc, bus adm, eco, law-bus, socio, counselling-guidance, soc w, law-adm.*

Hong Kong Association of University Women (IFUW)
President: Mrs. Susan Cameron.

Chairman (Internat. Rel): Mrs. Gillian Workman Markley.
G.P.O. Box 11708, Hong Kong.

World University Service (WUS)
c/o Students Union, University of Hong Kong,
Hong Kong.
Tel: 5-(859) 2111

Pax Romana Catholic Graduates' Association
Hong Kong Ltd.
c/o Catholic Centre, 16th floor, Grand Building, Connaught Road Central, Hong Kong.

Hong Kong Federation of Catholic Students (Pax
Romana)
Caritas Social Centre, 6th Floor, 134 Boundary
Street, Kowloon, Hong Kong.

Student Christian Movement of Hong Kong
(WSCF)
12A/F Kiu Kiu Building, 568 Nathan Road,
Kowloon, Hong Kong.
Tel: 3-852550

Hong Kong Federation of Students (ISMUN)
51 Nathan Road, Kowloon, Hong Kong.

*

Education Department
Hong Kong.

HUNGARY
HONGRIE

UNIVERSITIES AND TECHNICAL UNIVERSITIES—
UNIVERSITES ET UNIVERSITES TECHNIQUES

*Eötvös Loránd Tudományegyetem [U. Loránd
Eötvös], Egyetem tér 1, 1053 Budapest V. (M.
le Secrétaire).   1635
Tél: 180-820. Télex: 22-5467 elte h
dr-pol, let, sc.

*Budapesti Műszaki Egyetem [U. Technique de
Budapest], Műegyetemrakpart 3, 1111 Buda-
pest XI.   1872
Tél: 664-011. Télex: 22-5931 muegy
F : gé civ, méc, arc-urb, ch élec, gé trans.
E : nat, hyd.

Kossuth Lajos Tudományegyetem [U. Lajos
Kossuth], Egyetem tér 1-3, 4010 Debrecen.
                                                   1912
Tél: 16-666. Télex: 72200 univk h
F : let, sc.

*Nehézipari Műszaki Egyetem [U. Technique de
l'Industrie lourde], Egyetemváros, 3515
Miskolc.   1949
Tél: (46) 65-111. Télex: 62223 nmemis h
F : dr, méc, mét, mine.
E : nat (Dunaujváros); ch (Kazincbarcika).

Pécsi Janus Pannonius Tudományegyetem [U. de
Pecs], 48-as tér 1, 7601 Pécs.   1914
Tél: (72) 12-902. Télex: 12301
F : dr-pol, éco.

József Attila Tudományegyetem [U. Attila
József], Dugonics tér 13, 6701 Szeged.
                                             1872, 1921
Tél: 24-022. Télex: 82-401
F : dr-pol, let, sc.

Veszprémi Vegyipari Egyetem [U. Technique de

l'Industrie chimique], Schönherz Zoltán utca
10, 8200 Veszprém.   1949
Tél: (80) 125-50. Télex: 32397
F : ch tec.

Agrártudományi Egyetem [U. d'Agriculture],
Böszörményi út 138, 4079 Debrecen.
                                             1868, 1970
Tél: 17-888. Télex: 722111
Sections à Szarvas, Mezőtúr.

*Agrártudományi Egyetem [U. d'Agriculture],
Páter Károly út 1, 2100 Gödöllő.
Tél: (28) 10-200. Télex: 224892 h
F : agr, méc.
Section à Gyöngyös.

Agrártudományi Egyetem [U. d'Agriculture],
Deák Ferenc út 16, 8361 Keszthely. 1797, 1970
Tél: 123-30. Télex: 35-282
Section à Mosonmagyaróvár.

*Marx Károly Közgazdaságtudományi Egyetem
[U. Karl Marx des Sciences économiques],
Dimitrov tér 8, 1093 Budapest IX.   1948
Tél: 174-539. Télex: 224186
F : éco, com, ind.

Erdészeti és Faipari Egyetem [U. des Forêts et de
l'Industrie du Bois], Bajcsy Zsilinszky út 4,
9400 Sopron.   1809, 1962
Tél: (99) 11-100. Télex: 249126
Section à Székesfehérvár.

Kertészeti Egyetem [U. d'Horticulture], Villányi
út 35-43, 1114 Budapest.   1853, 1970
Tél: 850-666. Télex: 226011

Semmelweis Orvostudományi Egyetem [U. de

Médecine Semmelweis], Üllői út 26, 1450 Budapest VIII. *1769, 1951*
Tél: 134-610. Télex: 226720
F : méd, dent, phar.
Debreceni Orvostudományi Egyetem, Nagyerdei Körút 98, 4012 Debrecen. *1912, 1951*
Tél: 17-571. Télex: 72411
Pécsi Orvostudományi Egyetem, Szigeti út 12, 7643 Pécs. *1912, 1951*
Tél: (72) 24-122. Télex: 12311 pote

Szentgyörgyi Albert Orvostudományi Egyetem (U. de Médecine Szentgyörgyi Albert), Dugonics tér 13, 6720 Szeged. *1921, 1951*
Tél: 12-729
F : méd, phar.
Állatorvostudományi Egyetem [U. vétérinaire], Landler Jenő út 2, 1078 Budapest VII.
1782, 1962
Tél: 222-660. Télex: 224439
Section à Hódmezővásárhely.

OTHER UNIVERSITY INSTITUTIONS—
AUTRES ETABLISSEMENTS UNIVERSITAIRES

Magyar Iparművészeti Főiskola [E. sup. des Arts décoratifs], Zugligeti út 11-25, 1121 Budapest XII.
Tél: 364-547
Magyar Képzőművészeti Főiskola [E. sup. des Beaux-Arts], Népköztársaság utja 71, 1062 Budapest VI. *1871, 1949, 1970*
Liszt Ferenc Zeneművészeti Főiskola [E. sup. de Musique], Liszt Ferenc tér 8, 1061 Budapest VI. *1875*
Tél: 414-785
Szinház- és Filmművészeti Főiskola [E. sup. de

Théâtre et de Cinéma], Vas utca 2/c, 1088 Budapest VIII.
Tél: 342-550
Testnevelési Főiskola [E. sup. d'Education physique], Alkotás út 44, 1123 Budapest XII.
1925
Tél: 564-444
Orvostovábbképző Egyetem [U. d'Etudes avancées en médecine], Szabolcs utca 33/35, 1398 Budapest.
Tél: 408-900. Télex: 226595

OTHER INSTITUTIONS—AUTRES INSTITUTIONS

Apáczai Csere János Tanitóképző Főiskola [E. normale sup.], Liszt Ferenc út 42, 9200 Győr.
Állami Balettintézet [I. d'Etat du Ballet], Népköztársaság út 25, 1061 Budapest.
Bánki Donát Gépipari Müszaki Főiskola [E. sup. de mécanique], Népszinház utca 8, 1081 Budapest.
Tél: 131-460. Télex: 226803
Bárczi Gusztáv Gyógypedagógiai Tanárképző Főiskola [E. normale sup. médicopédagogique], Bethlen tér 2, 1071 Budapest.
Tél: 226-494
Berzsenyi Dániel Tanárképző Főiskola [E. normale sup.], Szabadság tér 4, 9701 Szombathely.
Bessenyei György Tanárképző Főiskola, Sóstói út 31/b, 4401 Nyiregyháza.
Tél: 11788. Télex: 73380 tkfre h
Budapesti Tanitóképző Főiskola, Kiss János altábornagy út 40, 1531 Budapest.
Comenius Tanitóképző Főiskola, Eötvös út 5, 3950 Sárospatak.
Debreceni Tanitóképző Főiskola, Péterfia út 1/7, 4001 Debrecen.
Eötvös József Tanitóképző Főiskola, Szegedi út 2, 6501 Baja.
Esztergomi Tanitóképző Főiskola, Makarenkó út

1/3, 2501 Esztergom.
Tél: 166
Gépipari és Automatizálási Müszaki Főiskola [E. sup de Mécanique et d'Automatisation], Izsáki út 10, 6000 Kecskemét.
Tél: (76) 21-611. Télex: 26328
Ho Si Minh Tanárképző Főiskola [E. normale sup.], Szabadság ter 2, 3301 Eger.
Tél: 10-466. Télex: 63309
Jászberényi Tanitóképző Főiskola, Rákóczi út 53, 5102 Jászberény.
Juhász Gyula Tanárképző Főiskola, Április 4-e út 6, 6701 Szeged.
Tél: 10-495
Kandó Kálmán Villamosipari Müszaki Főiskola [E. sup. d'Electricité], Tavaszmező utca 15/17, 1084 Budapest.
Tél: 335-530. Télex: 224897
Kaposvári Tanitóképző Főiskola [E. normale sup.], Bajcsy Zsilinszky út 10, 7401 Kaposvár.
Kecskeméti Tanitóképző Főiskola, Kaszap ut 6/14, 6001 Kecskemét.
Könnyűipari Müszaki Főiskola [E. sup de l'Industrie légère], Doberdó út 6, 1034 Budapest.
Tél: 803-333
Külkereskedelmi Főiskola [E. sup. du Commerce

extérieur], Ecseri út 3, 1097 Budapest.
Tél: 573-166

Pénzügyi és Számviteli Főiskola [E. sup. des Finances et de la Comptabilité], Buzogány út 10-12, 1426 Budapest.

Pollack Mihály Müszaki Főiskola [E. sup. technique], Boszorkány ut 2, 7624 Pécs.
Tél: (72) 24-277. Télex: 12501

Széchényi István Közlekedési és Távközlési Főiskola [E. sup. de Télécommunication et des Transports], Ságvári Endre út 25, 9026 Győr.
Tél: (96) 13-111. Télex: 24-267

Zsámbéki Tanitóképző Főiskola [E. normale sup.], Lenin tér 3, 2072 Zsámbék.
Tél: (26) 42-122

Ybl Miklós Építőipari Müszaki Főiskola [E. sup. de Construction], Thököly út 74, 1146 Budapest.
Tél: 229-602. Télex: 224699

Kereskedelmi és Vendéglátóipari Főiskola [E. sup. du Commerce et de l'Industrie Hôtelière], Alkotmány út 9/11, 1055 Budapest.
Tél: 327-150

Mezőgazdasági Főiskola [E. sup. d'Agriculture], Rákóczi út 69, 4400 Nyiregyháza.
Tél: (42) 15-034. Télex: 73209

Államigazgatási Főiskola [E. sup. de l'Administration publique], Ménesi út 5, 1118 Budapest.
Tél: 852-122. Télex: 225229

National Committee of Hungarian Student Organizations – NCHSO (IUS)
Ujpesti Rkp. 37-38, Budapest XIII.
Télex: 224244 (attn. nchso)

Express Yöuth and Student Travel Bureau
Szabadsag tér 16, Budapest V.

Ecumenical Council of Churches in Hungary (WSCF)
Szabadsag tér 2.1, 1054 Budapest.

Ministère de la Culture et de l'Education
Szalay út 10-14, 1884 Budapest Pf1.
Tél: 530-600. Télex: 225-935

Commission nationale hongroise pour l'Unesco
Ministère de la Culture et de l'Education, Szalay út 10-14, 1884 Budapest Pf1.
Tél: 313-526. Télex: 225-935 (attention commission nationale). Cables: hungarounesco budapest

ICELAND
ISLANDE

***Háskóli Íslands** [U. of Iceland], 101 Reykjavik. (The Secretary). *1911*
Tel: (1) 694300
F : *theo, med, dent, law, eco, arts, tec, nat, soc, nurs, physio.*

Háskólinn á Akureyri [U. at Akureyri], P.O. Box 875, 602 Akureyri. *1987*
F : *eco, nurs.*

Tækniskóli Íslands [Technical C. of Iceland], Höfdabakki 9, 110 Reykjavik. *1964*
Tel: 1-84833

Kennaraháskóli Íslands [U.C. of Teacher Training], 105 Reykjavik. *1971*
Tel: (1) 688700

Félag Íslenzkra Háskólakvenna (IFUW)
President: Mrs. Arndís Björnsdóttir.
Chairman (Internat. Rel): Mrs. Hildur Björnadóttir.
P.O. Box 327, Reykjavik.

Stúdentenárad Háskóli Íslands—SHI
Háskóli Íslands, Reykjavik.

SHI Travel Service
c/o Félagsstonun Studenta Gamba Gardi, Reykjavik.

Utanrikisraduneytud (Foreign Office)
Reykjavik.
Telex: 2050 extern is

*

Menntamáláraduneytud (Ministry of Culture and Education)
150 Reykjavik.
Tel: 250-00. Telex: 2111 iskult is

Icelandic National Commission for Unesco
Ministry of Culture and Education, 150 Reykavik.
Tel: 250-00. Telex: 2111 iskult is

INDIA
INDE

UNIVERSITIES AND TECHNICAL UNIVERSITIES— UNIVERSITES ET UNIVERSITES TECHNIQUES

Agra University, Paliwal Park, Agra 282004, Uttar Pradesh. (The Registrar).
1927
Tel: 64164-8. Cables: agra university, agra, uttar pradesh
F : *arts, sc, agr, com, ed, law, med, fa, homeopathic med.*
INSTITUTE OF SOCIAL SCIENCES. *1956*
INSTITUTE OF HOUSEHOLD ART AND HOME SCIENCE. *1968*
K.M. INSTITUTE OF HINDI STUDIES AND LINGUISTICS. *1953*
Also 47 affiliated colleges.
Ajmer University, Ajmer.
Alagappa University, Alagappa Nagar 623004, Karaikudi, Tamil Nadu. *1985*
Tel: 2584
F : *arts, com, ed, sc.*
UNIVERSITY COLLEGE OF EDUCATION.
UNIVERSITY COLLEGE OF PHYSICAL EDUCATION.
***Aligarh Muslim University**, Aligarh 202001, Uttar Pradesh. *1920*
F : *arts, sc, com, eng-techn, law, med, theo, soc.*
WOMEN'S COLLEGE. *1923*
Z.H. ENGINEERING COLLEGE. *1970*
JAWAHARLAL NEHRU MEDICAL COLLEGE. *1970*
INSTITUTE OF OPHTHAMOLOGY.
AJMAL KHAN TIBBIYA COLLEGE. *1942*
UNIVERSITY POLYTECHNIC.
WOMAN'S POLYTECHNIC. *1968*
University of Allahabad, Allahabad 211002, Uttar Pradesh. *1887, 1921*
Tel: 50668. Cables: university allahabad
F : *arts, sc, com, eng, law, med.*
KALI PRASAD UNIVERSITY COLLEGE.
MADAN MOHAN MALAVIYA COLLEGE.
MOTILAL NEHRU MEDICAL COLLEGE. *1961*
WILLIAM HOLLAND UNIVERSITY COLLEGE.
Also 11 associated colleges.
Amravati University, Vidarbha Mahavidyale Campus, Amravati 444604, Maharashtra.
1983
Tel: 3279. Cables: amuni
F : *arts, ayur, com, ed, eng-techn, hom sc, law,*

sc, soc.
Also 85 affiliated colleges.
Andhra University, Waltair, Visakhapatnam 530003, Andhra Pradesh. *1926*
Tel: 64871. Cables: university waltair, visakhapatnam
F : *arts, sc, com, eng, fa, law, med, orntl st, ayur, ed, pharmaceutical sc, ch eng & techn, phys.*
Also 87 colleges and 13 oriental colleges.
Andhra Pradesh Agricultural University, Rajendranagar, Hyderabad 500030, Andhra Pradesh. *1964*
Tel: 48161. Cables: agriversity
F : *agr, vet, hom sc.*
AGRICULTURAL COLLEGE, Bapatla. *1945*
COLLEGE OF AGRICULTURE. *1946*
COLLEGE OF HOME SCIENCE. *1961*
COLLEGE OF HOME SCIENCE, Bapatla. *1946*
COLLEGE OF VETERINARY SCIENCE.
COLLEGE OF VETERINARY SCIENCE, Tirupati. *1956*
S.V. AGRICULTURAL COLLEGE, Tirupati. *1962*
Andhra Pradesh Open University, 6-3-645 Somajiguda, Hyderabad 500482, Andhra Pradesh. *1982*
Tel: 30197. Cables: opvarsity
arts, com, sc, soc.
Anna University, Sardar Patel Road, Guindy, Madras 600025, Tamil Nadu. *1978, 1982*
Tel: 414545. Cables: anatech, madras
F : *eng, arc-reg plan, app eng, sc-hum, techn.*
ALAGAPPA COLLEGE OF TECHNOLOGY. *1944*
COLLEGE OF ENGINEERING, Guindy. *1794*
MADRAS INSTITUTE OF TECHNOLOGY. *1949*
SCHOOL OF ARCHITECTURE AND TOWN PLANNING.
Annamalai University, Annamalainagar 608002, Tamil Nadu. *1929*
Tel: CDM 249. Cables: anna malainagar
F : *arts, sc, ed, eng-techn, agr, Indian langs.*
Arunachal University, Itanagar 79111.
Tel: 559. Cables: arunversity, itanagar

Assam Agricultural University, Jorhat 785013, Assam.   *1969*
Tel: Rowriah 89. Cables: agrivarsity, jorhat
F : *agr, vet sc, hom sc.*
 COLLEGE OF AGRICULTURE.   *1948*
 COLLEGE OF VETERINARY SCIENCE, Gauhati.
                                                     1948
 COLLEGE OF HOME SCIENCE (for Girls).
                                                     1973
Avadh University, Faizabad 224001, Uttar Pradesh.   *1975*
Tel: 2135
F : *arts, sc, com, law, ed, eng-techn.*
Also 29 affiliated colleges.
Awadhesh Pratap Singh Vishwavidyalaya, Rewa 486003, Madhya Pradesh.   *1968*
Tel: 277
F : *arts, sc, com, ed, eng, law, ayur, hom sc, life sc, med, soc.*
Also 60 affiliated colleges.
*Banaras Hindu University, Varanasi 221005, Uttar Pradesh.   *1915*
Tel: pabx bhu 54291. Cables: hindu university varanasi
F : *arts, sc, ed, eng-techn, law, med-sc, mus, fa, soc, com, mangt st, orntl st-theo, Indian med, theo, agr, sanskrit.*
 WOMEN'S COLLEGE.   *1929*
Also 4 affiliated colleges.
Bangalore University, Jnana Bharathi, Bangalore 560056, Karnataka State.   *1964*
Tel: 601241. Cables: unibangalore
F : *arts, sc, com, ed, eng, law, med, techn, mental heal-neuro sc, commun.*
 CENTRAL COLLEGE.   *1864*
 UNIVERSITY LAW COLLEGE.   *1948*
 UNIVERSITY COLLEGE OF PHYSICAL
  EDUCATION   *1959*
 UNIVERSITY VISVESVARAYA COLLEGE
  OF ENGINEERING.   *1917*
Also 113 affiliated colleges.
*Maharaja Sayajiraot University of Baroda, Vadodara 390002, Gujarat State.   *1949*
Tel: 64238. Cables: university, vadodara
F : *arts, sc, com ed-psyc, fa, hom sc, law, med, soc w, techn-eng.*
 BARODA MEDICAL COLLEGE.   *1949*
 BARODA SANSKRIT MAHAVIDYALAYA.   *1915*
 COLLEGE OF INDIAN MUSIC, DANCE AND
  DRAMATICS.   *1886*
 MANIBHAI KASHIBAI AMIN ARTS AND
  SCIENCE COLLEGE AND COLLEGE OF
  COMMERCE, Padra.   *1965*
 ORIENTAL INSTITUTE.   *1927*
 POLYTECHNIC.   *1957*
Berhampur University, Bhanjabihar 760007, Ganjam District, Orissa.   *1967*
Tel: 3404. Cables: berham pur university, bhanja bihar, berhampur, dist. ganjam

F : *arts, sc, com, ed, law, med.*
Also 31 affiliated colleges.
*Bhagalpur University, Bhagalpur 812007, Bihar.   *1960*
Tel: 8153. Cables: university, bhagalpur, bihar, india
F : *arts, sc, com, ed, eng, fa-crafts, law, med.*
 AMARDYUTI EVENING COLLEGE, Satsang
  (Deoghar).
 B.N.M. COLLEGE, Barahiya.   *1959*
 B.R.M. COLLEGE, Munger.   *1959*
 BHAGALPUR EVENING COLLEGE.   *1965*
 DEO SUNDARI MEMORIAL COLLEGE, Jhajha
  (Munger).
 DEOGHAR COLLEGE, Deoghar.   *1969*
 G.B. COLLEGE, Naugachhia.   *1959*
 GODDA COLLEGE, Godda.   *1955*
 H.S. COLLEGE, Baveli-Kharagpur.
 J.M.S. COLLEGE, Munger.
 J.P. COLLEGE, Narayanpur.   *1955*
 J.R.S. COLLEGE, Jamalpur.   *1953*
 JAMTARA COLLEGE.
 K.D.S. COLLEGE, Gogri.
 K.K.M. COLLEGE, Jamui.
 K.K.M. COLLEGE, Pakur.   *1966*
 K.M.D. COLLEGE, Parbatta.
 K.S.S. MAHAVIDYALAYA, Khagalia (Monghyr).
 KOSHI COLLEGE, Khagaria.   *1948*
 MADHUPUR COLLEGE, Madhupur.   *1945*
 MARWARI COLLEGE.
 MURARKA COLLEGE, Sultanganji.   *1956*
 P.B.S. COLLEGE, Banka.   *1959*
 R.D. & D.J. COLLEGE, Munger.   *1898*
 R.S. COLLEGE, Tarapur.   *1959*
 RAMADHIN COLLEGE, Sheikhpura (Munger).
 SAHIBGANJ COLLEGE, Sahibganj.   *1953*
 S.K.R. COLLEGE, Barbigha.   *1956*
 S.M. MAHAVIDYALAYA.
 S.P. COLLEGE, Dumka.   *1955*
 S.P. MAHILA COLLEGE, Dumka.
 S.R.T. COLLEGE, Dhamri.
 SUNDRAVATI MAHILA MAHAVIDYALAYA. *1949*
 TEJ NARAIN BANAILI COLLEGE.   *1887*
Also 22 affiliated colleges.
Bharathiar University, Coimbatore 641046, Tamil Nadu.   *1982*
Tel: 4222. Cables: unibharathiar, coimbatore
F : *arts, com, eng, law, med, sc.*
38 affiliated colleges.
Bharathidasan University, Tiruchirapalli 620024, Tamil Nadu.   *1982*
Tel: 29605. Cables: bard, tiruchirapalli
F : *arts, com, agr, eng, law, med, sc.*
I : *mangt.*
S : *energy, ling-lit.*
Also 44 affiliated colleges.
Bhavnagar University, Gijubhai Badheka Marg, Bhavnagar 364002, Gujarat.   *1978*

Tel: 20006
F : *arts, com, ed, law, sc, eng.*
M.J. COLLEGE OF COMMERCE.   *1949*
SAMALDAS ARTS COLLEGE.   *1885*
SIR P.P. INSTITUTE OF SCIENCE.
Also 5 affiliated colleges and 1 recognized institution.
Bhopal University, Hoshangabad Road, Bhopal 462006, Madhya Pradesh.   *1970*
Tel: 62103. Cables: university bhopal
F : *arts, sc, com, ed, eng, law, med, hom sc, soc, life sc, techn ed.*
Also 34 affiliated colleges.
Bidhan Chandra Krishi Vishwavidyalaya [Agricultural U.], Haringhata, Nadia District 741252, West Bengal.   *1974*
Tel: 54. Cables: krishibidhan
F : *agr, vet-anim sc.*
Bihar University, Muzaffarpur 842001, Bihar.
                              1952, 1960
Tel: 3066. Cables: bihvarsity
F : *hum, sc, com, ed, eng, law, med, soc, mangt.*
B.M.D. COLLEGE, Dayalpur.   *1969*
B.P.S. COLLEGE, Bhore.   *1970*
B.T.T. COLLEGE, Chapra.   *1970*
C.N. COLLEGE, Sahebganj.   *1969*
D.A.V. COLLEGE, Siwan.   *1941*
DR. R.M.L.S. COLLEGE.   *1968*
DR. S.K.S. WOMEN'S COLLEGE, Motihari.
                                   1959
GANGA SINGH COLLEGE, Chapra.   *1965*
GOPALGANJ COLLEGE, Gopalganj.   *1957*
GOPESHAW COLLEGE, Hathwa.   *1957*
H.R. COLLEGE, Amnaur.   *1965*
H.R. COLLEGE, Mairwa.   *1966*
JAGDAM COLLEGE, Chapra.   *1955*
JAIPRAKASH MAHILA COLLEGE, Chapra.
                                   1957
JEEWACHCHA MAHAVIDYALAYA, Motipur.
                                   1969
J.L.N.M. COLLEGE, Ghorasahan.
J.S. COLLEGE, Chandauli.   *1959*
J.B.S.D. COLLEGE, Bakuchi.   *1971*
LALIL NARAYAN MISHRA COLLEGE OF BUSINESS MANAGEMENT.
L.N. COLLEGE, Bhagwanpur.   *1958*
L.N.D. COLLEGE, Motihari.   *1967*
L.N. TIRHUT COLLEGE.
LANGAT SINGH COLLEGE.   *1899*
MAHANT DARSHAN DASS MAHILA COLLEGE.
                                   1948
M.J.K. COLLEGE, Bettah.   *1955*
M.P. SINGH SCIENCE COLLEGE.   *1967*
M.S.S.G. COLLEGE, Areraj.   *1962*
MUNSHI SINGH COLLEGE, Motihari.   *1945*
NARAYAN MAHAVIDYALAYA, Gorea Kothi.
                                   1972
N.L. SINGH COLLEGE, Jaitpur.   *1969*
P.N. COLLEGE, Parsa.   *1959*

RAJA SINGH COLLEGE, Siwan.   *1971*
RAJENDRA COLLEGE, Chapra.   *1938*
RAM DAYALU SINGH COLLEGE.   *1948*
RAJ NARAIN COLLEGE, Hajipur.   *1952*
RAMESHWAR MAHAVIDYALAYA.   *1965*
RAM JAIPAL COLLEGE, Chapra.
R.B.B. MAHILA COLLEGE.   *1969*
R.B.G.R. COLLEGE, Maharajganj.   *1962*
R.D.S. COLLEGE.   *1948*
R.P.S. COLLEGE, Jaitpur.   *1958*
R.S. SINGH MAHILA COLLEGE, Sitamarhi.
                                   1970
SAKRA COLLEGE.   *1971*
S.L.K. COLLEGE, Sitamarhi.
S.N.S. COLLEGE, Motihari.   *1970*
S.R.A.P. COLLEGE, Barachkia.   *1969*
S.R.K. GOENKA COLLEGE, Sitamarhi. *1949*
T.P. VERMA COLLEGE, Shikarpur.   *1971*
VIGYAN MAHAVIDYALAYA, Chapra.   *1971*
V.N. COLLEGE, Dighwara.   *1967*
Also 10 affiliated colleges.
Birsa Agricultural University, Kanko, Ranchi 834006, Bihar.
Tel: 22212. Cables: agriversity ranchi
*University of Bombay, University Road, Fort, Bombay 400032, Maharashtra State.
                   1857, 1904, 1928, 1953, 1974
Tel: 273623. Cables: bombay university, bombay 32
F : *arts, sc, com, dent, ed, fa, law, med, techn, ayur.*
ACADEMY OF ARCHITECTURE.   *1955*
AKBAR PEERBHOY COLLEGE OF COMMERCE AND ECONOMICS.   *1969*
ALI YAVAR JUNG NATIONAL INSTITUTE FOR THE HEARING HANDICAPPED..   *1983*
ALL INDIA INSTITUTE OF PHYSICAL MEDICINE & REHABILITATION.   *1955*
AYURVEDA MAHAVIDYALAYA.   *1954*
BALASAHEB KHARDEKAR COLLEGE, Vengurla 416516, Sindhudurg.   *1961*
BHANDUP EDUCATIONAL SOCIETY'S COLLEGE OF COMMERCE AND ECONOMICS. *1982*
BHARAT EDUCATION SOCIETY'S COLLEGE OF COMMERCE AND ECONOMICS.   *1972*
BIRLA COLLEGE OF ARTS, SCIENCE AND COMMERCE, Kalyan 421304, Thane. *1972*
BOMBAY COLLEGE OF PHARMACY.   *1970*
BOMBAY LOKMANYA TILAK MUNICIPAL MEDICAL COLLEGE.   *1964*
BOMBAY PHYSICAL EDUCATION COLLEGE.
                                   1978
BOMBAY TEACHER'S TRAINING COLLEGE.
                                   1969
B.S.S.S. COLLEGE OF ARTS AND COMMERCE.
                                   1979
BURHANI COLLEGE OF COMMERCE AND ARTS.   *1970*
CHEMBUR COMPREHENSIVE COLLEGE OF

EDUCATION.   *1970*
CHETANA COLLEGE OF COMMERCE AND
ECONOMICS.   *1970*
COLLEGE OF HOME SCIENCE.   *1969*
COLLEGE OF SOCIAL WORK.   *1955*
THE C.S.S.S. AND LADY SHANTABAI P.
COLLEGE OF ARTS AND SCIENCE.   *1964*
COSMOPOLITAN EDUCATION SOCIETY'S AND
COMMERCE COLLEGE.
D.E. SOCIETY'S K.M.D. COLLEGE OF ARTS
AND SCIENCE.   *1954*
D.G. RUPAREL COLLEGE.   *1952*
DNYAN BHARATI SOCIETY'S SAU SITABAI
RAMKRISHNA KARNADIKAR COLLEGE OF
COMMERCE, Vadkhun 401602, Dahnu
Road, Thane.   *1981*
DNYAN SADHANA COLLEGE OF ARTS,
SCIENCE AND COMMERCE, Thana 401602,
Thane.   *1983*
DNYANVARDHINI SHAHAPUR COLLEGE OF
ARTS AND COMMERCE, Thane.   *1984*
DR. AMBEDKAR COLLEGE OF ARTS, SCIENCE
AND COMMERCE, Mahad 40230, Raigad.
                                                  1961
DR. CHINTAMANRAO DESHMUKH COLLEGE
OF COMMERCE, Roha 402109, Raigad
District.
D.S.P. MANDAL'S K.V. PENDHAKAR ARTS,
SCIENCE AND COMMERCE COLLEGE,
Dombivli 421203, Thane.   *1979*
ELPHINSTONE COLLEGE.   *1856*
GANDHI SHIKSAN BHAVAN.   *1969*
GHANSHYAMDAS SARAF GIRLS' COLLEGE OF
ARTS AND COMMERCE.   *1983*
GOKHALE EDUCATION SOCIETY'S ARTS,
SCIENCE AND COMMERCE COLLEGE.   *1979*
GOKHALE EDUCATION SOCIETY'S COLLEGE
OF EDUCATION AND RESEARCH.   *1970*
GOKHALE EDUCATION SOCIETY'S COLLEGE
OF ARTS AND COMMERCE, Taihar 401603,
Thane.
GOPALDAS JHAMATMAL ADVANI LAW
COLLEGE.   *1977*
GOVERNMENT DENTAL COLLEGE AND
HOSPITAL.   *1945*
GOVERNMENT COLLEGE OF EDUCATION,
Panvel 410206 Raigad.   *1970*
GOVERNMENT COLLEGE OF EDUCATION,
Ratnagiri 415612.   *1974*
GOVERNMENT COLLEGE OF PHYSICAL
EDUCATION.   *1933*
GOVERNMENT LAW COLLEGE.   *1855*
GRANT MEDICAL COLLEGE.   *1845*
HANSRAJ JIVANDAS COLLEGE OF EDUCA-
TION.   *1969*
HASSNAIN EDUCATIONAL AND WELFARE
SOCIETY'S JAWAHARLAL NEHRU LAW
COLLEGE, Zadgaon 415612, Ratnagiri.
                                                  1976

HAZARIMAL SOMANI COLLEGE OF ARTS AND
SCIENCE.   *1965*
H.R. COLLEGE OF COMMERCE AND ECO-
NOMICS.   *1960*
INDIAN CULTURAL LEAGUE'S EDUCATION
SOCIETY'S COLLEGE OF ARTS, SCIENCE AND
COMMERCE, Thane.   *1984*
THE INDIAN INSTITUTE FOR THE TEACHERS OF
THE DEAF.   *1938*
INSTITUTE OF NURSING.   *1960*
INSTITUTE OF SCIENCE.   *1920*
ISMAIL YUSUF COLLEGE.   *1930*
JAI HIND COLLEGE AND BASANT SINGH
INSTITUTE OF SCIENCE.   *1948*
JITENDRA CHAUHAN COLLEGE OF LAW. *1977*
J.S.M. COLLEGE, Alibag 402201, Raigad.
                                                  1961
KANKAVLI COLLEGE, Kankavali 416602,
Sindhudurg.   *1972*
THE KELKAR EDUCATION TRUST'S COLLEGE
OF ARTS, SCIENCE AND COMMERCE.
                                                  1984
K.J. SOMAIYA COLLEGE OF ARTS AND
COMMERCE.   *1960*
K.J. SOMAIYA COLLEGE OF ENGINEERING.
                                                  1983
K.J. SOMAIYA COLLEGE OF SCIENCE.   *1960*
K.M.S.P. MANDAL'S COLLEGE OF ARTS AND
COMMERCE, Sindhudurg.   *1985*
K.P.B. HINDUJA COLLEGE OF COMMERCE.
                                                  1974
K.P.B. HINDUJA COLLEGE OF LAW.   *1976*
KHALSA COLLEGE.   *1937*
KHOPOLI MUNICIPAL COUNCIL COLLEGE,
Khopoli 410203, Raigad.   *1979*
KISHINCHAND CHELLARAM COLLEGE.   *1954*
KISHINCHAND CHELLARAM LAW COLLEGE.
                                                  1955
LALALAJPATRAI COLLEGE OF COMMERCE
AND ECONOMICS.   *1972*
MAHARASHTRA COLLEGE OF ARTS AND
SCIENCE.   *1968*
MAHARISHI DAYANAND EDUCATION
SOCIETY'S COLLEGE OF ARTS AND SCIENCE.
                                                  1962
MAHATMA EDUCATION SOCIETY'S COM-
MERCE COLLEGE.
MAHATMA GANDHI'S MISSION'S COLLEGE OF
ENGINEERING AND TECHNOLOGY.
MALAD-KANDIVLI EDUCATION SOCIETY'S
COLLEGE OF COMMERCE.   *1983*
MANDAR EDUCATION SOCIETY'S COLLEGE OF
EDUCATION.
M.L. DHANUKAR COLLEGE OF COMMERCE.
MEGJI MATHRADAS ARTS AND NARRONDASS
M. INSTITUTE OF SCIENCE.   *1945*
M.H.SABOO SIDDIK COLLEGE OF ENGINEER-
ING.   *1984*
MULUND COLLEGE OF COMMERCE.   *1970*

NAIR HOSPITAL DENTAL COLLEGE. *1933*
NALANDA NRITYA KALA VIDYAPEETH. *1973*
NARSEE MONJEE COLLEGE OF COMMERCE AND ECONOMICS. *1964*
NATIONAL EDUCATION SOCIETY'S RATNAM COLLEGE OF ARTS, SCIENCE AND COMMERCE. *1983*
NAVAKONKAN EDUCATION SOCIETY'S DR. DATAR SCIENCE, SHRI PILUKALA JOSHI COMMERCE AND DR. BEHERE ARTS COLLEGE, Chiplun 415605, Ratnagiri. *1965*
N.G. ACHARYA AND D.K. MARATHE COLLEGE OF ARTS, SCIENCE AND COMMERCE. *1978*
NEW LAW COLLEGE. *1954*
N.K.V. ARTS AND DAPOLI COMMERCE COLLEGE, Dapoli 415712, Ratnagiri. *1974*
N.Y.A. TATYASAHEB ATHALYE ARTS AND VED. S.R. SAPRE COMMERCE COLLEGE, Devrukh 415804, Ratnagiri. *1972*
PARLE COLLEGE. *1959*
PEOPLE'S EDUCATION SOCIETY'S DR. AMBEDKAR COLLEGE OF COMMERCE AND ECONOMICS. *1972*
PEOPLE'S EDUCATION SOCIETY'S DR. AMBEDKAR COLLEGE OF LAW. *1977*
P.D.L. COLLEGE OF COMMERCE AND ECONOMICS. *1972*
PRINCIPAL K.M. KUNDANI COLLEGE OF PHARMACY. *1971*
R.A. PODAR MEDICAL (AYURVEDA) COLLEGE. *1941*
R.A. PODAR COLLEGE OF COMMERCE AND ECONOMICS. *1941*
RAMNARAIN RUIA COLLEGE. *1937*
RAMNIRANJAN JHUNJHUNWALA COLLEGE OF ARTS, SCIENCE AND COMMERCE. *1963*
RAMRAO ADIK INSTITUTE OF TECHNOLOGY'S COLLEGE OF ENGINEERING. *1983*
RAYAT SHIKSHAN SANSTHA'S ARTS, SCIENCE AND COMMERCE COLLEGE, Panvel 410206, Raigad. *1970*
RAYAT SHIKSHAN SANSTHA'S ARTS, SCIENCE AND COMMERCE COLLEGE, Mokhada 401604, Thane. *1984*
RAYAT SHIKSHAN SANSTHA'S MODERN COLLEGE, Vashi, New Bombay 400703, Thane. *1979*
RISHI DAYARAM AND SETH HASARAM NATIONAL COLLEGE AND SETH WASSIAMULL ASSOMULL SCIENCE COLLEGE. *1949*
R.K. TALREJA COLLEGE OF ARTS, SCIENCE AND COMMERCE, Ulhasnagar, Thane. *1961*
R.P.G. COLLEGE OF ARTS AND SCIENCE AND R.V.J. COLLEGE OF COMMERCE, Ratnagiri. *1945*
SADHANA EDUCATION SOCIETY'S L.S. PAHEJA COLLEGE OF ARTS AND COMMERCE

1980
SANSKAR SARJAN EDUCATION SOCIETY'S COLLEGE OF COMMERCE. *1984*
SARDAR PATEL COLLEGE OF ENGINEERING. *1962*
SECONDARY TRAINING COLLEGE. *1922*
SETH GORDHANDAS SUNDERDAS MEDICAL COLLEGE. *1926*
SETH L.U.J. COLLEGE OF ARTS AND SIR M.V. COLLEGE OF SCIENCE AND SIR MATHURADAS VISSONJI COLLEGE OF SCIENCE AND COMMERCE. *1963*
SEVA SADAN'S COLLEGE OF EDUCATION, Ulhasnagar, Thane. *1966*
SHIKSHAK SANCHALIT SHIKSHAN SANSTHA'S ARTS AND COMMERCE COLLEGE, Wada, Thane. *1981*
SHRI B.A. ALIAS BHAISEHEB SAVANT ADHYAPAK MAHAVIDYALAYA, Ratnagiri. *1985*
SHRI CHINAI COLLEGE OF COMMERCE AND ECONOMICS. *1963*
SHRI PANCHEM KHEMRAJ MAHAVIDYALAYA, 416510 Savantwadi, Sindhudurg. *1961*
SHRI PANT WALAWALKAR COLLEGE OF EDUCATION, Deogad 416613, Sindhudurg. *1984*
SHRI SWAMI VIVEKANAND SHIKSAN SANTHA'S ARTS AND COMMERCE COLLEGE, Pen, Raigad. *1984*
SHRIMATI MITHIBAI MOTIRIM KUNDANANI COLLEGE OF COMMERCE AND ECONOMICS. *1961*
SIDDARTH COLLEGE OF ARTS AND SCIENCE. *1946*
SIDDARTH COLLEGE OF COMMERCE AND ECONOMICS. *1953*
SIDDARTH COLLEGE OF LAW. *1956*
SIR J.J. COLLEGE OF ARCHITECTURE. *1896*
SIR J.J. INSTITUTE OF APPLIED ART. *1935*
SIR J.J. SCHOOL OF ART. *1857*
S.K.P.S. MAHAVIDYALAYA AND JUNIOR COLLEGE, Malvan 416606, Sindhudurg. *1965*
SMT. C.H.M. COLLEGE, Ulhasnagar, Thane. *1965*
SMT. K.G.M.P. AYURVEDA MAHAVIDYALAYA. *1957*
SMT. KAPILA KHANDWALA COLLEGE OF EDUCATION. *1962*
SOCIETY OF ST. FRANCIS XAVIER'S FR. AGNEZ ENGINEERING COLLEGE. *1984*
SONOPANT DANDEKAR ARTS COLLEGE AND V.S. APTE COMMERCE COLLEGE, Palghar 401404, Thane District. *1970*
SOPHIA COLLEGE FOR WOMEN. *1941*
SOUTH INDIAN EDUCATION SOCIETY'S COLLEGE OF ARTS AND SCIENCE. *1960*

SOUTH INDIAN'S WELFARE SOCIETY'S
COLLEGE OF COMMERCE AND ECONOMICS.
1980
ST. ANDREW'S COLLEGE OF ARTS, SCIENCE
AND COMMERCE. 1983
ST. GONSALO GARCIA COLLEGE OF ARTS AND
COMMERCE, Papdy, Vasai, Thane 401207,
Thane.
ST. TERESA'S INSTITUTE OF EDUCATION.
1973
ST. XAVIER'S COLLEGE. 1869
ST. XAVIER'S INSTITUTE OF EDUCATION.
1953
SYDENHAM COLLEGE OF COMMERCE AND
ECONOMICS. 1913
THADOMAL SHAHANI ENGINEERING
COLLEGE. 1983
TIBIA COLLEGE AND HOSPITAL. 1940
TOPIWALA NATIONAL MEDICAL COLLEGE.
1921
V.E.S. COLLEGE OF ARTS, SCIENCE AND
COMMERCE. 1979
VICTORIA JUBILEE TECHNICAL INSTITUTE.
1887
VIDYA PRASARAK MANDAL'S B.N.
BANDODKAR COLLEGE OF SCIENCE, Thane
400601. 1969
VIDYA PRASARAK MANDAL'S K.G.J. COL-
LEGE OF ARTS AND N.G.B. COLLEGE OF
COMMERCE, Chendani 400601, Thane.
1969
VIDYA PRASARAK MANDAL'S T.M.C. LAW
COLLEGE, Thana 400601. 1972
VNEKANAND EDUCATION SOCIETY'S COL-
LEGE OF ENGINEERING. 1984
WATUMAL INSTITUTE OF ELECTRONIC
ENGINEERING, COMPUTER TECHNOLOGY
AND ELECTRONIC INSTRUMENTATION. 1981
WILSON COLLEGE. 1861
Also 38 recognized postgraduate institutions,
and 20 recognized qualified institutions.
University of Bundelkhand, Jhansi 284001, Uttar
Pradesh. 1975
F : arts, sc, agr, com, ed, law.
M.L.B. MEDICAL COLLEGE.
Also 19 affiliated colleges.
University of Burdwan, Burdwan 713104, West
Bengal. 1960
F : hum, sc, eng, law, med.
HOOGHLY MOHSIN COLLEGE, Chinsurah 252.
1836
Also 62 affiliated colleges.
University of Calcutta, Senate House, College
Street, Calcutta 700073, West Bengal.
1857, 1951, 1954
Tel: 313036. Cables: university calcutta
F : arts, agr-vet, com, ed, eng, mus-hom, sc, fa,
med, sc-techn.
UNIVERSITY COLLEGE OF ARTS. 1954

UNIVERSITY COLLEGE OF COMMERCE. 1954
UNIVERSITY COLLEGE OF LAW. 1909
UNIVERSITY COLLEGE OF MEDICINE. 1957
UNIVERSITY COLLEGE OF SCIENCE. 1954
UNIVERSITY COLLEGE OF TECHNOLOGY.
1954
Also 196 affiliated colleges and 8 constituent
colleges.
Calicut University, Tenhipalam 673635, Kerala
State. 1968
Tel: 8361-3. Telex: 854243 unic in. Cables:
unical, calicut
F : hum, sc, com, ed, eng, fa, law, med, lang,
homeopathy, ayur, jour.
Also 72 affiliated colleges.
**Chandra Shekhar Azad University of Agriculture
and Technology,** Kanpur 208002, Uttar
Pradesh. 1975
Tel: 244446. Cables: agrivarsity, kanpur
F : agr, vet-an hus.
Cochin University of Science and Technology,
Cochin University P.O., Cochin 682022,
Kerala. 1971
Tel: (484) 855181. Telex: 885-5019 cu in.
Cables: cusat
F : hum, sc, law, eng, mar sc, soc, techn, env st.
*University of Delhi, Delhi 110007. 1922, 1952
Tel: 2521521. Cables: university, delhi, india
F : arts, sc, ed, law, med, mus-fa, soc, techn,
math, mangt st, ayur-Unani med.
ATMA RAM SANATAN DHARMA COLLEGE.
1959
AYURVEDIC AND UNANI TIBBIA COLLEGE.
1973
BHARTI MAHILA COLLEGE. 1971
CENTRAL INSTITUTE OF EDUCATION.
1948
COLLEGE OF ARTS. 1972
COLLEGE OF PHARMACY. 1971
COLLEGE OF VOCATIONAL STUDIES.
1972
DAULAT RAM COLLEGE FOR WOMEN.
1960
DELHI COLLEGE OF ENGINEERING.
1941
DELHI INSTITUTE OF TECHNOLOGY.
DESHBANDHU COLLEGE. 1952
EVENING COLLEGE. 1958
DYAL SINGH COLLEGE. 1959
DYAL SINGH EVENING COLLEGE. 1959
GARGI COLLEGE. 1967
GURU GOVIND SINGH COLLEGE OF COM-
MERCE.
GYAN DEVI SALWAN COLLEGE. 1970
HAMDARD COLLEGE OF PHARMACY. 1973
HAMDARD TIBBI COLLEGE. 1977
HANS RAJ COLLEGE. 1948
HINDU COLLEGE. 1922
INDRAPRASTHA COLLEGE FOR WOMEN. 1925

INSTITUTE OF HOME ECONOMICS. *1969*
JANKI DEVI MAHAVIDYALAYA. *1959*
JESUS AND MARY COLLEGE. *1968*
KALINDI COLLEGE. *1967*
KAMALA NEHRU COLLEGE FOR WOMEN. *1964*
KIRORI MAL COLLEGE. *1954*
LADY HARDINGE MEDICAL COLLEGE. *1916*
LADY IRWIN COLLEGE. *1950*
LADY SHRI RAM COLLEGE FOR WOMEN. *1956*
LAKSHMIBAI COLLEGE FOR WOMEN, Ashok
  Vihar. *1965*
MAITREYI COLLEGE. *1967*
MATA SUNDRI COLLEGE. *1967*
MAULANA AZAD MEDICAL COLLEGE.
  1958
MIRANDA HOUSE. *1948*
MOT LAL NEHRU COLLEGE. *1964*
MOT LAL NEHRU EVENING COLLEGE. *1965*
P.G.D.A.V. EVENING COLLEGE. *1958*
RAJ KUMARI, AMRITKAUR COLLEGE OF
  NURSING. *1946*
RAJDHANI COLLEGE. *1964*
RAMJAS COLLEGE. *1917*
RAM LAL ANAND COLLEGE. *1964*
RAO TULA RAM COLLEGE. *1970*
SATYAVATI CO-EDUCATIONAL COLLEGE. *1972*
S.G.T.B. KHALSA COLLEGE. *1951*
S.G.T.B. KHALSA EVENING COLLEGE. *1973*
SCHOOL OF CORRESPONDENCE COURSES AND
  CONTINUING EDUCATION. *1962*
SHAHEED BHAGAT SINGH COLLEGE. *1967*
SHIVAJI COLLEGE. *1961*
SHRI AUROBINDO COLLEGE. *1972*
SHRI RAM COLLEGE OF COMMERCE. *1926*
SRI VENKATESHWARA COLLEGE. *1961*
SHYAM LAL COLLEGE, Shahdara. *1964*
SHYAM LAL EVENING COLLEGE. *1969*
SHYAMA PRASAD MUKHERJI COLLEGE.
  1969
ST. STEPHEN'S COLLEGE. *1881*
SWAMI SHARDHANAND COLLEGE. *1967*
UNIVERSITY COLLEGE OF MEDICAL SCIENCES.
  1971
VALLABHBHAI PATEL CHEST INSTITUTE. *1955*
VIVEKANANDA MAHILA COLLEGE. *1970*
ZAKIR HUSSAIN COLLEGE. *1948*
ZAKIR HUSSAIN EVENING COLLEGE. *1958*
Also 1 affiliated college.
Devi Ahilya Vishwavidyalaya, Indore, Indore
452001, Madhya Pradesh. *1964, 1983*
Tel: 5730. Cables: university, indore
F : *arts, com, eng, law, med, ayur, ed, life sc,
soc, sc-techn, dent.*
Also 26 affiliated colleges.
Dibrugarh University, Dibrugarh 786004, Assam
  1965
Tel: 20631. Cables: university, dibrugarh
F : *arts, sc, com, med.*
Also 56 affiliated colleges.

Doctor Hari Singh Gour Vishwavidyalaya, Sagar,
Gour Nagar, Sagar 470003, Madhya Pradesh.
  1946
Tel: 2263. Cables: university, sagar
F : *arts, sc, law, eng-techn, soc, life, sc, com, ed,
ayur.*
  COLLEGE OF EDUCATION. *1961*
Also 72 affiliated colleges.
Garhwal University, Srinagar 246174 Distt.
Garhwal, Uttar Pradesh. *1973*
Tel: 141. Cables: unigarh, srinagar (garhwal)
F : *arts, sc, com, ed, law.*
  BIRLA COLLEGE, Srinagar. *1962*
  DR. B.G. REDDEY P.G. COLLEGE, Pauri.
  1970
  SWAMI RAMTIRTH COLLEGE, Tehri. *1970*
Also 16 affiliated colleges.
Gauhati University, Gauhati 781014, Assam.
  1948
Tel: 88412. Cables: university, gauhati
F : *arts, sc, com, eng, law, med.*
  UNIVERSITY LAW COLLEGE.
    F: *arts, sc, com, eng, law, med.*
Also 103 affiliated colleges.
Goa University, Bambolin, P.O. Santa Cruz
403005, Goa. *1985*
Tel: 4498. Cables: unigoa
F : *arts, sc.*
Also 19 affiliated colleges and 4 recognized
postgraduate institutions.
University of Gorakhpur, Gorakhpur 273001,
Uttar Pradesh. *1956*
Tel: 5201. Cables: university, gorakhpur
F : *arts, sc, com, agr, ed, law, med, eng.*
Also 100 affiliated colleges.
**Govind Ballabh Pant University of Agriculture
and Technology**, Pantnagar, Nainital 263145,
Uttar Pradesh. *1960, 1972*
  COLLEGE OF AGRICULTURE. *1960*
  COLLEGE OF HOME SCIENCE. *1971*
  COLLEGE OF POSTGRADUATE STUDIES.
  1963
  PANT COLLEGE OF TECHNOLOGY. *1962*
  COLLEGE OF VETERINARY SCIENCE. *1960*
  SCHOOL OF BASIC SCIENCES AND HUMANI-
    TIES. *1960*
Gujarat University, Navrangpura, Ahmedabad
380009, Gujarat State. *1949*
Tel: 440341. Cables: unigujarat
F : *arts, ed, sc, com, law, med, techn, phar,
dent.*
Also 153 affiliated colleges and 9 recognized
institutions.
Gujarat Agricultural University, Sardar Kri-
ushinagar 385506, Banaskantha, Gujarat.
  1969
Tel: 26. Cables: krushi, sardar, kriushinagar
F : *agr, eng-techn, agr, vet-an hus, dairy sc, hom
sc.*

ASPEE COLLEGE OF NUTRITIONAL SCIENCE
AND COLLEGE OF HOME SCIENCE AND FOOD
TECHNOLOGY, Sardar Krushinagaro.
B.A. COLLEGE OF AGRICULTURE, Anand.
                                        1947
COLLEGE OF AGRICULTURE, Junagadh.
                                        1960
COLLEGE OF AGRICULTURE, Sardar Kru-
shinagar.
SHETH MANSUKHAL DAIRY SCIENCE COL-
LEGE, Anand.   *1961*
GUJARAT COLLEGE OF VETERINARY SCIENCE
AND ANIMAL HUSBANDRY, Anand.   *1964*
COLLEGE OF VETERINARY SCIENCE AND
ANIMAL HUSBANDRY, Sardar Krushinagar.
N.M. COLLEGE OF AGRICULTURE, Navasari.
                                        1965
Gujarat Ayurved University, Jamnagar 361008,
Gujarat.   *1966*
Cables: ayu
F : *ayur.*
SHRI GULABKUNVERBA AYURVED MAHAVI-
DYALAYA.   *1946*
INSTITUTE OF POSTGRADUATE TEACHING AND
RESEARCH.
Also 8 affiliated colleges.
Gulbarga University, Jnana Ganga, Gulbarga
585105, Karnataka State.   *1980*
Tel: 21446. Telex: 0895-208 gulu in
F : *arts, com, ed, eng, law, med, sc-techn, soc.*
Also 78 affiliated colleges.
Guru Ghasidas University, Bilaspur 495001,
Madhya Prades.   *1983*
Tel: 4901. Cables: vishwavidyalaya, bilaspur,
madhya pradesh
F : *arts, com, ed, eng, law, life sc, sc, soc.*
Also 32 affiliated colleges.
Guru Nanak Dev University, Amritsar 143005,
Punjab.   *1969*
Tel: 64228. Cables: university, amritsar
F : *arts-soc, sc, ed, med, fa-arc, agr-for, laws,
lang, dent, phys, ayur, phys plan, eco-bus, hum-
relig, eng techn.*
Also 74 affiliated colleges.
Haryana Agricultural University, Hisar 125004,
Haryana.   *1970*
Tel: PABX 3721/294. Cables: agrivarsity, hisar
COLLEGE OF AGRICULTURE.   *1962*
COLLEGE OF ANIMAL SCIENCES.   *1966*
COLLEGE OF BASIC SCIENCES AND HUMANI-
TIES.   *1966*
COLLEGE OF VETERINARY SCIENCES.   *1948*
COLLEGE OF SPORTS.   *1972*
COLLEGE OF HOME SCIENCES.   *1973*
COLLEGE OF AGRICULTURE, Kaul.   *1974*
Himachal Pradesh Krishi Vishwavidyalaya,
Palampar 176062, Himachal Pradesh.   *1978*
Tel: 61. Cables: himkrishi palampur
agr.

Himachal Pradesh University, Shimla 171005,
Himachal Pradesh.   *1970*
Tel: 3513. Cables: himversity, shimla
F : *arts, sc, com-bus adm, ed, law, med.*
AGRICULTURAL COLLEGE, Solan.   *1962*
EVENING COLLEGE, Simla.   *1962*
Also 26 affiliated colleges.
*University of Hyderabad, Hyderabad 500134,
Andhra Pradesh.   *1974*
Tel: 558220. Cables: central varsity hyderabad
S : *hum, life sc, soc, ch, math, phys, sc.*
Indira Gandhi Krishi Vishwa-Vidyalaya, Raipur
492012.
Indira Gandhi National Open University,
Y.M.C.A. Cultural Centre, Jai Singh Road,
New Delhi 110001.   *1985*
Tel: 351189. Telex: 031-66470 igou in. Cables:
ignou, new delhi
Indira Kala Sangit Vishwavidyalaya, Khairagarh
491881, Madhya Pradesh.   *1956*
Tel: 32. Cables: university, khairagarh-raj
F : *mus, dancing, fa-arts, pnt, folk mus.*
Also 32 affiliated colleges.
Jadavpur University, P.O. Jadavpur University,
Calcutta 700032, West Bengal.   *1955*
Tel: 72-4044. Cables: jadavpur university,
calcutta
F : *arts, sc, eng-techn.*
Also 3 affiliated colleges.
*University of Jammu, Canal Road, Jammu Tawi
180001, Jammu and Kashmir.   *1969*
Tel: 43679. Cables: university, jammu
F : *arts, sc, com, ed, law, mus-fa, orntl st, soc,
med.*
GOVERNMENT COLLEGE OF EDUCATION. *1954*
GOVERNMENT MEDICAL COLLEGE.   *1971*
INSTITUTE OF CORRESPONDENCE EDUCATION.
Also 11 affiliated colleges and 1 oriental
institute.
Jawaharlal Nehru Krishi Vishwavidyalaya, P.O.
Box 80, Krishnigar, Jabalpur 482004, Madhya
Pradesh.   *1964*
Tel: PBX 23771-3. Cables: krisiviswa, jabalpur
4, m.p. state
F : *agr, vet-an hus, agr eng.*
COLLEGE OF AGRICULTURE, Gwalior.   *1950*
COLLEGE OF AGRICULTURE, Indore.
                                        1955
COLLEGE OF AGRICULTURE.   *1955*
COLLEGE OF AGRICULTURE, Raipur.   *1961*
COLLEGE OF AGRICULTURE, Rewa.
                                        1955
COLLEGE OF AGRICULTURE, Sehore.   *1956*
COLLEGE OF AGRICULTURAL ENGINEERING.
                                        1967
COLLEGE OF DAIRY TECHNOLOGY, Raipur.
COLLEGE OF VETERINARY SCIENCE AND
ANIMAL HUSBANDRY, Mhow.   *1955*
COLLEGE OF VETERINARY SCIENCE AND

ANIMAL HUSBANDRY.   *1948*
Jawaharlal Nehru University, New Mehrauli Road, New Delhi 110067.   *1969*
Tel: 66762. Telex: 73 167 jnu iw in. Cables: yayenu
S : *for lang, int st, life sc, soc, env sc, comp & systems sc, creative arts.*
Also 4 recognized institutions.

Jawaharlal Nehru Technological University, Mahaveer Marg, Saifabad, Hyderabad 500028, Andhra Pradesh.   *1972*
Tel: 228388. Cables: technology, hyderabad
F : *arc, ch, eng, hum-lang, mangt sc, math, phy.*
COLLEGE OF FINE ARTS AND ARCHITECTURE.   *1968*
COLLEGE OF ENGINEERING, Anantapur. *1946*
COLLEGE OF ENGINEERING, Kakinada. *1946*
COLLEGE OF ENGINEERING.   *1965*

Jiwaji University, Vidya Vihar, Gwalior 474011, Madhya Pradesh.   *1964*
Tel: 20095. Cables: university, gwalior
F : *arts, sc, ayur, com, ed, eng, law, hom sc, life sc, phys, soc, med.*
Also 50 affiliated colleges.

University of Jodhpur, Jodhpur 342001, Rajasthan.   *1962*
Tel: 24733. Cables: university, jodhpur
F : *arts-ed-soc, sc, com, ed, eng, law.*
KAMLA NEHRU UNIVERSITY COLLEGE FOR WOMEN.   *1962*
Also 3 affiliated colleges.

Kakatiya University, Vidyaranyapuri, Warangal 506009, Andhra Pradesh.   *1976*
Tel: (PMBX) 7701. Cables: kakatiya
F : *arts, sc, com, eng-techn, law, med, ed-soc.*
ARTS AND SCIENCE COLLEGE.   *1927*
UNIVERSITY COLLEGE OF LAW.
UNIVERSITY COLLEGE OF PHARMACEUTICAL SCIENCES.
UNIVERSITY COLLEGE.   *1976*
EVENING COLLEGE.   *1961*
Also 12 affiliated colleges.

University of Kalyani, Kalyani, Nadia 741235, West Bengal.   *1960*
Tel: 220
F : *arts, sc, ed.*
Also 3 affiliated colleges.

Kameshwar Singh Darbhanga Sanskrit Vishwavidyalaya, Kameshwarnagar, Darbhanga 846004, Bihar.   *1961*
Tel: 2178. Cables: savita, darbhanga
F : *Darshan, Samaj Shastra, Veda, Vyakaran-Sahitya, Dharmashastra-Purana, Ayur, Jyotisha.*
Also 33 affiliated colleges and 37 constituent colleges.

Kanpur University, 4/277 Kalyanpur Road, Kanpur 208024, Uttar Pradesh.   *1966*
Tel: 242239. Cables: university, kanpur

F : *arts, sc, agr, com, eng-techn, homeopathic med, law, med, ed, ayur-Unani med.*
G.S.V.M. MEDICAL COLLEGE.   *1955*
Also 78 affiliated colleges.

Karnatak University, Dharwad 580003, Karnataka.   *1949*
Tel: 1894. Cables: unikarnatak
F : *arts, sc-techn, com, eng, law, med, soc, ed, Indian system of med, mangt.*
KARNATAK ARTS COLLEGE.   *1917*
KARNATAK SCIENCE COLLEGE.   *1958*
UNIVERSITY COLLEGE OF EDUCATION.   *1962*
UNIVERSITY COLLEGE OF LAW.   *1962*
UNIVERSITY COLLEGE OF MUSIC.   *1975*
Also 123 affiliated colleges.

Kashi Vidyapeeth, Varanesi 221002, Uttar Pradesh.   *1921*
Tel: 54160. Cables: kashividyapith, varanasi
F : *arts-hum, soc, soc w.*

*University of Kashmir**, Hazratbal, Srinagar 190006, Jammu and Kashmir.   *1969*
Tel: PABX 76972-4. Cables: university, srinagar
F : *arts, sc, com, ed, eng, mus-fa, law, med, orntl st, soc.*
GANDHI MEMORIAL COLLEGE.
GOVERNMENT MEDICAL COLLEGE.   *1959*
M.E.T. TEACHERS' COLLEGE, Sopore.   *1973*
REGIONAL ENGINEERING COLLEGE.   *1960*
GOVERNMENT COLLEGE OF EDUCATION.   *1940*
GOVERNMENT COLLEGE OF PHYSICAL EDUCATION.   *1978*
VISHWA BHARTI WOMEN'S WELFARE INSTITUTION.   *1979*
Also 12 affiliated colleges.

Kerala Agricultural University, P.O. Vellanikkara, Trichur 680654, Kerala.   *1971*
Tel: 23432. Cables: agrivarsity, trichur
F : *agr, vet-anim sc, fish, hort.*
COLLEGE OF AGRICULTURE, Vellayani Trivandrum.   *1955*
COLLEGE OF HORTICULTURE.   *1972*
COLLEGE OF VETERINARY AND ANIMAL SCIENCES, Mannuthy.   *1955*
COLLEGE OF FISHERIES, Panangad.

University of Kerala, University Buildings, Trivandrum 695034, Kerala State.   *1937, 1957*
Tel: 695034. Cables: university, trivandrum
F : *arts, sc, ayur, com, ed, eng-techn, law, med, orntl st, fa, soc, homeopathy, dent.*
Also 152 affiliated colleges.

Konkan Krishi Vidyapeeth [Konkan Agricultural U.], Dapoli 415712, Ratnagiri, Maharashtra.   *1972*
Tel: 26. Cables: konkanagri dapoli

F : *agr, vet, fish.*
COLLEGE OF AGRICULTURE.   *1965*
BOMBAY VETERINARY COLLEGE, Parel,
Bombay.   *1885*
AGRICULTURAL SCHOOL, Raigad.
AGRICULTURAL SCHOOL.
COLLEGE OF FISHERIES.
Also 17 research stations.
Kota Open University, Kota 324009.
Kumaun University, Nainital 263001, Uttar
Pradesh.   *1973*
Tel: 2563. Cables: kumaum university, nainital
F : *arts, sc, com, ed, law.*
   D.S.B. COLLEGE.   *1951*
   ALMORA COLLEGE.   *1949*
Also 13 affiliated colleges.
Kurukshetra University, Kurukshetra 132119,
Haryana.   *1956*
Tel: 26. Cables: dharmakshetra, kurukshetra,
haryana
F : *arts-lang, sc, com-mangt, law, ed, soc, ayur,
Indic st, eng-techn, agr-an hus-dairying.*
   COLLEGE OF EDUCATION.   *1960*
   UNIVERSITY COLLEGE.   *1961*
Also 169 recognized colleges.
Kuvempu University, B.R. Project, Shimoga
District, Karnataka 577115.
*Lalit Narayan Mithila University, Darbhanga
846004, Bihar.   *1972*
Tel: 2582. Cables: unimithila, darbhanga
F : *arts, sc, com, med, ed, law.*
   A.P.S.M. COLLEGE, Barauni.   *1959*
   A.N.D. COLLEGE, Sahpur-Patori.   *1960*
   ARARIA COLLEGE.
   B.A. COLLEGE, Baheri.
   B.M. COLLEGE, Rohika.
   B.R.B. COLLEGE, Samastipur.
   B.S.S. COLLEGE, Supaul.   *1959*
   C.E. COLLEGE, Begusarai.
   C.M. ARTS AND COMMERCE COLLEGE.   *1938*
   C.M. SCIENCE COLLEGE.   *1974*
   C.M.B. COLLEGE, Deorh-Ghoghardiha.
   C.M.J. COLLEGE, Donwarihat.
   D.B. COLLEGE, Jainagar.   *1960*
   D.B.K.N. COLLEGE, Narhan.
   DR. L.K. COLLEGE, Taipur.
   D.S. COLLEGE, Katihar.   *1955*
   FORBESGANJ COLLEGE, Forbesganj.   *1960*
   G.D. COLLEGE, Begusarai.   *1977*
   G.L.M. COLLEGE, Banmankhi.   *1959*
   G.M.R.D. COLLEGE, Mohanpur.
   H.P.S. COLLEGE, Madhepur.
   H.S. COLLEGE, Uda-Kishanganj.   *1957*
   J.K. COLLEGE, Biroul.   *1969*
   J.N. COLLEGE, Madhubani.   *1959*
   J.N. COLLEGE, Nehra.
   K.P. COLLEGE, Murliganj.
   K.S. COLLEGE, Laheriasarai.
   K.V.S. COLLEGE, Uchchaith.   *1972*

L.N. JANTA COLLEGE, Jhanjharpur.   *1959*
L.N.M.S. COLLEGE, Birpur.
MAHILA COLLEGE, Purnhea.
MARWARI COLLEGE.   *1958*
MARWARI COLLEGE, Kishanganj.   *1961*
M.H.M. COLLEGE, Sonbarsa-Raj.
MILLAT COLLEGE, Laheriasarai.   *1957*
M.J.M. MAHILA COLLEGE, Katihar.   *1963*
M.K. COLLEGE, Laheriasarai.
M.L. ARYA COLLEGE, Kasba.
M.K.S. COLLEGE, Trimuhanghat.
M.L.S. COLLEGE, Sarisabpahi.   *1959*
M.R. MAHILA COLLEGE.   *1964*
NEHRU COLLEGE, Bahadurganj.
NIRMALI COLLEGE.
PURNEA COLLEGE, Purnea.   *1948*
R.B. COLLEGE, Dalsingsorai.   *1960*
R.B.S. COLLEGE, Andaur.
R.C.S. COLLEGE, Manjhaul.
R.JHA MAHILA COLLEGE, Saharsa.
R.D.S. COLLEGE, Salmari.
R.K. COLLEGE, Madhubani.   *1941*
R.M.M. LAW COLLEGE, Saharsa.
R.N.A.R. COLLEGE, Samastipur.
R.N. COLLEGE, Pandaul.   *1959*
SAHARSA COLLEGE, Saharsa.   *1953*
SAMASTIPUR COLLEGE, Samastipur.   *1949*
S.K. MAHILA COLLEGE, Begusarai.   *1958*
T.P. COLLEGE, Madhepura.   *1954*
U. ROSERA COLLEGE, Rosera.   *1960*
U.P. COLLEGE, Pusa.
V.S.J. COLLEGE, Rajnagar.
WOMEN'S COLLEGE, Samastipur.
Also 15 affiliated colleges.
University of Lucknow, Badshah Bagh, Lucknow
226007, Uttar Pradesh.   *1921*
Tel: 72761
F : *arts, sc, com, ayur, ed, fa, law, med, arc,
dent eng-techn.*
   KING GEORGE'S MEDICAL COLLEGE.   *1911*
   COLLEGE OF ARCHITECTURE.
   STATE COLLEGE OF AYURVEDA.   *1954*
   COLLEGE OF ARTS AND CRAFTS.   *1973*
Also 19 associated colleges and 2 recognized
institutions.
University of Madras, University Centenary
Building, Chepauk, Triplicane P.O., Madras
600005, Tamil Nadu.
                  1857, 1904, 1923, 1929, 1966
Tel: 568778. Telex: 416376 unom in. Cables:
university, madras
F : *arts, sc, com, eng, fa, law, med, Indian lang-
ling, teaching.*
   ORIENTAL RESEARCH INSTITUTE.
   POSTGRADUATE INSTITUTE OF BASIC MEDI-
   CAL SCIENCES.
Also 98 affiliated colleges and 26 recognized
institutions.
*Madurai-Kamaraj University, University

Buildings, Palkalai Nagar, Madurai 625021,
Tamil Nadu. *1966*
Tel: 33171-8. Cables: university, madurai
F : *arts, sc, com, eng, med, ed, bus adm, Indian
med, lang, law.*
Also 94 affiliated and 2 approved colleges.
Magadh University, Bodh-Gaya 824234, Bihar
State. *1962*
Tel: 835. Cables: magvarsity, bodh.gaya bihar
state
F : *hum, sc, com, soc.*
  J.J. College, Gaya. *1960*
  A.M. College, Gaya.
  A.N. College, Parna. *1961*
  A.N.S. College, Nabinagar.
  Arvind Mahila College, Patna.
  J.J. College, Arrah. *1960*
  A.N.S. College, Barh. *1951*
  A.S. College, Bikramganj. *1959*
  B.S. College, Dinapur. *1955*
  College of Commerce, Patna. *1955*
  Daudnagar College, Daudnagar.
  D.K. College, Dumraon, Duri, Bhojpur. *1956*
  J.D. Women's College, Patna.
  J.L.N. College, Dehri-on-Sone.
  J.L.N. College, Khagaul.
  K.L.S. College, Nawada. *1957*
  Kisan College, Sohsarai. *1958*
  M.D. College, Naubatpur. *1957*
  M.V. College, Buxar. *1958*
  Maharaja College, Arrah. *1955*
  Mahila College, Khagaul.
  Nalanda Mahila College, Biharsharif.
  Rajendra Memorial Mahila College, Nawadah.
  R.L.S. Yadav College, Bakhtiarpur.
  Rohtas Mahila College, Sasaram.
  R.P. Mahila College, Patna City.
  R.R.S. College, Mokameh. *1958*
  S.B. College, Arrah.
  Sheodani College, Kaler, Gaya.
  S.M.S.G. College, Sherghati.
  S.N. College, Shamal.
  S.N. Sinha College, Jehanabad.
  S.N. Sinha College, Tekari.
  S.N. Sinha College, Warsaliganj.
  S.P. Jain College, Sasaram. *1952*
  S.P.M. College, Udantpuri.
  S.S. College, Jahanabad. *1955*
  S.S. College, Sasaram.
  S. Sinha College, Aurangabad. *1944*
  S.U. College, Hilsa. *1957*
  S.V.P. College, Bhabua. *1951*
  S.M.D. College, PoonPoon. *1958*
  G.J. College, Rambagh, Bihta. *1959*
  G.B.M. College, Gaya. *1959*
  M.M. College, Bikram.
  M.M. Mahila College, Arrah. *1959*

  T.P.S. College, Patna. *1960*
  Gaya College, Gaya. *1949*
  H.D. Jain College, Arrah. *1962*
  Nalanda College, Biharsharif. *1920*
Also 60 affiliated colleges and 4 recognized
postgraduate institutions.
Maharshi Dayanand University, Rohtak 124001,
Haryana. *1976*
Tel: 2639. Cables: varsity, rohtak
F : *com-bus mangt, ed, phy sc, soc, ayur-Unani,
eng, hum, life sc, med.*
  University College.
Also 60 affiliated colleges.
Mahatma Gandhi University, Padinjareka Build-
ings, Kottayam 686002, Kerala. *1983*
Tel: 5136
F : *arts, ayur, com, ed, eng, fa, moneopathy,
law, med, orntl st, sc, soc.*
Also 55 affiliated colleges.
Mahatma Phule Krishi Vidyapeeth [Agricultural
U.], Rahuri 413722, Distt. Ahmednager,
Maharashtra. *1967*
Tel: MPKV 16. Cables: krishivid, rahuri
F : *agr, agr, eng.*
  College of Agricultural Engineering. *1971*
  College of Agriculture, Dhule. *1960*
  College of Agriculture, Kolhapur. *1963*
  College of Agriculture, Pune. *1908*
  Postgraduate Agricultural Institute. *1972*
Mangalore University, Light House Hill Road,
Mangalore 575003, Karnataka. *1980*
Tel: 21093. Telex: 258 pgc in. Cables: uni-
versity, mangalore
F : *arts, com, law, ed, med, eng, sc-techn.*
Also 53 affiliated colleges.
Manipur University, Canchipur, Imphal 795003,
Manipur.
Tel: 20529. Telex: 0286-205. Cables: man-
varsity, imphal
F : *arts-com, sc, soc.*
Also 23 affiliated colleges.
Marathwada University, Aurangabad 421004,
Maharashtra State. *1958*
Tel: 4431-7. Cables: marathsity, aurangabad
(deccan)
F : *arts, sc, com, ed, eng, law, med, ayur, soc.*
Also 120 affiliated colleges.
Marathwada Krishi Vidyapith [Marathwada
Agricultural U.], Parbhani 431402, Maha-
rashtra. *1972*
Tel: 301. Cables: university, parbhani
F : *agr, vet, agr techn, hom sc.*
  College of Agriculture. *1956*
  College of Agricultural Technology. *1976*
  College of Home Science. *1976*
  College of Veterinary and Animal

SCIENCES.   *1972*
Meerut University, Meerut 250001, Uttar
Pradesh.   *1965*
Tel: 75021-24
F : *arts, sc, agr, com, ed, law, med.*
    L.L.R.M. MEDICAL COLLEGE.   *1966*
Also 59 affiliated colleges.
Mohanlal Sukhadia University, Pratapragar,
Udaipur 313001, Rajasthan.   *1962*
Tel: 29166. Cables: university, udaipur
F : *hum-soc, sc, agr, com, ed, law, vet-anim sc,
agr eng, hom sc, dairy sc.*
    COLLEGE OF COMMERCE AND MANAGEMENT
       STUDIES.   *1984*
    COLLEGE OF DAIRY SCIENCE.   *1982*
    COLLEGE OF HOME SCIENCE.   *1966*
    COLLEGE OF LAW.   *1966*
    COLLEGE OF TECHNOLOGY AND AGRI-
       CULTURAL ENGINEERING.   *1964*
    COLLEGE OF VETERINARY AND ANIMAL
       SCIENCE, Bikaner.   *1954*
    RAJASTHAN COLLEGE OF AGRICULTURE. *1965*
    SCHOOL OF SOCIAL SCIENCES AND HUMANI-
       TIES.   *1922*
    S.K.N. COLLEGE OF AGRICULTURE, Jobner.
                                             1947
Mother Teresa Women's University, Kodaikanal
624102.
Tel: 377. Cables: women's university, kodai-
kanal
*University of Mysore, Karya Soudha, Crawford
Hall, P.B. 406, Mysore 570005, Karnataka
State.   *1916*
Tel: 20677. Telex: 0846226 uomin. Cables:
unireg misore
F : *arts, sc-techn, com, ed, eng, law, med.*
    COLLEGE OF FINE ARTS.   *1965*
    MAHARAJA'S COLLEGE.   *1833*
    UNIVERSITY COLLEGE OF PHYSICAL EDUCA-
       TION.   *1972*
    INSTITUTE OF CORRESPONDENCE COURSES
       AND CONTINUING EDUCATION.   *1970*
    UNIVERSITY EVENING COLLEGE.   *1965*
    YUVARAJA'S COLLEGE.   *1928*
Also 123 affiliated colleges.
Nagarjuna University, Nagarjunanagar 522510,
Andhra Pradesh.   *1976*
Tel: 23225. Cables: university, nagarjunanagar
F : *ayur, com, ed, eng, fa, hum, law, med, nat,
orntl st, phys sc, soc.*
Also 32 affiliated colleges.
*Nagpur University, Rabindranath Tagore
Marg, Nagpur 440001, Maharashtra State.
                                             1923
Tel: 25417. Cables: nagpur university, nagpur
F : *arts, sc, com, ed, eng-techn, law, med, soc,
hom sc, ayur.*
    LAXMINARAYAN INSTITUTE OF TECHNOLOGY.
                                             1942

UNIVERSITY COLLEGE OF LAW.   *1925*
UNIVERSITY COLLEGE OF EDUCATION.   *1945*
Also 96 affiliated colleges.
Nalanda Open University, Nalanda.
**Narendra Deva University of Agriculture and
Technology**, Narendranagar, Faizabad 224229,
Uttar Pradesh.   *1975*
Tel: 2748. Cables: agrivarsity, faizabad
North Bengal University, Rajarammohanpur,
Distt. Darjeeling 734430, West Kumarganj,
Bengal.   *1962*
Tel: 21455
F : *arts, sc, eng-techn, med-phar.*
    DARJEELING   GOVERNMENT   COLLEGE,
       Darjeeling.   *1948*
    JALPAIGURI   GOVERNMENT   ENGINEERING
       COLLEGE, Jalpaiguri.   *1962*
    RAIGANJ UNIVERSITY COLLEGE, Raiganj.
                                             1948
    UNIVERSITY B.T. AND EVENING COLLEGE,
       Cooch Behar.   *1968*
    UNIVERSITY LAW COLLEGE.   *1974*
Also 37 affiliated colleges.
North Eastern Hill University, Lower Lachu-
miere, Shillong 793001, Meghalaya.   *1973*
Tel: 23222. Cables: nehu, shilong
S : *lang, life, physical sc, ed, soc.*
    COLLEGE OF AGRICULTURE, Nagaland.
Also 26 affiliated colleges.
North Gujarat University, Patan 384265.
Orissa University of Agriculture and Technology,
New Capital, Bhubaneswar 751003, District
Puri, Orissa State.   *1962*
Tel: 51424. Cables: agritech, bhubaneswar
F : *agr, agr-eng-techn, vet-an hus.*
    COLLEGE OF AGRICULTURE.   *1954*
    COLLEGE OF AGRICULTURAL ENGINEERING
       AND TECHNOLOGY.   *1966*
    COLLEGE OF BASIC SCIENCE AND HUMANI-
       TIES.   *1964*
    COLLEGE OF VETERINARY SCIENCE AND
       ANIMAL HUSBANDRY.   *1955*
*Osmania University, Hyderabad 500007,
Andhra Pradesh. *1918, 1947, 1950, 1966, 1976*
Tel: 868951. Telex: 425-7090 osmu in. Cables:
university, hyderabad, deccan 500007
F : *arts, sc, com, ed, eng, law, med, techn, soc,
ayur-unani med.*
    EVENING COLLEGE OF ARTS AND COMMERCE.
                                             1949
    EVENING COLLEGE OF LAW.   *1951*
    POSTGRADUATE COLLEGE OF LAW (Morning
       Session).   *1972*
    EVENING COLLEGE, Secunderabad.   *1949*
    NIZAM COLLEGE OF SCIENCE.   *1887*
    POSTGRADUATE COLLEGE, Saifabad.   *1951*
    COLLEGE OF ARTS AND SCIENCE, Secun-
       derabad.   *1947*
    UNIVERSITY COLLEGE OF ARTS.   *1918*

University College of Commerce and Business Management. *1975*
University College of Education. *1928*
Postgraduate School, Bhiknoor, Nizamabad. *1976*
Postgraduate School, Godavarikhani. *1976*
Postgraduate School, Kothagudem. *1976*
University College of Engineering. *1928*
University College of Law. *1960*
University College of Science. *1918*
University College of Technology. *1969*
University College for Women. *1924*
Also 123 affiliated colleges and 22 recognized institutions.
*Panjab University, Chandigarh, Chandigarh 160014, Union Territory. *1947*
Tel: 23324. Cables: university, chandigarh
F : *arts, sc, com-bus mangt, ed, eng-techn, lang, law, med sc, des-fa, dairying-an hus-agr, phar.*
Panjab University Evening College. *1961*
Institute of Sanskrit and Indological Studies, Hoshiarpur.
Also 93 affiliated colleges and 1 postgraduate regional centre.
Patna University, Patna 800005, Bihar State. *1917, 1952, 1960, 1962*
Tel: 50444. Cables: patversity, patna, bihar
F : *hum, sc, com, ed, eng, law, med, soc.*
Bihar College of Engineering. *1924*
Bihar National College. *1880*
College of Arts and Crafts. *1979*
Institute of Music.
Magadh Mahila College. *1946*
Patna College. *1863*
Law College. *1907*
Patna Training College. *1908*
Patna Women's College. *1940*
Science College. *1927*
Vanijya Mahavidyalaya. *1974*
Patna Women's Training College. *1951*
Also 4 recognized institutions.
*Pondicherry University, Pondicherry 605001. *1949*
Tel: 6562
Arignar Anna Govt. Arts College, Karaikal. *1967*
Avvaiyar Govt. College for Women, Karaikal.
Mahatma Gandhi Govt. Arts College, Mahe.
Bharathidasan Govt. Arts College. *1968*
Dr. Ambedkar Govt. Law College. *1972*
Jawaharlal Institute of Postgrad. Medical Education and Research. *1956*
Pondicherry Engineering College. *1985*

Pope John Paul II College of Education. *1986*
Tagore Arts College. *1961*
Vector Control Research Centre. *1975*
Dr. S.R.K. Govt. Arts College, Yanam.
*University of Poona, Ganeshkhind, Pune, 411007, Maharashtra. *1949*
F : *arts, sc, ayur, com, ed, eng, law, med, mental-moral & soc sc.*
Also 163 affiliated colleges and 34 recognized institutions.
*Punjab Agricultural University, Ludhiana 141004, Punjab. *1962*
Tel: 22960. Cables: agrivarsity, ludhiana
College of Agriculture. *1947*
College of Agricultural Engineering. *1965*
College of Basic Sciences and Humanities. *1965*
College of Home Science.
College of Home Science, Kaoni. *1966*
College of Veterinary Science. *1969*
Punjabi University, Patiala 147002, Punjab. *1962*
Tel: 74312. Cables: university, patiala
F : *arts-soc, bus adm-com, ed, lang, med, ayur-unani, eng-techn, voc st, law, hum-relig st, physical sc.*
Also 52 affiliated colleges.
Punjabrao Krishi Vidyapeeth [Punjabrao Agricultural U.], Krishinagar, Akola 444104, Maharashtra. *1969*
Tel: 5372. Telex: 0725-215 pkv in. Cables: university, akola
F : *agr, agr eng, vet.*
College of Agriculture. *1955*
College of Agriculture, Nagpur. *1906*
College of Agricultural Engineering. *1970*
Nagpur Veterinary College. *1958*
Postgraduate Institute. *1970*
Also 2 affiliated colleges.
Purvanchal University, Jaunpur.
Rabindra Bharati University, 6/4, Dwarkanath Tagore Lane, Calcutta 700007, West Bengal. *1962*
Tel: 39-6601
F : *arts, vis arts, fa.*
Also 58 affiliated colleges.
*University of Rajasthan, Gandhinagar, Jaipur 302004, Rajasthan. *1947*
Tel: PABX 60271. Cables: university, jaipur.
F : *arts, sc, com, ed, eng-techn, law, med-phar, ayur, soc, Sanskrit, fa-mus-dram, mangt st.*
College of Commerce. *1956*
Maharaja's College (Science). *1944*
Maharani's College. *1944*
Rajasthan College (Arts and Social Sciences). *1962*

INSTITUTE OF CORRESPONDENCE STUDIES.
R.A. PODAR INSTITUTE OF MANAGEMENT.
Also 195 affiliated colleges.

Rajendra Agricultural University, P.O. Pusa, District Samastipur 848125, Bihar.   *1970*
Tel: 39
F : *agr, an hus-vet.*
BIHAR AGRICULTURAL COLLEGE, Sabour, Bhagalpur.   *1945*
BIHAR VETERINARY COLLEGE, Patna.
                                                        1930
RANCHI AGRICULTURAL COLLEGE   *1955*
RANCHI COLLEGE OF VETERINARY SCIENCE AND ANIMAL HUSBANDRY, Kanke, Ranchi.
                                                        1961
TIRHUT COLLEGE OF AGRICULTURE, Dholi, Muzaffarpur.   *1960*

Ranchi University, Ranchi 834008, Bihar State.
                                                        1960
Tel: 23600
F : *hum, sc, com, ed, eng, law, med, soc.*
BAHARAGORA COLLEGE, Baharagora.
BIRSA COLLEGE, Khunti.   *1961*
BOKARO STATE CITY COLLEGE, Dhanbad.
B.S. COLLEGE, Lohardaga.   *1962*
B.S.K. COLLEGE, Maithon, Dhanbad.
B.V. PARIKH JANTA COLLEGE, Jamshedpur.
CHATRA COLLEGE, Hazaribagh.   *1962*
DORANDA COLLEGE, Ranchi.   *1962*
GHATSILA COLLEGE, Ghatsila.
G.L.A. COLLEGE, Daltonganj.   *1954*
GIRIDIH COLLEGE.   *1957*
GUMLA COLLEGE, Gumla.   *1966*
GYAN CHAND JAIN COMMERCE COLLEGE, Chaibasa.
JAGANNATH NAGAR COLLEGE, Dhurwa. *1954*
JAMSHEDPUR CO-OPERATIVE COLLEGE.
JANTA SHIVRATRI COLLEGE, Daltonganj.
JAWAHARLAL NEHRU COLLEGE, Chakradharpur.
J.J. COLLEGE, Jhumritalaya, Hazaribagh.
                                                        1960
JODH SINGH NAMDHARI MAHILA COLLEGE, Daltonganj.
KASHI SAHU COLLEGE, Saraikela.
KATRAS COLLEGE, Katrasgarh.
K.B. COLLEGE, Bermo, Giridih.
K.B. WOMEN'S COLLEGE, Hazaribagh.   *1963*
LAL BAHADUR SHASTRI MEMORIAL COLLEGE, Jamshedpur.
MARWARI COLLEGE.
P.K. ROY MEMORIAL COLLEGE, Dhanbad.
                                                        1940
R.S. MORE COLLEGE, Govindpur, Dhanbad.
                                                        1959
R.S.P. COLLEGE, Jharia.   *1952*
S.S.L.N.T. MAHILA COLLEGE, Dhanbad.
                                                        1955
RAMGARH COLLEGE, Ramgarh.

RANCHI COLLEGE.   *1946*
RANCHI WOMEN'S COLLEGE.   *1950*
R.L. SINGH YAOAV COLLEGE.
SINDEGA COLLEGE, Sindega.   *1950*
SINDRI COLLEGE, Sindri.
SINGHBHUM COLLEGE, Chandil.
S.S.L.N.T. MAHILA COLLEGE, Dhanbad.
ST. COLUMBA'S COLLEGE, Hazaribagh. *1938*
SURAJ SINGH MEMORIAL COLLEGE.
TATA COLLEGE, Chaibasa.   *1953*
WOMEN'S COLLEGE, Jamshedpur.   *1960*
WORKER'S COLLEGE, Jamshedpur.   *1959*
Also 37 affiliated colleges and 1 regional institute.

Rani Durgavati Vishwavidyalaya, Jabalpur, Saraswati Vihar, Jabalpur 482001, Madhya Pradesh.   *1957*
Tel: 23567. Cables: unidurga, jabalpur
F : *arts, sc, com, ed, eng, hom sc, law, med, soc, life sc, ayur.*
GOVERNMENT COLLEGE OF EDUCATIONAL PSYCHOLOGY AND GUIDANCE.   *1962*
GOVERNMENT ENGINEERING COLLEGE. *1947*
GOVERNMENT MEDICAL COLLEGE.   *1955*
G.S. COLLEGE OF COMMERCE AND ECONOMICS.
HITKARINI MAHAVIDYALAYA.   *1933*
Also 30 affiliated colleges.

Rashtriya Sanskrit Vidyapeeth, Tirupati.

Ravishankar University, Raipur 492002, Madhya Pradesh.   *1964*
Tel: 23970. Cables: university, jaipur
F : *arts, sc, com, ed, eng, law, med, ayur, soc, life sc, hom sc.*
And 44 affiliated colleges.

Rohilkhand University, 204-B, Civil Lines, Bareilly 243001, Uttar Pradesh.   *1975*
Tel: 75815. Cables: ruversity
F : *arts, sc, agr, com, law.*

University of Roorkee, Roorkee 247667, Uttar Pradesh.   *1948*
Tel: 2405. Telex: 0597201 uor in
eng, sc, arc.

Sambalpur University, Jyoti Vihar, P.O. Burla, Sambalpur 768019, Orissa.   *1967*
Tel: 137. Cables: university, burla
F : *arts, sc, com, ed, eng, law, med.*
UNIVERSITY COLLEGE OF ENGINEERING. *1965*
LAJPATRAI LAW COLLEGE.   *1965*
Also 48 affiliated colleges.

Sampurnanand Sanskrit Vishwavidyalaya, Varanasi 221002, Uttar Pradesh.   *1958, 1974*
Tel: 64089. Cables: shrutam, varanasi
F : *Sanskrit.*
Also *c.* 2000 affiliated colleges.

Sardar Patel University, Vallabh Vidyanagar 388120, Gujarat.   *1955, 1966*
Tel: 7008. Cables: university, vallabh vidyanagar, gujarat

F : *arts sc, com, eng-techn, hom sc, ed, law.*
  M.B. PATEL COLLEGE OF EDUCATION. *1960*
Also 16 affiliated colleges.
Saurashtra University, University Campus, Kalavad Road, Rajkot 360005, Gujarat State. *1967*
Tel: 40450. Cables: university, raijkot
F : *arts, sc, com, ed, law, med-phar, rur sc, techn-eng, hom sc.*
Also 60 affiliated colleges, 2 recognized institutions and 1 approved institution.
Sher-e-Kashmir University of Agricultural Sciences and Technology, P.B. 262, Srinagar 190001, Jammu and Kashmir.
Tel: 73459. Cables: agrisity, srinagar
Shivaji University, Vidyanagar, Kolhapur 416004, Maharashtra State. *1962*
Tel: 20571. Cables: unishivaji, kolhapur
F : *arts sc, com, ed, eng, law, med, soc, ayur.*
Also 114 affiliated colleges and 1 recognized institution.
Shreemati Nathibai Damodar Thackers Women's University, 1 Nathibai Thackers Road, Bombay 400020, Maharashtra State. *1916*
Tel: 291879. Cables: uniwomen, bombay
F : *arts, ed, hom sc, nurs, fa, lib, soc.*
  C.U. SHAH COLLEGE OF PHARMACY.
  LEELABAI THACKERSEY COLLEGE OF NURSING FOR WOMEN. *1964*
  P.V. POLYTECHNIC, SIR VITHALDAS VIDYAVIHAR. *1976*
  P.V.D.T. COLLEGE OF EDUCATION FOR WOMEN. *1959*
  SHRI HANSRAJ PRAGJI THACKERSEY COLLEGE OF SCIENCE.
  SHRI HANSRAJ PRAGJI THACKERSEY SCHOOL OF LIBRARY SCIENCE.
  SIR VITHALDAS THACKERSEY COLLEGE OF HOME SCIENCE. *1962*
  S.N.D.T. COLLEGE OF ARTS AND SMT. C.B. COLLEGE OF COMMERCE FOR WOMEN. *1931*
  S.N.D.T. COLLEGE OF ARTS AND COMMERCE FOR WOMEN, Poona. *1916*
  S.N.D.T. COLLEGE OF EDUCATION FOR WOMEN, Poona. *1964*
  S.N.D.T. COLLEGE OF HOME SCIENCE, Poona. *1968*
Also 14 affiliated colleges.
Shri Jagannath Sanskrit Vishvavidyalaya, Puri 752001.
Tel: 2669
Shri Lal Bahadur Shastri Kendriya Sanskrit Vidyapith, Katwaria Sarai, New Delhi 110017.
South Gujarat University, Post Box 49, Udhna-Magdalla Road, Surat 395007, Gujarat State. *1967*
Tel: 87141-9. Cables: soguni surat
F : *arts, sc, com, ed, eng, law, med, rur st.*
Also 38 affiliated colleges and 3 approved

institutions.
Sri Krishnadevaraya University, Sri Venkateswarapuram (P.O.), Anantapur 515003, Andhra Pradesh. *1981*
Tel: 2923. Cables: s.k. university
F : *arts, sc, com, law.*
Sri Padmavati Mahila Visvadyalayam, Tirupati, Dist. Chittoor 517502, Andra Pradesh. *1983*
Tel: 2564. Cables: mahilalaya, tirupati
comp, nutr-diet, pre-school ed, seri culture (all postgrad.).
Sri Venkateswara University, Tirupati, Dist. Chittoor 517502, Andra Pradesh. *1954*
Tel: 2781. Cables: university, tirupati
F : *arts, sc, com, eng, fa, med, orntl st, hum-ext, teaching, biol-earth sc, math-physical sc, soc-behavioural sc, law, bus mangt.*
  UNIVERSITY COLLEGE OF ARTS AND SCIENCES.
  UNIVERSITY COLLEGE OF ENGINEERING. *1959*
Also 95 affiliated colleges and 7 oriental colleges.
Tamil University, Palace Buildings, Thanjavur 613001, Tamil Nadu. *1981*
Tel: 22221. Cables: valartamil, thanjavur
F : *arts, developing Tamil, lang, manuscriptology, sc.*
Tamilnadu Agricultural University, Lawlay Road P.O., Coimbatore 641003, Tamil Nadu State. *1971*
Tel: 41222. Telex: 855-360 tnau in. Cables: coimbatore, tamil nadu
F : *agr, agr eng, vet-anim sc, fish, hort.*
  AGRICULTURAL COLLEGE, Killikulam. *1984*
  AGRICULTURAL COLLEGE AND RESEARCH INSTITUTE. *1906*
  AGRICULTURAL COLLEGE AND RESEARCH INSTITUTE, Madurai. *1965*
  COLLEGE FOR AGRICULTURAL ENGINEERING. *1972*
  VETERINARY COLLEGE, Madras. *1935*
  VETERINARY COLLEGE, Namakkal. *1985*
  FISHERIES COLLEGE, Tuticorin. *1977*
Telugu University, Kala Bhawan 500004, Hyderabad.
Tel: 236045
Tilak Maharashtra Vidyapith, Pune 411037.
Tripura University, Agartala 799004.
University of Agricultural Sciences, Post Bag 2477, Hebbal, Bangalore 560065, Karnataka State. *1964*
Tel: 366753. Telex: 84583-93 uask in
F : *agr, vet-anim sc, basic sc-hum.*
  COLLEGE OF AGRICULTURE, Dharwad. *1947*
  COLLEGE OF AGRICULTURE. *1946*
  COLLEGE OF AGRICULTURE, Raichur. *1969*
  COLLEGE OF BASIC SCIENCES AND HUMANITIES. *1966*
  COLLEGE OF RURAL HOME SCIENCE,

Dharwad. *1974*
COLLEGE OF POSTGRADUATE STUDIES, Dharwad. *1966*
VETERINARY COLLEGE.
VETERINARY COLLEGE, Bidar. *1958*
FISHERIES COLLEGE, Mangalore. *1969*
University of Health Sciences, Guanadala, Vijaywada 520005. *1986*
Tel: 84276. Telex: 475269 uhs in
Utkal University, Vani Vihar, Bhubaneswar, Dist. Puri 751004, Orissa. *1948*
Tel: 52520. Cables: utkalvihar, bhubaneswar
F : *arts, sc, com, ed, law, med, eng.*
UNIVERSITY LAW COLLEGE. *1975*
MADHUSUDAN LAW COLLEGE, Cuttack.
1949
Also 88 affiliated colleges.
Vidyasagar University, P.O. and Dist. Midnapore 721101, West Bengal. *1981*
Tel: 329. Cables: university, midnapore
D : *anth, app math-comp, com-mangt, eco-rur dev, lib-infor, pol-rural adm* (all postgraduate).
Also 31 affiliated colleges.
Vikram University, University Road, Ujjain, 456010, Madhya Pradesh. *1957*
Tel: 3219. Cables: university, ujjain
F : *arts, sc, com, ed, eng, ayur, law, life sc, soc.*
B.S.N. GOVERNMENT COLLEGE, Shajapur.
1958
S.N. COLLEGE, Agar. *1966*
GOVERNMENT COLLEGE, Alirajpur. *1972*
GOVERNMENT COLLEGE, Barnagar. *1967*
GOVERNMENT COLLEGE, Barwaha. *1964*
GOVERNMENT COLLEGE, Barwani. *1958*
GOVERNMENT COLLEGE, Dhar. *1957*
GOVERNMENT BHAGATSINGH COLLEGE, Jaora. *1961*
GOVERNMENT COLLEGE, Jhabua. *1958*
GOVERNMENT COLLEGE, Khargone. *1958*
GOVERNMENT COLLEGE, Mandsaur. *1957*

GOVERNMENT COLLEGE, Mehidpur. *1969*
GOVERNMENT COLLEGE, Narsinghgarh. *1962*
GOVERNMENT COLLEGE, Neemuch. *1958*
GOVERNMENT COLLEGE, Rajgarh. *1958*
GOVERNMENT COLLEGE, Rampura. *1958*
GOVERNMENT COLLEGE, Ratlam. *1956*
GOVERNMENT COMMERCE COLLEGE, Ratlam. *1982*
GOVERNMENT GIRL'S COLLEGE, Ratlam.
1971
GOVERNMENT GIRL'S COLLEGE, Ujjain. *1959*
GOVERNMENT COLLEGE, Shujalpur. *1964*
GOVERNMENT COLLEGE OF EDUCATION. *1957*
KRISHNAJIRAO PAWAR MAHAVIDYALAYA, Dewas. *1958*
GOVERNMENT NEHRU MEMORIAL DEGREE COLLEGE, Sendhwa. *1964*
GOVERNMENT VIKRAM MAHAVIDYALAYA, Khachrand. *1967*
MADHAV COLLEGE. *1896*
MADHAV SCIENCE COLLEGE. *1969*
SANDIPANI COLLEGE. *1966*
Also 37 affiliated colleges.
Visva-Bharati, P.O. Santiniketan Dist. Birbhum 731235, West Bengal. *1921, 1951*
Tel: 451-456. Cables: visvabharati, santiniketan
CHEENA-BHAVANA (Sino-Indian Studies)
HINDI-BHAYANA (Hindi studies).
KALA-BHAVANA (Fine Arts and Crafts). *1919*
PALLI-SAMGATHANA VIBHAGA (Rural Construction). *1922*
PALLI-SIKSHA SADANA (Agriculture). *1963*
RABINDRA BHAVAN (Rabindra Literature).
1962
SANGIT BHAVANA (Music and Dancing). *1934*
SIKSHA BHAVANA (Science). *1921*
VIDYA-BHAVANA (Humanities, Postgraduate). *1918*
VINAYA-BHAVANA (Teachers' Training).*1948*

OTHER UNIVERSITY INSTITUTIONS— AUTRES ETABLISSEMENTS UNIVERSITAIRES

Technical Education—Enseignement technique

Birla Institute of Technology, Mesra 835215, Ranchi.
Tel: 21065. Cables: technology, mesra
Birla Institute of Technology and Science, P.O. Pilani 333031, Rajasthan. *1964*
Tel: 92. Cables: bits, pilani
F : *hum-soc, eng-techn, sc.*
Indian Institute of Technology, Powai, Bombay 400076, Maharashtra State. *1958*
Tel: 581421. Telex: 011-71385 iitb in. Cables: technology, bombay
Indian Institute of Technology, Kanpur 208016, Uttar Pradesh. *1960*
Tel: 40066. Telex: 325296 iit in. Cables: technology, kanpur
Indian Institute of Technology, P.O. Kharagpur Technology, Kharagpur 721302 West Bengal.
1951
Tel: 221224. Telex: 212760 itkg in. Cables: technology, kharagpur

*Indian Institute of Technology, I.I.T. P.O., Madras 600036, Tamil Nadu.   *1959*
Tel: 41-53-42. Telex: 41-7362 iitm in. Cables: technology, madras
Indian Institute of Technology, Hauz Khas, New Delhi 110029.   *1961*

Tel: 666979. Telex: 313687 iit in. Cables: technology, new delhi
Thapar Institute of Engineering and Technology, Patiala 147001.
Tel: 73270. Cables: thaparinst

Professional Education—Enseignement professionnel

*All India Institute of Medical Sciences, Ansari Nagar, New Delhi 110029.   *1956*
Tel: 661123. Cables: medinst new delhi
Banasthali Vidyapith, P.O. Banasthali Vidyaith, Rajasthan 304022.   *1935, 1983*
Tel: 24 59. Cables: banasthali vidyapith rajasthan
F : *ed, fa, hom sc, hum, sc, soc.*
Central Institute of English and Foreign Languages, Hyderabad 500007, Andhra Pradesh.   *1958*
Tel: 71131. Cables: english hyderabad
Dakshina Bharat Hindi Prachar Sabha, P.B. 68, Hyderabad 500004, Andhra Pradesh.
            1918, 1964
Tel: 441824. Cables: dakshin, madras
Hindi.
Dayalbagh Educational Institute, P.O. Dayalbagh Agra 282005, Uttar Pradesh.   *1981*
Tel: 73398. Cables: dayalinst, agra
F : *arts, com, ed, eng, sc.*
*Gandhigram Rural Institute, Gandhigram 624302, Madurai, Tamil Nadu.   *1976*
Tel: 323. Cables: gramvarity
F : *agr-an hus, English-for lang, rur heal-sani, rur oriented sc, rur soc, Tamil-Indian lang-rur arts.*
Gujarat Vidyapeeth, Ashram Road, Ahmedabad 380014, Gujarat State.   *1920*
Tel: 447292. Telex: 121-254 guvi in. Cables: gujarat vidyapith, ahmedabad
F : *ed, lang, soc, tribal welfare.*
*Gurukula Kangri Vishwavidyalaya, Hardwar 249404, Uttar Pradesh.   *1900*
Tel: 235. Cables: gurukula
F : *arts, sc, Veda.*
Indian Institute of Science, Bangalore 560012, Karnataka.   *1909*
Tel: 344411. Telex: 0845-8349 iisc in. Cables: science, bangalore, malleswaram
F : *sc, eng.*
Indian Statistical Institute, 203 Barrackpore

Trunk Road, Calcutta 700035.   *1932*
Tel: 52-6694. Telex: 21-2210 stat in. Cables: statistica, calcutta-35
Postgraduate Institute of Medical Education and Research, Chandigarh 160012.   *1962*
Sree Chitra Tirunal Institute for Medical Sciences and Technology, Trivandrum 695011, Kerala.
            1973, 1981
Jamia Millia Islamia, Jamia Nagar, New Delhi 110025.   *1920*
Tel: 630490. Cables: jamia, new delhi
F : *ed, eng-techn, hum-lang, nat, soc.*
Indian Agricultural Research Institute, New Delhi 110012.   *1905*
Tel: 582081. Cables: krishipusa, new delhi
F : *agr.*
*Indian Veterinary Research Institute, Izatnagar 243122, Uttar Pradesh.   *1889*
Tel: 74069. Telex: 577-205 ivry in. Cables: vetek, izatnagar
Indian School of Mines, Dhanbad 826004, Bihar State.   *1926*
Tel: 2866. Telex: 629-214 ism in. Cables: sholomin, dhanbad 826004
F : *mine eng, mine machinery, petro-eng, app geol, app geo-phy.*
School of Planning and Architecture, 4, Block-B, Indraprastha Estate, New Delhi 110002.
            1955
Tel: 3317892. Cables: schoolplan, new delhi
Tata Institute of Social Sciences, P.O. 8313, Deonar, Bombay 400088.   *1936*
Tel: 5510400. Cables: fernstalk, chembur, bombay 400071
soc, soc w.
Sri Sathya Sai Institute of Higher Learning, Prasanthinalayam, Anantapur Dist. 515134, Andhra Pradesh.   *1981*
Tel: 39. Cables: sainstitut
F : *arts, sc, soc-com.*
Sanjay Gandhi Postgraduate Institute of Medical Sciences, Rae-Bareli Road, Lucknow 226001.

Association of Indian Universities

The Association was established on the recommendation of the Conference of Vice-Chancellors of Universities, convened by the

Viceroy of India at Shimla in May 1924. A need was felt to have an organization which could serve as a common meeting ground for the universities as well as a repository of information

relating to the university system. A year later, in March 1925, representatives of the universities meeting at Bombay resolved to form "the Inter-University Board" (IUB), renamed in 1973: "Association of Indian Universities".

The Association has started a new activity of organizing group discussion/orientation programmes for the benefit of University Administrators. So far, programmes for Registrars, Senior Academics, Deputy/Assistant Registrars, Finance Officers and Public Relations Officers have been set up. These provide a forum for discussion and exchange of views for University Administrators of all categories. It is proposed to organize similar programmes for the Controller of Examinations, Deans of Students Welfare and Zonal, together with local workshops on specific issues. It is also proposed to hold public lectures on important issues given by distinguished educationists.

AIU is an accredited body at national level for the *equivalence* of degrees and diplomas obtained from India and abroad. The flow of foreign students has increased considerably and so has the Association's responsibilities in this regard. Over the years, AIU has collected specialized documentation and expertise on systems of education prevailing in different countries. The information is shared extensively with universities and other agencies involved with the admission of foreign students. It is represented on the Inter-Ministry Scholarship Committee of the Ministry of Human Resource Development which decides the award of scholarships to foreign students under Cultural Exchange Programmes and various other schemes. AIU is also one of the Implementing Agencies of the Cultural Exchange Programmes with other countries, so far as it relates to the recognition of degrees and diplomas. AIU is a member of the Standing Committee on Foreign Students constituted in the Ministry of External Affairs. The decision-making on the equivalence of foreign qualifications at the highest level is vested in the Equivalence/Standing Committees of Vice-Chancellors.

The *Evaluation and Information Unit* attends to thousands of visitors seeking information on parity of foreign qualifications or university courses and eligibility. This service is widely used by students, teachers, educational administrators and universities in India and abroad. The AIU publication 'Equivalence of Foreign Degrees' showing the recognition awarded by AIU and Indian Universities to various foreign examinations has recently been released.

The AIU 'Student Information Unit' of the Department of Education of the Central Ministry of Human Resource Development is responsible for providing extensive information on the university system and other educational institutions, including polytechnics, Industrial Training Institutes, Management and Computer Institutes, Professional Bodies and accredited courses conducted by Central and State agencies. Students and others in India and abroad may seek information on their eligibility at an Indian University or on the standing of an institution.

The Association's *Research Cell* has two units, Examinations and Economics of Education. The Association publishes a Question Bank Book Series. Question Banks on 10 different subjects in the first phase and 11 in the second phase have appeared. Each book contains between three and five thousand questions in a particular subject covering the undergraduate/postgraduate syllabus. The object is to paraphrase university syllabuses into questions, taking into account all the different techniques of testing and evaluation. The subjects so far covered are: Mathematics, Physics, Chemistry, Zoology, Botany, Automobile Engineering, Pharmacology, Political Science, English Language and Literature, Mathematics (P.G. Level), History, Geography, Psychology, Economics, Commerce, Physiology, Law of Contracts, Sociology, Food and Nutrition, Anatomy and Constitutional Law, Electrical Power System, and Zoology (Hindi version). Other subjects will be covered in the second phase.

In addition, there are monographs on a variety of topics including the Management of Examinations, Internal Assessment, Grading, Non-scholastic Aspects of Learners' Behaviour and Test and Item Analysis. The recent additions to the list are 'Scaling Techniques: What? Why? How?' Computer in Examinations and Monograph on Sample Free Item Analysis. The Research Cell has brought out reports of Task Forces on various subjects such as New Technologies in Higher Education; Working of Autonomous Colleges; Distance Education, etc.

Through a series of Workshops, University Registrars/Administrators and Controllers of Examinations have been exposed to the use of computers in processing the examination results and receiving the necessary feedback by analysing the performance of students. The Research Cell also runs regular correspondence courses at three levels, Basic, Intermediate, and Special Professional for university and college teachers in Evaluation Methodology and Examinations. Several Workshops have been conducted in the area of examination reforms in various universities/institutions. The Research Cell (Exams) is at present involved in conducting a series of seminars/workshops on 'Implementation and Monitoring of New Education Policy'.

These seminars are being sponsored and funded by the Department of Education, Ministry of Human Resource Development.

The Economics of Education Division carries out in-depth empirical and investigative research on economic aspects of education. It has three broad programmes: I-Research; II-Development of Research Resources; and III-Conduct of Seminars/Conferences. The select documents under the Research programme include: Three Aspects of University Education; University and College Finance—Seminar Papers; Economics of College Education—A Study of Hindu College; State Funding of Universities; Elite in the Making – A Socio-Economic Study of Delhi University Students; New Education Policy – AIU's Recommendations on Higher Education; Education and Economic Development – Perspectives for Policy Planning; Education and Culture – Perspectives on India; and Studies in Distance Education. The following studies are in progress; Financing of Non-Plan Expenditure on University Sector; Economics of Distance Education; Graduate Unemployment in India; and Survey of Scientific and Technical Manpower in the University Sector.

Under the programme of Development of Research Resources, relevant data on University education are compiled. To this end, the Division has the following publications to its credit: University Finance (Vols. I & II); and Educational Statistics at a Glance.

In order to exchange views on educational policy planning and development, Seminars/Conferences are organized every year. Conferences have been organized on such themes as educational technologies, distance education and National Policy on Education (1986). National seminars on University Finances and Graduate Unemployment are also proposed.

The Library has built over the years a specialized collection of books and documents. It maintains files of Annual Reports, Calendars, Syllabi and other publications put out by member universities. A select list of articles extracted from about 100 periodicals received is issued every month as 'Current Documentation in Education'. The Library also compiles a two-volume annual Bibliography of Doctoral Dissertations accepted by Indian Universities. One is devoted to Natural and Applied Sciences, the other covers Social Sciences and the Humanities. A record is also maintained of on-going Doctoral Research at different universities. Files of press clippings concerning higher education are also kept.

The Association plays a co-ordinating and supervisory role in Sports. Every year it organizes 43 Inter-University Tournaments (24 for men

and 19 for women) and manages 80 University Level Coaching Camps in selected sports disciplines. It sponsors Indian universities teams in national and international events and provides financial assistance to member universities towards the cost of managing Inter-University Tournaments and organizing University Level Coaching Camps. Liaison is maintained with the Government and with the National Sport Federations.

The Cultural Division was set up during International Youth Year in 1985 to organize a series of Inter-University Youth Festivals. This also coincided with AIU's Diamond Jubilee Celebrations. These festivals have turned into a regular feature and comprise cultural activities such as Music, Dance, Theatre, Literary Activities and Fine Arts at Zonal and National Level. Over 100 university youth from more than 15 universities participated in the Festival of India in the USSR during September–November 1987, and were selected from the Inter-University Youth Festivals held during 1986–87.

Publications: The regular publications of the Association include the Universities Handbook, Handbook of Medical Education, Handbook of Engineering Education, Handbook of Management Education, Handbook of Agricultural Education, Handbook of Distance Education and Bibliography of Doctoral Dissertations in Natural and Applied Sciences and Social Sciences and Humanities. The Association also publishes the Proceedings of its meetings and of Conferences of universities held under its auspices. University News, started in February 1963, became a weekly in January 1984.

L'Association tire son origine d'une Conférence des Vice-Chanceliers des Universités réunie par le Vice-Roi de l'Inde à Simla en mai 1924. On ressentait alors le besoin de disposer d'une organisation pouvant à la fois servir de lieu de rencontre entre les universités et de centre d'informations relatives au système universitaire. Un an plus tard, en mars 1925, les délégués des universités réunis à Bombay décidèrent de constituer le Conseil interuniversitaire (IUB), qui reçut en 1973 la nouvelle appellation d'Association des universités indiennes.

L'Association a entrepris d'organiser à l'intention des administrateurs d'université des discussions en groupe et des programmes d'orientation. Seuls existent jusqu'à présent les programmes destinés aux 'registrars', aux enseignants figurant en tête de la hiérarchie, aux 'registrars' adjoints, aux directeurs financiers et aux responsables des services de relations publiques. Ils constituent une tribune permettant à toutes les catégories d'administrateurs d'université de discuter et de

procéder à des échanges de vues. Il est prévu d'instituer des programmes similaires pour les directeurs des services d'examens, les doyens des oeuvres universitaires, ainsi que des ateliers régionaux et locaux sur des sujets précis. Un autre projet consiste à organiser sur de problèmes importants des conférences publiques avec la participation d'éminents spécialistes dans le domaine de l'éducation.

L'Association (AIU) est une institution acréditée au niveau national avec pour mission d'établir l'équivalence des diplômes obtenus en Inde et à l'étranger. Le nombre d'étudiants étrangers a considérablement augmenté et avec lui les responsabilités de l'Association dans ce domaine. Au fil des années, l'AIU a rassemblé une documentation spécialisée et des compétences sur les systèmes éducatifs dans les différents pays. Elle les partage avec les universités et les autres organisations chargées de l'admission des étudiants étrangers. Elle est représentée au Comité Interministériel des Bourses du Ministère du Développement des Ressources Humaines qui décide de l'attribution des bourses aux étudiants étrangers dans le cadre des Programmes d'Echanges Culturels et d'autres projets. L'AIU est aussi une des organisations qui s'occupents de la mise en place des programmes d'échanges avec d'autres pays mais seulement dans le cadre de la reconnaissance des diplômes. L'AIU est membre du Comité permanent des Etudiants Etrangers, constitué au sein du Ministère des Affaires Extérieures. Ce sont les Comités permanents des Equivalences et des Vice-Chanceliers qui prennent les décisions sur l'équivalence des diplômes étrangers du plus haut niveau.

L'Unité d'Evaluation et d'Information accueille des milliers de visiteurs qui cherchent des informations sur les titres étrangers, ou sur les cours à l'université et sur l'admissibilité. Ce service est largement utilisé par les étudiants, les professeurs, les administrateurs dans le domaine de l'éducation et les universités tant en Inde qu'à l'étranger. La publication de l'AIU 'Equivalence de diplomes étrangers', qui établit la reconnaissance accordée par l'AIU et les Universités indiennes aux divers examens étrangers est parue depuis peu.

'L'Unité d'information des Etudiants' de l'AIU, créée au sein du Département de l'Education du Ministère du Développement des Ressources Humaines, a pour mission de fournir des informations détaillées sur le système universitaire et les autres institutions éducatives, y compris les "polytechniques", les institutions de formation aux métiers de l'industrie, les instituts de gestion et d'informatique, les organismes professionnels et les cours organisés par les institutions du pouvoir central et des états et qui ont été accréditées.

Les étudiants et les autres personnes intéressées tant en Inde qu'à l'étranger peuvent y obtenir des informations soit sur leur admissibilité à une université indienne, soit sur le niveau d'une institution.

La Cellule de Recherche de l'Association a deux unités: les examens et l'économie de l'éducation. Les examens: l'Association publie une série de répertoires de questions d'examen. Un premier répertoire sur dix disciplines différentes, puis un deuxième portant sur 11 disciplines ont déjà paru. Chacun contient entre trois et cinq mille questions par discipline et couvre l'ensemble des programmes de prégraduation et de postgraduation. Le but est de présenter des programmes universitaires sous forme de questions, en tirant parti de toutes les différentes techniques de tests et d'évaluation. Sont déjà parues à ce jour les annales de mathématiques, physique, chimie, zoologie, botanique, génie de l'automobile, pharmacologie, sciences politiques, langue et littérature anglaises, mathématiques (études de postgraduation), histoire, géographie, psychologie, sciences économiques, commerce, physiologie, droit des contrats, sociologie, alimentation et nutrition, anatomie et droit constitutionnel, sustème d'énergie électrique, et zoologie (version en hindi). D'autres disciplines feront l'objet de publications dans une phase ultérieure.

Il existe en outre des monographies sur divers sujets, notamment l'organisation des examens, l'évaluation interne, l'obtention des titres, les aspects non scolaires du comportement et des tests des étudiants et l'analyse d'une question particulière. Les ouvrages "Scaling Techniques: What? Why? How?" et "Computer in Examinations and Monograph on Sample Free Item Analysis" ont récemment été rajoutés à la liste. La Cellule de recherche a publié les rapports d'experts sur divers sujets, tels que les nouvelles technologies dans l'enseignement supérieur, le fonctionnement des collèges autonomes, l'enseignement à distance, etc . . .

Grace à une série d'ateliers, les "Registrars", les administrateurs et les inspecteurs des examens dans les Universités ont pu se servir d'ordinateurs pour traiter les résultats des examens et les analyser afin d'en recevoir en retour les informations nécessaires. La Cellule de recherche organise également des cours à l'intention par correspondance à trois niveaux (élimentaire, moyen, et professionel) des enseignants des universités et des "colleges" sur la méthodologie de l'évaluation et sur les examens. Plusieurs ateliers ont porté sur la question de la réforme des examens dans différentes universités et institutions universitaires.

La Cellule de recherche (Examens) participe actuellement à l'organisation d'une série de séminaires/ateliers sur "La mis en oeuvres et

le suivi d'une nouvelle politique en matière d'éducation". Ces séminaires sont organisés sous les auspices du Département de l'Education du Ministère du Développement des Ressources Humaines, et financés par lui.

La Division L'Economie de l'Education en romain effectue des recherches approfondies de caractère empirique sur les aspects économiques de l'éducation. Elle s'occupe de trois grands programmes de caractère général: 1) recherche; 2) développement des ressources affectées à la recherche, 3) séminaires et conférences. Les documents sélectif figurant dans le cadre du programme de recherches comprennent: *Three Aspects of University Education, University and College Finance—Seminar Papers, Economics of College Education—A Study of Hindu College, State Funding of Universities, Elite in the Making – A Socio-Economic Study of Delhi University Students, New Education Policy – AIU's Recommendations on Higher Education, Education and Economic Development – Perspectives for Policy Planning.* Les études suivantes sont en cours: *Education and Culture – Perspectives on India; Financing of Non-Plan Expenditure on University Sector; Economics of Distance Education; Graduate Unemployment in India; Survey of Scientific and Technical Manpower in the University Sector.*

Une compilation des données utiles sur l'enseignement universitaire est effectuée dans le cadre du programme de développement des ressources affectées à la recherche. La Division dispose à cet effet des publications suivantes: *University Finance (Vols. I et II)* et *Educational Statistics at a Glance.*

Des séminaires et des conférences sont organisés chaque année dans le but d'échanger des opinions sur le développement et la planification de la politique de l'enseignement. Des conférences se sont tenues sur des thèmes tels que les technologies éducatives, l'enseignement à distance et la politique nationale d'éducation (1986). Des séminaires nationaux sur les finances des universités et le chômage des diplômés sont également prévus.

La Bibliothèque a constitué au fil des années une collection spécialisée de livres et de documents. Elle rassemble des séries de rapports annuels, de calendriers, de programmes et d'autres publications des universités membres. Elle reçoit une centaine de périodiques dont elle publie une liste sélective tous les mois sous le titre "Current Documentation in Education". La bibliothèque prépare également une bibliographie annuelle en deux volumes des thèses de doctorat approuvées par les universités indiennes. Le premier est consacré aux sciences naturelles et appliquées, le deuxième couvre les sciences sociales et humaines.

Elle conserve aussi des archives sur la recherche doctorale en cours dans les différentes universités, ainsi que des dossiers de coupures de presse sur l'enseignement supérieur en général.

L'Association joue un rôle de coordination et de contrôle dans le domaine des sports. Elle organise chaque année quarante-trois tournois inter-universitaires (vingt-quatre pour les hommes, dix-neuf pour les femmes) et dirige quatre-vingts camps universitaires d'entraînement dans un certain nombre de disciplines sportives. Elle patronne les équipes des universités indiennes qui participent à des manifestations nationales et internationales. Elle octroie une assistance financière aux universités membres pour subvenir aux frais d'organisation des tournois inter-universitaires et des camps d'entraînement. Elle assure une liaison avec le gouvernement et les fédérations sportives nationales.

La Division de la Culture a été créée pendant l'Année internationale de la Jeunesse (1985) afin d'organiser une série de festivals interuniversitaires de la jeunesse. Cette innovation coïncidait aussi avec la commémoration du jubilé de diamant de l'AIU. Ces festivals sont devenus une institution permanents et comportent l'organisation, aux niveaux régional et national, de manifestations culturelles dans les domaines de la musique, de la danse, du théâtre, des activités littéraires et des beaux-arts. Plus de cent jeunes gens venant de plus de quinze universités ont participé au Festival de l'Inde qui a eu lieu en URSS de septembre à novembre 1987; ils avaient été sélectionnés aux Festivals interuniversitaires de la Jeunesse tenus en 1986–87.

Parmi les publications périodiques de l'Association, il convient de mentionner *The Universities Handbook (India), Handbook of Medical Education, Handbook of Engineering Education, Handbook of Management, Handbook of Agricultural Education, Handbook of Distance Education* et *Bibliography of Doctoral Dissertations in Natural and Applied Sciences, Social Sciences and Humanities.* L'Association publie également les Actes de ses réunions et des conférences universitaires tenues sous ses auspices. En février 1963, elle a lancé la revue *University News* devenue hebdomadaire en janvier 1984.

President: Dr. Sukhdev Singh, Vice-Chancellor, Pubjab Agricultural University, Ludhiana 141004.
Secretary: Prof. S.K. Agrawala.
AIU House, 16 Kotla Marg, New Delhi 110002.
  Tel: (331) 5105. Telex: 315578 aiu in. Cables: asindu

University Grants Commission

The University Grants Commission was established in December 1953 by a resolution of the

Government of India and given autonomous status by an Act of Parliament in 1956. The University Grants Commission Act 1956, as amended up to 17 June 1972, has laid down that it shall be the general duty of the Commission to take in consultation with the universities or other bodies concerned, all such steps as it may think fit for the promotion and co-ordination of university education and for the determination and maintenance of standards of teaching, examination and research in the universities, and for this purpose the Commission may *inter alia* inquire into the financial needs of universities, allocate and disburse grants to universities, institutions deemed to be universities and colleges, and advise on matters connected with the improvement of university education, establishment of new universities, and other matters referred to it.

The Universities Grants Commission Act prohibits giving of any grant to a university established after 17 June 1972 not declared by the Commission fit to receive such grant from any Central Government source. Under the Act, the Commission is required to collect information on matters relating to university education in India and other countries as it thinks fit, and make the same available to any university.

Under the latest legislation, the Commission will consist of a Chairman, a Vice-Chairman and ten other members to be appointed by the Central Government.

La Commission des crédits universitaires a été créée en décembre 1953 par une résolution du gouvernement indien et s'est vu confirmer un statut autonome par un Acte du Parlement en 1956. Cet Acte, où figurent les amendements apportés jusqu'à la date du 17 juin 1972, stipule que la Commission aura pour tâche principale de prendre, en accord avec les universités ou autres organismes intéressés, toutes les mesures qu'elle jugera opportunes en vue de la promotion et de la coordination de la formation universitaire, ainsi que de la définition et du maintien du niveau de l'enseignement, de la recherche et des examens dans les universités. A cet égard, la Commission pourra notamment s'informer des besoins financiers des universités, affecter et verser des crédits aux universités ou aux établissements assimilés aux universités et collèges, donner ses avis sur les questions relatives à l'amélioration de l'enseignement universitaire et à la création de nouvelles universités ou sur tous autres problèmes qui lui sont soumis.

L'Acte constitutif de la Commission des crédits universitaires interdit l'octroi de tous crédits aux universités créées après le 17 juin 1972 que la Commission n'aurait pas déclarées aptes à recevoir de tels crédits du gouvernement central. En vertu de cet Acte, la Commission est chargée de recueillir des informations sur l'enseignement universitaire en Inde et, le cas échéant, dans les autres pays, et de les diffuser auprès des universités.

En vertu de la législation la plus récente, la Commission se composera d'un Président, d'un Vice-président et de dix autres membres à nommer par le gouvernement central.
Chairman: Prof. Yash Pal.
Secretary: Prof. S.K. Khanna.
Bahadur Shah Zafar Marg, New Delhi 110002.
  Tel: 3311241. Telex: 3165913 ugc in

Federation of Central Universities Teachers' Associations
Department of Urdu, Aligarh Muslim University, Aligarh.

All India Federation of University and College Teachers' Organizations (IAUPL)
Contact: 18, rue de docteur Roux, 75015 Paris (France).
Tel: (33-1) 47-83-31-65

Indian Federation of University Women's Associations (IFUW)
Secretary: 32 T.T.K. Road, Madras 600 018.

World University Service
R579 New Rajinder Nagar, New Delhi 110 060.
  Tel: 584056. Telex: 3177026 pe in

National Council of University Students of India — NCUSI
F–13 South Extension, Part 1, New Delhi 3.

All India Students' Federation – AISF (IUS)
4/7 Asaf Ali Road, New Delhi 110 002.
  Telex: 3165982 cns in (attn. aisf)

Students' Federation of India – SFI (IUS)
22 Vittal Bhai Patel House, New Delhi 11001.

Indian Student Travel Service – ISTS
R–583 New Rajinder Nagar, New Delhi 5.

Newman Association of India (Pax Romana)
North Janatha Road, Palanivattam, 682025 Cochin.

All India Catholic University Federation (Pax Romana)
AICUF House, 1/16A Sterling Road, Madras 34.

Student Christian Movement of India (WSCF)
29 CSI Compound, 2nd Cross, Mission Road, Bangalore 560 027.

Indian Union of Jewish Students
Contact: 89 Chaussee De Vleurgat, 1050 Brussels (Belgium).
Tel: (2) 647-7279. Telex: 20625

*

Ministry of Human Resources Development
Department of Education, "C" Wing, 534 Shastri Bhavan, New Delhi 110001.
  Tel: 333936. Telex: 3161336 eouc in
Indian National Commission for Co-operation

with Unesco
Ministry of Human Resources Development
Department of Education, "C" Wing, 534

Shastri Bhavan, New Delhi 110001.
Tel: 384589. Telex: 3161336 eouc in. Cables:
educind new delhi

INDONESIA
INDONESIE

UNIVERSITIES—UNIVERSITES

State Institutions—Etablissements d'Etat

Universitas Airlangga, Jalan Raya Sutomo 61, Surabaya. (The Rector). *1954*
Tel: 41348. Telex: 31138 unair sb
F : *med, law, eco, dent, phar, vet, soc-pol, math-nat.*

Universitas Andalas, Jalan Perintis Kemerdekaan 77, Padang. *1956*
Tel: 21535
F : *med, law, let, eco, agr, an hus, math-nat.*

Universitas Bengkulu, Jalan Raya Kandang Limun, Bengkulu. *1982*
Tel: 31170
F : *law, eco, soc-pol, agr, ed-teacher training.*

Universitas Brawijaja, Jalan Mayjen Haryono 169, Malang. *1963*
Tel: 51611
F : *law, eco, agr, adm, an hus, fish, eng, med.*

Universitas Cenderawasih, Jalan Sentani, Abepura, Irian Jaya. *1962*
Tel: Abe-151. Telex: 76138
F : *law, agr, soc-pol, ed-teacher training.*

Universitas Diponegoro, Jalan Imam Bardjo, Semarang. *1960*
Tel: 311513. Telex: 22315 ugm yk
F : *law, eco, eng, med, an hus, let, soc-pol.*

Universitas Gajah Mada, Bulaksumur, Yogyakarta. *1949*
Tel: 88688. Telex: 25135 ugm yk
F : *med, law, let, phil, eco, agr, vet, an hus, eng, phar, soc-pol, biol, math-nat, dent, geog, psyc, agr techn, for.*

Universitas Halu Oleo, Jalan Mayjen S. Parman, Kendari. *1981*
Tel: 21834
F : *eco, soc-pol, agr, ed-teacher training.*

Universitas Hasanuddin, Jalan Mesjid Raya 55, Ujung Pandang. *1965*
Tel: 6343. Telex: 71179 unhas up
F : *med, law, eco, eng, let, agr, math-nat, an hus, soc-pol, publ heal, dent.*

*Universitas Indonesia, Jalan Salemba Raja 4-6, Jakarta Pusat. *1950*
Tel: (21) 330-335. Telex: 45680 ui jkt
F : *med, eco, math-nat, psyc, let, law, soc-pol, publ heal, dent, eng.*

Universitas Jambi, Jalan Yos Sudarso, Telanaipura, Jambi. *1963*
Tel: 23198
F : *law, eco, an hus, agr, ed-teacher training.*

Universitas Jember, Jalan Veteran 3, Jember. *1964*
Tel: 21270
F : *law, soc-pol, eco, let, agr, eco, ed-teacher training.*

Universitas Jenderal Soedirman, Kampus UNSOED, Grendeng, Purwokerto. *1963*
Tel: 21292
F : *law, eco, agr, an hus, biol.*

Universitas Lambung Mangkurat, Jalan Kayu Tangi, Banjarmasin. *1960*
Tel: 4177
F : *law, agr, soc-pol, for, eco, ed-teacher training, fish, eng.*

Universitas Lampung, Kampus UNILA Gedung Meneng Kedaton, Bandar Lampung. *1965*
Tel: 52673
F : *law, eco, ed-teacher training, agr.*

Universitas Mataram, Jalan Pendidikan 37, Mataram. *1962*
Tel: 21166
F : *eco, an hus, agr, law, ed-teacher training.*

Universitas Mulawarman, Kampus UNMUL, Gunung Kelua, Samarinda. *1962*
Tel: 21118
F : *agr, for, soc-pol, eco, ed-teacher training.*

Universitas Nusa Cendana, Jalan Jenderal Suharto 72, Kupang. *1962*
Tel: 21680
F : *an hus, adm, ed-teacher training, law, agr.*

Universitas Padjadjaran, Jalan Dipati Ukur 35,

Bandung.   *1957*
Tel: 83271
F : *law, eco, med, dent, let, agr, psyc, math-nat, an hus, soc-pol, commun.*

Universitas Palangkaraya, Jalan Yos Sudarso BII–5, Tanjung Nyaho, Palangkaraya.   *1963*
Tel: 21722
F : *eco, ed-teacher training.*

Universitas Pattimura, Jalan Jenderal Achemad Yani, Ambon.   *1956*
Tel: 2189
F : *law, soc-pol, agr, eco, ed-teacher training, fish, eng.*

Universitas Riau, Jalan Pattimura 5, Pekanbaru.
                                            1962
Tel: 21341
F : *math-nat, eco, soc-pol, fish, ed-teacher training.*

Universitas Sam Ratulangi, Kampus UNSRAT, Kleak, Manado.   *1961*
Tel: 3586. Telex: 74131 unsrat mo
F : *med eco, law, an hus, agr, eng, let soc-pol, fish, ed-teacher training.*

Universitas Sebelas Maret, Jalan Ir. Soetami 36A, Kentingan, Surakarta.   *1976*
Tel: 6623
F : *ed-teacher training, let, soc-pol, law, eco, med, agr, eng.*

Universitas Sriwijaya, Jalan Arif Rachman Hakim, Palembang.   *1960*

Tel: 26388
F : *eco, law, eng, med, agr, ed-teacher training.*

Universitas Sumatera Utara, Jalan Universitas 9, Medan.   *1957*
Tel: 23210. Telex. 51753 usu mdn
F : *med, agr, eng, dent, math-nat, let, law, soc-pol, eco.*

Universitas Syiah Kuala, Kopelma Darusalam, Banda Aceh.   *1961*
Tel: 22721
F : *eco, law, vet, eng, agr, med, ed-teacher training.*

Universitas Tadulako, Kampus Bumi Bahari, Palu.   *1981*
Tel: 21590
F : *law, soc-pol, eco, agr, ed-teacher training.*

Universitas Tanjungpura, Jalan Imam Bonjol, Pontianak.   *1963*
Tel: 4399
F : *law, eco, agr, eng, soc-pol, ed-teacher training.*

Universitas Terbuka [Open U.], Jalan Terbang Layang, Pondok Cabe, Ciputat.   *1984*
Tel: 741023. Telex: 47498 uter ia
F : *ed-teacher training, eco, soc-pol, math-nat.*

Universitas Udayana, Jalan Panglima Besar Soedirman, Denpasar.   *1962*
Tel: 23791
F : *let, med, an hus, law, agr, eng, eco, ed-teacher training.*

Private Institutions-Etablissements privés

Universitas Amir Hamzah, Jalan HM Joni 22, Medan. (The Rector).   *1981*
F : *law, eco.*

Universitas Advent Indonesia, Jalan Parangpang Cisarua, Lembang, Bandung.
                                            1948
F : *eco, theo, ed-teacher training.*

Universitas Atmajaya, Jalan Demangan Baru 29, Yogyakarta.   *1965*
F : *law, eco, eng.*

Universitas Atmajaya, Jalan Thamrin 1-3, Ujung Pandang.   *1981*
F : *eng, eco, law.*

Universitas Bojonegoro, Jalan Jenderal Basuki Rakhmat 23A, Bojonegoro.   *1981*
F : *law, soc-pol, agr.*

Universitas Bung Hatta, Jalan Sumatera, Ulak Karang, Padang.   *1981*
Tel: 24439
F : *eco, law, ed-teacher training, let, eng.*

Universitas Darma Agung, Jalan Bantam 21, Medan.   *1957*
F : *law, soc-pol, eco, ed-teacher training, eng, agr, ind-tex, eng, let.*

Universitas Darul'ulum, Jalan Merdeka 29A,

Jombang.   *1965*
F : *law, soc-pol, ed, eng, eco.*

Universitas Dr. Soetomo Surabaya, Jalan Semolowaru, Surabaya.
F : *adm, fish, ed.*

Universitas Gresik, Jalan Jaksa Agung Suprapto 1, Gresik.   *1981*
F : *eng, ed, law, eco.*

Universitas HKBP Nommensen, Jalan Dr. Soetomo 4A, Medan.   *1954*
Tel: 511426. Telex: 51577
F : *eco, publ-bus adm, ed-teacher training, eng, an hus, law.*

Universitas IBNU Chaldun, Jalan Senen Raya 45-47, Jakarta.   *1956*
Tel: 4880599
F : *eco, law, soc-pol, publishing.*

Universitas IBNU Chaldun, Jalan R.E. Martadinata 2, Bogor.   *1961*
Tel: 21112
F : *ed, law, eco, eng.*

Universitas Indonesia Muda, Jalan Letjen Suprapto 22, Jakarta.   *1965*
F : *eng, law.*

Universitas Islam Bandung, Jalan Tamansari 1,

Bandung. *1959*
F : *law, psyc, eng, eco.*
Universitas Islam Indonesia, Jalan Cik Ditiro 1,
Yogyakarta. *1945*
Tel: 3091
F : *eng, tex techn, law, eco.*
Universitas Islam Jakarta, Jalan Nanas II, Utan
Kayu, Jakarta. *1951*
Tel: 45286
F : *eco, law.*
Universitas Islam Malang, Jalan Mayjen
Haryono 193, Malang. *1981*
F : *law, agr, eco, eng, ed-teacher training.*
Universitas Islam Nusantara, Jalan Sukarno
Hatta, Jalan Taman Halimun 37, Bandung.
1959
Tel: 56556
F : *eco, law, ed.*
Universitas Islam Riau, Jalan Prof. Muhd.
Yamin, SH, Pekanbaru. *1962*
Tel: 21016
F : *law, eng, agr, eco.*
Universitas Islam Syekh Yusuf, Jalan Tanjung
Duren Barat II/1, Jakarta. *1964*
Tel: 22340
F : *law, soc-pol.*
Universitas Islam Syekh Yusuf, Jalan Harapan II,
Babakan, Tangerang. *1975*
F : *soc-pol, law, tex techn, ed.*
Universitas Islam Sumatera Utara, Jalan Sisinga-
mangaraja, Teladan, Medan. *1952*
Tel: 24382
F : *eco, soc-pol, med, ed-teacher training, law,
let, eng, agr.*
Universitas Islam Sultan Agung, Jalan Raya
Kaligawe, Semarang. *1962*
F : *law, eco, eng, med.*
Universitas Jakarta, Jalan Pulo Mas Barat,
Jakarta. *1965*
F : *eng, law, publ-bus adm.*
Universitas Janabadra, Jalan KHA Dahlan 1,
Yogyakarta. *1958*
F : *law.*
Universitas Jayabaya, Jalan Jenderal A. Yani,
By Pass, Jakarta. *1958*
Tel: 414904. Telex: 49505 urbaya ia
F : *eng, eco, law, soc-pol.*
Universitas Katolik Indonesi Atmajaya, Jalan
Jenderal Sudirman 49A, Jakarta. *1960*
Tel: 586491
F : *law, eng, med, eco, ed-teacher training, soc-
pol.*
Universitas Kadiri, Jalan Sodanco Supriadi 3,
Kediri. *1980*
F : *law, soc-pol, agr, eco, eng.*
Universitas Katolik Parahyangan, Jalan Merdeka
30, Bandung. *1955*
Tel: 83691
F : *eco, law, eng.*

Universitas Katolik Soegiyo Pranoto, Jalan
Pandanaran 100, Semarang. *1966*
F : *eng, eco, law.*
Universitas Katolik Widya Karya, Jalan
Bondowoso 2, Malang. *1982*
F : *eco, agr, eng.*
Universitas Katolik Widya Mandala, Jalan
Dinoyo 42-44, Surabaya. *1960*
F : *ed-teacher training, phar, eco.*
Universitas Khairun, Jalan Hasan Esa, Ternate.
1964
F : *law, eco, ed.*
Universitas Klabat, Jalan Airmadidi, Manado.
1982
Tel: 4142
F : *theo, ed-teacher training, eco.*
Universitas Krisnadwipayana, Jatiwaringin,
Jakarta. *1952*
Tel: 51249
F : *eng, publ-bus adm, law, eco.*
Universitas Kristen Indonesia, Jalan Letjen
Sutoyo, Cawang, Jakarta 13650. *1953*
Tel: 800311
F : *eng, let, med, law, eco, ed-teacher training.*
Universitas Kristen Indonesia Paulus, Jalan
Cenderawasih 65, Ujung Pandang. *1963*
F : *eng, law, eco, let.*
Universitas Kristen Indonesia Tomohon, Jalan
Kakaskasen III, Tomohom. *1965*
F : *theol, ed-teacher training, psyc, nat.*
Universitas Kristen Jaya, Jalan Tanjung Duren
Raya 4, Jakarta 11470. *1967*
Tel: 599601
F : *med, eng, eco.*
Universitas Kristen Maranatha, Jalan Ciham-
pelas 169, Bandung. *1965*
Tel: 81212
F : *med, eng, psyc, let.*
Universitas Kristen Petra, Jalan Siwalankerto,
121-131, Surabaya 60002. *1961*
Tel: 813040
F : *eng, let.*
Universitas Kristen Satyawacana, Jalan Dipone-
goro 54-56, Salatiga 50711. *1956*
Tel: 81362. Telex: 22364 uks sa
F : *eng, ed-teacher training, law, eco.*
Universitas Madura, Jalan Slamet Riyadi 2,
Pamekasan. *1978*
F : *law, eco, soc-pol, ed.*
Universitas Mahasaraswati, Jalan Kembodja,
Denpasar. *1962*
F : *agr, law, eco, ed-teacher training, eng.*
Universitas Marhaen, Jalan Ken Arok 5,
Denpasar. *1963*
F : *soc-pol, law.*
Universitas Merdeka Madiun, Jalan Pahlawan
25, Madiun. *1979*
F : *law, eco, soc-pol, eng.*
Universitas Merdeka Pusat, Jalan Bandung 2,

Malang.   *1964*
Tel: 2893
F : *law, eco, soc-pol, eng.*

Universitas Methodist Indonesia, Jalan Hang
Tuah 8, Medan.   *1965*
F : *let, med, agr.*

Universitas Muhammadiyah Jakarta, Jalan
Limau I-II-III, Jakarta.   *1955*
F : *soc-pol, eng, eco, law.*

Universitas Muhammadiyah Jember, Jalan Gatot
Subroto 7, Jember.   *1981*
F : *agr, law, ed-teacher training.*

Universitas Muhammadiyah Magelang, Jalan
Tidar 21, Magelang.   *1964*
F : *eco, law, ed.*

Universitas Muhammadiyah Malang, Jalan
Bandung 1, Malang.   *1965*
F : *ed-teacher training, soc-pol, law, eco, eng,
agr.*

Universitas Muhammadiyah Mataram, Jalan
Anyelir 2, Mataram.   *1980*
Tel: 23723
F : *ed-teacher training, eng, soc-pol.*

Universitas Mohammadiyah Sumatera Utara,
Jalan Gedung Arca 53, Medan.   *1957*
F : *ed, soc, eco, agr.*

Universitas Muhammadiyah Ujung Pandang,
Jalan Ranggong 7, Ujung Pandang.   *1963*
F : *ed-teacher training, soc w, soc-pol, eco.*

Universitas Muhammadiyah Surakarta, Jalan
Dr. Rajiman 78, Surakarta.   *1958*
F : *ed-teacher training.*

Universitas Muhammad Seroedji, Jalan Bromo
89, Jember.   *1981*
F : *soc-pol, ed, eco, eng, law.*

Universitas Muria Kudus, Jalan Sunan Muria I/
Bawah, Kudus.   *1980*
F : *eco, law, ed-teacher training.*

Universitas Muslim Indonesia, Jalan Kakatua 27,
Ujung Pandang.   *1954*
F : *eco, law, eng.*

Universitas Narotama, Jalan Pahlawan 30,
Surabaya.   *1981*
F : *eco, law, eng.*

Universitas Nasional, Jalan Sawo Manila,
Pejaten, Pasar Minggu, Jakarta.   *1949*
Tel: 782700
F : *eco, let, math-nat, biol, soc-pol, eng.*

Universitas Ngurah Rai, Jalan Patih Jelantik 9,
Denpasar, Bali.   *1979*
F : *law, eco, soc-pol, eng.*

Universitas Pakuan, Jalan Pakuan, Bogor. *1980*
Tel: 26226
F : *law, eco, ed-teacher training.*

Universitas Pancasila, Jalan Borobudur 7,
Jakarta.   *1966*
Tel: 322267
F : *eng, phar, law, eco.*

Universitas Pancasila Tegal, Jalan Pancasila 2,

Tegal.   *1979*
F : *soc-pol, fish, teacher-training.*

Universitas Pasundan, Jalan Tamansari 8,
Bandung.   *1960*
F : *law, eco, eng, ed-teacher training.*

Universitas Pekalongan, Jalan Garuda 49,
Pekalongan.   *1981*
F : *eco, law, fish.*

Universitas Pembangunan Panca Budi, Jalan
Jenderal Gatot Subroto, Medan.   *1961*
F : *law, phil, eco, agr, arc.*

Universitas Pepabri Ujung Pandang, Jalan Syarif
Alqadri 32A, Ujung Pandung.   *1978*
F : *soc-pol, eng, adm.*

Universitas Prof. Dr. Mustopo (Beragama), Jalan
Hanglekir I/8, Kebayoran Baru, Jakarta. *1961*
F : *soc-pol, eco, commun, dent.*

Universitas Proklamasi 45, Jalan Dagen 129,
Yogyakarta.   *1964*
F : *eng, soc-pol, eco, law.*

Universitas Sarjana Wiyata Taman Siswa, Jalan
Kusumanegara 95, Yogyakarta.   *1955*
F : *ed-teacher training, eco.*

Universitas Siliwangi, Jalan Ir. H. Juanda,
Tasikmalaya.   *1976*
Tel: 21634
F : *ed-teacher training, eco.*

Universitas Simalungun, Jalan Merdeka 232,
Pematang Siantar.   *1966*
F : *eco, agr, law, eng, ed-teacher training.*

Universitas Slamet Riyadi Surakarta, Jalan
Munginsidi 40, Surakarta.   *1977*
Tel: 7839
F : *law, eco, soc-pol, ed.*

Universitas Soerjo, Jalan Jurusan Ngawi-Cepu,
Ngawi.   *1981*
F : *law, soc-pol, agr.*

Universitas Sunan Giri, Jalan Citarum 1,
Surabaya.   *1976*
F : *eng, eco, soc-pol, law.*

Universitas Surabaya, Jalan Ngagel Jaya Selatan
169, Surabaya.   *1968*
Tel: 60866
F : *law, phar, eco.*

Universitas Swadaya Gunung Jati, Jalan Dr.
Ciptomangunkusumo 1, Cirebon.   *1960*
F : *law, eco, ed-teaching training.*

Universitas Tamansiswa, Jalan Kusumanegara
95, Yogyakarta.
Tel: 87265
F : *ed-teacher training, agr, eco.*

Universitas Tarumanegara, Jalan Letjen S.
Parman 1, Jakarta.   *1962*
Tel: 591747
F : *eco, med, eng, law.*

Universitas Tidar Magelang, Jalan Kapten
Suparman, Magelang.   *1979*
F : *eco, ed-teacher training, agr, soc-pol, eng.*

Universitas Tri Dharma, Jalan Kapten Tendean

26, Balikpapan.   *1978*
F : *law, eng, ed-teacher training.*
Universitas Trisakti, Jalan Kiyai Tapa, Grogol,
Jakarta.   *1965*
Tel: 591356
F : *eco, law, eng, med, dent, arc.*
Universitas 17 Agustus 1945 Banyuwangi, Jalan
Adisucipto 26, Banyuwangi.   *1980*
Tel: 41980
F : *law, eco, agr, soc-pol.*
Universitas 17 Agustus 1945 Cirebon, Jalan Sili-
wangi 94, Cirebon.   *1964*
F : *publ-bus adm, law.*
Universitas 17 Agustus 1945 Jakarta, Jalan
Teuku Cik Ditiro 46, Jakarta.   *1952*
Tel: 343901
F : *eng, phar, soc, publ-bus adm, eco.*
Universitas 17 Agustus 1945 Samarinda, Jalan Ir.
H. Juanda, Samarinda.   *1965*
F : *law, soc-pol, eco, eng.*
Universitas 17 Agustus 1945 Semarang, Jalan

Seteran Dalam 9, Semarang.   *1963*
F : *law, soc-pol, eco, eng.*
Universitas 17 Agustus 1945 Surabaya, Jalan
Semolowaru 45, Surabaya.   *1964*
F : *publ-bus adm, eco, law, ind-techn.*
Universitas Tunas Pembangunan, Jalan Irian 22,
Surakarta.   *1980*
F : *eng, eco, agr, ed.*
Universitas Veteran R I, Jalan G. Bawakaraeng
72, Ujung Pandang.   *1961*
F : *ed-teacher training, soc-pol, eng.*
Universitas Wijaya Kusuma, Jalan Gatot
Subroto 101, Purwokerto.   *1980*
F : *law, soc-pol, eco, eng.*
Universitas Wijaya Kusuma Surabaya, Jalan
Dukuh Kupang 25, Surabaya.   *1980*
F : *eng, art, law, eco, soc-pol, ed-teacher
training.*
Universitas Wisnu Wardhana, Jalan Raya Dieng
1, Malang.   *1981*
F : *law, eco, agr, ed-teacher training.*

OTHER INSTITUTIONS—AUTRES INSTITUTIONS

Technical Education—Enseignement technique

Institut Pelayaran Niaga, Jalan Kebun Nanas,
Jakarta.   *1981*
F : *ship techn, ship-mangt.*
Institut Pertanian Bogor, Jalan Raya Pajajaran,
Bogor.   *1963*
Tel: 23081
F : *agr, an hus, vet, fish, for, agr techn, math-
nat.*
Institut Teknologi Bandung, Jalan Tamansari 64,
Bandung.   *1959*
Tel: 83047. telex: 28324 itb bd
F : *math-nat-phar, civ eng-urb, ind eng, arts-*

des, mineral eng.
Institut Teknologi Nasional, Jalan Bendungan
Sigura-gura 2, Malang.   *1962*
F : *eng, plan eng, ind eng.*
Institut Teknologi Pembangunan, Jalan Manyar
Tirtomoyo VIII/1, Surabaya.   *1980*
F : *eng, plan eng, ind eng.*
Institut Teknologi Sepulah Nopember, Jalan
Keputih, Sukolilo, Surabaja.   *1960*
Tel: 60651. Telex: 31224 intexs sb
D : *marine eng, elec, civ eng-plan, math-nat, ind
eng.*

Professional Education—Enseignement professionnel

Institut Kesenian Jakarta, Jalan Cikini Raya 73,
Jakarta.   *1970*
F : *art, theat.*

Institut Manajemen Koperasi Indonesia, Jalan
Raya Bandung, Sumedang.   *1981*
F : *mangt, dev mangt, ind mangt.*

Teacher Training—Formation pédagogique

Institut Keguruan dan Ilmu Pendidikan, Jalan
Setiabudi 229, Bandung.   *1954*
Tel: 83162
F : *ed, lang-arts, math-nat, soc, techn-voc ed,
sports.*
Institut Keguruan dan Ilmu Pendidikan, Kampus
IKIP, Rawamangun, Jakarta.   *1963*
Tel: 81811

F : *ed, lang-arts, math-nat, soc, techn-voc ed,
sports.*
**Institut Keguruan dan Ilmu Pendidikan
Muhammadiyah**, Jalan Limau II, Jakarta.
                                                    1957
F : *ed, lang-arts, math-nat, soc.*
**Institut Keguruan dan Ilmu Pendidikan
Muhammadiyah**, Jalan Komplek Pendidikan,

Karanganyar. 1969
F : ed.
Institut Keguruan dan Ilmu Pendidikan, Jalan
Bendogantungan, Klaten. 1965
F : lang-arts, soc.
Institut Keguruan dan Ilmu Pendidikan, Jalan
Semarang 5, Malang. 1954
Tel: 51312
F : ed, lang-arts, math-nat, soc, techn-voc ed,
sports.
Institut Keguruan dan Ilmu Pendidikan, Jalan
Yusuf Hasiru, Kleak, Mandado. 1965
Tel: 51193
F : ed, lang-arts, math-nat, soc, techn-voc ed,
sports.
Institut Keguruan dan Ilmu Pendidikan, Jalan
Pemuda, Mataram. 1967
F : ed, lang-arts, math-nat, sports.
Institut Keguruan dan Ilmu Pendidikan, Jalan
Merbabu 38A, Medan. 1965
Tel: 327704
F : ed, lang-arts, math-nat, soc, techn-voc ed,
sports.
**Institut Keguruan dan Ilmu Pendidikan Aswas-
liyah**, Jalan Sisingamangaraja, Medan. 1963
F : ed, lang-arts, math-nat, soc.
**Institut Keguruan dan Ilmu Pendidikan Gunung
Sitoli**, Jalan Labuhan Angin, Nias.
1965
F : ed, math-nat, soc.
Institut Keguruan dan Ilmu Pendidikan, Kampus
IKIP, Air Tawar, Padang. 1954
Tel: 21838
F : ed, lang-arts, math-nat, soc, techn-voc ed,
sports.
**Institut Keguruan dan Ilmu Pendidikan
Muhammadiyah**, Jalan dr. Angka 1,
Purwokerto. 1965
F : ed, soc.
**Institut Keguruan dan Ilmu Pendidikan
Muhammadiyah**, Jalan KHA Dahlan 6,
Purworejo. 1964
F : lang-arts, soc.
Institut Keguruan dan Ilmu Pendidikan, Jalan
Kelud Utara III, Semarang. 1965
Tel: 311501
F : ed, lang-arts, math-nat, soc, techn-voc ed,
sports.
**Institut Keguruan dan Ilmu Pendidikan Veteran
Jawa Tengah**, Jalan Pemuda 138, Semarang.
1962

F : ed, techn ed, soc.
Institut Keguruan dan Ilmu Pendidikan, Jalan
Dr. Muwardi, Sukoharjo. 1968
F : ed, lang-arts, soc.
Institut Keguruan dan Ilmu Pendidikan, Jalan
Kajun 72-74, Surabaya. 1965
Tel: 45907
F : ed, lang-arts, math-nat, soc, techn-voc ed,
sports.
**Institut Keguruan dan Ilmu Pendidikan
Muhammadiyah**, Jalan Kapasan 73-75,
Surabaya. 1980
F : ed, lang-arts, math-nat, soc.
Institut Keguruan dan Ilmu Pendidikan Pgri,
Jalan Ngagel Dadi III B, Surabaya. 1971
F : ed, lang-arts, math-nat, soc.
**Institut Keguruan dan Ilmu Pendidikan
Saraswati**, Jalan Pahlawan, Tabanan. 1965
F : soc.
Institut Keguruan dan Ilmu Pendidikan, Kampus
IKIP, Gunungsari Baru, Ujung Pandang. 1965
Tel: 82879. telex: 71173 ikip up
F : ed, lang-arts, math-nat, soc, techn-voc ed,
sports.
Institut Keguruan dan Ilmu Pendidikan, Kampus
IKIP, Karang Malang, Yogyakarta. 1965
Tel: 3262
F : ed, lang-arts, math-nat, soc, techn-voc ed,
sports.
Institut Keguruan dan Ilmu Pendidikan Pgri,
Jalan Stasiun 1, Wates. 1969
F : ed, soc.
Institut Keguruan dan Ilmu Pendidikan Pgri,
Jalan Wates 147, Yogyakarta. 1962
F : ed, soc.
**Institut Keguruan dan Ilmu Pendidikan Sanata
Dharma**, Mrican, Yogyakarta. 1955
Tel: 86168
F : ed, lang-arts, math-nat, soc.
**Institut Keguruan dan Ilmu Pendidikan
Muhammadiyah**, Jalan Kapas 6, Yogyakarta.
1960
F : ed, lang-arts, math-nat.
Institut Keguruan dan Ilmu Pendidikan Veteran,
Jalan Mantrigawen Lor 38, Yogyakarta. 1967
F : soc.
*Also 3 Universities and 42 Academies, Schools
and Institutes of professional training attached to
relevant Ministries (Government Departments),
and 316 private professional Academies and
Schools.*

Ikatan Sardjana Wanita Indonesia (IFUW)
Jalan Sriwijaya 4 No. 3, Kebayoran Baru,
Jakarta-Selatan.
Ikatan Sardjana Katolik (Pax Romana)
Jalan Patal Senajan 23, Jakarta-Pusat.

**Perhimpunan Mahasiswa Katolik Republik
Indonesia** – (PMKRI) (Pax Romana)
Jalan Sam Ratulangie 1, Jakarta 111/6.
Gerakan Mahaiswa Kristen Indonesia –
G.M.K.I. (WSCF)

Salemba 10, Jakarta, Pusat.

*

Direktorat Jenderal Pendidikan (Directorate-General for Higher Education)
Jalan Proklamasi 17A, Jakarta.

Tel: 581436
Indonesian National Commission for Unesco
c/o Department of Education and Culture, Jalan Jenderal Sudirman-Senayan, Jakarta. Tel: 581665. Telex: 44471. Cables: indonatcom jakarta

ISLAMIC REPUBLIC OF IRAN
REPUBLIQUE ISLAMIQUE D'IRAN

UNIVERSITIES AND UNIVERSITY COMPLEXES —
UNIVERSITES ET COMPLEXES UNIVERSITAIRES

Allmeh Tabatabai University, Karimkhan Zand Avenue, North Aban, Tehran. *1977*
Amir Kabir University of Technology, Hafez Avenue, Tehran. *1958*
Avicenna University, Mahdieh Avenue, Hammedan. *1974*
Tel: 99050
F : *heal-med sc, env sc, nat resources.*
Azzahra University, Vanak, Tehran 19934. *1964*
C : *sc, theo-lit-hum, soc-eco, fa.*
University of Engineering and Technology, 41, Shahin Alley, Seyed Khandan, Tehran. *1967*
*University of Esfahan, Shiraz Gate, Esfahan. *1950*
Tel: 71071. Telex: 312295 ireu ir
C: *let-hum, adm-eco, for lang, ed, sc, eng.*
Esfahan University of Technology, Tehran Gate, Esfahan. *1977*
Tel: 38043
*Ferdowsi University, Mashhad. *1949*
Tel: 31031
S : *let-hum, sc, theo-Isl st, ed, agr, eng.*
Gilan University, Laken Road, Rasht. *1969*
Tel: 35035. Telex: 232100.
F : *sc, agr, techn, hum.*
Imam Sadegh University, Martyr Chamran Park Way, Farahzad Road, Tehran. *1983*
Iran University of Science and Technology, Narmak, Tehran 16844.
Tel: 792991. Telex: 212965
C: *arc-urb plan, ch eng, civ eng, elec-electro eng, ind eng, mec, mat-met, sc.*
Martyr Bahonar University, Islamic Republic Boulevard, Kerman. *1975*
Tel: 24637
F : *agr, lit-hum, sc, tech.*
*Martyr Beheshti University, Evin, Tehran. *1959*
Tel: 214111

F : *let-hum, law, sc, eco-pol, arc, ed-psyc, comp-mangt.*
Martyr Chamran University, Ahwaz. *1955*
Tel: 30012
C : *agr, eco-soc, ed-psyc, eng, lit-for lang, phys, sc, theo-Isl st, vet; agr* (Mollasani).
Mazandaran University, Pasdaran Avenue, Bobolsar. *1974*
Tel: 32091. Telex: 215424
C : *eco-socio, sc, eng, nat resources; agr* (Gonbad, Sari).
I : *ch.*
University of Orumiyeh, Martyr Beheshti Avenue, Orumiyeh 57135. *1964*
Tel: 24051
C : *agr.*
F : *sc.*
S : *vet.*
I : *techn-eng.*
Razi University, Azadi Square, Bakhtaran. *1972*
Tel: 28066
C : *sc* (Kermanshah); *an hus* (Elam); *teacher training* (Sanandaj).
*Sharif University of Technology, Azadi Avenue, Tehran. *1965*
Tel: 97200
C : *ch eng, ch, elec, ind eng, math-comp, mec, met, phy, const eng.*
*Shiraz University, Zand Avenue Shiraz. *1959*
Tel: 51001. Telex: 65912
C : *agr, dent, eng, ed, sc, vet, arts, law.*
University of Sistan and Baluchestan, Khash Road, Zahedan. *1975*
Tel: 25981. Cables: dasibel
C : *ch, civ eng, elec, sc; naut* (Chah-Bahar); *agr* (Zabol).
*University of Tabriz, 29th Bahman Boulevard, Tabriz. *1946*

Tel: 31300. Telex: 412045

F : *agr, ed, eng, let-hum, sc; agr* (Ardabil).

*University for Teacher Education, 49 Martyr Mofatteh Avenue, Tehran.   *1930, 1976*

C : *teacher training; teacher training* (Yazd, Zahedan); *sc* (Arak, Kashan).

*University of Tehran, Enghelab Avenue, Tehran.   *1934*

Tel: (021) 6111. Telex: 213944 ir ibb

C : *lit-hum, bus adm-mangt, eco, ed, fa, law-pol, nat, theo-Isl st, vet, phar, sc, soc-co-operatives, agr.*

I : *geophy, psyc, Deh ghoda encyclopedias, geog, bioch, comparative law, env st* (all research).

University Faculty Training Centre, North Karegar Avenue, Tehran.   *1981*

Medical Sciences University of Iran, Gandhi Avenue, Tehran.   *1974, 1986*

Tel: 688191

S : *med, allied heal, publ heal, nurs-obst, med infor.*

University of Medical Sciences Martyr Chamran, Golestan Road, Ahwaz.   *1955, 1986*

University of Medical Sciences, Martyr Beheshti Boulevard, Bakhtaran.   *1974, 1986*

University of Medical Sciences of Mazandaran,

Gang Afrooz Avenue, Babol.   *1974, 1986*

University of Medical Sciences, Shiraz Gate, University Avenue, Esfahan.   *1950, 1986*

University of Medical Sciences, Ayattollah Kashani Boulevard, Hammedan.   *1974, 1986*

University of Medical Sciences, I.R.I. Boulevard, Kerman.   *1973, 1986*

University of Medical Sciences, University Avenue, Mashhad.   *1949, 1986*

University of Medical Sciences, Martyr Beheshti Avenue, Orumiyeh.   *1964, 1986*

University of Medical Sciences of Gilan, Saadi Avenue, Resht.   *1969, 1986*

University of Medical Sciences, Ghods Square, Shiraz.   *1959, 1986*

University of Medical Sciences, 29th Bahman Boulevard, Tabriz.   *1946, 1986*

University of Medical Sciences Martyr Beheshti, Evin, Tehran.   *1959, 1986*

University of Medical Sciences, Enghelab Avenue, Poorsina, Tehran.   *1934, 1986*

University of Medical Sciences, Bafgh Road, Safaeeyeh, Yazd.

University of Medical Sciences of Sistan and Baluchestan, Goorband Road, , Zahedan.   *1975, 1986*

OTHER INSTITUTIONS—AUTRES INSTITUTIONS

University Complex of Art, 499 Vali-Asr Avenue, Tehran.   *1980*

D : *cinema-television, pnt, des, int des, tex, photography, ind des, vis commun.*

Birjand Higher Education Complex, Birjand.   *1975*

Deh-Khoda Higher Educational Complex, University Avenue, Ghazvin.   *1978*

Lorestan Higher Educational Complex, Enghelab Avenue, Khorram Abad.   *1979*

Zanjan Higher Educational Complex, 6th Kilometer of Tabriz Road, Zanjan.   *1975*

Arak Higher Educational Research Complex, Martyr Shiroodi Avenue, Arak.   *1986*

Bushehr Higher Educational Research Complex, Bushehr.   *1986*

Hormozgan Higher Educational Research Complex, Iman Khomeini Boulevard, Bandar Abbass.   *1983*

Lorestan Higher Educational Research Complex, Enghelab Avenue, Khorram Abad.   *1983*

Sanandaj Higher Educational Research Complex, Towheed Hospital, Sanandaj.   *1978*

Semnan Higher Educational Research Complex, 17th of Shahrivar Avenue, Semnan.   *1975*

Shahrood Higher Educational Research Complex, Railway Road, Shahrood.   *1975*

Zanjan Higher Educational Research Complex,

Parvin Etesami Avenue, Zanjan.   *1986*

College of International Relations, North of Ostad Nejatollahi Avenue, Rahbar Alley, Tehran.   *1982*

College of I.R.I.B., Martyr Khaled Eslamboli Avenue, 1 Alley, Tehran.   *1983*

College of Judicial Law and Administrative Services, Ehghelab Avenue/Khark Avenue, Tehran.   *1981*

Abadan College of Petroleum, National Islamic Republic of Iran Oil Company, Ahwaz.   *1939*

Civil Aviation Training Centre, Mehr-Abad Airport, Meraj Avenue, Tehran.   *1961*

School of Industrial Safety and Occupational Health, Vali-Asr Avenue, Esteghlal Hotel Avenue, Tehran.   *1981*

School of Judicial Law, Salariyeh, Ghom.   *1984*

School of Martyr Motahari, Bahrestan Square, Tehran.   *1981*

School of Mining, Shahrood.   *1974*

Tel: 6000

National Bank of Iran School of Nursing, Ferdowsi Avenue, National Bank Building, Tehran.   *1974*

School of Psychiatry, Taleghani Avenue, Jahan Alley, Tehran.   *1977*

School of Technology, 17th of Shahrivar Boulevard, Semnau.   *1973*

Ahwaz Technical School, 20th Kianpars Avenue, Ahwaz.   *1967*
Baktaran Technical School, Martyr Jafari Avenue, Bakhtaran.   *1976*
Esfahan Technical School, Shiraz Gate, Esfahan.   *1973*
Hammedan Technical School, 2nd Kilometer of Shorin Road, Hammedan.   *1978*
Kashan Technical School, 6th Kilometer of Ravand Road, Kashan.   *1975*
Kerman Technical School, Shahab Avenue, Kerman.   *1975*
Mashhad Technical School, Reza City, Taleghani Road, Mashhad.   *1967*
Rasht Technical School, Rooman Road, Rasht.
                                                            1986
Sanandaj Technical School, Pasdaran Avenue, Sanandaj.   *1974*
Sari Technical School, Khazar Abad Boulevard, Tabarestan Alley, Sari.   *1975*

Shiraz Technical School, Horr Avenue, Shiraz.
                                                            1967
Tabriz Technical School, Tabriz.   *1979*
Tehran Technical School No. 1, Ray Avenue, Tehran.   *1976*
Tehran Technical School No. 2, Vanak Square, Brazil Avenue, Tehran.   *1975*
Tehran Technical School No. 3, Pasdaran Avenue, Sokhandan Avenue, Tehran.
                                                            1967
Tehran Technical School for Women, Damavand Avenue, Tehran.   *1983*
Towheed Technical School, 45th Kilometer of Esfahan Road, Shahre Kord, Esfahan.
                                                            1986
Orumiyeh Technical School, Sarve Road, Orumiyeh.   *1970*
Yazd Technical School, Student's Boulevard, Yazd.   *1973*
Zahedan Technical School, Goorhand 1st Boulevard, Zahedan.   *1978*

Ministry of Culture and Higher Education
Tehran.
Telex: 212889 irdc ir

Iranian National Commission for Unesco
1188 Enghelab Avenue, Rostam Give Building, P.O. Box 11365-4498, Tehran 13158.
Tel: 668365. Cables: irannatcom tehran

IRAQ
IRAK

UNIVERSITIES—UNIVERSITES

*Al-Mustansiriyah University, Baghdad.   *1968*
Tel: 4168511. Telex: 212566 musbad ik
C : *arts, med, sc, adm-eco, ed, eng, lib, tour & hotel mangt.*
University of Al-Anbar, Al-Anbar.   *1988*
C : *ed, ed for girls, sc, med.*
University of Al-Qadisiya, Al-Qadisiya.
                                                    1988
C : *adm-eco, ed, art.*
*University of Baghdad, Jadyriyah, Baghdad.
(The President).   *1908, 1949, 1958, 1969*
Tel: 93091
C : *arts, agr, sc, med, phar, dent, phys, fa, ed, nurs, eng, vet, adm-eco, Alsharea, law-pol, lang, ed for girls.*
Ce : *psyc-ed, med res, adm-eco res, Palestinian st, urb & reg plan, psyc, nat hist res, dent res.*

*University of Basrah, Basrah.   *1967*
Tel: 417951. Telex: 207025 univrsity ik
C : *arts, eng, sc, med, adm-eco, ed, agr, law, phys.*
Ce : *env beach res, Arabic Gulf st, manipulative teach.*
University of Kufa, Kufa.   *1988*
C : *med, fa, Al fikih, art, sc, eng, law, ed for girls.*
*University of Mosul, Mosul.   *1967*
Tel: 812611. Telex: 298011 mosunprs ik
C : *med, sc, eng, agr-for, arts, adm-eco, ed, vet, phys, dent, law.*
Ce : *appl med, appl ind, appl agr, archae-cult, eco-adm, vet* (all Research).
*University of Salahaddin, Arbil.   *1968*
Tel: 21422. Telex: 218510 anco ik

C : eng, sc, arts, ed, adm-eco, med, law.
*University of Technology, Baghdad.   *1975*
  Tel: 7196021. Telex: 214149 unitech ik
  D : elec, bui-const, prod eng-met, control &

systems, ch eng, tec ed, machinery-equipment,
appl sc, arc.
University of Tikrit, Tikrit.   *1988*
  C : ed for girls, eng, med.

OTHER INSTITUTIONS—AUTRES INSTITUTIONS

Institute of Administration, Al-Risafa, Baghdad.
                                                1969
Institute of Applied Arts, Baghdad.   *1969*
Institute of Technical Trainers, Baghdad.   *1986*
Institute of Technology, Baghdad.   *1972*
  Tel: 7731491. Telex: 212769 instech ik
Technical Institute of Administration, Baghdad.
                                                1976
Technical Institute, Al-Huwayja.   *1980*
Technical Institute, Al-Kufa.   *1988*
Technical Institute, **Al-Misayab**, Babylon. *1979*
Technical Institute, Al-Najaf.   *1978*
  Tel: 20938
Technical Institute, Al-Nasiriyah.   *1980*

  Tel: 231315
Technical Institute, Al-Ramadi.   *1977*
Technical Institute, **Al-Shatra**, Thikar. *1979*
Technical Institute, Al-Sowaira.   *1988*
Technical Institute, Al-Taamim.   *1976*
Technical Institute, Basrah.   *1973*
Technical Institute, Hilla, Babylon.   *1976*
Technical Institute, Misan.   *1979*
Technical Institute, Mosul.   *1976*
  Tel: 81891
Technical Institute, **Namrood**, Naynawa. *1980*
Technical Institute, Wasit.   *1980*
Technical Institute of Medicine, Baghdad.   *1972*
  Tel: 5153

National Union of Iraqi Students and Youth –
ODYSI (IUS)
Wazyriah, Baghdad.
Telex: 212747 nuis ik

                    *

**Ministry of Higher Education and Scientific
Research**
Baghdad.
Tel: Telex: 212385 balemali ik
Iraqi National Commission for Unesco
Ministry of Education, Baghdad.
Tel: 887-2947 (ext. 3714). Telex: 2259 educate
ik. Cables: incu baghdad

IRELAND
IRLANDE

UNIVERSITIES AND UNIVERSITY COLLEGES—
UNIVERSITES ET COLLEGES UNIVERSITAIRES

*University of Dublin.
  TRINITY COLLEGE, Dublin 2. (The Registrar)
                                                1591
  Tel: (1) 772941. Fax: (1) 772694. Telex:
  93782 tcd ei
  S : Hebrew, Biblical & theo st, mus, ed, eng,
  phy, dent, phil, eco pol, math, class, lang-lit,
  hist-pol, Hebrew & Semitic lang, Irish &
  Celtic lang, law, eco-soc st, mental & moral
  sc, remedial ling, nat, phar.
*National University of Ireland, 49 Merrion
Square, Dublin 2.   *1908*

  Tel: (1) 767246. Telex: 25278 ucd ei
  F : arts, phil-soc, Celtic, sc, law, med-dent, eng-
  arc, com, agr, dairy, vet.
  UNIVERSITY COLLEGE, Cork.
    Tel: (21) 276871. Telex: 26050 unic ei
  UNIVERSITY COLLEGE, Belfield, Dublin 4.
    Tel: (1) 693244. Fax: (1) 694409. Telex:
    32693 ucd ei
  UNIVERSITY COLLEGE, Galway.
    Tel: (91) 24411. Fax: (91) 25700. Telex:
    50023 unig ei
  ST. PATRICK'S COLLEGE, Maynooth, Co.

Kildare.
Tel: (1) 285222. Fax: (1) 286583
*Dublin City University, Albert College, Glasnevin, Dublin 9. *1975*
Tel: (1) 370077. Fax: 360830. Telex: 30690 nihe ei

*University of Limerick, Plassy House, Castleroy, Limerick. *1972*
Tel: (61) 333644. Fax: (61) 330316. Telex: 70609

OTHER INSTITUTIONS—AUTRES INSTITUTIONS

Technological and Technical Education— Enseignement technique et technologique

Dublin Institute of Technology, 14 Mount Street, Upper, Dublin 2. *1978*
Tel: (1) 611133
COLLEGE OF CATERING, Cathal Brugha Street, Dublin 1.
Tel: (17) 747886. Fax: (17) 743634
COLLEGE OF COMMERCE, Rathmines, Dublin 6.
Tel: (1) 970666
COLLEGE OF MARKETING AND DESIGN, 40 Mountjoy Square, Dublin 1.
Tel: (1) 363000
COLLEGE OF MUSIC, Adelaid Road, Dublin 2.
Tel: (1) 784393
COLLEGE OF TECHNOLOGY, Bolton Street, Dublin 1.
Tel: (1) 727177
COLLEGE OF TECHNOLOGY, Kevin Street, Dublin 8.
Tel: (1) 757541. Fax: (1) 780282
Crawford College of Art and Design, Emmet Place, Cork.
Tel: (21) 966777
Dun Laoghaire School of Art and Design, Carriglea Park, Kill Avenue, Dun Laoghaire, Co. Dublin.
Tel: (1) 801138
Limerick College of Art, Commerce and Technology, Moylish Park, Limerick.
Tel: (61) 51344
The National College of Art and Design, 100 Thomas Street, Dublin 8.
Tel: (1) 711377
Also Regional Technical Colleges at: Athlone; Carlow; Cork; Dundalk; Galway; Letterkenny; Sligo; Tralee; Waterford.

Professional Training—Enseignement professionnel

College of Industrial Relations, Sandford Road, Dublin 6.
Tel: (1) 972917
College of Hotel Management, Shannon Free Airport, Co. Clare.
Tel: (61) 61444
Dublin Institute for Advanced Studies, 9–10 Burlington Road, Dublin 4. *1940*
Tel: (1) 680748. Telex: 31687

S : *Celtic, theoretical phy, cosmic phy.*
The Royal College of Physicians of Ireland, 6 Kildare Street, Dublin 2. *1667, 1692*
Tel: (1) 616677
The Royal College of Surgeons, 123, St. Stephen's Green, Dublin 2. *1784*
Tel: (1) 780200. Fax: (1) 780934. Telex: 30795 rcsi ei

Teacher Training—Formation pédagogique

Church of Ireland College of Education, 96 Upper Rathmines Road, Dublin 6. *1811*
Tel: (1) 970033
Froebel College of Education, Sion Hill, Blackrock, Co. Dublin. *1943*
Tel: (1) 888520
Mary Immaculate College, South Circular Road, Limerick. *1898*

Tel: (61) 314923
Mater Dei Institute of Education, Clonliffe Road, Dublin 3.
St. Angela's College of Education for Home Economics, Lough Gill, Sligo.
Tel: (71) 42051
St. Catherine's College of Education for Home Economics, Sion Hill, Blackrock, Co. Dublin.

Tel: (1) 884989
St. Mary's Training College, Marino, Dublin 9.
   Tel: (1) 338756
St. Patrick's College, Drumcondra, Dublin 9.
                                                    1875

Tel: (1) 376191
Thomond College of Education, Castletroy, Limerick.   *1976*
Tel: (61) 334888

The Committee of the Heads of the Irish Universities

The Committee is comprised of the Provost of Trinity College, Dublin, and the Presidents of University College, Cork, University College, Dublin, University College, Galway, St. Patrick's College Maynooth, Dublin City University and the University of Limerick; the National University of Ireland is represented on the Committee by its Vice-Chancellor (one of the University College Presidents) and its Registrar. Meetings are held some five times a year, at which are discussed matters and problems of common interest. The Committee, as necessary, presents common views to the Higher Education Authority and to government ministries and, in turn, may be consulted by these agencies. Meetings rotate between the participating institutions and are chaired by the Head of the host institution. New arrangements are being provided for the secretariat which will be announced in the next edition.

Le Comité des Chefs des Universités irlandaises se compose du Principal de Trinity College, Dublin, et des Présidents des Collèges universitaires de Cork, Dublin, Galway, de l'Université de la Ville de Dublin et de l'Université de Limerick et du College universitaire St. Patrick, Maynooth; l'Université nationale d'Irlande est représentée au sein du Comité par son Vice-Chancelier (l'un des Présidents des Collèges universitaires) et son Secrétaire général. Les réunions se tiennent environ cinq fois par an; on y discute de problèmes et de questions d'intérêt commun. Le cas échéant, le Comité soumet à l'Autorité suprême en matière d'enseignement supérieur et aux ministères du gouvernement des points de vue communs et peut, à son tour, être consulté par ces institutions. Les réunions se tiennent, par roulement, dans les institutions membres et sont présidées par le Chef de l'institution hôte. Le Secrétariat est actuellement en voie de réorganisation. Les nouvelles dispositions seront annoncées dans la prochaine édition.

Chairman: Dr. Patrick Masterson, President, University College, Dublin.
Executive Officer: Salters Sterling. University of Dublin, Trinity College, Dublin 2.
   Tel: (1) 772941 (ext. 1558). Fax: (1) 772694.
   Telex: 93782 tcd ei

An Comhchaidreamh

Founded in 1935, the Irish Inter-University Association aims to maintain contact between Irish speaking districts and further the development of the Irish language in all aspects of Irish life, including literature, industry and government, placing particular emphasis on university activities. It founded COMHAR the Irish language monthly review of literature and current affairs in 1942, an important literary forum for young Irish writers and journalists. An Comhchaidreamh also founded GAEL-LINN in 1953, an organization actively engaged in promoting industries in Gaeltacht areas, in publishing records and in organizing highly successful courses in spoken Irish. Special emphasis has been placed in recent years on youth development. GAEL-LINN organizes debates, runs courses in Summer Colleges and Venture Sports, and funds scholarships to Irish-speaking districts.

Fondée en 1935, l'Association interuniversitaire irlandaise s'efforce de maintenir le contact entre les districts de langue irlandaise et de promouvoir le développement de l'utilisation de l'irlandais dans tous les aspects de la vie irlandaise, notamment la vie littéraire, l'industrie et le gouvernement, en mettant un accent particulier sur les activités universitaires. En 1942, elle a fondé COMHAR, revue mensuelle de littérature et d'actualité qui paraît en langue irlandaise, et importante tribune littéraire pour les jeunes écrivains et journalistes irlandais. An Comhchaidreamh a également fondé, en 1953, l'organisation GAEL-LINN, qui s'occupe activement de promouvoir les industries dans les districts de langue irlandaise, d'éditer des disques et d'organiser des cours d'irlandais parlé qui ont un grand succès. Au cours de ces dernières années un accent particulier a été mis sur le développement des activités pour les jeunes. GAEL-LINN organise des débats, ainsi que des cours d'été et des activités sportives, et finance des bourses dans les districts de langue irlandaise.
President: Uaitéar Ó Garuáin.
Secretary: Máiréad Ó Cathasaigh.
86, Sr. Gardnar Íocht., Baile Átha Cliath 1.
   Tel: (1) 365572

Irish Federation of University Women (IFUW)
No. 5, Trinity College, Dublin 6.

World University Service (WUS)
37 Wexford Street, Dublin 2.
Tel: (1) 714181. Telex: 91259 pi ei
Pax Romana
30 Fitzwilliam Place, Dublin 2.
Union of Students in Ireland – USI
8 Belvedere Place, Dublin 7.
Irish Student Travel Service – USIT
19 Aston Quay, Dublin 2.
Student Christian Movement of Ireland (WSCF)
13 Talbot Street, Dublin 1.
Tel: (1) 788484
World Union of Jewish Students (WUJS)

Contact: 89 Chausser De Vleurgat, 1050
Brussels (Belgium).
Tel: (2) 647-7279. Telex: 20625

*

An Roinn Oideachais (Department of Education)
Marlborough Street, Dublin 1.
Tel: (1) 734700. Fax: (1) 729553. Telex: 31136
Irish National Commission for Unesco
Department of Education, Marlborough
Street, Dublin 1.
Tel: (1) 717101 (ext. 87). Telex: 31136 educ ei.
Cables: neo dublin

ISRAEL
ISRAËL

UNIVERSITIES AND TECHNICAL UNIVERSITIES—
UNIVERSITES ET UNIVERSITES TECHNIQUES

Universitat Ben Gurion Ba'Negev [Ben-Gurion
U. of the Negev], Beer-Sheva 84120.
                                    1965, 1969
Tel: (57) 661111. Telex: 5254 unegil
*hum-soc, eng, heal sc, nat, desert res, app res,
Ben Gurion Heritage.*
***Universitat Haifa** [U. of Haifa], Haifa 31999.
                                          1963
Tel: (4) 240111. Telex: 46660 uniha il
hum, soc-math, ed, soc w.
***Ha'Technion—Machon Technologi Le'-Israel**
[Israel I. of Technology], Haifa 32000.
                                    1912, 1924
Tel: (4) 292111. Telex: 46406
*civ eng, arc-urb, mec, elec, ch eng, agr eng, ind
& mangt eng, biomed eng, math, phy, ch, mec,
nucl sc, aero eng, mater eng, food, comp, biol.*
***Ha'Universita Ha'Ivrit Bi'Yerushalayim** [The
Hebrew U. of Jerusalem], Mt. Scopus, Jerusa-
lem 91905. (The Academic Secretary).
                                          1925
Tel: (2) 882111. Telex: 26458 scopm il

F : *hum, soc, law, sc, agr, med, dent, math-nat.*
S : *phar, soc w, lib, occup ther.*
***Universitat Bar-Ilan** [Bar-Ilam U.], Ramat-Gan
52115.   *1952, 1955*
Tel: (3) 718111. Telex: 3613111
hum-Jewish st, soc, nat-math, law.
***Machon Weizmann Le'Mada** [The Weizmann I.
of Science], Rehovoth 76100.
                                    1934, 1949
Tel: (8) 482111. Telex: 361900 wix il
math, phy, ch, biophy-bioch, biol (all post-
grad).
***Universitat Tel-Aviv** [Tel-Aviv U.], Ramat-
Aviv, Tel-Aviv 69978.   *1953, 1956*
Tel: (3) 420111. Telex: 342171 versy il
*hum, arts soc, law, exact sc, eng, life sc, med,
bus adm-mangt.*
Ha'Universita Ha'Petuha [Everyman's (Open)
U.], P.O. Box 39328, Tel-Aviv 61392.
Tel: (3) 422511
hum, soc, nat, math.

OTHER INSTITUTIONS—AUTRES INSTITUTIONS

Professional Education—Enseignement professionnel

Hamihlala Leminhal [The College of Administra-
tion], 93 Arlozorov Street, Tel-Aviv 61480.
Tel: (3) 429297

Midreshet Ruppin [Ruppin C. of Agriculture],
Emek Hefer 60960.
Academia Bezalel [Bezalel A. of Arts and

Design], Bezalel Street, Jerusalam 94591.
Tel: (2) 225116. Telex: 26452 bezal il
*fa, graph des, env & ind des, cer des, silver-
smith, photo.*
**Ha-Academia Lemusika Ulemahol Biyerusha-
layim Al-Shem Rubin** [The Jerusalem Rubin A.
of Music and Dance], 7 Peretz Smolenskin
Street, Jerusalem 92101.
Tel: (2) 635271
Beit Sefer Gavoah Letechnologia [Jerusalem C.

of Technology], P.O. Box 16031, Jerusalem
91106.
Tel: (2) 423131
comp, appl phy-electro-optics, electro.
**Beit Hasefer Hagavoa Lemdaei Hatextile
Valeofna Al'Shem Shenkar** [Shenkar C. of
Textile Technology and Fashion], 24 Anna
Frank Street, Ramat-Gan 52526.
Tel: (3) 7521133. Telex: 341118 btv il (ext.
5790)

Teacher Training—Formation pédagogique

Mihlelet Beit Berl [Beit-Berl Teachers' Training
C.], Beit-Berl Post 44925.
**Hamihlala Lehinuch Gufani Al'Shem Zinman
Bermahon Wingate** [The Zinman C. of Physical
Education at the Wingate I.], Wingate Post
Office, Netanya 42902.
Tel: (53) 38044
Hamihlala Lehinuch Al'Shem David Yellin [The
David Yellin Teachers' C.], P.O. Box 3578,
Jerusalem 91035.

Tel: (2) 533111
Hamihlala   Lehinuch   Al'Shem   Levinsky
[Levinsky Teacher's C.], P.O. Box 48130, Tel-
Aviv 61480.
Tel: (3) 426162
Mihlala Yerushalayim Lebanot [Michala, Jerusa-
lem C. for Women], P.O. Box 16078, Bayit
Vegan, Jerusalem 91160.
Tel: (2) 422481

Council for Higher Education
The Council is a statutory body created by
the Council for Higher Education Law of 1958.
It is the State institution charged with higher
education in the country. It has 25 members,
including the Minister of Education and Culture,
who is *ex-officio* its Chairman. At least two-thirds
of its members must be academics of standing,
recommended by the Minister after consultation
with the institutions of higher education. The
members of the Council are appointed *ad
personam* by the President of the State.
The powers of the Council include: to recommend to the Government the granting of a licence
to open and maintain an institution of higher
education; to recommend to the Government the
partial or full accreditation of institutions
of higher education; to authorize accredited
institutions to award academic degrees and
appoint professors; to permit the use of
recognized academic nomenclature.
In January 1974, the Council appointed a
Planning and Grants Committee, consisting of six
members, including its chairman, who is *ex-
officio* a member of the Council. The Committee
acts as a buffer between institutions of higher
education and the Government. It is authorized
to submit proposals for the overall higher education budget to the Government and to allocate
it between the institutions, which are free to
conduct their academic and administrative affairs
as they see fit. The Committee is responsible

for the planning of higher education and must
present its opinion to the Council, which must
decide on the need for and creation of any new
institution or new unit in an existing institution,
and if there are any financial implications.
*Le Conseil de l'enseignement supérieur est
un établissement de droit public créé par la Loi
du Conseil pour l'enseignement supérieur en 1958.
C'est une institution d'Etat, chargée de l'enseignement supérieur dans le pays. Il comprend vingt-
cinq membres, y compris le Ministre de l'éducation et de la culture qui en est le président de droit.
Les deux-tiers au moins de ses membres doivent
être des personnalités éminentes de l'enseignement
supérieur, recommandées par le Ministre après
consultation avec les établissements d'enseignement supérieur. Les membres du Conseil sont
nommés personnellement par le Président de
la République. Le Conseil a pour fonctions:
d'appuyer auprès du gouvernement l'obtention
d'une autorisation pour ouvrir et faire fonctionner
un établissement d'enseignement supérieur;
de recommander au gouvernement d'agréer
pleinement ou partiellement des établissements;
d'autoriser des établissements agréés à délivrer
des diplômes et à nommer des professeurs; de
permettre l'utilisation de la nomenclature des
titres reconnus.
En janvier 1974, le Conseil a nommé un Comité
pour la planification et les crédits universitaires qui
comprend six membres, dont le président, lui-
même membre de droit du Conseil. Le Comité*

joue un rôle de modérateur entre les établissements d'enseignement supérieur et le gouvernement. Il est autorisé à soumettre des propositions au gouvernement pour le budget global de l'enseignement supérieur ainsi que l'affectation des crédits approuvés entre les divers établissements qui sont libres de mener leurs affaires académiques et administratives comme ils le jugent.

Le Comité est responsable de la planification de l'enseignement supérieur et doit présenter son opinion au Conseil. Ce dernier doit décider du besoin et de la création d'un nouvel établissement ou d'un nouveau département dans un établissement déjà existant, ainsi que des implications financières possibles.

P.O. Box 4037, Jerusalem 91040.
Tel: (2) 663131

Technion Academic Staff Association (IAUPL)
  Contact: 18, rue du Docteur Roux, 75015 Paris (France).
  Tel: (33-1) 47-83-31-65
The Hebrew University of Jerusalem Staff Association (IAUPL)

Sherman Building, Jerusalem.
Israel Association of University Women (IFUW)
  P.O. Box 4173, Jerusalem.
Israel Student Association for the United Nations (ISMUN)
  P.O. Box 7747, Jerusalem.
National Union of Israel Students (WUJS)
  Tel-Aviv University, Building 'G', Ramat Aviv.
  Tel: (3) 413671

*

Committee for the Evaluation of Foreign Academic Degrees
  Ministry of Education and Culture, 34 Shivtey Yisrael Street, Jerusalem.
  Tel: (2) 817251
Ministry of Education and Culture
  34 Shivtey Yisrael Street, Jerusalem.
  Tel: (2) 817251
Israel National Commission for Unesco
  Ministry of Education and Culture.
  34 Shivtey Yisrael Street, Jerusalem.
  Tel: (2) 817251 (ext. 266). Cables: isrunesco jerusalem

ITALY
ITALIE

UNIVERSITIES AND TECHNICAL UNIVERSITIES — UNIVERSITES ET UNIVERSITES TECHNIQUES

Università degli Studi di Ancona, Piazza Roma 22-23, 60100 Ancona.
Tél: (71) 28212. Télex: 561838 univan i
F : ing, méd-chir, éco-com.
Università dell'Aquila, Piazza dell'Annunziata 1, 67100 L'Aquila.   *1952*
Tél: 862-6461. Télex: 600213 univaq i
F : éd, math-phy-nat, ing, méd-chir.
*Università degli Studi di Bari, Palazzo Ateneo, Piazza Umberto I 1, 70100 Bari. (Sig. Rettore).
                                                             1924
Tél: (80) 314111. Télex: 810598 univba i
F : dr, éco-com, méd-chir, phar, agr, let-phil, math-phy-nat, ing, éd, lang-let étr, vét.
E : stat.
Università Libera di Bergamo, Piazza Vecchia 6, 24100, Bergamo.
Tél: (35) 217195
F : ling-let étr.

*Università degli Studi di Bologna, Via Zamboni 33, 40100 Bologna.   *1075*
Tél: (51) 220980. Télex: 511650 univbo i
F : dr, pol, éco-com, let-phil, méd-chir, éd, math-phy-nat, phar, ing, agr, vét.
Università degli Studi di Brescia, Via Cefalonia 49, 25100 Brescia.
Tél: (30) 298881. Télex: 304116 univbs i
F : méd-chir, ing, éco-com.
*Università degli Studi di Cagliari, Via Università 40, 09100 Cagliari.   *1606*
Tél: (70) 662493. Télex: 790269 unica i
F : dr, éco-com, pol, let-phil, éd, méd-chir, math-phy-nat, phar, ing.
E : stat.
Università degli Studi della Calabria, Via Matteotti, 87100, Calabria (Cosenza).   *1972*
Tél: (984) 861961. Télex: 800044 unical i
F : let-phil, math-phy-nat, ing, éco-soc.

*Università degli Studi di Camerino, Via del
Bastione 3, 62032 Camerino.   *1336, 1727*
Tél: (737) 401. Télex: 560024 unicam i
F : dr, phar, math-phy-nat.
Università degli Studi di Cassino, Via Marconi,
03043 Cassino (Frosinone).   *1979*
Tél: (776) 26633
F : éd.
D : éco-com, méc.
*Università degli Studi di Catania, Piazza della
Università, 95129 Catania.   *1434*
Tél: (95) 310355. Télex: 970255
F : dr, pol, éco-com, let-phil, méd-chir, math-
phy-nat, phar, agr, ing.
Ce : phy nucl.
Università abruzzese degli Studi «G. D'Annunzio»
di Chieti, Via dei Vestini, 66013 Chieti.   *1965*
Tél: (871) 586141
F : let-phil, méd-chir, dr, pol (Teramo); éco-
com, arc, lang-let étr (Pescara).
*Università degli Studi di Ferrara, Via Savona-
rola 9, 44100 Ferrara.   *1391*
Tél: (532) 39181. Télex: 570850 uniferr i
F : dr, méd-chir, phar, math-phy-nat, éd, ing.
Università degli Studi di Firenze, Piazza San
Marco 4, 50121 Firenze.   *1321, 1924*
Tél: (55) 27571. Télex: 572400 unifi i
F : agr, arc, éco-com, phar, dr, let-phil, éd,
méd-chir, math-phy-nat, pol, ing.
I : géog, paléo, papyrologie, psyc.
F : stat.
*Università degli Studi di Genova, Via Balbi 5,
16126 Genova.   *1471*
Tél: (10) 2099. Télex: 271114
F : dr, pol, éco-com, let-phil, méd-chir, math-
phy-nat, phar, ing, arc, éd.
Università degli Studi di Lecce, Viale Taranto 2,
73100.   *1959*
Tél: (832) 4711. Télex: 860830 unstle i
F : let-phil, éd, math-phy-nat.
*Università degli Studi di Macerata, Piazza della
Università 2, 62100 Macerata.   *1290*
Tél: (733) 41646
F : dr, let-phil.
E : rech soc.
Università degli Studi di Messina, Via Tommaso
Cannizzaro, 98100 Messina.   *1548*
Tél: (90) 711022. Télex: 980075 unime i
F : dr, pol, let-phil, éd, méd-chir, phar, vét,
éco-com, math-phy-nat.
E : stat.
*Università degli Studi di Milano, Via Festa del
Perdono, 20100 Milano.   *1923*
Tél: (2) 88461. Télex: 320484 unimi i
F : dr, let-phil, pol, méd-chir, math-phy-nat,
agr, vét, phar.
E : stat.
*Università Cattolica del Sacro Cuore, Largo A.
Gemelli 1, 20123 Milano.   *1924*

Tél: (2) 8856. Télex: 321033 ucatmi i
F : dr, pol, éco-com, let-phil, math-phy-nat, éd;
agr (Piacenza), méd-chir (Roma).
I : phys.
E : stat, jour.
D : ét relig.
Università di Economia e Commercio «Luigi
Bocconi», Via Sarfatti 25, 20136 Milano.   *1902*
Tél: (2) 83841. Télex: 316003 sdaboc i
F : éco-com, lang-lit étr.
I : pol, éco-com, stat, dr comparé, hist éco,
techn ind, math.
*Università degli Studi di Modena, Via
Università 4, 41100 Modena.
Tél: (59) 329111. Télex: 583257 fisimo i
F : dr, méd-chir, phar, math-phy-nat, éco-com.
Ce : biol mar (Livorno).
Università degli Studi del Molise, Campobasso.
Tél: (874) 63045
F : éco-soc, agr.
Università degli Studi di Napoli, Corso Umberto
1, 80100 Napoli.   *1224*
Tél: (81) 7819111. Télex: 722040 univna i
F : dr, éco-com, pol, let-phil, méd-chir (2),
math-phy-nat, phar, ing, arc, agr, vét.
*Università degli Studi di Padova, Via Otto
Febbraio 2, 35100 Padova.   *1222*
Tél: (49) 651400. Télex: 430176 unpadu i
F : dr, pol, let-phil, éd, méd-chir, math-phy-
nat, ing, agr, éco-com, phar, stat-démographie-
act.
Università degli Studi di Palermo, Piazza Marina,
90100 Palermo.   *1779, 1806*
Tél: (91) 283041. Télex: 910170 univpa i
F : dr, let-phil, éco-com, méd-chir, math-phy-
nat, ing, arc, agr, phar, éd.
*Università degli Studi di Parma, Via Cavestro 7,
43100 Parma.   *1064*
Tél: (521) 2041. Télex: 530327 univpr i
F : dr, méd-chir, phar, vét, math-phy-nat, éco-
com, éd.
E : adm des aff, paléo, mus, opt.
*Università degli Studi di Pavia, Corso Strada
Nuova 65, 27100 Pavia.   *1361*
Tél: (0382) 35491. Télex: 312841 unipav i
F : dr, pol, éco-com, let-phil, méd-chir, phar,
math-phy-nat, ing.
E : paléographie-phill mus.
*Università degli Studi di Perugia, Piazza della
Università, 06100 Perugia.   *1200, 1308*
Tél: (75) 4691. Télex: 662078 unipg i
F : dr, pol, éco-com, let-phil, méd-chir, math-
phy-nat, phar, agr, vét, éd.
Università degli Studi di Pisa, Lungarno Pacinotti
43, 56100 Pisa.   *1343*
Tél: (50) 590000. Télex: 590035 univpi i
F : dr, pol, let-phil, méd-chir, phar, agr, vét,
éco-com, math-phy-nat, ing, ling-let étr.
Università degli Studi Basilicata, Presso 1st Ex-

Enauli-Rione Francioso 85, 85100 Potenza.
1982
Tél: (971) 334111
F : math-phy-nat, ing, agr, let-phil.
Università degli Studi di Reggio Calabria, Via
Cimino 25, 89100 Reggio Calabria.
Tél: (965) 331701. Télex: 890099 univrc i
F : arc, méd-chir, dr.
*Università degli Studi di Roma I (La Sapienza),
Città Universitaria, Piazzale delle Scienze 5,
00100 Roma. *1303*
Tél: (6) 4991. Télex: 620564 unisap i
F : dr, pol, stat-démographie-act, éco-com, let-
phil, éd, méd-chir, math-phy-nat, phar, ing,
arc.
E : ing (aérospatiale), archives-bibl, bibl.
*Università degli Studi di Roma II (Tor Vergata),
Via Orazio Raimondo, 00100 Roma.
Tél: (6) 79791
F : dr, let-phil, méd-chir, math-phy-nat, ing.
**Libera Università Internazionale degli Studi
Sociali**, Viale Pola 12, 00198 Roma. *1966*
Tél: (6) 841051
F : éco-com, pol, dr.
E : lang.
I : ét soc, ét Amérique latine.
Università degli Studi di Salerno, Via Urbano II,
84100 Salerno.
Tél: (89) 225488. Télex: 722106 univas i
F : dr, éco-com, let-phil, éd, math-phy-nat.
*Università degli Studi di Sassari, Piazza
Università 21, 07100 Sassari, Sardegna. *1562*
Tél: (79) 236134. Télex: 790299 sacer i
F : dr, méd, phar, vét, agr, math-phy-nat, éd.
Università degli Studi di Siena, Via Banchi di
Sotto 55, 53100 Siena. *1240*
Tél: (577) 298000. Télex: 572459 univsi i
F : dr, let-phil, méd-chir, phar, math-phy-nat,
éco-banc, éd.
Università degli Studi di Torino, Via Giuseppe
Verdi 8, 10124 Torino. *1404*
Tél: (11) 519436. Télex: 220225 univto i
F : dr, éco-com, pol, éd, méd-chir, phar, agr,
vét, let-phil, math-phy-nat.

Università degli Studi di Trento, Via Bellenzani
12, 38100 Trento. *1966*
Tél: (461) 981136. Fax: (461) 881299. Télex:
400674 unitn i
F : éco-com, math-phy-nat, socio.
*Università degli Studi di Trieste, Piazzale
Europa 1, 34100 Trieste. *1877, 1924*
Tél: (40) 560038. Télex: 460865 univts i
F : dr, éco-com, pol, let-phil, éd, math-phy-nat,
phar, ing, méd-chir.
E : lang mod pour interp.
Università degli Studi di Tuscia, S. Giovanni
Decollato 1, 01100 Viterbo. *1979*
Tél: 761) 33073
F : agr, ling & let étr.
*Università degli Studi di Udine, Via Antonini 8,
33100 Udine. *1978*
Tél: (432) 297105. Télex: 450412 univud i
F : lang-lit étr, ing, math-phy-nat, agr, let-phil.
Università Libera di Urbino, Via Saffi 1, 61029
Urbino. *1506, 1826*
Tél: (722) 4511
F : dr, éco-com, let-phil, éd, math-phy-nat,
phar.
*Università degli Studi di Venezia, Palazzi
Foscari e Giustiniani di Vescovi, 30100 Venezia.
1868
Tél: (41) 5285420. Télex: 410638 univve i
F : let-phil, éco-com, lang lit étr, ch ind.
Università degli Studi di Verona, Via S.
Francesco 1, 37129 Verona.
Tél: (45) 591100. Télex: 431143 univer i
F : méd-chir, éco-com, éd.
*Politecnico di Milano, Piazza L. da Vinci 32,
20123 Milano. *1863*
Tél: (2) 23991. Télex: 333467 polimi i
F : ing, arc.
Ce : ét nucl.
*Politecnico di Torino, Corso Duca degli Abruzzi
24, 10129 Torino. *1859, 1906*
Tél: (11) 55661. Télex: 220646 polito i
F : arc, ing.
E : ing (aérospatiale), arts graph.

OTHER INSTITUTIONS—AUTRES INSTITUTIONS

Technical Education—Enseignement technique

Istituto Universitario di Architectura, S. Croce
Campazzo dei Tolentini 191, 30104 Venezia.
1926

Tél: (41) 703377
F : arc.

Professional Education— Enseignement professionnel

Istituto Universitario Navale, Via Acton 38, 80100 Napoli. *1920*
Tél: (81) 5512249. Télex: 710417 navale i
F : nav, éco mar.
Istituto Universitario Orientale, Piazza S. Giovanni Maggiore 30, 80133 Napoli.
1732, 1888

Tél: (81) 322597. Télex: 721089 iuo i
F : let-phil, pol.
E : ét isl.
Istituto Universitario di Lingue moderne, Piazza dei Volontari 3, 20145 Milano.
Tél: (2) 313922

Teacher Training—Formation pédagogique

Scuola Normale Superiore, Piazza dei Cavalieri 6, Pisa. *1813*
Tél: (50) 59711. Télex: 590548 snspi i
Scuola Superiore di Studi Universitari e di Perfezionamento, Via Carducci 40, 56100 Pisa.
Tél: (50) 45377
Istituto Universitario pareggiato di Magistero «Suor Orsola Benincasa», Corso Vittorio Emmanuele, 35100 Napoli. *1901*
Tél: (81) 418518
Istituto Universitario di Magistero «Maria SS Assunta», Via della Transpontina 21, 00100 Roma. *1939*
Tél: (6) 68277
Istituto Superiore pareggiato di Educazione Fisica dell'Aquila, Via F. Crispi, 67100 L'Aquila.
1968
Tél: (862) 22104
Istituto Superiore pareggiato di Educazione fisica di Bologna, Via S. Vitale 15, 40100 Bologna.
1960
Tél: (51) 239491
Istituto Superiore pareggiato di Educazione Fisica di Firenze, Via Nicolodi 2, 50137 Firenze.
1960
Tél: (55) 571997
Istituto Superiore pareggiato di Educazione Fisica

della Lombardia, Piazza S. Alessandro 1, 20123 Milano. *1968*
Tél: (2) 803431
Istituto Superiore pareggiato di Educazione Fisica di Milano, Via S. Agnese 2, 20123 Milano. *1964*
Tél: (2) 8856
Istituto Superiore pareggiato di Educazione Fisica di Napoli, Presso la Mastra d'Oltremare, 80100 Napoli. *1960*
Tél: (81) 615241
Istituto Superiore pareggiato di Educazione Fisica di Palermo, Via Imperatore Federico 61, 90100 Palermo. *1965*
Tél: (91) 546106
Istituto Superiore pareggiato di Educazione Fisica di Perugia, Via Canali 12, 06100 Perugia. *1967*
Tél: (75) 754206
Istituto Superiore statale di Educazione Fisica di Roma, Foro Italico, Piazza Lauro de Bosis 15, 00100 Roma.
Tél: (6) 390616
Istituto Superiore pareggiato di Educazione Fisica di Torino, Piazza Bernini 12, 10100 Torino.
Tél: (577) 745774
Istituto Superiore pareggiato di Educazione Fisica di Urbino, Via Saffi 12, 61029 Urbino. *1967*
Tél: (722) 39152

General Education—Enseignement général

Università Italiana per Stranieri di Perugia, Piazza Fortebraccio 4, 006100 Perugia.

Italien (pour étrangers).
Tél: (75) 64344. Télex: 662079 unstra i

Conferenza permanente dei Rettori delle Università italiane

La Conférence permanente des recteurs des universités italiennes, née après la deuxième guerre mondiale en tant que réunion des recteurs des universités de l'Italie du Nord, s'est étendue aux recteurs de toutes les universités d'Italie et est devenue finalement l'organe permanent de liaison entre les universités italiennes.

La Conférence a pour but de collaborer avec le gouvernement en ce qui concerne les initiatives visant aux solutions des problèmes universitaires, de proposer des mesures législatives et administratives pour une meilleure organisation pédagogique et scientifique des universités et pour assurer entre celles-ci une unité d'action et de directives.

Les organes de la Conférence sont: l'Assemblée,

le Président et le Comité de présidence. Il peut y avoir des commissions pour l'étude des problèmes particuliers.

The Standing Conference of Italian University Rectors, created after the Second World War as an assembly of university rectors from Northern Italy, developed to include the rectors of all the Italian universities and finally became the permanent liaison organization between Italian universities.

Its purposes are to collaborate with the government in seeking solutions to university problems, to propose legislative and administrative measures to improve the pedagogic and academic organization of universities, and to ensure unity of action and purpose between the universities.

The organs of the Conference are: the Assembly, the President and the Presidential Committee. Commissions may be set up to study particular problems.

Président: Prof. Vincenzo Buonocore.
Secrétaire: Prof. Gian Tommaso Scarascia Mugnozza.
Via Vittoria 64, 00187 Roma.
Tél: (6) 6785797. Télex: 622213 cprui i

Associazione Nazionale Professori Universitari di Ruolo – ANPUR (IAUPL)
Correspondant: 18, rue du Docteur Roux, 75015 Paris (France).
Tél: (33-1) 47-83-31-65
Federazione Italiana Laureate Diplomate Istituti Superiori (IFUW)
Viale XI Febbraio 2, 27100 Pavia.
Unione Nazionale Universitaria Rappresentativa Italiana – UNURI
Via Palestro 11, Roma.

Centro Relazioni Universitarie con l'Estero – CRUEI
Via Palestro 11, Roma.
Movimento Laureati di Azione Cattolica (Pax Romana)
Via della Conciliazione 1, 00193 Roma.
Federazione Universitaria Cattolica Italiana (Pax Romana)
Via della Conciliazione 1, 00193 Roma.
F.G.E.I.
c/o Michele Rostan, Via C. Poerio 37, 20159 Milano.
Movimento studentesco per l'Organizzazione internazionale (ISMUN)
Palazetto di Venezia, Via San Marco 3, 00186 Roma.
Federazione Giovanile Ebraica d'Italia (WUJS)
Correspondant: 89 Chaussee De Vleurgat, 1050 Brussels (Belgium).
Tél: (2) 647-7279. Télex: 20625

*

Centro Nazionale di Informazione in Materia di Equipollenza di Titoli di Studio
Direzione Generale degli Istruzione Universitaria, Via Trastevere, 00100 Roma.
Tél: (6) 658491. Télex: 614079 piuniv i
Ministero della pubblica Istruzione, Direzione generale per l'Istruzione universitaria
Via del Lavoro, Roma.
Tél: 1925543. Télex: 614079 piuniv i
Ministero degli Affari esteri
Palazzo Chigi, Roma.
Tél: 369011. Télex: 625368 faimae i
Commission nationale italienne pour l'Unesco
Piazza Firenze 27, 00186 Roma.
Tél: (6) 798240. Cables: italunesco roma

JAMAICA
JAMAÏQUE

*University of the West Indies, Mona, Kingston 7. (The Registrar). *1946, 1949, 1962*
Tel: P.B.X. 92-71660. Telex: 2123 univers ja
F : *med, arts, nat, soc, ed, gen st, law.*
I : *ed, soc-eco res, int rel, mass commun.*
See also:
  FACULTY OF ARTS AND GENERAL STUDIES, Barbados, p. 23.
  FACULTY OF EDUCATION, Barbados, p. 23.
  FACULTY OF NATURAL SCIENCES, Barbados, p. 23.

FACULTY OF SOCIAL SCIENCES, Barbados, p. 23.
FACULTY OF LAW, Barbados, p. 23.
INSTITUTE OF SOCIAL AND ECONOMIC RESEARCH (EASTERN CARIBBEAN BRANCH), Barbados, p. 23.
FACULTY OF AGRICULTURE, Trinidad, p. 420.
FACULTY OF ARTS AND GENERAL STUDIES, Trinidad, p. 420.
FACULTY OF EDUCATION, Trinidad, p. 420.
FACULTY OF ENGINEERING, Trinidad, p. 420.

FACULTY OF LAW, Trinidad, p. 420.
FACULTY OF NATURAL SCIENCES, Trinidad, p. 420.
FACULTY OF SOCIAL SCIENCES, Trinidad, p. 420.
College of Arts, Sciences, and Technology, 237 Old Hope Road, Kingston 6. *1958*
Tel: 92-71680
D : *bui, eng, com, sc, mangt, teacher ed.*
Ce : *comp.*
College of Agriculture, P.O. Box 170, Port Antonio, Postland. *1982*
Tel: 993 32-46
D : *nat, agr, anim sc, agr eng, agr ed, agr eco, hom eco.*
Cultural Training Centre, 1 Arthur Wint Drive, Kingston 5.
Tel: 926 28-00
S : *drama, art, dance, mus.*
West Indies College, Mandeville, Manchester.
Tel: 962 22-04
li arts.
Bethlehem Teacher College, Malvern P.O., St. Elizabeth.
Tel: 966 23-52
Church Teacher College, Mandeville, Manchester.
Tel: 962 26-62
Mico Teacher College, 1A Marescaux Road, Kingston 5.

Tel: 929 52-60
St. Josephs Teacher College, 16 Old Hope Road, Kingston 5.
Tel: 926 66-59
Shortwood Training College, 77 Shortwood Road, Kingston 8.
Tel: 924 10-95
Moneague Teacher College, Moneague P.O., St. Ann.
Tel: 972 32-89
Sam Sharpe Teacher College, Granville P.O., St. James.
Tel: 952 40-00
Passley Gardens Teachers Training College, Port Antonio P.O., Portland.
Tel: 993 26-21
G.C. Foster College of Physical Education and Sports.
Montego Bay Community College, Montego Bay P.O., St. James.
Tel: 952 17-05
Brown's Town Community College, Brown's Town P.O., St. Ann.
Tel: 975 23-39
Knox Community College, Spauldings P.O., Clarendon.
Tel: 964 24-10
Excelsior Education Centre Community College, 137 Mountain View Avenue, Kingston 3.
Tel: 928 22-87

Jamaica Union of Tertiary Students – JUTS (IUS)
CSO Box 8069, Kingston.
Guild of Undergraduates
University of the West Indies, P.O. Box 69, Mona, Kingston 7.
Student Christian Movement of Jamaica (WSCF) P.O. Box 527, Kingston 10.

Ministry of Education, Youth and Sports
2 National Heroes Circle, P.O. Box 202, Kingston.
Tel: 922 14-00
Jamaica National Commission for Unesco
25 Dominica Drive, Kingston 5.
Tel: 926 54-80. Cables jamunesco kingston

*

JAPAN
JAPON

UNIVERSITIES AND UNIVERSITY INSTITUTIONS
WITH GRADUATE SCHOOLS (1)—
UNIVERSITES ET ETABLISSEMENTS UNIVERSITAIRES
AVEC SECTIONS POUR GRADUES (1)

National Institutions—Institutions nationales

Aichi Kyoiku Daigaku [Aichi U. of Education], 1 Hirosawa Igawa-cho, Kariya-shi, Aichi 448.
1943, 1949
Tel: 566-36-3111
F : *ed.*

Akita Daigaku, Tegata Gakuen-cho, Akita-shi, Akita 010.   *1910, 1949*
Tel: 188-33-5261
F : *ed, med, mine.*

Asahikawa Ika Daigaku [Asahikawa Medical C.], 4-5 Nishikagura, Asahikawa-shi, Hokkaido 078
1973
Tel: 166-65-2111. Telex: 922492 asamel j
F : *med.*

*Chiba Daigaku, 1-33 Yayoi-cho, Chiba-shi, Chiba 260.   *1921, 1949*
Tel: 472-51-1111
F : *let, ed, phar, eng, hort, sc, med, law-eco, nurs.*

Denki-Tsushin Daigaku [U. of Electro-Communications], 1-5-1 Chofu-ga-oka, Chofu-shi, Tokyo 182.   *1942, 1949*
Tel: 424-83-2161
F : *electrocommun.*

Ehime Daigaku, 10-13 Dogo-himata, Matsuyama-shi, Ehime 790.   *1919, 1949*
Tel: 899-24-7111
F : *sc, ed, eng, agr, med, law-lit.*
S : *med.*
C : *agr.*

Fukui Daigaku, 3-9-1 Bunkyo, Fukui-shi, Fukui 910.   *1923, 1949*
Tel: 776-23-0500
F : *ed, eng.*

Fukui Ika Daigaku [Fukui Medical S.], 23 Shimoaizuki, Matsuoka-cho, Yoshida-gun, Fukui 910-11.   *1978*
Tel: 776-61-3111
F : *med.*

Fukuoka Kyoiku Daigaku [Fukuoka U. of Education], 729 Akama, Munakata-shi, Fukuoka 811-41.   *1943, 1949*
Tel: 940-32-2381

Fukushima Daigaku, 2 Sugumichi, Asakawa, Matsukawa-machi, Fukushima-shi, Fukushima 960-12.   *1921, 1949*
Tel: 245-48-5151
F : *ed, eco.*

Gifu Daigaku, 1-1 Yanagido, Gifu-shi, Gifu 501-4.   *1923, 1949*
Tel: 582-30-1111
F : *ed, med, eng, agr.*

Gunma Daigaku, 4-2 Aramaki-machi, Showa-machi 3, Maebashi-shi, Gunma 371. *1915, 1949*
Tel: 272-32-1611
F : *ed, med, eng.*

Hamamatsu Ika Daigaku [Hammamatsu U.S. of Medicine], 3600 Handa-cho, Hamamatsu-shi, Shizuoka 431-31.   *1974*
Tel: 534-35-2111

Hirosaki Daigaku, 1 Bunkyo-cho, Hirosaki-shi, Aomori 036.   *1920, 1949*
Tel: 172-36-2111
F : *hum, sc, agr, med.*

---

(1) It will be noted that all institutions of higher education included in this chapter bear the title 'Daigaku'. Their classification in various groups is based on a proposal made by the Ministry of Education of Japan.

(1) On notera que toutes les institutions d'enseignement supérieur figurant dans ce chapitre portent le titre de «Daigaku». Leur classement en différents groupes repose sur des propositions formulées par le Ministère de l'Education du Japon.

*Hiroshima Daigaku, 1-89 1-chome, Higashi-senda-machi, Naka-ku, Hiroshima 730.
1902, 1949
Tel: 82-241-1221
F : *let, ed, eco, sc, eng, integrated arts & sc, app biol, law, school ed.*

*Hitotsubashi Daigaku, 2-1 Naka, Kunitachishi, Tokyo 186. *1885, 1949*
Tel: 425-72-1101. Telex: 2842107 hitots j
F : *com, eco, law, soc.*

*Hokkaido Daigaku, Nishi 5-chome, Kita 8, Kita-ku, Sapporo-shi, Hokkaido 060. *1876, 1949*
Tel: 11-716-2111
F : *let, ed, law, eco, sc, phar, eng, agr, vet, fish, med, dent.*

Hokkaido Kyoiku Daigaku [Hokkaido U. of Education], Nishi-13, Minami-24, Sapporo, Hokkaido 064. *1943, 1949*
Tel: 11-561-4281
F : *ed*

Hyogo Kyoiku Daigaku [Hyogo U. of Teacher Education] 942-1 Shimokume, Yashiro-cho, Kato-gun, Hyogo 673-14. *1978*
Tel: 795-44-1101
F : *ed*

Ibaraki Daigaku, 2-1-1, Bunkyo, Mito-shi, Ibaraki 310. *1920, 1949*
Tel: 292-26-1621
F : *hum, ed, sc, eng, agr.*

Iwate Daigaku, 3-18-1 Ueda, Morioka-shi, Iwate 020. *1902, 1949*
Tel: 196-23-5171
F : *ed, eng, agr.*
C : *hum-soc.*

Joetsu Kyoiki Daigaku [Joetsu U. of Education], 1 Yamayashiki-machi, Joetsu-shi 943.
1978
Tel: 255-22-2411
F : *school ed.*

Kagawa Daigaku, Saiwai-cho, Takamatsu-shi, Kagawa 760. *1923, 1949*
Tel: 878-61-4141
F : *ed, eco, agr, law.*

Kagawa Ika Daigaku [Kagawa Medical S.], 1751-1 Ikenobe-oaza, Miki-cho, Kita-gun, Kagawa 761-07. *1978*
Tel: 878-98-5111
F : *med.*

*Kagoshima Daigaku, 1-21-24, Korimoto, Kagoshima-shi, Kagoshima 890. *1901, 1949*
Tel: 992-54-7141
F : *law-let, ed, sc, med, eng, agr, fish, dent.*

*Kanazawa Daigaku, 1-1 Marunouchi, Kanazawa-shi, Ishikawa 920. *1887, 1949*
Tel: 762-62-4281
F : *law, let, ed, sc, med, phar, techn, eco.*

Kanoya Taiiku Daigaku [National I. of Fitness and Sports], 1 Shiromizu, Kanoya-shi, Kagoshima 89-23. *1981*

Tel: 994-46-4111
F : *phys-recr.*

Kitami Kogyo Daigaku [Kitami I. of Engineering], 165 Koen-cho, Kitami-shi, Hokkaido 090.
1960, 1966, 1984
Tel: 157-24-7786

*Kobe Daigaku, 1-1 Rokkodai-cho, Nadu-ku, Kobe-shi, Hyogo 657. *1921, 1949*
Tel: 78-881-1212
F : *let, ed, law, eco, bus adm, sc, med, eng, agr.*

Kobe Shosen Daigaku [Kobe U. of Mercantile Marine], 5-1-1 Fukaeminami-machi, Higashi-ada-ku, Kobe-shi, Hyogo 658.
Tel: 78-453-2332
F : *mercantile mar.*

Kochi Daigaku, 2-5-1 Akebono-cho, Kochi-shi, Kochi 780. *1923, 1949*
Tel: 888-44-0111
F: *hum, eco, ed, agr, sc.*

Kochi Ika Daigaku [Kochi Medical C.], Kohasu, Okocho, Nankoku-shi, Kochi 781-51.
Tel: 888-66-5811
F : *med.*

*Kumamoto Daigaku, 2-40-1 Kurokami, Kumamoto-shi, Kurokamimachi, Kumamoto 860. *1887, 1949*
Tel: 96-344-2111
F : *law, let, ed, sc, med, phar, eng.*

*Kyoto Daigaku, Yoshida Honmachi, Sakyo-ku, Kyoto-shi, Kyoto 606. *1894, 1949*
Tel: 75-751-2111
F : *let, ed, law, eco, sc, med, phar, eng, agr.*

Kyoto Kogei Sen-i Daigaku [Kyoto I. of Technology], Hashigami-cho, Matsugasaki Sakyo-ku, Kyoto-shi, Kyoto 606. *1900, 1949*
Tel: 75-791-3211
F : *eng-des, tex.*

*Kyushu Daigaku, 6-10-1 Hakozaki, Higashi-ku, Fukuoka-shi, Fukuoka 812. *1910, 1949*
Tel: 92-641-1101
F : *lit, ed, law, eco, sc, med, dent, phar, eng, agr.*

Kyushu Geijutsukoka Daigaku [Kyushu I. of Design], 4-9-1 Shiobaru, Minami-ku, Fukuoka-shi, Fukuoka 815. *1968*
Tel: 92-541-143
F : *des.*

Kyushu Kogyo Daigaku [Kyushu I. of Technology], 1-1 Sensui-cho Tobata-ku, Kita-kyushu-shi, Fukuoka 804. *1907, 1949*
Tel: 93-871-1931
F : *eng, comp, systems eng.*

Mie Daigaku, 1515 Kamihama-cho, Tsushi-shi, Mie 514. *1921, 1949*
Tel: 592-32-1211
F : *ed, eng, agr, med, fish, hum-soc.*

Miyagi Kyoiku Daigaku [Miyagi U. of Educa-ion], Aramaki Aza Aoba, Sendai-shi, Miyagi 980. *1965*

Tel: 22-222-1021
F : *ed.*

Miyazaki Daigaku, 7710 Oaza Kumano, Miyazaki-shi, Miyazaki 889-21.   *1924, 1949*
Tel: 985-58-2811
F : *ed, agr, eng.*

Miyazaki Ika Daigaku [Miyazaki Medical C.], 5200 Kihara, Miyaazaki-gun, Miyazaki 889-16.   *1974*
Tel: 985-85-1510
F : *med.*

Muroran Kogyo Daigaku [Muroran I. of Techology], 27-1 Mizumoto-cho, Muroran-shi, Hokkaido 050.   *1918, 1949*
Tel: 143-44-4181
F : *eng.*

Nagaoka Gijutsukagaku Daigaku, [Technoogical U. of Nagaoka], 1603-1 Kamitomioka-machi, Nagaoka-shi, Niigata 940-21.   *1976*
Tel: 258-46-6000
F : *eng.*

*Nagasaki Daigaku, 1–14 Bunkyo-machi, Nagasaki-shi, Nagasaki 852.   *1905, 1949*
Tel: 958-47-111
F : *ed, eco, med, phar, fish, eng, dent.*

*Nagoya Daigaku, Furo-cho, Chikusa-ku, Nagoya-shi, Aichi 464.   *1871, 1949*
Tel: 52-781-5111. Telex: ntt 4477323 scunagj
F : *let, ed, law, eco, sc, med, eng, agr.*

Nagoya Kogyo Daigaku [Nagoya I. of Techology], Gokiso-cho, Showa-ku, Nagoya-shi, Aichi 466.   *1905, 1949*
Tel: 52-732-2111. Telex: ntt 4477355 scunag j
F : *eng.*

*Nara Joshi Daigaku [Nara Women's U.], Kitauoyahigshi-machi, Nara-shi, Nara 630.
                    1908, 1949
Tel: 742-23-1131
F : *let, sc, hom eco.*

Nara Kyoiku Daigaku [Nara U. of Education], Takabatake-cho, Nara-shi, Nara 630.
                    1886, 1949
Tel: 742-26-1101. Telex: 238057
F : *ed.*

Naruto Kyoiku Daigaku [Naruto U. of Teacher Education], Takashima, Naruto-shi, Tokushima 772   *1981*
Tel: 886-87-1311
F : *ed.*

*Niigata Daigaku, 8050 Ikarashi Nino-cho, Niigata-shi, Niigata 950-21.   *1910, 1949*
Tel: 25-262-6098
F : *hum, ed, sc, eng, agr, eco, law, med, dent.*

Obihiro Chikusan Daigaku [Obihiro U. of Agriulture and Veterinary Medicine], Nishi 2-11, Inada-cho, Obihiro, Hokkaido 080. *1941, 1949*
Tel: 155-48-5111
F : *an hus.*

*Ochanomizu Joshi Daigaku [Ochanomizu

Women's U.], 2-1-1 Otsuka, Bunkyo-ku, Tokyo 112.   *1874, 1949*
Tel: 3-943-3151
F : *let-ed, sc, hom eco.*

*Oita Daigaku, 700 Dannoharu, Oita-shi, Oita 870-11.   *1921, 1949*
Tel: 975-69-3311
F : *eco, eng.*

Oita Ika Daigaku [Medical C. of Oita], 1-1506 Idaigaoka, Hazama-cho, Oita-gun, Oita 879-56.   *1976*
Tel: 975-49-4411
F : *med sc.*

*Okayama Daigaku, 1-1-1 Tsushimanaka, Okayama-shi, Okayama 700.   *1900, 1949*
Tel: 862-52-1111
F : *law, let, teacher ed, sc, agr, eng, med, phar, eco.*
S : *dent.*

*Osaka Daigaku, 1-1 Yamadaoka, Suita-shi, Osaka 565.   *1931, 1949*
Tel: 6-877-5111
F: *let, law, eco, sc, hum, dent, med, eng, phar.*

Osaka Gaikokugo Daigaku [Osaka U. of Foreign Studies], 2734 Aomadani, Minoo-shi, Osaka 562.
Tel: 727-28-3111
F : *fgn lang.*

Osaka Kyoiku Daigaku [Osaka U. of Education], 4-88 Minami-kawahori-cho, Tennoji-ku, Osaka-shi, Osaka 543.   *1949, 1967*
Tel: 6-771-8131
F : *ed.*

Otaru Shoka Daigaku [Otaru U. of Commerce], 3-5-21 Midori, Otaru-shi, Hokkaido 047.
                    1910, 1949
Tel: 134-23-1101
F : *com.*

Ryukyu Daigaku [U. of the Ryukyus], 1 Senbaru, Nishiharacho, Okanawa 903-01. *1950*
Tel: 9889-5-2221
F : *law-let, ed, agr, sc, eng, med.*

Saga Daigaku [Saga U.], 1 Honjo-machi, Saga-shi, Saga 840.   *1920, 1949*
Tel: 952-24-5191
F : *ed, eco, sc-eng, agr.*

Saga Ika Daigaku [Saga Medical S.], Nabeshima-sanbonsugi, Nabeshima-machi, Saga-shi 840-01.   *1970, 1984*
Tel: 952-31-6511
F : *med.*

Saitama Daigaku, 255 Shimo-Okubo, Urawa-shi, Saitama 338.   *1921, 1949*
Tel: 488-52-2111
F : *li arts, ed, eco, sc, eng.*

Shiga Daigaku, 1-1-1 Banba, Hikone-shi, Shiga 522.   *1921, 1949*
Tel: 749-22-5600
F : *ed, eco.*

Shiga Ika Daigaku [Shiga U. of Medical Science],
Seta-tsukinowa-cho, Otsui-shi, Shiga 520-21.
                                            1974, 1981
Tel: 775-48-2111
F : *med.*
Shimane Daigaku, 1060 Nishikawatsu-cho,
Matsue-shi, Shimane 690.   *1949*
Tel: 852-21-7100
F : *law-lit, sc, ed, agr.*
Shimane Ika Daigaku [Shimane Medical U.],
89-1 Enya-cho, Iaumo-shi, Shimane 693.
                                        1975, 1982
Tel: 853-23-2111
F : *med.*
*Shinshu Daigaku, 3-1-1, Asahi, Matsumoto-shi,
Nagaro 390.   *1910, 1949*
Tel: 263-35-4600
F : *arts, eco, ed, sc, eng, med, agr, tex.*
Shizuoka Daigaku, 836 Onya, Shizuoka-shi,
Shizuoka 422.   *1922, 1949*
Tel: 542-37-1111
F : *hum-soc, ed, sc, eng, agr.*
*Tohoku Diagaku, 2–1–1 Katahira, Sendai-shi,
Miyagi 980.   *1907, 1949*
Tel: 22-227-6200
F : *arts-let, ed, law, eco, sc, med, dent, phar,
eng, agr.*
Tokushima Daigaku, 2-24 Shinkura-cho,
Tokushima-shi, Tokushima 770.   *1949*
Tel: 886-22-5131
F : *phar, eng, arts-sc.*
S : *dent.*
*Tokyo Daigaku, 7-3-1 Hongo, Bunkyo-ku,
Tokyo 113.   *1877, 1949*
Tel: 3-812-2111. Fax: 3-818-3163. Telex: kdd
25510 unitoky j
F : *let, ed, law, eco, sc, med, eng, agr, phar.*
C : *arts-sc.*
Tokyo Gaiakokugo Daigaku [Tokyo U. of
Foreign Studies], 4–51–21 Nishigahara, Kita-
ku, Tokyo 114.   *1897, 1949*
Tel: 3-917-6111
F : *fgn st.*
Tokyo Gakugei Daigaku, 4-1-1 Nukuikita-machi,
Koganei-shi, Tokyo 184.   *1943, 1949*
Tel: 423-25-2111
F : *ed.*
Tokyo Geijutsu Daigaku [Tokyo National U. of
Fine Arts and Music], 12–8 Ueno Koen, Taito-
ku, Tokyo 110.   *1949*
Tel: 3-828-6111
F : *fa, mus.*
Tokyo Ikashika Daigaku [Tokyo Medical and
Dental U.], 1-5-45, Yushima, Bunkyo-ku,
Tokyo 113.   *1928, 1946, 1955*
Tel: 3-813-6111
F : *med, dent.*
*Tokyo Kogyo Daigaku [Tokyo I. of Techno-
logy], 2-12-1, Ohokayama, Meguro-ku, Tokyo

152.   *1881, 1949*
Tel: 3-726-1111. Telex: 2466360 titech j
F : *sc, eng.*
Tokyo Noko Daigaku [Tokyo U. of Agriculture
and Technology], 3–8–1 Harumi-cho, Fuchu-
shi, Tokyo 183.   *1914, 1949*
Tel: 423-64-3311
F : *agr, techn.*
Tokyo Shosen Daigaku [Tokyo U. of Mercantile
Marine], 2-1-6 Etchujima, Koto-ku, Tokyo
135.   *1945, 1949*
Tel: 3-641-1171
F : *mercantile mar.*
Tokyo Suisan Daigaku [Tokyo U. of Fisheries],
4-5-7 Konan, Minato-ku, Tokyo 108.*1897, 1949*
Tel: 3-471-1251
F : *fish.*
Toshokan Joho Daigaku [U. of Libraray and
Information Sciences], 1-2 Kasuga, Yatabe-
machi, Tsukuba-gun, Ibaraki 305.   *1979*
Tel: 0298-52-0511
F : *lib-infor.*
Tottori Diagaku, 4-1101 Koyama-cho, Tottori-
shi, Tottori 680.   *1920, 1949*
Tel: 857-28-0321
F : *ed, med, eng, agr.*
Toyama Daigaku, 3190 Gofuku, Toyama.
                                       1920, 1949
Tel: 764-41-1271
F : *hum-sc, ed, eco, phar, eng.*
Toyama Ikayakka Daigaku, [Toyama Medical
and Pharmaceutical U.], 2630 Sugitoni,
Toyama-shi, Toyama 930-01   *1975*
Tel: 764-34-2281
F : *med, phar.*
Toyohashi Gijutsu Kagaku Daigaku [Toyohashi
U. of Technology], 1-1 Hibarigaoka, Tenpaku-
cho, Toyohashi-shi, Aichi 440.   *1976*
Tel: 532-47-0117
F : *eng.*
*Tsukuba Daigaku, 1-1-1 Tennodai, Sakura-
mura, Niihari-gun, Ibaraki 305.   *1973*
Tel: 298-53-2111. Telex: 3652580 untuku j
C : *hum, nat, soc, agr-for, biol, comparative
cult, hum, Japanese lang-cult, eng, infor, int rel,
socio-eco plan.*
S : *arts-des, phys, med.*
Utsunomiya Daigaku, 350 Mine-machi,
Utsunomiya-shi, Tochigi 321.   *1922, 1949*
Tel: 286-36-1515
F : *ed, eng, agr.*
Wakayama Daigaku, 930 Sakaedani,
Wakayama-shi, Wakayama 640.   *1922, 1949*
Tel: 734-54-0361
F : *ed, eco.*
Yamagata Daigaku, 1-4-12, Koshi-rakawa-
machi, Yamagata-shi, Yamagata 990.
                                       1910, 1949
Tel: 236-31-1421

F : *ed, sc, eng, agr, lit-soc, med.*
Yamaguchi Daigaku, 1677-1 Yoshida, Yama-
guchi-shi, Yamaguchi 753.   *1905, 1949*
Tel: 839-22-6111
F : *hum, ed, eco, eng, agr.*
S : *med.*
Yamanashi Daigaku, Takeda 4-chome 4-37,
Kofu-shi, Yamanashi.   *1924, 1949*
F : *ed, eng.*
Yamanashi Ika Daigaku [Yamanashi Medical

C.], 1110 Tamaho, Nakakoma-gun,
Yamanashi 409-38.   *1978*
Tel: 552-73-1111
F : *med sc.*
Yokohama Kokuritsu Daigaku [Yokohama
National U.], 156 Tokiwadai, Hodogaya-ku,
Yokohama-shi, Kanagawa 240.   *1920, 1949*
Tel: 45-375-1451
F : *ed, eng, eco, bus adm.*

Public Institutions—Etablissements publics

Aichi Kenritsu Geijutsu Daigaku [Aichi Pre-
fectural U. of Fine Arts], 1-1 Sagamine,
Yazako, Nagakute-cho, Aichi-gun, Aichi
480-11.   *1966*
Tel: 5616-2-1180
F : *mus, fa.*
Fukushima Kenritsu Ika Daigaku [Fukushima
Medical C.], 5-75 Sugitsuma-cho, Fukushima-
cho, Fukushima 960.   *1947, 1952*
Tel: 245-21-1211
F : *med.*
Gifu Yakka Daigaku [Gifu C. of Pharmaceutical
U.], 5-6-1 Mitahora-higashi, Gifu-shi, Gifu
502.   *1932, 1949*
Tel: 582-37-3931
F : *phar.*
Himeji Kogyo Daigaku [Himeji I. of Techn-
ology], 2167 Shosha, Himeji-shi, Hyogo
671-22.   *1944, 1949*
Tel: 792-66-1661
F : *eng.*
Kanazawa Bijutsu Kogei Daigaku [Kanazawa C.
of Art], 5-11-1 Kodatsuno, Kanazawa-shi,
Ishikawa 920.   *1946, 1955*
Tel: 762-62-3531
F : *art*
Kitakyushu Daigaku, Kokuraminami-ku,
Kitakyu-shi, Fukuoka 802.   *1946, 1950, 1984*
Tel: 93-962-4436
F : *fgn lang, eco-bus, lit, law, adm.*
Kobe Shoka Daigaku [Kobe U. of Commerce],
4-3-3 Seiryodai, Tarumi-ku, Kobe-shi, Hyogo
655.   *1929, 1948*
F : *eco-bu.*
Kobe-shi Gaikokugo Daigaku [Kobe City U. of
Foreign Studies], 9-1 Gakuen-higashi-machi,
Nishi-ku, Kobe-shi, Hyogo 673.
                                              1946, 1949
Tel: 78-794-8111
F : *fgn st.*
Kyoto Furitsu Daigaku [Kyoto Prefectural U.],
1-5, Shimogamo-Hangi-cho, Sakyo-ku, Kyoto-
shi, Kyoto 610-11.   *1944, 1949*
Tel: 75-232-0701
F : *let, sc of living, agr.*
Kyoto Furitsu Ika Daigaku [Kyoto Prefectural U.

of Medicine], 465 Kajii-cho, Kawaramachi-
dori, Hirokoji-agaru, Kamigyo-ku, Kyoto-shi
602.   *1921, 1952*
Tel: 75-251-5111-8
F : *med.*
Kyoto Shiritsu Geijutsu Daigaku [Kyoto City U.
of Arts], 13-6 Kutsukake-cho, Ooe, Nishigyo-
ku, Kyoto-shi, Kyoto 610-11.   *1880, 1969*
Tel: 75-332-0701
F : *arts, mus.*
Kyushu Shika Daigaku [Kyushu Dental C.], 2-6-1
Manazuru, Kokurakita-ku, Kitakyushu-shi,
Fukuoka 803.   *1921, 1949*
Tel: 93-582-1131
F : *dent.*
Nagoya Shiritsu Daigaku [Nagoya City U.], 1
Kawasumi, Mizuho-cho, Mizuho-ku, Nagoya-
shi, Aichi 467.   *1950*
Tel: 52-851-5511
F : *phar, eco, med.*
Nara Kenritsu Ika Daigaku [Nara Medical U.],
840 Shijo-cho, Kashihara-shi, Nara 634.
                                              1945, 1952
Tel: 7442-2-3051
F : *med.*
Osaka Furitsu Daigaku [U. of Osaka Prefecture],
4-804 Mozu-Umemachi, Sakai-shi, Osaka 591.
                                              1939, 1949
Tel: 722-52-1161
F : *agr, eco, eng, integrated arts & sc, soc
welfare.*
Osaka Joshi Daigaku [Osaka Women's U.], 2-1
Daisen-cho, Sakai-shi, Osaka 590.   *1924, 1949*
Tel: 722-22-4811
C : *arts-sc.*
*Osaka Shiritsu Daigaku [Osaka City U.],
3-3-138 Sugimoto, Sumiyoshi-ku, Osaka-shi,
Osaka 558.   *1928, 1949*
Tel: 6-605-2011
F : *eco, law let, sc, eng, sc of living, bus, med.*
Sapporo Ika Daigaku [Sapporo Medical C.],
Minami 1, Nishi 17, Chuo-ku, Sapporo-shi,
Hokkaido 060.   *1945, 1950*
Tel: 11-611-2111
F : *med.*
Shizuoka Yakka Daigaku [Shizuoka C. of

Pharmacy], 2–2–1 Oshika, Shizuoka-shi, Yamaguchi 751. *1945, 1953*
Tel: 832-52-0288
F : *phar.*

*Tokyo Toritsu Daigaku [Tokyo Metropolitan U.], 1-1-1 Yakumo, Meguro-ku, Tokyo 152.
1929, 1949
Tel: 3-717-0111
F : *hum-soc, sc, techn, law, eco.*

Wakayama Kenritsu Ika Daigaku [Wakayama

Medical C.], 9 Kyaban-cho, Wakayama-shi, Wakayama 640. *1948, 1952*
Tel: 734-31-2151
F : *med.*

Yokohama Shiritsu Daigaku [Yokohama City U.], 22-2 Seto, Kanazawa-ku, Yokohama-shi, Kanagawa 235. *1928, 1949*
Tel: 45-787-2311
F : *ecobus, adm, li arts-sc, med.*

Private Intitutions—Etablissements privés

Aichi Daigaku, 1-1 Machihata-machi, Toyohashi-shi, Aichi 440. *1946, 1949*
Tel: 532-45-0441
F : *law, eco, let.*

*Aichi Gakuin Daigaku, 12 Araike, Iwasaki, Nisshin-cho, Aichi-gun, Aichi 470-01.
1876, 1953
Tel: 5667-3-1111
F : *com, law, dent, let.*

Aichi Ika Daigaku [Aichi Medical U.], 21 Yazako Karimata, Nagakute-cho, Aichi-gun, Aichi.
1972
Tel: 5616-2-3311
F : *med.*

Aichi Kogyo Daigaku [Aichi I. of Technology], 1247 Yachigusa, Ya kusa-cho, Toyota-shi, Aichi 470-03. *1954, 1959*
Tel: 565-48-8121
F : *eng.*

Ajia Daigaku [Asia U.], 5-24-10 Sakai, Musashino-shi, Tokyo 180. *1941, 1955*
Tel: 0422-54-3111. Fax: 0422-558232
F : *eco, bus adm, law.*

*Aoyama Gakuin Daigaku, 4-4-25 Shibiya, Shibuya-ku, Tokyo 150. *1904, 1949*
Tel: 3-409-8111
S : *lit, eco, law, bus adm, sc-eng.*

Asahi Daigaku, 1851 Hozumi, Hozumi-cho. Motoso-gun, Gifu 501-02. *1971, 1985*
Tel: 5832-6-6131
S : *bus adm, dent.*

Ashiya Daigaku, 13-22 Rokurokusho-cho, Ashiya, Hyogo 659. *1964*
Tel: 797-23-0661
F : *ed.*

Azabu Daigaku 1-17-71 Fuchinobe, Sagamihara-shi, Kanagawa 229. *1934, 1950*
Tel: 427-54-7111
F : *vet, env heal.*

Baika Joshi Daigaku [Baika Women's C.], 2-19-5 Shukunosho, Ibaraki-shi, Osaka 567. *1964*
Tel: 726-43-6221
F : *lit.*

Bukkyo Daigaku, 96 Kitahanabo-cho, Murasakino, Kita-ku, Kyoto-shi, Kyoto 603.

1912, 1940
Tel: 75-491-2141
F : *let, socio.*

Bunka Joshi Daigaku [Bunka Women's C.], 3-22-1 Yogogi, Shibuya-ku, Tokyo 151.
1964
Tel: 3-370-3111
F : *dom eco.*

Chiba Kogyo Daigaku [Chiba I. of Technology], 2-17-1 Tsudanuma, Narashino-shi, Chiba 275.
1942, 1950
Tel: 474-75-2111
F : *techn.*

*Chiba Shoka Daigaku [Chiba U. of Commerce], 1-3-1 Konodai, Ichikawa-shi, Chiba 272.
1928, 1950
Tel: 473-72-4111
F : *com-eco.*

*Chubu Daigaku [Chubu U.], 1200 Matsumoto-cho, Kasugai-shi, Aichi 487. *1964, 1984*
Tel: 568-51-1111
C : *eng.*

Chukyo Daigaku, 101-2 Yagoto Honmachi, Showa-ku, Nagoya-shi, Aichi 466. *1954, 1956*
Tel: 52-832-2151
F : *com, phys, let, law, eco.*

*Chuo Daigaku, 742-1 Higashinakano, Higashikano, Hachioji-shi, Tokyo 192-03. *1903, 1949*
Tel: 426-74-2111
F : *law, eco, com, lit, sc-eng.*

Daito Bunka Daigaku, 1-9-1 Takashimadama, Itabashi-ku, Tokyo 175. *1923, 1949*
Tel: 3-935-1111
F : *let, eco, fgn lang, law, int rel.*

Dokkyo Daigaku, 1-1 Gakuen-cho, Soka-shi, Saitama 340. *1964*
Tel: 489-42-111
F : *fgn lang, eco, law.*

Dokkyo Ika Daigaku [Dokkyo Medical U.], Shimotsuga-gun, Tochigi 321-02.
Tel: 282-86-1111
F : *med.*

Doshisha Daigaku, 601 Gembu-cho, Karasuma Higashiiru, Kamikyo-ku, Kyoto 602.
1904, 1948

Tel: 75-251-3223
F : *law, eco, com, eng, theo, let.*
Doshisha Joshi Daigaku [Doshisha Women's C.of Liberal Arts], Imadegawa-dori, Teramachi Nishiiru, Kamikyo-ku, Kyoto-shi, Kyoto 602.
1912, 1949
Tel: 75-251-4113
F : *li arts, hom eco.*
Erizabeto Ongaku Daigaku [Elisabeth U. of Music], 4-15 Nobori-cho, Naka-ku, Hiroshima-shi, Hiroshima 730.   *1952, 1963*
Tel: 82-221-0918
F : *mus.*
Fujita-Gakuen Hoken'eisei Dargaku [Fujita-Gakuen Health U.], 1-98 Dengakugakubo, Kutsukake-cho, Toyoake-shi, Aichi 470-11.
1972
Tel: 562-93-2000
S : *hyg, med.*
Fukui Kogyo Dalgaku [Fukui I. of Technology], 3-6-1 Gakuen, Fukui-shi, Fukui 910.   *1965*
Tel: 776-22-8111
Fukuoka Daigaku, 8-19-1 Nanakuma, Jonan-ku, Fukuoka-shi, Fukuoka 814-01.   *1934, 1949*
Tel: 92-871-6631
F : *law, eco, com, phar, eng, hum, phys, sc.*
S : *med.*
Fukuoka Shika Daigaku [Fukuoka Dental C.], 700 Ta, Sawara-ku, Fukuoka-shi, Fukuoka 814-01.   *1972*
Tel: 92-661-3030
F : *dent.*
Fukuyama Daigaku, 985 Sanzo, Higashimura-cho, Fukuyama-shi, Hiroshima 729-02.   *1975*
Tel: 849-36-2111
F : *eco, eng, phar.*
*Gakushuin Daigaku, 1–5–1 Mejiro Toshima-ku, Tokyo 171.   *1877, 1949*
Tel: 3-986-0221
F : *law, eco, lit, sc.*
Gifu Kyoiku Daigaku [Gifu C. of Education], Takakuwa 2078, Yanaizu-cho, Hashima-gun, Gifu 501-61.   *1972*
Tel: 582-79-0804
F : *ed.*
Hanazono Daigaku, 8-1 Tsubonouchi-cho, Nishinokyo, Nakagyo-ku, Kyoto-shi, Kyoto 604.   *1908, 1949*
Tel: 75-811-5181
F : *let.*
Higashi Nippon Gakuen Daigaku, 1757 Kanazawa, Tobetsu-cho, Ishikari-gun, Hokkaido 061-02.   *1974*
Tel: 1332-3-1211
F : *phar.*
S : *dent.*
Hiroshima Bunkyo Joshi Daigaku [Hiroshima Bunkyo Women's C.], 1-2-1 Kabe-higashi, Asakita-ku, Hiroshima-shi, Hiroshima 731-02.

1948, 1966
Tel: 8266-4-3191
F : *let.*
Hiroshima Keizai Daigaku [Hiroshima U. of Economics], 5-37-1 Gion, Asa Minami-ku, Hiroshima 731-01.   *1967, 1984*
Tel: 82-874-3041
F : *eco.*
Hiroshima Shudo Daigaku, 1717 Otsuka, Numata-cho, Asa-Minami-ku, Hiroshima-shi, Hiroshima 731-31.   *1952*
Tel: 82-848-2121
F : *com, hum-sc, law.*
*Hokkaigakuen Daigaku, 4-1-40 Asahi-machi, Toyohira-shi, Sapporo-shi, Hokkaido 062.
1952
Tel: 11-841-1161
F : *eco, law, eng.*
Hokkaido Yakka Daigaku [Hokkaido I. of Pharmaceutical Science], 7-1 Katsuraoka-cho, Otaru-shi, Hokkaido 047-02.
Tel: 134-62-5111
F : *phar.*
Hokuriku Daigaku, Ho-3, Kanakawa-cho, Kanazawa-shi, Ishikawa 920-11.   *1975*
Tel: 762-29-1161
S : *phar.*
Hokusei Gakuen Daigaku, 828 Oyachi, Shiroishi-ku, Sapporo-shi, Hokkaido 004.   *1962*
Tel: 11-891-2731
F : *lit, eco.*
*Hosei Daigaku, 2-17-1 Fujimi, Chiyoda-ku, Tokyo 102.   *1903, 1949*
Tel: 3-264-9315
F : *law, let, eco, eng, soc, bus adm.*
Hoshi Yakka Daigaku [Hoshi C. of Pharmacy], 2-4-41 Ebara, Shinagawa-ku, Tokyo 142.
1941, 1950
Tel: 3-786-1011
F : *phar.*
Hyogo Ika Daigaku [Hyogo C. of Medicine], 1-1 Mukogawa-cho, Nishinomiya-shi, Hyogo 663.
Tel: 798-45-6111
F : *med.*
International University of Japan (See **Kokusai Daigaku**).
Iwate Ika Daigaku [Iwate Medical U.], 19-1 Uchimaru, Morioka-shi, Iwate 020.
1947, 1952
Tel: 196-51-5111
F : *med, dent.*
Jichi Ika Daigaku, 3311-1 Yakushiji, Minamikawachi-machi, Kawachi-gun, Tochigi 329-04.
Tel: 285-44-2111
F : *med.*
Jissen Joshi Daigaku [Jissen Women's U.], 4-1-1 Osakaue, Hino-shi, Tokyo 191.   *1925, 1949*
Tel: 425-85-0311

F : *lit, dom sc.*

*Jochi Daigaku [Sophia U.], 7-1 Kioi-cho, Chiyoda-ku, Tokyo 102.   *1913, 1948*
Tel: 3-238-3111. Telex: 24140 htlotani j
F : *eco, hum, law, theo, fgn st, sc-techn, comparative cult.*

Josai Daigaku, 1-1 Keyakidai, Sakado-shi, Saitama 350-02.   *1965*
Tel: 492-86-2233
F : *eco, sc, phar.*

Josai Shika Daigaku [Josai Dental C.], 1-1 Keyakidai, Sakado-shi, Saitama 350-92.
                                                       1970
Tel: 492-85-5511
F : *dent.*

Joshi Eiyo Daigaku [Kagawa Nutrition C.], 3-9-21 Chiyoda, Sakado-shi, Saitama 350-02.
                                                 1950, 1961
Tel: 492-83-2126
F : *nutr.*

Juntendo Daigaku, 2-1-1 Hongo, Bunkyo-ku, Tokyo 113.   *1843, 1951*
Tel: 3-813-3111
S : *med, heal-phys.*

Kanagawa Daigaku, 3-27-1 Rokkakubashi, Kanagawa-ku, Yokohama-shi, Kanagawa 221.
                                                 1929, 1949
Tel: 45-481-5661
F : *law, eco, fgn lang, eng.*

Kanagawa Shika Daigaku [Kanagawa Dental C.], 82 Inaoka-cho, Yokosuka-shi, Kanagawa 238.   *1964*
Tel: 468-25-1500
F : *dent.*

Kanazawa Ika Daigaku [Kanazawa Medical C.], 1-1 Uchinada-machi, Kawakita-gun, Ishikawa 920-02.   *1972, 1982*
Tel: 762-86-2211
F : *med.*

*Kanazawa Kogyo Daigaku [Kanazawa I. of Technology], 7-1 Ogigaoka, Nonoichi-machi, Ishikawa 921.   *1965*
Tel: 762-48-1100. Telex: ntt 5122456 kit lc j
F : *eng.*

*Kansai Daigaku, Suita-shi, Osaka 564.
                                                 1905, 1948
Tel: 6-388-1121
F : *law, let, eco, com, socio, eng.*

Kansai Gaikokugo Daigaku [Kansai U. of Foreign Studies], 16-1 Kitakatahoko-cho, Hirakata-shi, Osaka 573.   *1953, 1966*
D : *fgn lang.*

Kansai Ika Daigaku [Kansai Medical S.], 1 Fumizono-cho, Moriguchi-shi, Moriguchi, Osaka 570.   *1928, 1952*
Tel: 6-992-1001
F : *med.*

Kanto Gakuen Daigaku, 200 Fujiaku, Ota-shi, Gunma 370-04.   *1976*

Tel: 276-31-2711
F : *eco.*

*Kanto Gakuin Daigaku, 4834 Mutsuura-cho, Kanazawa-ku, Yokohama-shi, Kanagawa 236.
                                                 1944, 1949
F : *eco, eng, hum.*

Kawasaki Ika Daigaku [Kawasaki Medical C.], 577 Matsushima, Kurashiki-shi, Okayama 701-01.   *1970*
Tel: 864-62-1111
F : *med.*

*Keio Gijuku Daigaku, 2-15-45 Mita, Minato-ku, Tokyo 108.   *1858, 1949*
Tel: 3-453-4511. Telex: 34532 keiolc j
F : *let, eco, law, med, eng, bus-com, sc-techn.*

Kinki Daigaku, 3-4-1 Kowakae, Higashi-Osaka-shi, Osaka 577.   *1924, 1949*
Tel: 6-721-2332
F : *jurisprudence, eco-bus adm, sc-techn, phar, agr, med; eng* (Kure City).

Kitasato Daigaku, 5-9-1 Shirokane, Minato-ku, Tokyo 108.   *1962*
Tel: 3-444-6161
S : *hyg, phar, vet-an hus, med, fish, nurs.*

Kobe Gakuin Daigaku, 518 Arise, Ikawadani-cho, Nishi-ku, Kobe-shi, Hyogo 673.   *1966*
F : *nutr, law, eco, phar.*

*Kobe Jogakuin Daigaku, 4-1 Okadayama, Nishinomiya-shi, Hyogo 662.   *1909, 1948*
Tel: 798-52-0955
F : *lit, mus, hom eco.*

Kobe Joshi Daigaku [Kobe Women's U.], 2-23-1 Nakayamate-dori, Chuo-ku, Kobe-shi, Hyogo 650.   *1950, 1966*
Tel: 78-231-1001
F : *hom eco, lit.*

Kobe Joshi Yakka Daigaku [Kobe Women's C. of Pharmacy], 4-19-1 Motoyamakta-machi, Higashinada-ku, Kobe-shi, Hyogo 658.
                                                 1932, 1949
F : *phar.*

Kogakuin Daigaku, 1-24-2 Nishi-shinjuku, Shinjuku-ku, Tokyo 160.   *1887, 1949*
Tel: 3-342-1211
F : *eng.*

Kogakkan Daigaku, 1704 Kodakujimoto-cho, Ise-shi, Mie 516.   *1962*
Tel: 596-22-0201
F : *lit.*

*Kokugakuin Daigaku, 4-10-28 Higashi, Shibuya-ku, Tokyo 150.   *1904, 1949*
Tel: 3-409-0111
F : *eco, let, law.*

Kokusai Daigaku [International U. of Japan], Yamato-machi, Minamiuonuma-gun, Niigata 949-72.
Tel: 257-77-1111
S : *int rel* (graduate).

*Kokusai Kirisutokyo Daigaku [International

Christian U.], 3-10-2 Osawa, Mitaka-shi, Tokyo 181. *1949*
Tel: 422-33-3131
F : *li arts.*

Kokushikan Daigaku, 4-28-1 Satagaya, Setagaya-ku, Tokyo 154. *1917*
Tel: 3-422-5341
F : *pol-eco, eng, phys, law, lit.*

Komazawa Daigaku, 1-23-1 Komazawa, Setagaya-ku, Tokyo 154. *1925, 1949*
Tel: 3-418-9010
F : *arts-sc, budh, eco, law, bus mangt.*

*Konan Daigaku, 8-9-1 Okamoto, Higashinada-ku, Kobe-shi, Hyogo 658. *1923, 1951*
Tel: 78-431-4141
F : *eco, sc, law, bus adm, li arts.*

Konan Joshi Daigaku [Konan Women's C.], Higashinada-ku, Kobe-shi, Hyogo 658.
1955, 1964
Tel: 78-431-0391
F : *let.*

Koyasan Daigaku, Koyasan, Koya-cho, Ito-gun, Wakayama 648-02. *1926, 1949*
Tel: 7365-6-2921
F : *let.*

Kumamoto Kogyo Daigaku [Kumamoto I. of Technology], 4-22-1 Ikeda, Kumamoto-shi, Kumamoto 860. *1965, 1967, 1982*
Tel: 96-326-3111
F : *eng.*

Kunitachi Ongaku Daigaku [Kunitachi C. of Music], 5-5-1 Kashiwa-cho, Kunitachi-shi, Tokyo 190. *1926, 1950*
Tel: 425-36-0321
F : *mus.*

Kurume Daigaku, 67 Asahi-machi, Kurume-shi, Fukuoka 830. *1928, 1950*
S : *com, med.*

*Kwansai Gakuin Daigaku, 1-1-155 Uegahara, Nishinomiya-shi, Hyogo 662. *1908, 1948*
Tel: 798-53-6111
S : *theo, lit, law, eco, bus adm, socio, sc.*

Kyorin Daigaku, 6-20-2 Shinkawa, Mitaka-shi, Tokyo 181. *1970*
Tel: 422-47-5511
S : *med, allied heal.*

Kyoritsu Joshi Daigaku [Kyoritsu Women's U.], 2-2-1 Hitotsubashi, Chiyoda-ku, Tokyo 101.
1925, 1949
Tel: 3-237-2433
F : *hom eco, let-arts.*

Kyoritsu Yakka Daigaku [Kyoritsu C. of Pharmacy], 1-5-30 Shibakoen, Minato-ku, Tokyo 105. *1930, 1949*
Tel: 3-434-6241
F : *phar.*

*Kyoto Gaikokugo Daigaku [Kyoto U. of Foreign Studies], 6 Saiin-Kasame-cho, Ukyo-ku, Kyoto-shi, Kyoto 615. *1950, 1959*

Tel: 75-311-5181
F : *fgn lang.*

Kyoto Joshi Daigaku [Kyoto Women's U.], 35 Kitahiyoshi-cho, Imakumano, Higashiyama-ku, Kyoto-shi, Kyoto 605. *1949*
Tel: 75-531-7030
F : *lit, hom eco.*

Kyoto Sangyo Daigaku [Kyoto Industrial U.], Motoyama, Kamigamo, Kita-ku, Kyoto-shi, Kyoto 603. *1965*
F : *eco, sc, law, bus adm, fgn lang.*

Kyoto Yakka Daigaku [Kyoto C. of Pharmacy], 5 Misaginakauchi-cho, Yamashima-ku, Kyoto-shi, Kyoto 607. *1919, 1949*
Tel: 75-581-3161
S : *phar.*

Kyushu Sangyo Daigaku [Kyushu Industrial U.], 2-327 Matsukadai, Higashi-ku, Fukuoka-shi, Fukuoka 813. *1960*
Tel: 92-681-1831
F : *com, mangt, eng, art.*

Kyushu Tokai Daigaku, 223 Toroku, Oe-machi, Kumamoto-shi, Kumamoto 862. *1973*
Tel: 96-382-1141
S : *eng, agr.*

Matsuyama Shoka Daigaku [Matsuyama Commercial U.], 4-2 Bunkyo-cho, Matsuyama-shi, Ehime 790. *1923, 1949*
Tel: 899-25-7111
F : *eco, bus adm, hum.*

*Meiji Daigaku, 1-1 Kanda Surugadai, Chiyoda-ku, Tokyo 101. *1881, 1949*
Tel: 3-296-4545
S : *law, com, pol-eco, lit, eng, agr, bus adm.*

*Meiji Gakuin Daigaku, 1-2-37 Shirokanedai, Minato-ku, Tokyo 108. *1877, 1949*
Tel: 3-448-5110. Telex: 47762 prime j
F : *lit, int st, eco, law, socio-soc w.*

Meiji Yakka Daigaku [Meiji C. of Pharmacy], 1-35-23 Nozawa, Setagaya-ku, Tokyo 154.
1902, 1949
Tel: 3-434-1001
F : *phar.*

Meijo Daigaku, 1-501 Shiogamuchi, Tenpaku-ku, Nagoya-shi, Aichi 468. *1926, 1949*
Tel: 52-832-1151
F : *law, com, sc-eng, agr, phar.*

Meisei Daigaku, 2-1-1- Hodokubo, Hino-shi, Tokyo 191. *1964*
Tel: 425-91-5111
C : *sc-eng, hum.*

Mukogawa Joshi Daigaku [Mukogawa Women's U.], 6-46 Ikebiraki-cho, Nishinomiya-shi, Hyogo 663. *1939, 1949*
Tel: 798-47-1212
F : *let, mus, phar, home eco.*

Musashi Daigaku, 1-26 Toyotama-Kami, Nerima-ku, Tokyo 176. *1922, 1949*
Tel: 3-991-1191

D : *eco, hum.*

Musashi Kogyo Daigaku [Musashi I. of Technology], 1-28-1 Tamazutsumi, Setagaya-ku, Tokyo 158.   *1929, 1949*
Tel: 3-703-3111
F : *eng.*

Musashino Bijutsu Daigaku [Musashino Art U.], 1-736 Ogawa-cho, Kodaira-shi, Tokyo 187.
                                                  1957, 1962
Tel: 423-41-5011
F : *arts-des.*

Musashino Ongaku Daigaku [Musashino A. of Music], 1-13 Hazawa, Nerima-ku, Tokyo 176.
                                                  1929, 1949
Tel: 3-992-1121
F : *mus.*

Nagasaki Sogo Kagaku Daigaku [Nagasaki I. of Applied Science], 536 Aba-machi, Nagasaki-shi, Nagasaki 851-01.   *1942, 1965*
Tel: 958-39-3111
F : *eng.*

Nagoya Shoka Daigaku [Nagoya U. of Commerce and Business Administration], Sagamine, Nisshin-cho, Aichi-gun, Aichi 470-01.
                                                  1950, 1953
Tel: 5617-3-2111. Telex: ntt 4496002 nucba j
F : *com.*

*Nanzan Daigaku, 18 Yamazato-cho, Showa-ku, Nagoya-shi, Aichi 466.   *1946, 1949*
Tel: 52-832-3111
F : *arts-let, fgn lang, eco, bus adm, law.*

*Nihon Daigaku, 4-8-24 Kudan-Minami, Chiyoda-ku, Tokyo 102.   *1903, 1949*
Tel: 3-262-2271. Telex: 29496 nichidai j
C : *hum-sc, law, eco, com, art, ind techn, eng, agr-vet, int rel, sc-techn.*
S : *med, dent; dent* (Matsudo).

Nihon Fukushi Daigaku [Japan Social Welfare U.], Okuda, Mihama-cho, Chita-gun, Aichi 470-32.   *1953, 1957*
Tel: 569-87-2211
F : *soc welfare, eco.*

*Nihon Joshi Daigaku [Japan Women's U.], 2-8-1 Mejirodai, Bunkyo-ku, Tokyo 112. *1901, 1948*
Tel: 3-943-3131
F : *hom eco, hum.*

Nihon Ruteru Shingaku [Japan Lutheran Theological C.] Osawa 3-10-20, Mitaka-shi.
                                                        1916
F : *theo.*

Nihon Taiiku Daigaku [Nippon C. of Physical Education], 7-1-1 Fukazawa, Setagaya-ku, Tokyo 158.   *1941, 1949*
Tel: 3-704-7001
F : *phys.*

*Nippon Ika Daigaku [Nippon Medical S.], 1-1-5 Sendagi-cho, Bunkyo-ku, Tokyo 113.
                                                  1904, 1952
Tel: 3-822-2131

F : *med.*

Nippon Juichikusan Daigaku [Nippon Veterinary and Zootechnical C.], 1-7-1 Kyonan-cho, Musashino-shi, Musashino, Tokyo 180.
                                                  1938, 1949
S : *vet-an hus.*

Nippon Kogyo Daigaku [Nippon I. of Technology], 4-1 Gakuendai, Miyashiro-machi, Minamisaitama, Saitama 345.   *1961*
Tel: 480-34-4111
F : *eng.*

Nippon Shika Daigaku [Nippon Dental U.], 1-9-20 Fujimi, Chiyoda-ku, Tokyo 102.
                                                  1907, 1952
Tel: 3-261-8311
S : *dent; dent* (Niigata).

Nisho Gakusha Daigaku, 6 Sanban-cho, Chiyoda-ku, Tokyo.   *1928, 1949*
Tel: 3-261-7407
F : *lit.*

Okayama Rika Daigaku [Okayama U. of Science], 1-1 Ridai-cho, Okayama-shi, Okayama 700.   *1964*
Tel: 862-52-3161
C : *sc, eng.*

Osaka Gakuin Daigaku, 2-36-1 Kishibe-Minami, Suita-shi, Osaka 564.   *1963*
Tel: 6-381-8434
F : *com, eco, law, fgn lang.*

Osaka Geijutsu Daigaku [Osaka U. of Arts], 469 Higashiyama, Kanan-cho, Minamikawachi-gun, Osaka 585.   *1964*
Tel: 721-93-3781
F : *arts*

Osaka Ika Daigaku [Osaka Medical C.], 2-7 Daigaku-machi, Takatsuki-shi, Osaka 569.
                                                  1927, 1952
Tel: 726-83-1221
F : *med.*

Osaka Keizai Daigaku [Osaka U. of Economics], 2-2-8 Osumi, Higashi-yodogawa-ku, Osaka-shi, Osaka 533.   *1935, 1949*
Tel: 6-328-2431
F : *eco, bus adm.*

Osaka Kogyo Daigaku [Osaka I. of Technology], 5-16-1 Omiya, Asahi-ku, Osaka-shi, Osaka 535.
                                                  1922, 1949
Tel: 6-952-3131
F : *eng.*

Osaka Ongaku Daigaku [Osaka C. of Music], 1-1-8 Shonai-Sawai-machi, Toyonakashi, Osaka 561.   *1915, 1958*
Tel: 6-334-2131
F : *mus.*

Osaka Shika Daigaku [Osaka Dental U.], 1-47 Kyobashi, Higashi-ku, Osaka-shi, Osaka 540.
                                                  1947, 1952
Tel: 6-943-6521

F : *dent.*

*Osaka Shogyo Daigaku [Osaka U. of Commerce], 4-1-10 Mikuriya Sakae-machi, Higashiosaka-shi, Osaka 577. *1949, 1952*
Tel: 6-781-0381
F : *com-eco*

Osaka Taiiku Daigaku [Osaka C. of Physical Education], 1-1 Gakuen-cho, Ibarai-shi, Osaka 567. *1965*
Tel: 726-34-3141
F : *phys.*

Osaka Yakka Daigaku [Osaka C. of Pharmaceutical Sciences], 2-10-65 Kawai, Matsubara-shi, Osaka 580. *1925, 1950, 1986*
Tel: 723-32-1015
F : *phar.*

Otani Daigaku, Kamifusa-cho, Kita-ku, Kyoto-shi, Kyote 603. *1922, 1949*
Tel: 75-432-3131
F : *let.*

Otemae Joshi Daigaku [Otemae Women's C], 6-42 Ochayasho-cho, Nishinomiya-shi, Hyogo 662. *1966*
Tel: 798-34-6331
F : *let.*

Otemon Gakuin Daigaku, 2-1-15 Nishiai, Ibarai-shi, Osaka 567. *1966*
Tel: 726-43-5421
F : *eco, let.*

Otsuma Joshi Daigaku [Otsuma Women's U.], 12 Sanban-cho, Chiyoda-ku, Tokyo 102. *1942, 1949*
F : *lit, dom sc.*

Rakuno Gakuen Daigaku [C. of Dairy Agriculture], 582-1 Bunkyodai-Midorimachi, Ebetsu-shi, Hokkaido 069. *1950, 1960*
F : *dairy agr.*

*Rikkyo Daigaku [Rikkyo (St. Paul's) U.], 3-34-1 Nishi Ikebukuro, Toshima-ku, Tokyo 171. *1922, 1949*
Tel: 3-985-2204
F : *arts, eco, sc, soc rel, law-pol.*

Rissho Daigaku, 4-2-16 Osaki, Shinagawa-ku, Tokyo 141. *1904, 1949*
Tel: 3-492-5262
F : *eco, bus adm, budh, let.*

Ritsumeikan Daigaku, 56-1 Kitamachi, Tojiin, Kyoto-shi, Kyoto 603. *1903, 1949*
Tel: 75-463-1131
F : *let, law, eco, law, sc-eng, bus adm, soc.*

*Ryukoku Daigaku, 67 Tsukamoto-cho, Fukakusa, Fushimi-ku, Kyoto-shi, Kyoto 612. *1922, 1949*
Tel: 75-642-1111
F : *let, eco, bus adm, law.*

Ryutsu-Keizai Daigaku [U. of Transportation Economics], 120 Hirahata, Ryugasaki-shi, Ibaraki 301. *1965*
Tel: 297-62-3251

F : *eco.*

Saitama Ika Daigaku [Saitama Medical C.], Moroyama-machi, Iruma-gun, Saitama 350-04.
Tel: 492-95-1111
F : *med.*

Sangyo Ika Daigaku]U. of Occupational and Environmental Health], 1-1 Iseigoaka, Yahatanishi-ku, Kitayushu-shi, Fukuoka 807. *1977, 1984*
Tel: 93-603-1611
S : *med.*

*Seijo Daigaku, 6-1-20 Seijo, Setagaya-ku, Tokyo 157. *1926, 1950*
Tel: 3-482-1181
F : *eco, lit-arts, law.*

Seikei Daigaku, 3-3-1 Kichijoji-Kitamachi, Musashino-shi, Tokyo 180. *1949*
Tel: 422-51-5181
F : *eco, eng, hum, law.*

Sei Marianna Ika Daigaku [St. Marianna U., S. of Medicine], 2095 Sugao, Miyamae-ku, Kawasaki-shi, Kanagawa 213. *1971*
Tel: 44-977-8111
F : *med.*

Seinan Gakuin Daigaku, 6-2-92 Nishijin, Fukuoka-shi, Fukuoka 814. *1921, 1949*
Tel: 92-841-1311
F : *com, eco, lit, law, theo.*

Seiroka Kango Daigaku [St. Luke's C. of Nursing], 10-1 Akasi-cho, Chuo-ku, Tokyo 104.
Tel: 3-543-6391
F : *nurs.*

*Seishin Joshi Daigaku [U. of the Sacred Heart], 4-3-1 Hiroo, Shibuya-ku, Tokyo 150. *1915, 1949*
Tel: 3-407-5811
F : *li arts.*

*Senshu Daigaku, 3-8 Kandajimbo-cho, Chiyoda-ku, Tokyo 101. *1927, 1949*
Tel: 3-265-6211
F : *eco, law, com, lit, bus adm.*

Senzoku Gakuen Daigaku, 290 Hisamoto, Takatsu-ku, Kasawaki-shi, Kanagawa 213. *1967*
Tel: 44-877-3211
F *bus.*

Shibaura Kogyo Daigaku [Shibaura I. of Technology], 3-9-14 Shibaura, Minato-ku, Tokyo 108. *1926, 1949*
Tel: 3-452-3201
F : *eng.*

Shikoku Gakuin Daigaku [Shikoku Christian C.], 3-2-1 Bunkyo-cho, Zentsuji-shi, Kagawa 765. *1962*
Tel: 877-62-2111
F : *lit.*

Showa Daigaku, 1-5-8 Hatanodai, Shinagawa-ku, Tokyo 142. *1928, 1964*
Tel: 3-784-8000

F : *med, phar, dent.*
Showa Joshi Daigaku [Showa Women's U.], 1-7 Taishido, Setagaya-ku, Tokyo 154.
1946, 1949
Tel: 3-422-5131
F : *lit, dom sc.*
Showa Yakka Daigaku [Showa C. of Pharmaceutical Science], 5-1-8 Tsurumaki, Setagaya-ku, Tokyo 154. *1930, 1949*
Tel: 3-426-3381
F : *phar.*
*****Soka Daigaku**, 1-236 Tangi-cho, Hachioji-shi, Tokyo 192. *1971*
Tel: 426-91-2211
D : *eco, law, let, bus adm, ed.*
Sophia University (See **Jochi Daigaku**)
Sugiyama Jogakuen Daigaku [Sugiyama Women's C.], 17-3 Hoshigaoka-motomachi, Chikusa-ku, Nagoya-shi, Aichi 414.
1930, 1949
Tel: 52-781-1186
F : *lit, home eco.*
Taisho Daigaku, 3-20-1 Nishisugamo, Toshima-ku, Tokyo 170. *1926, 1949*
Tel: 3-918-7311
F : *let, budh.*
Takushoku Daigaku, 3-4-14 Kohinata, Bunkyo-ku, Tokyo 112. *1904, 1949*
Tel: 3-947-2261
F : *com, pol-eco, fgn lang, techn.*
Tama Bijutsu Daigaku [Tama Art U.], 3-15-34 Kaminoge, Setagaya-ku, Tokyo 158.
1935, 1953
Tel: 3-702-1141
F : *fa-des.*
*****Tamagawa Daigaku**, 6-1-1- Tamagawa Gakuen, Machida-shi, Tokyo 194. *1945, 1949*
Tel: 427-28-3111
F : *let, agr, techn.*
Teikyo Daigaku, 2-11-1 Kaga, Itabashi-ku, Tokyo 173. *1966*
Tel: 3-964-1211
F : *lit, eco, law, med, phar.*
Toho Daigaku, 5-21-16 Omori Nishi, Ota-ku, Tokyo 143. *1925, 1949*
Tel: 3-762-4151
S : *med, phar, physical sc.*
Toho Ongaku Daigaku [Toho C. of Music], 84 Imaizumi, Kawagoe-shi, Saitama 356. *1965*
Tel: 492-35-2157
F : *mus.*
Tohoku Fukushi Daigaku [Tohoku (Welfare) U.], 1-8-1 Kunimi, Sendai-shi, Miyagi 980.
1962
Tel: 22-233-3111
F : *soc welfare.*
*****Tohoku Gakuin Daigaku** [Fukushi Tohoku Gakuin U.], Sendai-shi, Miyagi 980.
1949

Tel: 22-264-6411
F : *let, eco, eng, law.*
Tohoku Shika Daigaku [Tohoku Dental U.], 31-1 Misumi-do, Tomita-machi, Kosiyama-shi, Fukushima 963. *1972*
Tel: 249-32-8931
F : *dent.*
Tohoku Yakka Daigaku [Tohoku C. of Pharmacy], 4-4-1 Komatsushima, Sendai-shi, Miyagi 983. *1939, 1949*
Tel: 22-234-4181
F : *phar.*
*****Tokai Daigaku**, 2-28 Tomigaya, Shibuya-ku, Tokyo 151. *1946, 1950*
Tel: 3-467-2211. Telex: ntt 2423402 unitok j
S : *pol-eco, let, eng, sc, hum-cult, mar sc, phys, med.*
Tokushima Bunri Daigaku [Tokushima Bunri U.], 1-8 Terashimahon-cho, Tokushima-shi, Tokushima 720. *1961, 1966*
Tel: 886-22-0097
F : *dom sc, mus, phar, lit.*
Tokyo Denki Daigaku [Tokyo Engineering C.], 2-2 Kanda-Nishikicho, Chiyoda-ku, Tokyo 101. *1939, 1949*
Tel: 3-294-1551
F : *eng.*
Tokyo Ika Daigaku [Tokyo Medical C.], 6-1-1 Shinjuku, Shinjuku-ku, Tokyo 160. *1918, 1952*
Tel: 3-351-6141
F : *med.*
Tokyo International University (See **Tokyo Kokusai Daigaku**)
*****Tokyo Jikei-kai Ika Daigaku** [Jikei U.S. of Medicine], 3-25-8 Nishi-shinbashi, Minato-ku, Tokyo 105. *1921, 1952*
Tel: 3-433-1111
F : *med.*
*****Tokyo Joshi Daigaku** [Tokyo Woman's Christian C.], 2-6-1 Zenpukuji, Suginami-ku, Tokyo 167. *1918, 1948*
Tel: 3-395-1211
C : *arts-sc.*
Tokyo Joshi Ika Daigaku [Tokyo Women's Medical C.], 8-1 Kawada-cho, Shinjuku-ku, Tokyo 162. *1912, 1952*
Tel: 3-353-8111. Telex: ntt 2322317 twmlib j
F : *med.*
Tokyo Keizai Daigaku [Tokyo C. of Economics], 1-7 Minami-cho, Kokubunji-shi, Tokyo 185.
1900, 1949
Tel: 423-21-1941
F : *eco, bus adm.*
Tokyo Kogei Daigaku [Tokyo I. of Polytechnics], 1583 Iiyama, Atugi-shi, Kanagawa 243-02.
1923
Tel: 462-41-0454
F : *eng.*
Tokyo Kokusai Daigaku [Tokyo International

U.], 4-23-20 Takadanobaba, Shinjuku-ku, Tokyo 160. *1965*
Tel: 3-362-9641
F : *bus-com, int rel-hum rel.*
Tokyo Nogyo Daigaku [Tokyo U. of Agriculture], 1-1-1 Sakuragaoka, Setagaya-ku, Tokyo 156. *1925, 1949*
F : *agr.*
*Tokyo Rika Daigaku [Science U. of Tokyo], Shinjuku-ku, Tokyo. *1880, 1949*
F : *sc, eng, phar, sc-techn.*
Tokyo Shika Daigaku [Tokyo Dental C.], 2-9-18 Misaki-cho, Chiyoda-ku, Tokyo 101 *1907, 1952*
Tel: 3-262-3421
F : *dent.*
Tokyo Yakka Daigaku [Tokyo C. of Pharmacy], 1432-1 Horinouchi, Hachioji-shi, Tokyo 192-02. *1880, 1949*
Tel: 426-76-5111
F : *phar.*
Toyo Daigaku, 5-28-20 Hakusan, Bunkyo-ku, Tokyo 112. *1903, 1949*
Tel: 3-945-7241
F : *lit, eco, law, eng, bus adm, socio.*

Toyota Kogyo Daigaku [Toyota Technological I.], 2-12 Hisakata, Tempaku-ku, Nagoya-shi, Aichi 468. *1981*
Tel: 52-802-1111
F : *eng.*
*Tsuda-Juku Daigaku, 2-1-1 Tsuda-machi, Kodaira-shi, Tokyo 187. *1904, 1948*
Tel: 423-41-2441
F : *li arts.*
Tsurumi Daigaku [Tsurumi U.], 2-1-3 Tsurumi, Tsurumiku, Yokohama-shi, Kanagawa 230. *1953*
Tel: 45-581-1001
F : *lit.*
S : *dent.*
Wako Daigaku, 2,160 Kanai-cho, Machida-shi, Tokyo 194-01. *1966*
Tel: 44-988-1431
F : *hum, eco.*
*Waseda Daigaku, 1-6-1 Nishi-Waseda, Shinjuku-ku, Tokyo 160. *1902, 1949*
Tel: 3-203-4141. Telex: ntt 2323280
S : *pol-eco, law, ed, lit, sc-eng, com, soc.*

OTHER UNIVERSITIES AND UNIVERSITY INSTITUTIONS— AUTRES UNIVERSITES ET ETABLISSEMENTS UNIVERSITAIRES

National Institutions—Etablissements nationaux

Kyoto Kyoiku Daigaku [Kyoto U. of Education], 7 Fukakusa-Fujinomori-cho, Fushimi-ku, Kyoto-shi, Kyoto 612. *1876, 1949*
Tel: 75-641-9281
F : *ed.*

Public Institutions—Etablissements public

Aichi Kenritsu Daigaku [Aichi Prefectural U.], 3-28 Takada-cho, Mizuho-ku, Nagoya-shi, aichi 467. *1950, 1966*
Tel: 52-851-2191
F : *lit, fgn st.*
Fukuoka Joshi Daigaku [Fukuoka Women's U.], 1-1-1 Kasumigaoka, Higashi-ku, Fukuoka-shi, Fukuoka 813. *1923, 1950*
Tel: 92-661-2411
F : *lit, hom life sc.*
Gunma Kenritsu Joshi Daigaku [Gunma Prefectural Women's U.], 1395-1 Kaminote, Tamamura-machi, Sawa-gun, Gunma 370-11. *1980*
Tel: 270-65-8511
F : *let.*
Hiroshima Joshi Daigaku [Hiroshima Women's U.], 1-1-71 Ujina-higashi, Minami-ku, Hiroshima-shi, Hiroshima 734. *1928, 1965*

Tel: 82-251-5178
F : *let, hom eco.*
Hoso Daijaku [U. of the Air], Tokyo. *1983*
Kochi Joshi Daigaku [Kochi Women's U.], 5-15 Eikokuji-cho, Kochi-shi, Kochi 780. *1949*
Tel: 888-73-2156
F : *lit, hom eco.*
Kumamoto Joshi Daigaku [Kumamoto Women's C.], 2432-1 Mizuarai, Kengun, Kumamoto-shi, Kumamoto 862. *1949*
Tel: 96-383-2929
F : *let-living sc.*
Nagasaki Kenritsu Kokusai Keizai Daigaku [Nagasaki Prefectural C. of International Economics], 123 Kawashimo-cho, Sasebo-shi, Nagasaki 858. *1957, 1967*
Tel: 956-47-2191
F : *eco.*

Okinawa Kenritsu Geijutsu Daigaku [Okinawa Prefectural C. of Fine Arts], 1-4 Tonokura-cho, Shuri, Naha-shi, Okanawa 903.   *1928*
Tel: 988-31-5000
F : *fa.*

Shimonoseki Shiritsu Daigaku [Shimonoseki City C.], 2-1-1 Daigaku-cho, Shimonoseki-shi, Yamaguchi 751.   *1956, 1962*
Tel: 832-52-0288
F : *eco.*

Shizuoka Joshi Daigaku [Shizuoka Women's U.], 409 Yata, Shizuoka-shi, Shizuoka 422.
                                                    1951, 1967
Tel: 542-62-0336
F : *lang-lit, food & clothing sc.*

Takasaki Keizai Daigaku [Takasaki City U. of Economics], 1300 Kaminamie-machi, Takasaki-shi, Gumma 370.   *1952, 1957*
Tel: 273-43-5417
F : *eco.*

Tokyo Toritsu Kagaku Gijutsu Daigaku [Tokyo Metropolitan I. of Technology], 6-6 Asahi-gaoka, Hino-shi, Tokyo 191.   *1986*
Tel: 425-83-5111
F : *eng.*

Tsuru Bunka Daigaku 3-81 Tahara, Tsuru-shi, Yamanashi 402.   *1953, 1959*
Tel: 554-43-4341
C : *hum.*

Yamaguchi Joshi Daigaku [Yamaguchi Women's U.], 3-2-1 Sakurabatake, Yamaguchi-shi, Yamaguchi 753.   *1941*
Tel: 839-28-0211
F : *lit, hom sc.*

Private Institutions—Etablissements privés

Aichi Shukutoku Daigaku, 9 Katahira, Nagakute, Nagakute-cho, Aichi-gun, Aichi 480-11.
                                                          1975
Tel: 5616-2-4111
F : *lit.*

Akita Keizai Hoka Daigaku [Akita U. of Economics and Law], 46-1 Morisawa, Tezakura, Shimokita, Akita-shi, Akita 010.
                                                          1953
Tel: 188-35-6625
F : *eco, law.*

Aomori Daigaku, 248 Abeno, Kohata, Aomori-shi, Aomori 030.   *1962, 1968*
Tel: 177-38-2114
F : *bus adm, socio.*

Asahikawa Daigaku, 113-3-23 Nagayama, Asahikawa-shi, Hokkaido 079.   *1968*
Tel: 166-48-3121
F : *eco.*

Ashikaga Kogyo Daigaku [Ashikaga I. of Technology], 268-1 Omae-cho, Ashikaga-shi, Tochigi 326.   *1967*
Tel: 284-62-0605
F : *eng.*

Atomi Gakuen Joshi Daigaku [Atomi Gakuen Women's C.], 1-9-6 Nakaro, Niiza-shi, Saitama 352.   *1969*
Tel: 484-78-3333
F : *lit.*

Baiko Jogakuin Daigaku, 365 Myoji-cho, Yoshimi, Shimonoseki-shi, Yamaguchi 759-65.
                                                    1964, 1967
Tel: 832-56-1111
F : *let.*

Beppu Daigaku, 82 Kita-ishigaki, Beppu-shi, Oita 874-01.   *1946, 1970*
Tel: 977-67-0101
F : *lit.*

Bunkyo Daigaku, 3337 Minami-Ogishima, Koshigaya-shi, Saitama 343.
Tel: 489-74-8811
F : *ed, hum sc, lang-lit.*

Chiba Keiai Keizai Daigaku [Chiba Keiai C. of Economics], 1-5-21 Anagawa, Chiba-shi, Chiba 260.   *1950, 1966*
Tel: 472-51-6363
F : *eco.*

Chukyo Joshi Daigaku [Chukyo Women's U.], 2-1-10 Daiko Minami, Higashi-ku, Nagoya-shi, Aichi 461.   *1963*
Tel: 52-723-0851
F : *phys, hom eco.*

Chuo Gakuin Daigaku, 451 Kujike, Abiko-shi, Chiba 270-11.   *1966*
Tel: 471-82-1311
F : *com, law.*

Daido Kogyo Daigaku [Daido I. of Technology], 2-21 Daido-cho, Minami-ku, Nagoya, Aichi 457.   *1964*
Tel: 52-612-6111
F : *eng.*

Dai-ichi Keizai Daigaku [Dai-ichi C. of Commerce and Industry], 3-11-25 Gojo, Dazaifu-shi, Chikushi-gun, Fukuoka 818-01.
                                                          1968
Tel: 92-922-5131
F : *eco.*

Dai-ichi Kogyo Daigaku, 1-10-2 Chuo, Kokubu-shi, Kagoshima 899-43.
Tel: 995-45-0640.
F : *techn.*

Dai-ichi Yakka Daigaku [Dai-ichi C. of Pharmaceutical Sciences], 22-1 Tamagawa-cho, Minami-ku, Fukuoka-shi, Fukuoka 815.   *1960*
Tel: 92-541-0161
F : *phar.*

Doho Daigaku, 7-1 Inabaji-cho, Nakamura-ku, Nagoya-shi, Aichi 453. *1921, 1950*
Tel: 52-411-1111
F : *lit, soc welfare.*

Dohto Daigaku [Dohto U.], 7 Ochiishi-cho, Mombetsu-shi, Hokkaido 094. *1978*
Tel: 1582-4-8101
F : *soc welfare, fa.*

Eichi Daigaku [Catholic U. of Osaka], 2-18-1 Nakoji, Amagasaki-shi, Hyogo 661. *1963*
Tel: 6-491-5083
F : *li arts.*

Ferisu Jogakuin Daigaku [Ferris Women's C.], 37 Yamate-cho, Naka-ku, Yokohama-shi, Kanagawa 231. *1947, 1965*
Tel: 45-662-4521
F : *lit.*

Fuji Daigaku, 450-3 Shimoneko, Hanamaki-shi, Iwate 025. *1965*
Tel: 198-23-6221
F : *eco.*

Fuji Joshi Daigaku [Fuji Women's C.], Nishi 2, Kita 16, Kita-ku, Sapporo-shi, Hokkaido 001. *1950, 1961*
Tel: 11-736-0311
F : *let.*

Fukuoka Kogyo Daigaku [Fukuoka I. of Technology], 3-30-1 Wajirohigashi, Higashi-ku, Fukuoka 811-02. *1963*
Tel: 92-606-3131
F : *eng.*

Gifu Joshi Daigaku [Gifu Women's C.], 80 Taromaru, Gifu-shi, Gifu 501-25. *1968*
Tel: 582-29-2111
F : *hom eco, lit.*

Gifu Keizai Daigaku [Gifu C. of Economics], 5-5 Kitagata-cho, Ogaki-shi, Gifu 176. *1967*
Tel: 584-74-5151
F : *eco.*

Hachinohe Daigaku, 13-98 Mihono, Hachinohe-shi, Aomori 031. *1981*
Tel: 178-25-2711
F : *com.*

Hachinohe Kogyo Daigaku [Hachinohe U. of Technology], 88-1 Obiraki, Myo, Hachinohe-shi, Aomori 031. *1972*
Tel: 178-25-3111
F : *eng.*

Hakodate Daigaku, 51-1 Takaoka-cho, Hakodate-shi, Hokkaido 042. *1965*
Tel: 138-57-1181
F : *com.*

Hakuoh Daigaku, 1177 Daigyoji, Oyama-shi, Tochige 323.
Tel: 285-22-1111
F : *mangt*

Hannan Daigaku, 5-4-33 Amamihigashi, Matsubara-shi, Osaka 580. *1950, 1965*
Tel: 723-32-1224

F : *com, eco.*

Hirosaki Gakuin Daigaku [Hirosaki Gakuin U.], 13-1 Minori-cho, Aomori 036.
Tel: 172-34-5211
F : *lit* (women).

Hiroshima-Denki Daigaku [Hiroshima Denki I. of Technology], 6-20-1 Nakano, Aki-ku, Hiroshima-shi, Hiroshima 739-03. *1967*
Tel: 82-893-0381
F : *eng.*

Hiroshima Jogakuin Daigaku, 4-13-1 Ushita-Higashi, Hiroshima-shi, Hiroshima 732. *1932, 1949*
Tel: 82-228-0386
F : *lit.*

Hiroshima Kogyo Daigaku [Hiroshima I. of Technology], 725 Miyake, Itsukaichi-cho, Saeki-ku, Hiroshima-shi, Hiroshima 731-51. *1961, 1963*
Tel: 829-21-3121
F : *eng.*

Hokkaigakuen Kitami Daigaku, 235 Hokko, Kitami-shi, Hokkaido 090. *1977*
Tel: 157-22-2721
F : *com.*

Hokkaido Kogyo Daigaku [Hokkaido I. of Technology], 419-2 Maeda, Teine, Nishi-ku, Sapporo-shi, Hokkaido 061-24. *1953, 1967*
Tel: 11-681-2161
F : *eng.*

Hokkaido Tokai Daigaku, 224 Chawa, Kamui-cho, Asahikawa-shi, Hokkaido. *1977*
Tel: 166-61-5111
S : *art-techn.*

Ibaraki Kirisutokyo Daigaku [Ibaraki Christian C.], 6-11-1 Omika-cho, Hitachi-shi, Ibaraki 319-12. *1967*
Tel: 294-52-3215
F : *lit.*

Jobu Daigaku, 634 Toyazuka-machi, Isezaki-shi, Gunma 372. *1986*
Tel: 276-32-1011
F : *com, mangt-infor.*

Joshi Bijutsu Daigaku [Women's C. of Fine Arts], Suginami-ku, Tokyo. *1929, 1949*
F : *fa.*

Kagoshima Joshi Daigaku [Kagoshima Women's C.], 1904 Uchi, Hayato-cho, Aira-gun, Kagoshima 899-51. *1978*
Tel: 995-43-1111
F : *lit.*

Kagoshima Keizai Daigaku [Kagoshima U. of Economics and Sociology], 8850 Shimo-fukomoto-cho, Kagoshima-shi, Kagoshima 891-01. *1950, 1959*
Tel: 992-61-3211
F : *eco, socio.*

Kamakura Joshi Daigaku [Kamakura Women's U.], 1420 Iwase, Kamakura-shi, Kanagawa

247.   *1943, 1959*
Tel: 467-44-2111
F : *hom eco.*

Kanagawa Kogyo Daigaku [Kanagawa I. of
Technology], 1030 Shimoogino, Atsugi-shi,
Kanagawa 243-02.   *1975*
Tel: 462-41-1211
F : *eng.*

Kanazawa Keizai Daigaku [Kanazawa C. of
Economics], 101 Ushi, Gosho-machi,
Kanazawa-shi, Ishikawa 920.   *1967*
Tel: 762-52-2236
F : *eco.*

Kinjo Gakuin Daigaku, 2-1723 Omori, Nagoya-
shi, Aichi 463.   *1927, 1949*
Tel: 52-798-0180
F : *lit, hom eco.*

Kobe Kaisei Joshi Gakuin Daigaku, [Kobe Kaisei
C., Stella Maris C.], 2-7-1 Aotani-cho, Nada-
ku, Kobe-shi, Hyogo 657.   *1950, 1965*
Tel: 78-801-2277
F : *lit.*

Koka Joshi Daigaku [Koka Women's C.], 38
Kadono-cho, Nishi-Kyogoku, Ukyo-ku,
Kyoto-shi, Kyoto 615.   *1944, 1964*
F : *let.*

Kokusai Budo Daigaku, 841 Aza Monomizuka,
Shinga, Katsuura-shi, Chiba 299-52.   *1984*
Tel: 4707-3-4111
F : *phys.*

Koriyama Joshi Daigaku [Koriyama Women's
C.], 3-25-2 Kasei, Koriyama-shi, Fukushima
963.   *1950, 1966*
Tel: 249-32-4848
F : *hom eco.*

Koshien Daigaku, 10-1 Momijigaoka,
Takarazuka-shi, Hyogo 665.   *1967*
Tel: 767-87-5111
F : *nutr, bus adm-infor.*

Kumamoto Shoka Daigaku [Kumamoto U. of
Commerce], 2-5-1 Oe, Kumamoto-shi,
Kumamoto 862.   *1950, 1954*
Tel: 96-364-5161
F : *com, eco.*

Kurume Kogyo Daigaku [Kurume I. of Tech-
nology], 2228 Kamitsu-machi, Kurume-shi,
Fukuoka 830.   *1971*
Tel: 942-22-1234
F : *techn.*

Kwassui Joshi Dayaku [Kwassui Women's C.],
1-50 Higashi-Yamate-machi, Nagasaki-shi,
Nagasaki 850   *1952, 1981*
Tel: 958-22-4107
F : *lit.*

Kyoto Gakuen Daigaku, Nanjo Otani, Sokabe-
cho, Kameoka-shi, Kyoto 621.   *1969*
Tel: 7712-2-2001
F : *eco.*

Kyoto Seika Daigaku, 137 Kino, Iwakura, Sakyo-

ku, Kyoto-shi, Kyoto 606.   *1968*
Tel: 75-791-6131
F : *fa.*

Kyushi Joshi Daigaku [Kyushu Women's U.],
1-1 Jiyagaoka, Yahatanishi-ku, Kitakyushu-
shi, Fukuoka 802.
Tel: 93-691-3331
F : *hom eco, lit.*

Kyushu Gakuin Daigaku, Kokubu, Kagoshima.
                                        1966
F : *eng.*

Kyushu Kyoritsu Daigaku, 1-1 Jiyugaoka,
Yahatanishi-ku, Kitakyushu-shi, Fukuoka 807.
                                        1965
Tel: 93-691-3331
F : *eco, eng.*

Matsumoto Shika Daigaku [Matsumoto Dental
C.], 1780 Hirooka, Gobara, Shiojiri-shi,
Nagano 399-07.   *1972*
Tel: 263-52-3100
F : *dent.*

Matsusaka Daigaku, 1846 Kubo-cho, Matsusaka-
shi, Mie 515.   *1982*
Tel: 598-29-1122
F : *pol-eco.*

Meiji Shinkyu Daigaku [Meiji C. of Oriental
Medicine], Hiyoshi-cho, Funai-gun, Kyoto
629-03.   *1983*
Tel: 7717-2-1181
F : *acupuncture-moxibustion.*

Mimasaka Joshi Daigaku [Mimasaka Women's
C.], 32 Kamigawara, Tsuyama-shi, Okayama
708.   *1951, 1967*
Tel: 862-2-7718
F : *hom eco.*

Minami Kyushu Daigaku, 6307 Tayoshi,
Miyazaki-shi, Koyu-gun, Miyazaki 880.
                                        1965, 1967
Tel: 985-51-6307
F : *hort.*

Miyagi Gakuin Joshi Daigaku [Miyagi Gakuin
Women's C.], 9-1-1 Sakuragaoka, Sendai-shi,
Miyagi 980.   *1946, 1949*
Tel: 22-279-1311
F : *li arts.*

Momoyama Gakuin Daigaku [St. Andrew's U.],
237-1 Nishino, Sakai-shi, Osaka.   *1959*
Tel: 722-36-1181
F : *eco, bus adm, socio.*

Morioka Daigaku, 5-4-1 Kurigawa, Morioka-shi,
Iwate 020-01.
Tel: 196-41-2193
F : *lit.*

Musashino Joshi Daigaku [Musashino Women's
C.], 1-1-20 Shin-machi, Hoya-shi, Tokyo 202.
                                        1950, 1965
Tel: 424-62-3111
F : *lit.*

Nagano Daigaku, Shimonogo, Ueda-shi, Nagano

386-12. *1966*
Tel: 268-38-2350
F : *ind socio.*
Nagoya Gakuin Daigaku, 1350 Kamishinano-cho, Seto-shi, Aichi 480-12. *1964*
Tel: 561-42-0250
F : *eco.*
Nagoya Geijutsu Daigaku [Nagoya U. of the Arts], Nishikasugai-gun, Aichi 481. *1970*
Tel: 568-24-0315
F : *mus, fa.*
Nagoya Keizei Daigaku [Nagoya Economics U.], 61-1 Uchikubo, Inuyama-shi, Aichi 484. *1979*
Tel: 568-67-0511
F : *eco.*
Nagoya Joshi Daigaku [Nagoya Women's C.], 4-30 Shioji-cho, Mizuho-ku, Aichi 467. *1964*
Tel: 52-852-1111
F : *hom eco.*
Nagoya Ongaku Daigaku [Nagoya Music C.], 7-1 Inabaji-cho, Nakamura-ku, Nagoya-shi, Aichi 468. *1976*
Tel: 52-411-1111
F : *mus.*
Nakamura Gakuen Daigaku, 5-7-1 Befu, Jonan-ku, Fukuoka-shi, Fukuoka 814. *1965*
Tel: 92-851-2531
F : *hom eco.*
Nara Daigaku, 1230 Horai-cho, Nara-shi, Nara 631. *1969*
Tel: 742-44-1251
F : *hum.*
Nara Sangyo Daigaku, 3-12-1 Tatsunokita, Sango-cho, Ikomo-gun, Nara 636. *1984*
Tel: 745-73-7800
F : *eco.*
Nihon Kuteru Shingaku Daigaku [Japan Lutheran Theological C.], 3-10-20 Osawa, Mitaka-shi, Tokyo 181. *1976*
F : *theo, lit.*
Nihon Sekijuji Kango Daigaku [The Japanese Red Cross C. of Nursing], 4-1-3 Hiroo, Shibuya-ku, Tokyo 150. *1966*
Tel: 3-409-0875
F : *nurs.*
Nihon Shakai-Jigyo Daigaku [Japan C. of Social Work], 1-4-19 Jingumae, Shibuya-ku, Tokyo 150. *1950, 1958*
Tel: 3-402-7507
F : *soc welfare.*
Nihon Joshi Taiiku Daigaku [Nippon Women's C. of Physical Education], 8-19-1 Kitakara-suyana, Setagayaku, Tokyo 157. *1965*
Tel: 3-300-2251
F : *phys.*
Niigata Yakka Daigaku [Niigata C. of Pharmacy], 5-13-2 Kamishin'ei-cho, Niigata-shi, Niigata 950-21. *1977*
Tel: 25-269-3171

F : *phar.*
Nippon Bunka Daigaku, Hachioji-shi, Tokyo 192. *1978*
Tel: 426-36-5211
F : *law.*
Nippon Bunri Daigaku, Ichigi, Oita-shi, Oita 870-03. *1967, 1982*
Tel: 975-92-1600
S : *bus-eco, eng.*
Nishikyushu Daigaku, 4490-9 Hirayama, Osaki, Kanzaki-machi, Kanzaki, Saga 842. *1968*
Tel: 952-52-4191
F : *hom eco.*
Nishinippon Kogyo Daigaku [Nishinippon I. of Technology], 1633 Aratsu, Kanda-cho, Miyako-gun, Fukuoka 800-03.
1967
Tel: 9302-3-1491
F : *techn.*
***Notorudamu Joshi Daigaku** [Notre Dame Women's C.], 1 Minami-Nonogami-cho, Shimogamo, Sakyo-ku, Kyoto-shi, Kyoto 606.
1961
F : *lit.*
Notre Dame Seishin Joshi Daigaku [Notre Dame Seishin U.], 2-16-9 Ifuku-cho, Okayama-shi, Okayama 700. *1944, 1949*
Tel: 862-52-1155
F : *lit, hom eco.*
Obirin Daigaku, 3758 Tokiwa-cho, Machida-shi, Tokyo 194-02. *1950, 1966*
Tel: 427-97-2661
F : *lit, eco.*
Okayama Shoka Daigaku [Okayama C. of Commerce], 2-10-1 Tsushima-Kyo-machi, Okayama-shi, Okayama 700. *1965*
Tel: 862-52-0642
F : *com.*
Okinawa Daigaku [U. of Okinawa], 747 Kokuba, Naha-shi, Okinawa 902. *1961*
Tel: 988-32-1768
F : *law-eco.*
Okinawa Kokusai Daigaku [Okinawa Kokusai U.], 276-2 Ginowan, Ginowanshi, Okinawa 901-22. *1961, 1962, 1972*
Tel: 9889-2-1111
C : *law, let, com-eco.*
Osaka Denkitsushin Daigaku [Osaka Electro-Communications U.], 18-8 Hatsu-cho, Neyagawa-shi, Osaka 572. *1961*
Tel: 720-24-1131
F : *eng.*
Osaka Keizai Hoka Daigaku [Osaka U. of Economics and Law], 6-10 Gakuoniji, Yao-shi, Osaka 581. *1971*
Tel: 729-41-8211
F : *eco, law.*
Osaka Sangyo Daigaku [Osaka Industrial U.], 3-1-1 Nakagaito, Daito-shi, Osaka 574. *1965*

Tel: 720-75-3001
F : *bus adm, eng, eco.*

Osaka Shoin Joshi Daigaku [Osaka Shoin Women's C.], 4-2-26 Hishiyanishi, Higashi Osaka-shi, Osaka 577.   *1925, 1949*
Tel: 6-723-8181
F : *li arts.*

Otani Joshi Daigaku [Otani Women's C.], Shigakudai, Nishikiori, Tondabayashi-shi, Osaka 584.   *1966*
Tel: 721-24-0381
F : *lit.*

Reitaku Daigaku, 2-1-1 Hikarigaoka, Kashiwa-shi, Chiba 277.   *1942, 1959*
Tel: 471-73-3601
F : *fgn lang.*

Sagami Joshi Daigaku [Sagami Women's U.], 2-1-1 Bukyo, Sagamihara-shi, Kanagawa 228.
                                                        1909, 1949
Tel: 427-42-1411
F : *li arts.*

Sagami Kogyo Daigaku [Sagami I. of Technology], 1-1-25 Tsujido, Nishikaigan, Fujisawa-shi, Kanagawa 251.   *1963*
Tel: 466-34-4111
F : *eng.*

Saitama Kogyo Daigaku [Saitama I. of Techology], 1690 Fusaiji, Okabe-machi, Osato-gun, Saitama 369-02.
F : *eng.*

Sakuyo Ongaku Daigaku [Sakuyo C. of Music], 1334-1 Yaide, Tsuyama-shi, Okayama708.
                                                                1966
Tel: 868-24-1811
F : *mus.*

Sangyo Noritsu Daigaku [Sanno C.], 1573 Kami-kasuya, Isehara-shi, Kanagawa 259-11.   *1979*
Tel: 463-92-2211
D : *mangt-informatics.*

Sapporo Daigaku, 3-1; 3-7 Nishioka, Toyohira-ku, Sapporo-shi, Hokkaido 062.   *1967*
Tel: 4-852-1181
F : *eco, fgn lang, bus adm.*

Sapporo Gakuin Daigaku [Sapporo Gakuin U.], 11 Bunkyodai, Ebetsu-shi, Hokkaido 069.
                                                    1946, 1968, 1984
Tel: 11-386-8111
F : *com, hum, law.*

Seisen Joshi Daigaku [Seisen Women's C.], 3-16-21 Higashi Gotanda, Shinagawa-ku, Tokyo 141.   *1950*
Tel: 3-447-5551
F : *let.*

Sendai Daigaku, Minami 2, 2-18 Funaoka, Shibata-machi, Shibata-gun, Miyagi 989-16.
                                                                1967
Tel: 2245-5-1121
F : *phys.*

Setsunan Daigaku, 17-8 Ikedanaka-machi,

Neyagawa-shi, Osaka 572.   *1975*
Tel: 720-26-5101
F : *eng, bus adm-infor, int lang-cult, phar.*

Shikoku Joshi Daigaku [Shikoku Women's U.], 123-1 Ebisuno, Furukawa, Ojin-cho, Tokushima-shi, Tokushima 771-11.   *1961, 1966*
Tel: 886-65-1300
F : *hom eco, lit.*

Shinwa Joshi Daigaku [Shinwa Women's C.], 7-13-1 Suzurandai-kitamachi, Kita-ku, Kobe-shi, Hyogo 651-11.   *1966*
Tel: 78-591-1651
F : *lit.*

Shirayuri Joshi Daigaku [Shirayuri Women's C.], Chofu, Tokyo.   *1946, 1965*
F : *let.*

Shitennoji Kokusai Bukkyo Daigaku [Shitennoji International Buddhist U.], 1308 Hanyuno, Habikino-shi, Osaka 583.   *592*
Tel: 729-56-3181
F : *lit.*

Shoin Joshigakuin Daigaku [Shoin Women's U.], 1-2-1 Shinoharaobaroyama-cho, Nadaku, Kobe-shi, Hyogo 657.   *1966*
Tel: 78-882-6122
F : *lit.*

Shokei Daigaku, 2155-7 Ninenoki, Shimizu-machi, Kumamoto-shi, Kumamoto 860.   *1975*
Tel: 96-338-8840
F : *lit.*

Shotoku Gakuen (See **Gifu Kyoiku Daigaku**)

Shuchiin Daigaku, 545 Toji-cho, Hachijo-sagaru, Mibu-dori, Minami-ku, Kyoto-shi, Kyoto 601.
                                                                1905
Tel: 75-681-6513
F : *budh.*

Shujitso Joshi Daigaku [Shujitso Women's U.], 1-6-1 Nishigawara, Okayama-shi, Okayama 703.   *1979*
Tel: 862-72-3185
F : *lit.*

Shukutoku Daigaku, 200 Daiganji-cho, Chiba-shi, Chiba 280.   *1965*
Tel: 472-65-7331
F : *soc welfare.*

Soai Daigaku, 4-4-1 Nanko-Naka, Suminoe-ku, Osaka-shi, Osaka 559.
Tel: 6-612-5900
F : *hum, mus.*

Sonoda Gakuen Joshi Daigaku [Sonoda Gakuen Women's C.], 7-29-1 Minami-Tsukaguchi-cho, Amagasaki-shi, Hyogo 661.   *1963, 1966*
Tel: 6-429-1201
F : *lit.*

Sophia University (See **Jochi Daigaku**)

Sugino Joshi Daigaku [Sugino Women's C.], 4-6-19 Kamiosaki, Shinagawa-ku, Tokyo 141.
                                                            1950, 1964
Tel: 3-491-8151

F : *hom eco.*
Tachibana Joshi Daigaku Kyoto [Tachibana Women's U.], 34 Oyake Yamada-cho, Yamashina-ku, Kyoto-shi, Kyoto 607. *1967*
Tel: 75-571-1111
F : *let.*
Takachiho Shoka Daigaku [Takachiho C. of Commerce], 2-19-1 Omiya, Suginami-ku, Tokyo 168. *1914, 1950*
Tel: 3-313-0141
F : *com.*
Teikoku Joshi Daigaku [Teikoku Women's C.], 6-173 Toda-cho, Moriguchi-shi, Osaka 570. *1965*
Tel: 6-902-0791
F : *hom eco.*
Tenri Daigaku, 1050 Somanouchi-cho, Tenri-shi, Nara 632. *1925, 1949*
Tel: 7436-3-1511
F : *lit, fgn lang, phys.*
Tezukayama Daigaku, 7-1-1 Tezukayama, Nara-shi, Nara 631. *1964*
Tel: 742-45-4701
F : *li arts.*
Tezukayama Gakuin Daigaku, 1823 Imakuma, Sayama-cho, Minamikawachi-gun, Osaka 589. *1966*
Tel: 723-65-0865
F : *lit.*
Toa Daigaku [U. of East Asia], 15-2 Kasuno, Shimonoseki-shi, Yamaguchi 751.
Tel: 832-56-1111
F : *bus adm, eng.*
Toho Gakuen Daigaku [Toho Gakuen S. of Music], 1-41-1 Wakaba-shi, Chofu-shi, Tokyo 182. *1955, 1961*
Tel: 3-307-4101
F : *mus.*
Tohoku Joshi Daigaku [Tohoku Women's C.], 1-2-1 Toyohara, Hirosaki-shi, Aomori 036. *1969*
F : *hom eco.*
Tohoku Kogyo Daigaku [Tohoku I. of Technology], 35-1 Yagiyama-kasumuho, Sendai-shi, Miyagi 982. *1964*
Tel: 22-229-1151
F : *eng.*
Tohoku Seikatsu Bunka Daigaku [Tohoku Living Culture C.], 1-18 Nijinooka, Izumi-shi, Miyagi 980. *1958*
Tel: 22-272-7511
F : *dom sc.*
Tokai Joshi Daigaku [Tokai Women's C.], Kirino-cho, Naka, Kakamigahara-shi, Gifu 504.
Tel: 583-89-2200
F : *li arts.*
Tokiwa Daigaku [Tokiwa U.], 1-430-1 Miwa, Mito-shi, Ibaraki 310. *1983*

Tel: 292-32-2611
F : *hum.*
Tokoha Gakuen Daigaku, 100 Sena, Shizuoka-shi, Shizuoka 420.
Tel: 542-63-1125
F : *ed, fgn lang.*
Tokuyama Daigaku [Tokuyama U.], 843-4-2 Kune-Kurigasako, Tokuyama-shi, Yamaguchi 745. *1971*
Tel: 834-28-0411
F : *eco.*
Tokyo International University (See **Tokyo Kokusai Daigaku**)
Tokyo Joshi Taiiku Daigaku [Tokyo Women's C. of Physical Education], 620 Tanikawakami, Aoyagi, Kunitachi-shi, Tokyo 186. *1962*
F : *phys.*
Tokyo Kasei Daigaku, 1-18-1 Kaga, Itabashi-ku, Tokyo 173. *1922, 1949*
Tel: 3-961-5226
F : *hom eco.*
Tokyo Kasei Gakuin Daigaku [Tokyo Women's C. of Home Economics], 2260 Aihara-cho, Machida-shi, Tokyo 194-02. *1963*
Tel: 427-82-9811
F : *hom eco.*
Tokyo Koka Daigaku [Tokyo Engineering U.], 1401-1 Katakura-cho, Hachioji-shi, Tokyo 192 *1986*
Tel: 426-37-2111
Tokyo Ongaku Daigaku [Tokyo Music C.], Toshima-ku, Tokyo 186. *1954, 1963*
Tel: 3-982-3186
F : *mus.*
Tokyo Zokei Daigaku [Tokyo U. of Arts and Design], 3-2707 Motohachiji, Hachioji-shi, Tokyo 193. *1966*
Tel: 426-61-4401
F : *arts.*
Towa Daigaku, 1-1-1 Chikushigaoka, Minami-ku, Fukuoka-shi, Fukuoka 815. *1967*
Tel: 92-541-1511
F : *eng.*
Ueno Gakuen Daigaku, 4-24-12 Higashiueno, Taito-ku, Tokyo 180. *1952, 1958*
Tel: 3-842-1021
F : *mus.*
University of East Asia (See **Toa Daigaku**)
Wayo Joshi Daigaku [Wayo Women's U.], Ichikawa-shi, Chiba 272. *1928, 1949*
Tel: 473-71-1111
F : *lit-hom eco.*
Yahata Daigaku, 5-9-1 Edamitsu, Yahata-ku, Kitakyushu, Fukuoka 805. *1947, 1950*
Tel: 93-661-3030
F : *law-eco.*
Yamanashi Gakuin Daigaku, 2-4-5 Sakaori, Kofu-shi, Yamanashi 400. *1951, 1962*
Tel: 552-33-1111

F: *law, com.*

Yashiro Gakuin Daigaku [St. Michael's U.],
5-1-1-Manabigaoka, Tarumi-ku, Kobe-shi,
Hyogo 655.   *1968*
Tel: 78-709-3851
F: *eco.*

Yasuda Joshi Daigaku [Yasuda Women's U.],
6-13-1 Yasuhigashi, Asaminami-ku, Hiroshima-shi, Hiroshima 731-01.   *1966*

Tel: 82-878-8111
F: *let.*

Yokohama Shoka Daigaku [Yokohama C. of
Commerce], 4-11-1 Higashi Terao, Tsurumi-
ku, Yokohama-shi, Kanagawa 230.
                                               1966, 1968
Tel: 45-571-3901
F: *com.*

Kokuritsu Daigaku Kyokai (National University
Association of Japan)

The object of the Association is to contribute
to the accomplishment of the mission of the
Government universities, through mutual co-
operation.

Activities: 1) investigation and research for
development of the universities; 2) matters
concerning mutual co-operation in scientific
research and education; 3) other necessary
matters.

Membership: Government universities.

*L'Association nationale des universités du
Japon a pour objet de contribuer à l'accomplissement de la mission des universités d'Etat par la
coopération mutuelle.*

*Activités: 1) études et recherches en vue du
développement des universités; 2) questions
relatives à la coopération mutuelle en matière de
recherche scientifique et d'enseignement; 3) autres
questions importantes.*

Membres: Les universités d'Etat.

President: Wataru Mori.

Vice-Presidents: Kenzo   Tanaka;   Shigeru
Tanese.

Hongo 7–3–1, Bunkyo-ku, Tokyo 113.
Tel: 813 0467

Koritsu Daigaku Kyokai (Association of the
Public (Local Government) Universities)

The object of the Association is to contribute
to the accomplishment of the mission of the
public (local government) universities, through
mutual co-operation.

Activities: 1) matters concerning administration and management in public (local government) universities; 2) matters required for the
scientific research and the realization of research
and plans on education; 3) other necessary
matters.

Membership: Public (local government)
universities.

*L'Association des universités publiques dé-
pendant des autorités locales a pour objet de
contribuer à l'accomplissement de la mission des
universités publiques (dépendant des autorités
locales) par la coopération mutuelle.*

*Activités: 1) questions concernant l'administra-
tion et la gestion des universités publiques;
2) questions relatives à la recherche scientifique et
à la réalisation des programmes de recherche et
d'enseignement; 3) autres questions importantes.*

*Membres: Les universités publiques (dépendant
des autorités locales).*

President: Ken-ichi Kusukawa.

c/o Kokuritsu Kyoiku Kaikannai, 3-2-3
Kasumigaseki Chiyoda-ku, Tokyo 100.
Tel: 580 20-46

Nihon Shiritsu Daigaku Kyokai (Association of
Private Universities of Japan)

The object of the Association is to contribute
to the accomplishment of the mission and
purpose of the private universities, through
mutual co-operation.

Activities: 1) matters concerning administration, management and student life in the private
universities; 2) matters concerning scientific
research and the realization of research and plans
on education; 3) matters concerning the National
Budget for education and the Law of Education;
4) publication of an organ newspaper (the
Kyoiku Gakujutsu) and other bulletins; 5) other
necessary matters.

Membership: 210 Private universities in Japan.

*L'Association des universités privées du Japon
a pour objet de contribuer à l'accomplissement de
la mission et de la fonction des universités par la
coopération mutuelle.*

*Activités: 1) questions concernant l'administra-
tion, la gestion des universités privées et
l'organisation de la vie des étudiants; 2) questions
concernant la recherche scientifique et la réalisation des programmes de recherche et d'enseignement; 3) questions concernant le budget national
pour l'enseignement et la législation de l'enseignement; 4) publication d'un journal (Kyoiku
Gakujutsu) et d'autres bulletins; 5) autres questions importantes.*

Membres: 210 universités privées du Japon.

President: S. Kittaka.

Vice-Presidents: T. Obara; N. Sato; M. Morimoto;
N. Watanabe; T. Tanioka; M. Ishida.

Secretary-General: Takao Maruyama.
c/o Shigaku-Kaikan, 4–2–25, Kudankita, Chiyoda-ku, Tokyo.
Tel: 3-261-7048

Daigaku Kijun Kyokai (Japanese University Accreditation Association)

The purpose of the Association is to conduct research and investigation on matters concerning higher education, foreign and domestic, to improve the standard of higher education in Japan and also to make a contribution to higher education in the world at large by co-operating with other nations.

Activities: 1) research and study on matters concerning higher education, foreign and domestic; 2) establishment of standards, their advancement and application in order to improve the quality of universities and colleges; 3) advice and assistance and distribution of information in order to promote higher education; 4) setting up of study groups and conferences necessary to improve the quality of higher education; 5) exchange of information and co-operation with other nations in matters concerning higher education; 6) publication of documents and materials on university education and conferences; 7) other activities necessary for the achievement of the purpose of the Association.

Membership: Limited to those universities which have existed more than four years since their establishment by, or approval of establishment by the Minister of Education and which are recognized by the Association as conforming to the University Standards.

L'Association japonaise d'accréditation universitaire a pour objet d'effectuer des études et des recherches concernant l'enseignement supérieur étranger et japonais, d'améliorer le niveau de l'enseignement supérieur japonais et de contribuer au progrès de l'enseignement supérieur dans le monde grâce à la coopération avec d'autres nations.

Activités: 1) recherches et études sur des questions relatives à l'enseignement supérieur étranger et japonais; 2) définition des niveaux et leur application en vue de l'amélioration de la qualité des universités et collèges; 3) diffusion d'informations et services consultatifs en vue de promouvoir l'enseignement supérieur; 4) organisation de groupes d'étude et de conférences en vue d'améliorer la qualité de l'enseignement supérieur; 5) échange d'informations et co-opération avec d'autres pays en matière d'enseignement supérieur; 6) publication de documentation sur l'enseignement et sur les conférences universitaires; 7) autres activités nécessaires à l'accomplissement des buts de l'Association.

Membres: Peuvent seules devenir membres les universités qui existent depuis plus de quatre ans à compter de leur création par le ministre de l'éducation et dont l'Association reconnaît qu'elles sont conformes aux normes universitaires.
President: Shuzo Toda.
Vice-Presidents: Izuko Tanaka; Haruo Nishi-hara.
20–3 Honshio-cho, Shinjuku-ku, Tokyo 160.
Tel: 35105-17

Chuo Kyoiku Shingikai (Central Council for Education)

The purpose of the Council is to carry out research and make proposals at the request of the Minister of Education or on its own initiative, on fundamental and important matters concerning education science and culture. The Council is a consultative body of the Minister of Education.

Membership: Not exceeding 20 (appointed by the Minister of Education after the approval of the Cabinet). If necessary, the Minister of Education may appoint *ad hoc* members for the Council.

Le Conseil central de l'éducation a pour objet d'effectuer des recherches et de formuler des propositions à la demande du ministre de l'éducation, ou de sa propre initiative, sur les questions fondamentales se rapportant à l'enseignement, à la science et à la culture. Le Conseil est un organe consultatif du Ministre de l'Education.

Membres: Jusqu'à 20 (nommés par le Ministre de l'Education avec l'approbation du Cabinet). Si nécessaire le Ministre de l'Education peut nommer des membres ad hoc pour le Conseil.
The Ministry of Education, Science and Culture, 3–2–2 Kasumigaseki, Chiyoda-ku, Tokyo.
Tel: 3-581-4211

Kokuritsu Kyoiku Kenkyu Sho (National Institute for Educational Research)

The Institute, established in 1949, is financed by the Ministry of Education, Science and Culture. Its main function is to carry out fundamental and comprehensive research in order to provide basic information and material for the use by national and local governments in formulating educational policies and educational researchers for study purposes. Its research areas range from pre-school to higher education, both formal and non-formal. One section is concerned exclusively with the study of higher education.

The Institute organizes and participates in international joint research projects on education and receives foreign scholars and educationalists visiting Japan to conduct education research. Since 1967 the Institute has assisted Unesco Member States in Asia and the Pacific

develop their educational research activities by organizing research workshops, experts' meetings, seminars and study tours.

L'Institut national de recherches pédagogiques, en éducation, créé en 1949, est financé par le Ministère de l'éducation, de la science et de la culture. Sa principale fonction consiste à effectuer sur une vaste gamme de sujets des recherches fondamentales et détaillées destinées à fournir aux gouvernements, national et locaux, des informations et de la documentation de base dont ils ont besoin pour formuler leurs politiques éducatives, ainsi que des chercheurs en éducation chargés d'effectuer des études. Le domaine de ses recherches va de l'enseignement préscolaire à l'enseignement supérieur, formel et non-formel. L'une de ses sections s'occupe exclusivement de l'étude de l'enseignement supérieur.

L'Institut met sur pied des projets internationaux de recherche conjoints en éducation et y participe; il reçoit des chercheurs étrangers venant au Japon pour y effectuer de la recherche en éducation. Depuis 1967, l'Institut aide les Etats membres de l'Unesco en Asie et dans le Pacifique à développer leurs activités de recherche en éducation en organisant des ateliers, des réunions d'experts, des séminaires et des voyages d'études.

Director-General: Isao Suzuki.
5–22 Shimomeguro, 6-chome, Meguroku, Tokyo.
Tel: 3-714-0111. Cables: ninstfedure tokyo

Nihon Ikueikai (Japan Scholarship Foundation)
The object of the Foundation is to provide loans for expenses to brilliant Japanese students who find it difficult to continue their studies for financial reasons, so as to give them an equal chance of education in order to become useful citizens in the community.

Activities: 1) providing students with loans for educational expenses; 2) refunding of the loans; 3) guidance of the students who are given loans; 4) business incidental to the execution of the above mentioned activities.

La Fondation japonaise des bourses a pour objet de fournir des prêts aux étudiants japonais particulièrement doués et qui éprouvent des difficultés à continuer leurs études pour des raisons financières, afin de rétablir leurs chances devant

l'éducation et leur permettre de devenir d'utiles citoyens.

Activités: 1) octroi de prêts aux étudiants pour leurs frais d'enseignement; 2) recouvrement des prêts; 3) orientation des étudiants bénéficiaires de prêts; 4) affaires résultant de l'accomplissement des activités susmentionnées.

President: Shigeru Fukuda.
Director-General: Tetsuo Misumi.
10–7 Ichigaya Honmura-cho, Shinjuku-ku, Tokyo 162.
Tel: 269-42-61

Daigaku Fujin Kyokai (IFUW)
241 Toyama Mansions, 7–17–18 Shinjuku, Shinjuku-ku, Tokyo 160.
Tel: 202-05-72
Zengakuren (All-Japan Federation of Student Autonomies) (IUS)
2–11–7 Chuou, Nakano-ku, Tokyo.
Cables: jpnstud tokyo
World Youth Visit Exchange Association – WYVEA
c/o Yoshida Building, 2–7 Kirakawacho, Chiyoda-ku, Tokyo.
Nippon Katorikku Gakushikai (Pax Romana)
Shinseikaikan 33 Shinano-machi, Shinjuku-ku, Tokyo.
Japan Student YMCA, National Council of YMCAs of Japan (WSCF)
3–18, Nishiwaseda, 2-chome, Shinjuku-ku, Tokyo 160.
Tel: 3-203-0171
United Nations Student Association of Japan (ISMUN)
Room 525, Nippon Building, 8–2-chome, Ohtemachi, Chiyoda-ku, Tokyo.

*

Ministry of Education, Science and Culture
3–2–2 Kasumigaseki, 3-chome, Chiyoda-ku, Tokyo.
Tel: 3-581-4211. Fax: (3) 5819149
Japanese National Commission for Unesco
Ministry of Education, Science and Culture, 3–2–2 Kasumigaseki, 3-chome, Chiyoda-ku, Tokyo.
Tel: 3-581-4211 (ext. 2551). Cables: unescocom tokyo

JORDAN
JORDANIE

UNIVERSITIES — UNIVERSITES

*Bethlehem University, Bethlehem, West Bank. (The President). *1973*
Tel: 74-1241. Telex: 26526 ndc il
F : *arts-sc, bus adm, nurs, ed.*

*Birzeit University, P.O. Box 14, Birzeit, West Bank. *1967*
Tel: 95-4381. Telex: 23076 birzeit jo
F : *arts, sc, com-eco, eng.*

*University of Jordan, Jubaiha, Amman, East Bank. *1962, 1965, 1971*
Tel: 84 3555. Telex: 21629 univj jo
F : *arts, sc, eco-com, med, Isl st, nurs, agr, eng-techn, ed, law, phar, dent.*

*Al Quds University [Open U.], P.O. Box 20002, Jerusalem. *1982*
Tel: 271753
C : *sc-techn, paramed, art* (for Women), *Isl theo.*

Jami'at Al Khalil [Hebron U.], P.O. Box 40, Hebron, West Bank. *1970, 1980*
Tel: (2) 963296

*Mu'tah University, P.O. Box 7, Mu'tah, East Bank. *1981*
Tel: 629545. Telex: 63003 mu'tah jo
D : *nat, eng, hum, law, adm, police sc.*

*An-Najah University, Nablus, West Bank. *1977*
Tel: (53) 70042
F : *arts-hum-soc, eco-adm, eng, phar, publ heal-med, nurs, dent.*

*Yarmouk University, Irbid, East Bank. *1975*
Tel: 71100 (Irbid) 842777 (Amman). Telex: 51533 yarmouk jo
F : *arts-hum-soc-ed-jour, sc, eco-adm, eng, med, phar, nurs, publ heal.*

*Jordan University of Science and Technology, Irbid, East Bank. *1986*
Tel: 29511. Telex: 55545 just jo
F : *eng, med, publ heal, dent, agr, phar, nurs.*

OTHER INSTITUTIONS — AUTRES INSTITUTIONS

Intermediate University College, P.O. Box 922380, Ein Ghazel Road, Allan, East Bank. *1979*
Tel: 664530
D : *eng-arc, com, paramed-phar, ed, soc w.*

UNRWA/Unesco Training Centre, Amman, East Bank. *1967*

Hussein Institute of Agriculture, P.O. Box 7, Tulkarm, West Bank. *1931, 1961*
Tel: 26

Princess Sumaya College for Informatics, P.O. Box 6945, Amman, East Bank. *1977, 1981*
Tel: 844700. Telex: 21276 ramah jo

Paramedical Institute, P.O. Box 10097, Amman, East Bank. *1973*
Tel: 775809

Amman Polytechnic, P.O. Box 15008, Marka, Amman, East Bank. *1975*
Tel: 892345
eng, voc training, com, app arc.

Hebron Polytechnic, P.O. Box 198, Hebron, West Bank. *1978*
Tel: 962550
D : *civ eng, arc, mec, elec, comp.*

Al-Huson Polytechnic, P.O. Box 50, Irbid-al-Husn, East Bank. *1981*
Tel: 210400

D : *ch eng, food techn, tex techn, app arc.*

Institute of Public Administration, Jubaiha, Amman, East Bank. *1968*

Jordan Co-operative Institute, P.O. Box 1343, Amman, East Bank. *1963*
Tel: 661513. Telex: 21835

Institute of Fine Arts, Amman, East Bank. *1967*

Jordan College of Nursing, P.O. Box 491, Amman, East Bank. *1966*
Tel: 773123

Royal Police College, P.O. Box 925425, Amman, East Bank.
Tel: 62168

Jordan Junior College of Social Work, P.O. Box 8088, Amman, East Bank. *1966, 1981*
Tel: 62936

Statistics Training Centre, P.O. Box 2015, Amman, East Bank. *1964*
Tel: 24313

Ajloun Community College, Ajloun, East Bank. *1964, 1980*
Tel: 26
D : *ed, com, soc w.*

Amman Community College, P.O. Box 1705, Amman, East Bank. *1952, 1980*
Tel: 3914

ed, com, lib-jour.

Al-Andulus Community College, P.O. Box 17215, Amman, East Bank.   *1979, 1981*
Tel: 816125

D : *com, eng, paramed, ed, comp.*

Arab Community College, P.O. Box 926845, Amman, East Bank.   *1979*
Tel: 842181

D : *eng, comty, com, ed, paramed-phar.*

Hittein Community College, P.O. Box 620914, Amman, East Bank.   *1984*
Tel: 780801

D : *eng, com, paramed, comp, soc w.*

Huwwara Community College, P.O. Box 1, Huwwara, Irbid, East Bank.   *1956, 1980*
Tel: 274967

ed, com, eng.

Irbid Community College, P.O. Box 1283, Irbid, East Bank.   *1978*

D : *ed, com, soc w.*

Jerash Community College, Jerash, East Bank.   *1980*

Tel: 51113

D : *eng, com, ed, comp, soc w.*

Jordan Community College, P.O. Box 19029, Amman, East Bank.   *1981*
Tel: 669141

ed, paramed-phar, eng, com, comp.

Al-Karak Community College, P.O. Box 52, Karak, East Bank.   *1979*
Tel: 51083

D : *ed, com, adm.*

Ibn Khaldoun Community College, P.O. Box 1202, Irbid, East Bank.   *1979*
Tel: 74731

D : *com, comp, eng, ed, paramed, adm, soc, comp.*

Khaleel Community College, Khaleel, West Bank.

Al-Khawarizmi Community College, P.O. Box 476, Amman, East Bank.   *1974, 1979*
Tel: 669377. Telex: 22372 jo

mangt st-comp-acc, ed, paramed, soc.

Al Quds Community College, P.O. Box 18334, Amman, East Bank.   *1980*
Tel: 22631

D : *ed, com, paramed, comp.*

Princess Tharwat Community College, Queen Misbah Street, P.O. Box 3179, Amman, East Bank.   *1980*
Tel: 44249

D : *com, ed, eng.*

Al-Razi Community College, P.O. Box 794, Irbid, East Bank.   *1979*
Tel: 71185

D : *ed, com, paramed.*

Salt Community College, Salt, East Bank.   *1975*
Tel: 55573

D : *ed, com, paramed.*

Shobak Community College, P.O. Box 5, Shobak, East Bank.   *1975*
Tel: 18

D : *eng, agr, com.*

Al-Zarqa Community College, P.O. Box 6390, Zarqa, East Bank.   *1978*
Tel: 986531

D : *ed, com, paramed, agr, comp.*

Al-Zarqa National Community College, P.O. Box 1027, Zarqa, East Bank.   *1979*
Tel: 985558

D : *com, eng, ed, paramed, comp, soc w.*

Community Teacher Training College of Arts and Science, Amman, East Bank.   *1967*

Women's Teacher Training Institute, Ramallah, West Bank.   *1952*

UNRWA/Unesco Men's Teacher Training Centre, Ramallah, West Bank.   *1960*

UNRWA Women's Training Centre, P.O. Box 214, Ramallah, West Bank.   *1962*
Tel: 952533

Najah National Teacher Training College, Nablus, West Bank.   *1965*

Teacher Inservice Centre, Amman, East Bank.   *1971*

Islamic Education Institute, P.O. Box 585, Amman, East Bank.   *1972*

Ministry of Education
Amman, East Bank.
Tel: 669181. Telex: 21396 educate jo
Jordan National Commission for Unesco

P.O. Box 1646, Ministry of Education, Amman, East Bank.
Tel: 669181. Telex: 21396 educate jo. Cables: unesco jordan ministry education amman

KENYA
KENYA

UNIVERSITIES — UNIVERSITES

*University of Nairobi, P.O. Box 30197, Nairobi.
1951, 1964, 1970
Tel: Nairobi 334244. Cables: varsity, nairobi
F : *agr, arc-des-dev, arts, com, eng, law, med, sc; vet* (Kabete).
I : *adult st, African st, dev st, comp.*
S : *jour.*
Egerton University, P.O. Private Bag, Njoro.
1987
Tel: Nakuru 61620. Telex: 33075 egerton.

Cables: college, njoro.
F : *agr.*
Kenyatta University, P.O. Box 43844, Nairobi.
1972, 1985
Tel: Kahawa 356. Cables: kenuco
F : *arts, sc, ed.*
Moi University, P.O. Box 3900, Eldoret. *1984*
Tel: (0321) 31660. Telex: 35047. Cables: moi varsity, eldoret
F : *for resources-wildlife mangt, sc, techn, ed.*

OTHER INSTITUTIONS — AUTRES INSTITUTIONS

Coast Institute of Technology, c/o Provincial Planning Office, P.O. Box 83059, Mombasa.
Tel: Voi 281/2
Eldoret Polytechnic, P.O. Box 4461, Eldoret.
Embu College of Technology, c/o District Commissioner, P.O. Box 3, Embu.
Government Secretarial College, P.O. Box 42243, Nairobi.
Government Training Institute, P.O. Box 84027, Mombasa.
Gusii Institute of Technology, P.O. Box 222, Kisii.
Tel: 81
Jomo Kenyatta College of Agriculture and Technology, P.O. Box 62000, Nairobi.
Tel: Thika 22646
Kagumo Teachers' College, P.O. Box 18, Nyeri.
Kaimosi College of Research and Technology, P.O. Box 150, Kaimosi.
Tel: Tir 64
Kenya Polytechnic, P.O. Box 52428, Nairobi.
Tel: 338231
Kenya Science Teachers' College, P.O. Box 30596, Nairobi.
Tel: 566072
Kenya Technical Teachers' College, P.O. Box 44600, Nairobi.
Tel: 520211
Kiambu Institute of Science and Technology (Private), P.O. Box 414, Kiambu.
Tel: 22236
Kimathi Institute of Technology, P.O. Box 657, Nyeri.
Tel: 4005

Kirinyaga Technical Institute, P.O. Box 143, Kerugoya.
Tel: 75
Kisii Teachers' College, P.O. Box 408, Kisii.
Medical Training Centre, P.O. Box 30195, Nairobi.
Tel: 336511
Meru Institute of Advanced Technology, P.O. Box 972, Meru.
Moi Institute of Technology, P.O. Box 30, Rongo.
Tel: 12
Moi Teachers' College, P.O. Box 1125, Eldoret.
Mombasa Polytechnic, P.O. Box 90420, Mombasa.
Tel: 492222
Murang'a College of Technology, P.O. Box 75, Murang'a.
Tel: 22906
Nyahururu Teachers' College, P.O. Box 1100, Nyahururu.
Ramogi Institute of Advanced Technology, P.O. Box 1738, Kisumu.
Tel: 41820
Rift Valley Institute of Science and Technology, P.O. Box 7182, Nakuru.
Tel: 2374
Sangalo Institute of Science and Technology, P.O. Box 158, Bungoma.
Tel: 7
Siriba Teachers' College, Private Bag, Maseno.
Western College of Arts and Applied Sciences, P.O. Box 190, Kakamega.
Tel: 20455

Kenya Association of University Women (IFUW)
P.O. Box 47010, Nairobi.
World University Service (WUS)
Administrator: African Refugees Training Programme, P.O. Box 30863, Nairobi.
Tel: 331248. Telex: 25443 lall
**Student Organization of Nairobi University –
SONU** (IUS)
P.O. Box 30344, Nairobi.
The University Catholic Society (Pax Romana)
P.O. Box 41512, Nairobi.
Christian Students' Council of Kenya (WSCF)
P.O. Box 54579, Nairobi.

Tel: 725921
United Nations Youth Association of Kenya (ISMUN)
P.O. Box 41946, Nairobi.

*

Public Service Commission
Nairobi.
Ministry of Education
P.O. Box 30040, Nairobi.
Tel: 28411
Kenya National Commission for Unesco
Ministry of Education, P.O. Box 30040, Nairobi.
Tel: 332546. Cables: education nairobi

DEMOCRATIC PEOPLE'S REPUBLIC OF KOREA
REPUBLIQUE POPULAIRE DEMOCRATIQUE DE COREE

UNIVERSITIES – UNIVERSITES

*Kim Il Sung University, Pyongyang.   *1946*
F : *hist, phil, lit-lang, eco, law, fgn lang, phy, math-dynamics, ch, biol, geog, geol, adm.*
Kim Chaek University of Technology, Pyongyang.   *1948*
F : *geol, mine, met, met process, machine-bui, mec, shipbui, elec, electro, nucl, ind adm, auto, semi-conductor.*
Pyongyang University of Agriculture, Pyongyang.   *1981*
F : *agr, stock, agr mec.*
Pyongyang University of Cinematics, Pyongyang.   *1953*
The University of Commerce, Pyongyang.   *1970*
F : *clothing, acc, bui.*
The University of Construction and Building Materials, Pyongyang.   *1959*
F : *arc, bui mater, bui eng, city plan, arc eng.*
The University of National Economy, Pyongyang.   *1946*
F : *ind mangt, agr mangt, fin-bank, plan, trade, stat.*
Pyongyang University of Fine Arts, Pyongyang.   *1947*
F : *Korean pnt, pictures, publication pnt, sculp, ind art, tec art.*
Pyongyang University of Foreign Studies, Pyongyang.   *1949*
F : *ed.*
The University of Light Industry, Pyongyang.

1959
F : *tex eng, food eng, mec.*
Pyongyang University of Mechanical Engineering, Pyongyang.   *1948*
F : *machine-bui, mec, const machine, met process, adm, des.*
Pyongyang University of Medicine, Pyongyang.   *1946*
F : *med, clin med, hyg, orntl med, phar, dent.*
Pyongyang Music and Dance University, Pyongyang.   *1948*
F : *national mus instruments, mus instruments, vocal mus, dance, composition.*
Pyongyang University of Physical Education, Pyongyang.   *1958*
Pyongyang University of Railways, Pyongyang.   *1959*
F : *railway operation, railway mec, railway const.*
Haeju University of Agriculture, South Hwanghae Province.   *1960*
F : *agr, pomiculture, agr adm, vet-stock, agr mec, for-potamology.*
Hambuk University of Agriculture, North Hamgyong Province.   *1970*
F : *agr, vet-stock, pomiculture.*
Hamhung University of Agriculture, South Hamgyong Province.   *1958*
F : *agr, vet-stock, agr mec, pomiculture.*
Hyesan University of Agriculture and Forestry,

Ranggang Province.   *1959*
F : *agr, for, vet-stock, for mangt, wood processing.*
Kanggye University of Agriculture, Chagang Province.   *1970*
F : *agr, vet-stock, sericulture, agr mec.*
Nampo University of Agriculture, Nampo.   *1967*
F : *agr, hort, agr mec.*
Sariwon University of Agriculture, North Hwanghae Province.   *1959*
F : *agr, pomiculture, agr mec, agr biol, forpotamology.*
Sinuiju University of Agriculture, North Pyongan Province.   *1969*
F : *agr, vet-an hus, agr mec, pomiculture.*
Wonsan University of Agriculture, Kangwon Province.   *1948*
F : *agr, pomiculture, agr mec, agr biol, forpotamology, agr mangt, vet-stock, garden-eco plant sericulture.*
Hamhung University of Chemical Industry, South Hamgyong Province.   *1947*
F : *inorganic ch, organic ch, mec, polymer ch, silicate eng.*
Wonsan University of Economics, Kangwon Province.   *1960*
F : *eco, fin, com mangt, mater supply-labour mangt.*
Nampo University of Fisheries, Nampo.   *1977*
F : *fish, mec.*
Wonsan University of Fisheries, Kangwon Province.   *1959*
F : *fish, mec, fish breeding-thremetology, fish processing.*
The University of Geology, North Hwanghae Province.   *1970*
F : *geol res, mec, geotechn.*
Hamhung University of Hydraulics, South Hamgyong Province.   *1959*
F : *irrig, elec, mec, hyd power-harbour const.*
Sinuiju University of Light Industry, North Pyongan Province.   *1982*
F : *tex eng, food eng, ch eng of daily necessity.*
Chongjin University of Medicine, North Hamgyong Province.   *1948*
F : *basic med, clin med, hyg, orntl med, phar.*
Haeju University of Medicine, South Hwanghae Province.   *1969*

F : *basic med, clin med, hyg, orntl med, dent.*
Hyesan University of Medicine, Ranggang Province.   *1971*
F : *basic med, clin med, orntl med.*
Kanggye University of Medicine, Chagang Province.   *1969*
F : *basic med, clin med, hyg, orntl med, dent.*
Hamhung University of Medicine, South Hamgyong Province.   *1946*
F : *med, clin med, hyg, orntl med, phar, dent.*
Pyongsong University of Medicine, South Pyongan Province.   *1972*
F : *med, clin med, hyg, orntl med.*
Sariwon University of Medicine, North Hwanghae Province.   *1971*
F : *basic med, clin med, orntl med.*
Sinuiju University of Medicine, North Pyongan Province.   *1969*
F : *basic med, clin med, hyg, orntl med, dent.*
Wonsan University of Medicine, Kangwon Province.   *1971*
F : *basic med, clin med, orntl med.*
Chongjin University of Mining and Metallurgical Engineering, North Hamgyong Province. *1959*
F : *coal eng, geotechn, mine eng, met, mineral analysis, atm.*
Pyongnam University of Coal Mining, South Pyongan Province.   *1968*
F : *coal eng, mec, geol.*
Hamhung University of Pharmacy, South Hamgyong Province.   *1968*
F : *pharmacology, pharmaceutical eng, med apparatus.*
The University of Sea Transport, North Hamgyong Province.   *1968*
F : *navigation, mar elec, ship eng, sea trans mangt.*
The University of Science, South Pyongan Province.   *1967*
F : *math, phy, ch, biol.*
Huichon University of Technology, Chagang Province.   *1958*
F : *radio eng, wire commun eng, mec, electro-apparatus, atm.*
The University of Veterinary and Animal Husbandry, South Pyongan Province.   *1955*
F : *vet, an hus, poultry.*

OTHER INSTITUTIONS — AUTRES INSTITUTIONS

Technical Education — Enseignement technique

Sariwon College of Agricultural Chemicals, North Hwanghae Province.   *1984*
Sinchon College of Agriculture, South Hwanghae Province.   *1984*

Sukchon College of Agriculture, South Pyongan Province.   *1984*
Tokchon Automobile College, South Pyongan Province.   *1984*

Chongsu College of Chemical Industry, North Pyongan Province. *1985*
Hamhung College of Chemical Industry, South Hamgyong Province. *1984*
Li Su Bok College of Chemical Industry, South Pyongan Province. *1984*
Pyongyang College of City Planning, Pyongyang. *1985*
Hamhung College of Computing Machines, South Hamgyong Province. *1985*
Pyongyang College of Computing Machines, Pyongyang. *1985*
Pyongyang College of Construction, Pyongyang. *1984*
Sinuiju College of Economics, North Pyongan Province. *1985*
Pyongyang Electrical College, Pyongyang. *1984*
Supung Electrical College, North Pyongan Province. *1984*
Chongjin College of Electronics and Automation, North Hamgyong Province. *1984*
Haeju College of Electronics and Automation, South Hwanghae Province. *1984*
Hamhung College of Electronics and Automation, South Hamgyong Province. *1984*
Songjin College of Fireproof Material Technology, North Hamgyong Province. *1983*
Sinpo College of Fisheries, South Hamgyong Province. *1984*
Ryongsong College of Food Industry, Pyongyang. *1982*
Kilju College of Forestry, North Hamgyong Province. *1984*
Tanchon College of Geological Prospecting, South Hamgyong Province. *1984*
Pukchong College of Horticulture, South Hamgyong Province. *1984*
Tokchon College of Hydraulic Power Construction, South Pyongan Province. *1985*
Chongjin College of Light Industry, North Hamgyong Province. *1984*
Haeju College of Light Industry, South Hwanghae Province. *1985*
Kaesong College of Light Industry, Kaesong. *1984*
Huichon College of Mechanical Engineering, Chagang Province. *1984*
Kusong College of Mechanical Engineering, North Pyongan Province. *1984*
Ryongsong College of Mechanical Engineering, South Hamgyong Province. *1961*
Nampo College of Medicine, Nampo. *1985*
Chongjin Mercantile Marine College, Chongjin. *1985*
Chongjin College of Metallugical Engineering, North Hamgyong Province. *1984*
Kangson College of Metallugical Engineering, Nampo. *1984*
Kimchaek College of Metallugical Engineering,

South Hamgyong Province. *1984*
Anju College of Coal Mining, South Pyongan Province. *1985*
Undok College of Coal Mining, North Hamgyong Province. *1985*
Pyongyang College of Printing, Pyongyang. *1984*
Chongju College of Railway Construction, North Pyongan Province. *1985*
Chongjin College of Railway Management, North Hamgyong Province. *1985*
Nampo College of Shipbuilding, Nampo. *1985*
Sunchon College of Silicate Engineering, South Pyongan Province. *1976*
Pyongyang College of Surgery, Pyongyang. *1985*
Anju College of Technology, South Pyongan Province. *1976*
Bukjung College of Technology, North Pyongan Province. *1960*
Chongjin College of Technology, North Hamgyong Province. *1960*
Chonnae College of Technology, Kangwon Province. *1982*
Dongrim College of Technology, North Pyongan Province. *1976*
February 26th College of Technology, Chagang Province. *1985*
Haeju College of Technology, South Hwanghae Province. *1961*
Hungnam College of Technology, South Hamgyong Province. *1960*
Hwasong College of Technology, Pyongyang. *1983*
Hyesan College of Technology, Ryanggang Province. *1971*
Hyongbong College of Technology, South Pyongan Province. *1979*
Kangson College of Technology, Nampo. *1960*
Kapsan College of Technology, Ryanggang Province. *1984*
Kiyang College of Technology, Nampo. *1960*
Kogonwon College of Technology, North Hamgyong Province. *1981*
Komdok College of Technology, South Hamgyong Province. *1961*
Kusong College of Technology, North Pyongan Province. *1968*
Kyongsong College of Technology, North Hamgyong Province. *1961*
May Fourth College of Technology, South Pyongan Province. *1984*
Munpyong College of Technology, Kangwon Province. *1960*
Musan College of Technology, North Hamgyong Province. *1960*
Namhung College of Technology, South Pyongan Province. *1983*
Nampo College of Technology, Nampo. *1960*
Pohang College of Technology, North Hamgyong Province. *1964*

Pukchang College of Technology, South Pyongan Province. 1976

Pyongchon College of Technology, Pyongyang. 1970

Pyongyang College of Technology, Pyongyang. 1960

Rahung College of Technology, South Hamgyong Province. 1976

Rakwon College of Technology, North Pyongan Province. 1960

Rakyon College of Technology, South Hwanghae Province. 1984

Ranam College of Technology, North Hwanghae Province. 1984

Ryongdung College of Technology, North Pyongan Province. 1979

Ryongyang College of Technology, South Hamgyong Province. 1976

Sapo College of Technology, South Hamgyong Province. 1961

Sinchang College of Technology, South Pyongan Province. 1961

Sinuiju College of Technology, North Pyongan Province. 1960

Songjin College of Technology, North Hamgyong Province. 1960

Songlim College of Technology, North Pyongan Province. 1961

Songpyong College of Technology, North Hamgyong Province. 1979

Sosong College of Technology, Pyongyang. 1976

Sunchon College of Technology, South Pyongan Province. 1961

Sungho College of Technology, Pyongyang. 1961

Taean College of Technology, Nampo. 1960

Tanchon College of Technology, South Hamgyong Province. 1971

Tokchon College of Technology, South Pyongan Province. 1960

Tokhyon College of Technology, North Pyongan Province. 1978

Uiju College of Technology, North Pyongan Province. 1984

Undok College of Technology, North Hamgyong Province. 1960

Unhung College of Technology, Ryanggang Province. 1985

Unsan College of Technology, North Pyongan Province. 1961

Chaeryong College of Tideland Reclamation, South Hwanghae Province. 1985

Teacher Training—Formation pédagogique

Kim Hyong Jik University of Education, Pyongyang. 1946

Kim Jong Suk University of Education, Ryanggang Province. 1967

Chongjin University of Education, No. 1, North Hamgyong Province. 1961

Chongjin University of Education, No. 2, North Hamgyong Province. 1946

Haeju University of Education, North Hamgyong Province. 1948

Hamnam University of Education No. 1, South Hamgyong Province. 1961

Hamnam University of Education No. 2, South Hamgyong Province. 1961

Hyesan University of Education No. 1, Ryanggang Province. 1967

Kanggye University of Education No. 1, Chagang Province. 1967

Kanggye University of Education No. 2, Chagang Province. 1953

Kim Jong Tae University of Education, South Hwanghae Province. 1961

Nampo University of Education, Nampo. 1963

Pyongsong University of Education, South Pyongan Province. 1967

Pyongyang University of Education No. 2, Pyongyang. 1946

Sariwon University of Education No. 1, North Hwanghae Province. 1953

Sariwon University of Education No. 2, North Hwanghae Province. 1963

Sinuiju University of Education No. 1, North Pyongan Province. 1961

Sinuiju University of Education No. 2, North Pyongan Province. 1947

Songdo University, Kaesong. 1961

Wonsan University of Education No. 1, Kangwon Province. 1961

Wonsan University of Education No. 2, Kangwon Province. 1949

Chongjin Teachers' Training College, North Hamgyong Province. 1968

Haeju Teachers' Training College, South Hwanghae Province. 1968

Hamhung Teachers' Training College No. 1, South Hamgyong Province. 1968

Hamhung Teachers' Training College No. 2, South Hamgyong Province. 1972

Hoiryong Teachers' Training College, North Hamgyong Province. 1972

Hyesan Teachers' Training College, Ryanggang Province. 1968

Kangge Teachers' Training College, Chagang Province. 1968

Nampo Teachers' Training College, Nampo. 1968

Pyongsong Teachers' Training College, South Pyongan Province. 1972

Pyongyang Teachers' Training College, Pyongyang. *1968*
Sariwon Teachers' Training College, North Pyongan Province. *1968*
Sinuiju Teachers' Training College, North Pyongan Province. *1972*
Sonchon Teachers' Training College, North

Pyongan Province. *1968*
Wonsan Teachers' Training College, Kangwon Province. *1968*

Also 67 other colleges in the field of technology, economics, foreign languages, and art.

Korean Students Committee – KSC (IUS)
Sarochung, Pyongyang.
Telex: 5989 kp (attn. sarochung)

*

Ministry of Higher Education
Education Commission, Pyongyang.

Research Institute of Higher Education
Pyongyang.
National Commission of the Democratic People's Republic of Korea for Unesco
Ministry of Foreign Affairs, Pyongyang.
Telex: 5350. Cables: unesco foreign ministry pyongyang

REPUBLIC OF KOREA
REPUBLIQUE DE COREE

UNIVERSITIES AND COLLEGES – UNIVERSITES ET COLLEGES

National Institutions – Etablissements nationaux

Andong National College, Songchon-dong, Andong CT, Kyungbuk 760-380. *1979*
Tel: 55-1661
Sec : *hum, ed, soc-law, nat, arts-phys.*
Busan National University, Changjon-dong, Kumjong-gu, Busan 609-735. *1946*
Tel: 56-0171
C : *eng, li arts-sc, nat, law-pol, ed, bus, med, dent, phar, hom eco.*
S : *grad, bus adm, publ adm, ed.*
Changwon National College, Teochon-dong, Changwon CT, Kyungnam 641-240. *1969*
Tel: 83-2151
Chonnam National University, Yongbong-dong, Puk-gu, Kwangju 500-757. *1951*
Tel: 55-0011
C : *eng, agr, hum soc, nat, law, ed, bus adm, med, dent.*
S : *grad, bus adm, publ adm, ed.*
Chungbuk National University, Kaeshin-dong, Chongju, Chungbuk 360-763. *1951*
Tel: 4-2131
C : *hum, soc-sc, nat, eng, agr, ed, phar.*
S : *grad, ed.*
Chungnam National University, Kung-dong, So-gu, Taejon CT, Chungnam 302-764. *1952*

Tel: 822-6121
C : *li arts, com-eco, agr, law, med, ind ed.*
S : *grad, ed, bus adm.*
Gunsan National University, Miryong-dong, Kunsan CT, Chonbuk 573-360. *1965*
Tel: 62-4171
Gyeongsang National University, Kajoa-dong, Chinju CT, Kyongnam 600-300. *1948*
Tel: 54-8331
C : *agr, law-bus adm, ed, nat-eng, hum.*
S : *grad, ed.*
Jeju National University, Ara-dong, Cheju CT, Cheju-do 690-121. *1952*
Tel: 23-6141
Jeonbug National University, Dukjin-dong, Chong CT, Chonbuk 506-756. *1951*
Tel: 70-2023. Telex: 760429
C : *hum, nat, com, eng, law-pol, med, ed, dent.*
S : *grad, ed, bus adm.*
Kangreung National University, Chipyen-dong, Kangreung CT, Kangwondo 210-320. *1979*
Tel: 42-7001
D : *bus adm, acc, Korean lang & lit, English lang & lit, phy-ch-biol, reg dev, mus-fa.*
*Kangweon National University, Hyoja-dong, Chunchon CT, Kangwondo 200–701. *1947*

Tel: 53-9000

C : *bus adm, eng, agr-an hus, ed, nat-phar, hum soc, for, law.*

S : *grad, ed, bus adm.*

Kong Ju National Teachers College, Shinkwan-dong, Kongju CT, Chungnam 314-110. *1948*
Tel: 53-2151

Korea Air Correspondence University, 169 Dongsung-dong, Chongro-ku, Seoul 110.
1972, 1981
Tel: 743-8420

D : *law, publ adm, eco, bus adm, agr, hom eco, comp-stat, ed; Korean, English, Chinese, French (lang & lit).*

Korea Maritime University, Dongsam-dong, Youngdo-gu, Pusan 606-791. *1945*
Tel: 49-0031

Korea National College of Physical Education, Karak-dong, Songpa-gu, Seoul 138–763. *1977*
Tel: 418-1001

Korea National University of Education, Darak-ri, Kangnae-myeon, Cheongwongun, Chung-buk 363-980, *1984*
Tel: 60-3114

*Kyungpook National University, Sankyuk-dong, Puk-gu, Taegu 702-701. *1951*
Tel: 955-5001. Telex: 54400

C : *hum, soc-pol-lib-psyc, eco-com, eng, agr-hort-vet, nat, law, ed, mus-vis arts.*

S : *med-nurs-phar, dent, grad.*

Mogpo National College, Torim-ri, Chonggae-myeon, Muan-gun, Chonnam 534-830. *1946*
Tel: 72-8153

National Fisheries University of Busan, Taeyon-dong, Nam-gu, Busan 608-023. *1946, 1964*
Tel: 622-3951

*Seoul National University, Shinnim-dong, Kwanak-gu, Seoul 151-742.
Tel: 886-0101

C : *hum, soc, nat, hom eco, bus adm, eng, agr, fa, law, ed, vet, phar, mus, med, dent.*

S : *grad, publ heal, publ adm, enc st.*

Sun Cheon National College, Maegok-dong, Sun-cheon, Chonnam 550-070.
Tel: 52-8131. Telex: 29664 snurok k

Yosu National Fisheries College, Kuk-dong, Yosu CT, Chonnam 550–180. *1917*
Tel: 2-7141

Public Institutions—Etablissements publics

Seoul City University, Chonnong-dong, Tong-daemun-gu, Seoul 130–743. *1918*
Tel: 245-5303

Private Institutions—Etablissements privés

Ajou University, Wonchon-dong, Suwon CT, Kyonggi 440-749. *1972*
Tel: 33-5141

C : *eng, bus adm, li arts-sc.*

S : *grad.*

Busan College of Foreign Studies, Uam-dong, Nam-gu, Busan 608-060. *1981*
Tel: 643-5111

Busan Women's University, Yonsan-dong, Tongnae-gu, Busan 607-080. *1969*
Tel: 865-1001

Catholic College, Haewha-dong, Chongno-gu, Seoul 110-530. *1947*
Tel: 762-2501

Cheongju University, Naedok-dong, Chongju CT, Chungbuk 360-764. *1946*
Tel: 54-2111

C : *eco-bus, adm, law-pol, li arts-sc, nat-eng, ed, arts.*

S : *grad.*

Chosun University, Sosok-dong, Dong-gu, Kwangju 501-759. *1946*
Tel: 232-8151

C : *li arts-sc, law-pol, com-eco, eng, ed, fgn lang, phys, med, dent, phar, women's ind.*

S : *grad ed, ind.*

*Chung Ang University, Huksok-dung, Dongs-sak-gu, Seoul 156-756. *1918*
Tel: 813-3811

C : *li arts-sc, law, pol-eco, bus adm, agr, med, phar, ed, eng, art.*

S : *grad, soc dev, int, mangt, ed, jour, broad-casting.*

Dankook University, Hannam-dong, Yongsan-gu, Seoul 140-714. *1947*
Tel: 797-0581

C : *li arts-sc, law-pol, com-eco, eng, ed.*

S : *grad, ed, publ adm, bus adm.*

Dong-A University, Hadan-dong, Saha-gu, Pusan 604-714. *1946*
Tel: 204-0171

C : *li arts-sc, nat, law-pol, bus-eco, agr, eng.*

S : *grad, ed, bus adm.*

Dong Eui University, Kaya-dong, Busanjin-gu, Busan 614-010. *1976*
Tel: 804-1500

F : *li arts, law-pol, bus adm-eco, sc, eng, fa-mus.*

Dong-shin Engineering College, Taeho-dong,

Naju CT, Chonnam 520-180.　　　*1985*
Tel: 33-2901

Dongduck Women's University, Hawolgok-dong, Songbuk-gu, Seoul 136-132.　　　*1950*
Tel: 913-2001
D : *soc, phar, hom eco, Korean lang-lit, fa, grad.*

Dongguk University, Pil-dong, Chung-gu, Seoul 100-715.　　　*1906*
Tel: 267-8131
C : *boudh, li arts-sc, law, pol, eco-com, agr, ed, eng.*
S : *grad, ed, publ adm, bus adm.*

Duksung Women's University, Sangmun-dong, Dobong-gu, Seoul 132-030.　　　*1950*
Tel: 902-8121

*Ewha Women's University, Tahyon-dong, Sodaemun-gu, Seoul 120-750.　　　*1886*
Tel: 362-6151
C : *li arts, nat, mus, fa, phar, phys, ed, law-pol, med, nurs, hom eco.*
S : *grad, ed.*

Hallym College, Okchon-dong, Chunchon CT, Kangwon 200-010.　　　*1982*
Tel: 53-5411

Han Nam University, Ojong-dong, Tong-gu, Taejon CT , Chungnam 300-210.　　　*1956*
Tel: 623-7111

Han Shin University, Yangsan-ri, Osan-eup, Hwasong-gun, Kyonggi 445-800.　　　*1940*
Tel: 45-8480

Hankook Aviation College, Hwajon-ri, Kwajon-eup, Koyang-gun, Kyonggi 411-910.　　　*1979*
Tel: 372-5771

Hankook University of Foreign Studies, Imun-dong, Tongdaemun-gu, Seoul 131-791.　　　*1954*
Tel: 965-7001
C : *occidental lang, orntl lang, law-pol, trad-eco, ed, li arts-sc.*
S : *grad, interp-trans, int trade, ed.*

Hansung University, Samson-dong, Songbuk-gu, Seoul 136-042.　　　*1972*
Tel: 742-2201

*Hanyang University, Haengdang-dong, Song-dong-gu, Seoul 133-791.　　　*1939*
Tel: 292-3111
C : *li arts-sc, eng, med, nat, law-pol, com-eco, ed, mus, phys.*
S : *grad, ed, publ adm, bus adm, ind.*

Hong Ik University, Sangsu-dong, Mapo-gu, Seoul 121-791.　　　*1946*
Tel: 322-0151
C : *eng, li arts-sc, fa, ed, com-eco.*
S : *grad, ind-fine arts, env st.*

Honam College, Ssangchon-dong, So-gu, Kwangju 502-260.　　　*1981*
Tel: 34-8211

Hyosung Women's University, Kumrak-dong, Hayang-eup, Kyungsan-gun, Kyungbuk

713-900.　　　*1952*
Tel: 52-8001
C : *li arts-sc, law-eco, ed, phar, art, hom eco.*
S : *grad.*

*In Ha University, Yonghyon-dong, Nam-gu, Inchon 402-751.　　　*1954*
Tel: 862-0077. Telex: 32771 in hauni k
C : *li arts-sc, eng, mat, com-eco, law-pol, ed.*
S : *grad, ed, bus adm.*

Incheon University, Towha-dong, Nam-gu, Inchon 402-749.　　　*1979*
Tel: 74-5301
F : *hum, nat, soc, eng-arc, bus adm.*

Inje College, Kaejum-dong, Busanjin-gu, Busan 614-110.　　　*1979*
Tel: 93-3421

International University, Chongneung-dong, Songbuk-gu, Seoul 136-104.　　　*1955*
Tel: 919-0411

Jeon Ju University, Hyoja-dong, Chonju CT, Chonbuk 560-759.　　　*1964*
Tel: 6-5011

Jeonju Woosuk University, Hujong-ri, Samrae-eup, Wanju-gun, Chonbuk 565-800.　　　*1979*
Tel: 73-8001

Keimyung University, Taemyong-dong, Nam-gu, Taegu 705-037.　　　*1954*
Tel: 626-1321
C : *hum, for st, bus adm, soc, nat-eng, mus, fa, ed, med.*
S : *grad, ed, int trade.*

King Sejong University, Kunja-dong, Songdong-gu, Seoul 133-150.　　　*1954*
Tel: 467-5121

*Konkuk University, Mojin-dong, Songdong-gu, Seoul 133-701.　　　*1946*
Tel: 445-0061
C : *li arts, sc, eng, law-pol, eco-bus, agr, an hus, dom sc, ed, hum, soc, nat.*
S : *grad, ed, publ adm, ind.*

Kookmin University, Chongrung-dong, Song-buk-gu, Seoul 136-702.　　　*1946*
Tel: 914-3141
C : *li arts-sc, law-pol, eco-bus, eng, arc-app arts, ed.*
S : *grad, ed.*

Korean Christian College, Deungchon-dong, Kangso-gu, Seoul 157-010.
Tel: 605-2989

Korean Tourism University, Hyohyen-dong, Kyongju CT, Kyungbuk 780-210.　　　*1988*
Tel: 3-5558

Korea Union College, Kongrung-dong, Nowon-gu, Seoul 139-242.　　　*1962*
Tel: 972-3606

Korea University, Anam-dong, Songbuk-gu, Seoul 136-701.　　　*1905*
Tel: 94-2641
C : *li arts-sc, law, bus adm, agr, pol-eco, nat,*

eng, med, ed.
S : *grad, ed, bus adm, food dev.*
Kosin College, Dongsam-dong, Youngdo-gu, Busan 606-080.
Tel: 256-3181
Kumoh Institute of Technology, Shinpyong-dong, Kumi CT, Kyungbuk 730-070. *1979*
Tel: 461-0131
Kwan Dong University, Naegok-dong, Kangreung CT, Kangwon 210-160. *1954*
Tel: 3-7721
C : *ed, hum, soc, eng-arc.*
S : *grad.*
Kwangju Catholic College, Sangchon-dong, So-gu, Kwangju 502-260. *1965*
Tel: 365-5111
Kwangwoon University, Wolkye-dong, Nowongu, Seoul 139-050. *1964*
Tel: 918-1021
D : *eng, nat, bus-eco, law-pol.*
Kyonggi University, Iui-ri, Suji-myon, Yongingun, Kyonggi 449-840. *1970*
Tel: 6-2175
Kyung Hee University, Hoegi-dong, Tongdaemungu, Seoul 131-701. *1949*
Tel: 966-0904
C : *li arts-sc, law, pol-eco, ed, med, orntl med, dent, phar, eng, ind, mus, phys.*
S : *grad, ed, publ adm, bus adm.*
Kyungnam University, Wolyoung-dong, Masan CT, Kyungnam 630-260. *1946*
Tel: 2-8112. Telex: 26834 kifes k
C : *li arts-sc, ed, com-ed, law-pol, eng-arc.*
S : *grad, ed, bus adm.*
Kyungsung University, Taeyon-dong, Nam-gu, Busan 608-020. *1955*
Tel: 622-5331
Kyungwon University, Pokjong-dong, Songnam CT, Kyonggi 461-200. *1981*
Tel: 752-3220
Mokwon Methodist College, Mok-dong, Chunggu, Taejon CT, Chungnam 301-070. *1965*
Tel: 252-9941
*Myong Ji University, Nam-ri, Yongin-gun, Kyonggi 120-728. *1948*
Tel: 32-4001
C : *hum, law-pol, bus adm-eco, sc, eng, hum-soc.*
S : *grad.*
Pai Chai College, Toma-dong, So-gu, Taejon CT, Chungnam 302-162. *1981*
Tel: 522-0335
Pohang Institute of Science and Technology, P.O. Box 125 Pohang CT, Kyungbuk 790-330. *1986*
Tel: 75-0900
Sacred Heart College of Women, Yokgok-dong, Puchon CT, Kyonggi 421-100. *1964*
Tel: 62-8251
Sang Myung Women's University, Hongji-dong,

Chongno-gu, Seoul 110-743. *1965*
Tel: 737-0291
Sang Ji College, Woosan-dong, Wonju CT, Kangwon 220-130. *1974*
Tel: 42-1121
Seoul Woman's University, Kongreung-dong, Nowon-gu, Seoul 139-240. *1960*
Tel: 972-203
D : *hum, soc-bus adm-eco-lib-phys, nat-food techn, fa-phys.*
Seowon University, Mochung-dong, Chungju CT, Chungbuk 360-140. *1972*
Tel: 62-8813
*Sogang University, Shinsu-dong, Mapo-gu, Seoul 121-110.
Tel: 715-0141
C : *li arts-sc, nat-eng, com-eco.*
S : *grad, bus adm.*
Sook Myung Women's University, Chongpa-dong, Yongsan-gu, Seoul 140-132. *1938*
Tel: 713-9391
C : *li arts-sc, pol-eco, mus, fa, phar, dom-sc, nat-sc.*
S : *grad.*
Soonchunhyang College, Asan-gun, Chungnam 337-880. *1978*
Tel: 42-4601
C : *hum, eco-com, sc, med..*
I : *cancer res, obst, ind med, population-cmty heal sc.*
*Soongsil University, Sangdo-dong, Dongssakgu, Seoul 156-743. *1897*
Tel: 814-9611
C : *li arts-sc, law-bus, eng.*
S : *grad, ind, reg dev.*
*Sung Kyun Kwan University, Myongryun-dong, Chongno-gu, Seoul 110-745. *992, 1953*
Tel: 762-5021. Telex: 27485
C : *confucian st, li arts-sc, law-pol, eco-bus, nat, eng, phar, hom eco, ed, agr.*
S : *grad, bus-publ adm, fgn trade.*
Sungshin Women's University, Tongson-dong, Songbuk-gu, Seoul 136-742. *1963*
Tel: 94-0124
Suweon University, Wawoo-ri, Pongdam-myon, Hwasong-gun, Kyonggi 445-890. *1981*
Tel: 33-1402
Suwon Catholic College, Wongrim-ri, Pongdam-myon, Hwasong-gun, Kyonggi 445-890. *1983*
Tel: 34-1081
Taegu Catholic College, Pongduk-dong, Nam-gu, Taegu 705-020. *1981*
Tel: 626-9581
Taegu Oriental Medical College, Chomchon-dong, Kyongsan-gun, Kyungbuk 713-800. *1980*
Tel: 83-0551
Taegu University, Taemyong-dong, Nam-gu, Taegu 705-030. *1956*

Tel: 67-2081
Taejeon College, Yongun-dong, Tong-gu, Taejon CT, Chungnam 300-120.   *1981*
Tel: 252-0213
University of Ulsan, Mugo-dong, Ulsan CT, Kyongnam 680-749.   *1969*
Tel: 77-3101
Won Kwang University, Shinyong-dong, Iri CT, Chonbuk 570-749.   *1953*
Tel: 52-2111
C : *boudh, li arts-sc, law-pol, com-eco, phar, ed, agr, orntl med, dent, eng, hom eco.*
S : *grad, ed.*

Yeungnam University, Taedong-dong, Kyungsan-eup, Kyungbuk 713-800.
Tel: 82-5111
C : *li arts-sc, nat, eng, law-pol, com-eco, med, phar, agr-an hus, dom sc, ed, mus, fa.*
S : *grad, bus adm, env st, ed.*
*Yonsei University, Shinchon-dong Sodaemun-gu, Seoul 120-749.   *1885*
Tel: 392-0131
C : *li arts-sc, bus-eco, mus, nat, eng, ed, theo, law, soc, med, dent, nurs, hom eco.*
S : *grad, ed, pol adm, bus adm, ind, publ heal, theo.*

OTHER INSTITUTIONS—AUTRES INSTITUTIONS

Teacher Training—Formation pédagogique

Busan National Teachers College, Koje-dong, Tongnae-gu, Busan 607-070.   *1946*
Tel: 84-5055
Che Ju National Teachers College, Hwabuk-dong, Cheju CT, 790 Cheju 690-060.   *1953*
Tel: 53-5691
Cheong Ju National Teachers College, Sugok-dong, Chongju CT, Chungbuk 360-150.   *1941*
Tel: 4-8151
Chuncheon National Teachers College, Soksa-dong, Chunchon CT, Kangwon 200-180.
                    1939
Tel: 2-5691
Inchon National Teachers College, Sungeui-dong, Nam-gu, Inchon 402-010.   *1962*
Tel: 883-5151
Jeon Ju National Teachers College, Dongsohak-dong, Chonju CT, Chonbuk 560-120.   *1936*

Tel: 6-0051
Jinju National Teachers College, Shinan-dong, Chinju CT, Kynungnam 660-100.   *1940*
Tel: 2-4206
Kongju National Teachers College, Ponghwang-dong, Kongju, Chungnam 314-060.   *1938*
Tel: 2-2661
Kwangju National Teachers College, Punghyang-dong, Puk-gu, Kwangju 500-090.   *1938*
Tel: 524-6001
Seoul National Teachers College, Socho-dong, Kangnam-gu, Seoul 137-070.   *1946*
Tel: 583-4091
Tae Gu National Teachers College, Taemyong-dong, Nam-gu, Taegu 705-030.   *1949*
Tel: 66-4971

Also 119 junior colleges.

Korean Council for University Education
   The Council was established in April 1982 and has as its legal basis the Korean Council for University Education Act legislated by the National Assembly in 1984. It is designed to promote autonomy and public accountability in university management, thus contributing to the healthy development of higher education in Korea. Its membership includes presidents of all the four-year institutions of higher education in Korea.
   The Council has a General Assembly, Board of Trustees and Secretariat. It has also established an advisory committee and six specialized research committees to help effectively carry out its functions. They comprise Committees for University Evaluation, University Finance, University Co-operation, University Development, Teachers'

College Development, and Journal Compilation.
   Its major activities include annual evaluation of member institutions, researches on university education, publication of a bimonthly journal, Higher Education, training of university administrators, international seminars, the operation of an Information Center for Higher Education, and the management of an Information Center for Faculty Resources.
   The Research Institute of Higher Education, attached to KCUE, was established in 1988 to effectively execute the research activities commissioned by both university and government sides.
   Le Conseil a été créé en avril 1982 en vertu de la loi qui porte son nom et a été votée par l'Assemblée nationale en 1984. Il est chargé de promouvoir l'autonomie et la responsabilité publique de la

gestion universitaire, contribuant ainsi à un développement harmonieux de l'enseignement supérieur en Corée. Tous les présidents de tous les établissements d'enseignement supérieur du pays, mandatés pour quatre ans, en sont les membres.

Le Conseil est doté d'une Assemblée générale, d'un Conseil d'administration et d'un Secrétariat. Il a créé un comité consultatif et six comités de recherche spécialisés pour l'aider à remplir ses fonctions (comités d'évaluation universitaire, des crédits universitaires, de la coopération universitaire, du développement universitaire, du développement des écoles de formation pédagogique, et de l'élaboration de la revue).

Les activités principales du Conseil sont: l'évaluation annuelle des institutions membres, des recherches sur l'enseignement universitaire, la publication d'une revue bimensuelle Higher Education, la formation d'administrateurs universitaires, l'organisation de séminaires internationaux, l'activité d'un centre d'information pour l'enseignement supérieur et la gestion d'un centre d'information pour la logistique du personnel enseignant.

L'Institut de recherche sur l'enseignement supérieur, qui est attaché au Conseil, a été créé en 1988 pour le bon déroulement des activités de recherche réalisées à la demande des milieux universitaire et gouvernemental.

Secretary-General: In-suk Chang.
27–2 Youido-dong, Youngdungpo-gu, Seoul 150-010.
Tel: 782-8310

The Korean Federation of Education Associations

The Federation is an independent, non-political and voluntary organization of professional teachers in Korea. It was founded on 23 November 1947 as the professional organization of Korean teachers.

It is composed of fourteen provincial associations under which are placed local associations at city and county level. In May 1988, KFEA had 264,000 members, or about 80% of all Korean teachers. KFEA consolidates teachers engaged in elementary, secondary and higher education, in order to improve their social and economic status as well as their professional and academic qualifications, and to promote their material and moral rights and interests, thereby contributing to the sound development of democratic education in Korea.

The governing body of KFEA is the Assembly of Delegates which meets annually. This Assembly determines policies outlining the general programme, adopts the annual budget, amends the KFEA Constitution and elects the Board of Directors. Between meetings of the Assembly of Delegates, the Board of Directors

is responsible for general policies and main interests of KFEA. The work of the Federation is carried out by the Secretariat under the direction of the Board of Directors.

KFEA raises the standard of teaching through various programmes such as study meetings, seminars, in-service-training and workshops. Official Journals: The Korea Education Weekly (newspaper); The New Education (monthly); The New Classroom (monthly); The Educational Year Book (biennially).

La Fédération coréenne des associations d'enseignement est un organisme indépendant, sans but politique et bénévole réunissant les enseignants professionnels de Corée. Elle fut fondée le 23 novembre 1947 comme organisation professionnelle des enseignants coréens.

Elle se compose de quatorze associations provinciales dont dépendent des associations locales au niveau de la ville ou du district. Elle comptait, en mai 1988, 264.000 membres, soit environ 80% de l'ensemble du corps enseignant coréen. La KFEA apporte son appui aux enseignants de l'enseignement élémentaire, secondaire, et supérieur, en vue d'améliorer leur statut tant économique que social, ainsi que leurs qualifications professionnelles et académiques, et de défendre leurs droits et intérêts, sur les plans matériel et moral. Elle contribue ainsi à un développement harmonieux de l'enseignement démocratique en Corée.

L'organe suprême de la KFEA est l'Assemblée des délégués, qui se réunit annuellement. L'Assemblée fixe l'orientation du programme général, établit le budget, modifie s'il y a lieu les Statuts de la Fédération et élit le Conseil d'administration. Entre les réunions de l'Assemblée, le Conseil dirige la politique générale de la KFEA et veille à ses principaux intérêts. Les tâches de la Fédération sont accomplies par le Secrétariat, sous la direction du Conseil d'administration.

La KFEA élève le niveau de l'enseignement grâce à différents programmes (journées d'études, séminaires, sessions de recyclage en cours de carrière et colloques). Périodiques officiels: The Korea Education Weekly; The New Education (mensuel); The New Classroom (mensuel); The Educational Year Book (tous les deux ans).

President: Dr. Bom-Suk Chung.
Secretary-General: Dr. Yong-Do Ha.
25, 1-ka Shinmun-ro, Chongro-ku, Seoul 110061.
Tel: 735-5981

Korean Association of University Women (IFUW)
423–44, Sangmun-dong, Dobong-gu, Seoul 132.

World University Service (WUS)
General Secretary: Suk Dong Choi.
Seoul Language Institute, Chung-Kang Build-
ing, 5-7 Sucho-Dong, Kangnam-ku, Seoul.
Catholic Students' Centre (Pax Romana)
Secretary: Peter H. Kim.
29–1, 4-ka, Myongryun-dong, Chongro-gu,
Seoul.
Korean Catholic Intellectuals Association (Pax
Romana)
President: Kun Lee.
Catholic Students' Centre (see above).
National Council of Student YMCAs (WSCF)

P.O. Box 1056, Seoul.
Korean Student Christian Federation (WSCF)
Rm. 708, Christian Building, 136–46 Yongji-
dong, Chongno-ku, Seoul.

*

Ministry of Education
17 Sejong-ro, Chong-ro-gu, Seoul.
Tel: 738-7981. Telex: 24758 munkyo k
Korean National Commission for Unesco
Unesco House, 50–16 2 Ka, Myung-Dong,
Choong-gu, Seoul.
Tel: 776-3950. Telex: 24758 munkyo k

KUWAIT
KOWEIT

*Kuwait University, P.O. Box 5969 Safat,
Kuwait, Safat 13060.   *1966*
Tel: 811188. Telex: 2616
F : *sc, arts, ed, law, Isl st (Shari'a), eng-pet,
com, eco-pol, med, allied heal sc-nurs, grad st.*

**Public Authority for Applied Education and
Training**, P.O. Box 23167, Safat 13092.   *1982*
Tel: 2413050. Telev: 22269
F : *bus st, basic e'' .chn st, heal st.*

**National Union of Kuwait Students – NUKS
(IUS)**
Kuwait University.
                                        *

Ministry of Education
Kuwait.
Kuwait National Commission for Unesco
Post Box 3266, Safat 13033.

LAO PEOPLE'S DEMOCRATIC REPUBLIC
REPUBLIQUE DEMOCRATIQUE POPULAIRE DE LAO

Université des Sciences médicales, Ministère de la Santé publique, Vientiane. *1958*
Ecole Supérieure de Pédagogie Dongdok, Ministère de l'Education, Vientiane. *1958*
Institut national polytechnique, Ministère de l'Education, Vientiane. *1984*
Ecole supérieure des Ponts et Chaussées, Ministère de la Communication et des Transports, Vientiane. *1983*

Ecole supérieure du Bâtiment, Ministère de la Construction, Vientiane. *1979*
Ecole technique supérieure d'Electrotechnique et d'Electronique, Ministère de l'Education, Vientiane. *1983*
Institut national des Sciences de l'Education, Ministère de l'Education, Vientiane. *1982*
Institut national des Sciences sociales, Ministère de l'Education. *1986*

Union de la Jeunesse populaire révolutionnaire de Lao – UJPRL (IUS)
30, rue Sisavat, Quartier Nahaidiao, B.P. 736, Vientiane.
Cables: jeulao vientiane (attn. uneul)
Catholic Students' Society (Pax Romana)
Mission catholique, Vientiane.

Ministère de l'Education
Vientiane.
Tél: 2213
Commission nationale lao pour l'Unesco
Ministère de l'Education, Vientiane.
Tél: 2213 (postes 132/3). Télex: 4317

*

LEBANON
LIBAN

UNIVERSITIES—UNIVERSITES

*Al-Jâmi'ah al-Lubnaniyah [U. libanaise], Bîr'Hassan, Beyrouth. (M. le Secrétaire général). *1953*
Tél: 386817. Télex: 42151 fansul le
F : dr-pol, let, sc, péd, gestion entrep.
I : soc, ba, jour.
*American University of Beirut, B.P. 236, Beirut. (The Registrar.) *1865*
Tél: 340740. Télex: 20801 amunob le
F : *arts-sc, eng-arc, agr.*
S : *publ heal, nurs, med, phar.*
*Jâmi'at al Qiddis Yussuf [U. Saint-Joseph], rue de l'Université Saint-Joseph, B.P. 293, Beyrouth. *1875*
Tél: 326636. Télex: 21486 usj le. Cables:

medifac
F : théo, dr-éco, méd-phar.
Ce : ét arabes.
E : gé.
I : let orntl.
*Jâmi'at Bayrût al-'Arabiyah [Beirut Arab U.], B.P. 5020, Beirut. *1960*
Tél: 300100. Télex: 22844 abu le
F : *let, law, eng-arc, com.*
*Jâmi'at al-Rûh'al-Qudos [U. Saint-Esprit], Kaslik. *1961*
Tél: 930124. Télex: 45777 usek le
F : théo, phil, let, dr, com, ba.
I : lit, mus.

OTHER INSTITUTIONS—AUTRES INSTITUTIONS

Al-Akadimiyah al-Lubnaniyah lil-Fûnûn al-Jamîlah [A. libanaise des Beaux-Arts], Beyrouth. *1937*
Tél: 480056
E : arc, mus, pnt, décor.

Ma'had Haïkazian [Haïgazian C.], rue du Mexique, B.P. 1748, Beyrouth. *1955*
Tél: 349230
D : arts, sc.

Kulliyat Bayrut al'Jâmi'yat [Beirut U.C.], B.P. 4080, Beirut. *1950*
Tél: 811968. Télex: 23389 buc le
D : arts, sc.

Ma'had al-'Hikmat al-'Ali li-I-'Huqûq [I. sup. de Droit de la Sagesse], 1961, rue de Hikmat, Beyrouth. *1961*

Kulliyat al-Sharq al-Awsat [Middle East C.], B.P. 1170, Beirut. *1949*
D : relig st, hist, bus adm, eng, nat.

Kulliyat Al-Imam Al-Ouzai li-Dirasat Al-Islamiyya [Imam Ouzaï C. of Islamic Studies], P.O. Box 14-5355, Beirut. *1979*
Tél: 317708
Isl st.

Kulliyat Idarat Al-Amal Al-Islamiya [Islamic C. of Business Administration], P.O. Box 14-5355, Beirut. *1986*
Tél: 317708
bus adm.

Association des Libanaises universitaires (IFUW)
B.P. 165039, Achrafieh 2300, Beyrouth.

Union nationale des Etudiants Universitaires du Liban—UNEUL (IUS)
B.P. 14/5632, Beyrouth.
Télex: 23308 cttd le (attn. uneul)

Conseil national du Tourisme au Liban, Service «Accueil des Jeunes» – CNTL
B.P. 5344, Beyrouth.

Union catholique des Intellectuels du Liban (Pax Romana)
Imm. Jabr., rue Patriarcat Arménien, Antélias.

Orthodox Youth Movement (WSCF)
P.O. Box 1375, Beirut.

*

Ministère de l'Education nationale et des Beaux-Arts
Beyrouth.
Tél: 305111

Commission nationale libanaise pour l'Unesco
Palais de l'Unesco, Beyrouth.
Tél: 300962. Cables: libanesco beyrouth

LESOTHO
LESOTHO

*National University of Lesotho, P.O. Roma 180.
(The Vice-Chancellor). *1945, 1964, 1966, 1975*
Tel: 64601. Telex: 4303 uniter lo. Cables: uniter

roma
F : *agr, ed, hum, law, sc, soc.*

International Association of University Professors
and Lecturers (IAUPL)
Contact: 18, rue du Docteur Roux, 75015 Paris
(France).
Tel: (33-1) 47.83.31.65
World University Service
National University of Lesotho, P.O. Roma
180.
Tel: 64336. Telex: 4303 uniter lo
Students' Representative Council—SRC (IUS)
National University of Lesotho, P.O. Roma
180, Maseru.

Student Christian Movement of Lesotho (WSCF)
P.O. 63, Morija 190.
Tel: 76233

*

Ministry of Education, Sports and Culture P.O.
47, Maseru.
Lesotho National Commission for Unesco Minis-
try of Education, Sports and Culture, P.O. 47,
Maseru.
Tel: 325932. Cables: unescom maseru

LIBERIA
LIBERIA

UNIVERSITIES—UNIVERSITES

*University of Liberia, P.O. Box 804, Monrovia.
(The President).   *1856, 1951*

Tel: 222448
F : *li arts, sc, law, ed, for-agr, med, bus adm.*

OTHER INSTITUTIONS—AUTRES INSTITUTIONS

Cuttington University College, P.O. Box 277,
Monrovia.   *1889, 1976*

Tel: 224243. Cables: pecusam
D : *sc-math, hum, soc, nurs, ed, theo.*

Liberian National Students Union—LNSU (IUS)
c/o University of Liberia, Monrovia.
Telex: 4560 (attn. linsu)
National Student Christian Council of Liberia
(WSCF)
P.O. Box 1010, Monrovia.
Tel: 262781
United Nations Student Association (ISMUN)
University of Liberia, P.O. Box 9020, Monrovia.

*

Ministry of Education
Monrovia
Tel: 222654
Liberian National Commission for Unesco Minis-
try of Education, Monrovia.
Tel: 222654 (ext. 67). Telex: 44449 rinedu

SOCIALIST PEOPLE'S LIBYAN ARAB JAMAJIRIYA
JAMAHIRIYA ARABE LIBYENNE POPULAIRE
ET SOCIALISTE

*University of Garyounis, P.O. Box 1308, Benghazi.   *1955, 1973, 1976*
Tel: 87462
F : *let-ed, eco-com, law, eng, sc, dent, agr.*
*University of Al-Fateh, P.O. Box 13482, Tripoli.
1957, 1973, 1976
Tel: 36010. Telex: 20629 ly
F : *let, sc, eng, agr, pet-miner, nucl techn-electro, med, phar, vet; ed* (Zawia).
University of Sebha, Sebha.   *1983*
Tel: 21575
F : *ed, sc.*

Al-Arab Medical University, Benghazi.
1984
F : *med, dent.*
Higher Institute of Electronics, P.O. Box 8645, Beni Walid/Souk Jin.   *1976*
Higher Institute of Mechanical and Electrical Engineering, P.O. Box 61160, Hon.   *1976*
Tel: 2154. Telex: 30254 ly
Higher Institute of Technology, P.O. Box 68, Brack.   *1976*
Tel: 45300
D : *med lab techn, food techn, env techn.*

General Congress of Students of Great Jama-hiriya–GCSGJ (IUS)
7 U-Ben Ashour Street, P.O. Box 10826, Tripoli.
Telex: 20830 slp ly

*

Secretariat of Education
Tripoli.
Tel: 41446
National Commission for Education, Science and Culture of the Socialist People's Libyan Arab Jamahiriya
P.O. Box 1091, Tripoli.
Tel: 41572. Telex: 20367 amanta ly

LUXEMBOURG
LUXEMBOURG

Centre Universitaire de Luxembourg, 162a, avenue de la Faïencerie, L-1511 Luxembourg. •
1969, 1974
Tél: 216-21
D : *let-hum, dr-éco, sc, jur, péd.*
Institut Universitaire International de Luxembourg, 162a, avenue de la Faïencerie, L-1511 Luxembourg.   *1958, 1974*
Ce : *ét jur-dr comparé, éco pol, ét-recheur.*
Institut Supérieur d'Etudes et de Recherches Pédagogiques, Walferdange.

1960, 1983
Tél: 33-14-14
Institut Supérieur de Technologie, rue R. Coudenhove-Kalergi, L-1359 Luxembourg.
1979
Tél: 43-66-61. Télex: 3586 istdr lu
Institut Européen pour la Gestion de l'Information, 13, rue de Bragance, L-1255 Luxembourg.
1982
Tél: 44-58-11

Association générale des Etudiants luxembourgeois
Case Postale 78, Luxembourg-Ville.

Fédération luxembourgeoise des Femmes universitaires (IFUW)
10, rue de l'Abbé-Lemire, 1927 Luxembourg.

Association luxembourgeoise des Universitaires catholiques—Akademiker Verein (Pax Romana)
12, avenue Marie-Thérèse, Luxembourg.

Cercle des Jeunes de l'Association luxembourgeoise pour les Nations Unies (ISMUN)
62, rue St. Joseph, Rumelange, Luxembourg.

World Union of Jewish Students (WUJS)
Correspondant: 89 Chaussee de Vleurgat, 1050 Brussels.
Tél: (2) 647-7279. Télex: 20625

*

Ministère de l'Education nationale et de la Jeunesse
6, boulevard Royal, 2910 Luxembourg.
Tél: 478-11

Commission nationale luxembourgeoise pour la Coopération avec l'Unesco
Ministère de l'Education nationale et de la Jeunesse, 6, boulevard Royal, 2910 Luxembourg.
Tél: 478-11. Télex: 2111. Cables: commission unesco luxembourg

MACAU
MACAO

*University of East Asia, University Hill, Taipa, P.O. Box 3001, Macau.   *1981*
Tel: 27322. Telex: 88397 uea om. Cables: ueastasia
S : *arts, soc, bus adm.*
C : *continuing ed, junior, open.*

Serviços de Educação e Cultura
Macau.
Telex: 88346 edu om

DEMOCRATIC REPUBLIC OF MADAGASCAR
REPUBLIQUE DEMOCRATIQUE DE MADAGSCAR

*Université d'Antananarivo, B.P. 566, Antananarivo. (M. le Recteur). *1961*
Tél: 241-14. Télex: 22304 recumt mg
E : dr-éco-adm des aff-socio, sc, let, sa, agr, poly, méd.
I : phys, math (rech).
Université d'Antsiranana, Antsiranana.
1975, 1988
E : poly, let.
Université de Fianarantsoa, B.P. 1264, Fianarantsoa. *1977, 1988*
E : sc, dr.
Université de Mahajanga, B.P. 652, Mahajanga.
1977, 1988
E : dent, sc, méd.
Université de Toamasina, B.P. 591, Toamasina.
1977, 1988
E : dr-éco-adm des aff-socio, let.
Université de Toliary.   *1977, 1988*
E : sc, let.

ECOLE NATIONALE D'INFORMATIQUE, Fianarantsoa.   *1980*
Ecole Normale du Niveau III.   *1979*
Sections à Antananarivo, Fianarantsoa, Toliary, Antsiranana.
  LABORATOIRE DE RADIO-ISOTOPES, B.P. 3383, Antananarivo.   *1956*
  MUSÉE D'ART ET D'ARCHÉOLOGIE, B.P. 564, Antananarivo.   *1964*
  STATION MARINE DE TOLIARY, B.P. 141, Toliary.   *1970*
  CENTRE NATIONAL D'ENSEIGNEMENT DE LA LANGUE ANGLAISE, Antananarivo.
          1985
  CENTRE DE DOCUMENTATION ET DE RECHERCHE SUR L'ART ET LES TRADITIONS ORALES À MADAGASCAR, Toliary.   *1985*
  CENTRE D'ETUDES ET DE RECHERCHES ETHNOLOGIQUES ET LINGUISTIQUES, Toamasina.   *1985*

Comité démocratique de la Jeunesse et des Etudiants pour le Soutien de la Révolution socialiste Malagasy—KDTM (IUS)
43, avenue Rakotomala Ratsimba, Antananarivo.
Fédération des Associations d'Etudiants de Madagascar—FAEM (IUS)
Mpianatra Kristiana Malagasi (WSCF)
B.P. 6309, Antananarivo.
Centre d'Etudes et d'Information sur le Développement (Pax Romana)
25, Cité des Professeurs, Antananarivo.

*

Ministère de l'Enseignement supérieur et de la Recherche scientifique
Antananarivo.
Tél: 272 92. Télex: 22539 mrstd
Commission nationale malgache pour l'Unesco
11, Naka Rabemanantsoa-Behoririka, Antananarivo.
Tél: 217. 61. Cables: comnat unesco tananarive

MALAWI
MALAWI

*University of Malawi, University Office, P.O. Box 278, Zomba. *1965*
Tel: 522.622. Cables: university, zomba
  BUNDA COLLEGE OF AGRICULTURE, P.O. Box 219, Lilongwe.
  Tel: 721.455
  CHANCELLOR COLLEGE, P.O. Box 280, Zomba.
  Tel: 522.222

S : *arts, sc, soc eco, law-adm, ed-hom eco.*
THE POLYTECHNIC, Private Bag 303, Chichiri, Blantyre 3.
Tel: 632.144
S : *techn, bus-st, eng.*
KAMUZU COLLEGE OF NURSING, Private Bag 1, Lilongwe.
Tel: 721.622

Catholic Student Society (Pax Romana)
c/o The Chaplain, Pius XII Seiminary, Box 603, Limbe.
Student Christian Movement of Malawi (WSCF)
c/o Kings M.G. Phiri, Chancellor College, P.O. Box 280, Zomba.

Ministry of Education and Culture
Lilongwe 3.
Tel: 733.922
Malawi National Commission for Unesco
Taurus House, P.O. Box 30278, Capital City, Lilongwe 3.
Tel: 733.077. Telex: 4769 unesco mi. Cables: unesco lilongwe 3 malawi

*

MALAYSIA
MALAISIE

UNIVERSITIES—UNIVERSITES

*Universiti Malaya, Lembah Pantai 59000, Kuala Lumpur. (The Registrar). *1949, 1957, 1962*
Tel: (3) 7560022. Telex: 39845 unimal ma. Cables: univsel kuala lumpur
F : *arts-soc, eng, sc, med, ed, eco-adm, dent, law.*
  AKADEMIC ISLAM [Islam A.], Kota Bharu, Kelantan. *1981*
  F : *Isl law & theo.*
*Universiti Kebangsaan Malaysia [National U.], 43600 Bangi, Selangor. *1970*
Tel: (3) 8250001. Telex: 31496 unikeb ma. Cables: unikeb
F : *soc-hum, eco, Isl st, ed, phy-app sc, bus mangt; sc, med* (Kuala Lumpur); *sc-nat resources* (Sabah).
Universiti Sains Malaysia [U. of Science],

Minden, 11800 Penang. *1969*
Tel: 883822 (PABX). Telex: 40254 usmlib ma. Cables: unisains malaysia
S : *phar, arc-bui-plan, hum, ed, soc, med, biol, ch, eng-ind, techn, math, phy.*
*Universiti Teknoloji Malaysia [U. of Technology], Jalan Gurney, 54100 Kuala Lumpur. *1972*
Tel: (3) 2929033. Telex: 30090 utekma ma. Cables: unitekma kuala lumpur
F : *arc, surv, sc, ch eng-nat resources, civ eng, comp, elec, mec, sc, hum.*
*Universiti Pertanian Malaysia [U. of Agriculture], Serdang, Selangor. *1931, 1971*
Tel: (3) 9486101. Telex: 37454 uniper ma. Cables: unipertama sungaibesi
F : *agr, for, vet-anim sc, agr eng, ed serv,*

resource eco & agri bus, sc-env st, fish, food techn, hum dev; fish, oceanog (Trengganu).

International Islamic University [U. Islam Antarabangsa], Jalan Universiti, P.O. Box 70, Jalan Sultan, Petaling Jaya, Selangor.   *1963*
laws, eco, lang, basic st, Quranic st.

Universiti Utara Malaysia, Bandar Darulaman, 06000 Jitra, Kedah.   *1984*
Tel: (4) 772066. Telex: 42052 utamas ma.
Cables: utamas
S : *bus mangt-acc, eco-publ adm, foundation st, lang-scientific thinking.*

OTHER INSTITUTIONS—AUTRES INSTITUTIONS
Technical Education—Enseignement technique

Institut Teknoloji MARA [Mara I. of Technology], Shah Alam, Selangor.   *1957*
Tel: 5592950. Telex: 38671 tekma ma
F : *acc, adm-law, bus st, app sc, math-comp, plan-surv, arc, des-fa, eng, lib, mass commun, hotel & catering mangt, sec.*
Also branches (9) in: Kelantan, Johor, Pahang, Perak Melaka, Perlis, Trengganu, Sabah, Sarawak.

Kolej Tunku Abdul Rahman [Tunku Abdul Rahman C.], Jalan Genting Kelang, Wilayah Persekutuan, Kuala Lumpur.   *1969*
Tel: 4233122
com, sc, techn, pre-U. st.

Politeknik Alor Setar, [Alor Setar Polytechnic], Bandar Baru Darylamen, 06000 Jitra, Kedha.   *1984*

eng.
Politeknik Batu Pahat, Jalan Tun Abdul Razak, Johor Bahru.   *1984*
eng.
Politeknik Kota Bahru, Bunut Susa, 17020 Pasir Mas, Kelantan.   *1985*
eng.
Politeknik Kuantan, Alor Akar, Kuantan, Pahang.   *1976*
eng, com, arc, surv, book-keeping, comp, sec, acc, food techn.
Politeknik Kuching, Tkt. 2, Lot 7417, Jalan Simpang 3, 93738 Kuching, Sarawak.   *1987*
eng, com, sec.
Politeknik Ungku Omar, Jalan Dairy, 31400 Ipoh, Perak.   *1969*
mar, acc, eng, com, arc, surv, acc, shipping.

Teacher Training—Formation pédagogique

Maktab Perguruan Batu Lintang [Teachers' Training C.], Batu Lintang, Sarawak.   *1947*
Maktab Perguruan Gaya, Kota Kinabalu, Sabah.   *1963*
Maktab Perguruan Ipoh, Hulu Kinta, Ipoh, Perak 19.   *1976*
Maktab Perguruan Islam, Jalan Pantai Baru, Kuala Lumpur, Wilayah Persekutuan.   *1977*
Maktab Perguruan Keningau, Beg Berkunci 11, 89009 Keningau, Sabah.   *1985*
Maktab Perguruan Kent, Tuaran, Sabah.   *1952*
Maktab Perguruan Kinta, Jalan Dairy, Ipoh, Perak.   *1974*
Maktab Perguruan Kota Bahru, Pengkalan Chepa, Kelantan.   *1954*
Maktab Perguruan Kuala Trengganu, Batu Rakit, Kuala Trengganu.   *1982*
Maktab Perguruan Kuantan, Kuantan, Jalan Kuantan, Pahang.   *1976*
Maktab Perguruan Lembah Pantai, Kuala Lumpur, Wilayah Persekutuan.   *1976*
Maktab Perguruan Perempuan Melayu [Women's Teachers' Training C.], Jalan Tun Fatimah, Melaka.   *1935*

Maktab Perguruan Mohd. Khalid, Jalan A. Samad, Johor Bahru, Johor.   *1957*
Maktab Perguruan Pasir Panjang, Kuala Trengganu, Trengganu.   *1959*
Maktab Perguruan Persekutuan [Malayan Teachers' College], Gelugor, Pulau Pinang.   *1956*
Maktab Perguruan Raja Melewar [Teachers' Training C.], Jalan Sikamat, Seremban, Negeri Sembilan.   *1957*
Maktab Perguruan Rajang, Binatang, Sarawak.   *1965*
Maktab Perguruan Sandakan, Sandakan, Sabah.   *1974*
Maktab Perguruan Sarawak Miri, Jalan Bakau, 98000 Miri, Sarawak.   *1957*
Maktab Perguruan Seri Pinang, Jalan Northam, Pulau Pinang.   *1957*
Maktab Perguruan Sri Kota, Jalan Kuantan, Kuala Lumpur.   *1957*
Maktab Perguruan Sultan Abd. Halim, Sungai Petani, Kedah.   *1980*
Maktab Perguruan Sultan Idris, Tanjong Malim, Perak.   *1922*
Maktab Perguruan Temenggong Ibrahim, Peti

Surat 731, Johor Bharu, Johor. *1965*
Maktab Perguruan Tg. Ampuan Afzan, Semamba, 25350 Kuantan, Pahang. *1984*
Maktab Perguruan Banasa [Language I.], Kuala Lumpur, Wilayah Persekutuan. *1958*
Maktab Perguruan Ilmu Khas [Specialist Teachers' Training I.], Cheras, Kuala Lumpur, Wilayah Persekutuan. *1960*
Maktab Perguruan Teknik [Technical Teachers' Training C.], Jalan Cheras, Kuala Lumpur, Wilayah Persekutuan. *1962*

Persatuan Kebangsaan Pelajar 2, Malaya – PKPM
Union House, University of Malaya, Pantai Valley, Kuala Lumpur.
Pergerakan Siswazah Katholik Malaysia (Pax Romana)
Xavier Hall, Jalan Gasing, Petaling Jaya, Selangor.
Graduates Movement Malaysia (Pax Romana)
St. John's Institution, Bukit Nanas, Kuala Lumpur.
Catholic Students' Society University of Malaya (Pax Romana)
University of Malaya, c/o Xavier Hall, Jalan Gasing, Petaling Jaya, Selangor.
National Student Christian Movement of Malaysia (WSCF)
26 Jalan University, Petaling Jaya, Selangor.

Persatuan Kebangsaan Pelajar-Pelajar Malaysia (ISMUN)
International Vice-President: Mohd. Radhi Mohd. Amin.
Union House, University of Malaya, Kuala Lumpur.

*

Ministry of Education
Kuala Lumpur.
Tel: 2922066
Malaysian National Commission for Unesco
20th Floor, Bank Pertanian Building, Jalan Leloh, Pasar, 50604 Kuala Lumpur.
Tel: (3) 2927767. Telex: 33547 ma. Cables: malnatcom kuala lumpur

MALI
MALI

Ecole des hautes Etudes pratiques, B.P. 242, Bamako. *1974*
Tél: 22-21-47
sec, comp-gestion.
Ecole nationale d'Administration, B.P. 276, Bamako. *1963*
Tél: 22-27-19
Sect : adm publ, jur, éco.
Ecole nationale d'Ingénieurs, B.P. 242, Bamako. *1963*
Tél: 22-21-47
Sect : topog, géol, const, civ, élec-méc.
Ecole nationale de Médecine et de Dentisterie Point-G, Point-G, Bamako. *1969*
Tél: 22-20-02

Ecole nationale des Postes et Télécommunications, Bamako. *1969*
Ecole normale supérieure, B.P. 241, Bamako. *1962*
Tél: 22-21-85
Sect : phil, let, hist-géog, lang, math, phy-ch, biol.
Institut polytechnique rural de Katibougou, B.P. 6, Koulikoro. *1966*
Tél: 26-20-12
Sect : élev, eaux et forêts, agr.
Institut supérieur de Formation et Recherche appliquée, B.P. 241, Bamako. *1970, 1982*
Sect : écol, entomologie, microbiol, lit comparée, géol, ling app, biol anim.

Ministère de l'Education nationale, Direction nationale des Enseignements supérieurs et de la Recherche scientifique
Bamako.

Tél: 22-21-26
Commission nationale malienne pour l'Unesco
Ministère de l'Education nationale, Bamako.
Tél: 22-25-15. Télex: 2602

MALTA
MALTE

*The University of Malta, Msida. (The Registrar).
1592, 1769, 1980
Tel: 333903/6

F : *law, med-surg-phar, arc, civ eng, mec, elec, sc, dent surg, arts, ed, eco-mangt, acc.*

Association of Teachers of The University of Malta (IAUPL)
The University of Malta, Msida.
Students' Representative Council – SRC
Student House, Tal-Qroqq, Msida.
University Students' Catholic Movement (Pax Romana)
The University of Malta, Msida.

National Equivalence Information Centre
Education Department, 32-33 Marzamwetto Road, Valletta.
Tel: 229842. Telex: 1115 mee mt
Ministry of Education
Lascarris, Valletta.
Maltese National Commission for Unesco
Ministry of Education, Lascarris, Valletta.
Tel: 231385. Telex: 1100 mod mlt mt. Cables: external malta

*

MARTINIQUE
MARTINIQUE

Université des Antilles-Guyane (1)
Faculté de Droit et d'Economie, B.P. 7209, 97275 Schœlcher Cedex.

Tel: 61.20.24
Faculté des Lettres et Sciences Humaines, B.P. 7207, 97275 Schœlcher Cedex.

Association générale des Etudiants de la Martinique – AGEM (IUS)

*

Inspection académique de la Martinique, Service de l'Organisation scolaire
B.P. 638 et 639, 97262 Fort-de-France, Cedex.
Tél: (596) 726060

---

(1) See also Guadeloupe, p. 185.
(1) Voir aussi Guadeloupe, p. 185.

MAURITANIA
MAURITANIE

Université de Nouakchott, B.P. 798, Nouakchott.
1981
Tél: 539-67
F : let-hum, sc jur-éco.
Centre supérieur d'Enseignement technique,
B.P. 986, Nouakchott.   *1982*
Tél: 530-17. Télex: 719 MTN Nktt
D : méc, élec.

Ecole normale supérieure, B.P. 990, Nouakchott.
1970
Tél: 531-84
D : let-hist-géog, lang, math, sc.
Institut supérieur scientifique, B.P. 5026,
Nouakchott.   *1985*
Tél: 513-82. Télex: 598 MTN Nktt
D : math, phy, ch, biol, géol.

Ministère de l'Education nationale
Nouakchott.
Tél: 523-62

Commission nationale pour l'Unesco
B.P. 5115, Nouakchott.
Tél: 528-02

MAURITIUS
MAURICE (Ile)

University of Mauritius, Reduit. (The Chancellor).   *1965*
Tel: 54-1041/9. Telex: 4621 unim iw. Cables:
university mauritius
S : *agr, adm, ind techn.*
   SIR SEEWOOSAGUR RAMGOOLAM CENTRE
   FOR MEDICAL RESEARCH AND STUDIES,
   Reduit. (The Head).   *1986*
**Sir Kher Jagatsing Industrial Trade Training
Centre**, Beau Bassin. (The Manager).
**Prof. Upadhyaya Industrial Trade Training
Centre**, Piton.   *1982*
Lycée Polytechnique Sir Guy Forget, Centre de

Flacq. (The Director).   *1982*
Tel: 53-28-70
Mauritius Institute of Education, Reduit. (The
Director).   *1974*
Tel: 541031
   MAURITIUS COLLEGE OF EDUCATION, Beau
   Bassin.   *1942*
   CURRICULUM DEVELOPMENT CENTRE, Beau
   Bassin. (The Director).   *1984*
**School of African, Oriental and Mauritian
Studies**, Moka.   *1977*
Tel: 48021

Socialist Working Youth League of Mauritius
(ISMUN)
P.O. Box 382, 12 Bourbon Street, Port Louis.
                     *

Ministry of Education, Arts and Culture
Port Louis.
Tel: 01-11-05

Mauritius National Commission for Unesco
Ministry of Education, Arts and Culture, Port
Louis.
Tel: 24915. Cables: unesco education ministry
port louis

MEXICO
MEXIQUE

UNIVERSITIES—UNIVERSITES

Public Institutions—Etablissements publics

Universidad Autónoma Agraria "Antonio Narro", Domicilio Conocido, Buena Vista, Saltillo, Coah.   *1923*
Tél: 4-31-00. Télex: 038128
gé, agr.
UNIDAD LA LAGUNA, Carretera a Santa Fe y Periférico, 27000 Torreón, Coah.   *1980*
E : vét-zoo.
*Universidad Autónoma de Aguascalientes, Jardin del Estudiante 1, 20100 Aguascalientes, Ags.   *1973*
Tél: 7-05-05
Ce : éco adm, bioméd, techn, arts-hum, agr, ét fond.
*Universidad Autónoma de Baja California, Avenida Alvaro Obregón y Julián Carrillo s/n, 21100 Mexicali, B.C.   *1957*
Tél: 54-22-00. Télex: 569888 uabcme
E : arc, soc-pol, comp-adm, dr, ing, vét-zoo, dent, éd, méd; agr (el Valle); comp-adm, ch, dr, éco, méd, dent, tour; océanog, biol, ing, comp-adm (Ensenada); comp-adm, ch, éco, méd, dent, tour, dr (Tijuana)
Universidad Autónoma de Baja California Sur, Ciudad Universitaria, Km. 5 Carretera al Sur, 23000 La Paz, B.C. Sur.   *1975*
Tél: 4-22-00
sc mar, agr, soc.
Universidad Autónoma del Carmen, Calle 31 x 56, 24176 Ciudad del Carmen, Camp.
Tél: 2-11-33
F : com-adm, dr, ch, éd.
E : prod pêch.
*Universidad Autónoma de Chapingo, Km. 32 Carretera México-Texcoco, 56230 Chapingo, Estado de México.   *1854, 1974*
Tél: 585-45-55
agr.
*Universidad Autónoma de Chiapas, 1a Avenida Norte-Poniente 151, 29050 Tuxtla Gutiérrez, Chis.   *1975*
Tél: 2-53-55
adm, phy-math, bioméd, hum; soc, dr (San Cristobal de las Casas); adm, comp, ch (Tapachula); agr (Villaflores); agr (Huehuetan).
*Universidad Autónoma de Chihuahua, Escorza y B. Carranza s/n, 31000 Chihuahua, Chih.
                                              1954
Tél: 5-24-27
F : comp-adm, dr, ing, méd, zoo, ch; adm publ-pol (Ciudad Juárez); agr (Ciudad Delicias).
E : phil-let, inf-obst.
E(sup.) : phys, fruit.
*Universidad Autónoma de Ciudad Juárez, Avenida López Mateos 20, Apartado postal 1594–D, 32310 Ciudad Juárez, Chih.   *1973*
Tél: 3-12-22
I : bioméd, soc-adm, ing-arc.
*Universidad Autónoma de Coahuila, Bulevard Constitución y Lic. Salvador González Lobo, 25280 Saltillo, Coah.   *1867, 1957*
Tél: 2-01-55
F : ch, gé civ, arc, éd, phil-let, dr; méd, dr, comp-adm, éco, dent (Torreón).
E : adm, commun, éco, inf, méd, march, dent, psyc, systèmes, mus, trav soc; arc, adm, biol, comté, pol-soc, inf, gé civ, méc-élec (Torreón); adm (Piedras Negras); comp-adm (Monclova).
*Universidad de Colima, Avenida Universidad 333, 28000 Colima, Col.   *1867, 1940, 1962*
Tél: 2-54-36. Télex: 62248 ucolme
F : adm-comp, dr, méd, péd; méc-élec (Coquimatlán); biol-agr (Tecomán).
E : arc, pol-soc, éco, let-commun, inf, gé civ, trav soc, éd; ch (Coquimatlán); comp-adm, sc mar (Manzanillo); comp-adm, vét-zoo (Tecomán); lang (Villa de Alvarez).
*Universidad Juárez del Estado de Durango, Constitución 404 Sur, 34000 Durango, Dgo.
                                              1933, 1957
Tél: 2-00-44
F : vét-zoo, soc, dr, math, trav soc.
E : biol, gé civ, alim, méd, agr, zoo (Gomez Palacio).
*Universidad Autónoma del Estado de Hidalgo, Abasolo 600, 42000 Pachuca, Hgo.   *1869, 1961*

Tél: 2-65-34

I : soc, sc exactes, comp-adm.

E : dent, méd.

*Universidad Autónoma del Estado de México, Instituto-Literio 100 Ote., 50000 Toluca, Estado de México.   *1956*

Tél: 5-45-04. Télex: 174426 uamme

F : arc, sc du comportement, pol-adm publ, comp-adm, dr, hum, ing, méd, agr, dent.

E : agr, ch, éco, inf, géog, vét, tour (Toluca).

*Universidad Autónoma del Estado de Morelos, Avenida Universidad 1001, 62210 Cuernavaca, Mor.   *1939, 1953, 1967*

Tél: 13-10-90. Télex: 173392 uaemme

F : comp-adm, ch ind.

E : arc, biol, dr-soc, psyc, méd, éd, agr.

*Universidad de Guadalajara, Avenida Juárez 975, 44100 Guadalajara, Jal.   *1791*

Tél: 25-22-42

F : adm, sc, arc, comp publ, ch, dr, dess, éco, phil-let, géog, ing, méd, vét-zoo, dent, agr, trav soc, tour; vét-zoo (Ciudad Guzmán).

E : psyc; agr (Autlán).

E(sup.) : phys.

*Universidad de Guanajuato, Lascuráin de Retana 5, 36000 Guanajuato, Gto.

                         1732, 1828, 1945

Tél: 2-03-04

F : arc, ch, comp-adm, dr, gé mine-mét, géol; méd, (León); méc-élec-électro (Salamanca).

E : phil-let, gé civ, rel ind, dess, topog, math; com-adm, inf-obst (Celaya); agr-zoo (Irapuato); inf, psyc (León).

*Universidad Autónoma de Guerrero, Avenida Abasolo 33, 39020 Chilpancingo, Gro.

                         1869, 1960

Tél: 2-25-36

F : com-adm (Acapulco).

E : dr-soc, ing, sc, ch-biol, arc-urb, phil-let; vét-zoo (Ciudad Altamirano); méd, écol mar, soc (Acapulco); sc de la terre (Taxco el Viejo).

*Universidad Autónoma Metropolitana, Boulevard Manuel Avila, Camacho 90, Col. El Parque, 53390 Naucalpán de Juárez, Estado de México.   *1973*

Tél: 576-79-00. Télex: 1764296 uamme

UNIDAD AZCAPOTZALCO, Avenida San Pablo 180, Col. Reynosa Tamaulipas, Delegación Azcapotzalco, 02200 México, D.F.

Tél: 382-5000

D : sc-ing, soc-hum, sc-arts dess.

UNIDAD IZTAPALAPA, Avenida Michoacán y la Purisima, Col. Vicentina, Delegación Iztapalapa, 09340 México, D.F.

Tél: 686-03-22

D : sc-ing, biol-sa, soc-hum.

UNIDAD XOCHIMILCO, Calz. del Huesco 1100, Col. Villa Quietud, Delegación Coyocán, 04969 México, D.F.

Tél: 594-78-33

D : biol-sa, soc-hum, sc-arts dess.

*Universidad Nacional Autónoma de México, Ciudad Universitaria, 04510 México, D.F. *1551*

Tél: 550-52-15. Télex: 1777429 unamme

F : arc, sc, pol-soc, comp-adm, dr, éco, phil-let, ing, méd, vét-zoo, dent, pysc, ch.

E : trav soc, arts plast, inf-obst, mus.

C : sc-hum.

ESCUELA NACIONAL DE ESTUDIOS PROFESIONALES ACATLÁN, Avenida Alcanfores y San Juan Totoltepec, 53150 Sta. Cruz Acatlán, Estado de México.

Tél: 373-23-18

act, arc, gé civ, pol-adm publ, dr, éco, phil, math appl-inft, hist, péd, jour-commun, lang-lit hisp, socio, rel int, lang anglaise.

ESCUELA NACIONAL DE ESTUDIOS PROFESIONALES ARAGÓN, Prof. Carlos Hank Gonzaléz y Hacienda Rancho-Seco de Aragón, 57170 Ciudad Nezahualcóyotl, Estado de México.

Tél: 796-04-88

arc, dr, dess ind, éco, gé civ, méc-élec, péd, jour-commun, rel-int, socio, inft, plan agr.

ESCUELA NACIONAL DE ESTUDIOS PROFESIONALES IZTACALA, Avenida Los Barrios s/n, Unidad Los Reyes Iztacala, 54090 Tlalnepantla, Estado de México.

Tél: 565-28-51

biol, dent, méd, psyc.

ESCUELA NACIONAL DE ESTUDIOS PROFESIONALES ZARAGOZA, J.C. Bonilla No. 66, Col. Ejército Oriente, 09320 México, D.F.

Tél: 765-11-84

biol, dent, gé ch, psyc, ch phar-biol.

FACULTAD DE ESTUDIOS SUPERIORES CUAUTITLÁN, Conjunto No. 1, Apartado postal 25, Cuautitlán Izcalli, Estado de México.

Tél: 3-01-42

adm, comp, gé agr, alim, méc-élec, vét-zoo, gé ch, phar-biol, ch.

*Universidad Michoacana de San Nicolás de Hidalgo, Edificio "A" Cd. Universitaria, Morelia, Mich.   *1580, 1917*

Tél: 2-05-69

F : méd, dent, dr-soc; agrobiol (Uruapan).

E : gé civ, méc, élec, ch, techn de bois, arc, ch, phar-biol, inf, comp-adm, phy-math, biol, phil, hist, vét-zoo.

E(sup.) : agr (Ciudad Apatzingan).

*Universidad Autónoma de Nayarit, Ciudad de la Cultura "Amado Nervo", 63190 Tepic, Nay.

                         1930, 1969

Tél: 3-38-39

E : dr, com-adm, dent, éco, tour, méd, gé ch, ind; pêch (San Blas); vét-zoo (Compostela).

E(sup.) : agr (Xalisco).

*Universidad Autónoma de Nuevo León, Ciudad Universitaria, 64000 Monterrey, N.L.
1857, 1933
Tél: 76-41-40. Télex: 382989 unanlme
F : biol, inf, méd, dent, psyc, vét-zoo, agr, arc, phy-math, ch, gé civ, méc-élec, comp-adm, dr-soc, éco, phil-let, sport, trav soc, arts vis, sa publ, commun, pol-adm publ, mus (Monterrey); agr (Marin); sc de la terre, for (Linares).

*Universidad Autónoma "Benito Juárez" de Oaxaca, Ciudad Universitaria, Ex-Hacienda "Cinco Señores", 68120 Oaxaca, Oax.
1827, 1955
Tél: 6-46-86. Télex: 18601 ubjome
F : comp-adm publ.
E : arc, dr-soc, méd-chir, vét-zoo, ch, dent, inf.

Universidad de Occidente, Avenida Benito Juárez 435 Pte., 81200 Los Mochis, Sin. *1980*
Tél: 2-66-17
D : psyc, adm, commun, biol, ing, math, dr; math, ing, adm, dr, commun (Culiacán); dr, adm, commun, ing, math (Guasave); psyc, adm (Mazatlán).
I : anth (Mochicahui).

*Universidad Autónoma de Puebla, 4 Sur No. 104, 72000 Puebla, Pue.
1578, 1825, 1937, 1956
Tél: 42-88-02. Télex: 178350 iuapme
adm publ, arc, dent, dr-soc, éco, phil let, phy-math, gé civ, gé ch, ch, méd; vét-zoo (Tecamachalco).

*Universidad Autónoma de Querétaro, Centro Universitario, Cerro de las Campanas, 76010 Querétaro, Qro. *1775*
Tél: 6-32-42
F : ch, comp-adm, psyc, ing.
E : méd, dr, socio, vét.

*Universidad Autónoma de San Luis Potosí, Alvaro Obregón 64, 78000 San Luis Potosí, S.L.P. *1859, 1934*
Tél: 2-34-61. Télex: 13512 unsine
F : ch, comp-adm, éco, sc, ing, dr, méd.
E : stom, psyc, inf; agr (Soledad Díez Gutiérrez).

*Universidad Autónoma de Sinaloa, Angel Flores y Riva Palacio, s/n, 80000 Culiacán, Sin.
1874, 1918, 1941, 1965
Tél: 2-35-50. Télex: 53298 unasme
E : dr-soc, ing, comp-adm, psyc, dent, vét-zoo, éco, méd, dent, phy-math, phil, ch; dr, soc, biol pêch, comp-adm, ing (Mazatlán); dr-pol, ing (Los Mochis); adm agr (Guamúchil).
E(sup.) : agr; agr (Juan José Ríos).

*Universidad de Sonora, Campos de la Universidad, 83000 Hermosillo, Son.
1938, 1942
Tél: 2-10-46
E : dr-soc, psyc-commun, ing, ch, agr-élev; ing, ch, dr-soc (Caborca); ing, ch, dr-soc, agr-élev

(Navojoa).
D : soc, comp-adm, éco, hum, phy, math, géol, ch-biol; géol, soc, comp-adm, éco, ch-biol, phy, math (Caborca); phy, math, géol, soc, comp-adm, éco, ch-biol (Navojoa).

Universidad del Sudeste, Ciudad Universitaria, 24030 Campeche, Camp. *1756, 1957*
Tél: 6-55-03
F : dr, ing.
E(sup.) : ch-biol, com, méd, pol-adm publ, dent.

Universidad «Juárez» Autónoma de Tabasco, Zona de la Cultura, 86020 Villa-hermosa, Tab.
1879, 1958
Tél: 2-29-93
D : éco, adm, soc-hum, sa; ing-techn, sc (Cunduacán); agr, ét fond (Ateapa).

Universidad Autónoma de Tamaulipas, Calle Matamoros 8-altos, 87000 Ciudad Victoria, Tamps. *1956*
Tél: 2-70-00. Télex: 31260 uatyme
F : dr, agr, com-adm, vét-zoo, éd, trav soc; agr (Ciudad Mante); com-adm (Nuevo Laredo); dr-soc, ing, arc, méd, inf, com-adm, dent (Tampico); inf, méd (Mata Moros); ch, agro-ind (Reynosa).
E(sup.) : mus (Tampico).

*Universidad Autónoma de Tlaxcala, Avenida Universidad 1, 90000 Tlaxcala, Tlax. *1976*
Tél: 2-11-67
D : com-adm, dr, idiome, trav soc, dent; ing, ch (Apizaco); agrobiol (Ixtacuixtla).

*Universidad Veracruzana, Zona Universitaria, Lomas del Estadio, 91090 Xalapa, Ver. *1944*
Tél: 8-23-97. Télex: 15516 diuvme
F : adm des aff, agr, anth, arc, bioanalyse, biol, sc de l'atmosphère, électro, inft, arts plast, dent, mus, théât, com, ing, phy, danse, dr, éco, stat, phil, hist, idiome, ch, let espagnoles, math, méd, nutr, péd, psyc, socio; dent, méd, méc-élec (Ciudad Mendoza); adm, ing, com-adm, ch (Coatzacoalcos); adm, biol, arc (Córdoba); méd, dent, trav soc (Minatitlán); com (Nogales); ch (Orizaba); arc, ing, ch, méd, dent, psyc, péd, trav soc (Poza Rica); com, adm, péd, tour, ing, phys, psyc, dent, gé nav, ch, vét-zoo, bioanalyse, méd, nutr, jour (Veracruz); agr, biol, vét-zoo, com (Tuxpan).

*Universidad de Yucatán, Calle 60 x 57, 97000 Mérida, Yuc. *1624, 1922, 1938*
Tél: 24-80-00
F : comp-adm, ing, méd, dent, gé ch, inf, psyc, éco, vét-zoo, arc, éd.
E : dr, math, ch, anth.

*Universidad Autónoma de Zacatecas, Galeana No. 1, 98000 Zacatecas, Zac. *1834, 1968*
Tél: 2-01-60
F : comp-adm.
E : dr, éco, agr, ing, gé mine-mét, vét-zoo,

méd, dent, ch.
Universidad Pedagógica Nacional, Km 1/2 Carretera al Ajusco, Héroes de Padierna, 14200

México, D.F. *1979*
Tél: 571-85-66
Avec 75 Unités dans tout le pays.

Private Institutions — Etablissements privés

Universidad de las Américas A.C., Calle Puebla 223, Col. Roma, 067000 México, D.F. (Sr. Secretario General).
Tél: 525-14-05
E : éco-adm, soc-hum.
Universidad Anáhuac, Lomas de Anáhuac, Apartado postal 10-844, 11000 México, D.F.
Tél: 589-22-00
F : méd, commun, soc, act, psyc, arc, inft, dr, éco, ing, éd, comp-adm, tour, dess ind.
Universidad Anáhuac del Sur, Avenida de las Torres 131, Col. Oliver de los Padres, 01780 México, D.F. *1964*
Tél: 589-22-00
adm des aff, tour, rel ind, dess, act, gé ind, élec-électro, inft.
Universidad de Bajio, A.C., Falda Cerro Gordo s/n, Fracc. Lomas del Campastre, 37150 León, Gto.
Tél: 7-17-40
E : dess ind, tour-hôtel, comp-adm, commun, méd, arc, dr, gé des systèmes, dent, vét-zoo.
Universidad Chapultepéc, A.C., Chihuahua 156, Col. Roma, 06700 México, D.F.
Tél: 584-57-74
E : comp-adm.
Universidad de la Comunicación, José Vasconcelos 70, Col. Condesa, 06140 México, D.F.
Tél: 286-08-49
E : adm-comp.
Universidad «Cristóbal Colón», Carretera Boticaria Km. 1½, 91930 Veracruz, Ver.
Tél: 7-21-89
E : arc, comp-adm, dr, péd, hist d'art, inft, dév agr, psyc.
Universidad Cuauhtémoc, Jalpan y Tlacomulco, Colonia La Paz, 72160 Puebla, Pue.
Tél: 48-20-44
E : ing, comp-adm, dr, dent, psyc.
Universidad Cuetlaxcoapan, S.C., Boulevard Valsequillo y 3B Sur, Residencial Boulevares, 72000 Puebla, Pue.
vét, sc anim.
Universidad Femenina de México, Avenida Constituyentes 151, 11850 México, D.F. *1943*
Tél: 515-13-11
psyc, dr, phil, péd, rel int, ch-phar-biol, trad, interp.
Universidad Femenina de Veracruz-Llave,

Balboa 524, 91910 Veracruz, Ver.
Tél: 7-14-60
trav soc.
Universidad Franco-Mexicana, Colina del Kan 1, Fracc. Boulevares, 53140 Naucalpán, Estado de México.
adm des aff-tour, commun, comp, dr, péd, psyc, rel ind.
Universidad Galilea, A.C., 5 de Mayo 535, Zona Centro, 78000 San Luis Potosí, S.L.P.
E : psyc, inf.
UNIDAD AGUASCALIENTES, Avenida Revolución 804, Esq. Anillo de Circunvalación, Aguascalientes, Ags.
E : dr.

Universidad del Golfo, Obregón 203 Pte., 89000 Tampico, Tamps. *1972*
Tél: 2-92-22
E : éco, comp-adm, dr.
Universidad Autónoma de Guadalajara, Avenida la Patria 1201, 3a, Sección Lomas del Valle, 44100 Guadalajara, Jal. *1935*
Tél: 41-50-51. Télex: 682785 uagpme
F : adm, éco, ch, dr, éd, méd, tour-comp.
E : gé agr, anth, commun, biol, inft, math, inf, phil-let, ing, dent, psyc.
Ce : dess.
Universidad Hispano Mexicana, Emilio Castelar 63 esq. con Eugenio Sué 44, Col. Polanco, 11590 México, D.F.
Tél: 545-17-82
tour, adm, rel int.
*Universidad Iberoamericana, Avenida Cerro de las Torres 395, Col. Campestre Churubusco, 04200 México 21, D.F. *1943*
Tél: 549-35-00
D : art, arc-urb, dess ind & graph, adm, comp, éco, gé civ, méc-élec, systèmes, phy, gé ch, nutr-alim, commun, dr, relig, psyc, socio-pol, phil, hist, let.
PLANTEL GOLFO-CENTRO, Calzada Ignacio Zaragoza 284, Col. Los Pinos, 72960 Puebla, Pue.
Tél: 35-00-74
adm des aff, commun, dess graph, rel ind.
PLANTEL LAGUNA, Pánuco 645, Colonia Navarro, 27010 Torreón, Coah.
Tél: 7-28-43

commun, dr, rel ind, gé civ.

PLANTEL LEÓN, Libramiento Norte Km. 3, 37000 León, Gto.
Tél: (471) 698-98
art-dess, sc de l'homme, ing, éco adm.

PLANTEL NOROESTE, Blvd. Aguacaliente y Privada Pinos, 22000 Tijuana, B.C.
Tél: 86-25-13
arc, dess graph, dr, électro-commun.

Universidad Intercontinental, Avenida Insurgentes Sur 4135, 14420 México, D.F.
Tél: 573-85-44
E : arc, commun, comp-adm, dr, phil, dent, péd, psyc, théo, rel tour, dess.

Universidad José Vasconcelos, Bruno Martínez 203-207 Nte., 34000 Victoria de Durango, Dgo.
psyc, commun.

Universidad Kino, Marruecos Final Oriente, Col. Casa Blanca, 83070 Hermosillo, Son.
comp publ, adm des aff, éd, jour.

*Universidad La Salle, A.C., Avenida Benjamin Franklin 47, 06140 México, D.F.
Tél: 516-99-60. Télex: 1772861 ulsame
E : arc, comp-adm, dr, méd, phil, ch, ing, phil, relig.

Universidad Lasallista Benavente, Avenida Universidad s/n, 38040 Celaya, Gto.
Tél: 2-45-08
E : dr.

Universidad Latina, A.C., Chihuahua 202, 06700 México, D.F.
Tél: 574-18-09
comp, adm.

Universidad Latinoamericana, S.C., Gabriel Mancera 1402, Col. de Valle, 03100 México, D.F.
Tél: 575-04-11
E : dent, commun-rel publ, comp-adm.

Universidad de Matamoros, Diagonal Cuauhtémoc y 7a, Zona Centro, 87300 Matamoros, Tamps.
E : commun, dr-soc, comp-adm, éco, dent, arc, agr.

Universidad de Mayab, Km. 15.5 Carretera Mérida-Progreso, 97000 Mérida, Yuc.
E : adm-comp, dr, inft, commun soc, psyc.

Universidad de Mazatlán, A.C., Guillermo Nelson 100 Desp. 104, 82000 Mazatlán, Sin.
méc adm, adm des aff, dr, comp publ, systèmes de inft adm.

Universidad Mexicana del Noreste, Quinta Zona 409, Col. Caracol, 64810 Monterrey, N.L.
Tél: 40-12-05
D : adm-soc, ing.

Universidad Mexicana de Tecnología, Calz. de Tlalpan 450, Col. Viaducto Piedad, 08200 México, D.F.
Tél: 530-98-04
adm des aff, comp, inft.

Universidad México Americana del Norte, Guerrero y Plutarco Elías Calles 1317, Col. de Prado, 88560 Ciudad Reynosa, Tamps.
Tél: 2-20-86
E : méd, dent, vét-zoo, éd, comp-adm, agr, let espagnoles, inft, arc, commun, dr, ing.

Universidad Miguel Alemán, Antonio Alzate y Press Palmito, Col. Hercilia, 88300 Ciudad Miguel Alemán, Tamps.
F : arc, com-adm, dr-soc.

Universidad de Montemorelos, Apartado postal 16, Montemorelos, N.L.
Tél: 3-30-80. Télex: 30104
E : méd, éd, comp-adm, inf, ba, nutr, ch-biol, théo.

*Universidad de Monterrey, San Pedro 100 Nte., Col. del Valle, 64020 Garza García, N.L. *1960*
Tél: 78-50-38
D : éco adm, sc nat & exactes, éd, art, hum-soc, sa, jur.

Universidad Motolinía A.C., Cerrado de Ameyalco 227, Col. del Valle 03100 México, D.F.
1919, 1974
Tél: 523-48-13
E : dr, ch.

Universidad Motolinía del Pedregal, Avenida de las Fuentes 525, Pedregal de San Angel, 01900 México, D.F.
E : dess.

Universidad del Noreste, Prol. Avenida Hidalgo s/n Km. 137, Apartado postal 469, Tampico, Tamps.
Tél: 3-58-31
E : méd, biol, commun-rel publ, psyc, ch, dent.

Universidad Autónoma del Noreste, Monclova 1430-2, 25280 Saltillo, Coah.
Tél: 2-44-22

UNIDAD SALTILLO, Enrique Reyna y Américas Unidad, Saltillo, Coah.
pol-adm publ, adm des aff, adm agr, gé ind adm, adm des ressources hum, comp publ, éd, socio, biol, psyc, systèmes inft, arc, gé ind et des systèmes, méc adm, tour, dr.

UNIDAD MONCLOVA, Blvd. Benito Juárez y Avenida de los Reyes s/n, Monclova, Coah.
adm des aff, gé ind adm, comp publ, éd, adm des ressources hum, psyc, arc, tour.

UNIDAD TORREÓN, Avenida Morelos 946 pte., Torreón, Coah.
adm des aff, adm agr, adm fin, gé ind adm, comp publ, banc-fin, éd, psyc, optom, arc, systèmes inft, tour, adm des ressources hum.

UNIDAD PIEDRAS NEGRAS, Avenida E. Carranza 1300, Col. Mondo Nuevo, Piedras Negras, Coah.
adm des aff, comp publ, éd, adm agr, systèmes inft, psyc, adm des ressources hum.

Unidad Sabinas, Juárez y Lamadrid 853 Pt., Sabinas, Coah.
comp publ, adm des aff, adm agr, adm des ressources hum.

Unidad Ciudad Acuña, Guerrero Villaldana s/n, Ciudad Acuña, Coah.
adm des aff, comp publ.

Universidad del Norte, Venustiano Carranza 1350 Nte., 64000 Monterrey, N.L.
D : ing, adm.

Universidad Nuevo Mundo, Bosque Moctezuma 124, 53920 Fracc. La Herradura, Estado de México.
Tél: 89-17-00
infor, dr, dess graph, dess ind, phil, méc-ind, psyc, adm des aff.

Universidad Panamericana, Augusto Rodín 498, Col. Mixcoac, 03910 México, D.F.
Tél: 563-00-22
E : adm-fin, dr, éco, phil, ing, péd, comp.

Unidad Guadalajara, Avenida Circunvalación Oriente 49, Ciudad Granja, 45010 Zapopar, Jal.
adm-fin, comp, dr, rel ind, gé ind.

Universidad Popular Autónoma del Estado de Puebla, Edificio Central, 21 Sur 1103, 72160 Pue.
Tél: 49-08-80. Télex: 178432
D : éco adm, sa, techn, agr, hum.

*****Universidad Regiomontana, A.C.**, Villagrán Sur 328, 64000 Monterrey, N.L. *1951, 1969*
Tél: 42-52-94. Télex: 382316 uracme
D : hum-soc, ing-sc exactes, arc-dess, commun-diffusion cult.

Universidad Regional "Miguel Hidalgo", 16 de Septiembre 102 Ote., Col. Arbol Grande, 89490 Ciudad Madero, Tamps.
Tél: 5-05-85
comp publ adm, phys, inf, trav soc, tour.

Universidad de Saltillo, Calle Juárez Ote., 595 25000 Saltillo, Coah.
comp publ, adm des aff, pol-adm, publ, dr, let anglais, psyc, commun.

Universidad de la Sierra, A.C., Avenida de los Técnicos s/n, Fracc. El Paraíso, 73160 Huauchinango, Pue.
adm des aff, comp publ, dr.

Universidad Regional del Sureste, Prolongación 20 de Noviembre s/n, Col. Alemán, 68120 Oaxaca, Oax.
Tél: 6-86-22
E : arc, dent, adm-comp, dr-soc, méd, psyc, ch.

Universidad Tecnológica de México, Avenida Marina Nacional 162, Col. Anáhuac, 11320 México, D.F. *1966*
Tél: 399-20-00
F : adm-soc.
E : dent.

Universidad del Tepeyac, A.C., Callao 842, Col.

Lindavista, 07300 México, D.F.
Tél: 781-40-33
E : arc, adm, comp publ, commun, dr, tour.

Universidad del Valle de Atemajac, Avenida López Mateos Sur y Rincón de los Ahuehuetes 1988, 45050 Guadalajara, Jal.
Tél: 22-56-22
D : soc-hum, ing, éco-adm.

Universidad Valle del Bravo, Herón Ramírez 155 Nte., Col. Rodríguez, 88630 Col. Reynosa, Tamps.

Unidad Reynosa.
adm des aff, comp publ, dr, commun, tour, let espagnoles, psyc, biol, méd-chir-obst, dent, gé agr adm, gé civ, méc-élec, élec adm, pét, gé agr-zoo, arc.

Unidad Tampico.
systèmes inft, tour, gé ind adm, comp publ, adm des aff, rel ind.

Unidad Monte.
tour, comp publ, adm des aff, psyc, commun, dr.

Unidad Ciudad Victoria.
méd-chir-obst, méd-chir-dent, tour, psyc, let espagnoles.

Unidad Nuevo Laredo.
commun, rel ind, dr, méd-chir-dent, psyc, gé agr-zoo.

Universidad del Valle de México, Tehuantepec 250, Col. Roma Sur, 06470 México, D.F. *1960*
Tél: 584-77-55

Plantel Lomas Verdes, Avenida de las Aves, 53220 Naucalpan, Estado de México.
éco adm, soc, phy-math.

Plantel San Angel, San Jerónimo 82, San Angel, 0100 México, D.F.
adm des aff, tour, systèmes inft adm.

Plantel San Rafael, Sadi Carnot 57, Col. San Rafael, 06470 México, D.F.
éco adm, soc, phy-math.

Plantel Tlalpan, San Juan de Dios 6, Col. Huipulco, 14380 México, D.F.
éco adm, soc, phy-math.

Plantel Xochimilco, Avenida México 6285, Col. San Marcos, 16050 México, D.F.
éco adm.

Universidad del Valle de Puebla, A.C., Avenida 12 Oriente 204, 72000 Puebla, Pue.
Tél: 40-61-35
adm, comp publ, rel ind, tour, inft adm.

Universidad del Valle de Toluca, Calle 21 de Marzo 101, Toluca, Estado de México.
Tél: 8-00-56
éco, adm, arc, comp, soc.

Universidad Ejecutivos de Ventas y Meradotecnia de México, A.C., Río Niágara 26, Col. Cuauhtémoc, 06500 México, D.F.
march.

Universidad Villa Rica, Avenida Díaz Mirón

2242, 91700 Veracruz, Ver.
Tél: 7-53-64
comp-adm, dr, éco, psyc.

Universidad Xicotepetl, A.C., Aldama 122, 73080
Col. Xicotepec de Juárez, Pue.
vét-zoo, gé agr-plantes, adm des aff agr.

OTHER INSTITUTIONS — AUTRES INSTITUTIONS

Technical Education — Enseignement technique

*Centro de Enseñanza Técnica y Superior, Calz.
CETYS s/n, Apartado postal 797, Mexicali,
B.C.
Tél: 8-1801
E : comp-adm, ing; comp-adm ing, psyc
(Tijuana); comp-adm, ing (Enseñada).
Centro de Enseñanza Técnica Industrial,
Avenida del Chaco 3223, Fraccionamiento
Providencia, 44620 Guadalajara, Jal.
Tél: 47-64-29
gé ind, méc, processus.
Escuela de Ingeniería Municipal, Dr. Lucio
191A, México, D.F.
Tél: 588-17-91
*Instituto Politécnico Nacional, Unidad Pro-
fesional Zacateco, 07738 México, D.F.   1937
Tél: 754-41-02
E : biol, méd homéopathique.
E (sup.) : élec-méc, ing-arc, gé ch-ind, gé tex,
phy-math, méd, biol, com-adm, éco, tour.
    Centro Interdisciplinario de Ciencias de
    la Salud, El Hacienda del Mayorazgo,
    Milpa Alta, Apartado postal 5, México 25,
    D.F.
    inf, méd, nutr, dent, optom, trav soc.
    Unidad Profesional Interdisciplinaria
    de Ingeniekría y Ciencias Sociales y
    Administrativas, Calle del The 950, Col.
    Granjas México, 08400 México, D.F.
    adm ind, infor, trans, gé ind.
*Instituto Tecnológico Autónomo de México, Río
Hondo 1, Col. Tizapán-San Angel, Delegación
Alvaro Obregón, 01000, México, D.F.
Tél: 550-93-00
comp publ, adm, soc, éco, math appl, dr, act,
stat, inft.
Instituto Tecnológico Mexicano, 5 de Febrero 91,
México, D.F.
Tél: 512-16-23
comp, adm des aff.
Instituto Tecnológico y de Estudios Superiores de
Monterrey, Avenida Eugenio Garza Sada
2501, Sucursal de Correos «J», Monterrey,
N.L.   1943, 1958
Tél: 58-20-00. Télex: 382975
D : adm-soc, agr-mar, sa, sc-hum, ing-arc.
Aussi unités à: Chiapas, Chihuahua, Colimas,

Ciudad Juárez, Irapuato, Laguna, León,
Mazatlán, Estado de México, Morelos, Obre-
gón, Querétaro, Saltillo, San Luis Potosí,
Sinaloa, Sonora Norte, Tampico, Toluca,
Veracruz, Zacatecas.
*Instituto Tecnológico y de Estudios Superiores
de Occidente, Avenida Niños Héroes 1342–8,
Guadalajara, Jal.   1957
Tél: 21-40-74
D : éco-adm, ing.
E : arc, psyc, commun.
Instituto Tecnológico y de Estudios Superiores
Potosino, Madero 335, Apartado postal 743,
San Luis Potosí, S.L.P.
comp.
Tél: 3-37-35
Instituto Tecnológico de Sonora, 5 de Febrero 818
Sur, 85000 Ciudad Obregón, Son.
Tél: 4-14-29
adm comp, éd, gé agr, gé civ, gé ind, gé ind-
systèmes, méc-élec, gé ch, vét-zoo, psyc, ch;
adm, comp, gé agr, gé civ, gé ind, gé ind-
systèmes, biotech, gé ch, ch (Navojoa); adm,
comp, gé ind-systèmes, ch (Guaymas).
Instituto Tecnológico Agropecuario No. 20,
Km. 18 Carretera Ags. S.L.P., 20270 Agua-
scalientes, Ags.
Tél: 5-56-60
phytotec.
Instituto Tecnológico Agropecuario No. 4, Km.
24.5 Carretera Tampico-Mante, Altamira,
Tamps.
Tél: 3-36-04
phyto.
Instituto Tecnológico Agropecuario No. 5, Ejido
China, 24000 Campeche, Camp.
phytotec, zoo.
Instituto Tecnológico No. 16, Avenida Insur-
gentes s/n, Apartado postal 207, 77000
Chetumal, Q. Roo.
Tél: 2-15-02
Instituto Tecnológico Agropecuario No. 25,
Domicilio Conocido, Municipio Pangarabato,
40660 Cd. Altamirano, Gro.
phytotec, dév rur.
Instituto Tecnológico Agropecuario No. 18, Prol.
de Pípila s/n, Mpio Ursulo Galván, 91680 Cd.

Cardel, Ver.
Tél: 2-91-13
phytotec, zoo.

Instituto Tecnológico Agropecuario No. 24, Km. 14.5 Carretera Cuauhtémoc, Col. Alvaro Obregón, 31500 Ciudad Cuauhtémoc, Chih.
phytotec, adm.

Instituto Tecnológico Agropecuario No. 31, Dom. Conocido, Rancho J.B., Comitán, Chis.
zoo, dév rur.

Instituto Tecnológico Agropecuario No. 22, Km. 4 de la Carretera Valles-Ingenio Plan de Ayala, 79000 Cd. Valles, S.L.P.
Tél: 2-32-75
phytotec, zoo.

Instituto Tecnológico Agropecuario No. 1, Carretera Durango-México Km. 22, Apartado postal 393, 34000 Durango, Dgo.
Tél: 2-95-56
phytotec, zoo, for, adm.

Instituto Tecnológico Agropecuario No. 6, Apartado postal 94, 43000 Huejutla de Reyes, Hgo.
phytotec, zoo.

Instituto Tecnológico Agropecuario No. 8, Centenario 61, San Pedro Comitancillo, Oax.
phytotec, zoo.

Instituto Tecnológico Agropecuario No. 13, Apartado postal No. 26, 71600 Santiago Pinotepa Nacional, Oax.
phytotec, zoo.

Instituto Tecnológico Agropecuario No. 12, Apartado postal 5, Ejido Emiliare Zapata, 67700 Linares, N.L.
phytotec, zoo, ind.

Instituto Tecnológico Agropecuario No. 2, Carretera Mérida-Motul Km. 16.3, Apartado postal 53-D, 97110 Mérida, Yuc.
Tél: 3-10-40
phytotec, zoo, dév rur.

Instituto Tecnológico Agropecuario No. 9, Cerro de la Trilla, Apartado postal 18, 62600 Miacatlán, Mor.
Tél: 4-34-00
phytotec, zoo.

Instituto Tecnológico Agropecuario No. 7, Km. 7 Carretera Morelia-Guanajuato, Apartado postal 39 "B", 58000 Morelia, Mich.
zoo, for, dév rur, phytotec.

Instituto Tecnológico Agropecuario No. 28, Km. 15 Carretera Villa Hermosa Fontera, Villahermosa, Tab.
phytotec, zoo.

Instituto Tecnológico Agropecuario No. 29, Km. 7.5 Carretera San Diego, 90122 San Diego. Xocoyucán, Tlax.
ind, zoo.

Instituto Tecnológico Agropecuario No. 23, Ex-Hacienda de Nazareno, Sta. Cruz Xoxocotlan,

Oax.
Tél: 6-18-94
phytotec, zoo.

Instituto Tecnológico Agropecuario No. 27, Pozo de Ibarra, 63300 Santiago Ixcuintla, Nay.
phytotec, dév rur.

Instituto Tecnológico Agropecuario No. 19, Apartado postal 79, 97700 Tizimín, Yuc.
Tél: 3-21-88
zoo, dév rur.

Instituto Tecnológico Agropecuario No. 26, Domicilio Conocido, Km. 4 Carretera Tlacomulco-San Miguel Coyutlán, Municipio Tlacomulco de Zúñiga, 45640 Tlacomulco, Jal.
zoo, phytotec, adm.

Instituto Tecnológico Agropecuario No. 10, Carretera Torreón, Km. 14.5, La Partida 27000 Torreón, Coah.
phytotec, zoo, dév rur.

Instituto Tecnológico Agropecuario No. 3, Daniel Soto No. 370, Esq. Sebastián Ortíz, Apartado postal 29, 68300 Tuxtepec, Oax.
Tél: 5-16-97
phytotec, zoo.

Instituto Tecnológico Agropecuario No. 21, Block No. 611, Municipio de Bacum, 85000 Valle del Yaqui, Son.
phytotec, adm, ind.

Instituto Tecnológico Agropecuario No. 30, Ejido el Mezquite, Villa de Arista, S.L.P.
phytotec, zoo.

Instituto Tecnológico Forestal de El Salto No. 1, Mesa del Tecnológico s/n, Apartado postal 59, El Salto, 34950 P. Nuevo, Dgo.
for.

Instituto Tecnológico del Mar, Km. 12 Carretera Internacional, Veracruz-México, Vía Córdoba, 94290 Boca del Río, Ver.
Tél: 6-01-39
adm des aff mar, pech ind, alim mar.

Instituto Tecnológico del Mar, Apartado postal 742, 85480 Quaymas, Son.

Instituto Tecnológico del Mar, Apartado postal 557, 82000 Mizatlán, Sin.

Instituto Tecnológico de Acapulco, Apartado postal 600, 39300 Acapulco, Gro.
Tél: 4-6-19
rel com, gé électro, gé bioch, arc, adm tour, alim.

Instituto Tecnológico de Aguascalientes, Blvd. Adolfo López Mateos, Apartado postal 263, 20000 Aguascalientes, Ags.
Tél: 5-01-51
gé ind, adm des aff, inft, élec, méc thermique, prod ch.

Instituto Tecnológico de Apizaco, Calz. Instituto Tecnológico s/n, Apartado postal 19, 90300 Apizaco, Tlax.
Télex: 128857 itrcme

gé ind, gé civ, adm des aff, dév comté, prod.

Instituto Tecnológico de Campeche, Apartado postal 347, 24500 Campeche, Camp.
gé ind, adm des aff, arc, prod.

Instituto Tecnológico de Celaya, Avenida Tecnológico Irrigación, Apartado postal 57, 38010 Celaya, Gto. *1958*
Tél: 2-10-23. Télex: 12857 itrcme
gé ind, adm des aff, gé bioch, alim, systèmes inft, prod, gé ch.

Instituto Tecnológico de Cerro Azul, Avenida Hidalgo s/n, Col. Campo Comercial, 92510 Cerro Azul, Ver.
Tél: 2-07-41
adm des aff, gé civ, électroméc.

Instituto Tecnológico de Chetumal, Avenida Andrés Q. Roo, Esq., Insurgentes Col. Centro, Ciudad Chetumal, Apartado postal 267, 77000 Othón Blanco, Q. Roo.
Tél: 2-10-19
adm des aff, gé civ, biol, adm tour, comp, gé ind, élec.

Instituto Tecnológico de Chihuahua, Avenida Tecnológico 2909, Apartado postal 119, 31310 Chihuahua, Chih. *1948*
Tél: 3-74-74. Télex: 349682 itchme
gé ind, mét, méc, élec, électro, prod, gé ch, rel ind, rel com.

Instituto Tecnológico de Chilpancingo, Avenida de la Juventud s/n, Col. Burócrata, Chilpancingo, Gro.
comp, inft, gé civ, géol.

Instituto Tecnológico de Ciudad Guzmán, Carretera al Fresnita s/n, Apartado 150, 49100 Ciudad Guzmán, Jal.
Tél: 2-17-18
adm des aff, électroméc, gé ind, rel ind, inft, comp, élec.

Instituto Tecnológico de Ciudad Juárez, Km. 6 Carretera Panamericana, 32000 Ciudad Juárez, Chih. *1964*
Tél: 7-36-46. Télex: 333888 itrjme
adm des aff, adm tour, comp, électro-systèmes, gé ind, méc, élec, électro, prod, électroméc.

Instituto Tecnológico de Ciudad Madero, Calle 1 de Mayo y Sor Juana Inés de la Cruz, 89440 Ciudad Madero, Tamps.
Tél: 5-21-53
gé ind, élec, méc, gé ch ind.

Instituto Tecnológico de Ciudad Victoria, Boulevard Lic. Emilio Portes Gil y Camino a La Libertad, Apartado postal 175, Ciudad Victoria, Tamps.
Tél: 2-43-58
gé civ, gé ind, biol, inft, prod.

Instituto Tecnológico de Colima, Avenida Tecnológico 1, 28000 Colima, Col.
Tél: 2-63-93. Télex: 62234 intrme
gé ind, gé bioch, adm des aff, tour, arc, inft.

Instituto Tecnológico de Culiacán, Avenida Ing. Juan de Dios Bátiz s/n y R. Corral, Apartado postal 1273 Culiacán, Sin.
Tél: 3-38-04. Télex: 665436 itrcme
gé ind, inft, gé bioch, alim, élec.

Instituto Tecnológico de Durango, Boulevard Felipe Pescador 1830, Apartado postal 465, 34080 Durango, Dgo.
Tél: 1-53-86. Télex: 66311 itrdme
gé ind, gé civ, inft, gé bioch, alim, méc, élec, électro, prod, gé ch.

Instituto Tecnológico de Hermosillo, Apartado postal 518, 83170 Hermosillo, Son.
Tél: 4-58-75
inft, gé ind, rel com, méc, électro.

Instituto Tecnológico de Juchitán, Carretera Panamericana, Apartado postal 63, 70000 Juchitán de Zaragoza, Oax.
Tél: 2-00-42
gé ind, gé civ, élec, électro, comp, dév comté, élec, prod, électroméc.

Instituto Tecnológico de Jiquilpán, Avenida de Presidente Lázaro Cárdenas 366, Jiquilpán, Mich.
Tél: 3-02-37
gé ind, comp, gé bioch, rel com, alim, prod, gé ch.

Instituto Tecnológico de La Laguna, Bulevard Revolución y Calz. Cuauhtémoc, Apartado postal 681, 27000 Torreón, Coah.
Tél: 3-18-23. Télex: 32834 itrlme
gé ind, méc, élec, électro, prod, gé ch.

Instituto Tecnológico de La Paz, Apartado postal 243, 23050 La Paz, B.C. Sur.
Tél: 2-24-24. Télex: 52516 itrme
gé civ, gé alim, comp, adm des aff, inft, bioch, gé ind, plan.

Instituto Tecnológico de León, Carretera a León-Silao, Avenida Tecnológico s/n, Fracc. Julián de Obregón, 37000 León, Gto.
Tél: 4-08-19
gé ind, adm ind, prod, électroméc.

Instituto Tecnológico de Los Mochis, Blvd. Juan de Dios Bátiz y Prolongación 20 de Noviembre, Apartado postal 766, 81200 Los Mochis, Sin.
Tél: 2-58-58. Télex: 53205 itrlme
adm des aff, comp, gé bioch, arc, gé ind, alim, gé ch.

Instituto Tecnológico de Matamoros, Km. 6, Carretera Lauro Villar, 87490 Matamoros, Tamps.
Tél: 2-41-62
gé ind, gé civ, rel ind, électroméc, trav urb, élec, gé ch, électroméc, prod.

Instituto Tecnológico de Mérida, Carretera Mérida-Progreso Km. 5, Apartado postal 561, 97118 Mérida, Yuc.
Tél: 27-23-00. Télex: 753760 itrmme
gé ind, adm des aff, gé bioch, gé civ, adm tour,

alim, systèmes inft, prod, gé ch, électro.

Instituto Tecnológico de Mexicali, Blvd. Lázaro Cárdenas, Col. P. Elías Calles, Mexicali, B.C.
Tél: 8-19-81
gé ind, élec, électro, ch, contrôle.

Instituto Tecnológico de Minatitlán, Km. 27, Carretera Transístmica, Apartado postal 777, 96700 Minatitlán, Ver.
Tél: 4-16-85
adm des aff, électroméc, gé ind, instruments, gé ch, prod.

Instituto Tecnológico de Morelia, Avenida Tecnológico 1500, Apartado postal 262, 58120 Morelia, Mich.
Tél: 2-15-70. Télex: 69654 itmlme
gé ind, élec, prod, sidérurgie, adm tour.

Instituto Tecnológico de Nogales, Calz. de los Nogales s/n, Apartado postal 796, 84000 Nogales, Son.
Tél: 2-10-88. Télex: 54125 itxnme
gé ind, adm des aff, gé civ, rel ind, adm tour, dév comté, électro, prod.

Instituto Tecnológico de Nuevo Laredo, Avenida Reforma Sur 2007, 88000 Nuevo Laredo, Tamps.
Tél: 2-34-44
gé civ, gé ind, adm tour, élec, électroméc, gé thermique, prod.

Instituto Tecnológico de Nuevo León, Avenida Eloy Cavazos s/n, Ciudad Guadalupe Nuevo León, 67170 Guadalupe, N.L.
Tél: 79-10-49. Télex: 36658 itnlme
gé ind, adm des aff, électro, systèmes inft, prod.

Instituto Tecnológico de Oaxaca, Calz. Tecnológico s/n, 68030 Oaxaca, Oax.
Tél: 6-17-22
gé ind, gé civ, adm tour, adm des aff, élec, méc thermique, gé ch, gé structures.

Instituto Tecnológico de Orizaba, Prol. Oriente 9 s/n, Apartado postal 324, 94320 Orizaba, Ver.
Tél: 4-40-96. Télex: 15439 itome
gé ind, inft, méc thermique, prod, gé ch.

Instituto Tecnológico de Pachuca, Apartado postal 276, 42080 Venta Prieta, Hgo.
Tél: 2-50-20
gé ind, gé civ, gé ch.

Instituto Tecnológico de Parral, Avenida Tecnológico s/n, Apartado postal 216, 33850 Parral, Chih.
Tél: 2-24-52
gé ind, comp, adm des aff, électroméc, mine, prod, gé ch, électroméc.

Instituto Tecnológico de Piedras Negras, Avenida Tecnológico Prolongación Poniente, 26080 Piedras Negras, Coah.
Tél: 2-10-41. Télex: 37258 itpnme
gé ind, adm des aff, électro, comp, plan.

Instituto Tecnológico de Puebla, Avenida Tecno-

lógico 420, Apartado postal 1145, 72000 Puebla, Pue.
Tél: 42-96-19
gé ind, élec, électroméc, dess.

Instituto Tecnológico de Querétaro, Avenida Tecnológico y Calle Marino Escobedo, 76000 Querétaro, Qro.   *1967*
Tél: 2-22-81. Télex: 121625 itqme
gé ind, gé arc, arc, adm, systèmes inft, méc, élec, prod.

Instituto Tecnológico de Saltillo, Avenida Universidad y Boulevard V. Carranza 2400, 25280 Saltillo, Coah.
Tél: 2-31-01. Télex: 38165 itrsme
gé ind, mét, méc, élec, prod.

Instituto Tecnológico de San Luis Potosí, Km. 1, Carretera San Luis Potosí Río Verde, 78070 San Luis Potosí, S.L.P.
Tél: 2-32-75. Télex: 13669
gé ind, adm tour, systèmes inft, rel ind, gé civ, élec, méc, électro, prod.

Instituto Tecnológico de Tapachula, Km. 2, Carretera Tapachula-Puerto Madero, Tapachula, Chis.
gé civ, gé ind.

Instituto Tecnológico de Tepic, Carretera Tepic-Guadalajara, Apartado postal 343, 63000 Tepic, Nay.
Tél: 2-60-83. Télex: 61155 inteme
rel com, gé civ, gé bioch, arc, gé ind, alim, dév.

Instituto Tecnológico de Tehuacán, Apartado postal 247, 75700 Tehuacán, Pue.
Tél: 2-24-48
gé civ, adm des aff, gé ind, gé bioch, comp, alim.

Instituto Tecnológico de Tijuana, Col. Fracc. Tomás de Aquino, 22000 Tijuana, B.C.
Tél: 82-10-55. Télex: 566796 itrtme
rel com, rel ind, électroméc, gé civ, bioch, gé ind, comp, arc, inft, alim, gé structures, trav urb, électro, prod.

Instituto Tecnológico de Tlalnepantla, Avenida Tecnológico s/n, Apartado postal 750, 54070 Tlalnepantla, Edo. de México.
Tél: 5-65-67-77
gé ind, élec, méc, électroméc, adm, prod.

Instituto Tecnológico de Toluca, Rancho de La Virgen Metepec, Apartado postal 890, 50000 Toluca, Estado de México.
Tél: 6-03-24. Télex: 174403 itrtme
électroméc, méc, gé ind, prod, gé ch, adm.

Instituto Tecnológico de Tuxtepec, Calz. Tecnológico s/n, Col. Centro, 68300 San Juan B. Tuxtepec, Oax.
électroméc, gé civ, comp, adm des aff, gé bioch, alim, comp, dév comté, adm.

Instituto Tecnológico de Tuxtla Gutiérrez, Carretera Panamericana Km. 1080, 29020 Tuxtla Gutiérrez, Chis.

Tél: 2-18-99
gé bioch, prod nat, gé ind, élec, prod.

Instituto Tecnológico de Veracruz, Circunvalación Norte e Icazo, 96700 Veracruz, Ver.
1944, 1957
Tél: 2-41-77. Télex: 151626 dirvme
gé ind, gé bioch, systèmes inft, alim, élec,
électro, prod, gé ch.

Instituto Tecnológico de Villahermosa, Carretera
a Frontera Km. 3, Apartado postal 424, 86000
Villahermosa, Tab.
Tél: 2-48-65

gé bioch, gé ind, ch, adm des aff, gé civ, alim,
dév comté.

Instituto Tecnológico de Zacatecas, Domicilio
Conocido, "La Escondida", 99559 Zacatecas,
Zac.
Tél: 2-41-08
gé ind, adm des aff, arc, mét, prod, électro.

Instituto Tecnológico de Zacatepec, Calz. Tecnológico 27, Apartado postal 45, 63780 Zacatepec, Morelos.
Tél: 2-13-94
gé ind, gé civ, adm tour, trav urb, prod, gé ch.

Professional Education−Enseignement professionnel

**Asociación Satélite de Estudios Culturales «Sor
Juana»** A.C., Colibri 6 Primera Sección de
Lomas Verdes, 53120 Naucalpán de Juárez,
Estado de México.

Centro de Arte Mexicano, A.C., Cascada 180,
Pedregal San Angel, 01900 México, D.F.
Tél: 568-32-44
hist de l'art.

**Centro de Bachilleres y Estudios Profesionales de
Salamanca**, Camino la Ordeña Km. 1, Fracc. el
Monte Apartado postal 462, Salamanca, Gto.
gé ind, arc, rel ind, psyc de trav.

Centro de Educación Profesional, S.C., Puebla
162, Col. Roma, 06700 México, D.F.
Tél: 514-26-54
adm des aff.

Centro Escolar «Benito Juárez», 5 de Febrero
No. 443 Sur, Ciudad Obregón, Son.
Tél: 3-32-82
trav soc.

Centro Escolar «Miguel Alemán V», Calle 27 No.
150, Fracc. San Miguel 97140 Mérida, Yuc.
comp publ, phys.

**Centro de Estudios en Ciencias de la Comunica-
ción**, Valle 23, Pedregal de San Angel, 01900
México, D.F.
Tél: 559-36-04
publicité, rel publ.

**Centro de Estudios Superiores de Diseño de
Monterrey**, Padre Mier 1545 Poniente, Col.
Obispado, 64000 Monterrey, N.L.
Tél: 43-35-63
dess.

**Centro de Estudios Superiores del Estado de
Sonora**, Americas y Tetabiate 2, Col. Valle
Verde, 83200 Hermosillo, Son.
D : éco, sc-ing, ch-biol.

**Centro de Estudios Superiores de Gua-muchil,
S.C.**, Silverio Trueba y Fernando Amilpa,
Guamuchil, Sin.
E : comp-adm, dr.

Centro de Estudios Superiores de Oaxaca, M.
Alcalá 801-A, 68000 Oaxaca, Oax.

commun.

Centro de Estudios Superiores, Andador 16 de
Septiembre 74 Oriente, 76000 Querétaro, Qro.
Tél: 4-17-79
trav soc.

**Centro de Estudios Superiores Turísticos, A.C.
(Coahuila)**, Presidente Cárdenas 651, 25000
Saltillo, Coah.
tour.

**Centro de Estudios Tecnológicos y Universitarios,
S.C.**, Guillermo Prieto No. 2, Col. San Rafael,
06470 México, D.F.
march.

Centro de Estudios Universitarios de Monterrey,
Avenida Hidalgo Pte. 546, 64000 Monterrey,
N.L.
E ; dr, vét, agr, psyc, com-adm, péd, ing, sa.

Centro de Estudios Universitarios de Xochicalco,
Avenida A. López Mateos 1277, Apartado
postal 1377, Ensenada, B.C. Norte.
E : méd, vét-zoo, arc, psyc.

**Centro de Investigaciones y Estudios Superiores
en Antropología Social**, General Victoria 75,
Apartado postal 22-048, Tlalpan, 14000
México, D.F.
soc, ling ethnique.

**Centro Sindical de Estudios Superiores de
la CTM, A.C.**, Camelia 108, Fracc. Rancho
Cortez, Apartado postal 134-C, Sucursal C.,
62050 Cuernavaca, Mor.
adm de trav, éco trav, dr.

Centro Universitario Hispanoamericano,
Avenida Cruz del Sol 3, Esq. Avenida Cerro de
las Torres, 53103 Col. Satélite, Estado de
México.
Tél: 393-15-33
adm des aff, comp publ, dr, péd; adm des aff,
comp publ, dr, rel tour, péd (Coacalco).

Centro Universitario Kennedy, Insurgentes 1616,
San Jerónimo, Apartado postal 1803, Monterrey, N.L.
adm des aff.

Centro Universitario de Mazatlán, Calle Cruz

No. 2, Apartado postal 275, Mazatlán, Sin.
adm des aff, comp, psyc.

Centro Universitario del Noreste, A.C., Lic.
Guillermo Martínez Domínguez 116, 87360 H.
Matamoros, Tamps.
Tél: 3-88-35
adm des aff, comp publ, psyc, dr, gé agr adm.

Centros Universitarios de Ciencias Humanas, Ex-
Convento de San Jerónimo, Plaza de San
Jerónimo 47, 06080 México 3, D.F.
Tél: 5-108999
hum.

El Colegio de México, Camino al Ajusco 20,
10740 México, D.F.   *1940*
Tél: 568-60-33. Télex: 1777585 colme
rel int, adm pub.

Colegio San Agustín, A.C., Calle 58 No. 484,
97000 Mérida, Yuc.
tour.

**Colegio Superior Agropecuario del Estado de
Guerrero**, Carretera Iguala Tuxpan Km. 2,
40000 Iguala, Gro.
gé agr.

Complejo Educativo Hispanoamericano, A.C.,
Avenida Morelos 220, Col. Peñitas, 37180
León, Gto.
E : psyc éd, éd, formation.

Colegio Español de México, Artículo 123 No. 44,
México, D.F.
Tél: 5212-98-34
comp.

**Escuela Superior de Administración de Institu-
ciones**, Canteras de Oxtopulco 16, 04310
México, D.F.
Tél: 548-41-79
adm.

**Escuela Superior de Administración de Recursos
Naturales**, Blvd. Ortíz Mena s/n, Col. Centro,
33800 Hidalgo del Parral, Chih.
Tél: 2-12-09
adm des ressources naturelles.

**Escuela Superior de Agricultura «Hermanos
Escobar»**, Apartado postal 29, Ciudad Juárez,
Chih.
Tél: 6-25-11
agr.

Escuela Superior de Agricultura y Veterinaria, de
la Puente 216 Poniente, San Buenaventura,
Coah.
gé agr, vét-zoo.

**Escuela Superior en Organización y Administra-
ción Agropecuaria de La Laguna, A.C. (Coa-
uila)**, Bravo y Degollado, 27000 Torreón,
Coah.
organisation et adm agr.

Escuela Nacional de Antropología e Historia,
Periférico Sur y Calle Zapote, Col. Isidro
Fabela, 14030 México, D.F.
Tél: 655-70-18

anth, arc, ethn, ling, hist, ethn-hist.

Escuela de Arquitectura de Chihuahua, A.C.,
Calzada H. Colegio Militar Antiguo Colegio La
Salle s/n, Chihuahua, Chih.
Tél: 4-18-42
arc.

Escuela de Arte Teatral, Auditorio Nacional,
México 18, D.F.
Tél: 520-71-66
art théât.

Escuela Bancaria y Comercial, Paseo de la
Reforma 202, 06600 México 6, D.F.
Tél: 566-01-77
comp, adm des aff, banc-fin.

**Escuela Nacional de Biblioteconomía y Archi-
vonomía**, Viaducto Miguel Alemán 155,
México 13, D.F.
Tél: 530-13-52
bibl, archives.

Escuela Nacional de Capacitación Aduanera,
Calz. Tlalpán 2775, Col. El Reloj, Tlalpán,
D.F.
Tél: 522-30-02
douane.

**Escuela Profesional de Comercio y Administra-
ción de León**, Independencia 1706, 37380 León,
Gto.
Tél: 2-09-38
comp, adm.

**Escuela Superior de Comercio y Administración
«Colegio Guasave»**, Domicilio Conocido,
Colonia Ejidal, 81020 Guasave, Sin.
Tél: 2-00-06
comp.

Escuela Superior de Comunicación Gráfica,
Avenida División del Norte 3102, Col. Bellavista, 31320 Altavista, Chih.
Tél: 7-03-05
commun graph.

Escuela de Comunicación Social, Riva Palacio
No. 684 Nte., 80000 Culiacán, Sin.
Tél: 3-58-29
jour, rel publ.

**Escuela Nacional de Conservación, Restauración
y Museografía «Manuel del Castillo Negrete»**,
Ex Convento de Churubusco, Xicoténcatl y
General Anava, Coyoacán, D.F.
Tél: 688-25-40

**Escuela Profesional de Contabilidad y Adminis-
tración «Maestro José Calvo» A.C.**, Avenida
Cuauhtémoc 60, México 7, D.F.
Tél: 578-78-27
comp, adm des aff.

**Escuela Superior de Contaduría y Administra-
ción**, Avenida Monterrey s/n, Col. Chapulte-
pec, 26860 Nueva Rosita, Coah.
Tél: 4-37-45
adm des aff, comp publ.

Escuela Libre de Derecho, Arcos de Belén, esq.

Dr. Vértiz, México 7, D.F.
Tél: 588-02-11
dr.
Escuela Libre de Derecho de Sinaloa, Rosales 266 Pte., Culiacán, Sin.
Tél: 2-71-68
dr.
Escuela de Dietética y Nutrición del ISSTE, Avenida San Fernando 15, Col. Toriello Guerra 14050, Tlalpán, D.F.
Tél: 559-55-54
diét-nutr.
Escuela de Diseño del INBA, Balderas 125, México 1, D.F.
Tél: 521-71-94
dess.
Escuela de Diseño, Belisario Domínguez 2202, Col. Obispado, 64010 Monterrey, N.L.
Tél: 46-20-42
dess.
Escuela de Ciencias de la Educación, Juan Escutia y M. del Llano, Col. Obrero, 64010 Monterrey, N.L.
Tél: 44-67-03
éd.
Escuela de Medicina Física y Rehabilitación, Avenida Observatorio y Esq. Sur 136, Col. Tacubaya, México 18, D.F.
Tél: 271-50-00
thér.
Escuela de Fisioterapía del Hospital ABC, Avenida Observatorio y Esq. Sur 136, Col. Tacubaya, México 18, D.F.
physio.
Escuela Libre de Homeopatía, Primera de Santa Lucía 6, México 2, D.F.
Tél: 526-09-49
homéopathie.
Escuela Panamericana de Hotelería, Prolong. Martín Mendalde 1795, Col. Valle, 03100 México, D.F.
adm hôtel.
Escuela de Ingeniería Municipal, Doctor Lucio 191A, Col. Doctores, 06720 México, D.F.
gé municipal.
Escuela Náutica Mercante «Cap. de Alt. Antonio Gómez Maqueo», Calz. Gabriel Leyva s/n, 82040 Mazatlán, Sin.
Tél: 1-24-86
ét nav.
Escuela Náutica Mercante de Tampico, Boulevard López Mateos y Constitución, 89070 Tampico, Tamps.
Tél: 12-55-21. Télex: 14763 enmtme
ét nav.
Escuela Náutica Mercante «Fernando Siliceo», Boulevard Avila Camacho s/n, 91700 Veracruz, Ver.
Tél: 31-08-73

ét nav, géog.
Escuela Superior de Pedagogía, A.C., División del Norte 3102, Col. Bellavista, 31320 Altavista, Chih.
Tél: 4-07-77
péd.
Escuela de Periodismo «Carlos Septien García», Basilio Badillo 43, ler Piso, 06030 México 1, D.F.
Tél: 510-49-01
jour.
Escuela Nacional de Pintura, Escultura y Grabado «La Esmeralda» del INBA, San Fernando 14, Col. Guerrero, 06300 México, D.F.
pnt, sculp, gravure.
Escuela de Psicología y Pedagogía «Sigmund Freud», Morelos 417-419, 31000 Chihuahua, Chih.
Tél: 3-19-23
psyc, péd.
Escuela Independiente de Psicología, Calle 3a y Méndez, Col. Santa Rosa, Chihuahua, Chih.
Tél: 5-71-86
psyc.
Escuela Libre de Psicología, Paseo Bolívar 419, Chihuahua, Chih.
psyc.
Escuela de Psicología del Valle de Tangamanga, 5 de Mayo 535, 78000 San Luis Potosí, S.L.P.
Tél: 4-17-47
psyc, inf.
Escuela Superior de Relaciones Industriales, Calz. Valle de Juárez 6922, Col. San Lorenzo, 32320 Col. Juárez, Chih.
Tél: 7-26-00
rel ind.
Escuela de Trabajo Social de Tampico, Boulevard López Mateos 3401, Col. Santo Niño, Tampico, Tamps.
trav soc.
Escuela de Trabajo Social de Tijuana, Calz. de Guadalupe 6, Fraccionamiento La Villa, La Mesa, Apartado postal 885, Tijuana, B.C.
Tél: 86-8911
trav soc.
Escuela Superior de Medicina Veterinaria y Zootecnia, A.C., Km. 125.5 Carretera Federal México Puebla, Momoxpán, 72760 San Pedro Cholula, Pue.
vét-zoo.
Facultades Universitarias de Saltillo, A.C., Hidalgo Norte 160, Saltillo, Coah.
Tél: 3-91-50
adm des aff, comp.
Instituto Superior de Arquitectura, Insurgentes Sur 1027-402, Col. Napoles, México 18, D.F.
Tél: 598-47-00
Instituto Mexicano de la Audición y el Lenguaje, A.C., Avenida Progreso 141-A, Col. Escan-

dón, 11800 México, D.F.
lang, audition.

Instituto Celayense, Paseo de Bajío y Magnolia, Celaya, Gto.
Tél: 2-48-37
psyc.

Instituto de Ciencia y Cultura, A.C., Victoria Pte. 525, Saltillo, Coah.
Tél: 3-00-53
adm, biol.

Instituto de Ciencia y Artes, 2a Avenida Norte y 3a Calle Ote., 29000 Tuxtla Gutiérrez 3, Chis.
Tél: 2-37-82
E (sup.) : topog, biol, dent, psyc.

Instituto de Ciencias y Estudios Superiores de Tamaulipas, A.C., Calle 7 Rayón y Victoria 706, 87300 H. Matamoros, Tamps.
Tél: 3-34-49
E : méd, psyc, trav soc, péd, adm, dess, inf-obst.

Instituto Superior de Ciencias y Tecnología de La Láguna, A.C., Héroes de Nacozari s/n, Col. Bellavista, 35050 Gómez Palacios, Dgo.
Tél: 4-26-33
arc, infor, dess graph, dess graph-et ind, gé civ, psyc.

Instituto de Enseñanza e Investigación Superior en Comercio Internacional, Monterrey 242, 96700 México 7, D.F.
Tél: 584-60-55
com ext, com int, douane.

Instituto Nacional de la Comunicación Humana, «Dr. Andrés Bustamante Gurría», Dr. Francisco P. Miranda 167, Col. Merced Gómez (Plateros), 01600 México, D.F.
Tél: 593-37-42
commun hum.

Instituto Tecnológico de la Construcción, A.C., Colima 254, Col. Roma, 06793 México, D.F.
gé const.

Instituto de Cultura Superior, Prado Norte 664, 11000 México, D.F.
Tél: 540-27-92
hist de l'art.

Instituto Superior de Cultura y Arte de Monterrey, Avenida San Jerónimo 201 Pte., 64640 Monterrey, N.L.
Tél: 47-19-17
dess, décor.

Instituto Cultural Don Vasco, Entronque Nueva Carretera a Pátzcuaro s/n, Apartado postal 66, Uruapán, Mich.
adm des aff, comp.

Instituto Cultural Isidro Fabela, S.C., Quintano Roo, Sur 836, Toluca, Estado de México.
Tél: 5-37-91
adm des aff, comp, anth, dr, hist, lit.

Instituto Michoacano de Ciencias de la Educación «Jose María Morelos», Calzada Juárez 1600,

580060 Morelia, Mich.   *1986*
Tél: 3-50-75

Instituto Universitario de Ciencias de la Educación, Calle Colegio Salesiano 35, Col. Anáhuac, México 3, D.F.
Tél: 531-40-42
péd, psyc, socio, commun.

Instituto de Estudios Profesionales, A.C., Hidalgo-Sur 468, 25000 Saltillo, Coah.
Tél: 3-34-38
E : adm des aff, arc, gé civ.

Instituto de Estudios Profesionales para la Administración del Tiempo Libre, Avenida Ejército Nacional 253, Col. Anzures, 11300 México, D.F.
Tél: 531-05-74
adm récréative.

Instituto Mantense de Estudios Profesionales, Calle Ocampo 212 Sur, 89800 Ciudad Mante, Tamps.
Tél: 2-17-78
E : com, adm, dr, gé agr.

Instituto Mexicano de Estudios Superiores, Avenida Ocampo con Privada Rayón 245, 27500 Torreón, Coah.
Tél: 2-32-54
nutr, trav soc.

Instituto de Estudios Superiores de Tamaulipas, Calle Divisonia Tampico, Altimara Ponientes s/n, Tampico, Tamps.
Tél: 2-11-02
adm, comp, phil, psyc, systèmes inft, gé civ-ind.

Instituto de Estudios Superiores Vasco de Quiroga, A.C., Prol. V. de Mendoza 1678, Col. Félix Ireta, 58070 Morelia, Mich.
Tél: 2-17-46
adm des aff, arc, comp publ.

Instituto de Estudios Superiores de Turismo, S.C., Privada del Lago 40, Col. Américas Unidad, 03610 México, D.F.
Tél: 539-03-08
tour.

Instituto Superior de Intérpretes y Traductores, Río Rhin 40, 06500 México 5, D.F.
Tél: 566-77-22
interp, trad.

Instituto Leonardo Bravo, Ezequiel Montes 115, México 4, D.F.
Tél: 535-29-40
comp.

Instituto Literario y de Estudios Superiores de Campeche, Avenida Malecón, Miguel Alemán s/n, 24000 Campeche, Camp.
Tél: 6-13-32
trav soc, tour, jour.

Instituto Mexicano Madero, 17 Poniente 503, 72000 Puebla, Pue.
Tél: 43-82-80

adm, comp, jour, plan-commun, éco, adm et dév zoo, gé agr.

Instituto del Noreste, Angel Flores 247 Ote, Culiacán, Sin.
Tél: 2-72-63
psyc.

Instituto Universitario del Norte, Calle Bolívar 112, 31000 Chihuahua, Chih.
Tél: 5-81-15
dent.

Instituto Regiomontano, Virgilio Garza y José Benitez, Col. Chepe Vera, Apdo. Postal 492, 64030 Monterrey, N.L.
Tél: 46-58-59
éd.

Instituto Superior de Turismo, Calle 9A No. 2211, 31000 Chihuahua, Chih.

Tél: 6-40-14
tour.

Liceo Profesional de Comercio y Administración, A.C., Bravo y 7a, H. Matamoros, Tamps.
Tél: 3-08-15
adm des aff, comp.

Tecnológico de Estudios Contables y Administrativos, Viaducto Pte. Miguel Alemán 255, Col. Roma Sur, 06760 México 7, D.F.
Tél: 564-25-54
adm des aff, comp, aff tour.

Tecnológico Universitario de México, Avenida Azcapotzalco 308, Col. Claveria, 02080 México, D.F.
Tél: 561-86-46
adm, comp publ.

Teacher Training—Formation pédagogique

Escuela Normal Superior Federal de Aguascalientes, Boulevard Nazario Ortíz Garza s/n, 20000 Aguascalientes, Ags.
Tél: 6-26-76

Escuela Normal Superior de Celaya, Luis de Velasco 225, Celaya, Gto.
Tél: 2-07-06

Escuela Normal Superior del Estado «José E. Madrane», Calle Ramírez y 6a, Chihuahua, Chih.
Tél: 2-12-32

Escuela de Educación Física «Profr. Antonio Estopier E.», Zaragoza 443 Norte, 35150 Col. Lerdo, Dgo.
phys.

Escuela Normal Superior de Ciudad Madero, Tamaulipas, A.C., Brasil y 5 de Mayo No. 406 Pte, 89400 Col. Madero, Tamps.

Escuela Normal Superior de Tamaulipas, A.C., Carretera Soto la Marina Km. 2, Apartado postal 338, Ciudad Victoria, Tamps.
Tél: 2-43-05

Escuela Normal Superior del Estado de Morelos, Avenida Palmas No. 13, Col. Bellavista, Apartado postal 1275, Cuernavaca, Mor.
Tél: 3-25-28

Escuela Normal Superior de Durango, Calle Pino Suárez 3000 Ote., Durango, Dgo.
Tél: 6-45-64

Escuela Normal Superior del Estado de México No. 2, Avenida Revolución y Avenida de Los Maestros, 55000 Ecatepec, Estado de México.
péd.

Escuela Normal Superior Labastida, José Vasconcelos Ote. 110, Col. del Valle, 66220 Garza Garcia, N.L.
Tél: 56-90-30

Escuela Normal Superior de Jalisco, Lisboa 488, Col. Sta. Elena Estadio, Guadalajara, Jal.
Tél: 24-54-01

Escuela Normal Superior «Nueva Galicia», Luis Pérez Verdía 361, 44680 Guadalajara, Jal. *1947*
Tél: 15-60-17

Escuela Normal de Especialización, Francisco Siles No. 1279, Fracc. Jardines Plaza del Sol, 04500 Guadalajara, Jal.
Tél: 22-52-71

Escuela Normal Superior de Guanajuato, Paseo de la Presa 76, Guanajuato, Gto.
Tél: 2-19-76

Escuela Normal Superior de La Laguna, Blvd. Miguel Alemán, Frentea a la Termoeléctrica, Gomez Palacio, Dgo.
Tél: 3-16-43

Escuela Normal Superior del Estado de Baja California Sur, República y Altamirano, La Paz, B.C. Sur.
Tél: 2-10-69

Escuela «Justo Sierra», Juárez 523, León, Gto.
psyc.

Instituto América, Calz. del Tepeyac s/n, León, Gto.
Tél: 3-14-72

Escuela Normal Superior de Sinaloa A.C., Tejeira No. 10C, Col. Juan Carrasco, Mazatlán, Sin.
Tél: 1-54-91

Escuela Normal Superior de Yucatán, Calle 59 No. 426, Mérida, Yuc.
Tél: 1-23-14

Escuela Normal Superior de México, Fresno 15, 06400 México 4, D.F. *1936*
Tél: 592-33-27

Escuela Normal de Especialización, Campos Elíseos y Bernard Shaw, México 25, D.F.
Tél: 540-29-61

Escuela Normal Superior «F.E.P.», Sadi Carnot 44, 06470 México 4, D.F.
Tél: 535-86-83

Escuela Superior de Educación Física, Puerta 4 Cd. Deportiva, Magdalena Mixcuca, 08010 México 8, D.F.
Tél: 519-50-60
phys.

Escuela Normal Superior del Estado de Nuevo León, Centro Escolar Venustiano Carranza, Venustiano Carranza y Ruperto Martínez, 64000 Monterrey, N.L.   1961
Tél: 43-83-66

Escuela Normal de Especialización, Avenida Tepeyac 1666 Pte. y Priv. Castelar "D", Colonia Pío X, 64710 Monterrey, N.L.

Escuela Normal Superior de Oaxaca, Arteaga No. 44, 68000 Oaxaca, Oax.
Tél: 6-98-68

Escuela Normal Superior de Hidalgo, Mina No. 110, 42000 Pachuca, Hgo.
Tél: 2-47-77

Escuela Normal Superior del Estado, 11, Sur No. 1102, 72000 Puebla, Pue.
Tél: 38-84-73

Escuela Normal Superior Benavente, Calle 25 Oriente 9, 72000 Puebla, Pue.   1956
Tél: 43-63-00

Escuela Normal Superior «Justo Sierra Mendez», A.C., Avenida Hermanas Serdán s/n, 72000 Puebla, Pue.

Tél: 45-37-78

Escuela Normal Superior de Querétaro A.C., Domicilio Conocido, Colonia Vista Alegre, 76090 Querétaro, Qro.

Escuela Normal Superior, Calle Aldama Pte. 858, Saltillo, Coah.
Tél: 3-65-39

Escuela Normal Regional de Especialización, Hildago y Aldama, Saltillo, Coah.
Tél: 3-61-59

Escuela Normal Superior del Sur de Tamaulipas, Ayuntamiento y Nicolás Bravo, Col. Martock, Tampico, Tamps.
Tél: 2-43-05

Escuela Normal Superior de Nayarit, Ciudad de la Cultura «Amado Nervo», Tepic, Nay.
Tél: 2-01-06

Escuela Normal Superior del Estado de México No. 1, Natalia Carrasco 400, Col. Federal, 50070 Toluca, Edo. de México.
Tél: 4-00-63

Escuela Normal Superior de Chiapas, Avenida 20 de Noviembre s/n, Col. Albania, Tuxtla Gutiérrez, Chis.
Tél: 2-68-76

Escuela Normal Superior «Juana de Asbaje», Dr. Verduzco 380 Sur, Zamora, Mich.
Tél: 2-07-14

Egalement 130 autres établissements de formation pédagogique.

Asociación Nacional de Universidades e Institutos de Enseñanza Superior

L'Association nationale des universités et institutions d'enseignement supérieur est un organisme qui s'occupe d'une part des rapports des institutions d'enseignement supérieur entre elles, et, d'autre part, des rapports de ces institutions aves les autorités éducatives, fédérales et des états. Le siège de l'Association est à Mexico.

L'Association se compose de 77 membres: 36 universités publiques, 34 instituts techniques et 7 instituts privés. Parmi les principaux établissements figurent l'Université nationale autonome du Mexique, l'Institut polytechnique national, le Collège du Mexique, le Centre national d'enseignement technique industriel.

Ses buts sont d'étudier les problèmes académiques et administratifs du système national de l'enseignement supérieur de la République à des fins de planification nationale et régionale.

Elle est dirigée par: l'Assemblée générale; le Conseil national; les Conseils régionaux; le Secrétariat général exécutif.

The National Association of Universities and Institutes of Higher Education is concerned with the relations between institutions of higher education themselves as well as with the relations of these institutions and the federal and state education authorities. The Association is located in Mexico City.

The Association consists of 77 members: 36 public universities, 34 technical institutions and 7 private institutions. Among the principal institutions are the National Autonomous University of Mexico, the National Polytechnic Institute, the College of Mexico, the National Centre for Technical Industrial Education.

Its purpose is to study the academic and administrative problems of the national system of higher education in the context of national and regional planning.

Its organs are the General Assembly: the National Council; the Regional Councils; and the General Secretariat.

Secrétaire général exécutif: Dr. Juan Casillas G de L.

Insurgentes Sur 2133, 3er Piso, Col. San Angel, Deleg. Alvaro Obregón, 01000 México, D.F.
Tél: 550-27-55

Asociación de Profesores Universitarios de México A.C. (IAUPL)
Correspondant: 18, rue du Docteur Roux, 75015 Paris (France).
Tél: (33-1) 47.83.31.65

Federación de Universitarias de México (IFUW)
Apartado postal 12-1044, Col. Navarte, Del. B. Juárez, 03020 México 12, D.F.

Servicio Universitario Mundial (WUS)
Correspondant: Axel Didriksson.
Avenida Copilco 181A, Colonia Copilco, 04360 México, D.F.
Tél: 658-9220

Confederación Nacional de Estudiantes – CNE
Apartado postal 756, San Luis Potosí, S.L.P.

Central Nacional de Estudiantes Democráticos – CNED
Córdoba 95, Despacho 102, Colonia Roma, México, D.F.

Movimiento de Profesionales Católicos (Pax Romana)
Apartado postal 20143, México 20, D.F.

Movimiento Estudiantil y Profesional (Pax Romana)
Apartado postal 1647, México 1, D.F.

Movimiento Estudiantil Cristiano de México (WSCF)
Apartado 20-256, 01000 México, D.F.

International Youth and Student Movement for the United Nations (ISMUN)
Colima 110, México 7, D.F.

*

Dirección General de Incorporación y Revalidación
Secretaría de Educación Pública, Añil 571, Col. Granjas, México, D.F.

Secretaria de Educación Pública
México, D.F.
Tél: 512-4992. Télex: 1773860 psepme

Comisión Nacional de los Estados Unidos Mexicanos para la Unesco
Secretaría de Educación Pública, México, D.F.
Tél: 521-65-42. Télex: 1773860 psepme.
Cables: conalmex mexico

MONGOLIA
MONGOLIE

***Mongolian State University**, p.b. 377, Ulan Bator 11. (The Rector).   *1942*
Tel: 20668
F : *phy-math, nat, phill, eco, trade & eco, soc.*

Mongolian Polytechnical Institute, P.O. 46, Box 520, Ulan Bator.   *1970*
Tel: 25109
F : *energ, mec-techn, arc-const, geol-mine, eng eco, sani-hydro eng.*

Russian Language Institute, p.b. 46/53, Ulan Bator.   *1979*

Institute for Management Personnel, University Street 3, Ulan Bator 6.   *1979*

Pedagogical Institute, Khobdo City, Khobdo Province.   *1979*
Tel: 2500
F : *nat, soc, phy-math.*

State Pedagogical Institute, p.b. 48/103, Peace Street 2, Ulan Bator.   *1951*
F : *Mongolian lang-lit, math-phy, nat-soc, art-labour-gen techn, teachers' refresher, external, sports-art.*

State Agricultural Institute, Post Office 53, Ulan Bator.   *1958*
F : *vet, zoo, agro-eng, agr eco.*

State Medical Institute, Post Office 48, Ulan Bator.   *1961*
F : *med, pedi, stom, phar, sani-hyg, ther.*

Union of Mongolian Students—UMS (IUS)
Small Ring Road 10, Ulan Bator.

*

State Committee for Science, Technology and Higher Education
Ulan Bator.

Mongolian National Commission for Unesco
Ministry of Foreign Affairs, Ulan Bator.
Tel: 21-6-78. Cables: mounesco ulan bator

MOROCCO
MAROC

UNIVERSITIES — UNIVERSITES

Université Hassan II, B.P. 9167, Mers-Sultan, Casablanca.   *1975*
Tél: 273-737
F : sc jur-éco-soc, let-hum (3), sc (2), méd-phar, dent; let-hum, sc (El Jadida).
***Université Mohammed I**, B.P. 524, Oujda. *1978*
F : let-hum, sc jur-éco-soc, sc.
***Université Mohammed V**, 3, rue Michlifen, Agdal-Rabat. (M. le Ministre de l'Enseignement supérieur).   *1957*
Tél: 713-18. Télex: 32603 recuniv m
F : sc jur-éco-soc, let-hum, sc, méd-phar, dent, péd; let-hum, sc (Kénitra).
E : ing.
I : ét arabisation (rech), scq, rech scq.

Université Sidi Mohammed Ben Abdallah, Dhar El Mahraz, Atlas-Fès.   *1975*
Tél: 416-64
F : sc jur-éco-soc, let-hum, sc; let-hum, sc (Meknès) Tél: 245-83; let-hum, sc (Tétouan).
Université Cadi Ayyad, B.P. 17, Marrakech.
                                                   1975
Tél: 346-49. Télex: 74013
F : let-hum, sc, sc jur-éco-soc.
Université Quaraouiyine, Dhar El Mahraz, B.P. 60, Fès.   *859*
Tél: 411-99
F : Ach-chariâ (Isl law), lang arabe (Marrakech); théo-phil (Tétouan); Ach-chariâ (Isl law) (Agadir).

OTHER INSTITUTIONS — AUTRES INSTITUTIONS

Ecole nationale d'Administration publique, 1, avenue de la Victoire, Rabat.   *1948*
Tél: 250-61
Ecole nationale d'Agriculture, Haj Kaddour, Route d'Ifrane, Meknès.   *1945*
Tél: 223-89. Télex: 41969
Institut Agronomique et Vétérinaire Hassan II, B.P. 704, Avenue Maa Al Aïnaïne, Haut-Agdal, Rabat.   *1966*
Tél: 717-58. Télex: 31873
Institut national d'Aménagement et Urbanisme, Avenue Maa Al Aïnaïne, Haut-Agdal, Rabat.
                                                   1981
Tél: 735-10
Ecole nationale d'Architecture, Rehba, Rabat.
                                                   1980
Tél: 224-27
Institut supérieur de Commerce et d'Administration des Entreprises, Km. 9, 5 route de Nouasser, Casablanca.   *1971*
Tél: 345-501. Télex: 22884 iscae m
Institut Dar-Al-Hadith Al-Hassania, Avenue de la Côte-d'Ivoire, Rabat.   *1964*
Tél: 225-87
ét Isl.
Ecole national forestière d'Ingénieurs, Tabriquet, B.P. 18, Salé.   *1968*
Tél: 871-49
Institut Royal de Formation des Cadres de la Jeunesse et des Sports, Belle-Vue, Avenue Ibn

Sina, Agdal, Rabat.   *1980*
Tél: 726-73
Centre de Formation des Conseillers en Planification de l'Education, Avenue Maa Al Aïnaïne, Haut Agdal, Rabat.
Tél: 30007
Centre de Formation des Contrôleurs de la Propriété foncière, c/o I.A.V. Hassan II, B.P. 704, Rabat.
Centre de Formation d'Inspecteurs, Bab Tamesna, Rabat.
Tél: 301-96
Ecole des Sciences de l'Information, Avenue Maa Al Aïnaïne, Haut Agdal, Rabat.   *1975*
Tél: 749-04
Institut supérieur de Journalisme, Avenue Maa Al Aïnaïne, Haut Agdal, Rabat.   *1970*
Tél: 709-15
Institut national d'Etudes Judiciaires, Avenue Beni Snassen, Haut-Souissi, Rabat.   *1970*
Tél: 502-53
Institut supérieur des Etudes Maritimes, Km. 7, Route d'El Jadida, Casablanca.   *1957*
Tél: 344-445
Ecole nationale de l'Industrie minérale, Rue Abderrahmen Errafiki, Agdal, Rabat.   *1972*
Tél: 713-60
Ecole normale supérieure, Avenue Victor Hugo, B.P. 9172 Casablanca.
Ecole normale supérieure, Kariat Bensouda

Ahouaz-Ouad, Fès.
Tél: 20

Ecole normale supérieure, Kariat Bensouda
Ahouaz-Ouad, Fès.
Tel: 20

Ecole normale supérieure, Cité Mohammadia,
Daoudiate, B.P. 415, Marrakech.

Ecole normale supérieure, Aïn Slougui, Meknès.
Tél: 229-50

Ecole normale supérieure (Enseignement technique), Avenue Maa Al Aïnaïne, Haut Agdal,
Rabat.

Ecole normale supérieure Takaddoum, Avenue
Oued Akrach, Takaddoum, Rabat.
Tél: 500-25

Ecole normale supérieure Souissi, Zankat Cadi
Ahmed Bennani, B.P. 773, Rabat.

Ecole de Perfectionnement des Cadres du Ministère de l'Intérieur, Base Aérienne, Kénitra.
                                                     1964

Tél: 32-18

Institut national des Postes et Télécommunica-
tions, Avenue Maa Al Aïnaïne, Haut Agdal,
Rabat.   1971
Tél: 730-77

Institut national des Statistiques et d'Economie
appliquée, Avenue Maa Al Aïnaïne, B.P. 406,
Haut Agdal, Rabat.   1967
Tél: 709-15. Télex: 32719

High Tech, Angle rue Fès-Meknès, Quartier de la
Résidence, Rabat.   1985
Tél: 333-31
inft.

Institut supérieur de Tourisme, 13, avenue Allal
Ben Abdellah, Tanger.   1972
Tél: 394-29

Institut national des Travailleurs sociaux, Ministère des Affaires sociales, 15, rue Marrakech,
Rabat.   1983

Ecole Hassania des Travaux publics et des
Communications, Km. 6, Route d'El Jadida,
Casablanca.   1971
Tél: 364-727

Service de Prospection, d'Information et d'Accueil (SPIA)

Le service de Prospection, d'information et d'Accueil (SPIA) (ex: BIDEP) relève de la Direction de la Formation des Cadres rattachée actuellement au Ministère de l'Equipement, de la Formation Professionnelle et de la Formation des Cadres. En liaison avec les universités et les établissements de formation des cadres nationaux et étrangers, le SPIA a pour tâches de: constituer et mettre à jour un fonds documentaire destiné à l'information des élèves des classes terminales et des élèves bacheliers sur les possibilités de formation disponibles aussi bien au Maroc qu'à l'étranger; et élaborer des brochures d'information à l'usage de ces élèves, dont la plus importante est la brochure "Carrière" qui est à sa 9ème édition.

The Prospecting, Information and Reception Service (ex: Bureau of Information and Documentation on Training and the Professions) is responsible to the Directorate of Higher Training of the Ministry of Equipment and Vocational and Higher Training. Working in liaison with the universities and training institutes for national and foreign students, the Service assembles detailed documentation aimed at informing pupils prepar-
ing for and holding the baccalauréat of training possibilities available in Morocco and abroad; and prepares information brochures for their use, of which the most important, "Carrière", is now in its Ninth Edition.

Ministère de l'Equipment, de la Formation Professionnelle, et de la Formation des Cadres (Direction de la Formation des Cadres), 35, avenue Ibn Sina, B.P. 707, Rabat Agdal.
Tél: 727.22. Télex: 32028 seforcad

*

Division de la Réglementation et des Equivalences de Diplômes
Ministère de l'Education nationale, Rabat.
Tél: 748-39. Télex: 31016 meps-mes

Ministère de l'Education nationale
Rabat.

Ministère d'Etat chargé des Affaires culturelles
Rabat.
Tél: 66054

Commission nationale marocaine pour l'Education, la Science et la Culture
24, rue Sénégal-Océan, B.P. 420, Rabat.
Tél: 712-21. Télex: 31016/61

PEOPLE'S REPUBLIC OF MOZAMBIQUE
REPUBLIQUE POPULAIRE DE MOZAMBIQUE

*Universidade Eduardo Mondlane, Praça 25 de Junho, P.O. Box 257, Maputo.
1962, 1968, 1976
Tel: 27851. Telex: 6374

F : *law, eco, med, vet.*
D : *geol, math, phy, elec, civ eng, ch.*
Course : *agr-for, biol, mec, let.*
Ce : *African st, ecol (Tel: 74-27-31)*

Organização da Juventude Moçambicana – OJM
(IUS)
Rua Pereira do Lago 147, Maputo.
Telex: 6-160 ojm mo

*

Ministero da Educação e Cultura
45 rua Dr. Egas Moniz, P.O. Box 3674, Maputo.
Tel: 744.090

Mozambique National Commission for Unesco
Ministry of Education and Culture, 45 rua Dr. Egas Moniz, P.O. Box 3674, Maputo.
Tel: 744.090. Telex: 6148 mec

NEPAL
NEPAL

*Tribhuvan University, Kirtipur, Kathmandu.
(The Registrar).   *1959, 1971*
Tel: 15313

Campuses : *hum-soc* (27), *sc* (11), *bus mangt-com-publ adm* (13), *Sanskrit* (4), *law* (4), *ed* (14), *for* (1), *eng* (2), *agr-anim sc* (7), *med* (11).

Nepal University Teachers' Association
Saraswati Sadan, Durbar Marga, Kathmandu.
World University Service (WUS)
Secretary: P.L. Shrestha.
P.O. Box 2431B, Bhotahity, Kathmandu.
Nepal National Federation of Students – NNFS
(IUS)
United Nations Student and Youth Association of Nepal (ISMUN)
188 Naxal, Kathmandu 20.

*

Ministry of Education
Kathmandu
Tel: 14064
Nepal National Commission for Unesco
Ministry of Education, Kaiser Mahal, Kantipah, Kathmandu.
Tel: 14064. Cables: nepnatcom kathmandou

NETHERLANDS
PAYS-BAS

UNIVERSITIES AND UNIVERSITY INSTITUTIONS—
UNIVERSITES ET INSTITUTIONS UNIVERSITAIRES

*Universiteit van Amsterdam [U. of Amsterdam], P.O. Box 19268, 1000 GG Amsterdam-C. *1632*
Tel: 5259111. Telex: 16526 unasd nl
F : *theo, law, med-dent, math-comp-astr-phy-ch-biol, arts-hist-hist of art-archae-musicology, eco, socio-pol-anth-psyc-ped-psyc-sc of ed.*
Inter F : *phil, geog, phy geog-plan, prehist, act-econometrics.*

Vrije Universiteit te Amsterdam [Free U., Amsterdam], P.O. Box 7161, 1007 MC Amsterdam. *1880*
Tel: 5489222. Telex: 11329 dpvvu nl
F : *theo, law, med-dent, math-comp-phy-ch-pharmoch-biol-geol, arts-hist-hist of art-archae, eco, psyc-ped-socio-pol-anth, sc of ed.*
Inter-F : *phil, phy, geog, econometrics, phys.*

Technische Rijksuniversiteit te Delft [Delft U. of Technology], P.O. Box 5, 2600 AA Delft. *1905*
Tel: 789111. Telex: 38151 bhthd nl
F : *civ eng, geod, arc, mec, nav, aero, elec, mine, met, ind des, phy eng, ch eng, math eng-comp.*

*Technische Rijksuniversiteit te Eindhoven [Eindhoven U. of Technology], P.O. Box 513, 5600 MB Eindhoven. *1956*
Tel: 479111. Telex: 51163 thehv nl
F : *mec, elec, arc, bus adm, phy eng, ch eng, math eng-comp.*

Technische Rijksuniversiteit te Enschede [Twente U. Technology], P.B. 217, 7500 AE Enschede. *1964*
Tel: 899111. Telex: 44200 thtes nl
F : *bus adm, elec, mec, phy eng, ch eng, math eng-publ adm-sc of ed-comp.*

Rijksuniversiteit Groningen [U. Groningen], P.O. Box 72, 9700 AB Groningen. *1614*
Tel: 119111. Telex: 53410 rugro nl
F : *theo, law, med-dent, math-sc, arts-hist-hist of art-archae, eco, socio-psyc-ped-sc of ed, organization-mangt.*
Inter-F : *phil, geog-prehist, econometrics, bus adm.*

Open Universiteit te Heerlen [Open U., Heerlen], P.O. Box 2960, 6401 DL Heerlen. *1984*
Tel: 762222. Fax: 711486. Telex: 56559 ouhrl nl
P : *law, eco, publ/bus adm, tec, sc, cult.*

*Rijksuniversiteit Leiden [Leiden U.], P.O. Box 9500, 2300 RA Leiden. *1575*
Tel: 272727. Telex: 39427
F : *theo, law, med, math-comp-astr-phy-ch-biol, arts-hist-hist of art-archae, socio-pol-anth-publ adm-psyc-ped.*
Inter-F : *phil, prehist.*

Rijksuniversiteit te Maastricht [U. of Limburg], P.O. Box 616, 6200 MD Maastricht. *1974, 1976*
Tel: 888888. Telex: 56726 rul nl
F : *med, law, eco.*

*Katholieke Universiteit te Nijmegen [Catholic U., Nijmegen], P.O. Box 9102, 6500 HC Nijmegen. *1923*
Tel: 519333. Telex: 48228 winat nl
F : *theo, law, med-dent, math-comp-phy-ch-biol, arts-hist-hist of art-archae, socio-pol-anth-psyc-ped-sc of ed.*
Inter-F : *phil, geog-plan.*

*Rijksuniversiteit te Rotterdam [Erasmus U., Rotterdam], P.O. Box 1738, 3000 DR Rotterdam. *1913, 1966, 1973*
Tel: 408111. Telex: 24421 ubrt nl
F : *eco-econometrics, law, socio-pol-publ adm, med.*
Inter-F : *phil, bus adm.*

*Katholieke Universiteit Brabant te Tilburg [Tilburg U.], P.O. Box 90153, 5000 LE Tilburg. *1927*
Tel: 669111. Telex: 52426 kht nl
F : *eco-econometrics, law, socio-psyc, theo.*
Inter-F : *phil.*

*Rijksuniversiteit te Utrecht [U. of Utrecht], P.O. Box 80125, 3508 TC Utrecht. *1636*
Tel: 535198. Telex: 40087 vluut nl
F : *theo, law, med, math-comp-astr-phy-ch-geol-geophy-biol-phar, arts-hist-hist of art musicology, vet, socio-psyc-ped-anth, sc of ed.*
Inter-F : *phil, geog-phy, geog.*

*Rijkslandbouwuniversiteit te Wageningen [Wageningen Agricultural U.], P.O. Box 9101, 6700 HB Wageningen. *1918*
Tel: 89111. Telex: 45917 burlh nl. Cables: elha wageningen
F : *agr, trop agr, an hus, hort, urb-rur plan, landscape arc, for, eco, socio, biol, hum nutr, soil sc, agr tec, biotechn.*

INSTITUTIONS OFFERING INTERNATIONAL COURSES—
INSTITUTIONS ORGANISANT DES COURS INTERNATIONAUX

*Institute of Social Studies, P.O. Box 90733, 2509 LS The Hague. *1951*
Tel: 510510. Telex: 31491 iss nl

Netherlands Universities Foundation for International Co-operation, P.O. Box 90734, 2509 LS The Hague. *1952*
Tel: 502681. Fax: 510513. Telex: 33565 nufic nl

International Agricultural Centre, P.O. Box 88, 6700 AB Wageningen. *1951*
Tel: 19040. Telex: 45888 intas nl

Institute for Housing Studies, P.O. Box 20718, 3001 JA, Rotterdam. *1946*
Tel: 4309540. Telex: 24548 ihs nl

International Institute for Aerospace Survey and Earth Sciences (ITC), P.O. Box 6, 7500 Enschede. *1951*
Tel: 320330. Telex: 44525 itc nl. Cables: aesur enschede

Philips' International Institute of Technological Studies, P.O. Box 218, 5600 MD Eindhoven. *1957*
Tel: 757511

Netherlands International Institute for Management(RVB), P.O. Box 143, 2600 AC Delft. *1955*
Tel: 569394. Telex: 38323 rvb nl

International Institute for Hydraulic and Environmental Engineering, P.O. Box 3015, 2601 DA Delft. *1957*
Tel: 783402. Telex: 38099 ihe nl

Royal Tropical Institute Amsterdam, Mauritskade 63, 1092 AD Amsterdam. *1960*
Tel: 5688477. Telex: 15080 kit nl. Cables: intropen amsterdam

Europa Institute of the University of Amsterdam, P.O. Box 19123, 1000 GC Amsterdam. *1960*
Tel: 5252162

International Institute for Land Reclamation and Improvement, P.O. Box 45, 6700 AA Wageningen. *1955*
Tel: 22938. Telex: 45888 intas nl. Cables: intas, iac, wageningen

International Union of Local Authorities, P.O. 90646, 2509 LP The Hague. *1964*
Tel: 244032. Telex: 32504 inta iula. Cables: iula, the hague

Hague Academy of International Law, Peace Palace, Carnegieplein 2, 2517 KJ The Hague.
Tel: 469680. Telex: 32323 icj nl. Cables: acintlaw

Telecommunication Institute PITTC, P.O. Box 1168, 1200 BD Hilversum.
Tel: 872750. Telex: 43894 phvs nl

International Agricultural College Deventer, P.O. Box 7, 7400 AA Deventer.
Tel: 22150. Telex: 49517 tgcon nl

Barneveld College, International Training Centre on Animal Husbandry and Milling Technology, P.O. Box 64, 3770 AB Barneveld.
Tel: 14881. Cables: barcol barneveld

Radio Nederland Training Centre, P.O. Box 222, 1200 JG Hilversum.
Tel: 16151. Telex: 43336 womr nl. Cables: mundivox hilversum

Nijenrode, The Netherlands School of Business, Straatweg 25, 3621 BG Breukelen.
Tel: 912111

Rectoren College

The College of Rectors, which meets at least five times a year, consists of the rector and another member of the Committee of Deans of each of the Netherlands universities. Its aim is to stress contact and consultation between rectors in matters of common interest.

The chairmanship is held in turn for a year by each university.

The Rectoren College appoints the editors of Universiteit en Hogeschool (bimonthly), which deals with various university problems.

Le Collège des recteurs, qui se réunit au moins cinq fois par an, se compose du recteur et d'un autre membre du Collège des Doyens de chacune des universités néerlandaises. Son objet est de stimuler les contacts et les consultations entre les recteurs sur des questions d'intérêt commun.

La présidence échoit par roulement annuel à chaque université.

Le Collège des recteurs désigne les rédacteurs de Universiteit en Hogeschool (bimestriel), qui traite de divers problèmes universitaires.

Chairman (1988–89): prof. dr. S.K. Thoden van Velzen, Rector, University of Amsterdam.
Secretary: Drs. H.W. Luttikholt
P.O. Box 19270, 3501 DG Utrecht.
Tel: 334441. Telex: 70055 vsnu nl

Adviesraad voor het Hoger Onderwijs (ARHO)

The Advisory Council for Higher Education was set up as part of the new advisory and consul-

tative structure for higher education (university education, higher vocational education and the Open University). Within this structure, unlike in the past, advisory and consultative functions are clearly separated with, on the one hand, bodies exclusively concerned with advising the government and, on the other, bodies which represent a particular group of interested parties in consultations with the government.

The ARHO was set up on 17 June 1985. Its function is to advise the Minister of Education and Science in the initial phase of policy development on general aspects of higher education policy, with a view to the harmonization and integration of higher education. The Council may draw up recommendations either at the Minister's request or on its own initiative.

The Council consists of independent experts and has between five and nine permanent members. Temporary members may also be appointed. All members are appointed on a part-time basis with the exception of the chairman and vice-chairman. The members are appointed by the Minister.

Le Conseil consultatif de l'Enseignement supérieur (ARHO) a été créé en tant qu'élément de la nouvelle structure a caractère consultative de l'enseignement supérieur (enseignement universitaire, enseignement professionnel supérieur, Université ouverte). Contrairement à ce qui était autrefois le cas, la consultation et la concertation sont deux éléments distincts au sein de cette structure. En d'autres termes, certains organes ont à l'égard du gouvernement une fonction purement consultative alors que d'autres ont pour fonction de procéder au nom de groupes d'intéressés à des concertations avec le gouvernement.

L'ARHO a été créé le 17 juin 1985. Il a pour tâche de conseiller le ministre de l'Enseignement et de la Science lors de la phase préliminaire de l'élaboration d'une politique sur les aspects généraux de la politique relative à l'enseignement supérieur, en vue de l'harmonisation et de l'intégration de l'enseignement supérieur. Le Conseil formule des recommandations soit à la demande du Ministre, soit de sa propre initiative.

Le Conseil se compose d'experts indépendants. Il comprend au moins cinq et au plus neuf membres permanents. A l'exception du président et du vice-président, les membres exercent leur fonction à temps partiel. En plus des membres permanents, il peut aussi y avoir des membres temporaires. Les membres sont nommés par le Ministre.

Chairman: drs. C. de Hart.
Prinsessegracht 22, 2514 AP Den Haag.
Tel: 924221

Vereniging van Samenwerkende Universiteiten (VSNU)

The Association of Co-operating Universities in the Netherlands was founded on 18 January 1985 and has as members all universities in the Netherlands and the Open University.

It is the centre for consultation and co-operation between the universities in general, and between their Executive Boards in particular. It serves the interests of the universities and prepares and supports the negotiations between the universities on the one hand, and the Minister of Education on the other. The new body is an association established under private law, and is supported by a Bureau located in Utrecht.

Policy-specific areas such as university research, building and construction and personnel matters will be dealt with by the appropriate members of the Executive Boards in sectorial fields. An important element is the interdisciplinary consultations as a basis, if not a precondition, for linking developments within each discipline with general university policy. In addition, a Student Advisory Committee has been established.

Both the sectorial consultation and discipline-related matters are supervised and co-ordinated in the Governing Board of the Association, comprising one member from each university.

L'Association chargée de la coopération entre les universités néerlandaises a été fondée le 18 janvier 1985 et se compose de toutes les universités néerlandaises (dont l'Université ouverte).

Elle constitue le centre chargé d'assurer la consultation et la coopération entre les universités en général, et entre leurs conseils exécutifs en particulier. Elle défend les intérêts des universités, et prépare et favorise les négociations entre les universités, d'une part, et le Ministre de l'éducation, d'autre part. La nouvelle organisation est une association créée conformément aux règles du droit privé ; elle comporte un Bureau situé à Utrecht.

Les questions relevant de domaines spécifiques tels que la recherche universitaire et celles relatives à la politique en matière de bâtiments, de locaux, et de personnel sont traitées par les membres compétents des Conseils exécutifs, dans les secteurs en question. Les consultations interdisciplinaires en tant que fondement, sinon condition préalable, de la relation évolution et innovation de chaque discipline/politique universitaire en général, constituent un élément important de la politique de l'Association. Un Comité consultatif étudiant a par ailleurs été créé.

Le Conseil d'administration de l'Association, formé d'un membre de chaque université, contrôle et coordonne la consultation entre les divers

secteurs et les questions relatives aux domaines d'études mêmes.

Chairman: Ir. P. van der Schans.
Director: Dr. F. E. H. van Eijkern.
P.O. Box 19270, 3501 DG Utrecht.
Tel: 334441. Telex: 70055 vsnu nl

Netherlands Universities Foundation for International Co-operation (NUFFIC)

NUFFIC, set up in 1952, is the organization in the Netherlands that both stimulates and serves the universities, professional colleges and international education institutes in matters involving international cooperation. Although particular attention is given to cooperation with the Third World, activities related to exchanges and joint projects with industrialized countries have been on the increase in recent years.

NUFFIC provides many services to the academic community and to government. These include:
- coordinating cooperative links between Dutch institutions and counterparts in the Third World;
- providing information and other services to people from developing countries who come to the Netherlands for specialized training;
- collecting surplus scientific literature from Dutch universities and sending it to universities in the Third World (the NUFFIC Periodicals Project);
- stimulating international cooperation and mobility;
- coordinating activities in the Netherlands for the European Action Scheme for the Mobility of University Students (ERASMUS), the European Community Programme for Education and Training (COMETT) and the United States' International Student Exchange Programme (ISEP);
- evaluating foreign diplomas at the request of universities, ministries and labour exchanges.

NUFFIC can offer published information on a wide variety of topics related to its work. It also has a large databank on higher education in other countries, with details on institutions and study programmes, admission procedures, fees and scholarships, possibilities for exchange, etc.

Publications: *Overzicht.* A monthly magazine (in Dutch) with news about education, research and development cooperation. Subscription: FL 35 a year; *VISUM-Nieuws.* Quarterly magazine (in Dutch) with information and news about student mobility and educational cooperation. Free; Projects. Loose-leaf book (in English) with descriptions of the projects undertaken by Dutch

universities and counterpart institutions in the Third World within the context of cooperative links financed by the Dutch government from development-aid funds. Price: FL 15; Basic Data on International Courses Offered in the Netherlands. The study catalogue for International Education: the special system of advanced courses offered in English especially for the benefit of people from other countries. Free; Studying at a University in Holland. Folder (in English, French, German or Spanish) for the person who is trying to decide whether or not to apply. Free. NUFFIC in a Nutshell. Folder (in English) briefly describing NUFFIC and its activities. Free.

Créée en 1952, la NUFFIC est la fondation néerlandaise chargée de promouvoir la coopération internationale entre les universités, les établissements d'enseignement supérieur professionnel et les établissements organisant des cours internationaux. Ses activités sont essentiellement axées sur le Tiers Monde mais, depuis quelques années, la coopération avec les pays industrialisés s'accroît.

La NUFFIC assure de nombreux et importants services à l'Etat et à l'enseignement supérieur, par exemple:
- *coordonner la coopération entre les établissements d'enseignement néerlandais et les établissements du Tiers Monde;*
- *informer et aider les étudiants du Tiers Monde comptant suivre ou suivant des cours spécialisés aux Pays-Bas;*
- *fournir aux universités du Tiers Monde, dans le cadre du "NUFFIC Periodicals Project" (Projet de périodiques de la NUFFIC) de la documentation scientifique dont les universités néerlandaises ne se servent plus;*
- *promouvoir la coopération et la mobilité internationales;*
- *coordonner le Programme d'action communautaire en matière de mobilité des étudiants (ERASMUS), le Programme communautaire d'éducation et de formation en matière de technologies (COMETT) et le Programme international d'échanges d'étudiants (ISEP). Ce dernier programme concerne uniquement l'échange avec les Etats-Unis;*
- *évaluer des diplômes étrangers. Ce service est uniquement rendu aux universités, aux ministères et aux agences nationales pour l'emploi, à l'exclusion des particuliers.*

La NUFFIC dispose de beaucoup de matériel d'information sur les activités qu'elle déploie. Elle possède, en outre, une importante banque de données sur l'enseignement supérieur à l'étranger qui comporte notamment des données relatives aux procédures d'admission, aux droits d'études et aux bourses, ainsi qu'aux possibilités d'échanges.

Publications: Overzicht, mensuel sur l'enseigne-ment, la recherche et la coopération au dévelop-pement (en néerlandais). Abonnement: FL 35,- par an; VISUM-Nieuws, revue trimestrielle sur la mobilité des étudiants et la coopération universi-taire (en néerlandais) (gratuite); Dossier à feuilles mobiles contenant la description des projets de coopération entre les universités néerlandaises et les universités du Tiers Monde (projets entrant dans le cadre du programme de coopération due gouvernement néerlandais) (en anglais), Prix FL 15,-; Basic Data on International Courses offered in the Netherlands, guide sur les cours inter-nationaux (en anglais, avec résumés en français et en espagnol) (gratuit); Etudier dans une université néerlandaise (également disponible en versions anglaise, espagnole et allemande) (gratuite); NUFFIC in a Nutshell (en englais) brève descrip-tion de la NUFFIC et de ses activités (gratuite).
Director: drs. T.G. Veenkamp.
Badhuisweg 251, B.P. 90734, 2509 LS Den Haag.
Tel: 510510. Fax: 510513. Telex: 33565 nufic nl

Nederlandsche Vereniging van Vrouwen met Academische Opleiding (IFUW)
Postbus 13226, 3507 LE Utrecht.
World University Service (WUS)
Oranje Nassaulaan 5, Amsterdam Z.

Platform Landelijke Studenten Organisaties (PLSO)
Nieuwe Koekstraat 97, 3514 EC Utrecht.
Thijmgenootschap (Pax Romana)
Huygensweg 14, Nijmegen.
Nederlandse Christen Studenten Vereniging (WSCF)
c/o Marten Janse, Van Eeghenstraat 90, Amsterdam.
S.I.B. (ISMUN)
Secretary-General: Laurens Narraina.
Box 2228, Leiden.
I.J.A.R. (WUJS)
Contact: 89 Chaussee De Vleurgat, 1050 Brussels (Belgium).
Tel: (2) 647-7279. Telex: 20625

*

National Equivalence Information Centre
NUFFIC, Badhuiseg 251, 2509 LS Den Haag.
Tel: 510510. Fax: 510513. Telex: 33565 nufic nl
Ministerie van Onderwijs en Wetenschappen
(Netherlands Ministry of Education and Science, Department of University Education)
Europaweg 4, P.O. Box 25000, 2700 LZ Zoetermeer.
Tel: 531911. Fax: 512651
Netherlands National Commission for Unesco
Oranjestraat 10, 2514 JB Den Haag.
Tel: 644655. Telex: 32636 mino nl. Cables: ministerie o.w. zoetermeer nederland

NETHERLANDS ANTILLES
ANTILLES NEERLANDAISES

Universiteit van de Nederlandse Antillen, Jan Noorduynweg 111, P.O. Box 3059, Willem-stad, Curaçao.   *1979*

Tel: 84422. Telex: 1411 una na
F : *law, social eco, tec.*

Department of Education
Curaçao.
Tel: 612000/611879

NEW CALEDONIA
NOUVELLE-CALEDONIE

Université du Pacifique, (Centre Universitaire), B.P. 4477, Nouméa.
Tél: 687.25.49.55. Télex: 175

Centre Régional Associé du C.N.A.M. (Centre des Arts et Métiers) (1), Chambre de Commerce et d'Industrie de Nouvelle-Calédonie, B.P. 3562, 10, rue de Verdun, Nouméa. *1971*
Tél: 283707

Centre de Droit de Nouméa (2), Vice-Rectorat, B.P. G4, Nouméa Cedex. *1962, 1966*
Tél: 27-59-44

Ecole normale d'Instituteurs, B.P. 19, Nouméa. *1954, 1976*

Centre de Formation et de Recherche péda-gogique (Ecole normale d'Instituteurs de l'Enseignement Catholique), B.P. 3580, Nouméa.
Tél: 27-63-95

Ecole de Formation des Personnels Médicaux «V. Budillon», B.P. 3278, Nouméa.

Lycée La Pérouse, B.P. M5, Nouméa Cedex.

Lycée Jules Garnier de Nouville, B.P. H3, Nouméa Cedex.

Ecole de Techniciens du Commerce et de la Gestion, Chambre de Commerce et de l'Industrie, Rue de Verdun, Nouméa.

Vice-Rectorat
B.P. G4, Nouméa Cedex.
Tél: 27-59-44

Centre d'Information et d'Orientation
B.P. 500, Nouméa.
Tél: 27-53-28

---

(1) Attached to the Conservatoire national des Arts et Métiers, Paris.
(2) Attached to the Université de Bordeaux I.

(1) Rattaché au Conservatoire national des Arts et Métiers, Paris.
(2) Rattaché à l'Université de Bordeaux I.

NEW ZEALAND
NOUVELLE-ZELANDE

UNIVERSITIES — UNIVERSITES

*University of Auckland, Private Bag, Auckland.
(The Registrar).   *1882*
Tel: 737999. Fax: (64)-(9)-799317. Telex: 21480
unilib nz. Cables: university, auckland
C : *arts, sc, arc, law, mus, com, eng, fa, urb, med.*
University of Canterbury, Private Bag, Christ-church.   *1873*
Tel: 67001. Telex: 4144 unicant nz. Cables:
university, christchurch
C : *arts, sc, law, com, eng, mus, fa, ed, for.*
 LINCOLN COLLEGE, Canterbury.   *1878*
  C : *agr, agr eng, hort, com, parks & recr mangt, land arc.*
Massey University, Private Bag, Palmerston
North.   *1964*
Tel: 69099. Telex: 30974 mas uni. Cables:
massey university

C : *agr, hort, vet, hum, sc, bus st, ed, soc, techn.*
University of Otago, P.O. Box 56, Dunedin.
                                             1869
Tel: 771640. Fax: (64)-(24)-741-607. Cables:
university, dunedin
C : *arts, mus, com, dent, hom sc, law, med, sc, theo, phys, surv.*
S : *clin.*
University of Waikato, Private Bag, Hamilton.
                                             1964
Tel: 62889. Fax: (64)-(71) 60135. Telex: 61109
uniwkto nz. Cables: university of waikato
C : *hum, ed, sc, mangt, soc, comp.*
Victoria University of Wellington, P.O. Box 600,
Wellington C.1.   *1897*
Tel: 721000. Telex: 30882 vuwlib nz
C : *arts, sc, biol, arc, law, com, soc, lang, lit, adm, mus.*

The New Zealand Vice-Chancellors' Committee
The Committee provides administrative machinery for the formulation and implementation of policies on any matters where collective action is considered to be to the advantage of the university institutions, both internally among themselves, and externally when a collective viewpoint is needed. The Committee is also a useful and important forum for the exchange of views on all aspects of university development.

Membership of the Committee consists of the six Vice-Chancellors of New Zealand's universities and the Principal of Lincoln College. In addition to the main Committee there are a number of standing committees dealing with libraries, computers, graduate employment, non-academic staffing matters. *Ad hoc* sub-committees or working parties are also established as required.

The Committee, through its Chairman, is represented on the Association of Commonwealth Universities Council, co-ordinates a number of overseas visitor schemes, and is widely represented on a number of national committees and councils. It is also represented on a number of important scholarship selection committees.

The Secretariat is based in the capital city, Wellington.

Le Comité des vice-chanceliers de Nouvelle-Zélande constitue le dispositif administratif permettant de définir et de mettre en oeuvre des politiques pour toutes questions où une action collective est jugée bénéfique pour les institutions universitaires, tant sur le plan intérieur entre elles que sur le plan extérieur quand un point de vue collectif s'avère nécessaire. Le Comité est également une importante et utile tribune permettant des échanges de vues sur tous les aspects du développement universitaire.

Le Comité se compose des six vice-chanceliers des universités néo-zélandaises et du Principal de Lincoln College. Il comporte, outre le comité principal, un certain nombre de comités permanents s'occupant de questions relatives aux bibliothèques, aux ordinateurs, à l'emploi des diplômés, et au personnel non académique. Des sous-comités ou des groupes de travail ad hoc sont, le cas échéant, également constitués.

Le Comité est représenté, par son Président, au Conseil de l'Association des Universités du Commonwealth; il assure la coordination d'un certain nombre de programmes d'enseignants

étrangers en visite, et est également représenté au sein d'un certain nombre de comités et conseils nationaux. Il est également représenté au sein de plusieurs importants comités de sélection pour l'attribution de bourses.

Le Secrétariat a son siège dans la capitale, Wellington.

Chairman: Bruce Ross, Principal, Lincoln College, Canterbury.

Secretary: B.P. Hampton.

Victoria University of Wellington, Private Bag, Wellington.

Tel: 46-040

University Grants Committee

The Committee was established from 1 January 1961, by Act of Parliament, as a statutory body with the following main functions:

to examine the needs of New Zealand in university education and research; to investigate and study the financial needs of university education and research, including the recurring and non-recurring needs of the universities; to initiate and consider, in consultation with the universities and other bodies, plans for such balanced university development as may be required to make the universities fully adequate to the needs of New Zealand;

to determine the allocation of grants of money to be recommended by it for appropriation by Parliament to meet the needs of university education and research, and to review the expenditure by the universities of money appropriated by Parliament;

to advise and make recommendations to the Government of New Zealand through the Minister of Education on any matters relating to university education and research requiring the consideration of the Government;

to provide secretarial and administrative services for the Universities Entrance Board, and a number of other statutory committees. These include the Curriculum Committee, the Research Committee, and the Council of Legal Education.

The Committee consists of a full-time Chairman, who is the chief executive officer of the Committee, and seven part-time members, three of whom are professors or teachers in the universities. All are appointed by the Governor-General after consultation between the Minister of Education and the universities and colleges.

Le Comité des crédits universitaires a été créé le 1er janvier 1961 par Acte du Parlement en tant qu'organisation officielle dont les attributions sont les suivantes:

examiner les besoins de la Nouvelle-Zélande en matière d'enseignement universitaire et de recherche;

étudier les besoins financiers de l'enseignement universitaire et de la recherche, et notamment les besoins des universités en crédits de fonctionnement et en crédits d'investissement;

établir ou étudier, en consultation avec les universités et d'autres organismes, des plans destinés à assurer le développement équilibré des universités et à les adapter pleinement aux besoins de la Nouvelle-Zélande;

déterminer le montant des crédits nécessaires pour satisfaire aux besoins de l'enseignement universitaire et de la recherche et en recommander l'affectation au Parlement;

examiner l'emploi fait par les universités des crédits consentis par le Parlement;

formuler des avis et des recommandations au gouvernement néo-zélandais, par l'intermédiaire du ministre de l'éducation, sur toutes questions relatives à l'enseignement universitaire et à la recherche requérant l'attention du gouvernement;

fournir des services de secrétariat et d'administration au Conseil d'admission des universités et à une série d'autres comités officiels dépendant de lui, notamment le Comité des programmes, le Comité de la recherche et le Conseil de l'enseignement juridique.

Le Comité se compose d'un président à plein temps qui est son chef exécutif et de sept membres à temps partiel, dont trois sont professeurs ou enseignants des universités. Tous sont nommés par le gouverneur général après consultation entre le ministre de l'éducation et les universités et collèges.

Chairman: Prof. David Hall.

Apple & Pear Board Building, 11-19 Bolton Street, P.O. Box 12–348, Wellington North.

Tel: 728-600. Cables: unigrants

The New Zealand Council for Educational Research

The Council, founded in 1933 as a result of a grant from the Carnegie Corporation of New York, is an autonomous, national research organization. Its functions are: to promote and undertake research into a variety of educational problems or issues, at all levels from pre-school through to higher education; to prepare and publish reports as a result of such investigations; and to provide an information and clearing-house service on educational topics to individuals or institutions within New Zealand and the South Pacfic region. Since 1945, the Council has operated under its own act of parliament, revised in 1972, and is now funded jointly from Government and independent sources within New Zealand.

Fondé en 1933 grâce à une subvention de la Carnegie Corporation de New-York, le Conseil néo-zélandais pour la recherche en éducation est

un organisme de recherche national et autonome. Il a pour fonctions: de promouvoir et d'entreprendre des recherches sur des problèmes éducatifs très divers, et ce à tous les niveaux, de l'enseignement préscolaire à l'enseignement supérieur; de préparer et de publier des rapports contenant les résultats de ces recherches; et de constituer, pour les particuliers ou les institutions de Nouvelle-Zélande et de la région du Pacifique Sud, un service central d'information sur les problèmes éducatifs. Depuis 1945, le Conseil exerce ses activités aux termes d'une loi qui lui est propre et a été modifiée en 1972; il est maintenant financé conjointement par le Gouvernement et par des bailleurs de fonds indépendants.
Director: Ian D. Livingstone.
P.O. Box 3237, Wellington.
   Tel: 847-939. Cables: edsearch

New Zealand Federation of University Women
(IFUW)

P.O. Box 2006, Wellington.
New Zealand University Students' Association –
NZUSA
P.O. Box 806, 2 Whitehall Apartments, Boulcott Street, Wellington C.1.
New Zealand Student Christian Movement
(WSCF)
P.O. Box 9792, Courtenay Place, Wellington.

*

Department of Education
Government Buildings, Lambton Quay, Wellington 1.
   Tel: 735-499. Cables: deped wellington
New Zealand National Commission for Unesco
c/o Department of Education, Lambton Quay, Wellington 1.
   Tel: 735-499. Cables: unesco wellington

NICARAGUA
NICARAGUA

UNIVERSITIES—UNIVERSITES

*Universidad Centroamericana, Apartado postal 69, Managua, D.N.   *1960*
Tél: 70532. Télex: 2296
F : ing, éco-adm, dr-soc, hum, agr, lang.
*Universidad Nacional Autónoma de Nicaragua, León.   *1812*
Tél: 2612
F : dr-soc, méd, ch, dent, sc; agr, éd, éco, phymath (Managua).

E : éd; sc, méd (Managua).
Universidad Nacional de Ingeniería «Simón Bolívar», Managua.   *1984*
Tél: 73709
inft, arc, gé ch, méc, gé ind, élec, gé civ.
Universidad Politécnica de Nicaragua, Apartado postal 3595, Managua, D.N.   *1968*
Tél: 97740
E : éd tec, dess, inf, adm-com-fin.

OTHER INSTITUTIONS—AUTRES INSTITUTIONS

Centro Popular de Estudios Superiores, Apartado postal 115, Matagalpa.   *1983*
Tél: 2474
comp agr, comp publ & fin.
Escuela de Agricultura y Ganadería, Apartado postal 81, Estelí.   *1982*
Tél: 2347
zoo, agr.
Escuela Internacional de Agricultura y Ganadería, Apartado postal 5, Rivas.   *1969*
zoo, agr.

Escuela de Enfermería, Jinotepe-Carazo.   *1984*
inf.
Escuela de Enfermería, Puerto Cabezas.   *1982*
inf.
Escuela de Enfermería de la Trinidad, Estelí.   *1982*
inf.
Instituto Politécnico de la Salud, Apartado postal "Antiguo Colegio Francés", Managua.   *1980*
alim ind, inf, stat méd, lab clin, physio.
Instituto Técnico Aeronáutico, Managua.   *1982*

Instituto Técnico "La Salle", Apartado postal 4, León. *1982*
Tél: 2584
méc ind, électro, méc agr, élec-réfrigération.
Instituto Tecnológico de Estudios Superiores "Pedro Aráuz Palacios", Apartado postal 3526,

Managua. *1979*
gé civ, méc, téléc, électro-énerg.
Instituto Tecnológico Nacional, Apartado postal 162, Granada. *1974*
méc ind, électro-énerg, ch ind, méc agr.

Asociación Nicaragüense de Instituciones de Educación Superior (ANIES)

L'Association nicaraguayenne des institutions d'enseignement supérieur a été créée en novembre 1968. Elle assure d'une part la coordination entre les travaux des institutions membres et d'autre part celle des institutions avec d'autres organismes, nationaux et internationaux, publics ou privés. Son organe suprême est le Conseil d'administration composé des recteurs, directeurs généraux ou directeurs des institutions membres. La Présidence de l'ANIES est assurée par roulement annuel au sein de ses quatre institutions membres.

Les buts de l'Association sont de: a) promouvoir le progrès des institutions membres, en coordonnant leurs activités; b) étudier les problèmes académiques et administratifs de l'enseignement supérieur en vue de sa planification intégrale dans le cadre du système national d'enseignement; inviter les institutions membres, ou les autorités universitaires, le cas échéant, à adopter les recommandations qu'elle approuve en vue de l'amélioration de l'enseignement à tous les niveaux; c) favoriser les échanges de personnes, d'informations et de services entre les institutions membres; d) promouvoir le développement des activités d'enseignement, de recherche et de diffusion de la culture au sein des institutions membres dans le cadre d'un programme national global, tout en tenant compte des caractéristiques propres à chacune d'elles.

Les institutions membres sont tenues de reconnaître réciproquement les études effectuées et, en cas de transfert d'étudiants, d'accorder à ceux-ci des équivalences compatibles avec les statuts respectifs des établissements.

The Nicaraguan Association of Institutions of Higher Education was established in November 1968. It co-ordinates relations between member institutions and between them and national and international bodies, both public and private. The governing body is the Administrative Council composed of the rectors and directors-general or directors of the member institutions. The Presidency of ANIES is a yearly rotary system among its four member institutions.

The aims of the Association are: a) to promote the progress of the member institutions by co-ordinating their activities; b) to study academic and administrative problems of higher education with a view to its integrated planning within the framework of the national system of education; to encourage member institutions and the university authorities, as appropriate, to adopt the recommendations which the Association approves concerning the improvement of education at all levels; c) to encourage the exchange of persons, information and services between member institutions; d) to promote the development of educational activities and research, and the spread of culture amongst the member institutions within the framework of a national programme, having always due regard for the individual characteristics of each institutions.

The Member institutions are required to recognize studies reciprocally, and in the case of transfer of students, to grant equivalences consistent with their respective constitutions.

Universidad Nacional Autónoma de Nicaragua, León.
Tél: 2612

Servicio Universitario de Nicaragua (WUS)
Secrétaire général: Joaquín Solís.
CNES, Apartado 5416, Managua.
Centro Universitario de la Universidad Nacional – CUUN
Universidad Nacional Autónoma de Nicaragua, Apartado 135, León.
Unión Nacional de Estudiantes de Nicaragua – UNEN (IUS)
Colonia Miquel Bonilla 215, Ap. 663, Managua.
Télex: 1251 dri atn. unen
Juventud Universitaria Católica (Pax Romana)
Apartado postal 3368, Managua, D.N.
Movimiento Estudiantil Cristiano de Nicaragua (WSCF)
Apartado T-290, Managua.
Movimiento Nacional de la Juventud (ISMUN)
Colonia Maximo Jérez E-312, Managua, D.N.
*

Ministerio de Educación
Managua, D.N.

Tél: 50344. Télex: 2427 med nk

Comisión Nacional Nicaragüense de Cooperación con la Unesco
Ministerio de Educación, Complejo cívico

«Camilo Ortega Saavedra», Managua, D.N.
Tél: 50344. Télex: 2427 med nk. Cables: comision nacional unesco mineducacion managua

NIGER
NIGER

*Université de Niamey, B.P. 237, Niamey.
1971, 1973
Tél: 73-2713. Télex: 5258 uninim ni
F : sc, agr, sc sa, let-hum, péd, éco-jur.
I : rech hum, rech math, radio-isotopes.
Université islamique du Niger, Say.   *1987*
(In process of development).
Ecole nationale d'Administration niveau supérieur, B.P. 542, Niamey.

Tél: 72-2853
Ecole Africaine et Malgache de l'Aviation civile, B.P. 746, Niamey.
Tél: 72-3661
Ecole nationale de la Santé publique niveau supérieur, B.P. 290, Niamey.
Tél: 72-3001
Centre Agrhymet, Niamey.

Ministère de l'Education nationale, de l'Enseignement supérieur et de la Formation professionnelle
B.P. 557, Niamey.
Tél: 72-2365

Commission nationale nigérienne pour l'Unesco
Ministère de l'Education nationale, de l'Enseignement supérieur et de la Formation professionnelle, B.P. 557, Niamey.
Tél: 72-2365. Télex: 5512 ni. Cables: mineducation niamey

NIGERIA
NIGERIA

UNIVERSITIES — UNIVERSITES

Federal University, Abuja, Federal Capital Territory. *1988*
F : *agr, sc, ed, hum.*

Abubakar Tafawa Balewa University, P.M.B. 0248. Bauchi. *1980, 1988*
Tel: 77-42065
F : *agr, eng-techn, sc.*

University of Agriculture, P.M.B. 2373, Makurdi, Benue State. *1980, 1988*
F : *agr, eng.*

University of Agriculture, P.M.B. 2240, Abeokuta, Ogun State. *1982, 1988*
Tel: 39-230847
F : *agr, eng.*

*Ahmadu Bello University, Samaru, Zaria, Kaduna State. *1962*
Tel: Zaria (69) 32581/5. Telex: 75252 wzza. Cables: unibello, zaria
F : *arts-soc, arts-Isl st, ed, sc, env des, agr, eng, vet, med, adm, law, phar.*
C : *ed* (Maduna).
I : *adm, ed, heal; agr res* (Samaru).
Ce : *et techn, Isl legal st, comp, soc & eco res, Nigerian cult st, ad ed.*
S : *basic st, postgrad st.*
   DIVISION OF AGRICULTURAL COLLEGES. *1971*
   C : *agr* (3), *anim sc.*
Also 2 affiliated Advanced Teachers' Colleges (Kano, Zaria).

*Anambra State University of Technology, P.M.B. 01660, Enugu. *1981*
Tel: Enugu 331244. Cables: unitech, enugu
F : *app biol, app phys sc, eng-techn.*

Bayero University, P.M.B. 3011, Kano. *1975, 1977*
Tel: 64-601280. Telex: 77189 unibayero ng. Cables: unibayero ng
F : *arts-Isl st, soc-mangt, sc ed, law, med, techn.*
Ce : *audio-vis, Nigerian langs, comp.*
S : *gen st, postgrad st.*

Bendel State University, P.M.B. 14, Ekpoma, Bendel State. *1981*
F : *arts-soc, nat, med sc, eng-techn, agr-nat resources, legal st, env des.*
   ABRAKA CAMPUS, Abraka. *1985*
   Tel: 54-66027
   F : *ed.*

*University of Benin, P.M.B. 1154, Benin City, Bendel State. *1971*
Tel: (52) 200250/89. Cables: uniben, benin
F : *sc, eng, arts, ed, soc, phar, law, agr.*
C : *med sc.*
I : *child heal, ed, comp, publ adm-extension serv.*
Ce : *instructional resource, soc-cult-env res.*
D : *gen st.*
S : *postgrad st.*

University of Calabar, P.M.B. 1115, Calabar, Cross River State. *1975*
Tel: 222695. Telex: 65103, unical ng. Cables: unical, calabar
F : *arts, ed, sc, soc, law, agr.*
C : *med sc.*
I : *ed, oceanog, publ policy st.*
Ce : *comp, radio-isotope, cult st.*
S : *postgrad st.*

*University of Cross River State, P.M.B. 1017, Uyo, Akwa Ibom State. *1983*
Tel: uyo 699. Cables: unicross, uyo
F : *arts-soc, ed, nat-app sc.*

*University of Ibadan, Ibadan, Oyo State. *1948, 1962*
Tel: Ibadan 400550. Telex: campus 31228 ng. Cables: university, ibadan
F : *arts, sc, basic med sc, agr-for, vet, soc, ed, techn, law, clin sc & dent, phar.*
I : *African st, child heal, ed.*
Ce : *heal ed, audio-vis, biomed commun, comp, Abadina media resource.*
S : *postgrad st.*

*University of Ilorin, P.M.B. 1515, Ilorin, Kwara State. *1975, 1977*
Tel: Ilorin (31) 221694. Telex: 33144 unilon ng. Cables: unilorin
F : *arts, sc, ed, eng-techn, bus & soc, law, agr.*
C : *heal sc.*
I : *sugar res, ed.*
Ce : *comp.*
S : *postgrad st.*

Imo State University, P.M.B. 2000, Okigwe, Imo State. *1981*
C : *arts-sc, bus adm-legal st.*

*University of Jos, P.M.B. 2084, Jos, Plateau State. *1975*
Telex: 81136 unijos ng
F : *arts, ed, med sc, soc, law, env st.*

I : *ed.*
Ce : *dev st, continuing ed.*
D : *gen st.*
S : *postgrad st.*

*University of Lagos, Akoka, Lagos.   *1962*
Tel: Lagos 82111. Cables: university, lagos
F : *sc, arts, soc, bus adm, eng, law, env des, ed.*
C : *med-phar-dent.*
I : *ed, advanced legal st.*
Ce : *continuing ed, cult st, open st, comp.*
S : *postgrad st.*

Lagos State University, Ojo.   *1983*
Tel: 884096. Cables: Lasu
F : *arts-soc, ed, eng-techn-env sc, law, sc.*
C : *med sc* (planned).

University of Maiduguri, P.M.B. 1069, Maiduguri, Borno State.   *1975*
Tel: (76) 232537. Cables: university maiduguri
F : *arts, ed, sc, soc-mangt, vet, agr, law, eng.*
C : *med sc.*
Ce : *ed techn.*
S : *postgrad st.*

*University of Nigeria, Nsukka, Anambra State.
                                                      1960
Tel: Nsukka 6251. Cables: nigersity, nsukka
F : *agr, arts, bus adm, ed, eng, law, vet, phar, med sc-dent, heal sc-techn, soc, biol, env st, physical sc.*
I : *eco dev, African st, ed.*
Ce : *demographic res, curriculum dev, co-op & rur dev st.*
S : *postgrad st.*
    ENUGU CAMPUS, Enugu, Anambra State.
    Tel: Enugu 252080. Cables: nigersity enugu
    F : *bus adm, law, med sc-dent, heal sc-techn, env st.*

*Obafemi Awolowo University, Ile-Ife, Oyo State.   *1962*
Tel: Ile-Ife 2291
F : *agr, arts, ed, law adm, heal sc, phar, sc, soc, techn, env des.*
I : *cult st, ecol.*
Ce : *comp, ind res & dev.*
D : *continuing ed.*

*Ondo State University, P.M.B. 5363, Ado-Ekiti, Ondo State.   *1982*
Tel: 30-240370. Cables: ondovarsity, ado ekiti
F : *arts, ed, sc, soc, eng.*

Ogun State University, P.M.B. 2002, Ago-Iwoye, Ogun State.   *1982*
F : *agr sc, arts, ed, law, sc, soc-mangt.*
C : *heal sc.*

*University of Port-Harcourt, P.M.B. 5323, Port-Harcourt, Rivers State.   *1975, 1977*
Tel: 84-334400. Telex: 61184 phuni ng. Cables: university pharcourt
F : *hum, soc, ed, sc eng, mangt-bus adm.*
C : *heal sc.*
I : *ed, agr res.*
Ce : *comp, instructional resources.*
Ut : *gen st.*
S : *postgrad st, basic st.*

Rivers State University of Science and Technology, P.M.B. 5080, Port-Harcourt.
                                                1979, 1982
Tel: 335823. Cables: riverstech port harcourt
F : *agr, eng, env sc, law, mangt, med-phar, sc, techn & sc ed.*
I : *agr res, flood res, gen st, pollution st.*
S : *postgrad st.*

University of Sokoto, P.M.B. 2346, Sokoto.
                                                1975, 1977
Tel: 60-232134. Telex: 73134 unisok ng. Cables: unisokoto, sokoto
F : *art-Isl st, soc, agr, vet, agr, law.*
C : *heal sc.*
Ce : *Isl st.*
D : *gen st.*
S : *postgrad st.*

Federal University of Technology, P.M.B. 704, Akure, Ondo State.   *1981*
Tel: Akure 34-230358. Cables: fedunitech, akure
S : *agr-agr techn, pure-app sc, earth-mineral sc.*
Ut : *gen st.*

Federal University of Technology, P.M.B. 1526, Owerri, Imo State.   *1980*
Tel: 83-230974. Cables: fedunitech, owerri
S : *agr-agr techn, eng-techn, mangt techn, nat-appl sc.*

Federal University of Technology, P.O. Box 656, Minna, Niger State.   *1982*
Tel: 66-222397. Cables: futech minna
S : *agr-agr techn, eng-techn, env techn, sc.*

Federal University of Technology, P.M.B. 2076, Yola, Gongola State.   *1981, 1988*
F : *adm, sc, eng-techn.*

OTHER INSTITUTIONS—AUTRES INSTITUTIONS

Federal Polytechnic, Ado-Ekiti, Ondo State.
                                                      1977
Tel: 34-230727
F : *civ eng, bui eng, elec, mec, mine, acc-bus st, sec, sc techn.*

Federal Polytechnic, Bauchi State.   *1977*
Tel: 77-42562
F : *civ eng, elec, mec, estate mangt, bus st, sec, food techn-hotel mangt.*

Federal Polytechnic, Bida, Niger State.   *1977*

Tel: 66-461707

F : *civ eng, bui eng, elec, ch eng, mec, surv, bus adm, acc-marketing, sec, sc lab techn, stat.*

Federal Polytechnic, Idah, Benue State.   *1977*
Tel: 40

F : *civ eng, elec, mec, met, acc, bus adm, sec, food techn, sc techn, catering-hotel mangt.*

Federal Polytechnic, Ilaro, Ogun State.   *1979*
Tel: 39-440005

F : *civ eng, bui techn, elec, mec, bus adm, marketing, sec, sc lab techn.*

Federal Polytechnic, Mulsi, Gongola State.   *1979*
F : *civ eng, elec, mec, surv, acc, bus adm, food techn.*

Federal Polytechnic, Nassarawa.   *1982*
F : *bui techn, art-urb-quantity surv, estate mangt, acc, bus st-bus adm, sec.*

Federal Polytechnic, Unwani Afikpo, Imo State.   *1982*
Tel: 54

F : *civ eng, elec, mec, acc, bus st, bus adm, sec, agr mec-irrig eng.*

Federal Polytechnic, Kaura Namoda, Sokoto State.

F : *bui techn, quantity surv, acc, bus st-bus adm, sec, agr-mec-irrig eng.*

Yaba College of Technology, Yaba, Lagos State.   *1948, 1963*
Tel: 800160. Cables: tekinst

F : *civ eng, bui techn, elec, mec, urb, quantity surv, acc, bus adm, sec, sc, techn, fa-app arts-des.*

Auchi Polytechnic, P.M.B. 13, Auchi, Bendel State.   *1964, 1972*
Tel: 57-200148

F : *civ eng, elec, mec, urb, surv, quantity surv, estate mangt, acc, bus st, sec, sc, techn, fa-app arts-des.*

Calabar Polytechnic, P.M.B. 1110, Calabar, Cross River State.   *1973*
Tel: 87-222418

F : *civ-eng, elec, mec, arc, urb, estate mangt, acc, bus adm, sec, sc, techn, stat, mass commun, pap.*

Kaduna Polytechnic, P.M.B. 2121, Kaduna, Kaduna State.   *1968*
Tel: 62-211551

F : *civ eng, bui eng, elec, electro, mec, mine, arc, urb, surv, quantity surv, estate mangt, acc, bus adm-marketing, purchasing-supply, sec, comty dev, printing techn.*

The Polytechnic, Ogwashi-Uku, Bendel State.
F : *civ eng, elec, mec, arc, urb, surv, bus adm.*

Ozoro Polytechnic, Ozoro, Bendel State.
F: *civ eng, bui eng, elec, mec, urb surv, quantity surv, estate mangt, bus adm.*

Ramat Polytechnic, P.M.B. 1070, Maiduguri, Borno State.   *1972, 1976*

Tel: 76-232264

F : *civ eng, elec, mec, arc, urb, surv, bus adm.*

Sokoto State Polytechnic, P.M.B. 90, Birnin Kebbi, Sokoto State.   *1976*
F : *civ eng, bui techn, elec, mec, quantity surv, acc, agr mec-irrig eng.*

Kano Institute of Higher Education, Kano State Polytechnic, P.M.B. 3481, Kano, Kano State.   *1977, 1978*
F : *elec, mec, arc, quantity surv, bus adm, marketing, purchasing-supply, coop st-cmty dev, printing techn, fa-app arts-des.*

Benue Polytechnic Ugbokolo, Markurdi, Benue State.   *1977*
F : *civ eng, elec, mec, acc, bus adm, marketing, sec, sc techn, catering-hotel mangt, fa-app arts.*

Katsina Polytechnic, P.M.B. 2052, Katsina, Kaduna State.   *1973*
F : *civ eng, bui eng, elec, quantity surv, acc, bus adm, sec.*

Ogun State Polytechnic, P.M.B. 2210, Abeokuta, Ogun State.   *1978*
F : *civ eng, elec, arc, urb, acc, bus adm, sec, food techn, mass commun.*

Ondo State Polytechnic, Owo, Ondo State.   *1980*
F : *civ eng, elec, mec, arc, urb, surv, quantity surv, acc, bus adm, sec.*

Ibadan Polytechnic, P.M.B. 5063, Ibadan, Oyo State.   *1960, 1970*
Tel: 22-410255. Telex: 31222 polyib ng

F : *civ eng, elec, electro, mec, arc, urb, quantity surv, estate mangt, acc, bus ad, ins, bank, marketing, purchase-supply, sec, sc techn, mass commun, fa-app arts-des, comp-systems sc.*

College of Arts, Science and Technology, Oko, Anambra State.

Institute of Management and Technology, P.M.B. 1079, Enugu, Anambra State.   *1958, 1965, 1973*
Tel: 330416

F : *civ eng, bui eng, elec, ch eng, mec, acc, bus adm, ins, fin, bank, marketing, purchasing-supply, sec, coop st-cmty dev, food techn, catering-hotel mangt, sc lab techn, mass commun, fa-app arts-des, comp.*

Kwara State College of Technology, P.M.B. 1375, Ilorin, Kwara State.   *1972*
Tel: 221441

F : *civ eng, bui, techn, elec, electro, mec, auto eng, met-mine eng, prod eng, arc, urb, surv, acc, bus adm, marketing, sec, agr mec-irrig eng, catering-hotel mangt, sc lab techn, stat.*

Murtala C.A.S. Technology, Makurdi, Benue State.

College of Technology, P.M.B. 1036, Owerri, Imo State.   *1975*
Tel: 83-230974

F : *civ eng, bui techn, elec, ch eng, mec, met, arc,*

urg, surv, estate mangt, acc, bus adm, fin, marketing, purchasing-supply, sec, agr elec-irrig eng, nutr-diabetic, catering-hotel mangt, sc lab techn, opt-photo, infor techn, trans st.

Plateau State College of Technology, P.M.B. 23, Barakin Ladi, Jos, Plateau State.

F : *elec, mec, acc, sec, catering-hotel mangt.*

Lagos State College of Science and Technology,

P.M.B. 1606, Ikeja, Lagos State.   *1977*
Tel: 523528
F : *civ eng, elec, ch eng, mec, arc, urb, acc, bus adm, ins, sec, food techn, catering-hotel mangt, sc lab techn, drug-ch.*

Also 51 Colleges of Education.

Committee of Vice-Chancellors

The Committee is an informal body established in 1962 by a resolution adopted at a meeting of the Vice-Chancellors and Principals of the Nigerian Universities.

The aims of the Committee are: (i) to provide a forum for Vice-Chancellors of Nigerian universities to discuss matters of mutual interest: (ii) to act as an informal co-ordinating body among the universities in Nigeria: (iii) to act as a channel through which the joint opinion of the universities on any matters affecting education is expressed: (iv) to offer advice to Government and university governing councils on matters of general concern to the universities.

The Committee is composed of the Vice-Chancellors of all the Federal universities in Nigeria. When the Committee was established in 1962 it had five members. Membership now consists of the Vice-Chancellors of all the twenty-one Federal Government-owned universities in Nigeria. A Chairman is elected from among members, and serves for one academic year.

The Committee meets five times in an academic session (October–June) to discuss a number of issues affecting the universities presented by the Secretariat. The meetings also provide the Vice-Chancellors with opportunities for personal contact and informal exchange of views and experience. There is also provision for special meetings, usually at the request of members, to consider issues that have a significant impact on the affairs of the universities and need urgent attention.

The Committee appoints *ad hoc* Sub-Committees of its members and other university staff to examine specific matters affecting the university system and to make necessary recommendations to it. The Committee has, however, a standing Sub-Committee for the Commonwealth Scholarship and Fellowship Plan, responsible for the placing of postgraduate candidates for Nigerian awards under this Plan.

The Committee organizes and sponsors conferences, seminars, workshops and training courses on higher education in Nigerian universities. The activities of the Committee and the

Secretariat are supported by contributions from its members.

Le Comité des vice-chanceliers des universités nigériannes est un organisme officieux créé en 1962 en vertu d'une résolution adoptée lors d'une réunion des vice-chanceliers et principaux des universités nigériannes.

Le Comité a pour objectifs: 1) de fournir aux vice-chanceliers des universités nigériannes une tribune pour la discussion des questions d'intérêt commun; 2) de constituer un organe officieux de coordination entre les universités du Nigéria; 3) de constituer un relais par lequel puisse s'exprimer l'opinion collective des universités sur tous problèmes intéressant l'enseignement; 4) de donner des avis au Gouvernement et aux organes directeurs des universités sur les questions d'intérêt commun pour ces dernières.

Le Comité est formé des vice-chanceliers de toutes les universités fédérales du Nigeria. Il comprenait lors de sa création cinq membres et se compose maintenant des vice-chanceliers des vingt-et-une universités du pays appartenant au Gouvernement fédéral. Un président est élu au sein des membres, et est nommé pour une année académique.

Le Comité se réunit cinq fois par année universitaire (octobre-juin) pour discuter d'un certain nombre de problèmes intéressant les universités, qui lui sont soumis par le Secrétariat. Les réunions donnent aussi aux vice-chanceliers l'occasion de nouer des contacts personnels et de procéder à des échanges de vues et d'expériences informels. Des séances extraordinaires peuvent également être organisées, généralement à la demande des membres, pour étudier les questions qui ont d'importantes répercussions sur les affaires des universités et doivent être examinées dans les plus brefs délais.

Le Comité nomme des sous-comités ad hoc composés de ses membres et d'autres universitaires pour examiner des questions précises concernant le système universitaire et formuler les recommandations nécessaires en la matière. Le Comité compte néanmoins un sous-comité permanent chargé du "Commonwealth Scholarship and Fellowship Plan", qui assure le placement

de candidats de niveau post-gradué sollicitant des bourses dans le cadre de ce Plan.

Le Comité organise et patronne des conférences, des séminaires, des ateliers et des cours de formation dans le domaine de l'enseignement supérieur, qui se tiennent dans les universités nigériannes. Les activités du Comité et du Secrétariat sont financées par les contributions versées par ses membres.

Chairman: Prof. A.N. Mohammed, Vice-Chancellor, Ahmadu Bello University, Zaria
4, Idowu Taylor Street, Victoria Island, P.M.B. 12022, Lagos.
Tel: 612465. Telex: 23555 comvic ng. Cables: rivcom lagos

National Universities Commission

The Commission is the legal body set up by the Federal Government to co-ordinate university education and provide money to the Federal universities.

Its terms of reference include: a) advising the Head of Government, through the Minister charged with the responsibility for higher education, on the creation of new universities and other degree-granting institutions; b) preparing, after consultation with all the states' governments, the universities, the National Manpower Board and other appropriate bodies, periodic master-plans for the balanced and co-ordinated development of universities in Nigeria, including general programmes to be pursued by the universities in order to ensure that they are fully adequate to the national needs and objectives, recommendations for the establishment of new faculties or post-graduate institutions in existing universities, or the approval or rejection of proposals to establish such faculties or institutions; c) conducting investigations relating to higher education generally and making such other recommendations to the Federal and State Governments of the universities as the Commission would consider fit to the national interest; d) assessing and advising the Government on the financial needs (recurrent and capital) of university education and also the financial needs for university research and, based on these needs, to receive annually block grants from the Government for allocation to the individual universities in accordance with such formulas as may be laid down by the Federal Executive Council; e) undertaking periodic reviews of the terms and conditions of service of personnel engaged in the universities and making recommendations thereon to the Government where appropriate; f) acting as the agency for channelling all external aid to the universities in Nigeria; g) recommending to the Visitor of a university that a Visitation be made to such a university as and when it

considers it necessary and h) accrediting all degree-granting programmes in universities and other institutions.

The Commission is, therefore, concerned with the development, finance and performance audit of the universities in Nigeria.

Seven new universities were established during the academic year 1975/76. Seven new Universities of Technology were also established between 1980 and 1983, but the Federal Government has decided to reduce their number to three from the 1984-85 session, with the remaining four to be run as campuses of other Universities. The total number of Federal Universities is now sixteen. There are also eight Universities established by the State Governments.

The Commission is under the direction of a board composed of a part-time Chairman and members drawn from various disciplines in the universities and various interests outside the universities. The day-to-day affairs of the Commission are conducted by full-time professional staff with an Executive Secretary as Chief Executive.

La Commission nationale des Universités est l'organisme légal institué par le Gouvernement fédéral pour coordonner l'enseignement universitaire et répartir entre les universités fédérales les fonds qui leur sont alloués.

Elle a pour attributions: a) de conseiller le Chef du Gouvernement, par l'intermédiaire de l'officier ministériel chargé de l'enseignement supérieur, sur la création de nouvelles universités et d'autres institutions délivrant des diplômes; b) d'élaborer périodiquement, après avoir consulté les gouvernements de tous les Etats, les universités, le Conseil national de la main-d'œuvre et les autres organismes appropriés, des plans d'ensemble pour le développement équilibré et coordonné des universités du Nigeria, notamment les programmes généraux que doivent suivre les universités pour assurer qu'elles répondent totalement aux besoins et aux objectifs nationaux, des recommandations pour la création de nouvelles facultés ou institutions post-graduées dans les universités existantes ou son accord sur des propositions visant à établir ces facultés ou institutions – ou le rejet de ces propositions; c) de poursuivre des recherches sur l'enseignement supérieur en général et de faire au Gouvernement fédéral, aux Gouvernements des Etats et aux universités des recommandations que la Commission jugerait être d'intérêt national; d) d'établir des estimations et de conseiller le Gouvernement sur les besoins financiers (dépenses initiales et dépenses qui reviennent périodiquement) de l'enseignement universitaire, ainsi que sur les crédits nécessaires à la recherche universitaire et, sur la base de ces besoins, de recevoir chaque

année un crédit global du Gouvernement qu'il doit répartir entre les universités selon les règles que le Conseil exécutif fédéral peut établir; e) de procéder périodiquement à l'examen des termes et des conditions de service du personnel engagé dans les universités et de faire si nécessaire des recommandations à ce sujet au Gouvernement; f) de répartir entre les universités du Nigeria toute l'aide reçue de source extérieure; g) de recommander à l'Inspecteur d'une université d'effectuer une Inspection à l'université en question dans tous les cas et au moment où elle le juge nécessaire et h) d'accréditer tous les programmes menant à l'obtention d'un grade dans les universités et les autres institutions.

La Commission s'occupe donc du développement, de la vérification des comptes et du fonctionnement des universités du Nigeria. Sept universités nouvelles ont été créées au cours de l'année académique 1975–76. Sept nouvelles universités de technologie ont également été créées entre 1980 et 1983, mais le gouvernement fédéral a décidé de réduire leur nombre à trois dès l'année 1984–85, les quatre autres étant administrées en tant que campus d'autres universités. Le nombre total des universités fédérales est maintenant de seize. Le pays compte aussi huit universités créées par les gouvernements des Etats.

La Commission est placée sous la direction d'un Conseil composé d'un président à temps partiel, d'universitaires de diverses disciplines ainsi que de personnalités extérieures à l'université et représentant des domaines divers. Un personnel professionnel à plein temps à la tête duquel se trouve un Secrétaire exécutif dirige les affaires quotidiennes de la Commission.

Executive Secretary: National Assembly Complex, Tafawa Balewa Square, P.M.B. 12694, Lagos.
Tel: 635233

Nigerian Association of University Women (IFUW)

Chairman (Internat. Rel.) and Secretary: Dr. Abimbola Ogumodede.
P.O. Box 611, Ibadan.

World University Service
c/o WUS Office, Room 14, Students Union Building, University of Ibadan, Ibadan.
Telex: 31448

National Association of Nigerian Students – NANS (IUS)
c/o Student's Union, Kaduna Nzeogwu Complex, University of Nigeria, Nsukka.

Nigeria Federation of Catholic Students (Pax Romana)
University of Ife, Ile-Ife.

Association of Catholic Graduates and Professionals (Pax Romana)
College of Science ad Technology, Kaduna.

Student Christian Movement of Nigeria (WSCF)
14 Awosika Avenue, Bodija Estate, P.O. Box 4014, Ibadan.
Tel: 413201

All Nigeria United Nations Student Association (ISMUN)
146 Fajuyi Hall, University of Ife, Ile-Ife.

*

National Standing Committee for the Evaluation of Foreign Qualifications.
c/o Federal Ministry of Education, Science and Technology, Victoria Island, Lagos.
Tel: 12793

Federal Ministry of Education, Science and Technology
Victoria Island, Lagos.
Tel: 12793

Nigerian National Commission for Unesco
Federal Ministry of Education, Science and Technology, Victoria Island, Lagos.
Tel: (Secretary-General) 615795. Cables: seceducate lagos

NORWAY
NORVEGE

UNIVERSITIES AND UNIVERSITY INSTITUTIONS—
UNIVERSITES ET ETABLISSEMENTS UNIVERSITAIRES

*Universitetet i Bergen, Muséplass 1, 5000 Bergen. (Universitetsdirektøren). *1948*
Tel: (5) 213050. Fax: (5) 328585 - 40/1. Telex: 8441023 uibta n. Teletex: 441023 = uibta
F : *soc, med, dent, hist-phil, math-nat, law.*
*Universitetet i Oslo, Blindern, Oslo 3. *1811*
Tel: (2) 455050. Telex: 72425 unios n. Cables: oslo 3
F : *theo, law, med, dent, hist-phil, math-nat, soc.*
*Universitetet i Tromsø, Postboks 635, 9001 Tromsø. *1968*
Tel: (83) 86560. Telex: 64427 ubhov n
F : *fish, med, soc, math-nat, hist-phil, law.*
*Universitetet i Trondheim, Kollegiet, Håkon Magnussonsgt. 1B, 7000 Trondheim. *1969*
Tel: (4717) 955000. Telex: 55273 dragv n
NORGES TEKNISKE HØGSKOLE [Technical U.], 7000 Trondheim. *1900, 1910*
D : *arc, mine, civ eng, elec, ch, mec.*
DEN ALLMENNVITENSKAPELIGE HØGSKOLEN [C. of Arts and Science], 7000 Trondheim.

1922
D : *hum, soc, sc.*
Norges landbrukshøgskole [Agricultural C.], 1432Ås—NLH. *1859*
Tel: (2) 949060. Telex: 77125 nlhbi n
Arkitekthøgskolen i Oslo [S. of Architecture], St. Olavsgt. 6, Oslo 1.
Tel: (2) 208316
Norges handelshøgskole [C. of Economics and Business Administration], Helleveien 30, 5000 Bergen. *1917*
Tel: (5) 256500. Telex: 40462 nhh n
Norges idrettshøgskole [National C. of Physical Education and Sport], Sognsveien 220, Oslo 8.
Tel: (2) 234685
Norges musikkhøgskolen [C. of Music], Postboks 6877, St. Olavsplass, 0165 Oslo 1. *1972*
Tel: (2) 207019
Norges veterinaerhøgskole [Veterinary C.], Ullevålsveien 72, Oslo 4. *1936*
Tel: (2) 693690

OTHER INSTITUTIONS—AUTRES INSTITUTIONS

Regional, Engineering and other Colleges—
Colleges régionaux, d'ingénieurs et autres

Agder distriktshøgskole [Agder C.], Postboks 607, 4601 Kristiansand.
Tel: (42) 27040
eco-adm, publ adm, nautical st, electro comp, techn-eco st, English, math, analytical ch, translation-interp, French, Norwegian lang-lit, Third World st, heal adm.
Hedmark distriktshøgskole, Postboks 104, 2451 Rena.
Tel: (64) 40800
eco-adm, informatics.
Finnmark distriktshøgskole, Postboks 301, 9501 Alta.
Tel: (84) 34011
eco-adm, electro comp, phys, Chris st, Finnish.
Sogn og Fjordane distriktshøgskole, Postboks 39, 5801 Sogndal.

Tel: (56) 71311
eco-adm, ecol, soc, local hist, civics, nat, tour.
Høgskolen i Harstad, Postboks 2140, 9405 Kanebogen.
eco-adm, heal adm.
Møre og Romsdal distriktshøgskole, Postboks 208, 6401 Molde.
Tel: (72) 51077
eco-adm, trans, electro comp, math, pol.
Møre og Romsdal distriktshøgskole, Postboks 188, 6101 Volda.
Tel: (70) 770666
Norwegian lang-lit, Ger, local hist st, local plan, child welfare, Chris st, media commun.
Nord-Trøndelag distriktshøgskole, Postboks 145, 7701 Steinkjer.
eco-adm, agr eco, electro, comp.

Høgskolesenteret i Nordland, Postboks 6003, 8016 Mørkved.
Tel: (81) 17200. Fax: (81) 17457
eco-adm, fish, hist, civics, soc w, electro comp, publ adm, soc, eco-bus adm.
Oppland distriktshøgskole, Postboks 1004 Skurva, 2601 Lillehammer.
Tel: (62) 55600
eco-adm, ped, tour, pol, publ adm, hist.
Østfold distriktshøgskole, Os Alle 9, 1750 Halden.
Tel: (4731) 85400
eco-adm, electro comp, Ger bus lang, heal adm.
Høgskolesenteret i Rogaland, Postboks 2557 Ullandhang, 4001 Stavanger.
Tel: (4) 874100. Fax: (4) 874300
hum-aesthetic st, soc, techn-nat, eco-adm, pet.
Telemark distriktshøgskole, 3800 Bø.
Tel: (36) 60200
eco-adm, env st, hist, Norwegian, English, art dissemination-cult w, agr eco, bookstore mangt, phys, math, English, hist, Norwegian.
Agder ingeniør- og distriktshøgskole, Postboks 94, 4891 Grimstad.
Tel: (41) 41811

Bergen ingeniørhøgskole, Lars Hillesgt 34, 5008 Bergen.
Tel: (5) 333040
Gjøvik ingeniørhøgskole, Postboks 191, 2801 Gjøvik.
Tel: (61) 73548
Hærens ingeniørhøgskole, Hvalsmoen, 3500 Hønefoss.
Horten ingeniørhøgskole, Skippergt. 6, 3190 Horten.
Tel: (4735) 43091
Kongsberg ingeniørhøgskole, Postboks 235, 3601 Kongsberg.
Tel: (3) 734060
Møre og Romsdal ingeniørhøgskole, Fogd. Greves vei, 6009 Ålesund.
Narvik ingeniørhøgskole, Postboks 385, 8501 Narvik.
Tel: (82) 44130. Telex: 64446
NKIs tekniskehøgskole, Ingeniørhøgskolen [NKI Polytechnic, C. of Engineering], Postboks 10, 1321 Stabekk.
Oslo ingeniørhøgskole, Cort Adelergst. 30, 0254 Oslo 2.
Tel: (2) 553000
Østfold ingeniørhøgskole [Østfold C. Engineering], Postboks 192, Valaskjold, 1701 Sarpsborg.
Tel: (31) 42011
Telemark ingeniørhøgskole, Kjølnes, 3900 Porsgrunn.
Tel: (35) 55080
Trondheim ingeniørhøgskole, Gunnerusgt. 1, 7013 Trondheim.

Tel: (75) 21670

Agder maritime høgskole [Agder C. of Maritime Studies], Fløyveien 28, 4800 Arendal.
Cables: maskiniskolen
Bergen maritime høgskole, Haugeveien 28, 5000 Bergen.
Haugesund maritime høgskole, Skåregt. 103, 5500 Haugesund.
Oslo tekniske maritime skole, Postboks 6009, Etterstad, 0601 Oslo 1.
Tel: (2) 193131
Tromsø maritime høgskole, Sommerfeldsgt. 74/76, 9000 Tromsø.
Trondheim maritime høgskole, Ladehammerveien 6, 7041 Trondheim.
Tønsberg maritime høgskole, Postboks 38, 3101 Tønsberg.

Statens kunstakademi [National A. of Art], St. Olavsgt. 32, 0166 Oslo 1.
Tel: (2) 200150
Vestlandets kunstakademi, C. Sundtsgt. 53, 5000 Bergen.
Tel: (5) 317350
Kunstakademiet i Trondheim, Aasta Hensteens vei 22, 7000 Trondheim.
Tel: (7) 912400
Statens høgskole for kunsthåndverk og design i Bergen [C. of Art and Design], Strømsgt. 1, 5000 Bergen.
Tel: (5) 312214
Statens håndverks- og kunstindustriskole [Norwegian C. of Arts and Crafts], Ullevålsveien 5, 0165 Oslo 1.
Tel: (2) 201235
Statens balletthøgskole [C. of Ballet], Tjuvholmen, Bygning B, 0250 Oslo 2.
Den norske balletthøgskole, Sørbyhaugen 33, 0377 Oslo 3.
Statens teaterhøgskole [C. of Dramatic Art], Dokkveien 1, 0250 Oslo 2.
Tel: (2) 140539
Statens operahøgskole [C. of Operatic Art], Dokkveien 1, 0250 Veitvetveien 8, Oslo 2.
Tel: (2) 425274

Økonomisk College [Oslo C. of Business and Economics], Parkveien 65, 0245 Oslo 2.
Trondheim økonomiske høgskole, Klostergt. 90, 7000 Trondheim.
eco-adm, auditing.
Bedrifsøkonomisk institutt [Oslo S. of Business and Management], Postboks 69, 1341 Bekkestua.
Stifelsen Norges Markedshøgskole [Norwegian S. of Marketing], Postboks 210 Økern, 0510 Oslo 5.
Norges fiskerihøgskole [C. of Fishery]. *1972*

[Courses are given by 4 separate institutions: the Universities of Bergen and Tromsø; the Technical University of Trondheim; and the National College of Economic and Business Administration in Bergen).

Møre og Romsdal fiskeritekniske høgskole [C. of Fishery Technology], Postboks 1555 Nørve, 6021 Ålesund.

Statens næringsmiddeltekniske høgskole [C. of Food Technology], Tungaveien 32, 7004 Trondheim.

Norsk hotell høgskole, Box 2536, Ullandhung, 4001 Stavanger.

Norsk journalisthøgskole [C. of Journalism], Frysjaveien 33c, 0883 Oslo 8.
Tel: (2) 236385

Statens bibliotekhøgskole [C. of Library Science], Daelenggt. 26, 0567 Oslo 5.
Tel: (2) 357390

Det norske diakonhjem Sosialhøgskolen [Norwegian Lutheran Hospital and C., D. of Social Work], Postboks 23 Vindern, 0319 Oslo 3.
Norges kommunal-og sosialhøgskolen [National C. of Social Work], Tjernveien 12, 0957 Oslo 9.
Tel: (472) 16430
Sosialhøgskolen, Stavanger, Møllergt. 66, 4000 Stavanger.
Tel: (4) 521080
Sosialhøgskolen, Trondheim, Lade gård, 7000 Trondheim.
Rudolf Steinerhøgskolen, Skoklefall, 1450 Nesodden.
Norsk diakonihøgskole, Lovisenberggt. 11, 0456 Oslo 4.
Misjonshøgskolen [S. of Theology and Missiology], Misjonsveien 34, 4000 Stavanger.
1843, 1977
Tel: (4) 521000
Det Teologiske Menighetsfakultet [Free F. of Theology], Gydas vei 4, 0363 Oslo 3.   *1908*
Tel: (2) 467900

Colleges of Nursing and Health Sciences—
Collèges d'Enseignement infirmier et des sciences de la santé

Statens sykepleierhøgskole [C. of Nursing], Bjerregaardsgt. 21, 0172 Oslo 1.
Aker sykepleierhøgskole, Trondheimsveien 235, 0514 Oslo 5.
Tel: (2) 150892
Aust-Agder sykepleierhøgskole, 4800 Arendal.
Bergen Diakonissehjems sykepleierhøgskole [Bergen Nursing Sisters' C.], Haraldsplass Ulriksdal 8, 5009 Bergen.
Betanien sykepleierhøgskole, Vestlundveien 19, 5033 Fyllingsdalen.
Betanien sykepleierhøgskole, Akersbakken 35, 0172 Oslo 1.
Diakonhjems sykepleierhøgskole, Postboks 23 Vindern, 0391 Oslo 3.
Diakonissehusets sykepleierhøgskole, Lovisenberggt. 15, 0456 Oslo 3.
Tel: (2) 357135
Finnmark sykepleierhøgskole, Postboks 1216, 9601 Hammerfest.
Tel: (84) 12022
Haugesund sjukepleierhøgskole, Skåregt 105, 5500 Haugesund.
Haukeland sykepleierhøgskole, Haukelandsbakken 45, 5000 Bergen.
Tel: (5) 298090
Hedmark sykepleierhøgskole, 2400 Elverum.
Tel: (64) 10066
Innherred sykepleierhøgskole, 7600 Levanger.
Tel: (76) 80022

Kristiansand sykepleierhøgskole, Postboks 2238, Posebyen, 4602 Kristiansand.
Menighetssøsterhjemmets sykepleierhøgskole, Rosenborggt. 8, 0356 Oslo 3.
Tel: (2) 693890
Namdal sykepleierhøgskole, 7800 Namsos.
Sykepleierhøgskole i Oppland, Ludvig Skattumsgt. 30/32, 2800 Gjøvik.
Tel: (61) 74064
Nordland sykepleierhøgskole, Leiteveien 7, 8000 Bodø.
Drammen sykepleierhøgskole, Konggt. 51, 3000 Drammen.
Sykepleierhøgskole i Lørenskog, 1474 Nordbyhagen.
Sykepleierhøgskole i Tromsø, Åsgårdveien 9A, 9000 Tromsø.
publ heal nurs, psyc, nurs, obst.
Høgskolen i Harstad sykepleierutdanningen, Postboks 2144, 9405 Kanebogen.
Sjukepleierhøgskolen i Ålesund, Postboks 40, 6017 Åsestranda.
Tel: (71) 41990
Sjukepleierhøgskolen i Molde, Glomestuveien 33, 6400 Molde.
Tel: (72) 51944
psyc nurs.
Sogn og Fjordane sjukepleiarhøgskolen, 6800 Førde.
Tel: (57) 22011

Stavanger sykepleierhøgskole, Madlaveien 13, 4000 Stavanger.
Tel: (4) 533095

Stord sjukepleierhøgskole, 5400 Stord.

Sykepleierhøgskolen i Sør-Trøndelag, Håkon Jarlsgt. 12, 7000 Trondheim.
Tel: (75) 29145

Telemark sjukepleierhøgskole, Postboks 1408, 3701 Skien.
Tel: (35) 25583

Ulleval sykepleierhøgskole, Kirkeveien 166, 0450 Oslo 1.

Vestfold sykepleierhøgskole, Kong Halvdansgt. 14, 3100 Tønsberg.
Tel: (33) 17010

Østfold sykepleierhøgskole, Rektor Østbyesgt. 2, 1600 Fredrikstad.
Tel: (32) 11245
psyc nurs.

Statens utdanningssenter for helsepersonell høgskole for helsepersonell, høgskole for helsesøstre, jordmødre og psykiatriske sykepleiere, Huk Aveny 56, 0287 Oslo 2.
publ heal nurs, obst, psyc nurs.

Statens spesialskole i pyskiatrisk sykepleie [C. of Psychiatric Nursing], Neståsen, 8000 Bodø.
Tel: (81) 22315

Høgskolen i psykiatrisk sykepleie, Postboks 2225, 5001 Bergen.
Tel: (5) 298090

Ullevål sykepleierhøgskole Spesialutdanning i psykiatrisk sykepleie, Dikemark, 1385 Solberg.

Bergen jordmorhøgskole [C. of Midwifery], Sundtsvei 57, 5050 Nesttun.

Helsesøsterhøgskolen i Trondheim [C. of Public Health Nursing], Eirik Jarlsgate 4, 7000 Trondheim.

Høgskolen i Harstad [C. of Mental Nursing], Vernepleierutdanninger, Postboks 2144, 9405 Harstad.

Akershus vernepleierhøgskole, Emma Hjorthsvei 1, Postboks 372, 1301 Sandvika.

Bergen vernepleierhøgskole, Postboks 2235, 5001 Bergen.
Tel: (5) 342210

Oslo vernepleierhøgskole, H.N. Haugesgt. 44, 0481 Oslo 4.

Rogaland vernepleierhøgskolen, Nærlands-

heimen, 4350 Nærbø.

Vernepleierhøgskolen i Sør-Trøndelag, 7060 Klæbu.

Østfold vernepleierhøgskole, Postboks 1189, Gamle Fredrikstad, 1601 Fredrikstad.
Tel: (32) 22089

Statens reseptarhøgskole [C. of Dispensers], Sven Oftedalsvei 8, 0950 Oslo 9.
Tel: (2) 257850

Radiografhøgskolen [C. of Radiography], Bergen, 5016 Haukeland sykehus.

Radiografhøgskolen, Rikshospitalet, Pilestredet 32, 0027 Oslo 1.

Radiografhøgskolen i Tromsø, Breivika videregående skole, Postboks 3038 Guleng, 9001 Tromsø.

Ullevål radiografhøgskole, Ullevål sykehus, Kirkeveien 166, 0407 Oslo 4.
Tel: (2) 461870 (ext. 8155)

Bioingeniørhøgskolen [C. for Medical Laboratory Engineers], Rikshospitalet, Pilestredet 32, 0027 Oslo 1.

Bioingeniørlinjen, Østfold ingeniørhøgskole, Postboks 1192, Valaskjold, 1701 Sarpsborg.

Bioingeniørhøgskolen, Bergen, 5016 Haukeland sykehus.

Bioingeniørhøgskolen i Tromsø, Breivika vid. skole, Postboks 3038 Guleng, 9001 Tromsø.

Ullevål bioingeniørhøgskole, Ullevål sykehus, Kirkeveien 166, 0467 Oslo 1.
Tel: (2) 461870

Bioingeniørutdanningen, Trondheim ingeniørshøgskole, Gunnerusgt. 1, 7000 Trondheim.

Fysioterapihøgskolen i Oslo [C. of Physiotherapy], Trondheimsveien 132, 0565 Oslo 5.

Fysioterapihøgskolen i Bergen, Møllendalsveien 6, 5000 Bergen.
Tel: (5) 298085

Mensendieck-skolen i Oslo, Grønnegt. 10, 0350 Oslo 3.

Ergoterapihøgskolen i Oslo [C. of Occupational Therapy], Grenseveien 32, 0571 Oslo 5.

Ergoterapihøgskolen i Trondheim, Ulstadløkkveien 15, 7042 Trondheim.

Statens høgskole i ortopediteknikk [C. of Orthopaedics], Sophies Minde, Trondheimsveien 132, 0570 Oslo 5.

Teacher Training—Formation pédagogique

Alta lærarhøgskole, 9500 Alta.
Tel: (84) 34044

Barnevernsadademiet i Oslo, Pedagogisk høgs-

kole, Plogveien 22, 0612 Oslo 6.
Tel: (2) 277860

Bergen lærerhøgskole, Landåssvingen 15, 5030

Landås.
Bodø lærerhøgskole, Rønvik, 8000 Bodø.
Tel: (81) 2
Dronning Mauds Minne, Høgskole for førskoleutdanning, Th. Owesensgt. 18, 7000 Trondheim.
Tel: (7) 512477
Eik lærarhøgskole, 3109 Lofts-Eik.
Tel: (33) 17530
Elverum lærarhøgskole, 2400 Elverum.
Tel: (64) 11655
Halden lærerhøgskole, Rommen, 1750 Halden.
Tel: (31) 84444
Hamar lærarhøgskole, 2300 Hamar.
Kristiansand lærerhøgskole, Kongsgård alle 20, 4600 Kristiansand.
Levanger lærarhøgskole, 7600 Levanger.
Tel: (76) 81211
Nesna lærarhøgskole, 8700 Nesna.
Tel: (86) 56102
Oslo lærarhøgskole, Wergelandsveien 29, 0167 Oslo 1.
Tel: (2) 465512
Sagene lærarhøgskole, Biermannsgt. 2, 0473 Oslo 4.
Tel: (2) 380498
Sogndal lærerhøgskole, Postboks 211, 5801 Sogndal.
Tel: (56) 71311
Stabekk høgskole [National C. of Home Economics], 1340 Bekkestua.
Tel: (2) 120720
Statens lærerhøgskole i forming Blaker [National C. for Teachers of Arts and Crafts], 1925 Blaker.
Statens lærerhøgskole i forming, Oslo, Cort Adelersgt. 33, 0254 Oslo 2.
Tel: (2) 562385
Statens lærerhøgskole i handels- og kontorfag [National C. of Commercial Education], Stubbveien 3, 3500 Hønefoss.
Tel: (67) 25100
Statens spesiallærerhøgskole [State C. of Special Education], Granåsen 4, 1347 Hosle.
Tel: (472) 248490
Statens yrkespedagogiske høgskole, Skedsmogt. 25, 0655 Oslo 6.
Tel: (2) 674585
Stavanger lærerhøgskole, Postboks 2521, Ullandhaug, 4001 Stavanger.
Tel: (45) 55072
Stord lærarhøgskole, 5414 Rommetveit.
Tel: (54) 10288
Telemark lærarhøgskole, 3670 Notodden.
Tromsø lærerhøgskole, Mellomveien 110, 9000 Tromsø.
Trondheim lærerhøgskole, Breidablikkveien 39, 7000 Trondheim.
Tel: (7) 511266
Volda lærarhøgskole, 6100 Volda.

The Council of Universities and Colleges in Norway

The Council, formerly the Conference of Rectors, is composed of the Rectors and the Directors (plus up to two persons) of the Norwegian universities and university level colleges and representatives of the Norwegian Union of Students. Each delegation (or institution) has one vote.

The Council elects a chairman for one year. The meetings rotate every half year between the different universities and colleges. The Secretary-General of the Council is elected for a period of five years.

The Council discusses and may give statements on matters of common interest, such as long-term planning, to the universities. The Council appoints members to *ad hoc* committees and to more permanent organs for higher education and research in Norway. It elects representatives to Nordic, European or other common organs.

A representative of the Ministry of Education and a representative from the Ministry of Agriculture are regularly invited to take part in the discussions.

Le Conseil, précédemment Conférence des Recteurs, est composé des Recteurs et des Directeurs (plus un ou deux membres) des universités et des collèges de niveau universitaire norvégiens et des représentants de l'Union norvégienne des étudiants. Chaque délégation (ou institution) a droit à une voix.

Le Conseil élit un président pour une année. Les réunions se tiennent tous les six mois par roulement dans les différents collèges et universités. Le Secrétaire général du Conseil est élu pour une période de cinq ans.

Le Conseil délibère et peut faire des déclarations sur des questions d'intérêt commun aux universités, telles que la planification à long terme. Le Conseil nomme les membres de comités ad hoc ou des organismes plus permanents de l'enseignement supérieur et de la recherche norvégiens, et choisit des représentants aux organisations nordiques, européennes ou communautaires.

Un représentant du ministère de l'éducation et un représentant du ministère de l'agriculture sont régulièrement invités à participer aux débats.

Secretary-General: Magne Lerheim, Director of the University of Bergen, Box 25, 5027 Bergen.
Tel: (5) 213050. Fax: (5) 328585

Norske Kvinnelige Akademikeres Landsforbund (IFUW)
Skytterveien 33, 5035 Bg/Sandviken.
World University Service – S.A.I.H. (WUS)
Chr. Krohgsgt. 3213, Oslo 1.
Tel: (047) 2.11.37.15. Telex: 74523 saih n
Norsk Studentunion – NUS
Lokkeveien 7, Oslo 1.
Studenternes Reiskontor – SR
Universitetssentret, Blindern, Oslo 3.
Katolsk Studentlag (Pax Romana)
Dominikanerne, Neuberggatan 15, Oslo 3.
Norges Kristelige Studenterbevegelse (WSCF)
Universitetsgate 20, Oslo 1.
National Union of Jewish Students (WUJS)

Contact: 89 Chaussee De Vleurgat, 1050 Brussels (Belgium).
Tel: (2) 647.7279. Telex: 20625

*

Det Kongelige Kirke- og Undervisnings-department (The Royal Ministry of Church and Education)
Oslo.
Tel: (2) 41.90.00. Telex: 17241 nsbp n
Norwegian National Commission for Unesco
Klingenberggatan 5, 0117 Oslo 1.
Tel: (472) 42.62.63. Telex: 71004. Cables: norunesco oslo

OMAN
OMAN

Sultan Qaboos University, Al Khoudh, Muscat.
1980
Tel: 513333. Telex: 5602 squ on

C : *ed-Isl sc, eng, sc, agr, med.*
Ce : *comp, lang, Isl res.*

Ministry of Education
Muscat.
Tel: 704852. Telex: 3369 tarbia on

The Oman National Commission for Education, Science and Culture
Ministry of Education, Muscat.
Tel: 704582. Telex: 3369 tarbia on

PAKISTAN
PAKISTAN

UNIVERSITIES AND TECHNICAL UNIVERSITIES — UNIVERSITES ET UNIVERSITES TECHNIQUES

Allama Iqbal Open University, Sector H-8, Islamabad. *1974*
Tel: 854246. Cables: openvarsity
F : *soc-hum, sc, ped.*
I : *ed techn.*

Azad Jammu and Kashmir University, Muzaffarabad. *1980*
Tel: 2060
F : *sc, eng, agr, adm.*

Bahaudin Zakariya University, Multan. *1975*
Tel: 33162. Cables: univzakariya
F : *arts-soc, sc-eng-agr, Isl st-lang, com-law-bus adm, med-dent-phar.*
D : *ch, math, phy, stat, eco, English, pol-int aff, Urdu, phar, hist, bus adm.*
Also 34 affiliated colleges.

Islamia University of Bahawalpur, Bahawalpur. *1975*
Tel: 4273
F : *arts, sc, law-Isl st.*
Also 12 affiliated colleges.

University of Baluchistan, Sariab Road, Quetta. *1970*
Tel: 70431
F : *arts, sc.*
D : *phy, ch, math, geol, eco, pol, soc w, Urdu, English, Isl st, com, ed, socio.*
Ce : *mines, Pakistan st.*
Also 13 affiliated colleges and institutes.

University of Agriculture, Faisalabad. *1961*
Tel: P.B.X. 25911/19. Cables: agrivarsity
F : *agr, an hus, vet, sc, agr eng-techn, eco-rur socio, sc.*
D : *ed, extension.*
COLLEGE OF VETERINARY SCIENCES, Lahore.
PAKISTAN MEN'S CO-OPERATION TRAINING RESEARCH INSTITUTE, Chak-Faiz, Multan.
Also *c.* 65 departments.

Gomal University, Dera Ismail Khan. *1974*
Tel: 9235. Cables: unigml
F : *sc, arts, agr.*
COLLEGE OF COMMERCE. *1974*
COLLEGE OF AGRICULTURE. *1980*
WENSAM COLLEGE. *1979*
UNIVERSITY LAW COLLEGE. *1974*
Also 8 affiliated colleges.

International Islamic University, P.O. Box 1243, Islamabad. *1980*

Tel: 852566. Telex: 54068. Cables: aljamia

University of Karachi, University Road, Karachi 32. *1951*
Tel: 462011/7
F : *arts, sc, bus adm-com, law, med, Isl st, phar, ed.*
I : *bus adm, ch, Eur st, marine sc, env st, clin psyc, appl eco.*
Also 43 affiliated colleges.

Agha Khan University of Health Sciences, P.O. Box 3500, Stadium Road, Karachi 5. *1983*
Tel: 420051/5

NED University of Engineering and Technology, University Road, Karachi 32. *1977*
Tel: PABX Exchange 464061/5
F : *eng, math, arc-plan.*
D : *civ eng, elec, mec, math, hum.*
Also 4 affiliated colleges.

Lahore University of Management Sciences, 103-C/2, Gulberg 111, Lahore. *1985*
Tel: 870385/9. Telex: 44291 ums pk. Cables: lgsba
S : *bus adm* (graduate).

*University of Engineering and Technology, Grand Trunk Road, Lahore 31. *1961*
Tel: 331875. Cables: univengtech
F : *arc-urb, nat-hum-Isl st, civ eng.*
Also 7 affiliated colleges.

Mehran University of Engineering and Technology, Jamshoro. *1977*
Tel: 71197. Cables: muetjam
F : *eng, techn, arc-urb plan.*
Also 3 affiliated colleges.

University of Peshawar, Peshawar. *1950*
Tel: 41200
F : *arts, sc, Isl st-Arabic, orntl lang.*
INSTITUTE OF EDUCATION AND RESEARCH.
COLLEGE OF HOME ECONOMICS.
JINNAH COLLEGE FOR WOMEN.
ISLAMIA COLLEGE.
LAW COLLEGE.
QUAID-E-AZAM COLLEGE OF COMMERCE.
Also 43 affiliated colleges.

NWFP Agricultural University, P.O. Pat., Forest Institute, Peshawar. *1981*
Tel: 40491
F : *agr, an hus-vet, rur soc.*

NWFP University of Engineering and Tech-

nology, Peshawar.   *1980*
Tel: 40573
F : *eng.*
*University of the Punjab, Lahore.   *1882*
Tel: 54428
F : *arts, sc, com, Isl & orntl st, law, med-dent, eng-techn, phar, ed.*
D : *adm sc, bus adm, eco, hist, jour, lib, phil, pol, socio, app psyc, space sc, bot, geog, geol, math, phy, zoo, Arabic, Persian, Punjabi, Urdu, soc w, fa, Isl st, phar, English, French.*
I : *eng-techn, stat, ch, ed-res, South Asian st.*
Ce : *solid state phy, soc, Urdu Encyclopedia of Islam, Urdu dev, literacy hist* (all res).
  HAILEY COLLEGE OF COMMERCE.   *1927*
  UNIVERSITY LAW COLLEGE.   *1870*
  ORIENTAL COLLEGE.   *1970*
Also 135 affiliated colleges.
Quaid-e-Azam University, P.O. Box 1090, Islamabad.   *1965, 1967*
Tel: 824801

F : *nat, soc, med.*
*University of Sind, Jamshoro (Hyderabad).   *1947*
Tel: 71291/5 Cables: unisind
F : *arts, ed, med, Isl st, law, sc.*
D : *comparative relig-Isl cult, pol, int rel, hist, eco, com, Urdu, Sindhi, English, phil, psyc, geog, socio, soc w, fa, lib, bot, zool, geol, stat, fresh water biol-fish, physiology, jour, milit sc, phar.*
I : *ed res, ch, lang, Sindhology, phy-techn, math-comp, bus st.*
Also 69 affiliated colleges.
Shah Abdul Latif University, Khairpur.   *1987*
Tel: 3091
F : *sc, arts.*
Sind Agricultural University, Tandojam, (Hyderabad).   *1977*
Tel: 40436. Cables: sauni
F : *agr, an hus-vet, agr eng.*

University Grants Commission

The Commission was established in June 1973 and given a Charter on 27 April 1974 by an Act of Parliament for, "the promotion and co-ordination of university education, the determination and maintenance of standards of teaching, examination and research in universities, the promotion of national unity and solidarity, and the orientation of university programmes to national needs." It consists of 7 members: the Chairman, a Wholetime Member, 2 Honorary members, the Secretary to the Government of Pakistan, Ministry of Education (*ex officio*), the Chairman of the Pakistan Science Foundation (*ex officio*), and the Chairman of the Vice-Chancellors' Committee (*ex officio*). The first 4 are appointed by the Federal Government from amongst eminent educationalists including scientists of repute for a period of 3 years and are eligible for reappointment.

It acts on behalf of the Federal Government as a funding agent and assesses the financial needs of universities; evaluates development programmes on higher education in general, collects and disseminates data on higher education; develops educational manpower by organizing grants, fellowships, scholarships and visiting professorships within and outside the country; supports and co-ordinates research programmes; and advises the government on the expansion of higher education, the establishment of new universities or improvement of existing institutions. These functions are carried out through several Statutory Committees. The Vice-Chancellors' Committee advises the

Commission on all academic decisions and is the main policy developing body. It appoints its own Chairman by rotation and meets frequently.

The Commission makes special studies on problems of higher education. Current programmes for Qualitative Improvement of University Education include: Educational Development; Research Capability Enhancement; Teaching Training and Development; Faculty Development; Language Training Centre; Curriculum and Material Resource Development; Study Groups on various subjects; Centre of Basic Sciences; Centre of Social Sciences and Humanities; Development and Maintenance Equipment; Centralized Services for Universities; Student Development; Women's Education Studies; and Linkages with other Universities and Agencies.

The commission has established at various universities Centres of Excellence and Advanced Studies, as well as Centres for the Study of various contemporary societies, particularly those affecting the national interest in the regional areas. Pakistan Study Centres have also been established in order to strengthen national cohesion and integration, and to help people understand the language and literature, social structure, customs, trends and traditions of the people from other regions of the country.

In order to meet the urgent need for the improvement of the quality of education at university and college level, the Commission has established the National Academy of Higher Education, whose primary function is to inform existing teachers of new methods. It also provides

initial training for newly-recruited teachers in methods and techniques in order to help in the development of better interaction with students. In addition, the Academy arranges Seminars, Conferences, and Workshops for the improvement of the quality of teaching and research in various disciplines.

La Commission des crédits universitaires a été créée en juin 1973 et s'est vu accorder une charte le 27 avril 1974 en vertu d'une loi du Parlement, "afin de promouvoir et coordonner l'enseignement universitaire, définir et maintenir les niveaux de l'enseignement, des examens et de la recherche dans les universités, promouvoir l'unité et la solidarité nationales, et orienter les programmes universitaires vers la réalisation des besoins nationaux." Elle comprend sept membres: le Président, un Membre à plein temps, deux membres honoraires, le Secrétaire du Ministère de l'éducation du Gouvernement du Pakistan (membre de droit), le Président de la Fondation pakistanaise de la Science (membre de droit), et le Président du Comité des Vice-Chanceliers (membre de droit). Les quatre premiers sont nommés pour trois ans par le Gouvernement fédéral parmi d'éminents responsables de l'éducation comprenant des scientifiques en renom, et sont rééligibles.

Elle agit, au nom du gouvernement fédéral, en tant qu'organisme de financement et examine les besoins financiers des universités; procède à des évaluations des programmes de développement des universités et de l'enseignement supérieur en général; rassemble et diffuse des données sur l'enseignement supérieur; améliore la formation des étudiants et du personnel enseignant en octroyant des subventions et en créant, notamment pour les enseignants, des bourses qui sont valables aussi bien dans les universités du pays qu'à l'étranger; soutient et coordonne les programmes de recherche, et conseille le Gouvernement pour le développement de l'enseignement supérieur, la création d'universités nouvelles ou l'amélioration des institutions existantes. Ces fonctions sont remplies par plusieurs comités créés en vertu d'une loi. Le Comité des Vice-Chanceliers conseille la Commission pour toutes les questions relatives à l'enseignement et est l'organisme principal pour l'élaboration de la politique. Il nomme par roulement son propre Président et se réunit fréquemment.

La Commission effectue des études spéciales sur les problèmes de l'enseignement supérieur. Parmi les programmes en cours portant sur l'amélioration de la qualité de l'enseignement supérieur, il convient de citer: le développement de l'éducation; le développement des possibilités en matière de recherche; la formation à l'enseignement et l'amélioration de la pédagogie; l'amélioration de

la formation pédagogique des enseignants; le centre de formation linguistique; les programmes d'enseignement et l'accroissement des ressources matérielles; les groupes d'études sur divers sujets; le Centre de sciences fondamentales; le Centre de sciences sociales et sciences humaines; le développement et le matériel d'entretien; la centralisation des services dans les universités; les études sur l'enseignement dispensé aux femmes; et les associations avec d'autres universités et institutions.

La Commission a créé dans diverses universités des centres d'excellence et d'études avancées, ainsi que des centres pour l'étude des divers groupes sociaux de l'époque actuelle, particulièrement ceux qui exercent une influence sur l'intérêt national dans les régions. Des centres pour l'étude du Pakistan ont également été créés afin de renforcer la cohésion et l'intégration nationales et d'aider la population à comprendre la langue, la littérature, la structure sociale, les coutumes, les traditions et les tendances que l'on constate au sein des populations des autres régions du pays.

Afin de faire face à l'urgente nécessité d'améliorer la qualité de l'enseignement aux niveaux tant de l'université que du collège, la Commission a créé un organisme intitulé National Academy of Higher Education, qui a essentiellement pour but d'informer les enseignants sur la pédagogie nouvelle. Elle dispense également aux enseignants récemment entrés en fonctions une formation initiale aux méthodes et techniques destinées à les aider à établir une meilleure interaction avec les étudiants. L'Academy organise en outre des séminaires, des conférences, et des ateliers visant à améliorer la qualité de l'enseignement et de la recherche dans diverses disciplines. Sector H-9, Islamabad.

Tel: 853811. Cables: unigrant

National Science Council
63 School Road, Shalimar 7/4, Islamabad.
Pakistan Association of University Professors and Lecturers (IAUPL)
Contact: 18, rue du Docteur Roux, 75015 Paris (France).
Tel: (33-1) 47.83.31.65.
Pakistan Federation of University Women (IFUW)
165—L, Block III, P.E.C.H.S., Karachi.
World University Service (WUS)
Correspondent: Manzoor Ahmad.
University of Karachi, Karachi.
Tel: 462011. Telex: 54157 peer pk
Student Christian Movement in Pakistan (WSCF)
c/o Gordon College, P.O. Box 260, Rawalpindi.

*

Ministry of Education
Islamabad.
Tel: 811879
Central Bureau of Education
Sector H9, Cultural Area, Islamabad.

Pakistan National Commission for Unesco
Ministry of Education, Islamabad.
Tel: 811879. Telex: 5591 ugc pk. Cables:
education islamabad

PANAMA
PANAMA

*Universidad de Panamá, Estafeta Universitaria, Panamá. (Sr. Secretario General).
                                                        1935
Tél: 63-6133
F : phil-let-éd, adm publ-com, ing, dr-pol, sc, méd, dent, arc, nat-phar-inf, agr.
Universidad Santa María La Antigua, Apartado 6—1696, Panamá 6.   *1965, 1973*
Tél: 60-6311
D : adm, soc, techn-nat-arc, hum-ét relig, dr-pol.

Universidad Tecnológica, Panamá.   *1984*
F : *gé civ, élec, méc, inft.*
Escuela Náutica de Panamá, Apartado 5936, Panamá 2.
Tél: 64-8625
Escuela Superior de Secretarias Ejecutivas Bilingües, Panamá.   *1971*
Instituto Superior de Turismo, Panamá.
                                                        1972
Instituto Superior de Enseñanza, Panamá.
                                                        1969

Servicio Universitario Mundial (WUS)
Apartado 6—3093, El Dorado, Panamá.
Tél: 27-2136
Federación de Estudiantes de Panamá – FEP (IUS)
Editora Bayono, Apartado 1699, Panamá 9A.
Telex: 2771 pgs
Juventud Universitaria Cristiana (Pax Romana)
Apartado 439, Panamá 9A.
Movimiento de Profesionales Católicos (Pax Romana)
Calle Colombia 6, Apartado 1510, Panamá 7.

*

Organismo Provisional para la Implementación de la Aplicación del Convenio de México
Ministerio de Educación, Apartado 2440, Panamá 3.
Tél: 62.4177
Ministerio de Educación
Apartado 2440, Panamá 3.
Tél: 62.4177
Comisión Nacional Panameña de Cooperación con la Unesco
Ministerio de Educación, Apartado 2440, Panamá 3.
Tél: 62.4177. Cables: Comision unesco mineduc panama

PAPUA NEW GUINEA
PAPOUASIE NOUVELLE GUINEE

*University of Papua New Guinea, P.O. Box 320, University, National Capital District. (The Registrar).   *1965*
Tel: 253900. Fax: 245187. Telex: 22366 unipng ne. Cables: university, port moresby
F : *arts, sc, law, ed, med.*

UNIVERSITY OF PAPUA NEW GUINEA – GOROKA TEACHERS' COLLEGE, P.O. BOX 1078, Goroka, Eastern Highlands Province. (The Principal).   *1976*

Papua New Guinea University of Technology, Private Mail Bag, Post Office, Lae, Morobe Province. (The Registrar).   *1972*

Tel: 434999. Fax: 424067. Telex: 42428 utech ne. Cables: utech, lae
D : *acc-bus, appl phy, arc-bui, chemical techn, civ eng, elec, mec, for, surv-land st, lang-soc, math, agr.*

Divine Word Institute, P.O. Box 483, Madang. (The Registrar).   *1980*
F : *commun arts, bus st, relig st.*

Pacific Adventist College, Private Mail Bag, Post Office, Boroko, National Capital District. (The Principal).   *1984*
Tel: 281112
D : *com, ed, theo.*

World University Service (WUS)
P.O. Box 79, University of PNG P.O., Waigani.
Tel: 253900. Telex: 22366 ne

Papua New Guinea National Union of Students – PNGNUS (IUS)
Papua New Guinea University of Technology, Lae.
Telex: 42428 ne

Student Christian Movement (WSCF)
P.O. Box 195, University of Papua New Guinea, Waigani.

Commission for Higher Education
P.O. Box 5117, Boroko.
Tel: 272000

Papua New Guinea National Commission for Unesco
Ministry of Education, Boroko.
Tel: 276111. Telex: 22193 ne. Cables: eduoff moroko

*

PARAGUAY
PARAGUAY

Universidad Católica «Nuestra Señora de la Asunción», Calle Independencia Nacional y Comuneros, Asunción. (Rectorado).   *1960*
Tél: 41044
F : phil-éd, dr-ét dipl, pol-soc, comp-adm; dr, phil-éd, comp-adm (Villarrica); phil, comp-adm (Concepción); phil-éd, dr, comp-adm (Encarnación); comp-adm (Pedro Juan Caballero).
I : ét relig.
Universidad Nacional de Asunción, España 1198, Asunción.   *1890*
Tél: 204960

F : dr-soc, phil, ch-phar, phy-math, arc, méd, dent, éco, agr, vet.
E : bibl.
I : serv soc, inf, obst.
Escuela Superior de Filosofía, Ciencias y Educación, Asunción.   *1944*
D : ch, éd, phil-let, sc, soc.
Instituto Superior de Educación, Avenida Eusebio Ayala Km. 4.5, Asunción.
Instituto Nacional de Investigaciones Científicas, P.O. Box 1141, Asunción.   *1957*
D : phy, ch, math, psyc-éd.

Movimiento de Egresados Universitarios Católicos (Pax Romana)
Casilla Correos 394, Asunción.
Juventud Estudiantil Católica (Pax Romana)
Casilla de Correos 394, Asunción.
Juventud Paraguaya por los Derechos Humanos (ISMUN)
Colón 871, Asunción.

Ministerio de Educación y Culto
Casilla de Correos 1080, Asunción.
Tél: 43919
Comisión Nacional Paraguaya de Cooperación con la Unesco
Chile 864, Casilla de Correos 1080, Asunción.
Tél: 43919. Cables: mineducation y culto chile 864 asunción

*

PERU
PEROU

UNIVERSITIES AND TECHNICAL UNIVERSITIES—
UNIVERSITES ET UNIVERSITES TECHNIQUES

National Institutions—Etablissements nationaux

*Universidad Nacional de «San Agustin», Siglo XX No. 227, Apartado 23, Arequipa, Arequipa.   *1825, 1928, 1969*
Tél: 227678
P : dr, hum, sc, éd, méd-inf, éco-comp, hist-soc, géol, biol, ch, arc, agr, gé ind, mét, phy, techn phy.

Universidad Nacional «San Cristóbal de Hua-manga», Portal Independencia 57, Apartado 120, Ayacucho, Ayacucho.
1677, 1959, 1969
Tél: 2522. Télex: 64753 unsch pe
P : agr, biol, éd, soc, inf-obst, mine, gé ch, éco-comp-adm, dr.

Universidad Nacional de «Cajamarca», Jr. Lima No. 549, Apartado 16, Cajamarca, Cajamarca.
1962, 1969
Tél: 922516
P : éd, agr, inf, gé civ, vét, socio, comp, zoo, obst.

Universidad Nacional del «Callao», Avenida Saenz Peña 1060, Apartado 138, Callao, Callao.   *1966*
Tél: 291600
P : comp, éco, élec, méc, gé ch, gé pêch.

Universidad Nacional «Daniel Alcides Carrión», Edificio Estatal 4, Apartado 77, Cerro de Pasco, Pasco.   *1965, 1969*
Tél: 2197
P : éd, éco-comp, ing, zoo, inf, géol.

Universidad Nacional de Santa, Avenida Pacífico 508, Urb. Buenos Aires, Chimbote, Ancash.
Tél: 311556

Universidad Nacional «San Antonio Abad», Avenida de la Cultura s/n., Apartado 367, Cusco, Cusco.   *1598, 1692, 1969*
Tél: 222271. Telex: 52209 unsaac pe
P : éco, comp, éd, techn, géol, mét, mine, zoo.

Universidad Nacional «José Faustino Sánchez Carrión», Avenida Grau 592, Apartado 81, Huacho, Lima.   *1967*
Tél: 324741
P : adm, comp, gé pêch, bromatologie-nutr, sociol-trav soc, gé ind, inf.

Universidad Nacional del «Centro del Perú», Calle Real 160, Apartado 77, Huancayo, Junín.
1959, 1962, 1969
Tél: 233032. Télex: 6400 pe
P : arc, agr, éco-adm, éd, zoo, for, méc-élec, gé ch, inf-serv soc, ind alim.
FILIAL DE LA UNIVERSIDAD DEL CENTRO, Huacho, Lima.
P : pêch, éco-com, let-éd.

Universidad Nacional «Hermilio Valdizán», Dos de Mayo 680, Huánuco, Huánuco.   *1964, 1969*
Tél: 2340
P : agr, éd, éco-com, inf, gé civ, gé ind.

Universidad Nacional «Santiago Antúnez de Mayolo», Avenida Centenario s/n, Apartado 70, Huaráz, Ancash.   *1977*
Tél: 721393
P : mine, gé civ, gé agr, gé ind alim.

Universidad Nacional «San Luis Gonzaga», Jr. Cajamarca 194, Ica, Ica.   *1955, 1961, 1969*
Tél: 233201
P : éco-adm, sc app, nat, éd, dr, ing, méd, vét, dent.

Universidad Nacional de la «Amazonía Peruana», Jr. Próspero 584, Apartado 496, Iquitos, Loreto.   *1967, 1969*
Tél: 235351
P : biol, inf, éd, ing, adm, comp.

Universidad Nacional «Pedro Ruiz Gallo» [National U. of Lambayeque], Jr. 8 de Octubre 637, Casilla 557, Lambayeque, Lambayeque.
1963, 1970
Tél: 2080
P : ing, biol, vét, inf, soc-éco, dr.

Universidad Nacional Agraria, Avenida de la Universidad s/n, Apartado 456, La Molina, Lima.   *1901, 1960, 1969*
Tél: 352035
P : zoo, gé agr, gé for, gé pêch, éco-plan, gé alim.

Universidad Nacional de Educación «Enrique Guzmán y Valle», La Cantuta, Chosica, Lima.
1967
Tél: 910052

P : sc-hum, éd, phys, éd techn.

Universidad Nacional de «Ingeniería», Avenida Túpac Amaru s/n, Apartado 1301, San Martín de Porres, Lima. *1875, 1954, 1969*
Tél: 811035
P : sc, arc-urb-art, géol-mine-mét, gé civ, méc-élec, ing ind, ing sani, pét, plan, gé ch.

Universidad Nacional «Mayor de San Marcos», República de Chile 295, Lima, Lima. *1551, 1861, 1969*
Tél: 314629
P : biol, soc, comp-adm, dr-pol, éco, éd, phar-bioch, phil-psyc-art, géol, ing, mét, lit-jour-ling-phill, math-phy, méd, vét, od, ch, nutr.

Universidad Nacional de Piura, Prolongación Avenida Grau s/n, Piura, Piura. *1961*
Tél: 321931. Telex: 21360 limaudep pe
P : agr-zoo, mine, comp, éco, gé ind, gé pêch, adm, méd; comp, gé pêch, agr (Tumbes).

Universidad Nacional de Pucallpa, Pucallpa, Ucayali. *1979*
Tél: 6044

Universidad Nacional del «Altiplano», Ciudad Universitaria, Apartado 291, Puno, Puno. *1961, 1969*
Tél: 324673. Telex: 54772 undapun pe
P : soc, vét-zoo, gé agr, mine, biol, éd.

Universidad Nacional «Federico Villarreal»,
Calle Carlos González 285, San Miguel, Lima. *1963, 1969*
Tél: 644370
P : arc-urb, soc-adm, éd, éco-com, océanog, dr-pol, gé ind, pêch techn, méd, dent, gé civ, géog, psyc.

Universidad Nacional «Jorge Basadre Grohmann», Avenida Bolognesi, Ciudad 15, Apartado 316, Tacna, Tacna. *1971*
Tél: 721385
P : mét, mine, comp, adm, gé pêch, agr-ind alim, obst.

Universidad Nacional de San Martín, Tarapoto, San Martín. *1979*

Universidad Nacional «Agraria de la Selva» [U. d'Agriculture tropicale], Apartado 156, Tingo María, Huánuco. *1964*
Tél: 2341
P : agr, zoo, gé ind alim.

Universidad Nacional de «La Libertad», Independencia 431, Trujillo, La Libertad. *1824, 1969*
Tél: 243721
P : biol, dr-pol, éco, ch, sc méd, éd, méc, gé ind, gé ch, mét, phy-math, phar-bioch, soc.

Universidad Nacional de Tumbes, Bolognesi 218, Tumbes, Tumbes.
Tél: 3081

Private Institutions—Etablissements privés

Universidad Particular de Apurimac, Jr. Apurimac 408, Abancay, Apurimac.

Universidad Católica de Santa María, Apartado 1350, Arequipa, Arequipa. *1961, 1969*
Tél: 224401
P : éco-com, soc, dr, sa, éd-théo, arché.

Universidad Particular de Chiclayo, Avenida Quiñones 615, Chiclayo, Lambayeque.
Tél: 226670

Universidad Particular «Los Angeles» de Chimbote, José Olaya 981, Chimbote, Ancash.
Tél: 321621

Universidad Andina del Cusco, Parque La Madre 186, Cusco, Cusco.
Tél: 226377

Universidad Privada «Los Andes», Jr. Cuzco 259, Huancayo, Junín.
Tél: 234480

Universidad «Víctor Andrés Belaúnde», Avenida 28 de julio 1127, Oficina 204, Huánuco, Huánuco.
Tél: 2094

*Universidad del Pacífico, Avenida Salaverry 2020, Apartado 4683, Jesús María, Lima. *1962, 1969*
Tél: 712277
P : éco, adm, comp.

Universidad Andina «Néstor Cácares Velásquez», Carretera Km. 19, Apartado 4896, Juliaca, Puno.
Tél: 540

Universidad Unión Incaica, Edificio El Campin, Oficina 301, Naña, Lima.
Tél: 910842

Universidad «Ricardo Palma», Avenida Prolongación Benavides Gda. 54, Las Gardenias, Surco, Lima. *1963*
Tél: 459035
P : arc, biol, éco, psyc, ing, interp-trad.

Universidad «San Martín de Porres», Calle Bolívar 348, Miraflores, Lima. *1962, 1969*
Tél: 442905
P : let, éd.
I : phil-soc, hist, géog.

*Pontificia Universidad Católica del Perú, Avenida Bolívar s/n, Pueblo Libre, Lima. *1917, 1942, 1969*
Tél: 622540
P : let, hum, ing, agr, soc, éd, dr, adm.
E : ét soc, éd, jour, arts plast, nor.
Ce : lang.

Universidad Femenina del Sagrado Corazón, Avenida Los Frutales s/n, Monterrico, Lima. *1962, 1967, 1969*

Tél: 36461
P : éd, trad, ét gén, socio, psyc, arc.
Universidad de Lima, Avenida Javier Prado s/n, Apartado 852, Monterrico, Lima. *1962, 1969*
Tél: 350677
P : adm, commun, cinéma-télévision, comp, éco, gé ind, gé des systèmes, mét, adm de l'éd, dr-pol.
Universidad de Piura, Ciudad Universitaria San Eduardo, Apartado 3208, Piura, Piura. *1968*
Tél: 328171
P : arts lib, ing, adm des aff, infor, gé ind.
Universidad Particular Inca Garcilaso de la Vega, Avenida Arequipa 1841, Lince, Lima.

1964, 1969
Tél: 711421
P : adm, gé adm, psyc, socio-trav soc, comp, éco, éd, gé ind, pol.
*Universidad Peruana Cayetano Heredia, Avenida Honorio Delgado 932, Apartado 5045, San Martín de Porres, Lima. *1961, 1969*
Tél: 815772
P : méd, sc-phil, math app, stom.
Universidad de Tacna, Opus Sacerdotale Co-operationis Hispano Americanao P.J. Vigil, Calle San Camilo 1000, Tacna, Tacna.
Tél: 725343

OTHER INSTITUTIONS—AUTRES INSTITUTIONS

Professional Education—Enseignement professionnel

Amazonas

Instituto Superior Tecnológico «Gustavo Lananta Luján», Chachapoyas-Leymebariba. *1980*
agr, const, méc.
Instituto Superior Tecnológico «Peru-Japan», Jr. Amazonas 120, Chachapayas. *1984*
Tél: 179
Instituto Superior Tecnológico «Utcubamba», Bagua Grande. *1987*
agr, inf tec.
Instituto Superior Tecnológico «Bagna», Distrito La Peca. *1987*
for, const civ.
Instituto Superior Tecnológico «Amazonas», Jr. Comercio 849, Bagua. *1984*
comp, inf tec.

Ancash

Instituto Superior Tecnológico «Aija», Fundo Monserrate, Aija. *1985*
agr.
Instituto Superior Tecnológico «Daniel Villar», Caraz. *1984*
élec, méc.
Instituto Superior Tecnológico «Casma», Casma. *1987*
inf tec, const civ.
Instituto Superior Tecnológico «Carlos Salazar Romero», Avenida Pacífico s/n Urban, Buenos Aires, Chimbote, Ancash. *1977*
Tél: 31-1581
méc, mét, élec-électro, adm, comp.
Instituto Superior Tecnológico «Chiquián», Mishay Alto, Chiquián. *1984*
élec, méc.

Instituto Superior Tecnológico «Eleazer Guzmán, Huaraz, Ancash. *1984*
méc, sa, agr, tour, élec-électro, mét.
Instituto Superior Tecnológico «Huaraz», Huaraz.
comp.
Instituto Superior Tecnológico «Huarí», Barrio Magisterial, Huarí.
agr.
Instituto Superior Tecnológico «Huarmey», Huarmey.
agr.
Instituto Superior Tecnológico «Piscobamba», Piscobamba.
agr.

Apurimac

Instituto Superior Tecnológico «Abancay», Abancay.
agr, const civ.

Arequipa

Instituto Superior Tecnológico «Pedro P. Diaz», Francisco Pizarro, 130 Porongoche, Arequipa. *1976*
Tél: 22-5672
adm, élec-électro, mét.
Instituto Superior Tecnológico «Monseñor Júlio González Ruiz», Catahuasi, La Unión, Arequipa.
agr, const civ.
Instituto Superior Tecnológico Ciencias Tecnológicas, Calle Santa Marcha 209, Arequipa.
Tél: 21-4045
Instituto Técnico Superior de Administración de Empresas, Calle Paral, 217, Arequipa.

adm des aff.

Instituto Superior Tecnológico «Cayetana Heredia», Avenida Independencía 946, Arequipa.
Tél: 225441
comp, inf tec.

Instituto Superior Tecnológico «Ecan», Avenida Salaverry 302, Vallacito, Arequipa.
Tél: 22-2705
adm.

Instituto Superior Tecnológico «Arequipa», Calle Rivero 311, Arequipa.
Tél: 21-4074
électro, inft.

Instituto Superior Tecnológico «Albert Einstein», Calle Rivero 306 y la Nerced 425, Arequipa.
Tél: 21-9125
électro, inft.

Instituto Superior Tecnológico «Isiproda», Calle Rivero 306, Arequipa.
comp-inft.

Instituto Superior Tecnológico «Del Sur», Calle Palacio Viojo 114, Arequipa.
adm, banc, comp.

Instituto Superior Tecnológico «La Recoleta», Calle Recoleta 117, Yanahuara, Arequipa.
méc, élec.

Instituto Superior Tecnológico «Javier Prado», Avenida Prolongación, Mariscal Castilla 72LB, Arequipa.
inf tec.

Instituto Superior Tecnológico «Maria Montessori», La Merced 212, Arequipa.
Tél: 21-3521
inf tec.

Instituto Superior Tecnológico «Faustino B. Franco», Camaná.
agr.

Ayacucho

Instituto Superior Tecnológico «Victor Alvarez Huapaya», Jr. San Martín 367, Ayacucho.
1978
Tél: 2335
agr, méc, sa.

Instituto Superior Tecnológico «Chipas», Chipas-Lucanas, Ayacucho.
agr, inf tec.

Instituto Superior Tecnológico «Aucara», Aucara-Lucanas, Ayacucho.
agr.

Instituto Superior Tecnológico «Cora Cora», Coracora.
agr. const civ.

Instituto Superior Tecnológico «Huancapi», Huancapi.
agr, inf tec.

Instituto Superior Tecnológico «Huanta», Huanta.
agr, élec.

Cajamarca

Instituto Superior Tecnológico «Bambamarca», Miguel Grau s/n, Bambamarca.
agr, mét, élec.

Instituto Superior Tecnológico «Cajabamba», Balta 193, Cajabamba.
agr, méc, élec.

Instituto Superior Tecnológico «Cajamarca», Km 3½ Carretera Baños del Inca, Cajamarca.
agr, for.

Instituto Superior Tecnológico «Cascas», Cascas-Contumaza, Cajamarca.
agr.

Instituto Superior Tecnológico «Mariano Iberico Rodríguez», José Gálvez 683, Cajamarca.
comp, adm.

Instituto Superior Tecnológico «Pedro Ortiz Montoya», Celendin.   1980
agr, const, sa, méc.

Instituto Superior Tecnológico «Chota», Fundo Tuctuhuasi, Chota.
agr, méc de prod.

Instituto Superior Tecnológico «Felipe Alva y Ava», Contumaza.
agr, comp.

Instituto Superior Tecnológico «Cutervo», Cutervo.
agr, élec, inf tec.

Instituto Superior Tecnológico «4 de Junio de 1821», Jaén.   1980
agr, const, méc, agroind.

Instituto Superior Tecnológico «San Ignacio», Santa Rosa Cdra. 3, San Ignacio.
agr, for, comp, adm.

Instituto Superior Tecnológico «San Marcos», Huayabamba, San Marcos.
agr, comp.

Instituto Superior Tecnológico «San Miguel», San Miguel.
agr.

Instituto Superior Tecnológico «13 de Julio», Jr. Cajamarca s/n, San Pablo.
agr, comp.

Instituto Superior Tecnológico «Santa Cruz», Santa Cruz.
agr, comp, inf tec.

Callao

Instituto Superior Tecnológico «Simón Bolívar», Avenida Colonial Cdr. 32, Callao, Callao.
1976
Tél: 65-1774
sa, élec-électro, tec lab, ch.

Instituto Superior Tecnológico «San Antonio»,
Avenida Saenz Peña 1330, Bellavista, Lima 2.
Tél: 292524

Cusco

Instituto Superior Tecnológico «Tupac Amaru»,
Avenida La Cultura s/n. San Sebastián, Cusco.
1976
Tél: 231187
agr, tour, méc, sa, adm, élec-électro.
Instituto Superior Tecnológico «Espinas»,
Espinas.
agr, inf tec.
Instituto Superior Tecnológico «Vilcanota»,
Sicuani.
agr, const civ.
Instituto Superior Tecnológico «Tayapampa»,
Tayapampa.
agr.
Instituto Superior Tecnológico «Urubamba»,
Urubamba.   *1978*
agr, for, const civ.

Huancavelica

Instituto Superior Tecnológico «Huancavelica»,
Jr. Huayna Cápac 350, San Cristobal,
Huancavelica.
agr, comp, inf tec.
Instituto Superior Tecnológico «Pampas»,
Pampas-Tayacaja.
agr, élec.

Huánuco

Instituto Superior Tecnológico «Ambo», Ambo.
agr.
Instituto Superior Tecnológico «Aparicio
Pomares», Huánuco.   *1980*
adm, const, sa.
Instituto Superior Tecnológico «Glicerio Goméz
I.», Huamalies, Llata, Huánuco.
agr, const civ.
Instituto Superior Tecnológico «Naranjillo»,
Huánuco.
agr, élec.
Instituto Superior Tecnológico «Ricardo Salinas
Vara», Dos de Mayo, Huánuco.
agr, inf tec.

Ica

Instituto Superior Tecnológico «Chincha»,
Avenida Unión s/n, Pueblo Nuevo, Chincha.
1978

agr, adm, const.
Instituto Superior Tecnológico «Catalina Buendía
de Pecho», Ica.   *1980*
Tél: 23-2246
méc, élec, comp, mét.
Instituto Superior Tecnológico «Marcona»,
Colugio Nacional San Juan, Ica.
électro, inf tec.
Instituto Superior Tecnológico «San Agustin»,
Municipalidad 234, Ica.
Tél: 23-4540.
comp, adm, inf tec.
Instituto Superior Tecnológico, Nazca, Ica.
1980
agr, méc, élec-électro, arts vis.
Instituto Superior Tecnológico «Palpa», Río
Grande, Palpa, Pisco.
agr.
Instituto Superior Tecnológico «Pisco», Pisco.
agr, comp.

Junín

Instituto Superior Tecnológico «Andrés Avelino
Cáceres», Huancayo.   *1980*
Instituto Superior Tecnológico «Santiago
Autúnex de Mayolo», Apartado 287, Palián,
Huancayo.   *1976*
Tél: 23-1632
agr, méc, sa, adm, mét, const.
Instituto Superior Tecnológico «Continental»,
Calle Real 125, Huancayo.
adm, inft, élec.
Instituto Superior Tecnológico «San Pedro», Real
235, Huancayo.
comp-inft.
Instituto Superior Tecnológico «Alejandro O.
Deustua», Jr. Ancash 441, Huancayo.
comp, adm.
Instituto Superior Tecnológico «San Ignacio de
Layola», Calle Simón Bolívar 250, Junín.
agr, comp.
Instituto Superior Tecnológico «Sausa», Augusto
Hector Aliaga E., Jauja, Junín.
agr.
Instituto Superior Tecnológico «Ramiro Priale
Priale», 9 de Julio, Concepción, Junín.
agr.
Instituto Superior Tecnológico «Huasicancha»,
Victor Raúl Castellar Z, Junín.
agr.
Instituto Superior Tecnológico «Parakas», Urb.
«La Morales», Ica.
tour.
Instituto Superior Tecnológico «Adolfo Vien-
rich», Malecón Galvez s/n, Casilla 232, Tarma.
1978
méc, const, adm.

La Libertad

Instituto Superior Tecnológico «Chocope», Chocope, Ascope.
agr.

Instituto Superior Tecnológico «Paiján», Ascope.
inf tec, ind alin.

Instituto Superior Tecnológico «Bolívar», Bolívar.
agr.

Instituto Superior Tecnológico «Ciro Alegría Bazán», Avenida Panamericana Norte s/n, Chepén.
comp, adm, méc, inf tec.

Instituto Superior Tecnológico «Guadalupe», Avenida Ayacucho 284, Guadalupe.
agr, comp

Instituto Superior Tecnológico «Jorge Demaison S.», Jr. Sarmiento 1138, Pacasmayo.
Tél: 2305.
agr, élec, méc.

Instituto Superior Tecnológico «Erasmo Arellano G.», Pataz.
mine.

Instituto Superior Tecnológico «Huamachuco», Sanchez Carrión, Santiago de Chuco.
agr, const civ.

Instituto Superior Tecnológico «Víctor Andrés B.», Santiago de Chuco.
agr.

Instituto Superior Tecnológico «Chan Chan», Trujillo.
Tél: 23-5305
élec, const civ, méc prod, méc agr, pêch.

Instituto Superior Tecnológico «Del Norte», Avenida del Ejército 940, Trujillo.
Tél: 24-6152
comp, sec, inft, tec.

Instituto Superior Tecnológico «John F. Kennedy», Jr. Bolívar, Trujillo.   1980
Tél: 25-0911
comp, tour.

Instituto Superior Tecnológico «Nueva Esperanza», Avenida José Castelli s/n, Trujillo.

Instituto Superior Tecnológico «Trujillo», Calle Albrecht 319, Urb. Los Quinteros, Trujillo.
comp, sec, tour.

Instituto Superior Tecnológico «Trujillo», Jr. Amazonas 202, Trujillo.   1979
agr, adm, comp.

Instituto Superior Tecnológico «Manuel Gonzáles Prada», El Porvenir, Trujillo.
méc, élec.

Instituto Superior Tecnológico «Indoamericano», Trujillo.
agr, const civ, comp.

Instituto Superior Tecnológico «Cima», Calle San Martín 540, Trujillo.
inft, élec.

Instituto Superior Tecnológico «Jorge Basadre», Ricardo Palma 348-Urb. Palermo, Trujillo.
Tél: 23-4561
inft, dess int, inf tec.

Instituto Superior Tecnológico «Los Libertadores», Avenida 29 de Diciembre 113, Trujillo.
tour, lab.

Instituto Superior Tecnológico «San Luis», Avenida Salvador Lara 30, Urb. Huerta Granda, Trujillo.
inft, inf tec.

Instituto Superior Tecnológico «Virú», Virú.
agr, comp, tec lab.

Lambayeque

Instituto Superior Tecnológico «Chiclayo», Avenida Batta 658, Chiclayo.
Tél: 23-2801

Instituto Superior Tecnológico «República Argentina», Calle Arica 845, Chiclayo.
Tél: 23-3573

Instituto Superior Tecnológico «República Federal Alemania», Avenida Elvira García y García 755, Chiclayo.
adm, comp, élec-électro, méc, processus ind.

Instituto Superior Tecnológico «Elias Aguirre», Jr. Torres Paz 199, Chiclayo.
Tél: 22-7065
inft.

Instituto Superior Tecnológico «Bertrand Russell», Calle 7 de Enero 632, Chiclayo.
Tél: 23-4442
élec, comp, inf tec.

Instituto Superior Tecnológico «Cayetano Heredia», Batte 1624, Chiclayo.
inf tec.

Instituto Superior Tecnológico «Manuel Mesones Muro», Alica 1168, Chiclayo.
inf tec, comp.

Instituto Superior Tecnológico «Enrique López Alburjar», Ferrenafe.   1980
Tél: 57
agr, const.

Instituto Superior Tecnológico «Motupe», Motupe.
agr, adm.

Instituto Superior Tecnológico «Olmos», Calle Sto. Domingo 112, Via Chiclayo, Olmos.
Tél: 12
agr, méc.

Lima

Instituto Superior Tecnológico «Cosmetologia», Psje. Nacarino 120, Breña, Lima 5.
Tél: 321644

Instituto Superior Tecnológico, Apartado 11, Quilmaná, Cañete.   1977

Tél: 007
adm, agr.
Instituto Superior Tecnológico Amauta, Avenida
Bolivis 284, Cercado, Lima.   *1979*
Tél: 24-1673
adm.
Instituto Superior Tecnológico de Lima, Avenida
Arequipa 979, Cercado, Lima 1.   *1980*
Tél: 720419
adm, élec-électro, méc, inf tec, tec phar.
**Instituto Superior Tecnológico «Pedro Ruíz
Gallo»**, Plaza 2 de Mayo 26, Altos 201,
Cercado, Lima 1.   *1980*
Tél: 285941
**Instituto Superior Tecnológico «ADEC»-Asesoría
de Empresas Comerciales**, Cercado, Lima 1.
sec, comp.
Instituto Superior Tecnológico «SEGUROS»,
Cercado, Lima 1.
Tél: 283986
adm.
**Instituto Superior Tecnológico «Peruano
Alemán»**, Avenida Garcilazo de la Vega 1218,
Cercado, Lima 1.
Tél: 236427
tec de lab clin, inft tec, tec phar, comp, sec.
**Instituto Superior Tecnológico «Victor Andrés
Belaunde»**, Jr. Miroquesada 11, Cercado,
Lima 1.   *1980*
Tél: 286458
comp, sec.
**Instituto Superior Tecnológico «Computronic
Tech»**, Avenida Uruguay 135, Cercado,
Lima 1.
inft.
Instituto Superior Tecnológico «Lima», Cara-
baua 474, Jr. de la Unión 1143, Cercado,
Lima 1.
Tél: 330510
comp, élec, électro, inf tec.
Instituto Superior Tecnológico «IDAT», Avenida
Arequipa 599, Cercado, Lima 1.
comp, adm, élec.
**Instituto Superior Tecnológico «Santa María
Reyna»**, Avenue Uruguay 316, Cercado,
Lima 1.
Tél: 247084
comp, inf tec.
Instituto Superior Tecnológico «San Marcos 2»,
Jr. Rufino Torrico 640, Cercado, Lima 1.
comp, adm.
**Instituto Superior Tecnológico «Federico W.
Taylor»**, Jr. Chancay 515, Cercado, Lima 1.
Tél: 311208
comp.
Instituto Superior Tecnológico «Max Uhle», Jr.
Carabaya 1127, Cercado, Lima 1.
comp, const civ, inft.
Instituto Superior Tecnológico «Sebastián

Salazar», Jr. Puno 722, Cercado, Lima 1.
comp.
**Instituto Superior Tecnológico «Daniel Alcides
Carrión»**, Avenida Arequipa 955, Cercado,
Lima 1.
Tél: 237246
comp, adm, phar, inf tec.
Instituto Superior Tecnológico «ESAE», Jr.
Chancay 869, Cercado, Lima 1.
Tél: 277798
compt, tour.
Instituto Superior Tecnológico «ETA», Jr.
Carabava 1133, Cercado, Lima 1.
Tél: 2219858
comp, électro.
**Instituto Superior Tecnológico «Garcilazo de la
Vega»**, Psje. Nueva Rosita 175, Lima.
Tél: 323020
comp, électro, agr, inf tec.
Instituto Superior Tecnológico «Julio C. Telio»,
Avenida 28 de Julio 787, Cercado, Lima 1.
Tél: 246959
comp, inft, dess publicité.
Instituto Superior Tecnológico «CESAEN», Jr.
Chancay 834, Cercado, Lima 1.
Tél: 239327
comp, adm.
**Instituto Superior Tecnológico «Nuestra Señora
del Carmen»**, Jr. Washington 1270, Cercado,
Lima 1.
comp.
**Instituto Superior Tecnológico «Alberto Leopoldo
Barton»**, Pqseo de la Republica 786, Cercado,
Lima 1.
Tél: 232235
comp, inf tec.
**Instituto Superior Tecnológico «Federico Villa-
real»**, Jr. Callao 229, Cercado, Lima 1.
Tél: 285274
comp, tec lab clin, inf tec, ch ind.
Instituto Superior Tecnológico «ESADE»,
Avenida Arequipa 331, Cercado, Lima 1.
Tél: 244563
comp, inft, adm.
**Instituto Superior Tecnológico «Oscar Miro
Quesada de la Guerra-Racso»**, Avenida Garci-
lazo de la Vega 1538, Cercado, Lima 1.
Tél: 236792
comp, adm, inft.
Instituto Superior Tecnológico «COOPIP»,
Avenida Rep. de Portugal 181, Brena, Cer-
cado, Lima 1.
comp, élec, électro.
**Instituto Superior Tecnológico «Señor de los
Milagros»**, Jr. 338, Cercado, Lima 1.
Tél: 272976
comp, adm.
**Instituto Superior Tecnológico «Santiago de
Surco»**, Jr. Chancay Cdra. 7, Cercado, Lima 1.

comp, adm, sec.

Instituto Superior Tecnológico «Óptica y Optometría», Camana 615, Cercado, Lima 1.
opt.

Instituto Superior Tecnológico «Cayetano Heredia de Lima», Avenida Uruguay 315, Cercado, Lima 1.
inf tec.

Instituto Superior Tecnológico «Datapro», Avenida Los Rosales 373, Lima 7.
Tél: 424914
comp, électro.

Instituto Superior Tecnológico «Perú», Es. Jr. Chota y Pasco Coló, Cercado, Lima 1.
Tél: 240405
comp, sec, tour.

Instituto Superior Tecnológico «Almirante Grau», Calle Acieclo Villaren 330, Cercado, Lima 1.
Tél: 324313
comp, inft, sec.

Instituto Superior Tecnológico «Harvard», Avenida España 267, Cercado, Lima 1.
sec, inf tec, comp, lab clin.

Instituto Superior Tecnológico «Sergio Bernales», Avenida Arequipa 991, Cercado, Lima 1.
Tél: 248248
lab clin, tec phar, inf tec.

Instituto Superior Tecnológico «George Boole», Avenida Arequipa 2865, Cercado, Lima 1.
Tél: 240204
comp-inft, électro.

Instituto Superior Tecnológico «Peruano», Jr. Washington 1369, Cercado, Lima 1.
méc, élec, électro, const civ.

Instituto Superior Tecnológico «Salesiano», Avenida Brasil 210, Cercado, Lima 1.
méc, phil-relig, élec, électro.

Instituto Superior Tecnológico «Gran Mariscal Ramón Castilla», Avenida Arequipa 199, Cercado, Lima 1.
inft.

Instituto Superior Tecnológico «Diseño», Jr. Ica 376, Cercado, Lima 1.
dess.

Instituto Superior Tecnológico «Manuel Seoane G.», Avenida Fernado Wiesso y Avenida Bayevar, Canto Grande, Lima 36.
méc, élec, ch ind.

Instituto Superior Tecnológico «Manuel Arévalo C.», Avenida Alises y Avenida Las Palmeras, Lima 31.
inf tec, ind alim, élec.

Instituto Superior Tecnológico «Antenor Orrogo Espinoza», Avenida Ciro Alegrín, Buenos Aires de Villa, Lima 9.
ind alim, inft, élec.

Instituto Superior Tecnológico «Luis Negreires Vega», Avenida José Granda, Cendevilla, Lima 31.
élec, const civ.

Instituto Superior Tecnológico «Huarochirí», Huarochirí, Urb. Chacarilla.
agr.

Instituto Superior Tecnológico «Comercio Exterior», Avenida Salaveray 1910, Jesús María, Lima 11.
Tél: 717007
adm des aff int.

Instituto Superior Tecnológico «Peruano de Computación e Informática», Jr. Arnaldo Marquez 1513, Jesús María, Lima 11.
Tél: 235726
inft.

Instituto Superior Tecnológico «CEPEA», Avenida República de Chile 314, Jesús María, Lima 11.   *1979*
Tél: 245441
comp, adm, tour, sec.

Instituto Superior Tecnológico «CESCA», Jr. Talara 774, Jesús María, Lima 11.
Tél: 328853
comp, électro, tour, inft, inf tec, tec de lab clin.

Instituto Superior Tecnológico «José Pardo», Avenida Grau 620, La Victoria, Lima 1.
Tél: 315040
élec, électro, const civ, méc.

Instituto Superior Tecnológico «Victor Raúl Haya de la Torre», E.P.S. «18 de Enero», Jirón Sta. Catalina, Malva Rosa-Barranca.
agr, comp.

Instituto Superior Tecnológico «César Vallejo», Avenida Arequipa 2515, Lince, Lima.
Tél: 450895
tour, adm.

Instituto Superior Tecnológico «Ernest Wilhelm Middendorf», San Antonio, Miraflores, Lima 18.   *1976*
Tél: 450895
adm, tec de lab, trad.

Instituto Superior Tecnológico «ITAE», Jr. Bolognesi 364, Miraflores, Lima 18.
comp, tec, sec, tour.

Instituto Superior Tecnológico-Escuela de Decoración de Interiores, Avenida 2 de Mayo 535, Miraflores, Lima 18.
Tél: 461386
dess.

Instituto Superior Tecnológico Metropolitano, Avenida Central 126, Cd. 36, Miraflores, Lima 18.   *1980*

Instituto Superior Tecnológico «San Ignacío de Loyola», Avenida Santa Cruz 410, Miraflores, Lima 18.
Tél: 459366
inft, comp, sec, tec.

Instituto Superior Tecnológico «SISE», Avenida 28 de Julio 745, Miraflores, Lima 18.

Tél: 44958
inft.
Instituto Superior Tecnológico «Siglo XXI», León García 3ra Cuadra, Miraflores, Lima 18.
Tél: 485781
inft, élec, électro.
Instituto Superior Tecnológico «Toulouse Lautrec», Malicón Batta 1070, Miraflores, Lima 18.
Tél: 467168
dess.
Instituto Superior Tecnológico «Antonio Raimondi», Antonieta Angelica, Avenida 28 de Julio 487, Miraflores, Lima 18.
inft, sec.
Instituto Superior Tecnológico Unión, Km. 19 Carretera Central, Ñaña, Lima 8. *1979*
Tél: 910842
adm, comp, sa, élec, alim ind.
Instituto Superior Tecnológico «CIBERTEC», Jr. Manuel Bañón 360, San Isidro, Lima 27.
inft.
Instituto Superior Tecnológico «Montemar», Avenida Arequipa 3420, San Isidro, Lima 27.
Instituto Superior Tecnológico «ISETEC», Avenida Coronel Portillo 474, San Isidro, Lima 27.
Tél: 406511
inft, dess.
Instituto Superior Tecnológico «Instituto Peruano de Publicidad», Avenida El Bosque 350, San Isidro, Lima 27.
Tél: 406238
Instituto Superior Tecnológico «Sentur», Avenida Arequipa 2633, San Isidro, Lima 27.
Tél: 404841
tour.
Instituto Superior Tecnológico «Sistema Perú», Juan de Arona 150, San Isidro, Lima 27.
Tél: 428186
télévision.
Instituto Superior Tecnológico «Montessori», Los Pinos 530, San Isidro, Lima 27.
Tél: 409576
dess.
Instituto Superior Tecnológico «San Agustin», Avenida Javier Prado 980, San Isidro, Lima 27.
inft.
Instituto Superior Tecnológico «Gilda Liliana Ballivián Rosado», Lizardo Montero s/n, San Juan de Miraflores, Lima 29.
1980
adm, comp, const, élec-électro.
Instituto Superior Tecnológico «María Rosario Araoz Pinto», José Marti 150, San Miguel, Lima 32. *1976*
adm, const, arts vis, méc.
Instituto Superior Tecnológico «Tusan», Jr. Cantuarias 155, San Miguel, Lima 32.

électro, inft.
Instituto Superior Tecnológico «TECSUP», Avenida Industrial s/n, Carretera Central KM. 5.7, Santa Anita, Lima 8.
Tél: 371905
élec ind.
Instituto Superior Tecnológico «Jatum Yauyos», Yauyos, Lima.
agr, const civ.
Instituto Superior Tecnológico «Julio César Tello», Avenida Maríategui s/n, Villa El Salvador, Lima 42. *1980*
adm, comp, méc, mét, processus ind.
Instituto Superior Tecnológico «Santa Mariana de Jésus», Jr. Tiachuanaco 679, Zarate, Lima 36.
Tél: 811914
ch ind, inf tec.
Instituto Superior Tecnológico «Pedro del Aguila Hidalgo», Aveynida del Ejército s/n, Iquitos. *1976*
Tél: 23-4451
sa, méc, adm, const, agr, for, élec-électro.
Instituto Superior Tecnológico «Corpus Christi», K. 4 Carretera Abelardo, Quillones.
inf tec, tour, comp.

Madre de Dios

Instituto Superior Tecnológico «Jorge Basadre G.», Aveynida Fitzcarrald Cdra. 14, Puerte Maldonado. *1980*
agr, méc, sa.

Moquegua

Instituto Superior Tecnológico «José Carlos Mariategui», Samegua. *1976*
Tél: 374
sa adm, mét, méc, comp.
Instituto Superior Tecnológico «Mariano Lino Urquieta», Avenida Uruguay 173, Urb. Garibaldi I 20, Moquegua.
inft, inf tec, comp.
Instituto Superior Tecnológico «Luis E. Valcarcel», Ilo.
comp, sec.

Pasco

Instituto Superior Tecnológico, Avenida Los Incas s/n, San Juan Pampa, Pasco. *1980*
Tél: 2110
méc, const civ, élec, électro.
Instituto Superior Tecnológico «Huariaca», Carretera Central de Tunaspampa s/n, Huariaca. *1982*
agr, comp, inf tec.
Instituto Superior Tecnológico «Daniel A. Car-

rión G.», Avenida 28 de Julio s/n, Yanahuanca.
agr, inf tec.
Instituto Superior Tecnológico «Oxapampa», Jr.
Enrique Battger s/n, Oxapampa.
inf tec, comp.
Instituto Superior Tecnológico «Paucartamba»,
Pasco.
agr.

Piura

Instituto Superior Tecnológico «Almirante Miguel Grau», Prolongación Avenida Grau, Apartado 466, Piura. *1976*
Tél: 32.3068
agr, élec-électro, méc, adm, mét.
Instituto Superior Tecnológico Cosmos, Jr.
Libertad 714, Piura. *1980*
sc publicité, comp, adm, sec.
Instituto Superior Tecnológico «Sullana»,
Sullana. *1980*
agr, const civ, comp, inf tec, méc de production.
Instituto Superior Tecnológico «San Juan», Jr.
José de Lama 195, Sullana.
Tél: 2354
comp, sec, tour, inft, élec.
Instituto Superior Tecnológico «San Miguel de Piura», Avenida Guardia Civil 222, Piura.
inft.
Instituto Superior Tecnológico «Otto Tonsmann», Huancavelice G-10, Buenos Aires, Piura.
inf tec, tec phar.
Instituto Superior Tecnológico «Nestor Martes Garrido», Huancabamba.
agr.
Instituto Superior Tecnológico «Vicus», Calle Lima 323, Chulucanas.
agr, inf tec.
Instituto Superior Tecnológico «Ayabaca», Piura.
agr.
Instituto Superior Tecnológico «Hermanes Carcamo», Paita.
élec, agr.
Instituto Superior Tecnológico «Luciano Castillo C.», Talara.
ch ind, méc, comp.
Instituto Superior Tecnológico «La Unión», La Unión.
agr, élec.

Puno

Instituto Superior Tecnológico «Juli», Ciudad de Juli.
agr.

Instituto Superior Tecnológico «José Antonio Encinas», Fundo Salcedo Rinconada, Puno. *1976*
Tél: 207
agr, méc, adm, const, élec-électro.
Instituto Superior Tecnológico «Manuel Nuñez Butrón», Morales Huascar 762, Juliaca, Urb. La Capilla. *1976*
méc, comp, sec, inf tec.
Instituto Superior Tecnológico «Ayaviri», Balsaspata, Ayaviri.
comp, agr.
Instituto Superior Tecnológico «Huancané», Huancané.
agr, inf tec.
Instituto Superior Tecnológico «Pedro Vilcapaza», Azangaro.
agr, inf tec.
Instituto Superior Tecnológico «Yunguyo», Yunguyo.
agr, inf tec.

San Martin

Instituto Superior Tecnológico «Nor Oriental de la Selva», Calle Tupac Amarú 398, Banda Silcayo, Tarapoto. *1978*
méc, élec, agr, const civ, for.
Instituto Superior Tecnológico «Alto Mayo», Mayamba.
agr, comp.
Instituto Superior Tecnológico «Rioja», Rioja.
agr, méc, inf tec.
Instituto Superior Tecnológico «Huallaga», Saposa.
agr, inf.
Instituto Superior Tecnológico «Tocache», Tocache.
agr.
Instituto Superior Tecnológico «Bellavista», Bellavista.
agr, const civ.
Instituto Superior Tecnológico «Santo Cristo de Bogazón», Ramón Castillo 268, Tarapoto.
adm, comp, inf tec.

Tacna

Instituto Superior Tecnológico «Francisco de Paula Gonzales Vigil», Avenida Circunvalción s/n, Tacna. *1977*
Tél: 72-1201
agr, élec-électro, const civ, méc, comp.
Instituto Superior Tecnológico «Ramón Copaja», Tarata.
agr.

Tumbes   *Ucayali*

Instituto Superior Tecnológico «José Abelardo Quiñones», Apartado 73, Tumbes.   *1977*
Tél: 3833
méc, inf tec, électro, const civ, sec, adm.

Instituto Superior Tecnológico «Suiza», Km. 6 de la Carretera «Federico Basadre», Coronel Portillo, Pucallpa.   *1980*
agr, for, sa, méc, const civ, élec, comp, sec.
Instituto Superior Tecnológico «Atalaya», Raymundy.
agr.

Teacher Training—Formation pédagogique

Instituto Superior Pedagógico «San Juan Bautista de La Salle» de Abancay, Calle Lima 135, Apartado 60, Abancay, Apurímac.   *1981*
Instituto Superior Pedagógico «José María Arquedas» de Andahuaylas, Coyahuacho s/n, San Jeronimo, Andahuaylas, Apurímac.
Instituto Superior Pedagógico de Arequipa, Jr. La Merced 313, Arequipa, Arequipa.
Instituto Superior Pedagógico «Nuestra Sra. de Lourdes» de Ayacucho, Avenida 28 de Julio 393, Ayacucho, Ayacucho.
Instituto Superior Pedagógico de Azángaro, Jr. Villacampa s/n, Azángaro, Puno.
Instituto Superior Pedagógico Particular «Salesiana», Avenida Brasil 210, Apartado 999, Lima 6, Lima.
Instituto Superior Pedagógico «Ciro Alegría Bazán», Jr. Odonován 740, Cajabamba, Cajamarca.
Instituto Superior Pedagógico de Cajamarca, Avenida El Maestro, Apartado 15, Cajamarca, Cajamarca.
Instituto Superior Pedagógico Particular «San José», Yauyos, Cañete, Lima.
Instituto Superior Pedagógico de Cañete, Mercado Modelo Norte, Cañete, Lima.
Instituto Superior Pedagógico de Celendín «Aristides Merino Nerino», Jr. Pardo 731, Celendín, Cajamarca.
Instituto Superior Pedagógico de Cerro de Pasco, Avenida 6 de Diciembre, San Juan de Yanacancha, Cerro de Pasco, Pasco.
Instituto Superior Pedagógico «Toribio Rodríguez de Mendoza» de Chachapoyas, Jr. Triunfo s/n 6ta., Chachapoyas, Amazonas.
Instituto Superior Pedagógico «Sagrado Corazón de Jesús» de Chiclayo, Jr. Leonardo Ortíz Cahuide s/n, Chiclayo, Lambayeque.
Instituto Superior Pedagógico Particular «Sto. Toribio de Mogrovejo», Jr. Leticia 318, Chiclayo, Lambayeque.
Programa de Formación de Prof. de Educación Primaria, Chimbote, Ancash.
Instituto Superior Pedagógico de Chincha, Avenida América 201, Chincha, Ica.
Instituto Superior Pedagógico «Nuestra Sra. de

Chota», Jr. Atahualpa 106, Chota, Cajamarca.
Instituto Superior Pedagógico «Teodoro Peñaloza» de Chupaca, Avenida Los Héroes 380, Chupaca-Huancayo, Junín.
Instituto Superior Pedagógico «Gregorio Mendel» de Chuquibambilla, Prelatura de Chuquibambilla, Graú, Apurímac.
Programa de Formación de Profesores de Primaria, Jr. Melgar s/n, Contumazá, Cajamarca.
Instituto Superior Pedagógico de Coracora, Plaza Jorge Chávez, Coracora, Ayacucho.
Instituto Superior Pedagógico «Octavio Matta Contreras» de Cutervo, Jr. Obrero s/n, Cutervo, Cajamarca.
Instituto Superior Pedagógico «Santa Rosa» de Cuzco, Calle San Andrés, Apartado 267, Cusco, Cusco.
Instituto Superior Pedagógico «Faustino Sánchez Carrión» de Huamachuco, Prolongación Sánchez Carrión s/n, Huamachuco, La Libertad.
Instituto Superior Pedagógico de Huancavelica, Plaza Santo Domingo s/n, Huancavelica, Huancavelica.
Instituto Superior Pedagógico «José Salvador Cavero» de Huanta, Jr. Ayacucho 567, Huanta, Ayacucho.
Instituto Superior Pedagógico «Marcos Durán Martel», Carretera Central s/n, Paucarbamba, Huánuco, Huánuco.
Instituto Superior Pedagógico de Huaráz, Jr. Víctor Vélez s/n, Barrio de Nicrupampa, Apartado 82, Huaráz, Ancash.
Instituto Superior Pedagógico de Ica «Juan XXIII», Calle Dos de Mayo 158, Ica, Ica.
Instituto Superior Pedagógico de Iquítos, Jirón Putmayo 355, Maynas, Iquítos, Loreto.
Instituto Superior Pedagógico «Victor Andrés Belaundé» de Jaén, Jirón Bolívar 1695, Jaén, Cajamarca.
Instituto Superior Pedagógico de Juliaca, Carretera Norte Salida al Cuzco, Juliaca, Puno.
Instituto Superior Pedagógico «Hermilio Valdizán» de La Unión, Jr. San Antonio s/n, La Unión, Huánuco.
Instituto Superior Pedagógico de Educación

Física de Lampa, Prolongación J.M. Ríos s/n, Lampa, Puno.

Instituto Superior Pedagógico Particular «Sto. Domingo de Guzmán», Prolongación Arenales 420, Lima, Lima.

Instituto Pedagógico Nacional de Educación Inicial, Jr. Victor Criado Tejado 2712, Urb. Elio, Lima, Lima.

Instituto Superior Pedagógico Particular «Marcelino Champagnat», Jr. Martír Olaya 162, Lima, Lima.

Instituto Pedagógico Nacional de Monterrico, Apartado 247, Monterrico, Lima.

Instituto Superior Pedagógico «Mercedes Cabello de Carbonara», Carretera Moquegua, Moquegua.

Instituto Superior Pedagógico «Generalísimo José de San Martín» de Moyobamba, Jr. Pedro Pascasio Noriega s/n, Moyobamba, San Martín.

Instituto Superior Pedagógico «Ntra. Señora de la Asunción» de Otuzco, Otuzco, La Libertad.

Instituto Superior Pedagógico «David Sánchez Infante» San Pedro de Lloc, Panamericana Norte Km. 659, San Pedro de Lloc, La Libertad.

Instituto Superior Pedagógico de Piura, Avenida Chulucanas s/n, Santa Rosa, Piura.

Instituto Superior Pedagógico de Pomabamba, Pomabamba, Ancash.

Instituto Superior Pedagógico de Pucallpa, Jirón Sáenz Peña s/n, Pucallpa, Ucayali.

Instituto Superior Pedagógico Bilingue de Yarinacochas, Yarinacochas, Pucallpa, Ucayali.

Instituto Superior Pedagógico Particular Cate-quética, Avenida Sucre 1200, Lima 21, Lima.

Instituto Superior Pedagógico «Ntra. Señora del Rosario» de Puerto Maldonado, Puerto Maldonado, Madre de Dios.

Instituto Superior Pedagógico de Puquio, Avenida Mariano Salas s/n, Lucanas, Ayacucho.

Instituto Superior Pedagógico de Puno, Fundo Salsedo s/n, Apartado 81, Puno, Puno.

Instituto Superior Pedagógico «Fray Florencio Pascual Alegre Gonzáles» de Requena, Barrio Tarapacá s/n, Requena, Loreto.

Instituto Superior Pedagógico «Victorino Elorz Goicoechea» de Sullana, Avenida Victorino Elorz s/n, Apartado 122, Sullana, Piura.

Instituto Superior Pedagógico «José Jiménez Borga», Jr. Billingurst 150, Tacna, Tacna.

Instituto Superior Pedagógico de Tarapoto, Jirón Orellana s/n, Tarapoto, San Martín.

Instituto Superior Pedagógico de Tarma, Tarma, Junín.

Instituto Superior Pedagógico de Tayabamba, Jirón Sucre 200, Tayabamba, La Libertad.

Instituto Superior Pedagógico «Túpac Amaru» de Tinta, Tinta, Cusco.

Instituto Superior Pedagógico de La Libertad, Avenida América Sur, Trujillo, La Libertad.

Instituto Superior Pedagógico Particular «Santo Tomás de Aquino» de Trujillo, Jr. Ayacucho 510, Trujillo, La Libertad.

Instituto Superior Pedagógico «José Antonio Encinas» de Tumbes, Panamericana, Norte Km. 03, Tumbes, Tumbes.

Instituto Superior Pedagógico de Urubamba, Apartado 379, Urubamba, Cuzco.

Instituto Superior Pedagógico «Ignacio A. Ramos Olivera» de Yungay, Jr. Yungay s/n, Yungay, Ancash.

Instituto Superior Pedagógico «Elias Olazar» de Yurimaguas, Avenida Mariscal Castilla, Yurimaguas, Loreto.

Asamblea Nacional de Rectores

L'Assemblée nationale des Recteurs (ANR) a été créée en 1983 par la Loi universitaire en remplacement de la Commission nationale interuniversitaire. Investie d'attributions nouvelles, cette Assemblée réunit tous les recteurs des universités publiques et privées du pays. Elle est l'organisme supérieur chargé, d'une part, de définir l'orientation générale des activités universitaires et d'assurer leur coordination et, d'autre part, de veiller à leur développement sur le plan économique et à l'accomplissement de la mission des universités vis-à-vis de la communauté nationale. A sa tête se trouve un Président élu en leur sein pour une période de deux ans par les Recteurs qui la composent.

Les organes de l'Assemblée nationale des Recteurs sont: les Conseils régionaux interuniversitaires, la Commission de coordination interuniversitaire (CCI) et le Conseil des contentieux. Organes formés des recteurs des universités publiques et privées, les Conseils régionaux interuniversitaires ont une vocation spécifiquement régionale; ils ont notamment pour fonctions de faciliter la coordination des plans et programmes de recherche et la prestation des services des universités à la société, de formuler des opinions sur certains aspects de la réalité locale et régionale, en proposant des critères destinés à servir de guides aux gouvernements régionaux et locaux en ce qui concerne la création, la suppression ou la fusion

d'universités à vocation régionale, avant leur approbation par l'Assemblée nationale des Recteurs.

La Commission de coordination interuniversitaires (CCI) représente l'Assemblée afin que les décisions de celle-ci soient adoptées comme il convient. Elle est présidée par le Président de l'Assemblée nationale des Recteurs et se compose des recteurs des universités nationales et privés ci-aprés: Mayor de San Marcos, «San Antonio Abad» del Cusco, «La Libertad», «San Agustín» de Arequipa, de Ingeniería, Agraria-La Molina, et Pontificia Universidad Católica del Perú, «San Cristóbal de Huamanga»-Ayacucho, de Piura, «Agraria de la Selva»-Tingo María, «Santiago Antúnez de Mayolo», Huaráz, Peruana Cayetano Heredia et «Ricardo Palma».

Le Secrétariat exécutif est l'organe administratif chargé de la mise en oeuvre de la coordination interuniversitaire.

The National Assembly of Rectors was created by law in 1983, replacing the National Interuniversity Commission. Vested with new functions, the Assembly is comprised of all the public and private university rectors. It is responsible for, on the one hand, defining general objectives concerning university activities and assuring their co-ordination, and, on the other hand, the over-seeing of their development from the economic point of view, and the carrying out of the tasks of the universities in relation to the needs of the community. A President is elected from among the Rectors of the member institutions and serves for two years.

The organs of the Assembly are: the regional interuniversity councils; the interuniversity co-ordinating commission (CCI), and legal council. Comprising the rectors of the public and private universities, the regional interuniversity councils play a specifically regional role. Their main function is to facilitate the co-ordination of plans and programmes of research and the benefits to society of university services, to formulate opinions on aspects of local and regional needs by proposing suitable criteria for local and regional authorities concerning the creation, suppression or integration of universities before their approval by the National Assembly of Rectors.

The CCI represents the Assembly in order that its decisions may be suitably adopted. It is headed by the President of the Assembly and comprises the rectors of the following national and private universities: Mayor de San Marcos, «San Antonio Abad» del Cusco, «La Libertad», «San Agustín» de Arequipa, De Ingeniería, Agraria La Molina; and Pontificia Universidad Católica del Perú, «San Cristóbal de Huamanga», Ayacucho, De Piura, «Agraria de la Selva»-Tingo María, «Santiago Antúnez de Mayolo», Huarez, Peruana Cayetano Heredia y «Ricardo Palma».

The Secretariat, headed by an Executive Secretary, is the administrative body responsible for the carrying out of university co-ordination.

Président: Alberto Fujimori Fujumori, Rector, Universidad Nacional Agraria-La Molina.

Secrétaire exécutif: Héctor Lú\njan Peralta, ex-Rector, Universidad Nacional de Trujillo.
Universidad Nacional de Trujillo.
Calle Aldabas, Cdra. 3, Lima 33.
Tél: 36-0068

Asociación de Universitarias Graduadas del Perú (IFUW)
Félex Dibós 308, Magdalena del Mar, Lima 17.
World University Service (WUS)
Correspondent: María Elena Alva.
Orquideas 2750, Lima 27.
Tél: 401741
Federación de Estudiantes del Perú – FEP
Casilla 5262, Lima.
Movimiento Intelectuales Católicos (Pax Romana)
Montero Rosas 1326, Lince, Lima 3.
Unión Nacional de Estudiantes Católicos (Pax Romana)
Apartado postal 3234, Ucayali 346, Lima.

*

Ministerio de Educación, Oficina de Asuntos Internacionales
Lima.
Tél: 281209. Télex: 25803 mesc pe
Comisión Nacional Peruana de Cooperación con la Unesco
Ministerio de Educación, Lima.
Tél: 281209. Télex: 25803 mesc pe. Cables: comision unesco ministerio educacion lima

PHILIPPINES
PHILIPPINES

UNIVERSITIES—UNIVERSITES

Public Institutions—Etablissement publics

Benguet State University, La Trinidad, Benguet.
1916, 1955
Tel: 432.2401
agr, for, agri-bus, eng, vet, ed, tec.

Bicol University, Regan Barracks, Legaspi City, Albay. *1969*
Tel: 49.13
arc, bus adm, ed, eng, arts, sc, nurs, agr, fish, soc w.

Cagayan State University, Tuguegarao, Cagayan. *1979*
Tel: 446-1949
agr eng, arts, sc, agr-bus, agr ed, ind techn.

Central Luzon State University, Muñoz, Nueva Ecija. *1984*
Tel: 107
ed, agr, arts, sc, food techn, fish, vet, bus adm, eng, an hus, home eco.

*Central Mindanao University, University Town, Musuan, Maramag, Bukidnon.
1910, 1952, 1965
agr, ed, arts, sc, for, eng, agr-bus, agr eng, vet.

Don Mariano Marcos Memorial State University, Bacnotan, La Union.
1960, 1972, 1980
agr, agro-for, sc, bus adm, ed, hom techn, fish, hotel & restaurant mangt, arts, law, ind techn, midwifery, tec.

Isabela State University, Echague, Isabela.
1926, 1963, 1978
Tel: 22013
bus adm, agr, for, agr eng, arts, sc, ed, hom techn, vet, food eng, for, comty dev, tec.

*Mariano Marcos State University, Batac, Ilocos Norte. *1964, 1978*
Cables: mmsu, batac, ilocos norte
sc, agr, fish, ed, nurs, eng, hom techn, bus adm, ind techn, tec.

*Mindanao State University, Marawi City. *1955*
Tel: 222 A
agr, fish, for, bus adm, hotel & restaurant mangt, arts, sc, eng, math, soc w, ed, lib.

*Iligan Institute of Technology, Tibanga, Iligan City. *1946, 1968*
Tel: 2 0800/1
S : eng, eng techn, arts-hum, sc-math, mangt techn, dev techn, ind, ed.

*Pamantasan ng Lungsod ng Maynila (University of the City of Manila), Intramuros, Manila.
1967
Tel: 407621
bus mangt, arts, sc, eng, ed, med, comp, soc w, voc.

Pangasinan State University, Lingayen, Pangasinan. *1978*
Tel: 1-4-2
ed, agr, arts, fish, ind techn, nutr, math, eng, tec.

*Polytechnic University of the Philippines, Anonas Street, Santa Mesa, Metro Manila.
1952, 1978
Tel: 616775
bus mangt, hotel & restaurant mangt, eng, lib, arts, ind psyc, tour, food techn, nutr, broadcast commun, bus jour, ed.

*Technological University of the Philippines, Ayala Boulevard, Ermita, Manila.
1901, 1959, 1978
Tel: 586355
fa, eng, ed, tec.

University of Eastern Philippines, University Town, Catarman, Northern Samar. *1964, 1965*
fish agr, for, bus adm, eng, vet, arts, sc, ed.

University of Northern Philippines, Tanay, Ilocos Sur. *1965*
Tel: 30-93
arts, sc, ed, nurs, eng, fa, arc, com, crim, soc w, lib.

*University of the Philippines System, Quezon Hall, Diliman, Quezon City 3004. (The Registrar). *1908*
Tel: 976061
arc, fa, bus adm, hotel & restaurant mangt, arts, sc, nutr, law, geol, eng, math, tour, mus, lib, soc w, ed.

UP at Los Baños.
agr, for, sc-hum, agrarian reform, agr dev & adm, agr eng-techn, hum-ecology.

Philippine Center for Advanced Studies, Diliman.
I : *Asian st, Isl st, Philippine st, strategic st.*

UP College Manila.
C : *med, publ adm.*

I : *population, publ heal.*
Ce : *stat.*
UP COLLEGE BAGUIO, Baguio City.
C : *arts-sc.*
UP COLLEGE CEBU, Lahug, Cebu City.
arts-sc, bus mangt, hotel-restaurant mangt.
UP EXTENSION DIVISION CLARK AIR BASE,
Angeles City.
arts-sc.
UP COLLEGE ILOILO, Iloilo City.
arts-sc, fish.
UP COLLEGE TACLOBAN, Tacloban City.
arts-sc.

University of Southeastern Philippines, Barrio
Obrero, Davao City. *1978*

Tel: 7-86-53
agr, eng, arts, sc, stat, ed, ind techn, for, agri-bus.
University of Southern Mindanao, ⁻ar,
North Cotabato.
Cables: kabacan, north cot
agr, agri-bus, eng, nutr, sc, vet, ed, ind techn, tec.
West Visayas State University, Iloilo City. *1924*
agr, for, arts, ed, nurs, med.
Western Mindanao State University, Baliwasan,
Zamboanga City. *1978*
Tel: 34.86
agr, for, arc, agri-bus, law, eng, arts, sc, math, nutr, nurs, soc w, ed, tec.

Private Institutions—Etablissements privés

*Adamson University, 500, San Marcelino,
Ermita, Manila. (The Executive Secretary).
1932, 1941
Tel: 50-20-11
arc, com, eng, arts, law, sc, phar, ed.
*Angeles University Foundation, Angeles City
2017. *1962*
Tel: 29.58
com, eng, arts, crim, sc, med, nurs, ed, tec.
Aquinas University Inc., Legaspi City.
1948, 1969
Tel: 22.27
arc, com, eng, arts, sc, nutr, law, nurs, ed.
Arellano University, 2600 Legarda, Sampaloc,
Manila. (The Registrar). *1938, 1947*
Tel: 60-74-41
law, ed, com, arts, nurs.
Ateneo de Davao University, E. Jacinto Street,
Davao City. *1948, 1951, 1977*
Tel: 7-87-71
com, eng, arts, sc, law, soc w, ed.
Ateneo de Manila University, P.O. Box 154,
Loyola Heights, Quezon City. *1859, 1865, 1959*
Tel: 99-87-21. Telex: 63199. Cables: ateneo
manila
mangt, eng, arts, sc, law.
Baguio Central University, 18, Bonifacio Street,
Baguio City. *1951, 1977*
Tel: 442-3071
com, eng, ed, publ adm, law, arts.
*Central Philippine University, Jaro, Iloilo City.
1956
Tel: 7-34-73
arts, sc, agr, com, ed, eng, law, nurs, theo, nutr, med techn, soc w, agr eng, ch.
*Centro Escolar University, 9, Mendiola Street,
San Miguel, Manila. (The Secretary-Treasurer).
1907
Tel: 741-0446. Cables: ceuniv

phar, dent, optom, hom eco-nutr, nurs, med techn, arts, sc, ch, com, ed, mus, soc w, phys.
*De La Salle University, 2401, Taft Avenue,
Manila. *1911, 1917, 1975*
Tel: 50-46-11. Cables: delasal
arts, sc, ed, com, eng, comp.
Divine Word University, Imelda Avenue,
Tacloban City 7101, Leyte. *1929, 1945, 1966*
Tel: 321-2307. Cables: dwut
arts, sc, ed, com, law, eng, nurs, soc w, med.
*Far Eastern University, Nicanor Reyes Street,
Manila. *1928*
Tel: 21-98-31. Cables: farsternu
com, arts, sc, ed, law, med, med techn, nurs, eng, arc, fa.
Feati University, Helios Street, Santa Cruz,
Manila. *1946, 1959*
Tel: 48-59-51
eng, arts, arc, com, fa, mar trans, tec.
*Foundation University, Dr. Miciano Road,
Dumaguete City, J–409. *1949, 1969*
Tel: 33.89
agr techn, arc, com, arts, sc, law, ed, const techn.
*Gregorio Araneta University Foundation,
Victoneta Park, Malabon, Metro Manila,
Rizal. *1946, 1958*
Tel: 361-9053
agr, for, vet, eng, com, food techn, ed, arts, sec adm, sc, agronomy, for, hom extension, recr & park adm.
Holy Angel University, Sto. Rosario Street,
Angeles City. *1933, 1969, 1981*
Tel: 35.28
bus adm, eng, arts, law, ed, sec adm.
International Harvardian University, 123,
Malvar Street, Davao City. *1950, 1969*
Tel: 7-50-14
ed, crim, law, arts, com, eng.

*Manila Central University, Zurbaran Cor, Oroquieta, Manila.   *1904*
Tel: 711-7341. Cables: mcu manila
phar, med techn, dent, ed, com, med, nurs, optom, sc, midwifery.

*Manuel L. Quezon University, 916, R. Hidalgo Street, Quiapo, Manila.   *1947*
Tel: 47-05-41. Cables: miqu manila
law, arts, sc, ed, com, eng, arc, crim.

Manuel S. Enverga University Foundation Inc., Lucena City.   *1947*
Tel: 71-25-41
arts, ed, eng, agr, arc, com.

Misamis University, Mabini and Bonifacio Streets, Ozamis City.   *1929, 1955, 1979*
agr, com, eng, arts, sc, law, crim, nurs, dent, midwifery, soc w, ed, comty dev.

*National University, 551, M.F. Jhocson Street, Sampaloc, Manila.   *1900, 1921*
Tel: 60-81-67
com, dent, ed, eng, arts, phar, law, arc, tec.

*Notre Dame University of Cotabato, Notre Dame Avenue, Cotabato City.   *1948, 1969*
Tel: 26.98
ed, arts, com, law, eng, nurs.

Ortañez University, 942, Aurora Boulevard, Quezon City.   *1945, 1958, 1973*
eng, arts, law, crim, nurs, ed, tec.

Pamantasan ng Araullo [Araullo U.], Del Pilar Street, Bitas, Cabanatuan City.   *1950*
Tel: 963-2215
arc, com, eng, arts, sc, nutr, law, crim, ed, interior des.

Philippine Christian University, Desmariñas, Cavite.   *1946*
agr techn, bus adm, ed, soc w.

*Philippine Christian University, 1648 Taft Avenue, Corner Pedro Gil, Manila.   *1947*
Tel: 50-82-80
agr techn, arts, com, ed, nurs, soc w, nutr.

*Philippine Women's University, Taft Avenue, Manila. (The Registrar).   *1919, 1932*
Tel: 59-25-15
bus adm, fa, arts, sc, nutr, comp, med techn, nurs, mus, hotel & restaurant mangt, soc w, ed.

*Saint Louis University, P.O. Box 71, Baguio City, B–202.   *1952, 1963*
Tel: 442-2793
ed, eng, arc, law, com, phar, arts, sc, med, med techn, nurs, soc w.

St. Paul University, Taguegarao, Cagayan.   *1939, 1982*
Tel: 446-1863
com, eng, arts, nutr, nurs, soc w, ed.

Silliman University, Dumaguete City, 6501. *1938*
Tel: 32.00
arts, sc, ed, eng, nurs, bus adm, mus, agr, med techn, soc w.

Southwestern University, Villa Azuar, Urgello, Private Road, Cebu City.   *1946*
Tel: 9-70-90
med, law, arts, sc, optom, ed, phar, eng, com, med techn, nurs, agr techn, nutr, vet, soc w, home eco, comp.

University of the Assumption, Unisite Subd., Del Pilar, San Fernando, Pampanga.   *1963*
Tel: 61-36-17. Cables: san fernando, pamp phil
arc, com, eng, arts, nutr, ed.

*University of Baguio, 17, Gen Luna, Baguio City.   *1948, 1969*
Tel: 442-3071
eng, com, arts, dent, med techn, hotel & restaurant mangt, for, nutr, crim, tec.

*University of Bohol, Tagbilaran City.   *1946, 1970*
Tel: 3101 ITT
law, eng, phar, nurs, arts, agr, crim, sec adm, hom eco.

*University of the East, Claro M. Recto Avenue, Manila.   *1946, 1948*
Tel: 741-9501. Cables: philcolcom
bus adm, arts, sc, ed, dent, eng, nutr, fa.
COLLEGE OF DENTISTRY, Aurora Boulevard, Quezon City.   *1948*

University of Iloilo, Rizal Street, La Paz, Iloilo City.   *1947, 1968*
ed, law, arts, sc, com, crim, eng, agr, nutr, nurs, soc w.

*The University of Manila, 588, Dr. M.V. de los Santos Street, Manila.   *1913, 1914, 1921*
Tel: 7413637. Cables: univman
ed, bus adm, arts, crim, sc, eng.

*University of Mindanao, Bolton Street, Davao City.   *1946, 1965*
Tel: 7-54-56
arts, sc, ed, eng, arc, law, com, crim, for, mus, soc w, tec.
Branches in: Bansalan, Digos, Guiana, Ilang-Tobungco, Panabo, Penaplata, Santa Ana, Tagum.

*University of Negros Occidental-Recoletos, Lizares Avenue, Bacolod City.   *1941, 1950, 1957*
Tel: 25036
arts, law, eng, ed, com, med techn.

*University of Northeastern Philippines, Iriga City.   *1948*
law, ed, com, nurs-midwifery, crim, arc, eng, arts, soc w, tec.

*University of Nueva Caceres, Naga City.   *1948, 1954*
law, arts, sc, ed, com, eng.
Tel: 9287. Cables: unc

University of Pangasinan, Arellano Street, Dagupan City.   *1925, 1941, 1968*
Tel: 3850
ed, eng, arc, arts, law, sc, com, nutr, med techn,

nurs, tec, voc.

University of Saint Anthony, Iriga City, Camarines Sur. *1947*
Tel. 401
arc, com, eng, arts, sc, hom eco, nurs, ed, crim, midwifery, tec-voc.

University of San Agustin, Gen. Luna Street, Iloilo City. *1904, 1935, 1953*
Tel: 7-48-41
arc, com, eng, mus, nutr, arts, sc, law, med techn, phar, nurs, ed.

University of San Carlos, P. del Rosario Street, P.O. Box 182, Cebu City. *1595, 1606*
Tel: 7-24-10
law, arts, sc, ed, com, eng, arc, phar, fa, nutr, nurs.

University of San Jose-Recoletos, Cebu City. *1947, 1984*
Tel: 5-38-02. Cables: recoletos, cebu
com, eng, arts, sc, law, comp, ed, hom eco, hotel & restaurant mangt.

*University of Santo Tomas, España Street, Sampaloc, Manila. *1611, 1619, 1645*
Tel: 731-3101
law, med, med techn, phar, arts, eng, ed, sc, com, arc, fa, nurs.

*University of Southern Philippines Foundation, Mabini Street, Cebu City. *1935*
Tel: 7-23-31
arts, com, ed, arc, eng, nutr, soc w.

*University of the Visayas, Colon Street, Cebu City. *1919, 1948*
Tel: 60.42
arts, ed, com, law, arc, customs adm, sc, crim, nurs, med, phar, mar trans, eng.

Wesleyan University-Philippines, Mabini Street, Cabanatuan City. *1946*
agr, com, eng, arts, sc, nutr, nurs, soc w, ed, tec-voc.

*Xavier University, Corrales Street, Cagayan de Oro City, L-305. *1933, 1938, 1958*
Tel: 37.42
law, arts, sc, ed, com, agr, eng, med.

OTHER INSTITUTIONS—AUTRES INSTITUTIONS

Public Institutions—Etablissements publics
Chartered—Dotés d'une charte

Abra State Institute of Science and Technology, Langangilang, Abra. *1908, 1983*
agr, for, agr ed, agr tec.

Basilan State College, Santa Clara, Lamitan, Basilan. *1966, 1984*
tec, agr ed.

Bukidnon State College, Malaybalay, Bukidnon. *1924, 1952, 1976*
com, arts, soc w, ed.

Bulacan College of Arts and Trades, Malolos, Bulacan. *1957, 1965*
Tel: 797-4114
arc, eng, ed, ind techn, tec-voc.

Camarines Sur State Agricultural College, Pili, Camarines Sur. *1954, 1982*
agr, agri-bus, agr eng, food techn.

Camarines Sur Polytechnic Colleges, Nabua, Camarines Sur. *1983*
office adm, eng, acc, food techn, fish.

Catanduanes State Colleges, Virac, Catanduanes. *1971*
agr, fish, com, eng, arts, nutr, nurs, ed.

Cebu State College, Osmeña Boulevard, Cebu City. *1954, 1976*
arts, nurs, tour, ed, agr, ed, sec, tec.

Central Luzon Polytechnic College, Cabanatuan City. *1964*
Tel: 963-2621
eng, ind eng.

Central Visayas Polytechnic College, Dumaguete City. *1910, 1968, 1983*
Tel: 3072
ind ed, ind techn.

Cotabato City State Polytechnic College, Cotabato City. *1924, 1983*
fish, ind techn, agr, agr techn, for ind ed.

Cotabato Foundation College of Science and Technology, Dorolumna, Magpet, North Cotabato. *1973, 1983*
agr, hom eco, for, agri-bus, anth.

Don Honorio Ventura College of Arts and Trades, Bacolor, Pampanga. *1978*
arc, eng, ed.

Don Mariano Marcos Memorial Polytechnic State College, Lapasan, Cagayan de Oro City. *1927, 1953, 1978*
Tel: 38.40. Cables: dmmmpsc, cagayan deoro
agr, fish, for, eng, ed, ind techn.

Don Severino Agricultural College, Indang, Cavite. *1964*
agr.

Eastern Samar State College, Borongan, Eastern Samar. *1983*
agr, agr ed, agr eng, ed, arts, com, hom sc, tec.

Eulogio "Amang" Rodriguez Institute of Science and Technology, Nagtahan, Manila.

1945, 1972, 1978
Tel: 601366
ed, fa, hotel & restaurant mangt, sc, arc, eng, ind techn, sec adm, tec.
Ifugao State College of Agriculture and Forestry, Mayon, Lamut, Ifugao.   *1973, 1983*
agr, for, ed, hom techn.
Iloilo State College of Fisheries, Tiwi, Barotac, Nuevo, Iloilo.   *1962, 1978*
Cables: iscof btac, nvo, phil
fish, mar eng, ed, prac arts, mar biol.
Jasaan College of Science and Technology, Jasaan, Misamis Oriental.
eng, ed, midwifery.
Kalinga-Apayao State College.
Laguna State Polytechnic College, Wawa East, Sinaloan, Laguna.   *1983*
agr, agr ed, agr techn.
Leyte State College, Tacloban City.   *1921, 1976*
Tel: 321-2177
arts, hotel & restaurant mangt, tour, ed.
Leyte Institute of Technology, Salazar Street, Tacloban City.   *1907, 1966, 1976*
Tel: 321-2185
arc, eng, arts, sc, hom techn, hotel & restaurant adm, ed.
Mambusao Agricultural and Technical College, Mambusao, Capiz.
agr, ed, tec.
Marinduque Institute of Science and Technology, Boac, Marinduque.   *1954*
ed, ind techn, agr, fish, eng.
Misamis Oriental State College of Agriculture and Technology, Claveria, Misamis Oriental.   *1963, 1983*
agr techn, ed, eng.
National Maritime Polytechnic, Barangay Cabalawan, Tacloban City.   *1978, 1980*
Naval Institute of Technology, Naval, Biliran Sub-Province.   *1965, 1972*
ed, tec.
Northern Iloilo Polytechnic State College, Estancia, Iloilo.   *1965, 1983*
fish, ed, eng, bus mangt, tec.
Northern Mindanao State Institute of Science and Technology, Ampayon, Butuan City.   *1946, 1963, 1982*
agr, ed.
Nueva Vizcaya State Institute of Technology, Bayombong, Nueva Vizcaya. *1916, 1964, 1973*
Tel: 4-8-2
agr, fish, for, agri-bus, eng, ed, hom techn, tec.
Nueva Vizcaya State Polytechnic College, Bambang, Nueva Vizcaya.   *1947, 1957, 1983*
ed, arts, tec.
Occidental Mindoro National College, San Jose, Occidental Mindoro.   *1983*
agr, com, ed, midwifery, voc.
Pablo Borbon Memorial Institute of Technology,

Rizal Avenue, Batangas City.   *1963, 1978*
Tel: 725-2138. Cables: pbmit, batangas city
eng, ed, tec.
Paglaum State College, Talisay, Negros Occidental.   *1983*
Tel: 57.13
com, ed, ind techn, tec.
Palawan National Agricultural College, Aborlan, Palawan.   *1963*
agr, eng, arts, ed, tec.
Palawan State College, Puerto Princesa City.   *1972, 1984*
bus adm, eng, arts, ed, midwifery.
Palompon Institute of Technology, Palompon, Leyte.   *1964, 1972*
hom techn, ed, ind techn, mar trans, eng, tec.
Pampanga Agricultural College, Magalang, Pampanga.   *1965*
agr, agri-bus, eng, ed, for tec.
Panay State Polytechnic College, Pontevedra, Capiz.   *1980*
ed, agr, fish, tec.
***Philippine Normal College,** Taft Avenue, Corner Ayala Boulevard, Manila. *1901, 1949*
Tel: 3-53-14
ed, arts, sc, math, eng.
Branches at Alicia, Cadiz City, Prosperidad.
Polytechnic State College of Antique, Sibalom, Antique.   *1976, 1984*
Cables: psca, sibalom, antique
com, ed.
Quirino State College, Diffun, Quirino.   *1969, 1983*
agr, ed, hom techn.
Rizal College of Agriculture and Technology, Sampaloc, Tanay, Rizal.   *1974, 1983*
Tel: 79-20-24
hom techn, livelihood mangt, agr.
Rizal Technological Colleges, Boni Avenue, Mandaluyong, Metro Manila.   *1969, 1975, 1978*
ed, arc, eng, arts, sc, bus techn, ind mangt, tec.
Romblon State College, Odiongan, Romblon.   *1976, 1982*
agr, hom techn, ed.
Samar State Polytechnic College, Catbalogan, Samar.   *1912, 1959, 1982*
Tel: 285
eng, ed, ind techn.
Southern Luzon Polytechnic College, Lucban, Quezon.   *1968, 1982*
Tel: 278
agr, fish, for, com, fa, arts, nurs, ed, tec.
Sulu State College, Jolo, Sulu.   *1970, 1985*
com, arts, ed.
Tarlac College of Agriculture, Camiling, Tarlac.   *1974*
agr, for, eng, hom techn, art-sc, ed, vet.
Tarlac College of Technology, Tarlac, Tarlac.

1965

Tel: 29-05
arc, bus adm, end, hom techn, ed, com.

Tawi-Tawi Regional Agricultural College, Bongao, Tawi-Tawi, Sulu.   *1963, 1983*
agr.

Tiburcio Tancinco Memorial Institute of Science and Technology, Calbayog City, Samar.
1960, 1975, 1982
Tel: 4-71. Cables: timist, calbayog city
eng, ind techn.

Visayas State College of Agriculture, Baybay, Leyte.   *1924, 1953, 1974*

Tel: 521-2027
ed, sc, for, agr, agri-bus, eng, math.

West Visayas State Colleges, Iloilo City, Iloilo.
1924, 1965
Tel: 7-49-05
agr, for, arts, ed, nurs, med.

Western Luzon Agricultural College, San Marcelino, Zambales.   *1957*
agr, ed.

Zamboanga College of Marine Science and Technology, Zamboanga City.   *1956, 1970*
Tel: 39-41
fish, ed, mar trans, ed.

Non-Chartered—Non dotés d'une charte

Abra School of Arts and Trades, Santiago Street, Bangued, Abra.   *1957, 1966*
ind techn, ind ed, trade techn.

Aklan Agricultural College, Banga, Aklan.
1918, 1963
agr, hom techn, agr ed, agr techn.

Aklan National College of Fisheries, New Washington, Aklan.   *1949, 1965*
fish, ed.

Alangalang Agro-Industrial School, Alangalang, Leyte.   *1971, 1975*
agr, ed, agr techn.

Antique College of Agriculture, Hamtic, Antique.   *1952, 1978*
agr, agr techn.

Antique National School, San Jose, Antique.
1976
agr, sec, arts.

Apolinario R. Apacible School of Fisheries, Nasugbu, Batangas.   *1952*
fish.

Arteche National Agricultural School, Cadian, Oran, Eastern Samar.   *1952*

Bago City School, Bago City.   *1980*
arts, agr, sec, tec.

Bais Developmental College, Bais City.   *1980*
ed, tec.

Barotac Viejo National Agricultural College, Barotac, Viejo, Iloilo.   *1963, 1976*
agr, homemaking.

Bataan National Agricultural School, Abucay, Bataan.   *1963*

Bataan National School of Arts ɪd Trades, Balanga, Bataan.   *1967*
ed, ind techn.

Benguet School of Arts and Trades, Bokod, Benguet.
ed, ind techn, ind.

Bicol College of Arts and Trades, Peñafrancia Avenue, Naga City.   *1911, 1970*

Biliran National Agricultural College, Biliran Sub-Province.   *1949, 1972*

Bohol Agricultural College, Zamora, Pilar, Bohol.   *1912, 1971*

Bohol School of Arts and Trades, Tagbilaran City.   *1907, 1959*
Tel: 32-88
ind techn, tec.

Bohol School of Fisheries, Cogtong, Candijay, Bohol.   *1959*

Bulacan National Agricultural School, San Ildefonso, Bulacan.

Calabanga National School of Arts and Trades, Calabanga, Camarines Sur.   *1971, 1984*
ed, ind techn.

Caloocan City Polytechnic Colleges, General San Miguel Road, Sangandaan, Caloocan City.
1971
ed, com.

Calinog Agricultural and Industrial College, Calinog, Iloilo.   *1959*

Camarines Norte Agricultural School, Lobo, Camarines Norte.   *1960*

Can-avid Jr. Agro-Industrial School, Canavid, Eastern Samar.   *1962, 1974*

Capiz Institute of Technology, Hemingway Street, Roxas City.   *1969*
Tel: 577
eng, ed.

Carigara School of Fisheries, Barugohoy Norte, Carigara, Leyte.   *1961, 1976*

Catanduanes Agricultural and Industrial College, Panganiban, Catanduanes.   *1956*

Cauayan Rural School, San Fermin, Cauayan, Isabela.   *1976*
agr, techn.

Cavite College of Arts and Trades, Rosario, Cavite.   *1960, 1970*
ind ed, ind techn.

Cavite College of Fisheries, Bucana, Naic, Cavite.   *1960, 1969*

Concepcion College of Fisheries, Concepcion, Iloilo.   *1979*

Daniel Z. Romualdez Memorial School of

Fisheries, Barangay, Tanghas, Tolosa, Leyte.
1971, 1974

Dingle Agricultural and Technical College, Dingle, Iloilo. *1977*

Dipolog School of Fisheries, Dipolog City.
1960, 1975

Dr. Emilio B. Espiñosa Sr. Memorial Agricultural College, Cabitan, Mandaon, Masbate.
1952

Felipe J. Abrigo Memorial School of Arts and Trades, Buiuan, Eastern Samar.
1962, 1968
ind ed, ind techn.

Fort A. Bonifacio College, Fort Bonifacio, Metro Manila. *1967*
com, arts, ed.

Gamu Rural School, Gamu, Isabela. *1960*
agr techn.

Glan School of Arts and Trades, Glan, South Cotabato. *1977*
ind ed.

Hadji Butu School of Arts and Trades, Jolo, Sulu. *1928, 1965*
ind techn.

Ibajay National Agricultural and Industrial School, Ibajay, Aklan. *1971*

Ilocos Sur Agricultural Colleges, Sta. Maria, Ilocos Sur. *1922, 1974*

Iloilo National College of Agricultural, Lambunao, Iloilo. *1964*
agr, for.

Kalinga-Apayao School of Arts and Trades, Conner, Kalinga-Apayao. *1971, 1977*
com, arts, ed.

Katipunan National Agricultural School, Katipunan, Zamboanga del Norte. *1957, 1975*

La Carlota City College, La Carlota City. *1966*
agr, crim, midwifery.

Laguna School of Arts and Trades, Santa Cruz, Laguna. *1984*
ed, tec.

Lambunao Institute of Science and Technology, Lambunao, Iloilo. *1945, 1974*
prac arts, tec.

Lanao Agricultural College, Lumbatan, Lanao del Sur. *1963*

Lanao National College of Arts and Trades, Marawi City, Lanao del Sur. *1920, 1975*
ed, tec.

Lanao del Norte Agricultural College, Karomatan, Lanao del Norte. *1969*

Laoang National Trade School, Laoang, Northern Samar. *1959, 1972*
ind techn, tec.

Lapak Agricultural School, Lapak, Siasi, Sulu.

Leon National College of Agriculture, F. Cabarles Street, Leon, Iloilo. *1977*

Leyte Agro-Industrial School, Leyte, Leyte.
1971, 1979

Leyte National Agricultural College, Villaba, Leyte. *1960, 1976*

Los Baños College of Fisheries, Los Baños, Laguna. *1959*

Maigo School of Arts and Trades, Maigo, Lanao del Norte. *1948, 1969*
ed, ind techn, tec.

Marikina Institute of Sciences and Technology, Shoe Avenue, Sta. Elena, Marikina, Metro Manila. *1969*
Tel: 947-2130
ed, tec.

Maydolong National Agricultural School, Maydolong, Eastern Samar. *1978*

McArthur National Agricultural School, General McArthur, Eastern Samar. *1962*

Mindoro College of Agriculture and Technology, Victoria, Oriental Mindoro. *1962*

Negros Occidental Agricultural College, Kabankalan, Negros Occidental. *1947, 1971*

Negros Occidental School of Fisheries, Enclaro, Binalbagan, Negros Occidental. *1961, 1973*

North Cotabato College of Arts and Trades, Kidapawan, North Cotabato. *1962*
tec.

Palawan Schools of Arts and Trades, Cuyo, Palawan. *1958*
ind techn.

Pedro Rebadulla Memorial Agricultural College, Catubig, Northern Samar. *1958, 1980*

Pototan College of Arts and Trades, Pototan, Iloilo. *1983*
ed, agr techn, tec, sciences.

Quezon National Agricultural School, Malicboy, Pagbilao, Quezon. *1960*

Ramon Magsaysay Memorial School of Arts and Trades, Iba, Zambales.
ed, ind techn.

Rizal Technological and Polytechnic Institute, Morong, Rizal. *1983*
Tel: 23-051
arts, sc, ind ed, tec.

Romblon College of Fisheries and Forestry, San Agustin, Romblon.

Roxas Memorial College of Arts and Trades, Andagao, Kalibo, Aklan. *1983*
ind ed, ind techn, tec.

Sabani Estate Agricultural College, Cabaldon, Nueva Ecija. *1960*

Samar National Agricultural School, San Jorge, Western Samar. *1954, 1975*

San Enrique Agricultural College, San Enrique, Iloilo. *1983*

San Pablo City School of Arts and Trades, San Pablo City. *1965*
ind techn.

Santiago Vocational and Industrial School, Santiago, Isabela. *1967, 1975*
tec.

School for Philippine Craftsmen, Polangul, Albay. *1959, 1976*
ed, tec.

Sindangan National Agricultural School, Sindangan, Zamboanga del Norte. *1947, 1975*

Sorsogon College of Arts and Trades, Sorsogon, Sorsogon. *1907, 1975*
ind ed, ind techn, tec.

Sorsogon National Agricultural School, Mayon, Castilla, Sorsogon. *1975, 1979*

Southern Agusan National Agricultural College, Bunawan, Agusan del Sur. *1948, 1969*

Southern Iloilo Polytechnic College, Miagao, Iloilo.
tec.

Southern Leyte Agro-Fishery Technical School, Bonton, Southern Leyte. *1967, 1974*

Southern Leyte School of Arts and Trades, Sogod, Southern Leyte. *1982*
ed, ind techn, tec.

Southern Samar Agricultural College, Salcedo, Eastern Samar. *1960, 1964*

Surigao del Norte College of Agriculture and Technology, Magpayang, Mainit, Surigao del Norte. *1983*

Surigao del Norte School of Arts and Trades, Narciso Street, Surigao City. *1969*
ed, ind techn, tec.

Surigao del Sur Institute of Technology, Cantilan, Surigao del Sur. *1983*

Tangub Agro-Industrial School, Tangub, Tangub City.
Cables: tanais, tangut city

Tublay School of Home Industries, Acop, Tublay, Benguet.
ind ed, ind techn.

Zamboanga del Norte Agricultural College, Tampilisian, Zamboanga del Norte. *1958, 1968*

Zamboanga del Norte School of Arts and Trades, Dipolog City. *1960*
tec.

Zamboanga del Sur Agricultural School, Dumingag, Zamboanga del Sur. *1954, 1975*

Zamboanga School of Arts and Trades, Justice R.T. Lim Boulevard, Zamboanga. *1912, 1962*
ind techn, ed, mar trans, tec.
Also c. 100 Technical/Vocational Schools and 25 Community Colleges.

Private Institutions—Etablissements privés

Abada College, Pinamalayan, Oriental Mindoro. *1950*
com, arts, ed.

Abra Valley College, Mckinley Street, Bangued, Abra. *1948*
Tel: 2-0-8
arts, ed, sec.

Adelphi College, Lingayen, Pangasinan. *1945*
com, arts, ed.

Agama-Islam Academy, Ganassi, Lanao del Sur.
com, arts, ed.

Agno Valley College, Malasiqui, Pangasinan.
com, arts, ed.

Ago Medical & Educational Center, Rizal Street, Legaspi City. *1975*
Tel: 41-36
sec adm, arts, sc, nutr, dent, med, med techn, nurs, hotel & restaurant mangt, phys ther, radiologic ther, midwifery.

Agro Far East Foundation College, San Isidro, Davao Oriental. *1977*
agr, agr techn.

Agro-Industrial Foundation College of the Philippines, Bolton Unit, Bolton Riverside, Davao City. *1978*
customs adm, mar eng, arts, crim, ed, mar trans.

Agro-Industrial Foundation College of the Philippines, Tanglad, Santa Maria, Davao del Sur. *1968*
fish.

Agusan Colleges, Butuan City. *1951*
com, arts, ed.

Agusan del Sur College, Bayugan, Agusan del Sur. *1966, 1971*
com, arts, ed.

Aklan College, Archbishop Reyes Street, Kalibo, Aklan. *1945*
com, eng, arts, ed, home eco.

Aldersgate College, Solano, Nueva Vizcaya. *1965*
com, arts, ed, sec adm.

Alliance Française, 3rd Floor, UPRC Building, 315 Buendia, Makati, Metro Manila.
Tel: 818-6298

AMA Computer College, 5486, South Super Highway, Cor. Hen. M. Tinio Street, Makati, Metro Manila. *1980, 1981*

Andres Bonifacio College, College Park, Dipolog City. *1940, 1946*
agr, com, eng, arts, sc, crim, laws, soc w, ed.

Andres Soriano College, Bislig, Surigao del Sur. *1952*
com, arts, ed, sec.

Annunciation College, 479 Magsaysay Avenue, Sorsogon, Sorsogon. *1961, 1967*
Tel: 507
agr techn, com, arts, eng, publ adm, sec adm.

Annunciation College of Gubat, Gubat, Sorsogon. *1981*
arts.

Asbury College, Anda, Pangasinan.
arts.
Assembleyman Mariano Marcos Memorial Foundation College, Kiblawan, Davao del Sur.
1968, 1973
agr, agr techn.
Asian Institute of Arts, CCP Building, 117 Gamban Street, Legaspi Village, Makati, Metro Manila.
Asian Institute for Distance Education, Makti Stock Exchange Building, Ayala Avenue, Makati, Metro Manila. *1983, 1984*
Tel: 851186
arts, bus adm, port adm-mangt.
Asian Institute of Journalism, Journal Building, Port Area, Manila. *1980*
Asian Social Institute, 1518 Leon Guinto Street, Malate, Manila.
Tel: 59-56-13. Telex: 40793 ohd pm
soc w.
Assumption College, Inc., San Lorenzo Village, Makati, Metro Manila. *1892, 1940*
Tel: 817-9264
com, ed, arts, sc.
Assumption College of Nabunturan, Nabunturan, Davao del Norte. *1955, 1960*
com, arts, ed.
Ateneo de Naga, Ateneo Avenue, Naga City.
1940
Tel: 31-75
com, arts, sc, ed, pre-eng.
Ateneo de Zamboanga, La Purisima Street, Zamboanga City. *1912, 1950*
Tel: 51-51
com, arts, ed, sec adm, nurs, publ adm.
Baguio Colleges Foundation, Harrizon Street, Baguio City. *1946*
Tel: 442-3316
arc, com, eng, laws, arts, sc, ed, tec-voc, mass commun.
Balatan Institute, Balatan, Camarines Sur.
1959, 1979
arts, sec.
Balayan Colleges, Palikpikan Street, Balayan, Batangas. *1926, 1964*
Tel: 397
arts, com, ed, sec.
Baliuag Colleges, Baliuag, Bulacan. *1925, 1969*
Tel: 767-2045
com, arts, nurs, ed, eng.
Bataan Educational Institution, Orani, Bataan.
1977, 1978
com, eng, arts.
Bataan Heroes Memorial College, Balanga, Bataan. *1979*
com, eng, arts, ed, mar trans.
Batac Junior College, Batac, Ilocos Norte.
arts.
Bicol College, Daraga, Albay. *1941, 1960, 1964*

Tel: 4613
com, arts, eng, crim, law, ed.
Binalbagan Catholic College, Binalbagan, Negros Occidental. *1961*
com, eng, ed.
Brokenshire College, Brokenshire Heights, Davao City. *1954, 1978*
Tel: 7-56-36
arts, sc, nurs.
Burias Academy, Claveria, Masbate. *1962*
arts.
Butuan City Colleges, Butuan City. *1950*
com, arts, ed.
Butuan Doctors' College, Butuan City. *1971*
nutr, nurs, sc, midwifery.
Cabalum Western College, Iznart Street, Iloilo City. *1945, 1951*
Tel: 7-25-36
bus adm, sec adm.
Cabanatuan City College, Burgos Avenue, Cabanatuan City.
agr techn, com, arts, midwifery.
Cagayan Capitol College, Cagayan de Oro City.
1971
agr techn, com, customs adm, eng, arts, nurs, ed, mar trans, midwifery.
Cagayan Colleges Tuguegarao, Tuguegarao, Cagayan.
com, arts, laws, soc w, ed.
Cagayan de Oro Colleges, Carmen, Cagayan de Oro City. *1948*
Tel: 42-81
arc, com, eng, arts, crim, ed, sec adm.
Calauag Central College, Calauag, Quezon. *1933*
arts, ed.
Camarines Norte College, Labo, Camarines Norte. *1947, 1976*
arts, ed, agr ed.
Camarines Sur Institute, Goa, Camarines Sur.
1979, 1980
com, arts, crim, ed.
Camiling Colleges, Camiling, Tarlac. *1946*
com, ed.
Canossa Colleges, San Pablo City, Laguna.
1955, 1963
Tel: 24-80
com, arts, ed, math, psyc.
Catanduanes State College, Virac, Catanduanes.
Tel: 473
agr, agr tech, com, pre-eng, arts, ed, tec voc.
Cebu Aeronautical Technical School, Lahug Airport, Cebu City. *1953, 1978*
aero eng, aircraft techn.
Cebu Central College, Osmeña Boulevard, Cebu City. *1964*
Tel: 91164
nav arc, com, customs adm, crim, arts, comp, nurs, hotel & restaurant mangt, ed, mar trans, midwifery, sec adm.

Cebu Doctors' College, Osmeña Boulevard, Cebu City. *1975*
Tel: 5-36-92
sec adm, med tec, phys ther, dent, optom, biol.

Cebu Eastern College, Leon Kilat Street, Cebu City. *1915, 1974*
com.

Cebu Institute of Medicine, F. Ramona Street, Cebu City.
Tel: 76240

Cebu Institute of Technology, Rizal Avenue, Cebu City. *1946, 1957*
com, eng, arc, arts, comp, math.

Cebu Polytechnic School, D. Jakosalem Street, Cebu City. *1932, 1962*
mar trans, tec voc.

Cebu Roosevelt Memorial Colleges, Bogo, Cebu. *1947*
agr, com, arts, ed, agr techn.

Center for Research and Communication, Pearl Drive, Pasig, Metro Manila. *1967, 1979*
Tel: 673-77-81. Telex: etp 65524 crcrp pn. Cables: metro manila

Central Colleges of the Philippines, 52 Aurora Boulevard, Quezon City. *1954*
Tel: 60-78-53
arc, eng, arts, optom, ed, comp, bus adm.

Central Institute of Technology, P. Paredes Quezon Boulevard, Sampaloc, Manila. *1945, 1950*
com, ed, ind arts, ind ed.

Central Institute of Technology, Burgos Street, Paniqui, Tarlac. *1945, 1967*
com, arts, ed, ind ed, ind arts.

Central Luzon Doctor's Hospital Educational Institution, San Vicente, Tarlac, Tarlac. *1976*
nurs, arts.

Central Lyceum of Catanduanes, Bato, Catanduanes.
ind ed, arts, bus adm.

Central Maguindanao Institute, Buayan, Datu Piang, Maguindanao. *1960, 1982*
arts, agr techn.

Central Mindanao College, Kidapawan, North Cotabato. *1946, 1947*
com, eng, arts, ed, home eco, civ eng.

Central Negros College, Severino Street, San Carlos City. *1951, 1974*
com, arts, ed.

Central Sulu College, Siasi, Sulu.
arts, ed.

Chiang Kai Shek College, 1274 Padre Algue Street, Tondo, Manila. *1939, 1965*
Tel: 26-38-81
com, ed.

Chinese General Hospital College of Nursing, 286 Blumentritt, Sta. Cruz, Manila. *1921, 1980*
arts, nurs.

Christ the King College, Magsaysay Boulevard, Calbayog City. *1905, 1951*
com, arts, soc w, laws, psyc, ed.

Christ the King College, Gingoog City. *1947, 1950*
com, hom eco, ed, midwifery, arts, sec adm.

Christian Colleges of the Philippines, Burgas Avenue, Cabanatuan City. *1946*
agr, com, eng, ed.

Claret College of Isabela, Isabela, Basilan Province. *1949, 1966*
com, arts, ed.

Colegio de la Immaculada Concepcion, 45 Gorordo Avenue, Cebu City. *1880, 1947*
Tel: 7-65-85. Cables: CIC. CEBU
com, mus, arts, ed, piano.

Colegio de la Immaculada Concepcion, Pototan, Iloilo. *1932, 1973*
arts, sec.

Colegio de la Milagrosa, Sorsogon, Sorsogon. *1937, 1938*
com, arts, ed.

Colegio de la Purisima Concepcion, 1, Arzobispo Street, Roxas City. *1948*
com, eng, arts, ed.

Colegio del Sagrado Corazon de Jesus, Iloilo City.
Tel: 7-16-54
arts.

Colegio de Saint Rita, San Carlos City. *1932, 1946*
com, arts, ed.

Colegio de San Agustin, Bacolod City. *1962, 1964*
com, eng, arts, sc, med techn, nurs, ed, sec adm, ch.

Colegio de San Jose, Jaro, Iloilo City. *1872, 1946*

Colegio de San Juan de Letran, Bucal, Calamba, Laguna. *1979*
Tel: 545-1829
com, arts, sc, eng.

***Colegio San Juan de Letran**, 151 Muralla Street, Intramuros, Manila. *1620, 1930*
Tel: 491236
com, arts, bus adm.

Colegio de Sta. Isabel, Naga City. *1968*
Tel: 3100
com, arts, mus, nutr, nurs, soc w, ed, home eco.

College of the Holy Spirit, 163 E. Mendiola Street, Manila. *1913, 1926*
Tel: 7410916
fa, sc, nutr, med techn, com, ed, ch, arts.

College of the Holy Spirit, Tarlac, Tarlac. *1939, 1968*
arts, ed, bus adm.

College of the Immaculate Conception, del Pilar Street, Cabanatuan City.
Tel: 963-2438
agr, com, civ eng, arts, nutr, soc w, ed, agr

techn.

College of Maasin, Maasin, Southern Leyte.
1924, 1948
arts, ed.

College of the Republic, San Jose City.
1948
com, arts, ed.

Columban College, Inc, 1 Mt. Apo Street, East
Tapinas, Olongapo City.   *1961*
com, civ eng, arts, sc, ed, psyc, math.

Concord Technical Institute, Jakosalem España
Street, Cebu City.   *1956*
mar trans.

Concordia College, 1739 Pedro Gil Street, Paco,
Manila.   *1947, 1967*
com, nurs, soc w, ed, mus, arts.

Congress College, San Nicolas Sur, Agoo, La
Union.   *1946, 1947*
com, arts, ed.

COR Jesu College, Digos, Davao del Sur.
1959, 1961
com, civ eng, arts, sc, laws, ed, psyc.

Corrigidor College, Guimba, Nueva Ecija.
com, arts, ed.

Dalubhasaang Epifanio de los Santos, Bernales
Street, Malabon, Metro Manila.   *1945*
ed.

Daniel B. Peña Memorial College Foundation,
Tabaco, Albay.   *1949, 1962*
com, arts, ed.

Dansalan Junior College, Marawi City.   *1951*
arts, ed.

Davao Central College, Toril, Davao City.
1948, 1965
Tel: 812-10
arts.

Davao Doctor's College, E. Quirino Avenue,
Davao City.   *1975*
Tel: 7-84-11
nurs, sc, biol.

Davao Institute of Agricultural Foundation, Inc.,
Toril, Davao City.   *1962*
agr, vet, for.

Davao Medical School Foundation, Bajada,
Davao City.
Tel: 7-21-94. Cables: davaomedschool
med, dent.

De Los Santos College, 201 E. Rodriguez Sr.
Boulevard, Quezon City.   *1975, 1979*
Tel: 78-70-11
nurs, midwifery, nutr-diet, arts.

De Ocampo Memorial College, 2921 Nagtahan
Street, Sta. Mesa, Manila.
Tel: 61-27-86
*arts, sc, nutr, dent, optom, med techn, nurs,
midwifery.*

De Paul College, E. Lopez Street, Jaro, Iloilo
City.   *1948, 1961*
com, arts, soc w, ed.

Divina Pastora College, Gapan, Nueva Ecija.
1958, 1967
com, arts, ed.

Divine Word College of Urdaneta, Urdaneta,
Pangasinan.   *1967, 1968*
com, arts.

Divine Word College of Bangued, Rizal Street,
Bangued, Abra.   *1920, 1948*
Tel: 203. Cables: divine bangued
com, arts, ed, midwifery.

Divine Word College of Calapan, Oriental
Mindoro.   *1946*
Cables: dwcc
com, arts, ed, eng.

Divine Word College of Laoag, Barangay 17,
General Segurado Avenue, Laoag City (Ilocos
Norte).   *1946*
com, eng, arts, ed, hom eco.

Divine Word College of Legazpi, Rizal Street,
Legazpi City.   *1961, 1965*
com, eng, arts, ed.

Divine Word College of San Jose, San Jose,
Occidental Mindoro.   *1960, 1961*
bus adm, arts, ed.

Divine Word College, Tagbilaran City.   *1947*
Tel: 33-87
com, eng, arts, laws, nurs, ed, hom eco.

Divine Word College of Vigan, Vigan, Ilocos
Sur.   *1925*
com, arts, ed.

Dr. Aurelio Mendoza Memorial College, Ipil,
Zamboanga del Sur.   *1958, 1964*
com, arts, ed.

Dr. Concepcion A. Aguila Memorial College, San
José, Batangas.   *1950*
com, arts, ed.

Dr. Faustino Legaspi Uy College, Pilar Village,
Almanza, Las Piñas, Metro Manila.   *1975*
bus adm, eng, arts, nurs, midwifery, tec.

Dr. Nicanor Reyes Memorial Colleges, Paniqui,
Tarlac.   *1950*
com, ed, arts.

Dr. Yanga's F. Balagtas College, McArthur
Highway, Bocaue, Bulacan.   *1950, 1977*
agr, com, arts, vet, midwifery.

Dominican College, 179, Blumetrit Street, San
Juan, Metro Manila.   *1924, 1966*
com.

Don Bosco Technical College, 736 Kalentong
Street, Mandaluyong, Metro Manila.
1953, 1966
Tel: 70-11-26
eng.

**Don Jose Ecleo Memorial Educational Founda-
tion**, San Jose, Dinagat, Surigao del Norte.
1981
arts, ed, com.

Dumaguete Cathedral College, Dumaguete City.
1959, 1969

Tel: 36-59
com, arts, ed.
DWU-RTR Medical Foundation College of Medicine, Tacloban City.   *1980*
Dynamic Computer Centrum, Legazpi City.
East Central Colleges, B. Mendoza Street, San Fernando, Pampanga.   *1945, 1958*
bus adm, civ eng, arts, ed.
East Negros College, Tanjay, Negros Oriental.
                                                    1947, 1953
agr techn, com, arts, ed, agr tec.
Eastern Laguna Colleges, J. Rizal Street, Paete, Laguna.   *1947, 1967*
com, ed, arts.
Eastern Mindoro College, Bongabong, Oriental Mindoro.   *1945, 1967*
com, arts, ed.
Eastern Quezon College, Ipil-Ipil Avenue, Gumaca, Quezon.   *1947, 1950*
com, arts, ed.
Eastern Tayabas College, Lopez, Quezon. *1920*
arts.
Elenton Mission College, Maitum, South Cotabato.
agr, arts, ed.
Emilio Aguinaldo College, Bagong Bayon, Dasmariñas Cavite.   *1977*
Tel: 741-92-71
bus adm, arts, sc, phys ther, phar, nurs, biol, crim, radiologic techn, nutr-diet, ed, midwifery, sec.
Emilio Aguinaldo College, 918 U.N. Avenue, Ermita, Manila.   *1973*
bus adm, nutr-diet, nurs, phar, phys ther, radiologic techn, sc, tour, midwifery, arts, sec adm.
Emilio Aguinaldo College of Medicine (Medical School Foundation), Bayong Bayan, Desmariñas Cavite.
med.
Emmanuel College, Magsaysay Avenue, General Santos City.   *1962, 1964*
arts.
Eveland Junior College, San Mateo, Isabela.
                                                         1942
arts.
The Family Clinic Inc., 1452 A. Mendoza Street, Sta. Cruz., Manila.   *1961, 1979*
radiologic techn, nurs, arts.
Fatima College of Camiguin, Mambajao, Camiguin.   *1922, 1956*
com, arts, ed.
Fatima Medical Science Foundation, Inc., 120, McArthur Highway, Valenzuela, Metro Manila.   *1979*
med, vet.
Fellowship Baptist Academy, Rizal Street, Kabankalan, Negros Occidental.   *1954, 1983*
Tel: 210
bus adm, arts, midwifery.

Fernandez Piano School, 110 Bonifacio Street, Davao City.
mus.
Filamer Christian Institute, Roxas City. *1904*
Tel: 210-471
com, arts, nurs, ed.
Franciscan College of the Immaculate Concepcion, Baybay Leyte, Inc., Baybay, Leyte. *1948*
Tel: 6-4-5
com, arts, ed.
Galang Medical Center College, 1240, Batangas Street, Sta. Cruz, Manila.
nurs, midwifery.
Gallego Institute of Agriculture and Industry, Nampicuan, Nueva Ecija.   *1952, 1973*
Garcia College of Technology, Kalibo, Aklan.
com, arts, civ eng, mec, elec, geodetic eng.
Gingoog Institute, Gingoog City.   *1946, 1951*
arts.
Golden Gate Colleges, Batangas City.
                                                         1946
agr, com, eng, arts, nurs, ed, sec, midwifery.
Good Samaritan Colleges, Burgos Ave., Cabanatuan City.   *1973, 1978*
arts, nurs, radiologic techn, midwifery.
Good Shepherd's Fold Academy, Buenavista, Gumaras, Iloilo.   *1965, 1969*
arts.
Grace Mission College, Socorro, Oriental Mindoro.   *1976, 1978*
arts, midwifery.
Great Plebian College, Plaridel Street, Alaminos, Pangasinan.   *1947, 1968*
com, arts, ed, midwifery, tec.
Guagua National Colleges, Guagua, Pampanga.
                                                  1918, 1932
com, eng, arts, ed.
Guzman Institute of Technology, 509 Mendoza Street, Quiapo, Manila.   *1947, 1975*
Tel: 47-48-06
sec adm, ed.
Harris Memorial College, 1267, General Luña Street, Ermita, Manila.   *1903, 1936*
arts, ed.
Harvardian Colleges, San Fernando, Pampanga.
                                                         1945
com, arts, law, ed.
Heroes Memorial Colleges, Daet, Camarines Norte.   *1947*
com, arts, ed.
Holy Cross of Bansalan College, Bansalan, Davao del Sur.   *1959, 1984*
ed.
Holy Cross College of Calinan, Calinan, Davao City.   *1948, 1964*
com, arts, ed.
Holy Cross of Davao College, Sta. Ana Avenue, Davao City.   *1956, 1966*
com, customs adm, arts, ed voc.

Holy Infant College, Tacloban City.
1924, 1963
com, mus, arts, piano, ed.

Holy Rosary College, Tala, Caloocan, Metro Manila. *1951, 1955*
Tel: 905721
ed.

Holy Trinity Academy, Ginatilan, Cebu.
1945, 1979
arts.

Holy Trinity College, Puerto Princesa City, Palawan. *1940, 1950*
bus adm, arts, ed, eng.

Holy Trinity College, Domingo P. Fontivo Street, Bato, Camarines Sur. *1966, 1970*
arts, ed.

I.B. Calingasan Memorial Institution, Nasugbu, Batangas. *1976*
Tel: 26-85-71
arts, com, ed, midwifery.

Iligan Capital College, Mahagahaz, Iligan City.
agr com, arts, crim, ed, midwifery, mar trans.

Iloilo Doctors' College, West Avenue, Molo, Iloilo City. *1972*
Tel: 7-91-22
nurs, dental med, med, radio, midwifery, tour.

Immaculate Conception College, Balayan, Batangas. *1935, 1955*
arts, com, ed.

Immaculate Conception College, Boac, Marinduque. *1920, 1964*
com, arts, ed.

Immaculate Conception College, Fr. Selgas Street, Davao City. *1905, 1951*
com, eng, mus, arts, nutr-diet, med techn, phar, ch, ed, home eco, soc w, ed, relig ed.

Immaculate Conception College, Ozamis City.
1933, 1948
com, geodetic eng, arts, soc w, ed, home eco, sec adm, English.

Immaculate Conception College, Daraga, Albay.
1963
arts, nurs, midwifery.

Imus Institute, Imus, Cavite. *1923*
Tel: 435-2967
com, arts, ed.

Isabela Colleges Foundation, Cauayan, Isabela.
1948
bus adm, arts, ed, bus adm.

Jamaitul Philippine Al-Islamia, Raya-Maday, Marawi City. *1955, 1967*
com, eng, arts, ed.

John B. Lacson College Foundation, M.M. del Pilar Street, Molo, Iloilo City. *1948, 1949*
Tel: 77267
customs adm, mar eng, mar trans.

John B. Lacson Colleges Foundation, Tangub, Bacolod City. *1948*
mar trans.

Jose Rizal College, 80 Shaw Boulevard, Mandaluyong, Metro Manila. *1919*
com, arts, law, ed.

Kabankalan Catholic College, Kabankalan, Negros Occidental. *1927, 1963*
com, arts, ed.

King's College of Isulan Inc., Isulan, Sultan Kudarat. *1957, 1984*
arts.

King's College of Marbel, Koronadal, South Cotabato. *1959, 1965*
agr techn, fish, arts, ed.

Kolehiyo ng Mamamayan-San Isidro, Pili Camarines Sur.
bus adm, arts.

La Consolacion College, Bacolod City.*1919, 1938*
Tel: 2-10-64
arc, com, eng, fa, arts, ed.

La Consolacion College, La Carlota City. *1966*
com.

La Consolacion College, Mendiola Street, Manila.
com, arts, ed, hotel & restaurant mangt, tour.

La Salle College, La Salle Avenue, Bacolod City. *1952*
Tel: 2-05-77
com, eng, arts, sc, nurs, ed, bus adm, ed mangt.

La Sallete College, Santiago, Isabela. *1951, 1952*
Tel: 721-71-82. Cables: salamid, manila
bus adm, eng, arts, ed, home eco, sec adm, dev ed.

Lacson College, 2188, F.B. Harrison Street, Pasay, Metro Manila. *1915, 1938*
com, arts, ed, law.

Laguna College, Zulueta Street, San Pablo City.
1923
com, arts, nurs, ed, eng.

Laguna College of Business and Arts, Calamba, Laguna. *1930, 1953*
com, arts, ed, teaching.

Laguna Northwestern Institute, 192, Mabinit Street, San Antonio, San Pedro, Laguna.
1978, 1981
Tel: 846-0738
arts, com, ed.

Learning Center of the Arts, San Pedro and Ladislava Villages, Buhangin, Davao City.
fa.

Leon Guinto Memorial College, Osmeña Street, Atimonan, Quezon. *1971*
arts, ed, law.

Leyte Colleges, Tacloban City. *1945*
com, arts, ed, law.

Liceo de Cagayan, Cagayan de Oro City.
1954, 1955
com, eng, arts, nurs, midwifery, law.

Liceo de San Jacinto, Almonte Street, San Jacinto, Masbate. *1981*
arts.

Lipa City Colleges, Lipa City, Batangas.
                                                    1947
arts, com, nurs, ed.
Lisun Institute, Liloy, Zamboanga del Norte.
arts.
Lorma College, San Fernando, La Union.
                                             1934, 1970
Tel: 26-16
*arts, nurs, midwifery, med techn, comp, radio-
logic techn.*
Lourdes College, Capistrano Street, Cagayan de
Oro City.   *1928, 1938*
Tel: 36-83
*com, hotel & restaurant mangt, mus, arts, nutr-
diet, ed, home eco.*
Luna Colleges, Tayug, Pangasinan.   *1934, 1945*
arts, ed, com.
Luzon Colleges, Perez Boulevard, Dagupan City.
Tel: 30–10
*com, sc, eng, arts, crim, diet-nutr, med techn,
nurs, hotel & restaurant mangt, ed, ind techn,
midwifery, arc, jour, home eco, sec adm, publ
adm.*
Lyceum of Aparri, Aparri, Cagayan.   *1967*
Tel: 2-2075. Cables: lyceumparri
bus adm, arts, eng, ed, midwifery.
Lyceum of Batangas, Capital Site, Batangas
City.   *1966*
Tel: 725-3313
*com, customs adm, arts, nurs, med techn, mar
trans, eng, radiologic techn, midwifery, crim,
dent, bus adm, publ adm.*
Lyceum of Cabagan, Cabagan, Isabela.
arts, ed.
Lyceum Northwestern, Tapuao, Dagupan City.
                                                    1969
*agr techn, com, eng, arts, med techn, nurs,
radiologic techn, dent, sc, ed, midwifery, bus-
adm, tec-voc.*
*Lyceum of the Philippines, Intramuros, Manila.
                                                    1952
Tel: 47-04-81
law, bus & publ adm, eng, arts, ed, sc, tec.
Mabini Colleges, Daet, Camarines Norte.
                                             1924, 1949
Tel: 23-70
com, arts, hom eco, nurs, soc w, ed, tec-voc.
Mabini Junior College, Talaga, Batangas.   *1949*
arts.
Magsaysay Memorial College, Koronadal, South
Cotabato.   *1967*
com, arts, ed.
Magsaysay Memorial College, Isulan, Sultan
Kudarat.   *1965*
com, arts, ed.
Magsaysay Memorial College, Tacurong, Sultan
Kudarat.   *1962, 1964*
com, arts, ed.
Magsaysay Memorial College, San Narciso,

Zambales.   *1947, 1962*
com, arts, ed, sec adm.
Mandawe Academy, Plaridel Street, Mandawe
City.   *1952, 1982*
arts.
Manila Doctors College, 667, United Nations
Avenue, Ermita, Manila.   *1975*
Tel: 50-30-11
sc, nurs.
Manuel V. Gallego Foundation College, Cabana-
tuan City, Nueva Ecija.   *1952, 1960*
Tel: 963-3277
agr, eng, nurs, sc, ed, voc.
Mapua Institute of Technology, Muralla Street,
Intramuros, Manila.   *1928*
Tel: 40-25-46
ch, eng, arc, ch.
Marian College, Ipil, Zamboanga del Sur.
                                             1958, 1962
com, arts, ed.
Mariners' Polytechnic College Foundation, 323,
Baras.   *1974, 1980*
customs adm, eng.
Martinez Memorial Colleges, 198, A. Mabini
Street, Caloocan, Metro Manila.   *1962*
Tel: 23-8861
*bus adm, arts, med techn, nurs, radiologic
techn, midwifery, arc, adm.*
Mary Chiles General College, 667 Gastambide,
Sampaloc, Manila.   *1930, 1980*
nurs, midwifery, voc, respiratory ther.
Maryhill School of Theology, 13th Street, Corner
Gilmore, Quezon City.   *1972, 1977*
Masbate Colleges, Rosero Street, Masbate,
Masbate.   *1964*
Tel: 103. Cables: mascoin
com, arts, ed.
Mater Dei College, Tubigon, Bohol.   *1983, 1984*
com, arts, ed.
Mats College of Technology, R. Castillo Street,
Agdao, Davao City.   *1970, 1973*
*nav, com, customs adm, eng, dent, tour mangt,
customs adm, optom, mar trans, tec-voc.*
**Medical Center of Lucena Educational Institu-
tion**, Lucena City.   *1973*
arts, nurs, midwifery.
Medina Colleges, Ozamis City.   *1963*
Tel: 20036
*com, arts, sc, nutr, nurs, phar, radiologic techn,
ed, agr, sec adm, tec-voc.*
Metro Manila College, Suite 201, Miranda
Buildings, 966 Plaza Novaliches, Quezon City.
Tel: 90–18-55. Cables: mirenter, manila
agr techn, com, arts, sc, crim, ed, sec adm.
Metropolitan Hospital School of Nursing, 1357
Masangkay, Sta. Cruz, Manila.   *1976*
arts, nurs, diet-nutr.
Mindanao Institute of Technology, Circuit Road,
Rosary Heights, Cotabato City.   *1982, 1983*

bus adm, mar trans, customs adm.

Mindanao Polytechnic College, General Santos City.   *1980*
Tel: 26-71
customs adm, eng, mar trans.

Mindanao School of Business Administration, Marawi City.   *1979, 1980*
bus adm.

Misamis Institute of Technology, Pingol/Bañadero, Ozamis City.   *1965, 1968*
customs adm, eng, ed, mar trans, tec-voc, mar eng.

Molave Institute, Molave, Zamboanga del Sur.
sec adm.

Mount Apo Science Foundation College, Eden-Bayabas, Toril, Davao City.   *1960*
agr techn.

Mount Carmel College, Baler, Aurora, Quezon.
1948, 1961
com, arts, ed.

Mount Carmel College, New Escalante, Negros Occidental.   *1961, 1963*
com, arts, ed.

Mount Carmel School of Quezon City, 48, N. Domingo Street, Quezon City.
com, arts.

Mountain View College, Malaybalay, Bukidnon.
1953
agr, com, arts, sc, nurs, ed, sec adm.

Naga College, Peñafrancia Avenue, Naga City.
1947
com, arts, ed, eng, food techn, crim, ind arts, midwifery.

Namei Polytechnic Institute, 123 A. Mabini, Mandaluyong, Metro Manila.
Tel: 79-42-21
eng, mar eng.

National College of Business and Arts, Lepanto Cor. R. Papa Street, Sampaloc, Manila.
1967, 1969
NATIONAL COLLEGE OF BUSINESS AND ARTS, 3394, V. Mapa Street, Sta. Mesa, Manila.
1982

National Radio School and Institute of Technology, 1813, C.M. Recto Avenue, Manila.
1931, 1960
Tel: 27-49-68

National Teachers College, 629 Nepomuceno Street, Quiapo, Manila.   *1928*
Tel: 741-09-51
ed, arts.

Negros Institute of Technology, Galo Street, Bacolod City.
com, civ eng.

New Era College, Don Mariano Marcos Avenue, Diliman, Quezon City.   *1975, 1978*
bus adm, arts, sc, ed, theo, eng.

North Negros College, Cadiz City, Negros del Norte.   *1979, 1985*

bus adm, arts.

Northeast Luzon Academy, Alicia, Isabela.
arts.

Northeastern College, Villasis, Santiago, Isabela.
1941, 1950
Tel: 6-5-9
com, eng, arts, ed.

Northern Bataan Institute, Dinalupihan, Bataan.
1945, 1967
com, arts, ed.

Northern Cagayan Academy, Ballesteros, Cagayan.   *1930, 1985*
arts, ed.

Northern Cebu Colleges, Cor. D. Rubio Street, Bogo, Cebu.   *1932, 1949*
ed.

Northern Christian College, General Ablan Avenue and Mabini Street, Laoag City.   *1946*
Tel: 22-00-521
com, arts, nurs, ed, home eco.

Northwestern Visayan College, Kalibo, Aklan.
1948
agr, com, arts, crim, ed, agr techn.

Notre Dame of Dadiangas College, Marist Avenue, General Santos City.   *1953, 1959*
Tel: 4351. Cables: marist dadiangas
com, arts, sc, nurs, ed, sec adm.

Notre Dame of Jolo College, Jolo, Sulu.   *1954*
com, arts, soc w, ed, midwifery, tec-voc.

Notre Dame of Kidapawan College, Datu Ingkal Street, Kidapawan, Cotabato.   *1948, 1960*
Tel: 181
arts, com, ed.

Notre Dame of Marbel College, Alunan Avenue, Koronadal, South Cotabato.   *1946, 1955*
Tel: 218. Cables: marist marbel phil
com, arts, sc, ch, theo, ed, eng, agr techn, agr ed, agr bus, guidance, sec adm.

Notre Dame of Midsayap College, Midsayap, North Cotabato.   *1960*
com, arts, ed.

Notre Dame of Tacurong College, Tacurong, Sultan Kudarat.   *1950, 1963*
com, arts, ed.

Nueva Ecija College, Cagayan Valley Road, Cabanatuan City.
nurs, arts.

Olivarez College, Sucat Road, Parañaque, Metro Manila.   *1976*
arts, nurs, voc, radiologic techn, nutr-diet, com, bus adm.

Osias College Educational Foundation, Balaoan, La Union.   *1947*
com, arts, ed.

Osias Colleges, F. Tañedo Street, Tarlac, Tarlac.
1949, 1950
com, arts, ed.

Osmena College, Masbate, Masbate.   *1948*
com, arts, ed.

Our Lady of Fatima College, 120, McArthur Highway, Valenzuela, Metro Manila.   *1973*
arts, nurs, midwifery, sc.

Our Lady of the Pillar's Institute, Cauayan, Isabela.   *1956, 1969*
bus adm, arts.

Ovilla Technical College, 38 Danao Street, Masbate, Masbate.   *1964*
arts, ed, ind ed, ind arts.

Pacasum College, Marawi City.
com, arts, ed.

Palaris College, San Carlos City, Pangasinan.
1947, 1954
bus adm, arts, ed.

Palawan Polytechnic College, Manalo Extension, Puerto Princesa City, Palawan.   *1979*
com, customs adm, eng, sc.

Pampanga Colleges, Macabebe, Pampanga.
1938, 1950
com, ed.

Pangarungan Islam College, Marawi City.
com, arts, ed.

Pangasinan Memorial College, Lingayen, Pangasinan.
com, arts, ed.

Pangasinan Merchant Marine Academy, Perez Boulevard, Dagupan City.   *1973, 1978*

Pasig Catholic College, Plaza Rizal, Pasig, Metro Manila.   *1915, 1951*
Tel: 682-2675
bus adm, ed, acc.

PATS School of Aeronautics, PATS Hanger, Domestic Airport, Pasay City, Metro Manila.
1969

Perpetual Help College of Manila, 1240 V. Concepcion Street, Sampaloc, Manila.   *1968*
com, arts, sc, nurs, sec adm, bus adm.

Perpetual Help College of Laguna, Sto. Niño, Biña, Laguna.
com, arts, eng, nutr, nurs, ed.

Perpetual Help College of Rizal, Pamplona, Las Piña, Metro Manila.   *1975*
Tel: 801-00-80
com, eng, arts, nutr, nurs, hotel & restaurant mangt, ed, zoo, crim, sec adm.

Perpetual Help School of Laguna (Foundation for Medicine and Health Science), Biñan, Laguna.
1976
phys ther, occ ther, med.

Philippine Advent College, Sindangan, Zamboanga del Norte.
arts, midwifery, ed, com, sec.

Philippine College of Criminology, 641 Sales Street, Sta. Cruz, Manila.   *1954*
com, arts, crim, laws.

Philippine College of Technological Resources, Maysan Road, Valenzuela, Metro Manila.
1980
bus adm, sec adm, tec.

Philippine Harvardian Colleges, 68, Almonte Street, Cotabato City.   *1969*
Tel: 23-18
com, eng, arts, ed, crim, agr techn, voc.

Philippine Maritime Institute, 730 Roosevelt Avenue, Quezon City.

Philippine Merchant Marine School, 745 Raon, Quiapo, Manila.

Philippine Merchant Marine School, 5th Floor, Filipinas Bank Building, Plaza Sta. Cruz, Manila.   *1950*
mar trans, eng.

Philippine Muslim-Christian College of Medicine Foundation Inc., Circumferential Road, Antipolo, Rizal.   *1981*
Tel: 695-0369
med.

Philippine School of Business Administration, 826 R. Papa Street, Sampaloc, Manila.   *1963, 1967*
Tel: 27-31-09

Philippine School of Business Administration, 1029, Aurora Boulevard, Quezon City.   *1980*

Philippine Statesman College, Cabanatuan City.
1947
ed, psyc.

Philippine Union College, Putking Kahoy, Silang, Cavite.   *1917, 1925*
com, mus, arts, sc, nutr, nurs, med techn, sec, ed.

Philippine Union College, Alicia, Isabela.   *1983*
arts.

Philippine Union College, Naga View Campus, Panicuason, P.O. Box 35, Naga City.
1965, 1971
Cables: puc-nvc c/o tony's grocery igualdad, naga city
arts.

Philippine Women's College, Juna Subdivision, Matina Street, Davao City.   *1953*
bus adm, hotel & restaurant mangt, arts, sec adm.

Pilar College, Zamboanga City.
mus.

Pines City Educational Center, Maysaysay Avenue, Baguio City.
Tel: 43-08
nurs, optom, midwifery.

Pius XII Institute of Catechitical and Social Studies, Jaro, Iloilo City.   *1959, 1961*
Tel: 7-23-39
ed.

PMI Colleges, 419, David Street, Sta Cruz, Manila.
customs adm, mar trans.

PMI Colleges, Bohol, CPC Avenue, Tagbilaran City.   *1973*
com, customs adm, arts, mar trans, mar eng.

President Magsaysay Memorial College, Urdaneta, Pangasinan.   *1961*

com.

Quezon City Medical Center and Colleges, 960, Aurora Boulevard, Quezon City.
1971, 1979
psyc, nutr-diet, nurs, midwifery.

Quezon Colleges of Southern Philippines, Tacurong, Sultan Kudarat.   *1959, 1962*
com, arts, ed.

Quezon Memorial Colleges, 9, Tomas Morato Avenue, Quezon City.   *1945*
Tel: 70-12-38
com, arts, ed.

R.G. de Castro College, Bulan, Sorsogon.
com, arts, ed.

Ramon Magsaysay Memorial College, General Santos City.   *1960*
com, customs adm, eng, arts, crim, soc w, ed, sec adm.

Recaredo Castillo College, Mangagoy, Bislig, Surigao del Sur.
com, arts.

Regina Carmeli College, Barasoain, Malolos Bulacan.   *1937, 1945*
com, arts, ed.

Remedios Trinidad Romualdez Memorial School, S. Amorsolo Street, Makati, Metro Manila.
arts, nurs.

Republic Central Colleges, Plaridel Street, Angeles City.   *1946, 1948*
agr, com, eng, arts, ch, agr ed, agr techn, ed.

Republic Colleges, G. Alban Street, Guinobatan, Albay.   *1947*
agr, bus adm, arts, ed, agr techn.

Republican College, 42, 18th Avenue, Murphy, Quezon City.   *1949*
com, arts, ed.

Riverside College, 23rd Street, Capitol Sub-division, Bacolod City.   *1954, 1972*
Tel: 2-70-31
nurs, midwifery.

Rizal College of Taal, Taal, Batangas. *1923, 1947*
arts, com, ed.

Rizal Memorial Colleges, A. Bichon Sr. Street, Davao City.   *1948*
agr, com, arts, ed, guidance-counselling, sec adm, eng, math, psyc.

Rizal Memorial Institute, Gov. Carnicero Street, Dapita City.   *1946, 1950*
com, arts.

Roosevelt College, Sumulong Highway, Cainta, Rizal.   *1933, 1977*
eng.

Roosevelt College, Marikina, Metro Manila.
1962, 1963
Tel: 947-70-66
com, arts, sec adm, ed.

Roxas College, Roxas, Oriental Mindoro.
1946, 1961
com, arts, ed.

Sacred Heart College, Merchant Street, Lucena City.   *1884, 1947*
com, arts, soc w, ed, nurs.

Sacred Heart College, Catbalogan, Samar. *1946*
com, arts, ed.

Sacred Heart School, Calamba, Misamis Occidental.   *1947, 1979*
arts, agr techn.

St. Anthony's College, San Jose, Antique. *1958*
com, arts, ed.

St. Anthony College of Technology, Mabalacat, Pampanga.   *1945, 1969*
ed.

St. Anthony College of Roxas City, San Roque Street, Roxas City.   *1958*
arts, nurs, midwifery.

St. Augustine College, Dr. Gonzales Street, Baliwag, Bulacan.   *1940, 1966*
com, ed.

St. Bridget's College, M.H. del Pilar Street, Batangas City.   *1913, 1946*
Tel: 725-2394
arts, com, ed, soc w.

St. Columban College, Lingayen, Pangasinan.
com, arts, ed.

St. Columban College, Pagadian City.
Tel: 202
com, arts, sec adm, ed.

St. Dominic College, Basco, Batanes.
com, arts, ed, tec-voc, agr techn.

St. Ferdinand College, Ilagan, Isabela.
Tel: 2-21-25
com, arts, sec adm, ed.

St. Francis Educational Institution, Allen, Northern Samar.   *1946, 1984*
arts.

Saint Gabriel College, G. Pastrana Street, Kalibo, Aklan.   *1970*
Tel: 3001
nurs, radiologic techn, midwifery.

Saint John the Baptist College, Jimenez, Misamis Occidental.   *1939, 1951*
com, arts, ed.

St. Joseph's College, Borongan, Eastern Samar.
1949, 1982
com, ed.

St. Joseph College, Cavite City.
Tel: 431-1937
ed, nurs.

St. Joseph's College, 295, E. Rodriguez Sr. Boulevard, Quezon City.   *1932, 1949*
com, arts, soc w, ed, psyc, mus.

St. Joseph College, Maasin, Southern Leyte.
1928, 1940
Tel: 631
com, eng, arts, ed.

Saint Joseph College, Sindangan, Zamboanga del Norte.   *1968, 1974*
com, arts, ed.

Saint Joseph Institute of Technology, Corners Montilla Boulevard and Rosales Streets, Butuan City. *1971, 1974*
com, customs adm, eng, arts, crim, mar trans, tec-voc.

St. Jude Agro-Industrial College, Topas Nabua, Camarines Sur. *1965, 1973*
agr techn.

St. Jude College, Don Quijote Street, Sampaloc, Manila. *1968, 1974*
bus adm, eng, nurs, radiologic techn, sec adm, midwifery, nurs-diet.

Saint Louis College, Carlatan, San Fernando, La Union. *1964*
arc, com, eng, arts, soc w, ed, sec adm.

Saint Louis College of Tuguegarao, Tuguegarao, Cagayan. *1965, 1968*
Tel: 446-1872
arc, com, eng, arts, ed.

St. Mary's College, Sta. Maria, Ilocos Sur. *1948, 1968*
arts, ed.

St. Mary's College, Bayombong, Nueva Vizcaya. *1928, 1947*
com, eng, arts, sc, ed.

St. Mary's College, SMC Tagum, Davao. *1948, 1960*
com, eng, arts, ed.

St. Michael's College, Cantilan, Surigao del Sur.
com, arts, ed.

St. Michael's College of Guagua, Inc., Guagua, Pampanga. *1941, 1948*
com, arts, ed.

St. Michael's College, Quezon Avenue, Iligan City. *1915, 1951*
com, eng, arts, ed.

St. Michael's College of Laguna, Biñan, Laguna. *1976*
com, arts, nurs, ed, midwifery.

St. Paul College, Dumaguete City. *1904, 1941*
Tel: 2959
bus adm, arts, ed, home eco.

St. Paul College of Iloilo, Iloilo City. *1946, 1974*
com, arts, sc, nutr, nurs.

St. Paul College, 680, Pedro Gil Street, Malate, Manila. *1912, 1936*
com, mus, arts, sc, nutr, nurs, math, psyc, sec adm, home eco, comp, hotel & restaurant mangt, ed.

St. Paul College, Aurora Boulevard, Corner Gilmore Avenue, Quezon City. *1946, 1965*
com, arts, sc, nutr-diet, hotel & restaurant mangt, sec adm.

St. Paul College, San Miguel, Bulacan *1938, 1966*
com, arts, ed.

St. Paul College, 432, Quirino Avenue, La Huerta, Parañaque, Metro Manila. *1945*
arts, sec.

St. Paul College, Vigan, Ilocos Sur. *1905, 1945*

bus adm, arts, ed.

St. Peter College, Balingasag, Misamis Oriental. *1950*
com, arts, ed.

Saint Peter's College, Ormoc City. *1914, 1965*
Tel: 2321
com, arts, ed.

St. Peter's College of Daliaon, Inc., Toril, Davao City. *1948*
Tel: 84-71
com, arts, ed.

St. Rita's College, Balingasag, Misamis Oriental. *1929, 1945*
com, arts, ed.

Saint Rita College, Plaza del Carmen, Quiapo, Manila. *1907, 1945*
arts, ed.

Saint Rita College, Dr. A. Santos Avenue, Sucat, Parañaque, Metro Manila.
com, arts.

St. Scholastica's College, 2560 Leon Guinto Street, Malate, Manila. *1906, 1914*
com, mus, piano, arts, math, psyc, sec adm, sc, nutr, hotel & restaurant mangt, ed.

St. Theresa's College, R. Aboitiz Street, Cebu City. *1933*
Tel: 7-70-21
com, arts, ed, soc w, mus, sc.

St. Theresa College, Tandag, Surigao del Sur.
com, arts, ed.

Saint Vincent De Paul College, Mangagoy, Bislig, Surigao del Sur. *1983*
arts.

Saint Vincent's College, Padre Ramona Street, Dipolog City. *1917, 1947*
com, arts, ed.

St. William's Academy, Bulanao, Tabuk, Kalinga-Apayao. *1967*
com, arts, ed.

Samal Institute, Babak, Davao del Norte. *1948, 1965*
arts.

Samar College, Catbalogan, Samar.
com, arts, law, ed.

San Agustin Institute of Technology, Valencia, Bukidnon. *1960, 1971*
eng, arts, midwifery, ind ed.

San Antonio de Padua Institute, Pila, Laguna. *1979*
com, arts.

San Beda College, P.O. Box 4457, Mendiola Street, Manila. *1901*
Tel: 40-69-71. Cables: sambeda
arts, com, law.

San Carlos College, San Carlos City, Pangasinan. *1946*
com, arts, ed, sec adm.

San Estanislao Kotska College, Manukan, Zamboanga del Norte. *1955, 1978*

arts.

San Ildefonso College, Tanay, Rizal.   *1947*
Tel: 2-4005
com, arts, ed.

San Isidro College, Malaybalay, Bukidnon.
                                        1949, 1962
com, arts, ed.

San Jose Colleges, San Nino Street, San Jose
City.   *1947*
com, arts, ed.

San Juan de Dios College, Roxas Boulevard,
Pasay City.   *1913, 1973*
Tel: 831-97-31
nurs, med techn.

San Nicolas College, Surigao City.   *1915, 1947*
Tel: 623
com, arts.

San Pablo Colleges, San Pablo City.   *1947*
com, arts, law, nurs, ed.

San Pedro College, 12 de Guzman Street, Davao
City.   *1956*
Tel: 6-44-61
med techn, nurs, arts, sc.

San Sebastian College, Sablayan, Occidental
Mindoro.   *1957, 1970*
com, arts, sec adm.

San Sebastian College, Santa Cruz, Cavite.
                                            1966
arts, com, sec adm.

San Sebastian College, C.M. Recto Avenue,
Quiapo, Manila.   *1946*
com, arts, law, bank-fin.

Sta. Catalina College, 2660, Legarda Street,
Sampaloc, Manila.   *1946, 1955*
com, arts, ed.

Sta. Cruz Institute, Sta. Cruz, Marinduque.
                                            1951
ed.

Santa Isabel College, 210, Taft Avenue, Metro
Manila.   *1594, 1932*
com, piano, arts, publ rel, ed, voice cult.

Santa Rita College, Santa Rita, Pampanga.
                                      1945, 1965
com, arts, ed.

Santo Niño Institute, Jasaan, Misamis Oriental.
                                      1972, 1980
midwifery.

Scout Ramon Albano Memorial College, 2407, T.
Earnshaw Street, Gagalangin, Tondo, Manila.
                                      1956, 1968
nurs, midwifery.

Siena College, Del Monte Avenue, Quezon City.
                                            1959
*sec adm, food serv adm, hotel & restaurant
mangt, bus adm, arts, nutr-diet, voc-tec.*

Silay Institute, Rizal Street, Silay City.
                                      1925, 1975
com.

SMC Agro-Tech, Dumalinao, Zamboanga del

Sur.   *1969, 1972*
agr techn, agr ed.

Southern Baptist College, M'lang, Cotabato.
                                          1952, 1954
Cables: bapto, m'lang, RCPI
com, arts, ed, theo.

Southeastern College, Padada, Davao del Sur.
                                          1951, 1967
arts, ed, voc, agr techn.

Southeastern College, College Road, Pasay,
Metro Manila.   *1946*
Tel: 831-84-84
bus adm, ed, com ed.

Southern Capital Colleges, Washington Street,
Oroquieta City.   *1946*
com, arts, ed.

Southern Christian College, Midsayap, North
Cotabato.   *1949*
agr techn, bus adm, arts, ed, midwifery.

Southern City Colleges, Pilar Street, Zamboanga
City.   *1946, 1951*
Tel: 38-47
com, customs adm, eng.

Southern Masbate Roosevelt College, Placer,
Masbate.   *1950, 1969*
arts.

Southern Mindanao Colleges, Pagadian City.
com, eng, arts, ind ed, ed.

Southern Negros College, Binalbagan, Negros
Occidental.   *1947*
com, ed.

Southern Philippines College, Julio Pacona
Street, Cagayan de Oro City.   *1981, 1982*
com, customs adm, arts, mar trans, sec adm, ed.

Stella Maris College, Oroquieta City. *1935, 1964*
arts, com, ed.

**Sultan Kudarat Educational Institution College of
Liberal Arts, Nursing and School of Midwifery**,
Tacurong, Sultan Kudarat.

                                          1978, 1984

T. del Rosario Academy, Capitol Drive, Balanga,
Bataan.   *1950, 1971*
bus adm, ed.

Tabaco College, 5, Tomas Cabeles Avenue,
Tabaco, Albay.   *1982*
Tel: 334
bus adm, arts, entrepreneurial mangt.

Tanauan Institute, J.V. Pagaspas Street,
Tanauan, Batangas.
art, com, ed.

Tayabas Western Academy, Candelaria,
Quezon.   *1928, 1967*
com, arts, ed.

Technological Institute of the Philippines, 888,
Gonzales Puyat Street, Quiapo, Manila. *1962*
Tel: 47-18-90
arc, com, eng, voc-tec.

Toledo Gullas College, Toledo City.   *1947*
arts, ed.

Tomas Claudio Memorial College, Morong, Rizal. *1950*
Tel: 23169
com, arts, ed.

Toril Community Educational Institution, McArthur Highway, Crossing Bayabas, Toril, Davao City. *1963*
com, arts.

Trinity College, Cathedral Heights, Quezon City. *1963*
Tel: 70-78-79
arts, bus adm, nurs, med techn, ed.

Unciano Paramedical College, V. Mapa Guadalcanal Street, Sta. Mesa, Manila. *1977*
arts, dent, nurs, midwifery, radiologic techn.

Union Christian College, San Fernando, La Union. *1910, 1947*
arts, com, nurs, ed.

Union College, Mabini Street, Sta. Cruz, Laguna. *1947*
Tel: 645-1083
arts, com, ed, ind ed.

United Doctors' Medical Center, 6 Ramirez Street, Quezon City. *1975*
nurs.

University of Mindanao Panabo College, Panabo, Davao. *1953*
com, arts, ed.

Urios College, Butuan City. *1900, 1949*
Tel: 20-40
com, eng, arts, ed, sec adm.

Velez College, F. Ramos Street, Cebu City. *1966*
Tel: 9-68-12
arts, sc, med techn, nurs, biol.

Veritas College of Irosin, Irosin, Sorsogon.
arts.

Villaflores College, Legaspi Street, Negros Oriental. *1952, 1956*
com, arts, ed.

Virgen Milagrosa Educational Institution, Taly District, San Carlos City. *1957, 1961*
Tel: 152
bus adm, eng, arts, sc, nutr, med techn, nurs, phar, phys ther, dent, med, vet, radiologic techn, midwifery, sec adm.

Visaya's Data Computer College, RBL Building, Gatuslao Street, Bacolod City. *1969, 1979*

Visayan Maritime Academy, Sum-ag, Bacolod City
mar trans.

West Negros College, Burgos Street, Bacolod City. *1948*
Tel: 2-23-13
com, eng, arts, sc, ed, psyc, ind mangt.

Western Colleges, Naic, Cavite. *1945, 1946*
com, ed.

Western Institute of Technology, Luna Street, La Paz, Iloilo City. *1953, 1964*
Tel: 7-42-13
com, eng, arts, sc, ch, mar eng.

Western Leyte College, Bonifacio Street, Ormoc City. *1945*
Tel: 2599
com, arts, ed.

Western Philippine Colleges, Batangas City. *1947*
Tel: 725-37-62
arts, com, ed, eng, agr techn, sec adm.

Zamboanga A.E. Colleges, Juan S. Alano Street, Zamboanga City. *1948*
Tel: 41-35
agr techn, com, eng, arts, crim, med techn, ed, laws, agr bus.

Zaragosa College, Tayug, Pangasinan.
com, arts, ed.

Also c. 230 Private Technical/Vocational Schools.

Philippine Association of State Universities and Colleges (PASUC)

Founded in 1966, the Association is a national organization of chartered state institutions of higher learning. It has a membership of 78 institutions.

PASUC serves as a forum for the exchange of ideas in the promotion of continuing contacts among state colleges and universities. It maintains co-operation among its members, with other educational associations, and with the Department of Education, Culture and Sports to attain excellence in higher education. It takes initiative and provides leadership in innovative approaches to educational reform that enables the Association to participate meaningfully in transforming higher education into a dynamic force for national development. The Association actively participates in decision-making on educational policies and plans.

The three organic bodies of the Association are the: General Assembly; Executive Board; and Secretariat.

Through its Executive Board and Secretariat, PASUC maintains an increasing sensitivity to social and economic change that affects higher education, and responds to such change through relevant projects and other activities.

Fondée en 1966, l'Association est une organisation nationale regroupant les institutions

d'enseignement supérieur d'Etat ayant reçu une charte. Elle comprend 78 institutions.

La PASUC constitue un forum permettant de procéder à des échanges d'idées afin de promouvoir l'établissement de contacts permanents entre les collèges et les universités d'Etat. Elle assure le maintien de la coopération entre ses membres, avec d'autres associations éducatives et avec le Département de l'Education, de la Culture et des Sports, en vue d'atteindre à un niveau d'excellence dans l'enseignement supérieur. En ce qui concerne la réforme de l'éducation, elle prend l'initiative d'élaborer des approches nouvelles et assure des fonctions de direction à cet égard, ce qui lui permet de participer sciemment à la transformation de l'enseignement supérieur en force dynamique de développement national. L'Association participe activement à la prise de décision en ce qui concerne les politiques éducatives et les plans en matière d'enseignement.

Les trois organes exécutifs de l'Association sont: l'Assemblée générale, le Conseil exécutif et le Secrétariat.

Grâce à son Conseil exécutif et à son Secrétariat, la PASUC se maintient et s'affirme toujours davantage à l'écoute des changements sociaux et économiques qui intéressent l'enseignement supérieur, et répond à ces changements par des projets pertinents et d'autres activités.
President: Dr. Frederick So. Pada.
Vice-President: Dr. Fortunato Battad.
Executive Secretary: Alicia O. Asuncion.
Department of Education, Culture and Sports, Arroceros Street, Manila.
Tel: 49-28-87

Philippine Association of Colleges and Universities (PACU)
Founded in 1932, the Philippine Association of Colleges and Universities is a voluntary, non-sectarian, non-profit organization. It was organized to raise the standard of instruction in all private schools, colleges and universities in the Philippines, and to foster the ideals of service among the youth of the land as a means to mould their character and prepare them to be good citizens and future leaders of the country.

The PACU is governed by a Board of Directors with a permanent staff headed by an Executive Vice-President. The President of the Association is elected from among the fifteen members of the Board. It has standing and special committees created to perform specific functions.

Membership in PACU is by educational institution, and not by individual. To be admitted into the Association, a school has to meet all the requirements prescribed in its constitution and by-laws.

L'Association des collèges et universités des Philippines, fondée en 1932, est une organisation bénévole, non confessionnelle et sans but lucratif. Elle a été créée afin d'élever le niveau de l'enseignement dans les universités, collèges et écoles privés des Philippines et de promouvoir parmi les jeunes l'idéal de service à la nation, pour former leur caractère et les préparer à leur rôle de citoyens et de futurs cadres du pays.

L'Association est dirigée par un Conseil d'administration assisté d'un personnel permanent à la tête duquel se trouve un Vice-Président Exécutif. Le Président de l'Association est élu parmi les quinze membres du Conseil. Le Conseil désigne des comités permanents et spéciaux en vue de certaines tâches particulières.

Les membres de l'Association sont des établissements d'enseignement et non des particuliers. Pour être admis à l'Association un établissement doit satisfaire à toutes les conditions requises par ses statuts et règlements.
244 Isabel Building, España Street, Manila.

Catholic Educational Association of the Philippines (CEAP)
Founded in 1941 and incorporated as a non-stock, non-profit religious-educational corporation in 1965, CEAP is a voluntary association of Catholic schools. The main objective of the Association is to advance and promote the educational work of the Catholic Church in the Philippines and contribute to the development of responsible citizenship among young people. Within this framework, CEAP represents the interests of the Catholic educational institutions in the Philippines to the Department of Education, Culture and Sports and also acts as liaison with other government offices. The Association operates through 31 regional educational associations as affiliate organizations. It is affiliated with the International Office of Catholic Education (OIEC) in Brussels and with the International Federation of Catholic Universities (IFCU) in Paris.

Membership of CEAP is composed of 1250 Catholic institutions, including 17 universities, 24 graduate schools, 178 colleges, 1099 high schools and 397 elementary schools. The Association is governed by a Board of Directors of 21 members.

CEAP publishes the CEAP Bulletin (monthly); the Perspective (quarterly) dubbed as the national education magazine in the Philippines.

L'Association de l'enseignement catholique aux Philippines (CEAP), fondée en 1941 et constituée en 1965 en une corporation à caractère religieux et éducatif, sans capital et sans but lucratif, est une association bénévole d'écoles catholiques. Son principal objectif est d'encourager et de promouvoir l'œuvre éducative de l'Eglise catholique aux

Philippines et de contribuer à développer, chez les jeunes, le sens des responsabilitiés civiques. Dans cette optique, la CEAP représente les intérêts des institutions d'enseignement catholique aux Philippines auprès du Département de l'Education, de la Culture et des Sports et sert d'organe de liaison avec les autres services gouvernementaux. L'Association fonctionne par l'intermédiaire de 31 associations régionales d'éducation qui lui sont affiliées. Elle est affiliée à l'Office international de l'enseignement catholique (OIEC), Bruxelles, et à la Fédération internationale des universités catholiques (FIUC), Paris.

La CEAP comprend 1250 institutions catholiques membres, dont 17 universités, 24 écoles postgraduées, 178 collèges, 1099 écoles secondaires et 397 écoles élémentaires. L'Association est administrée par un Conseil de Directeurs formé de 21 membres.

La CEAP publie régulièrement le Bulletin de la CEAP (mensuel); Perspective (trimestrielle) consideré aux Philippines comme le périodique national en matière d'éducation.

President: Jose D. Ante O.M.I.
Vice-President: Miguel Ma. Varela, S.J.
Executive Secretary: Carol C. Porio.
P.O. Box 1214, Zip Code 1007, 1175 United Nations Avenue, Paco, Manila.

Association of Catholic Universities of the Philippines (ACUP)

The Association was organized on 21 June 1973 as a voluntary, non-profit, organization. The objective of the Association is to foster co-operation among the 18 Catholic universities of the Philippines to be able to improve the quality of education in general and strengthen Catholic education in particular.

The ACUP is governed by a Board of Directors with a permanent staff headed by a Secretary-General. The Association sponsors projects in the areas of faculty development, student financial assistance, development education and educational research.

Membership in ACUP is by educational institution, and not by individual. To be admitted to the Association, a university must be a recognized Catholic university and must be able to satisfy the requirements as promulgated by the Board of Directors.

L'Association des Universités catholiques des Philippines (ACUP) a été créée le 21 juin 1973 comme organisation bénévole et sans but lucratif. Elle a pour objectif de promouvoir la collaboration entre les 18 universités catholiques des Philippines afin d'améliorer la qualité de l'enseignement en général et de renforcer l'enseignement catholique en particulier.

L'ACUP est administrée par un Conseil d'administration et dispose d'un personnel permanent, à la tête duquel se trouve un Secrétaire général. L'Association s'occupe de la mise sur pied de projets dans les domaines de la formation des enseignants, de l'aide financière aux étudiants, de l'éducation pour le développement et de la recherche pédagogique.

Ce ne sont pas les particuliers, mais les institutions qui peuvent solliciter leur adhésion à l'ACUP. Pour être admise à la qualité de membre, l'université doit être une université catholique reconnue et satisfaire aux conditions prescrites par le Conseil d'administration.

Secretary-General: Rafael B. Lusuegro, O.P.
Rm. 106-C Mezz. Floor., Main Bldg., University of Santo Tomas, España, Manila.
Tel: 731-3139.

Association of Christian Schools and Colleges

The objectives of the Association are: 1) to provide a centre of co-operative and united effort for Christian schools and colleges; 2) to act as a medium of expression of their common objectives, common ideals, and common desires; 3) to promote a high sense of unity, understanding, and fellowship among themselves and with the co-operating Mission Boards, agencies, and other bodies, both in the Philippines and abroad, interested in Christian schools and education in general in the Philippines; 4) to serve as an accrediting body for the church-related schools; 5) to provide special services, provided such services are requested by the member schools; and 6) to serve as liaison for member schools in connection with government and related agencies.

Membership: All Protestant church-related schools from elementary to university level that qualify for membership, and non-church-related schools that uphold the Association's objectives and meet its standards.

Les objectifs de l'Association des écoles et collèges chrétiens sont: 1) de fournir un centre de coopération à l'ensemble des écoles et collèges chrétiens; 2) d'être le porte-parole de leurs objectifs, de leurs aspirations et de leurs idéaux communs; 3) de promouvoir le sens de la solidarité, de la compréhension et de l'unité entre ses membres et avec les conseils de mission et autres organismes des Philippines ou de l'étranger qui s'intéressent aux écoles et à l'éducation chrétiennes aux Philippines; 4) de servir d'organisme «d'accréditation» pour les écoles reliées à l'Eglise; 5) d'assurer les services spéciaux qui peuvent lui être demandés par les écoles membres; et 6) d'assurer la liaison entre les écoles membres et le gouvernement et les autres organismes d'Etat.

Membres: Toutes les écoles reliées à l'Eglise protestante, du niveau élémentaire au niveau universitaire, qui remplissent les conditions requises, et les écoles non reliées à l'Eglise qui soutiennent les objectifs de l'Association et satisfont à ses conditions.
President: Dr. Lino Q. Arquiza.
General Secretary: Modesto G. Rico.
1664 Taft Avenue, Manila.
Tel: 58-63-40.

Philippine Association of University Women (IFUW)
124 Matatag Corner Matulungin Street, Diliman, Quezon City.
World University Service (WUS)
General Secretary: Ruben C. Caluya.
Manila Central University, University Affairs Center, Santa Cruz, Manila D404.
Tel: 2645-86. Telex: 27311 dac ph
Democratic Youth Council – Philippines – DYCP (IUS)
Rm. 403, Insurance Center Building, General Luna Street, Intramuros, Manila.

Philippine Movement for Intellectual and Cultural Affairs (Pax Romana)
10 Salud Street, Pasay City.
Agency for Community Educational Services (Pax Romana)
Cynthia-Marie Building (Rm. 206), 6 New York Corner E. Rodriguez Sr. Boulevard, Cubao, Quezon City.
Student Catholic Action of the Philippines (Pax Romana)
National Office, Pius XII Centre, United Nations Avenue, Manila.
Student Christian Movement of the Philippines (WSCF)
c/o National Council of Churches, 879 Epifano de los Santos Avenue, Quezon City.
*
Department of Education, Culture and Sports
Manila.
Tel: 49-28-87
Unesco National Commission of the Philippines
Department of Foreign Affairs, Padre Faura, Manila.
Tel: 831-88-73. Telex: 40257. Cables: minforaf unacom manila

POLAND
POLOGNE

UNIVERSITIES AND TECHNICAL UNIVERSITIES— UNIVERSITES ET UNIVERSITES TECHNIQUES

Uniwersytet Gdański, ul. Bażyńskiego la, 80-309
Gdańsk. *1970*
Tél: 52-50-71. Télex: 0512024 rekug pl
F : hum, math-phy-ch, biol-géog, dr-adm, éco prod, éco trans.
E : péd.
*Uniwersytet Jagielloński, ul. Gotębia 24, 31-
007 Kraków. *1364*
Tél: 22-10-33. Télex: 0322297 ujpl
F : dr-adm, phil-hist, phill, biol-géog, sc.
Uniwersytet Śląski w Katowicach, ul. Bankowa 12, 40-007 Katowice. *1968*
Tél: 587-231. Télex: 0315584 usk pl
F : soc, let, math-phy-ch, dr, adm, éd tec, biol-écologie.
E : péd (Cieszyn).
Uniwersytet Łódzki, ul. Narutowicza 65, 90-131
Łódź. *1945*

Tél: 34-98-85. Télex:886291 ulpl
F : dr-adm, phil-hist, phill, math-phy-ch, biol-géog, éco-socio.
*Katolicki Uniwersytet Lubelski, Al. Racławicke 14, 20–950 Lublin. (M. le Secrétaire). *1918*
Tél: 304-26. Télex: 0643235
F : hum, théo, dr can, phil chré.
Uniwersytet Marii Curie-Skłodowskiej, Plac M. Curie-Skłodowskiej 5, 20–031 Lublin. *1944*
Tél: 37-51-07. Télex: 0643223 umcs pl
F : dr-adm, let, math-phy-ch, biol-géol, éco, éd-psyc.
E : pol, lang étr, phys.
Section à Rzeszów.
Uniwersytet Mikołaja Kopernika w Toruniu, ul. Gagarina 11, 87–100 Toruń. *1945*
Tél: 226-94. Télex: 0552324 trao pl
F : ba, math-phy-ch, dr-adm, hum, biol-géol, éco.
Uniwersytet im. Adama Mickiewicza w Poznaniu,

ul. Stalingradzka 1, 61–712 Poznań. *1920*
Tél: 699-251. Télex: 0413260 uam pl
F : dr-adm, phil-hist, phill, math-phy, ch, biol-géol.
I : pol, trav, éd.
Uniwersytet Szczeciński, 70–451 Szczecin. *1984*
Tél: 429-92. Télex: 0422719
F : *eco, hum phy-ch-math.*
*Uniwersytet Warszawski, ul. Krakowskie Przedmieście 26/28, 00–325 Warszawa. *1818*
Tél: 200-381. Télex: 815439 uw pl
F : biol, ch, phill, phy, géol, hist, math-méc, soc, dr-adm, psyc-péd.
I : géog, soc, gestion.
Section à Białystok.
*Uniwersytet Wrocławski im. Bolesława Bieruta, plac Uniwersytecki 1, 50–957 Wrocław 3. *1945*
Tél: 368-47. Télex: 0712791 uwr pl
F : let, dr-adm, phil-hist, math-phy-ch, nat.
E : péd.
I : pol.
Akademia Górniczo-Hutnicza im. Stanisława Staszica [A. des Mines et de la Sidérurgie], Al. Mickiewicza 30, 30–059 Kraków. *1919*
Tél: 33-76-00. Télex: 0322203 agh pl
F : mine, géol, mét mine, cér, mét, élec mine, pét, méc mine.
Politechnika Białostoka, ul. Wiejska 45a, 15–351 Białystok. *1951, 1974*
Tél: 223-93. Télex: 852424 pb pl
F : arc, gé civ, élec, méc, math-phy.
Politechnika Częstochowska [E. polytechnique], ul. Deglera 31, 42–201 Częstochowa.
1949, 1955
Tél: 552-11. Télex: 037341 metal pl
F : méc, mét, élec.
I : math, phy, soc-éco.
*Politechnika Gdańska, ul. Majakowskiego 11/12, 80–952 Gdańsk 6. *1945*
Tél: 41-57-91. Télex: 0512302 plg pl
F : const nav, gé civ, const-arc, ch, élec, électro, techn-méc.
Politechnika Krakowska im. Tadeusza Kościuszki, ul. Warszawska 24, 31–155 Kraków.
1945
Tél: 33-03-00. Télex: 0322468 pk pl

F : arc, méc, gé civ, tec sani-hyd, ch.
I : math, phy, soc-éco.
Ce : inft, lang mod, techn éd.
Politechnika Łódzka, u. Żwirki 36, 90–924 Łódź.
1945
Tél: 36-55-22. Télex: 886136 polit pl
F : méc, ch alim, tex, élec, gé civ, gé ch.
Politechnika Lubelska, ul. J. Dąbrowskiego 13, 20–950 Lublin. *1953, 1977*
Tél: 222-01. Télex: 0642745 pl pl
F : gé civ, électro, méc.
Politechnika Poznańska, ul. Marii Curie Skłodowskiej 5, 60–965 Poznań. *1915*
Tél: 33-40-81. Télex: 0413250 polp pl
F : méc-tec, méc-véhicules, gé civ, élec, ch.
Politechnika Rzeszowska im. Ignacego Łukasiewicza, ul. Wincentego Pola 2, 35-959 Rzeszów.
1963, 1974
Tél: 432-81. Télex: 0632224 prz pl. Cables: inwsz
F : méc, const, élec, techn ch, gé civ.
Politechnika Śląska im. Wincentego Pstrowskiego, ul. Pstrowskiego 7, 44–100 Gliwice *1945*
Tél: 31-23-49. Télex: 036304 posl pl
F : mine, méc-énerg, const-arc, tec-ch, élec, tec sani, automatisation, méc-tec, math-phy, prod org, mét.
Politechnika Świętokrzyska, Al. Tysiąclecia Państwa Polskiego, 25–314 Kielce. *1951, 1974*
Tél: 24-100. Télex: 0613225 psbi pl
F : méc, gé civ, élec, auto, trans, éco.
Politechnika Szczecińska, Al. Piastów 17, 70–310 Szczecin. *1946*
Tél: 467-51. Télex: 0422141 ps pl
F : gé civ-arc, méc, gé ch, élec.
Politechnika Warszawska, Plac Jedności Robotniczej 1, 00–661 Warszawa 10. *1898*
Tél: 21-00-70. Télex: 813307 pw pl
F : arc, ch, gé civ, tec sani-hyd, techn-méc, méc-énerg-aéro, élec, téléc, méc-véhicules, géod-cartog, méc de précision, trans.
Section à Płock.
Politechnika Wrocławska, Wybrzeże Stanisława Wyspiańskiego 27, 50–370 Wrocław. *1945, 1968*
Tél: 22-73-36. Télex: 0712254 pwr pl
F : méc-énerg, méc, gé civ, arc, électro, élec, ch, tec sani, mine, éco-techn.

OTHER INSTITUTIONS—AUTRES INSTITUTIONS

Technical Education—Enseignement technique

Akademia Techniczno Rolnicza im. Jana i Jędrzeja Sniadeckich, ul. Jana Olszewskiego 20, 85–225 Bydgoszcz. *1951, 1974*
Tél: 314-50. Télex: 0562569 atr pl
F : méc, électro-élec, techn ch.

Wysża Szkoła Inżynierska, ul Racławicka 15/17, 75-620 Koszalin.
Tél: 278-81. Télex: 0532296 wsi pl
F : méc, const.
Wyższa Szkoła Inżynierska, ul. Oleska 114,

45–233 Opole.   *1966*
Tél: 260-41. Télex: 0732598 wsi pl
F : const, élec, méc.
Wyższa Szkoła Inżynierska, ul. Malczewskiego
29, 26–600 Radom.   *1978*
F : méc, trans, éco.
Wyższa Szkoła Inżynierska, ul. Podgórna 51,
65–246 Zielona Góra.   *1965*

Tél: 707-35. Télex: 0432215 wsi pl
F : const, méc, élec.
Akademia Rolnicza w Krakowie im. H. Kołłątaja
[Cracow U. of Agriculture], Al. Mickiewicza
21, 31–120 Kraków.   *1953*
Tél: 323-55. Cables: akrol
F : agr, zoo, hyd, for, hort.

Professional Education—Enseignement professionnel

Akademia Rolnicza, ul. Akademicka 13, Lublin.
                                 1955
Tél: 335-49. Télex: 0643176 ar pl
F : agr, zoo, vét, techn agr, hort.
Akademia Rolnicza-Techniczna, Blok 21, 10-957
Olsztyn-Kortowo.   *1950, 1972*
Tél: 233-10. Télex: 0526419 art pl
F : agr, zoo, lait-tec alim, vét, méc, gé civ-géod-
agr équipement.
*Akademia Rolnicza, ul. Wojska Polskiego 28,
60–637 Poznań.   *1951, 1972*
Tél: 403-34. Télex: 0413322
F : agr, zoo, hort, for, tec agr alim, ind du bois.
Akademia Rolnicza, ul. Janosika 8, 71–424
Szczecin.   *1954*
Tél: 22-08-51. Télex: 0425494 ar pl
F : agr, pêch, zoo.
Akademia Rolnicza w Warszawie, ul. Rakowiecka
26/30, 02–528 Warszawa.   *1906*
Tél: 49-22-51. Télex: 814790 sggw.ar pl
F : agr, zoo, hort, vét, hyd, éco agr, for, techn
alim, ind du bois.
Akademia Rolnicza, ul. Norwida 25, 50–375
Wrocław.   *1951, 1972*
Tél: 21-66-61. Télex: 0715327 arw pl
F : agr, zoo, vét, hyd.
Wyższa Szkoła Rolniczo-Pedagogiczna, ul. 3 Maja
54, Siedlce.   *1977*
F : agr, zoo, ch, péd.
Akademia Ekonomiczna im. K. Adamieckiego
[E. sup. d'Economie], ul. 1 Maja 50, 40–287
Katowice.   *1936*
Tél: 59-84-21. Télex: 0312455 ae pl
F : ind, com, ét éco alim.
Akademia Ekonomiczna, ul. Rakowiecka 27,
31–510 Kraków.   *1926*
Tél: 21-00-99. Télex: 0325414 aek pl
F : prod-com, opération-com.
Akademia Ekonomiczna, ul. Marchlewskiego
146, 60–967 Poznań.   *1926, 1974*
Tél: 69-92-61. Télex: 0413390 ae pl
F : com, prod-com.
Akademia Ekonomiczna im. O. Langego, ul.
Komandorska 118/120, 53–345 Wrocław. *1946*
Tél: 67-12-36. Télex: 0712427
F : éco-adm des aff, éco ind; éco (Jelenia
Góra).

Wyższa Szkoła Nauk Społecznych przy KC PZPR
[E. nationale supérieure de Sciences sociales du
Com. C. du POUP], ul. Bagatela 2, 00–585
Warszawa.   *1957, 1971*
Tél: 28-18-01
F : éco-adm, eco-pol, phil.
Szkoła Główna Planowania i Statystyki [E. cen-
trale de Planification et de Statistique], ul.
Niepodległości 162, 02–554 Warszawa. *1915*
Tél: 49-55-14
F : éco-prod, com, com ext, fin-stat, éco-soc.
Akademia Medyczna im. Juliana March-
lewskiego [A. de Médecine], ul. Kilińskiego 1,
15–320 Białystok.   *1950*
Tél: 217-05. Télex: 852200 am pl
F : méd.
D : dent.
Akademia Medyczna, Bydgoszcz.   *1984*
Akademia Medyczna, ul. Marii Curie-
Skołodowskiej 3a, 80–210 Gdańsk-Wrzeszcz.
                                 1945
Tél: 41-92-69. Télex: 0512997 amg pl
F : méd, phar.
D : dent.
Section à Bydgoszcz.
Śląska Akademia Medyczna im. Ludwika
Waryńskiego, ul. Poniatowskiego 15, 40–952
Katowice.   *1948*
Tél: 51-20-01. Télex: 0315338 slam pl
F : méd.
D : dent.
Akademia Medyczna im. M. Kopernika, ul. Św.
Anny 12, 31–008 Kraków.   *1950*
Tél: 22-04-11. Télex: 325766 amptg pl
F : méd, phar.
D : dent, lang étr, phys.
Akademia Medyczna, Al. Kościuszki 4, 90–419
Łódź.   *1950*
Tél: 57-50-74. Télex: 88-54-10 amel pl
F : méd, phar.
D : dent.
Akademia Medyczna, ul. Cicha 4, 20–078
Lublin.   *1950*
Tél: 246-33. Télex: 0642345
F : méd, phar, inf.
Akademia Medyczna, ul. Fredry 10, 60–701
Poznań.   *1950*

F : méd-dent, phar.
Pomorska Akademia Medyczna im. Gen. Karola Świerczewskiego, ul. Rybacka 1, 70-952 Szczecin. *1948*
Tél: 802-41. Télex: 0422596 dzapa pl
F : méd.
Akademia Medyczna, ul. Filtrowa 30, 02–032 Warszawa. *1950*
Tél: 25-00-51. Télex: 815403 akmed pl
F : méd, phar.
D : dent.
Akademia Medyczna, ul Pasteura 1, 50–367 Wrocław. *1950*
Tél: 22-70-23. Télex: 715354 am pl
F : méd, phar.
D : dent.
Akademia Muzyczna im S. Moniuszki w Gdańsku [E. nationale sup. de Musique], ul. Łagiewniki 3, 80–847 Gdańsk. *1947*
Tél: 31-77-15
Akademia Muzyczna im K. Szymanovskiego w Katowicach, ul. Zacisze 3, 40–025 Katowice. *1929*
Tél: 51-54-21
Akademia Muzyczna w Krakowie, ul, Bohaterów Stalingradu 3, 31–038 Kraków. *1945*
Tél: 22-32-50
Section à Rezeszów.
Akademia Muzyczna w Łódzi, ul. Gdańska 32, 90–716 Łódź. *1945*
Tél: 32-67-40
Section à Bydgoszcz.
Akademia Muzyczna im I. Paderewskiego w Poznaniu, ul. Czerwonej Armii 87, 61–808 Poznań. *1920*
Tél: 551-32
Akademia Muzyczna im F. Chopina w Warszawie, ul Okólnik 2, 00–368 Warszawa.
Tél: 27-72-41

1810
Section à Białystok.
Akademia Muzyczna im K. Lipinskiego we Wrocławiu, ul. Powstańców Ślaskich 204, 53–140 Wrocław. *1949*
Tél: 67-74-18
Akademia Sztuk Pięknych [A. des Beaux-Arts], Plac Matejki 13, 31–157 Kraków.
Tél: 22-24-50. Télex: 0325606 asp pl
Akademia Sztuk Pięknych, ul Krakowskie Przedmieście 5, Warszawa. *1904*
Tél: 26-92-01
Państwowa Wyższa Szkoła Sztuk Platycznych [E. nationale sup. d'Arts visuels], ul. Targ Weglowy 1, 80–836 Gdańsk. *1945*
Tél: 31-28-01
Państwowa Wyższa Szkoła Sztuk Plastycznych, ul. Wojska Polskiego 121, 90–138 Łódź. *1945*
Tél: 55-21-50
Państowa Wyższa Szkoła Sztuk Plastycznych, ul. Marcinkowskiego 29, 61–745 Poznań. *1946*
Tél: 575-51
Państwowa Wyższa Szkoła Sztuk Plastycznych, plac Polski 3/4, 50–151 Wrocław. *1946*
Tél: 315-58
Państwowa Wyższa Szkoła Teatralna im. Ludwika Solskiego [E. nationale sup. d'Art dramatique], ul. Bohaterów Stalingradu 3, 31–038 Kraków. *1946*
Tél: 22-18-55
Państwowa Wyższa Szkoła Teatralna im. Aleksandra Zelwerowicza, ul. Miodowa 24, 00–246 Warszawa. *1949*
Tél: 31-02-15
Państwowa Wyższa Szkoła Filmowa, Telewizyjna i Teatralna im. Leona Schillera [E. nationale sup. de Cinéma, de Télévision et d'Art dramatique], ul. Targowa, 61, 90–323 Łódź. *1948*
Tél: 74-39-43

Teacher Training—Formation pédagogique

Wyższa Szkoła Pedagogiczna, ul. Chodkiewicza 30, 85–084 Bydgoszcz. *1971, 1974*
Tél: 41-32-03. Télex: 0562573 wsp pl
F : phill, math-techn, péd.
Wyższa Szkoła Pedagogiczna, ul. A. Zawadzkiego 13/15, Czestochowa. *1971, 1974*
Tél: 550-321. Télex: 037261 puniv pl
F : péd, psyc, math-biol, phy.
Wyższa Szkoła Pedagogiczna, ul. Wesoła 56, 25–363 Kielce. *1969, 1973*
Télex: 0613478 wsp pl
F : phill-hist, math-biol-géo-phy.
Wyższa Szkoła Pedagogiczna im. Komisji Edukacji Narodowej, ul. Podchorążyck 2,

30–084 Kraków. *1946*
Tél: 37-47-77. Télex: 0322444 wsp pl
F : phill-hist, math-phy, géog-biol.
Wyższa Szkoła Pedagogiczna, ul. Żołnierska 14, 10–950 Olsztyn. *1969, 1974*
Tél: 245-09. Télex: 0526223 wsp pl
F : phill-hist, math-biol, péd-psyc.
Wyższa Szkoła Pedagogiczna im. Powstańców Sląskich, ul. Oleska 48, 45–052 Opole. *1950*
Tél: 358-41. Télex: 0732230 wsp pl
F : phill-hist, math-phy-ch.
Wyższa Szkoła Pedagogiczna, ul. Turkienicza 24, Rzeszów. *1965*
Télex: 0633343 wsp pl

F : phill, math-phy-éd, techn.
Wyższa Szkoła Pedagogiczna, ul. Arciszewskiego
22a, 76–200 Słupsk.   *1969, 1974*
Tél: 72-91
F : phill-hist, math-phy-ch-géo.
**Wyższa Szkoła Pedagogiki Specjalnej im. M.
Grzegorzewskiej**, ul. Szcześliwicka 40, 02–353
Warszawa.   *1970, 1976*
Tél: 22-16-31
F : péd spéciale.
Wyższa Szkoła Pedagogiczna, Pl. Słowiański 6,
65–625 Zielona Góra.   *1971, 1973*
Tél: 635-20. Télex: 0433467 wsp pl
F : phill, math-phy, techn, péd.
Wyższa Szkoła Wychowania Fizycznego [E. sup.
d'Education physique], ul. Wiejska 1, 80–336
Gdańsk-Oliwa.   *1969*
Tél: 52-50-51. Télex: 0512496 awf pl
Wyższa Szkoła Wychowania Fizycznego, ul.
Mikołska 72a, 40–065 Katowice.   *1970*
Tél: 51-40-66. Télex: 0315581 awf pl

Akademia Wychowania Fizycznego, ul. Planu
6-letniego 62a, 31–571 Kraków.   *1950*
Tél: 48-50-06. Télex: 0325235 awf pl
Akademia Wychowania Fizycznego, ul. March-
lewskiego 27/39, 61–871 Poznań.   *1950*
Tél: 33-00-81. Télex: 0413230 awf pl
**Akademia Wychowania Fizycznego im. K.
Świerczewskiego**, ul. Marymoncka 34,
Warszawa 45.   *1929*
Tél: 34-08-13. Télex: 816213 awf pl
Section à Biała Podlaska.   *1970*
Akademia Wychowania Fizycznego, Al. Pader-
ewskiego 35, 51–612 Wrocław.   *1950*
Tél: 48-25-27. Télex: 0712103 awf pl
Wyższa Szkoła Morska [E. sup. de Navigation],
ul. Czerwonych Kosynierów 83, 81–962
Gdynia.   *1969*
Tél: 20-75-12. Télex: 054568 wsm pl
Wyższa Szkoła Morska, ul. Wały Chrobrego 1,
70–500 Szczecin.   *1969*
Tél: 326-31. Télex: 0422585 wsm pl

Institut de Recherches sur la Politique scientifique et l'Enseignement supérieur

Les tâches de l'Institut comprennent a) des etudes de politique scientifique (indication des tendances, du rythme et des conditions de progrès de l'activité de recherche et de développement, et évaluation de son efficacité du point de vue tant économique que social); b) des recherches sur l'enseignement supérieur (recherches en pédagogie, détermination de la taille, de la structure et des modèles d'institutions d'enseignement supérieur, et évaluation de leur efficacité tant à l'intérieur qu'à l'extérieur).

L'Institut comprend les départements suivants: Economie et Organisation; Planification et Prévisions; Politique scientifique; Innovations de l'Education et Expertises; Recherches sociologiques; Pédagogie; ainsi qu'une Bibliothèque et un Centre de Documentation comportant une collection de plus de 17.000 volumes.

Il effectue des études et travaux de recherche pour son propre compte et met sur pied des recherches sur l'enseignement supérieur. L'Institut coopère avec des organismes homologues à l'étranger.

L'Institut publie 2 périodiques: Dydaktyka Szkoły Wyzszej (Didactique de l'Ecole supérieure); Sovremennaya Vysshaya Skoła (Ecole supérieure contemporaine)—périodique international publié en versions russe et espagnole. En outre, les résultats des recherches effectuées par l'Institut et d'autres institutions sont diffusés dans ses nombreuses séries de publications.

The Research Institute for Science Policy, and Higher Education is responsible for: a) studies on science policy (identifying and defining the trends, rhythm and progress of research and development, and its evaluation from economic and social points of view); b) research into higher education (research into educational methods, decisions about size, structure and forms of institutions of higher education, and evaluation of their internal and external efficiency).

The Institute comprises the following departments: Economics and Organization; Planning and Forecasting; Science Policy; Educational Innovations and Expertises; Sociology; Pedagogics; as well as Library and Documentation Centre with a collection of more than 17,000 volumes.

It carries out research studies on its own account and initiates research into higher education. The Institute co-operates with similar recognized bodies abroad.

The Institute publishes 2 periodicals: Dydaktyka Szkoły Wyzszej (Didactics of Higher Education); Sovremennaya Vysshaya Skoła (Contemporary Higher Education)—an international periodical published in Russian and Spanish versions. In addition, the results of research carried out by the Institute and other institutions are made known in the numerous series of its publications.
00–046 Warszawa, ul. Nowy Świat 69.
Tél: 26-07-46. Télex: 812285 pl

Polish Students Association – ZSP (IUS)
ul. Ordynacka 9, Warszawa 37.
Télex: 813878 alma attn. zsp
Travel and Tourism Bureau of the Polish Student Association—ALMATUR
ul. Ordynacka 9, Warszawa 37.
Klub Intelligencji Katolickiej (Pax Romana)
Kopernika 34, 00950 Warszawa.
Polish Ecumenical Council (WSCF)
A. Świerczewskiego 76a, Warszawa 1.
United Nations Student Association of Poland (ISMUN)
ul. Ordynacka 9, 364 Warszawa.

Comité de coopération économique avec l'étranger
Aleja I Armii W.P. 14, 00-918 Warszawa.
Ministerstwo Edukacij Narodowej (Ministère de l'Education nationale)
Aleja I Armii W.P. 25, 00-918 Warszawa.
Tél: 29-72-41. Télex: 81-35-23
Commission nationale polonaise pour l'Unesco
Pałac Kultury i Nauki (17. pietro), 00.901 Warszawa.
Tél: 20-33-55. Cables: polunesco varsovie

*

PORTUGAL
PORTUGAL

UNIVERSITIES AND UNIVERSITY INSTITUTIONS— UNIVERSITES ET ETABLISSEMENTS UNIVERSITAIRES

Public Institutions—Etablissements publics

Universidade dos Açores, Rua da Mãe de Deus, 9502 Ponta Delgada Codex. (Senhor Reitor). *1976*
Tél: 35318. Fax: 096-35278. Télex: 02115 unifpdl p
D : géosc, hist-phil-soc, lang & lit mod, math, éco-gestion, éd, biol; agr (Angra do Heroismo); océanog-pêch (Horta).
Universidade do Algarve, Quinta da Penha, Estrada da Penha, 8000 Faro. *1979*
Tél: 29130. Télex: 56168 ipfaro p
Ut : biol mar-pêch, sc-techn agr, éco-adm, sc exactes.
Universidade de Aveiro, Bairro da Gulbentian, 3800 Aveiro. *1973*
Tél: 25085. Télex: 37373 aveiro p
D : math, phy, ch, géosc, biol, électro-télécommun, cér, ambiance, lang.
Universidade da Beira Interior, Calçada de S. Martinho, 6200 Covilhã. *1973*
D : éco-gestion, math-inft, phy, ch, tex, soc-hum, pap, éd.
*****Universidade de Coimbra**, Pátio da Universidade, 3000 Coimbra. *1290*
Tél: 335410. Télex: 52273 unicoi p
F : dr, méd, let, phar, éco, psyc-éd.

Universidade de Évora, Largo dos Colegiais 2, 7000 Évora. *1973*
Tél: 25572. Télex: 18771 unievr p
D : phytologie, zoo, let, socio, éco, hist-arché, écologie, éd-péd, math, phy, géosc, ch, sa, biol, ing, plan rég, adm des aff.
Universidade de Lisboa, Praça da Universidade, 1600 Lisboa. *1911*
Tél: 767624
F : dr, méd, let, sc, phar, psyc-ed.
Universidade do Minho, Largo do Paço, 4700 Braga Codex. *1973*
Tél: 27021. Télex: 32135 uminho p
Ut : ing, sc exactes & nat, soc, éd, let, éco-gestion.
*****Universidade Nova de Lisboa**, Praça do Príncipe Real 26, 1200 Lisboa. *1973*
Tél: 366669. Télex: 44733 unbrtr p
F : sc-techn, soc-hum, éco, méd.
I : sa-méd trop.
Universidade do Porto, Rua Di Manuel II, 4003 Porto Codex. *1911*
Tél: 699519. Télex: 23121 unipor p
F : sc, méd, ing, phar, éco, let, psyc-éd, arc.
I : bioméd, phys.
Universidade Técnica de Lisboa, Alameda de

Santo Antônio dos Capuchos 1, 1100 Lisboa.
1930
Tél: 545434. Télex: 62067 utl p
F : arc.
I : agr, éco, ing, phys, soc-pol.
E: vét.
Universidade de Trás-os-Montes e Alto Douro,
Avenida Almeida Lucena 1, 5000 Vila Real
Codex. *1979*
Tél: 25031. Télex: 24436 utad p

agr, sc exactes & nat, hum-soc, techn.
Universidade Aberta (Open U.), 1200 Lisboa.
1988
Escola Superior de Medicina Dentária de Lisboa,
Avenida Prof. Gama Pinto, 1600 Lisboa. *1975*
Escola Superior de Medicina Dentária do Porto,
Rua Dr. Roberto Frias, 4200 Porto. *1976*
**Instituto Superior de Ciências do Trabalho e da
Empresa**, Avenida das Forças Armadas, 1600
Lisboa. *1972*

Private Establishments—Etablissements privés

**Universidade Autónoma de Lisboa Luís de
Camões**, Rua Sta. Marta 56, 1100 Lisboa.
1986
Tél: 528426
D: dr, hist, gestion, éco, math app, lang & lit
mod.
Universidade Católica Portuguesa, Caminho de
Palma de Cima, 1600 Lisboa. *1971*
Tél: 7265550. Télex: 65094 unicat p
F : hum, phil, théo.
I: théo, promotion sociale.
E: biotechn.

Universidade Internacional, Estrada de Benfica
275, 1500 Lisboa. *1986*
D: dr, gestion.
Universidade Lusíada, Rua da Junqueira 194,
1300 Lisboa. *1986*
D: dr, hist, gestion, éco, rel int, math app.
Universidade Portucalense, Rua Rodrigues de
Freitas 349, 4000 Porto. *1986*
Tél: 579823. Télex: 20091
D: dr, hist, adm des aff, éco, math, inft-gestion,
math app.

OTHER INSTITUTIONS—AUTRES INSTITUTIONS

Public Establishments—Etablissements publics

Instituto Politécnico de Beja, Rua de Sto.
António, 1-A, 7800 Beja.
E: agr, éd.
Instituto Politécnico de Bragança, Rua 1 de
Dezembro 8, 5300 Bragança. *1979*
E : agr, éd.
Instituto Politécnico de Castelo Branco, Rua São
João de Deus 25–2°, 6000 Castelo Branco.
1979
Tél: 23082. Télex: 27750 inspol p
E : agr, éd.
Instituto Politécnico do Coimbra, Rua Pinheiro
Chagas, 96, 2°, 3000 Coimbra.
E: agr, éd.
I: comp-adm.
Instituto Politécnico de Faro, Quinta da Penha,
Estrada da Penha, 8000 Faro. *1979*
Tél: 20461. Télex: 5616 ipfaro p
E : éd, techn-gestion, hôtel-tour.
Instituto Politécnico da Guarda, Rua Comand-
ante Salvador do Nascimento, 6300 Guarda.
1979
Tél: 21364. Télex: 53549 ipgua p
E : éd, gestion.
Instituto Politécnico de Leiria, Edifício Maringa
Torre 2, 2°, 2400 Leiria. *1980*
E: éd, gestion.

Instituto Politécnico de Lisboa, Campo dos
Mártires da Pátria 2, 1100 Lisboa. *1979*
E : dance, éd, mus, jour, sa, theât & cinema.
I: comp-adm.
Instituto Politécnico de Portalegre, Praça da
República, Apartado 125, 7301 Portalegre.
1980
E: éd, techn-gestion.
Instituto Politécnico do Porto, Rua Dr. Roberto
Frias, 4200 Porto. *1979*
Télex: 28506 esep p
E : éd, mus, sa.
I: comp-adm.
Instituto Politécnico de Santarém, Complexo
Andaluz, Apartado 279, 2000 Santarém. *1979*
Tél: 27521. Télex: 43003 ipsant p
E : éd, agr, gestion, techn.
Instituto Politécnico de Setúbal, Largo dos
Defensores da República 1, 2900 Setúbal. *1979*
Tél: 35301
E : techn, éd.
Instituto Politécnico de Viana do Castelo, Rua de
Escola Industrial e Comercial Nun'Alvares,
4901 Viana do Castelo Codex. *1980*
Tél: 261881. Télex: 32941 ispam p
E : éd, agr, techn, gestion.
Instituto Politécnico de Viseu, Rua Alexandre

Lobo 55, 3500 Viseu. *1979*
Tél: 25528
E : éd, techn.
Instituto Gregoriano de Lisboa, Avenida 5 de
Outubro 258, 1600 Lisboa. *1976*

Escola Superior de Belas Artes de Lisboa, Largo
da Biblioteca Pública, 1200 Lisboa. *1836*
Tél: 368174
D : pnt, sculp, dess.
Escola Superior de Belas Artes do Porto, Avenida
Rodrigues de Freitas 265, 4000 Porto. *1881*
D : pnt, sculpt, dess.
Instituto Superior de Artes Plásticas da Madeira,
Rua da Carreira 56, 9000 Funchal. *1977*
Tél: 26209
Escola Superior de Educação da Madeira, Rua do
Castanheiro, 9000 Funchal. *1982*
Instituto Superior de Contabilidade e Admini-

stração, Rua João Mendonça 17, 3800 Aveiro.
1976
Instituto Superior de Contabilidade e Admini-
stração, Rua Luís de Camões, Quinta de São
Jerónimo, 3000 Coimbra. *1975*
Instituto Superior de Contabilidade e Admini-
stração, Avenida Miguel Bombarda 20, 1000
Lisboa. *1975*
Instituto Superior de Contabilidade e Admini-
stração, Rua Entreparedes 48, 4000 Porto.
1975
Instituto Superior de Engenharia de Coimbra,
Quinta da Nora, 3000 Coimbra. *1975*
Instituto Superior de Engenharia de Lisboa, Rua
Conselheiro Emílio Navarro, 1900 Lisboa.
1975
Instituto Superior de Engenharia de Porto, Rua
de São Tomé, 4200 Porto. *1975*

Private Establishments—Etablissements privés

Cooperativa de Ensino Superior Artístico, Arvore
I, Rua Passeio das Virtudes 14, 4000 Porto.
1986
Cooperativa de Ensino Superior de Técnicas
Avançadas de Gestão e Informática, Campo dos
Mártires da Pátria 67, 2° Dto, 1100 Lisboa.
1986
gestion-inft.
Escola Superior de Jornalismo, Rua do Melo 2,
4000 Porto. *1986*
jour.
Instituto Superior de Administração e Gestação,
Avenida da Boavista 1043, 4100 Porto. *1986*
adm, gestion.
Instituto Superior de Assistentes e Intérpretes,
Rua António Pedro 24, 4000 Porto.
interp.

Instituto Superior de Gestão, Estrada da
Ameixoeira 112/116, 1700 Lisboa. *1986*
gestion.
Instituto Superior de Línguas e Administração,
Isla Sarl, 47 Pracas Lisboa. *1986*
Télex: 63501 isla p
Instituto Superior de Matemáticas Modernas,
Rua das Flores 59, 1200 Lisboa. *1971*
math mod.
Instituto de Novas Profissões, Avenida Duque de
Loulé 47, 1100 Lisboa. *1971*
gestion, publicité, tour.
Instituto Superior Politécnico Internacional,
Estrada de Benfica 275, 1500 Lisboa. *1987*
gestion, sec. securité sociale.
Instituto Superior de Psicologia Aplicada, Rua
Jardim do Tabaco 44, 1100 Lisboa.

Conselho dos Reitores das Universidades Portu-
guesas
Le Conseil des Recteurs des Universités
Portugaises (CRUP) est un organisme de
coordination des activités universitaires; il
dispose d'un pouvoir de décision en ce qui
concerne les fonctions qui incombent normalement aux recteurs d'université. Il sert également
d'organe gouvernemental de consultation sur
l'enseignement supérieur.
Il se compose des recteurs des douze universités d'Etat (Coimbra, Lisboa, Porto, Técnica de
Lisboa, Nova de Lisboa, Aveiro, Minho, Evora,
Açores, Algarve, Trás-os-Montes e Alto Douro
et Beira Interior). Le Président est élu au sein des

membres du Conseil, par roulement; son mandat
est de deux ans.
Normalement, les réunions se tiennent tous les
trois mois, mais le CRUP se réunit, en fait, une
fois par mois. Parfois, le Ministre de l'Education
ou le Secrétaire d'Etat à l'Enseignement
supérieur assistent aux réunions et les président.
Actuellement le CRUP s'occupe, entre autres
choses, d'examiner un important avant-projet de
loi sur l'autonomie universitaire. Il joue également un rôle important dans la coordination de
l'administration des universités et dans les
échanges et la collaboration scientifiques internationaux.

The Portuguese Council of University Rectors (CRUP) is a co-ordinating body of university activities with decisive powers in matters normally attributed to university Rectors. It also acts as a government organ of consultation on higher education.

It is composed of the Rectors of the twelve State universities (Coimbra, Lisboa, Porto, Técnica de Lisboa, Nova de Lisboa, Aveiro, Minho, Evora, Açores, Algarve, Trás-os-Montes e Alto Douro and Beira Interior). The President is elected from among members by rotation, and serves for two years.

Officially, meetings are held every three months but, in practice, the Council meets once a month and is sometimes presided over by the Minister or Secretary of State for Higher Education.

CRUP is at present engaged, among other things, in the study of the draft of an important bill concerning university autonomy. It also plays an important role in the coordination of university administration and international scientific exchange and collaboration.

Président: J.A. Esperança Pina, Recteur, Universidade Nova de Lisboa.
Secrétaire: Mário Marchante.
Campo Mártires da Pátria 2-2°, 1100 Lisboa.
Tél: 54.91.70. Télex: 44733 unlrtr p

Departamento de Turismo Universitário— SIAEIST
Associação dos Estudantes do Instituto

Superior Técnico, Avenida Rovisco Pais, Lisboa 1.
Movimento Eclesial de Professionais (Pax Romana)
R. Marquês de Fronteira 113, Lisboa 1.
World University Service Correspondante (WUS)
Correspondant: Ana Mendonça.
CDAC, 77 rua Pinheiro Chagas 2e esq., 1000 Lisboa.
Federação dos Diplomados Católicos Portugueses (Pax Romana)
Campo dos Mártires da Pátria 43, Lisboa 1.
Juventud Universitária Católica do Portugal (Pax Romana)
Avenida da República, 84–5 Dto, Lisboa 1.
Juventude Estudantil Católica (Pax Romana)
Campo de Santana 43, Lisboa.
Movimento Académico Cristão (WSCF)
c/o Silas Lopes do Oliveira, Rua da Arraibida 30, 1200 Lisboa 2.

*

Ministério da Educação
Avenida 5 de Outubro 107-1, 1051 Lisboa.
Tél: 778793. Fax: 76 4219. Télex: 18428 educa p
Commission nationale portugaise pour l'Unesco
Ministère des Affaires étrangères, Avenida Infante Santo 42, 1300 Lisbonne.
Tél: 60-49-42. Télex: 18332 etran p. Cables: cunesco c/clt nestrangeiros lisboa portugal

QATAR
QATAR

*University of Qatar, P.O. Box 2713, Doha.
1973, 1978
Tel: 83-2222. Telex: 4630 unvsty dh
F : ed, sc, hum-soc, Isl law & st.

CENTRE FOR SCIENTIFIC AND APPLIED RESEACH.
EDUCATIONAL RESEARCH AND DEVELOPMENT CENTRE.

Supreme Council of Education
Doha.
*
Ministry of Education
P.O. Box 80, Doha.

Tel: 41-64-61. Fax: 41-38-86. Telex: 4316 min ed dh
Qatar National Commission for Unesco
Ministry of Education, P.O. Box 80, Doha.
Tel: 41-64-61. Telex: 4316 min ed dh

REUNION
REUNION

Université de la Réunion, 15 avenue René Cassin, 97489 Saint-Denis Cedex. *1971*
Tél: 29-45-45. Télex: 916645 re
F : dr-éco-pol, sc, let-hum.
CENTRE D'ETUDES ADMINISTRATIVES, 2426 avenue de la Victoire, 97489 Saint-Denis Cedex.
Tél: 21-21-20
SERVICE COMMUN DE LA FORMATION CONTINUE, 2426, avenue de la Victoire, 97489 Saint-Denis Cedex.
Tél: 21-18-69

INSTITUT D'ADMINISTRATION DES ENTREPRISES, B.P. 356, 97468 Saint-Denis Cedex.
Tél: 21-16-26
INSTITUT DE LINGUISTIQUE ET D'ANTHROPOLOGIE, B.P. 225, 97490 Sainte-Clotilde.
1977
Tél: 29-45-45 (Postre 265)
Muséum d'Histoire naturelle, Jardin d'Etat, rue de Paris, 97489 Saint-Denis (1).
1854, 1961
Tél: 20-02-19

Union générale des Etudiants Créoles de la Réunion—UGECR (IUS)

(1) Attached to the Muséum national d'Histoire naturelle, Paris.
(1) Rattaché au Muséum national d'Histoire naturelle, Paris.

ROMANIA
ROUMANIE

UNIVERSITIES AND TECHNICAL UNIVERSITIES—
UNIVERSITES ET UNIVERSITES TECHNIQUES

*Universitatea din Bucureşti, Bulevardul
Gheorghe Gheorghiu-Dej 64, Bucureşti. *1864*
Tél: 15-71-87
F : math, phy, biol-géol-géog, dr, hist-phil,
phill.
Universitatea din Braşov, Bulevardul Gheorghe
Gheorghiu-Dej 29, Braşov. *1956, 1971*
Tél: 41580. Télex: 61381
F : méc, constr méc, for, ind du bois.
*Universitatea din Cluj-Napoca, Strada Mihail
Kogălniceanu 1, Cluj-Napoca. *1959*
Tél: 16101
F : math, phy, techn ch, biol-géog-géol, dr, éco,
hist-phil, phill.
Universitatea din Craiova, Strada Alexandru
Ioan Cuza 13, Craiova. *1966*
Tél: 16574
F : nat, phill, éco, méd, électro, méc, agr.
Universitatea din Galaţi, Bulevardul Republicii
47, Galaţi. *1951*
Tél: 1-41-12. Télex: 51292
F : méc, alim-pêch.
*Universitatea din Iaşi, Calea 23 August 11,
Iaşi. *1860*
Tél: 47540. Télex: 022212
F : math-phy, biol-géog-géol, dr, phill, hist-
phil, éco.

Universitatea din Timişoara, Bulevardul Vasile
Pârvan 4, Timişoara. *1948*
Tél: 1-28-05
F : nat, phill, éco.
*Institutul politehnic din Bucureşti, Splaiul
Independenţei 313, Bucureşti. *1854*
Tél: 31-40-10
F : constr méc, méc, méc agr, aérospatiale,
trans, mét, élec, électro-téléc, automatisation,
élec-énerg.
Institutul national de chimie, Splaiul Independ-
enţei 202, Bucureşti. *1977*
Tél: 15-67-05
F : techn ch.
Institutul politehnic din Cluj-Napoca, Strada
Emil Isac 15, Cluj-Napoca. *1948*
Tél: 34565
F : méc, élec, constr.
Institutul politehnic din Iaşi, Calea 23 August 22,
Iaşi. *1937*
Tél: 46577. Télex: 22216 ipol r
F : méc, élec, constr, gé hyd, techn-ch tex,
techn-ch.
Institutul politehnic din Timişoara, Bulevardul 30
Decembrie 2, Timişoara. *1920*
Tél: 34713
F : méc, méc agr, élec, const, techn ch.

OTHER INSTITUTIONS—AUTRES INSTITUTIONS

Technical Education—Enseignement technique

Institutul de construcţii din Bucureşti, Bule-
vardul Republicii 176, Bucureşti. *1946*
Tél: 42-42-00
F : const, outillage, hyd-chaussées, ferroviaire.
Institutul de arhitectură din Bucureşti, Strada
Academiei 18–20, Bucureşti. *1904*
Tél: 13-80-80
F : arc-urb.

Institutul de mine din Petroşani, Strada Institu-
tului 20, Petroşani. *1948*
Tél: 42580
F : mine, méc mine.
Institutul de petrol şi gaze din Ploieşti, Bulevardul
Bucureşti 39, Ploieşti. *1948*
Tél: 42451
F : for, outillage-techn ch.

Professional Education—Enseignement professionnel

Institutul agronomic din Bucureşti, Bulevardul
Mărăşti 59, Bucureşti.   *1852*
Tél: 18-39-55
F : agr, zoo-vét.

Institutul agronomic din Cluj-Napoca, Strada
Mănăştur 3, Cluj-Napoca.   *1910*
Tél: 18792
F : agr.

Institutul agronomic din Iaşi, Aleea Mihail
Sadoveanu 3, Iaşi.   *1918*
Tél: 40801
F : agr.

Institutul agronomic din Timişoara, Calea
Aradului 119, Timişoara.   *1945*
Tél: 43016
F : agr.

Academia de studii economice din Bucureşti,
Piaţa Romană 6, Bucureşti.   *1913*
Tél: 11-06-10. Télex: 11863 asero r
F : éco ind-agr, plan-cyb éco, com, fin-comp.

Institutul de medicină şi farmacie din Bucureşti,
Strada Dionisie Lupu 37, Bucureşti.   *1857*
Tél: 11-17-07
méd, pédi, stom-phar.

**Institutul de medicină şi farmacie din Cluj-
Napoca**, Strada 1 Mai 13, Cluj-Napoca.   *1918*
Tél: 16585
F : méd, stom-phar.

Institutul de medicină şi farmacie din Iaşi, Strada
Universităţii 16, Iaşi.   *1879*
Tél: 63845
F : méd, stom-phar.

**Institutul de medicină şi farmacie din Tîrgu
Mureş**, Strada Gheorghe Marinescu 38, Tîrgu
Mureş.   *1945*
Tél: 13127
F : méd-phar.

Institutul de medicină din Timişoara, Piata 23
August 2, Timişoara.
Tél: 37612
F : méd stom.

**Institutul de artă teatrală şi cinematograficá din
Bucureşti**, Strada Matei Voievod 75–77,
Bucureşti.   *1864*
Tél: 42-27-26
F : théât-cinéma-télévision.

Institutul de teatru din Tîrgu Mureş, Strada
Köteles Samuel 6, Tîrgu Mureş.   *1948*
F : théât.

Institutul de arte plastice din Bucureşti, Strada
General Budişteanu 19, Bucureşti.   *1864*
Tél: 13-05-56
F : arts plastiques-décor.

Institutul de arte plastice din Cluj-Napoca, Piaţa

Liberăţii 31, Cluj-Napoca.   *1948*
Tél: 11577
F : arts plastiques-décor.

Conservatorul de muzică din Bucureşti, Strada
Stirbei Vodă 33, Bucureşti.
Tél: 14-63-41
F : mus.

Conservatorul de muzică din Cluj-Napoca,
Strada 23 August 25, Cluj-Napoca.   *1919*
Tél: 15973
F : mus.

Conservatorul din Iaşi, Strada Cloşca 9, Iaşi.
                                                        1864
Tél: 47246
F : mus-arts plast.

Institutul de subingineri din Bacău, Calea
Mărăşeşti 151, Bacău.   *1961*
Tél: 32673
F : tec.

Institutul de subingineri din Baia Mare, Strada
Victor Babeş 65, Baia Mare.   *1961*
Tél: 15-43
F : tec-péd.

Institutul de subingineri din Constanţa, Bulevardul V.I. Lenin 124, Constanţa.   *1961*
F : tec.

Institutul de subingineri din Hunedoara, Strada
Karl Marx 5, Hunedoara.   *1972*

Institutul de subingineri din Oradea, Calea
Armatei Roşii 5, Oradea.   *1963*
Tél: 3-28-30
F : tec.

Institutul de subingineri din Piteşti, Strada Draga
11, Piteşti.   *1962*
Tél: 14305
F : tec.

Institutul de subingineri din Reşiţa, Piaţa Lenin
1–4, Reşiţa.   *1972*
F: tec.

Institutul de subingineri din Sibiu, Bulevardu
Victoriei 5–7, Sibiu.   *1969*
Tél: 17989
F : tec.

Institutul de subingineri din Suceava, Strada Emil
Bodnăraş 13, Suceava.   *1963*
Tél: 2366
F : tec.

Institutul de subingineri din Tîrgu Mureş, Strada
Nicolae Iorga 1, Tîrgu Mureş.   *1960*
F : tec.

Institutul de educatie fizică şi sport din Bucureşti,
Strada Stefan Furtună 140, Bucureşti.   *1922*
Tél: 49-53-65
F : phys.

Union des syndicats de l'Enseignement, de la Science et de la Culture de la République socialiste de Roumanie

L'Union comprend les syndicats des institutions de l'enseignement (préscolaire, primaire, secondaire, supérieur), de recherche scientifique appartenant au Ministère de l'Education, des institutions d'art et de culture (théâtres dramatiques et lyriques, orchestres philharmoniques, musées, bibliothèques), de la cinématographie (studios cinématographiques, offices et entreprises pour la diffusion des films) les syndicats des unions de création artistique, ainsi que ceux du Ministère de l'Education, du Conseil de la Culture et de l'Education Socialiste, et de l'Académie de la République Socialiste de roumanie.

The Union of Associations of Education, Science and Culture includes the Staff Unions of institutions of education (pre-school, primary, secondary and higher), research institutes attached to the Ministry of Education, the artistic and cultural institutes (drama and lyric theatres, philharmonic orchestras, museums, libraries), the cinema (film studios and distribution centres), staff Unions of the artistic Unions, as well as those of Ministry of Education, of the Council of Socialist Culture and Education and of the Academy of the Romanian Socialist Republic.
Str. Stefan Gheorghiu 14, Bucureşti.

Union of Associations of Communist Students of Romania—UASCR (IUS)
Str. Onesti 8, Bucureşti.
Télex: 11415 daciat att. uascr
Bureau de Tourisme pour la Jeunesse— BTT
Str. Onesti 6–8, Bucureşti.
Romanian Theological Institute (WSCF)
c/o Department of Foreign Relations, The Romanian Patriarchate, Str. Antim 29, 70666 Bucureşti VI.
Tél: 31-24-86
Asociatia Tineretului si Studentilor din Romania pentru Natiunile Unite (ISMUN)
Président: Vasile Bontas.
Str. Onesti 6–8, Bucureşti.

*

Equivalence Commission
Ministry of Education, 30 Str. Nuferilor, Bucureşti.
Télex: 11637 meidb r
Ministerul Educaţiei şi Invăţămîntului—Directia Relatii externe (Ministère de l'Enseignement — Direction des Relations étrangères) Str. Spiru Haŕet 12, 70738 Bucureşti.
Tél: 15-74-30
Commission nationale de la République socialiste de Roumanie pour l'Unesco
Soseaua Kiseleff 47, B.P. 712698, Bucureşti.
Tél: 17-42-49. Cables: romunesco bucarest

RWANDA
RWANDA

*Université nationale du Rwanda, B.P. 56, Butare. (M. le Secrétaire général). *1963, 1981*
Tél: 302. Télex: 605 rw
CAMPUS DE BUTARE, B.P. 117, Butare.
Tél: 3071
F : agr, méd, dr, éco-soc-gestion, sc app, phar.
Ce : énerg, pharmacopée-méd trad.
CAMPUS DE RUHENGERI, B.P. 44, Ruhengeri.
F : let, sc, éd.
E : tec mod.
Ce : rech app-formation permanent.
Université Adventiste d'Afrique Centrale, B.P. 118, Gisenyi. *1984*

F : théo, sc, let, éd, adm-gestion.
Ce : rech tec-sc appl.
Institut Africain et Mauricien de Statistiques et d'Economie appliquée, B.P. 1109, Kigali. *1976*
Tél: 5359
Institut Saint Fidèle (Ecole supérieure de Gestion et d'Information), B.P. 210, Gisenyi. *1985*
Tél: 306
gestion-comp, inft, sec.
Institut supérieur Catholique de Pédagogie appliquée, Nkumba. *1986*
Institut supérieur des Finances publiques, B.P. 158, Kigali. *1986*

Entr'aide universitaire mondiale (WUS)
Université nationale du Rwanda, B.P. 117, Butare.
Tél: 73309 (Francois Nzabhahimama)
Association générale des Etudiants de l'Université du Rwanda—AGEUNR (IUS)
Campus de Butare, B.P. 117, Butare.
Conseil Pastoral (Pax Romana)
Université nationale du Rwanda, B.P. 117, Butare.
MESSORWA (WSCF)
c/o Université nationale du Rwanda, B.P. 117, Butare.

Ministère de l'Enseignement supérieur et de la Recherche scientifique
B.P. 624, Kigali.
Tél: (8)2745
Commission nationale rwandaise pour l'Unesco
Ministère de l'Enseignement supérieur et de la Recherche scientifique, B.P. 1326, Kigali.
Tél: 72747. Télex: 502 minaffet rw. Cables: rwaunesco minesupres kigali

*

SAUDI ARABIA
ARABIE SAOUDITE

UNIVERSITIES—UNIVERSITES

*Jamiat Al-Malik Saud [King Saud U.], P.O. Box 2454, Al-Darieya, Riyadh 11451. (The Secretary-General). *1957, 1982*
Tel: 481-1000. Telex: 401019 ksu sj
F : arts, adm, sc, phar, com-eco, agr, ed, eng, med, dent, Arabic lang; ed, med (Abha); eco-adm, agr-vet (Qaseem).

Jamiat Al-Malik Faisal [King Faisal U.], P.O. Box 380, Ahsa 13982. *1974*
Tel: 42254
F : med, med sc, arc-plan, agr-nutr, vet-zoo, ed, adm-plan.

Al-Jamiat Al-Islamiah [Islamic U.], P.O. Box 170, Al-Madinah-Al-Munawara. *1961*
Tel: 24080. Telex: 470022 islamia. Cables: alislamia
F : Sharia (Isl law), Quranic st, Hadith Sharif, Dawa-Usul-Al-Din, Arabic lang.

Jamiat Al-Imam Mohamed Ibn Saaud Al-Islamiah [Imam Mohammad Ibn Saud Islamic U.], P.O. Box 5701, Riyadh 11432. *1974*
Tel: 4054448. Telex: 201166
F : Sharia (Isl law), Arabic lang, theo; soc, Isl

law-Arabic lang (Abha and Qaseem).
HIGHER JUDICIAL INSTITUTE, Riyadh-El-Chemeissi.
HIGHER INSTITUTE FOR ISLAMIC TEACHING, Riyadh.
Branch at Al-Madinah Al-Munawara.

Jamiat Al-Malik Fahd Lil Betrol wal Ma'din [U. of Petroleum and Minerals], Dhahran 1326. *1963*
Tel: 860-0000. Telex: 601060
F : sc, app eng, eng sc, ind mangt, sc-comp eng, env des.

Jamiat Al-Malik Abdulaziz [King Abdulaziz U.], P.O. Box 1540, Jeddah 21441. *1964*
Tel: 6879033. Telex: 401141
F : eco-adm, arts-hum, sc, eng, earth sc, mar sc, meteo-arid land st, med; ed (Madinah).

Jamiat Umm Al-Qura [Umm al-Qura U.], P.O. Box 715, Makkah 214215. *1981*
Tel: 5564770. Telex: 440026
F : Sharia (Isl law)-Isl st, ed, app sc-eng, Arabic language, Dawa-Usul al-Din; ed (Taif).

Supreme Council of Universities

The Council comprises the President of the Supreme Committee for Higher Education, the Minister of Higher Education, the Chief of the Central Planning Organization, the Head of the General Personnel Bureau, the Rectors of the Universities and Institutions members of the Council. The latter are designated by Royal decree on the recommendation of the President. The Secretary-General, appointed by the President and proposed by the Minister of Education, supervises and directs the financial, managerial and technical functions of the Secretariat and is responsible for preparing data and studies needed by the Council.

The President may raise with the Council any matter concerned with higher education for study and consideration. The Council also: reviews any questions presented to it by the universities; executes the general policies laid down for higher education, particularly in matters of scientific research and its orientation in relation to national development needs; co-ordinates university courses, degrees and academic staff affairs, and establishes admission requirements; it promotes and co-ordinates the development of higher education and notably that of laboratories and libraries; sets up permanent or ad hoc committees to consider matters within its competence; and makes proposals for general policy in matters of higher education. It presents an Annual Report to the Prime Minister.

Le Conseil suprême des universités se compose du Président du Comité suprême pour l'enseignement supérieur, du Ministre de l'enseignement supérieur, du Chef de l'Organisation centrale pour la planification, du Chef du Bureau général du personnel, des Recteurs des universités et institutions membres du Conseil. Ces dernières sont désignées par Décret royal sur la recommandation du Président. Le Secrétaire général, qui est nommé par le Président sur proposition du

Ministre de l'éducation, dirige et contrôle les activités financières, techniques et de gestion du Secrétariat; il est également chargé d'établir les données et de préparer les études demandées par le Conseil.

Le Président peut soumettre à l'examen du Conseil toute question concernant l'enseignement supérieur. En outre, le Conseil examine toute question lui étant soumise par les universités; il met en oeuvre la politique générale établie en matière de recherche scientifique, dont les orient-ations sont définies en fonction des besoins du développement national; il encourage et coordonne le développement de l'enseignement supérieur, notamment dans le domaine des laboratoires et des bibliothèques; il crée des comités ad hoc ou permanents pour examiner les problèmes de sa compétence; et il fait des propositions relatives à la politique générale de l'enseignement supérieur. Il présente un Rapport annuel au Premier Ministre.

President: The Chairman, Supreme Committee for Educational Policy.
Vice-President: The Minister of Higher Education.
Secretary-General: Mahmoud M. Safar, Riyadh Airport St., P.O. Box 4379, Riyadh.

*

Ministry of Education
Riyadh.
Tel: 404-28-88. Telex: 401673 maaref sj
National Commission for Unesco
c/o Ministry of Education, Riyadh.
Tel: 404-28-88 (Ext. 1485). Telex: 401673 sj saudunesco

SENEGAL
SENEGAL

*Université Cheikh Anta Diop de Dakar, Fann Parc, Dakar. (M. le Recteur).   *1949, 1957*
Tél: 22-05-30. Télex: 262 sg. Cables: unndak sg
F : dr-éco, méd-phar, let-hum, sc.
I : dent, math app, sc de l'env.
Ce : rech éco app, rech biol sur la Lèpre, ét afro-ibéro-am, rech sur les institutions & légis-lations africaines.
INSTITUT FONDAMENTAL D'AFRIQUE NOIRE.
ECOLE NORMALE SUPÉRIEURE.
ECOLE NATIONALE SUPÉRIEURE DE TECH-NOLOGIE.
ECOLE DES BIBLIOTHÉCAIRES, ARCHIVISTES ET DOCUMENTALISTES.   *1967*
INSTITUT DE MÉDECINE TROPICALE APPLIQUÉE.   *1964*
INSTITUT DE RECHERCHES SUR L'ENSEIGNE-MENT DE LA MATHÉMATIQUE, DE LA PHYSIQUE ET DE LA TECHNOLOGIE.   *1975*
INSTITUT DE FRANÇAIS POUR LES ETUDIANTS ÉTRANGERS.   *1979*
INSTITUT DE TECHNOLOGIE NUCLÉAIRE APPLIQUÉE.   *1980*
INSTITUT DE PÉDIATRIE SOCIALE.   *1964*
INSTITUT DES DROITS DE L'HOMME ET DE LA PAIX.   *1983*
CENTRE D'ETUDES DES SCIENCES ET TECH-NIQUES DE L'INFORMATION.   *1970*
CENTRE DE LINGUISTIQUE APPLIQUÉE DE DAKAR.   *1966*

CENTRE DE RECHERCHES PSYCHOPATHOL-OGIQUES ET SOCIALES.   *1981*
CENTRE D'ETUDES ET DE RECHERCHES SUR LES ENERGIES RENOUVELABLES.   *1980*
Ecole Inter-Etats des Sciences et de Médecine Vétérinaires, Dakar.
Ecole nationale d'Administration et de Magis-trature, Rue Dial-Diop, Dakar.
Tél: 21-69-71
Ecole Polytechnique, B.P. 10, Thiès.   *1973*
Tél: 51-13-84. Télex: 7758 epthies
Institut national de Développement rural, Thiès.
Ecole nationale d'Economie appliquée, Route de Ouakam, Dakar.   *1968*
Tél: 22-31-76
Ecole normale supérieure d'Enseignement tech-nique et professionnel, Km 4, Route de Ouakam, Dakar.   *1979*
Tél: 21-76-69
Institut Sénégalo-Britannique d'Enseignement de l'Anglais, B.P. 35, Rue du 18 juin, Dakar.
Tél: 22-40-23
Centre de Formation pédagogique spéciale, B.P. 149, Ex-Base aérienne, Thiès.   *1968*
Tél: 51-13-82
Ecole nationale de Formation maritime, Km 4, 5, route de Rufisque.
Tél: 21-38-23
Ecole nationale d'Horticulture, Cambérène, Dakar-lie.

Tél: 21-78-21

Ecole nationale de Cadres ruraux, B.P. 41, Bambey. *1960*
Tél: 58-63-60
agr, élev, for.

Centre de Formation et de Perfectionnement administratif, Cité Hersent, Boulevard de l'Est-Point E, Dakar-Fann. *1965*
Tél: 22-00-58

Centre africain d'Etudes supérieures en Gestion, 72, boulevard de la République, Dakar. *1980*
Tél: 21-92-23

Ecole nationale des Assistants Sociaux et Educateurs spécialisés, Km 4, Route de Ouakam, Dakar. *1968*
Tél: 23-07-70

Ecole nationale des Postes et Télécommunications, Rue Ousmane Socé Diop, Rufisque.
Tél: 36-00-29

Ecole supérieure multinationale des Postes et Télécommunications, Rue Ousmane Socé Diop, Rufisque. *1971*
Tél: 36-44-43

Ecole d'Architecture et d'Urbanisme, Dakar-Immeuble Seydou Nourou Tall, Dakar.

Tél: 22-39-81

Ecole nationale des Beaux-Arts, 124126 Avenue A. Peytavin, Dakar. *1979*
Tél: 22-35-53

Ecole normale supérieure d'Enseignement artistique, 124126, Avenue A. Peytavin, Dakar. *1979*
Tél: 22-35-53

Conservatoire national de Musique, de Danse et d'Art dramatique, 36, avenue Faidherbe prolongée, Dakar. *1978*
Tél: 21-25-11

Institut national supérieur de l'Education populaire et de Sport, Stade Iba Mar Diop, Dakar.
Tél: 21-33-84

Centre de Perfectionnement en Langue anglaise, Dakar.

Ecole nationale des Douanes, Avenue Carde, Rue René Ndiaye, Dakar. *1970*
Tél: 22-45-73

Ecole nationale de Police et de la Formation permanente, B.P. 5025, Dakar-Fann. *1954*
Tél: 22-28-18

Union démocratique des Etudiants de Dakar—UDED (IUS)
B.P. 10221, Dakar-Liberté.

Communauté catholique des Etudiants de Dakar (Pax Romana)

Association protestante des Etudiants et Elèves (WSCF)
Centre de Liberté, B.P. 10027, Dakar.

*

Ministère de l'Education nationale
Dakar.
Tél: 22-57-30. Télex: 3239 miensup sg

Commission nationale du Sénégal pour l'Unesco
Ministère de l'Education nationale, 87, rue Carnot x Bayeux, Dakar.
Tél: 22-57-30. Cables: comnat unesco min education dakar

SIERRA LEONE
SIERRA-LEONE

*University of Sierra Leone, Private Mail Bag 87, Freetown. (The Registrar).   *1966*
Tel: 26859. Cables: unisaal, freetown
   FOURAH BAY COLLEGE, Private Mail Bag 87, Freetown.   *1827, 1960, 1966*
   Tel: 27260. Cables: fourahbay
   F : *arts, eco-soc st, pure & app sc, eng.*
   D : *acc, bot, ch, class, eco, ed, eng, English, geog, geol, hist, law, math, mod lang, phil, phy, pol, socio, theo, zool, cmty heal.*
   I : *African st, marine biol & oceanog.*
   NJALA UNIVERSITY COLLEGE, Private Mail Bag, Freetown.   *1964, 1966*
   Tel: 4. Cables: njalun
   F : *agr, ed, basic sc.*
   D : *African ecol, agr, ed, agr eng, agronomy, anim sc, audio-vis ed, biol, ch, English, env st-geog, hom eco, math, phys, phy.*
   Ce : *sc curriculum dev.*
Institute of Public Administration and Management, c/o University of Sierra Leone, Private Mail Bag 87, Freetown.
Tel: 24476

Technical Institute, Congo Cross, Freetown.
Tel: 31368
sec, bui-civ eng, elec, bus st.
Bo Teachers' College, Private Mail Bag, Bo.
English, agr, math, geog, hist, rur dev st, handicrafts, hom eco, sc ed.
Bunumbu Teachers' College, Private Mail Bag, Kenema.
English, agr, math, geog, hist, rur dev st, handicrafts, hom eco, sc ed.
Freetown Teachers' College, Private Mail Bag, Freetown.
English, agr, math, geog, hist, rur dev st, handicrafts, hom eco, sc ed.
Makeni Teachers' College, Private Mail Bag, Makeni.
English, agr, math, geog, hist, rur dev st, handicrafts, hom eco, sc ed.
Milton Margai Teachers' College, Goderich.
Tel: 024305
D : *arts-crafts, biol, ch, ed, English, French, geog, hist, hom eco, mus, phys, phy, relig.*

Sierra Leone Association of University Women (IFUW)
P.O. Box 1001, Freetown.
National Union of Sierra Leone Students—NUSS (IUS)
Fourah Bay College, University of Sierra Leone, Freetown.
The Newman Society (Pax Romana)
Fourah Bay College, University of Sierra Leone, Freetown.
Sierra Leone Student Christian Movement (WSCF)
47 Siaka Stevens Street, Freetown.
Tel: 22989

Sierra Leone United Nations Student Association (ISMUN)
57 Dundas Street, Freetown.

*

Ministry of Education, Cultural Affairs and Sports
New England, Freetown.
Tel: 40560
Sierra Leone National Commission for Unesco
Ministry of Education, Cultural Affairs and Sports, New England, Freetown.
Tel: 40560. Cables: unesco mineduc freetown

SINGAPORE
SINGAPOUR

UNIVERSITIES—UNIVERSITES

National University of Singapore, Kent Ridge, Singapore 0511.   *1980*
Tel: 7756666. Fax: 7786570. Telex: 33943 unispo rs. Cables: univspore singapore
F : *arts-soc, soc, med, law, dent, eng, arc-bui, bus.*
S : *postgrad med, postgrad dent, postgrad mangt.*

Nanyang Technological Institute, Nanyang Avenue, Singapore 2263.   *1981*
Tel: 2651744. Fax: 2641604. Telex: 38851 nti rs. Cables: sinnti
S : *civ & structural eng, elec-electro, mec-prod eng.*

OTHER INSTITUTIONS—AUTRES INSTITUTIONS

College of Physical Education, 489 Bt Timah Road, Singapore 1025.
Institute of Education, 469 Bukit Timah Road, Singapore 1025.   *1950, 1973*
Tel: 4695151. Telex: 33778 ie rs
Ngee Ann Polytechnic, 535 Clementi Road, Singapore 2159.   *1963, 1982*
Tel: 4666555. Telex: 39206 ianpol rs
D : *mec, elec, electro, shipbuilding-offshore*

eng, bui mangt, bus st, comp st, publ heal eng.
Singapore Polytechnic, Dover Road, Singapore 0513.   *1954*
Tel: 7751133. Fax: 7721971. Telex: 50208 sinpol rs
D : *arc techn, civ eng, bui, ch process techn, elec, electro-commun, marine eng, mec, nautical st, bus-commun, surv, manufacturing eng.*

Catholic Students' Society of the University of Singapore (Pax Romana)
c/o Affiliates' Room, Union House, Cluny Road, University of Singapore, Singapore 0511.
Singapore Catholic Movement for Intellectual and Cultural Affairs—SICMICA (Pax Romana)
Correspondent: Philip Motha.
1 Leyden Hill, Singapore 11.
Student Christian Movement of Singapore (WSCF)
14 Dalvey Estate, Singapore 1025.

United Nations Student Association (ISMUN)
University of Singapore Students Union, Bukit Timah Road, Singapore 11.

*

Kementerian Pelajaran Singapura (Ministry of Education, Singapore)
Kay Siang Road, Singapore 1024.
Tel: 4739111. Fax: 4756128. Telex: edun rs 34366. Cable: education

SOLOMON ISLANDS
SALOMON (ILES)

University of the South Pacific, (see p. 131) University Centre, P.O. Box 406, Honiara.
Solomon Islands Training College, P.O. Box 1, Honiara. *1959*

College of Higher Education, P.O. Box G23, Honiara. *1969*
S : *trades, marine, surv-drafting, com.*

Ministry of Education and Training
P.O. Box 584, Honiara.

SOMALIA
SOMALIE

*Jaamacadda Ummadda Soomaaliyeed [Somali National U.], P.O. Box 15, Mogadiscio. (The President). *1954, 1959, 1970*

Tel: 80404
F : *law, eco, ed, agr, ch ind, eng, geol, vet, med, polytec.*

Somali Revolutionary Youth Union—SRYU (IUS)
P.O. Box 1810, Mogadiscio.
Telex: 639 (att. SRYU)

*

Ministry of Education and Culture
Mogadiscio.
Somali National Commission for Unesco
Ministry of Education and Culture, Mogadiscio.
Tel: 80204 (Ext. 57). Cables: secgen natcom ministry higher education mogadiscio

REPUBLIC OF SOUTH AFRICA
REPUBLIQUE D'AFRIQUE DU SUD

UNIVERSITIES – UNIVERSITES

*University of Cape Town, Private Bag, Rondebosch 7700. (The Registrar). *1829, 1918*
Tel: 6509111. Telex: 522208 sa
F : *arts, soc-hum, sc, eng, law, med, ed, com, mus, soc, fa-arc.*
S : *env st, ballet, opera.*

University of Durban-Westville, Private Bag X54001, Durban 4000. *1961, 1971*
Tel: 8209111. Telex: 623228 sa. Cables: inkol
F : *arts, sc, com-adm, ed, law, eng, heal sc, theo.*

University of Fort Hare, Private Bag X1314, Alice 5700. *1916, 1970*
Tel: 0404-32011. Telex: 242192 sa
F : *arts, ed, sc, theo, law, agr, eco.*

Medical University of Southern Africa-MEDUNSA, P.O. Medunsa 0204, Pretoria 0001. *1976*
Tel: (012)58-2844. Telex: 3-0580 sa
F : *med, dent, vet.*

University of Natal, King George V Avenue, Durban 4001 or P.O. Box 375, Pietermaritzburg 3200. *1909, 1949*
Tel: 81-69111. Telex: 623467 sa
F : *arc & allied disciplines, arts, sc, ed, law, com, eng, agr, med (for non-white students only), soc.*

University of the North/Universiteit van die Noorde, Private Bag X5090, Pietersburg 0700. *1959, 1970*
Tel: (01522)4310. Telex: 331813 sa. Cables: unikol
F : *arts, ed, eco-adm, theo, math-nat, law, agr.*

Universiteit van die Oranje-Vrystaat, [U. of the Orange Free State], P.O. Box 339, Bloemfontein 9300. *1855, 1950*
Tel: (051)401-9111. Telex: 267666 sa
F : *arts, soc, sc, law, eco-adm, ed & teachers' C., agr, med, theo.*

University of Port Elizabeth/Universiteit van Port Elizabeth, P.O. Box 1600, Port Elizabeth 6000. *1964*
Tel: (041)5311-9281. Telex: 243342 sa
F : *arts, sc, eco, ed, law.*

Potchefstroomse Universiteit vir Chirstelike Hoër Onderwys [Potchefstroom U. for Christian Higher Education], Potchefstroom 2520. *1869, 1951*
Tel: (01481)27511. Telex: 421363 sa. Cables: pup

F : *arts, sc, theo, ed, eco, law, eng.*

Universiteit van Pretoria [U. of Pretoria], Hillcrest, Pretoria 0001. *1908, 1930*
Tel: (012)420-9111. Telex: 322723 sa. Cables: puniv
F : *arts, sc-math, eco-pol, ed, law, vet, med, dent, eng, agr, theo.*

Randse Afrikaanse Universiteit [Rand Afrikaans U.], P.O. Box 524, Johannesburg 2000. *1966*
Tel: (011)726-5000. Telex: 424526 sa. Cables: rauniv
F : *arts, eco-mangt, law, sc, ed, eng.*

Rhodes University, P.O. Box 94, Grahamstown 6140. *1855, 1951*
Tel: (0461)22023. Telex: 244219 sa. Cables: rhodescol
F : *arts, ed, com, div, law, soc, phar, sc.*

Universiteit van Suid-Afrika/University of South Africa, P.O. Box 392, Pretoria 0001.*1873, 1916*
Tel: 440-3111. Teletex: 350068 unisa
F : *arts, theo, ed, sc, law, eco-mangt sc* (Teletuition).

Universiteit van Stellenbosch [U. of Stellenbosch], Stellenbosch 7600. *1866, 1918*
Tel: (02231)77911. Telex: 520383 sa. Cables: university
F : *arts, sc, ed, agr, for, theo, law, eng, com-adm, med, dent, milit.*

University of Venda, Private Bag X2220, Sibasa. *1982*
Tel: (01559)21071. Telex: 321619 sa
F : *art, sc, law, ed, bus-adm.*

University Vista/Universiteit Vista (Decentralized campuses), Private Bag X634, Pretoria 0001. *1983*
Tel: (012)322-8967
F : *arts, eco-mangt sc, ed.*
Soweta Campus, Private Bag X03, Tshiawelo 1818.
Batho Campus, Private Bag X380, Bloemfontein 9300.
Zwide Campus, Private Bag X613, Port Elizabeth 6000.

University of the Western Cape/Universiteit van Wes-Kaapland, Private Bag X17, Bellville 7530. *1960, 1970*
Tel: 959-2746. Telex: 526661 sa. Cables: unibell
F : *arts, ed, sc, dent, eco-mangt sc, law, theo.*

University of the Witwatersrand, Jan Smuts

Avenue, Johannesburg 2001.   *1896, 1923*
Tel: (011)716-1111. Telex: 427125 sa. Teletex:
450297 juill. Cables: uniwits
F : *arts, sc, med, eng, law, arc, dent, com, ed,
bus adm.*

University of Zululand/Universiteit van Zululand,
Private Bag X001, Kwadlangezwa, 3886.
1959, 1970
Tel: (0351)93911. Telex: 631311 sa. Cables:
unizul
F : *arts, ed, sc, eco-pol, law, theo.*
I : *publ serv & voc training.*

OTHER INSTITUTIONS—AUTRES INSTITUTIONS
Technical Education—Enseignement technique

Kaapse Technikon/Cape Technikon, P.O. Box
652, Cape Town.   *1968*
Tel: (021)46-6220. Telex: 521666 sa. Cables:
teccom
D : *art, civ eng-bui, elec, food & clothing techn,
mangt-adm, mec, paramed-biol sc, physical sc-
math, sec, teacher training (com).*
Technikon   Northern   Transvaal/Technikon
Noord-Transvaal,   Private   Bag   X24,
Soshunguve 0152.   *1981*
Tel: (01214)2005. Telex: 323239 sa
S : *elec, mangt-adm, mec, med-heal sc, physical
sc, sec-commun-lang, surv-mine-civ eng, bui,
ed-ed techn.*
Technikon Mangosuthu, P.O. Box 12363, Jacobs
4026.   *1979*
Tel: (031)907-1855. Telex: 621841 sa
D : *elec, heal sc, ch eng, civ eng-bui, mec, sec-
bus st.*
Technikon Natal, P.O. Box 953, Durban 4000.
1907, 1968
Tel: (031)318711. Telex: 620187 sa. Cables:
nattechnikon
S : *app sc, bui-civ eng, creative des, ed-ind eng,
elec, fa, food & clothing techn, heal serv, lang-
commun-performing arts, mangt, mec, phar,
sec.*
Technikon OVS/Technikon OFS, Private Bag
X20539, Bloemfontein 9300.   *1981*
Tel: 71003
D : *art-des, sec-mangt, eng, paramed.*
Technikon   Peninsula/Technikon   Skiereiland,
Private Bag X3, Kasselsvlei 7533, Cape.
S : *app sc, art-des, bus st, eng-bui, sec-comp,
teacher training.*

Port Elizabeth Technikon, Private Bag X6011,
Port Elizabeth 6000.   *1977*
Tel: 53-31-21. Telex: 243051 sa
S : *app sc, art-des, civ eng-bui, mangt, mec, elec,
phar, sec.*
Technikon Pretoria, 420 Church Street East,
Pretoria 0002.   *1968*
Tel: (012)28-3811. Cables: techpret
S : *agr sc, art, biol, ch, civ eng, comp, elec, food
& tex, heal sc, commun, mangt, mec, perform-
ing arts, phar, physical sc, sec.*
Technikon RSA (Teletuition), Private Bag X7,
Braamfontein 2017.   *1980*
Tel: (011)403-6918
S : *eng, mangt, adm-teacher training, math,
physical & biol sc.*
M.L. Sultan Technikon, P.O. Box 1334, Durban
4000.   *1946*
Tel: (031)316681. Cables: sulkon
S : *app sc, apprentice, art-des, bui-civ eng, elec-
mec, heal serv, hotel & catering, adm, mangt,
adm-comp, sec, commun-lang.*
D : *hom eco, phys-speech.*
Vaaldriehoekse   Technikon/Vaal   Triangle
Technikon, Private Box X021, Vanderbijlpark
1900.   *1972*
Tel: (016)81-2141. Telex: 748014 sa
S : *app sc, art-des, elec, food & clothing, mangt-
adm, mec.*
Technikon Witwatersrand, P.O. Box 3293,
Johannesburg 2000.   *1968*
Tel: (011)29-7136. Telex: 489539 sa
S : *comp, art-des, biol, ch-ch eng, civ eng-bui-
arc, elec, heal serv, hotel, lang-commun, mine-
met, opt, phar, mangt, mec-ind eng, sec.*

Agricultural Education—Enseignement agricole

Agricultural Research Station and College of
Agriculture, Glen 9360.
Tel: 05214-2051. Telex: 267690 sa
Cedara College of Agriculture, Pietermaritzburg
3200.
Elsenburg College of Agriculture, Private Bag

X5023, Stellenbosch 7600.
College of Agriculture, Grootfontein, Middel-
burg 5900.
College of Agriculture and Research Station,
Private Bag X804, Potchefstroom 2520.

Nursing Education – Enseignement infirmier

Carinus Nursing College, Private Bag, Rochester 7940.

Nico Malan-verplegingskollege [Nico Malan C. of Nursing], Private Bag, Athlone 7760.

Otto du Plessis-verpleegsterskollege [Otto du Plessis C. of Nursing], Private Bag, Tygerberg 7505.
Tel: 9310111

Sarleh Dollie-verplegingskollege [Sarleh Dollie C. of Nursing], Private Bag, Tygerberg 7505.

Sharleh Cribb-verplegingskollege [Sharleh Cribb C. of Nursing], Private Bag X6047, Port Elizabeth 6000.

College of Nursing, Lion Street, Welkom 9460.

Boitemelo-hospitaalkollege [Boitemelo Hospital C.], Private Bag, Kroonstad 9500.

Pelonomi Hospital Lecture Unit, Private Bag X20581, Bloemfontein 9300.

Vrystaat-opleidingskollege vir Verpleging [Free State C. of Nursing], Private Bag X20598, Bloemfontein 9300.

Pretoria-kollege vir Verpleging [Pretoria C. of Nursing], Private Bag X169, Pretoria 0001.

B.G. Alexander College of Nursing, 309 Smit Street, Hillbrow, Johannesburg 2001.

Weskoppies-opleidingskool vir Verpleegkundiges [Weskoppies Training S. for Nurses], Private Bag X113, Pretoria 0001.

Wes-Transvaalse Verplegingskollege [Western Transvaal C. of Nursing], Private Bag X14, Klerksdorp 2570.

Tara, The H. Moross Training School for Nurses, Private Bag X7, Randburg 2125.

Training School for Nurses, No. 1 Military Hospital, Voortrekkerhoogte 0187.

Frere Nursing College, Private Bag X9023, East London 5200.

Teacher Training – Formation pédagogique

Barkly House Training College, Molteno Road, Claremont 7700.

Teachers' College, Highbury Road, Mowbray, Cape Town 7700.

Teachers' College, P.O. Box 102, Graaff-Reinet 6280.

Teachers' College, Private Bag X649, Oudtshoorn 6620.

Teachers' College, P.O. Box 311, Paarl 7620.

Teachers' College, Belmont Terrace, Port Elizabeth 6001.
Tel: (041)532177

Denneoord College, Van Riebeeck Street, Stellenbosch 7600.

Teachers' College, Van Riebeeck Street, Wellington 7655.

Opleidingskollege Athlone [Training C. Athlone], 1 Sanddrift Street, Paarl 7646.

Athlone Training Centre for Pre-primary Teachers, 1 Sanddrift Street, Paarl 7646.

Bechet Training College, P.O. Box 3746, Greyville 4023.

Bellville Training College, Private Bag X8, Kasselsvlei 7533.

Dower Training College, Private Bag 6059, Port Elizabeth 6000.

St. Francis Remote Campus, P.O. Box 77, Crawford 7700.

Phatsimang College of Education, Private Bag X5029, Kimberley 8300.

College for Continuing Education, Private Bag X49, Soshanguve 0152.

Kagisanong College of Education, Private Bag X20523, Bloemfontein.

Rand Training College, Private Bag X6, Langlaagte 2102.

Opleidingskollege Roggebaai [Training C. Roggebaai], Prestwich Street, Cape Town 8001.

Suid-Kaaplandse Opleidingskollege [Southern Cape Training C.], Private Bag X646, Oudtshoorn 6620.

Peninsula Technikon, Private Bag X3, Kasselsvlei 7533.

Bethel College of Education, Bodenstein 2726.

Cape College of Education, Private Bag X2041, Fort Beaufort 5720.

East Rand College of Education, Private Bag X52, Springs 1560.
Tel: (0435)31179

Indumiso College of Education, Private Bag 9077, Pietermaritzburg 3200.

Mphohadi College of Education, Private Bag X66, Kroonstad 9500.

Sebokeng College of Education, Private Bag X01, Sebokeng 1982.
Tel: (016)337163

Soweto College of Education, P.O. Box 90064, Bertsham 2013.
Tel: 933-1093

Transvaal College of Education, Private Bag X11, Soshanguve 0152.

Hozane College of Education, Private Bag, Hazy View 1242.

Tivumbeni College of Education, Private Bag X1420, Letaba 0870.
Tel: 01523-41701. Cables: yiyani

Springfield College of Education, Private Bag, Dormenton, Durban 4015.

Transvaal College of Education, Private Bag, Fordsburg, Johannesburg 2033.

Mgweny College of Education, Private Bag X1008, Kanyamazane 1214.

Ndebele College of Education, Private Bag X4011, Siyabuswa 0472.

Amanzimtoti Zulu College of Education, PO Adams Mission 4100.

Appelbosch College of Education, Private Bag X202, Ozwatini 3476.

Esikhawini College of Education, Private Bag X520, Esikhawini 3887.
Tel: (0358)63041

Eshowe College of Education, Private Bag X503, Eshowe 3815.
Tel: 42131

Madadeni College of Education, Private Bag X5001, Madadeni 2951.

Mpumalanga College of Education, Private Bag X1004, Hammersdale 3700.

Ntuzuma College of Education, Private Bag X02, Kwa-Mashu 4360.

Umbumbulu College of Education, Private Bag X12, Amanzimtoti 4125.

Umlazi College of Education, Private Bag X04, Isipingo 4110.

Dr C.N. Phatudi College of Education, Private Bag X1020, Burgersfort 1150.

Kwena Moloto College of Education, Private Bag X4015, Seshego 0742.

Mamokgalake Chuene College of Education, Private Bag X629, Groblersdal 0470.

Mojadji College of Education, Private Bag X746, Duiwelskloof 0833.

Mokopane College of Education, Private Bag X601, Mahwelereng 0626.

Sekhukhune College of Education, P.O. Lefalene 0741.

Setoltolwane College of Education, Private Bag X7372, Pietersburg 0700.

Durbanse Onderwyskollege [Durban C. of Education], Queen Mary Avenue, Durban 4001.

Edgewood College of Education, Private Bag X2001, Pinetown 3600.
Tel: (031)7001455

Natal College of Education, Private Bag 9007, Pietermaritzburg 3200.
Tel: 54515

Teachers' College of the OFS, Park Road Bloemfontein 9301.

Bonamelo College of Education, Private Bag X849, Witsieshoek 9870.

Sefikeng College of Education, Private Bag X827, Witsieshoek 9870.

Tshiya College of Education, Private Bag X809, Witsieshoek 9870.

Goudstadse Onderwyskollege [Goudstad C. of Education], Private Bag X2, Cottesloe 2092.

Johannesburg College of Education, 17 Hoofd Street, Braamfontein 2001.

Onderwyskollege Potchefstroom [Potchefstroom C. of Education], Cr. Borcherd and Hoffman Streets, Potchefstroom 2520.

Onderwyskollege Pretoria [Pretoria C. of Education (Afrikaans-medium)], Private Bag X382, Pretoria 0001.

Pretoria College of Education, Private Bag X380, Pretoria 0001.
Tel: 325-14-31

College of Education for Further Training, Private Bag X460, Pretoria 0001.
Tel: (0331)58200

Hebron College of Education, Private Bag X1084, Garankuwa 0208.

Moretele College of Education, Private Bag X376, Makapanstad 0404.

Strydom College of Education, Private Bag X217, Seloshesha 9785.

Taung College of Education, Private Bag X03, Pudimoe 8581.

Tlhabane College of Education, Private Bag X2003, Tlabane 0305.

Lennon Sebe College of Education, P.O. Box 685, King Williams Town 5600.

Dr. W.B. Rubanase College of Education, Private Bag 140, Mdantsane 5219.

Masibulele College of Education, Private Bag 338, Whittlesea 5360.

Makhado College of Education, Private Bag X1004, Dzanani.

Tshisimani College of Education, Private Bag X1302, Tshakhuma.

Venda College of Education, Private Bag X2269, Sibasa.

Arthur Tsengiwe Teachers' Training College, P.O. Box 2, Cala.

Bensonvale Teachers' Training College, P.O. Bensonvale, Herschel.

Butterworth Teachers' Training College, P.O. Butterworth.

Cioira Teachers' Training College, Private Bag X5034, Umtata.

Clarkebury Teachers' Training College, Clarkebury.

Maluti Teachers' Training College, P.O. Box 87, Matatiele.

Mount Arthur Teachers' Training College, Private Bag X123, Lady Frere.

Shawbury Teachers' Training College, P.O. Qumbu.

Sigcau Teachers' Training College, Private Bag X514, Flagstaff.

Committee of University Principals

The Committee of University Principals was constituted by the Universities Act No. 61 of 1955 and empowered to take over the functions hitherto performed by the Vice-Chancellors' Committee. The Committee consists of the Principals of universities, and in an advisory capacity, such other persons as may be appointed by University Councils. In the exercise of powers conferred by the Act of 1955 the Committee may make recommendations to the Minister of National Education regarding any matter that it considers to be of common interest to the universities or which may be referred to it by the Minister or the Director-General for National Education. It may also make joint statutes and regulations relating to the Joint Matriculation Board, the administration of the Joint Scholarship Funds of the Universities, and admission of registered students of any one of the universities to any of the others, and a minimum period of attendance for the degree of Bachelor. The Committee has power to formulate regulations dealing with any matters of common interest such as the rotation between the universities of post-graduate scholarships administered by the Committee and the conditions and award of essay prizes, etc.

Le Comité des «principaux» d'université a été créé en vertu de la Loi universitaire no 61 de 1955 et est habilité à reprendre les fonctions jusqu'alors exercées par le Comité des vice-chanceliers. Il se compose des «principaux» des universités, et à titre consultatif, de personnes éventuellement désignées par les conseils d'université. En vertu des pouvoirs qui lui sont conférés par la Loi de 1955, le Comité peut faire des recommandations au Ministre de l'Education nationale concernant toute question qu'il juge d'intérêt commun pour les universités ou qui peuvent lui être soumises par le Ministre ou par le Directeur général de l'éducation nationale. Il peut également arrêter des dispositions statutaires ou réglementaires communes concernant l'Office conjoint des immatriculations, le Fonds commun des bourses universitaires, l'admission à telle université des étudiants inscrits à telle autre, les périodes d'études minima pour l'obtention du grade de Bachelor. Le Comité est en outre habilité à établir des règlements sur toutes questions d'intérêt commun: par exemple, l'ordre de roulement entre les universités des bourses d'études avancées administrées par lui et leurs conditions d'octroi, les conditions de délivrance de certains prix, etc.

The Chief Director
P.O. Box 27392, Sunnyside, Pretoria 0132.
 Tel: (012)341-7746

The Joint Matriculation Board

The Board consists of representatives of the seventeen South African universities; the Committee of University Principals; Departments of Education and Culture, Administration: House of Assembly; Education and Training; Education and Culture, Administration: House of Representatives; Education and Culture, Administration: House of Delegates; the four Provinces; and the secondary schools (public and private) of the four Provinces. Its function is to control and conduct the matriculation examinations on behalf of the seventeen universities in South West Africa and to deal with all applications for exemption therefrom.

Le Conseil paritaire pour l'admission aux études supérieures se compose des représentants des dix-sept universités sud-africaines; de la Conférence des présidents d'université; des départements de l'éducation et de la direction culturelle: Chambre de l'Assemblée; de l'éducation et de la formation professionnelle, de l'éducation et de la direction culturelle: Chambre des Représentants; de l'éducation et de la direction culturelle: Chambre des Délégués; des départements d'éducation des quatre Provinces; ainsi que des représentants des écoles secondaires (du secteur public et du secteur privé) des quatre Provinces. Le Conseil paritaire a pour mission d'homologuer et d'organiser les examens terminaux du secondaire de la part des dix-sept universités sud-africaines et de statuer sur toutes les demandes d'exemption de ces examens.

The Secretary,
P.O. Box 3854, Pretoria.
 Tel: (012)429-4128. Cables: matric

The University Teachers' Association of South Africa (IAUPL)
Contact: 18 rue du Docteur Roux, 75015 Paris, France.
 Tel: (33-1)47-83-31-65

South African Association of University Women/ Suid Afrikaanse Vereniging van Universiteitsvroue (IFUW)
6 Woodlands Park, 68 Camp Ground Road, Rondebosch 7700.

World University Service (WUS)
Correspondent: John Samuel.
SACHED, P.O. Box 11350, Johannesburg 2000.
 Tel: 8341341. Telex: 487413

Kolbe Association of South Africa (Pax Romana)
c/o St. John Vianney Seminary, Water-kloof, Pretoria.

National Catholic Federation of Students (Pax Romana)

37 Roseland Road, Rondebosch 7700.
South African Union of Jewish Students (WUJS)
Contact: 89 Champsee De Vleurgat, 1050
Brussels, (Belgium).
Tél: (02)647-7279. Telex: 20625
          *

Human Sciences Research Council
Private Bag X270, Pretoria 0001.
Tel: (012)325-1837. Telex: 320893 sa. Cables:
ragen

SPAIN
ESPAGNE

UNIVERSITIES — UNIVERSITES

Universidad de Alcalá de Henares, Carretera de
Barcelona, Km. 33, Alcalá de Henares
(Madrid).   *1977*
Tél: 889-0404. Télex: 23896 unah e
F : sc, méd, éco-adm des aff, phar, dr, phil-let.
E : éd.
Universidad de Alicante, San Vicente del
Raspeig, Alicante.   *1979*
Tél: (65)66-11-50. Télex: 66616 undea e
F : sc, phil-let, méd, dr, éco-adm des aff.
E : aff, éd, inf, trav soc, opt.
*Universitat de Barcelona, Gran Vía de las
Cortes Catalanas 585, Barcelona 11.   *1430*
Tél: (3)318-4266. Télex: 98871 unbe e
F : phil-éd, ba, ch, math, géol, phy, biol, géog-
hist, phill, dr, méd, phar, éco-adm des aff, psyc.
E : aff, éd, inf, bibl.
   LÉRIDA.
      Tél: (73)26-43-58
      E : inf.
   TARRAGONA.
      Tél: (77)22-52-54
      F : phil-let, ch.
      E : éd, inf, trav soc; inf (Tortosa)
      D: bioch; méd (Reus)
   VICH.
      E : éd.
*Universidad Autónoma de Barcelona, Campus
de Bellaterra, Avenida Santa Antoni Ma.
Claret 171, Barcelona.   *1968*
Tél: (3)692-0000. Télex: 52040 educi e
F : phil-let, sc, dr, méd, éco-adm des aff, infor,
vét, phill, géog, hist, phil-éd.
E : éd, trad-interp, inf.
   GERONA.
      E : éd, inf.
   LÉRIDA.
      E : éd.
   SABADELL.
      E : aff.

   VICH.
      E : inf.
Universidad de Cádiz, Plaza de Fragela s/n,
Cádiz.   *1979*
Tél: (56)22-38-08. Télex: 76197 Uncd e
F : sc, méd, phil-let.
E : aff, éd, inf, gé ind, gé nav.
   ALGECIRAS.
      E : gé ind.
   JÉREZ DE LA FRONTERA.
      F : dr.
      E : aff, inf, éd.
   LA LÍNEA DE LA CONCEPCIÓN.
      E : éd.
*Universidad de Cantabria, Avenida de los
Castros s/n, Santander.   *1972*
Tél: (42)21-78-11. Télex: 35861 educi e
F : sc, méd, phil-let.
E (tec sup.) : ponts et chaussées.
E : aff, éd, inf, gé ind.
   CANTABRIA.
      F : dr.
   TORRELAVEGA.
      E : éd, gé mine.
*Universidad de Castilla-La Mancha, Calle
Paloma 9, 13071 Ciudad Real.   *1985*
Tél: (26)25-19-00. Télex: 48127 ucma e
F : ch, phil-let.
E (tec. sup.) : gé agr.
E : gé agr, éd.
   ALBACETE.
      F : dr.
      E (tec. sup.) : gé ind.
      E : gé ind, gé agr, gé for, inft, éd, inf.
   ALMADÉN.
      E : gé ind, gé min.
   CUENCA.
      F : ba.
      E (tec. sup.) : arc.
      E : éd, inf.

GUADALAJARA.
　E : éd, inf.
TOLEDO.
　E : éd, élec.
Universidad Politécnica de Cataluña, Avenida
Dr. Gregorio Marañón s/n, Barcelona 14. *1971*
Tél: (3)249-3804
F : inft, éco, adm des aff.
E : gé téléc, gé agr, gé ind.
　CANET DE MAR.
　　E : gé tex.
　EL VALLÉS.
　　E : arc.
　GERONA.
　　E : arc, gé agr, gé ind.
　IGUALADA.
　　gé ind.
　LÉRIDA.
　　E (tec. sup.) : tec agr.
　　E : gé agr.
　MANRESA.
　　E : gé ind, gé mine.
　MATARÓ.
　　E : gé ind.
　TARRAGONA.
　　E : gé ind.
　TARRASA.
　　E (tec. sup.) : gé ind.
　　E : gé ind, opt.
　VILLANUEVA Y GELTRÚ.
　　E : gé ind, gé téléc.
*Universidad Pontificia Comillas, Canto Blanco,
Madrid 34. *1935, 1967*
Tél: (1)734-3950. Télex: 2486569 G3
F : phil-let, théo, dr can.
*Universidad de Córdoba, Alfonso XIII, 19,
Córdoba. *1972*
Tél: (57)47-31-25. Télex: 76561 educi e
F : méd, vét, sc, phil-let, dr.
E (tec. sup.) : gé agr.
E : éd, gé ind, aff, inf.
　BÉLMEZ.
　　E : mine.
*Universidad de Deusto, Avenida Universidades
s/n, Duesto-Bilbao (Vizcaya). *1886, 1963*
Tél: (4)445-3100. Télex: 34221 udd e
F : dr, phil-éd, éco-adm des aff, phill, géog-hist,
inft, pol-soc, théo.
　SAN SEBASTIÁN.
　　F : éco-adm des aff.
*Universidad Nacional de Educación a Distancia,
Madrid 3. *1972*
Tél: (1)449-3600. Télex: 45256 uned e
F : dr, géog-hist, phill, phil-éd, sc, psyc, éco-
adm des aff, pol-soc.
E (tec. sup.) : gé ind.
Aussi 58 Centres associés.
*Universidad de Extremadura, Avenida de Elvas
s/n, Badajoz. *1973*

Tél: (24)23-88-00. Fax: (24)23-69-58. Télex:
28638 educi e
F : sc, méd, éco-adm.
E : aff, éd, inf, gé agr, gé ind.
　ALMENDRALEJO.
　　E : éd, gé agr.
　CÁCERES.
　　Tél: (27)24-56-50. Fax: (27)23-69-58. Télex:
　　28638 educi e
　　F : phil-let, dr, vét.
　　E : éd, inft, aff, gé trav publ, inf.
　DON BENITO-VILLANUEVA DE LA SERENA.
　　E : inf.
　MÉRIDA.
　　E : inf, topog, inft.
　PLASENCIA.
　　E : inf, aff.

*Universidad de Granada, Hospital Real,
Avenida del Hospicio s/n, Granada. *1531*
Tél: (58)27-84-00. Télex: 78435 educi e
F : sc, dr, phar, phil-let, méd, ba.
E : éd, aff, trad-interp, inf, bibl, arc.
I : phys.
　ALMERÍA.
　　E : aff, inf, éd.
　CEUTA.
　　E : éd, inf.
　GUADIX.
　　E : éd.
　JAÉN.
　　E : aff, inf, éd, gé ind.
　LINARES.
　　E : gé ind, gé mine, éd.
　MELILLA.
　　E : aff, inf, éd.
　ÚBEDA.
　　E : éd.
**Universidad Hispanoamericana «Santa María de
La Rábida»**, Huelva. *1943*
*Universidad Internacional Menéndez Pelayo,
Amador de los Ríos 1, Madrid 4.
1932, 1945, 1980
Tél: (1)27-26-50
D : pol comparatives, éco-énerg ressources,
dév soc, hum, dr européen, sc expé, hist-soc,
art-commun.
Universidad Internacional «Pérez Galdós», Las
Palmas de Gran Canaria. *1962*
*Universidad de Islas Baleares, Miguel de los
Santos Oliver 2, Palma de Mallorca. *1978*
Tél: (71)29-52-00. Fax: (71)20-71-11. Télex:
69121
F : phil-let, sc, dr.
E : aff, éd, inf, inft, trav soc.
Universidad de La Laguna, Avenida de la
Universidad s/n, La Laguna (Santa Cruz de
Tenerife). *1701, 1927*
Tél: (22)25-81-19. Télex: 93137 educi e

F : éco-adm des aff, dr, phil-éd, méd, phar, biol, math, ch, phill, géog-hist.
E : éd, inf.
  LAS PALMAS.
    F : éco-aff.
    E : aff, éd, inf.
  SANTA CRUZ DE TENERIFE.
    F : ba.
    E : éd, aff, inf.
Universidad Politécnica de Las Palmas, Paseo de Tomás Morales 70, Las Palmas (Gran Canaria). *1979*
Tél: (28)24-23-40. Télex: 95238 uplp e
Ce U. : sc de la mer.
E (tec. sup.) : arc, gé ind.
E : gé ind, gé trav publ, gé nav, gé téléc, topog, inft.
  LA LAGUNA.
    E : arc, gé agr.
Universidad de León, Carretera de Santander s/n, León. *1979*
Tél: (87)24-04-51. Télex: 89892 educi e
F : biol, vét, dr, phil-let.
E : aff, éd, inf, trav soc, gé agr, gé mine, gé ind.
  PONFERRADA.
    E : éd.
*Universidad Complutense de Madrid, Ciudad Universitaria, Madrid 3. *1508*
Tél: (1)49-02-56. Télex: 22459 educi e
F : éco-adm des aff, infor, pol-socio, dr, géog-hist, phill, biol, phy, géol, math, ch, phar, phil-éd, méd, vét, ba, psyc.
E : aff, éd, opt, stat, inf, trav soc.
Universidad Autónoma de Madrid, Carretera de Colmenar Viejo, Km. 15, (Cantoblanco), Madrid 34. *1968*
Tél: (1)734-0100. Télex: 27810 educi e
F : sc, éco-adm des aff, dr, phil-let, méd, psyc.
E : éd, inf, physio.
  SEGOVIA.
    E : éd, inf.
*Universidad Politécnica de Madrid, Ramiro de Maeztu s/n, Madrid 3. *1971*
Tél: (1)254-5000. Télex: 23780 upmad e
F : inft.
E (tec. sup.) : arc, aéro, gé agr, ponts et chaussées, gé ind, mine, gé nav, gé téléc, gé des montagnes.
E : inft, arc, gé téléc, gé aéro, gé agr, gé for, gé ind, gé trav publ, topog.
  ALCALÁ DE HENARES.
    E : gé agr.
  VILLAVA.
    E : gé agr.
Universidad de Málaga, Zona Universitaria "El Ejido", Málaga. *1972*
Tél: (52)2550. Télex: 77173 educi e
F : éco-adm des aff, méd, sc, phil-let, dr.
E : aff, éd, ing, inf, gé ind, inft.

  ANTEQUERA.
    E : éd.
  RONDA.
    E : inf.
Universidad de Murcia, Santo Cristo 1, Murcia. *1915*
Tél: (68)24-92-00. Télex: 67058 educi e
F : sc, dr, phil-éd, méd, phil-let, éco-adm des aff, vét.
E : aff, inft, inf, éd.
  CARTAGENA.
    E : aff, inf, gé agr, gé ind, gé mine, gé nav.
*Universidad de Navarra, Campus Universitario, Pamplona (Navarra). *1962*
Tél: (48)25-27-00. Télex: 37917 unav e
F : dr, phil, phil-éd, méd, phar, infor, géog-hist, biol, dr can, théo, éco-adm des aff.
E (tec. sup.) : arc.
E : inf, gé ind, techn-lab, bibl.
  SAN SEBASTIÁN.
    E (tec. sup.) : gé ind.
    I: sec-adm.
  BARCELONA.
    I: adm des aff.
Universidad de Oviedo, San Francisco 1-3, Oviedo. *1604*
Tél: (85)21-98-85. Télex: 87322 educi e
F : dr, phil-éd, méd, éco-adm des aff, phill, géog-hist, géol, biol, ch.
E (tec. sup.) : mine.
E : aff, inft, éd, inf, trav soc.
  GIJÓN.
    E (tec. sup.) : gé ind.
    E : aff, gé ind, inft, inf.
  MIERES.
    E : gé mine.
*Universidad del País Vasco, Apartado 1397, 48080 Bilbao (Vizcaya). *1968*
Tél: (4)464-7700. Fax: (4)464-7446. Télex: 32098 educi e
F : ba, sc, méd, éco-adm des aff, infor.
E (tec. sup.) : gé ind.
E : aff, inf, éd, gé ind.
  BARACALDO.
    E : mine.
  EIBAR.
    E : gé ind.
  ESCORIAZA.
    E : éd.
  MONDRAGÓN.
    E : gé ind.
  OÑATE.
    E : aff.
  SAN SEBASTIÁN.
    F : ch, dr, phil-éd, inft.
    E (tec. sup.) : arc.
    E : aff, éd, gé ind, inf.
  VITORIA.
    F : phill, géog-hist.

E : gé ind, éd, inf.

*Universidad de Salamanca, Patio de Escuelas 1, Salamanca. *1218*
Tél: (23)21-45-18. Télex: 26828 educi e
F : sc, dr, phil-éd, méd, phar, biol, ch, phill, géog-hist, ba.
E : aff, éd, inf, bibl, trad-interp.
ÁVILA.
E : éd.
BÉJAR.
E : gé ind.
ZAMORA.
E : éd, gé ind, inf.

Universidad Pontificia de Salamanca, Paseo Agustinos Recoletos 2, Salamanca. *1940*
Tél: (23)21-22-60
F : phil-éd, théo, dr can, phill.
E : éd.
MADRID.
F : pol-socio.

*Universidad de Santiago de Compostela, Plaza Obradoiro s/n, Santiago de Compostela (La Coruña). *1495*
Tél: (81)58-38-00
F : éco-adm des aff, dr, phar, phil-éd, méd, biol, phill, géog-hist, math, phy, ch, vét.
E (tec. sup.) : téléc.
E : éd, inf, trav soc.
EL FERROL.
E : gé nav, inf.
LA CORUÑA.
E (tec. sup.) : arc.
E : aff, éd, arc, inf.
LUGO.
E : aff, gé agr, inf.
ORENSE.
E : éd.
PONTEVEDRA.
E : éd, inf.
VIGO.
Télex: 83280 euit e
E (tec. sup.) : gé ind.
E : gé ind, éd, inf, aff.

Universidad de Sevilla, Valle San Fernando 4, Sevilla. *1505*
Tél: (54)21-86-00. Télex: 72161
F : dr, phil-éd, éco-adm des aff, géog-hist, phill, biol, phy, math, ch méd, phar, ba.
E (tec. sup.) : arc, gé ind.
E : aff, éd, arc, inf, gé ind, inft, gé agr.
HUELVA.
E : éd, inf.
LA RÁBIDA.
F : géol.
E : gé ind, gé mine, gé for, gé agr.

Universidad de Valencia, Nave 2, Valencia 3.
1500
Tél: (6)351-1737. Télex: 62523
F : éco-adm des aff, dr, géog-hist, phil-éd, psyc, phill, ch, phy, biol, math, méd, phar.
E : aff, éd, physio, inf.
CASTELLÓN DE LA PLANA.
E : éd, inf.
CHESTE.
E : éd.

*Universidad Politécnica de Valencia, Camino de Vera s/n, Valencia 15. *1968, 1971*
Tél: (6)361-5051. Télex: 62808 upva e
F : ba, inft.
E (tec. sup.) : arc, gé agr, ponts et chaussées, gé ind.
E : gé agr, gé ind.
ALCOY.
E : gé ind.
ALICANTE.
E : gé trav publ, inft.
ORIHUELA.
E : gé agr.

Universidad de Valladolid, Palacio de Santa Cruz, Plaza de Santa Cruz 8, Valladolid. *1346*
Tél: (83)29-14-67. Télex: 26357
F : sc, dr, phil-let, méd, éco-adm des aff.
E (tec. sup.) : arc, gé ind.
E : aff, éd, trav soc, inf, gé agr, gé ind, inft.
BURGOS.
F : dr.
E : aff, éd, inf, gé ind, gé trav publ.
PALENCIA.
E : éd, inf, gé agr.
SORIA.
E : éd, inf.

*Universidad de Zaragoza, Plaza de San Francisco s/n, Zaragoza. *1474*
Tél: (76)35-41-00. Fax: 23-27-62. Télex: 58064 educi e
F : sc, dr, phil-let, méd, vét, eco-adm des aff.
E (tec. sup.) : gé ind.
E : aff, éd, inf, gé ind, physio, trav soc.
HUESCA.
E : éd, inf, gé ind.
LA ALMUNIA DE DOÑA GODINA.
E : gé ind, gé agr.
LOGROÑO.
E : aff, éd, inf, gé ind.
PAMPLONA.
E : aff, éd, inf, trav soc.
TERUEL.
F : éd, inf.

Egalement 31 Colegios Universitarios (1er cycle).
Also 31 Colegios Universitarios (1st cycle).

OTHER PRIVATE INSTITUTIONS—
AUTRES INSTITUTIONS PRIVEES

Academia Universitaria de Derecho, Burgos.
1956

Escuela Superior de Administración y Dirección de Empresas, Avenida de Pedralbes 60-62, 08034 Barcelona. *1958*
Tél: (3)203-7800. Télex: 98286 esad e

Escuela Superior Empresarial Agrícola, Casillas s/n, Córdoba. *1964*
Tél: (57)29-61-33

Escuela Superior de Relaciones Públicas, Barcelona. *1969*

Estudio Superior, Lérida.

Estudios Universitarios y Tecnicos de Guipúzcoa, Paseo del Urumea, San Sebastián. *1956*
Tél: (43)27-31-00

Facultad de Ciencias Económicas y Empresariales, Paseo de Mundaiz s/n, 20012 San Sebastián. *1956, 1979*
Tél: (43)27-31-00

Instituto Católico de Artes e Industrias, Calle de Alberto Aguilera 23, Madrid 15.

Instituto Católico de Dirección de Empresas, 23 Calle Alberto Aguilera, Madrid. *1960*

Instituto Químico de Sarriá, Barcelona 17. *1916*
Tél: (3)203-89-00

Consejo de Universidades

Créé en vertu de la Loi de Réforme Universitaire (LRU) approuvée en 1983, le Conseil des Universités a pour fonctions de régir, de planifier l'enseignement supérieur, de faire des propositions et de fournir des avis consultatifs à son sujet. Il a pour Président le Ministre de l'éducation et de la science et comprend les trente-et-un Recteurs des universités publiques, les responsables de l'enseignement universitaire siégeant aux gouvernements des Communautés autonomes (l'équivalent, en quelque sorte, des entités régionales, actuellement la Catalogne, le Pays basque, la Galice, l'Andalousie, Valence et les Canaries), plus quinze membres désignés parmi des personnalités ou des spécialistes des milieux de l'enseignement et de la recherche de la Chambre des Députés; du Sénat; et du Gouvernement de la Nation).

Les Recteurs des quatre universités privées assistent aux réunions où l'on débat de questions les concernant.

Le Conseil se réunit en Assemblée générale et en commissions intitulées: la Commission académique, essentiellement composée des Recteurs; la Commission de coordination et de planification, comprenant principalement les Conseillers d'éducation des Communautés autonomes.

Les principales fonctions du Conseil sont notamment: disposer de compétences dans le domaine de la simple gestion administrative, surtout en ce qui concerne le corps enseignant et l'établissement de statistiques universitaires; élaborer des rapports-guides pour la création d'universités, de centres et d'instituts et, de façon générale, sur les normes juridiques élaborées par les Administrations publiques; résoudre des questions d'intérêt particulier relatives, pour la plupart, au corps enseignant; résoudre des problèmes d'intérêt général et notamment: approuver les plans d'étude établis par les divers Centres et qui conduisent à l'obtention de titres officiels; établir la capacité maxima d'admission des étudiants dans les divers centres universitaires, afin d'assurer la qualité de l'enseignement; préciser les limites à l'intérieur desquelles les administrations publiques fixeront, chaque année, les droits d'études; et définir les critères d'évaluation des mérites des candidats aux concours de recrutement d'enseignants universitaires. Enfin, le Conseil des Universités peut proposer au Gouvernement des dispositions de caractère général dans les domaines suivants: réglementation des études de troisième cycle; normes de base en matière de création de départements universitaires; définition des titres dont la valeur sera officiellement reconnue sur tout le territoire national; grandes lignes des programmes d'études élaborés, conformément à l'autonomie accordée, par les universités et aboutissant à l'obtention de titres officiels; et définition des normes réglementant la responsabilité des étudiants vis-à-vis du respect de leurs obligations sur le plan académique.

En définitive, le Conseil des Universités coordonne l'enseignement universitaire en harmonisant les politiques des diverses universités, des Communautés autonomes et du Ministère de l'éducation et de la science, tout en adoptant, dans le même temps, des résolutions relatives à des questions strictement académiques.

Le Conseil des Universités dispose d'un Secrétariat général permanent comprenant plus de soixante fonctionnaires à la tête desquels se

trouve le Secrétaire général, désigné par le Président, et qui a rang de Directeur général du Ministère de l'éducation et de la science.

The Council of Universities was established by the University Reform Law (LRU) of 1983 for the purpose of governing and planning higher education, drawing up proposals for higher education and giving consultative advice. Its Chairman is the Minister of Education and Science and it comprises the thirty-one rectors of the public universities, those responsible for higher education within the governments of the Autonomous Communities, which are comparable to regional entities (Catalán, Basque, Galicia, Andalousia, Valencia, and the Canaries), and fifteen appointed representatives from the Chamber of Deputies, Senate, and Government who are well acquainted with higher education. The rectors of the four private universities attend the meetings at which questions debated concern them.

The Council meets at the General Assembly and at special Commissions: the Academic Commission, comprising the rectors; and the Co-ordinating and Planning Commission, composed of the education counsellors of the Autonomous Communities.

The main responsibilities of the Council are notably: to give advice in administrative matters, particularly those concerning academic staff and the compiling of university statistics; to set up guides for the creation of universities, centres and institutes and, in a general way, for legal standards set by the public administration; to deal with questions of individual interest relative, for the most part, to academic staff; to resolve any problems of general concern, including: the approval of curricula set by the different Centres which lead to the award of official qualifications, fixing the maximum student admission numbers in the university centres; clarifying the means within which the public administration should set annual tuition fees; and the defining of criteria for evaluating candidates in the competitive examination for the recruitment of university teachers. The Council can also propose measures concerning: regulations concerning advanced postgraduate studies; basic standards governing the setting up of university departments; the defining of qualifications to be officially recognized throughout the country; guidelines for the curricula set by the universities according to the autonomy granted to them and which lead to the award of degrees; and setting of standards for students' academic responsibilities.

Finally, the Council co-ordinates university training by bringing together the policies of the different universities, the Autonomous Communities, and the Ministry of Education and Science,

and adopting, simultaneously, all the different resolutions on academic questions.

The Council of Universities has a permanent Secretariat with a staff of more than sixty, headed by the Secretary-General who is appointed by the President and holds the rank of Director-General of the Ministry of Education and Science.

Secrétaire général: Prof. Elisa Pérez-Vera.
Ciudad Universitaria s/n, 28040 Madrid.
  Tél: (1)449-74-37

Conferencia de Rectores de Universidades del Estado

La Conférence des Recteurs des universités d'Etat a été créée en 1977. Il existait précédemment un Conseil des Recteurs ou Commission permanente du Conseil national des Universités qui était présidé par le Ministre de l'éducation et des sciences. Il avait pour objet de conseiller le Ministre.

La Conférence actuelle regroupe les Recteurs de toutes les universités d'Etat conférant des grades et son but est de défendre leurs intérêts et de promouvoir des relations entre elles et les universités d'autres pays.

Ses organes de direction sont: le Président, l'Assemblée générale, le Comité exécutif et le Secrétariat général.

The Conference of Rectors of State Universities was established in 1977. Previously there was a Council of Rectors, or Permanent Commission of the National Council of Universities presided over by the Minister of Education and Science. Its purpose was to advise the Minister.

The present Conference comprises the Rectors of all degree-conferring state universities and its purpose is to defend their interests and to promote relations between them and the universities of other countries.

Its governing bodies are the Presidency, the General Assembly, the Executive Committee and the Secretariat-general.

Président: R. Portaencasa, Recteur, Universidad Politécnica de Madrid.
Secrétaire: Manuel Peláez del Rosal.
Universidad de Córdoba, Escuela de Enfermería, Avenida Méndez Pidal s/n, 14004 Córdoba.
Tél: (57)20-19-0. Télex: 76561

Consejo Superior de Investigaciones Científicas
Serrano 117, Madrid 6.
Tél: (1)261-9800. Télex: 42182.

Dirección General de Enseñanza Superior
Subdirección General de Centros y Profesorado, C/Serrano 150, 28006 Madrid.

Oficina Nacional de Turismo e Intercambio de Jóvenes y Estudiantes
C/José Ortega y Gasset 71, 28006 Madrid.

Asociación Española de Mujeres Universitarias (IFUW)
Calle Miguel Angel 8, Madrid 280010.
Amistad Universitaria (fem.)
Velásquez 114, Madrid 6.
Agrupación Católica de Graduadas (Pax Romana)
Calle de Alfonso XI, No. 4, Madrid 14.
Juventud Estudiantil Católica (Pax Romana)
Immaculada Franco, Alfonso XI, 4, Madrid.
Federación Española de Comunidades Universitarias de Vida Cristiana—FECUN (Pax Romana)
Santa Catalina 8-2, Madrid 1.
Moviment d'Universitaris I Estudiants Cristians—MUEC (Pax Romana)
c/o Lauria 126, 3-1, Barcelona 9.
Movimiento Español de Jóvenes y Estudiantes pro Naciones Unidas (ISMUN)
Marqués de Urguijo 11, Madrid 8.
The Jewish Community (WUJS)
Correspondant: 89 Chaussee De Vleurgat, 1050

Brussel (Belgique).
Tél: (02)647-7279. Télex: 20625

*

Sección de Convalidaciones de Estudios Extranjeros
Ministerio de Educación y Ciencia, Calle Cartagena 83, Madrid 14.
Tél: (1)532-1300
Dirección General de Organismos Internacionales
Ministerio de Asuntos Exteriores, Plaza de Provincia 1, Madrid 12.
Tél: (1)266-4800. Télex: (1)22646
Ministerio de Educación y Ciencia
Calle Alcalá 34, Madrid 14.
Tél: (1)532-1300. Télex: 22510
Comisión Nacional Española de Cooperación con la Unesco
Escuela Diplomática, Paseo de Juan XXIII 5, 28040 Madrid 3.
Tél: (1)233-9639. Télex: 49924. Cables: hispaunesco madrid

SRI LANKA
SRI LANKA

University of Colombo, College House, Cumaratunge Munidasa Mawatha, Colombo 03.   *1942, 1967, 1972, 1978*
Tel: 581835. Telex: 22039. Cables: university
F : *arts, ed, law, med, sc.*
  INSTITUTE OF INDIGENOUS MEDICINE, Bandaranayake Place, Rajagiriya.   *1980*
  POSTGRADUATE INSTITUTE OF MEDICINE.
                                              1981
  INSTITUTE OF WORKERS' EDUCATION.   *1980*
  INSTITUTE OF COMPUTER TECHNOLOGY.   *1987*
University of Jaffna, Thirunelvely, Jaffna.
                                        1974, 1978
Tel: 22481. Cables: university, jaffna
F : *arts, sc, med.*
University of Kelaniya, Kelaniya.
                                  1959, 1972, 1978
Tel: 521391. Cables: university, kelaniya, sri lanka
F : *hum, soc, sc.*
  POSTGRADUATE INSTITUTE OF PALI AND BUDDHIST STUDIES.   *1980*
  INSTITUTE OF AESTHETIC STUDIES.   *1980*
  POSTGRADUATE INSTITUTE OF ARCHAEOLOGY.   *1986*

University of Moratuwa, Katubedda, Moratuwa.
                                        1972, 1978
Tel: 072301. Cables: ceyeoltee
F : *arc, eng.*
Open University of Sri Lanka, Nawala Road, Nugogoda.   *1980*
Tel: 553615. Cables: open university
F : *hum-soc, eng techn, nat.*
***University of Peradeniya**, Peradeniya.
                                  1942, 1972, 1978
Tel: (08)88301. Cables: university, peradeniya
F : *agr, arts, eng, med, sc, vet-anim sc, dent.*
  POSTGRADUATE INSTITUTE OF AGRICULTURE.   *1980*
University of Ruhuna, Wellamadama, Matara.
                                        1979, 1984
Tel: 041-2681. Cables: university of ruhuna sri lanka, matara
F : *agr, med, sc, hum-soc.*
***University of Sri Jayewardenepura**, Gangodawila, Nugegoda.   *1959, 1972, 1978*
Tel: 522695. Cables: unisjay, sri lanka
F : *app sc, arts, mangt-com.*
  POSTGRADUATE INSTITUTE OF MANAGEMENT.   *1986*

Eastern University of Sri Lanka, Vanthara-moolai, Chenkaladi, Batticaloa.   *1981, 1986*
Tel: 065-2302. Cables: eastern university, chenkaladi, sri lanka
F : *agr, com-mangt, cult st, sc.*

Buddhist and Pali University of Sri Lanka, 214 Bauddhaloka Mawatha, Colombo 7.   *1982*
Tel: 580609
Buddhist & Pali st.

Committee of Vice-Chancellors and Directors (CVCD)
Chairman: Prof. S. Vithiananthan, Vice-Chancellor, University of Jaffna, Thirunelvely, Jaffna. (See below).

University Grants Commission

The University Grants Commission was established in December 1978 under the provisions of the Universities Act. It is responsible for: the planning and co-ordination of university education so as to conform to national policy; the allocation to institutions of higher education of funds voted by Parliament in respect of University education, and the control of expenditure by each institution; the maintenance of academic standards; the control of administration in the institutions; and the regulation of student admission to each institution of higher education.

The Commission consists of a Chairman, Vice-Chairman and five other members, all appointed by the President of the Democratic Socialist Republic of Sri Lanka, and all specialized in the fields of science, medicine, arts and engineering.

There are five Standing Committees responsible for: Medical and Dental Sciences; Biological Sciences; Engineering; Humanities and Social Sciences, and Physical Sciences. In addition, the Commission has set up Standing Committees on University Staff Service Conditions, and on the Open University. These Committees have representatives from the universities' academic staff as well as from outside the university system.

The universities function independently and are administered by a Vice-Chancellor and a Council. The Senate and the Faculty Boards control the academic activities. Almost all the funds of the universities in Sri Lanka are voted by Parliament through the national budget. The university system has 9 universities, including an Open University, 9 institutes, 4 for undergraduate students, and 5 for postgraduate students.

The Universities Act also provides for a Committee of Vice-Chancellors and Directors (CVCD) of the universities and university colleges whose main function is to consider all matters of common interest and to advise the Commission in such matters. The Chairman of the University Grants Commission meets monthly with the Committee of Vice-Chancellors and Directors.

La Commission des crédits universitaires a été créée en décembre 1978 en vertu de la loi sur les Universités. Elle est responsable de: la planification et la coordination de l'enseignement universitaire en conformité avec la politique nationale; l'attribution de fonds votés par le Parlement pour l'enseignement universitaire, à des établissements d'enseignement supérieur et le contrôle de leurs dépenses; le maintien des niveaux académiques; le contrôle de l'administration dans les établissements et les règles d'admission des étudiants dans chaque établissement d'enseignement supérieur.

La Commission comprend un Président, un Vice-Président et cinq membres nommés par le Président de la République Socialiste démocratique du Sri Lanka. Ils sont tous des spécialistes dans les domaines de la science, la médecine, les lettres et les sciences de l'ingénieur.

Il y a cinq Comités permanents chargés de la médecine et de la dentisterie, de la biologie, des sciences de l'ingénieur, des sciences humaines et sociales, de la physique. En outre, la Commission a établi des Comités permanents sur les conditions de recrutement et de service du personnel universitaire, et sur l'Université 'ouverte'. Ces Comités ont à la fois des délégués du personnel universitaire enseignant et des représentants étrangers à l'université.

Les universités sont autonomes et administrées par un Vice-Chancelier et un Conseil. Le Sénat et les Conseils de faculté contrôlent les activités d'enseignement. La quasi totalité des fonds attribués aux universités du Sri Lanka est votée par le Parlement dans le cadre du budget national. Le système universitaire comprend neuf universités dont l'Université ouverte, et neuf instituts (quatre dispensant des enseignements de prégraduation et cinq des enseignements post-gradués).

La Loi sur les Universités prévoit aussi un Comité des Vice-Chanceliers et des Directeurs (CVCD) des universités et des collèges universitaires dont la fonction principale est d'examiner toutes les questions d'intérêt commun, ainsi que de conseiller la Commission à ce propos. Le Président de la Commission des crédits universitaires se réunit tous les mois avec le Comité des Vice-Chanceliers et des Directeurs.

Chairman: Prof. A.P.R. Aluwihare, Vice-Chancellor, University of Peradeniya.
20, Ward Place, Colombo 7.
Tel: 595301

Sri Lanka Federation of University of Women (IFUW)
120/10 Wijerama Mawatha, Colombo 7.
World University Service (WUS)
General Secretary: Dr. Hema Goonetileke.
c/o Research Assistant, Institute of Workers', University of Colombo, P.O. Box 557, Colombo 3.
University of Sri Lanka Students' Federation
36/53 Edmonton Road, Colombo 6.
Sri Lanka National Union of Students— SLNUS (IUS)
91 Cotta Road, Borella, Colombo 8.

The Xaverians (Pax Romana)
35/9 Gregory's Road, Colombo 7.
Student Christian Movement of Sri Lanka (WSCF)
P.O. Box 381, Colombo 1.

*

Ministry of Higher Education, Science and Technology
Colombo.
Tel: 545777
Sri Lanka National Commission for Unesco
Ministry of Justice, Transworks House, Lower Chatham Street, Colombo 01.
Tel: 33301. Cables: unesco natcom ministry of justice colombo

SUDAN
SOUDAN

UNIVERSITIES — UNIVERSITES

University of Khartoum, P.O. Box 321, Khartoum. (The Vice-Chancellor).
                              1902, 1951, 1956, 1975
Tel: 75100. Telex: 22113 gama sd
F : *agr, arts, eco-soc, eng-arc, law, med-dent, sc, vet, phar, ed.*
I : *extramural st, Africa-Asian st, bui-road res.*
C : *grad st.*
S : *math sc.*
Ce : *res-dev st.*
Cairo University, Khartoum Branch, P.O. Box 1055, Khartoum.   *1955*
Telex: 22811 cakhr sd
F : *arts, law, com, sc.*

Gezira University, P.O. Box 20, Wad Medani, 2667 Khartoum.   *1970, 1975*
Telex: 22115
F : *med, agr, sc-techn, eco-rur, dev.*
Juba University, P.O. Box 8, Juba.   *1975*
Tel: 2113
F : *nat resources, soc-env st, ed, med.*
Omdurman Islamic University, P.O. Box 382, Omdurman.   *1912, 1965, 1973, 1975*
Tel: 54220
F : *Isl st, arts, soc, wom.*
Ahfad University of Women, P.O. Box 167, Omdurman.   *1966, 1985*
Tel: 53363

OTHER INSTITUTIONS — AUTRES INSTITUTIONS

Technical Education — Enseignement technique

Khartoum Polytechnic, P.O. Box 407, Khartoum.   *1950, 1971, 1975*
Tel: 80459
C : *eng, bus, agr, fa-appl art, further ed.*
ABU HARAZ COLLEGE OF AGRICULTURE AND NATURAL RESOURCES, ABU HARAZ. *1976*

ABU NAAMA COLLEGE OF AGRICULTURE AND NATURAL RESOURCES, ABU NAMA. *1976*
COLLEGE OF MECHANICAL ENGINEERING, ATBARA.   *1971, 1976*
Institute of Optometry and Visual Science, P.O. Box 9007, Khartoum.   *1954*

Tel: 73055
Telecommunication Training Centre, Khartoum South.   *1903, 1969*
Tel: 44848

Wad El Magboul Higher Institute, Rural Water Corporation, P.O. Box 381, Khartoum.   *1962*
Tel: 893561
D : *drilling, surv.*

Professional Education—Enseignement professionnel

College for Police Officers, P.O. Box 1416, Khartoum.   *1950*
Tel: 80109
College for Prison Officers, P.O. Box 1703, Khartoum.   *1950*
Tel: 71013
Forest Rangers' College, P.O. Box 12, Khartoum.   *1946, 1976*
Higher Institute of Radiography and Radiotherapy, P.O. Box 1908, Khartoum.

1933, 1970, 1978
Tel: 71818. Telex: 22115 sd
Institute of Music and Drama, P.O. Box 291, Khartoum.   *1967, 1977*
Khartoum Nursing College, P.O. Box 1063, Khartoum.   *1956, 1976*
Tel: 72865
School of Hygiene, P.O. Box 205, Khartoum.
1967, 1977
Tel: 72690

Teacher Training—Formation pédagogique

Higher Physical Education Institute, P.O. Box 12, Khartoum Dume.   *1969, 1978*
Tel: 42331

National Council for Higher Education

The Council was first founded in 1972 and was re-established in 1975 by Presidential Decree in accordance with the High Education Systemization Act 1975. It is responsible for the planning and co-ordination of higher education in the light of national needs and high level manpower requirements. It draws up admissions policy and is responsible for the planning of new institutions. Its membership includes: the Minister of Education and Guidance (Chairman), the Ministers of Finance and National Planning, the Chairmen of the Universities Councils and their Vice-Chancellors, five members well acquainted with higher education, the Chairman of the Higher Education Grants Committee, and Chairman of the National Council for Research. The General Secretariat of the National Council for Higher Education, the Higher Education Grants Committee, and the Higher Education Admissions Committee form the executive arm of the Council. The Higher Education Grants Committee is responsible for the allocation of grants to universities and other institutions in accordance with the general policy laid down by the Council. It negotiates the total grant offered by the State with the Minister of Finance on behalf of the Council. The major part of the Higher Education Grants Committee's finance comes from the State.

The Council has also established five specialized academic councils to help achieve its main functions. They are councils for: the Humanities; Health and Medical Studies; Economics and Social Studies; Science and National Resources; and Engineering and Technological Studies.

Le Conseil national de l'enseignement supérieur a d'abord été créé en 1972, puis a, après une période d'interruption, été rétabli en 1975 par décret présidentiel, conformément à la Loi de 1975 sur la systématisation de l'enseignement supérieur. Il est chargé de planifier et de coordonner l'enseignement supérieur en fonction des impératifs nationaux et des besoins en main-d'œuvre hautement qualifiée. Il élabore la politique à suivre en matière d'accès à l'enseignement supérieur et s'occupe de la planification des institutions nouvelles. Il est présidé par le Ministre de l'éducation et de l'orientation, ses autres membres étant le Ministre des finances et de la planification nationale, les présidents des conseils universitaires et leurs vice-chanceliers, cinq membres connaissant bien le domaine de l'enseignement supérieur, le Président du Comité des crédits pour l'enseignement supérieur, et le Président du Conseil National de la Recherche. Le Secrétariat général du Conseil national de l'enseignement supérieur, le Comité des crédits pour l'enseignement supérieur, et le Comité des admissions à l'enseignement supérieur constituent

le dispositif exécutif du Conseil. Le Comité des crédits pour l'enseignement supérieur est chargé d'octroyer les crédits aux universitiés et aux autres institutions conformément à la politique générale définie par le Conseil. Il négocie avec le Ministre des Finances, au nom du Conseil, le montant global des crédits affectés par l'Etat à l'enseignement supérieur. La majeure partie des ressources du Comité des crédits pour l'enseignement supérieur provient de l'Etat.

Le Conseil a créé également, pour l'aider à remplir ses fonctions principales, cinq conseils académiques spécialisés. Il s'agit respectivement des conseils des lettres et des sciences humaines; de la santé et des études médicales; des sciences économiques et des études sociales; de la science et des ressources nationales; et des sciences de l'ingénieur et des études techniques.

Secretary-General: Prof. Salah Omer El Karib.
Director-General, Grants Committee: Dr. Ibrahim A. Sobahi.
Director-General, Higher Education Admissions Committee: Ibrahim Mohamed Ibrahim.
P.O. Box 2081, Khartoum.
Tel: 79970

Democratic Front of Sudanese Students—DESS (IUS)
P.O. Box 4148, Khartoum.

St. Augustine's Society (Pax Romana)
c/o St. Matthews Cathedral, P.O. Box 49, Khartoum.

Sudan International Student and Youth Movement for the United Nations (ISMUN)
P.O. Box 1850, Khartoum.

Khartoum University Christian Association (WSCF),
P.O. Box 32126, Khartoum.

*

Ministry of Education
P.O. Box 2324, Khartoum East.
Tel: 79888

Sudanese National Commission for Unesco
Ministry of Education, P.O. Box 2324, Khartoum East.
Tel: 79888. Telex: 22051 escom sd. Cables: natcom khartoum

SURINAME
SURINAME

Anton de Kom Universiteit van Suriname,
Leysweg 26, Paramaribo, Suriname.
1882, 1948, 1968
Tel: 65558. Telex: 311 adekus sn
F : *med, soc, techn.*
Also 4 Research Institutes.

Surinaamse Studenten Unie—SSU (IUS)
Swalembergstraat 7, Paramaribo.
Tel: 2364. Telex: 258 sna sn (att. ssu)

*

Ministerie van Onderwijs en Volksontwikkeling (Ministry of Education, Science and Culture)
Paramaribo.
Tel: 61865

Suriname National Commission for Unesco
Ministry of Education, Science and Culture, P.O. Box 3017, Paramaribo.
Tel: 61865. Telex: 376. Cables: nucs paramaribo

SWAZILAND
SWAZILAND

*University of Swaziland, P/Bag Kwaluseni.
                                      1976, 1982
Tel: (194)84011. Telex: 2087 wd. Cables:
university kwaluseni
F : *agr, ed, hum, sc, soc.*
   LUYENGO CAMPUS, P/Bag Luyengo.
   F : *agr.*
   NAZARENE TEACHERS' COLLEGE, P.O. Box
   602, Manzini.   *1933*
   Tel: 52211
   NGWANE TEACHERS' COLLEGE, P.O. Box
   474, Nhlangaro.   *1982*
   WILLIAM PITCHER TEACHERS' COLLEGE,
   P.O. Box 87, Manzini.   *1962*
   Tel: 52081
Mananga Agricultural Management Centre,
P.O. Box 86, Tjaneni.   *1972*
Tel: 31133. Telex: 2320
Institute of Development Management, P.O. Box
1534, Mbabane.   *1979*
Mlalatini Development Centre, P.O. Box 547,
Mbabane.   *1970*
Luthern Farmer Training Centre, P/Bag Piggs
Peak.
Ezulwini Handicraft Training Centre, P.O. Box
974, Ezulwini.   *1975*
Institute of Health Sciences, P.O. Box 396,
Mbabane.   *1980*
Tel: 22171
**Swaziland Institute of Management and Public
Administration**, P.O. Box 495, Mbabane.
Tel: 42981
Nazarene Nursing College, P.O. 14, Manzini.
                                         1968
Tel: (268)52211
Swaziland College of Technology, P.O. Box 69,
Mbabane.   *1974*
Tel: 42681

World University Service (WUS)
University of Swaziland, P.O. Kwaluseni,
Kwaluseni.
Tel: (268)52255 (Manzini). Telex: 2087 wd
             *

Ministry of Education
P.O. Box 39, Mbabane.
Tel: 42491
Swaziland National Committee for Unesco
Ministry of Education, P.O. Box 39, Mbabane.
Tel: 42491. Telex: 2293. Cables: imfundvo (for
unesco natcom) mbabane

SWEDEN
SUEDE

UNIVERSITIES AND UNIVERSITY INSTITUTIONS—
UNIVERSITES ET ETABLISSEMENTS UNIVERSITAIRES

Universitetet i Göteborg [Gothenburg U.], Vasaparken 411 24 Göteborg. *1891, 1954* Tel: (31)631000. Telex: 20897 ubmgbg s F : *med, hum, soc, math-nat, dent.*
CHALMERS TEKNISKA HÖGSKOLA [Chalmers U. of Technology], 412 96 Göteborg. *1829, 1937* Tel: (31)721000. Telex: 2369 chalbib s F : *techn.*
HÖGSKOLAN I BORAS, Box 55067, 501 15 Borås. Tel: (33)164000
HÖGSKOLAN I KARLSTAD, Box 9501, 650 09 Karlstad. Tel: (54)130020
HÖGSKOLAN I SKÖVDE, Box 264, 541 26 Skövde. Tel: (500)86760
Universitetet och tekniska högskolan i Linköping [Linköping U.], 581 83 Linköping. *1970, 1975* Tel: (13)281000. Fax: (13)142231. Telex: 50966 unlin s. Teletex: 8155076-liuida F : *med, techn, arts-sc.*
HÖGSKOLAN I JÖNKÖPING, Box 1026, 551 11 Jönköping. Tel: (36)165160
*Universitetet i Lund [Lund U.], Box 1703, 221 01 Lund. *1668, 1682* Tel: (46)46-107000. Telex: 33533 iuniver s F : *theo, law, med, hum, dent, soc, math-nat, techn.*
HÖGSKOLAN I HALMSTAD, Box 70 14, 300 07 Halmstad. Tel: (35)37800
HÖGSKOLAN I KALMAR, Box 905, 391 29 Kalmar. Tel: (480)97500
HÖGSKOLAN I KRISTIANSTAD, Box 59, 291 21 Kristianstad. Tel: (44)115645
HÖGSKOLAN I VÄXJÖ, Box 5053, 350 05 Växjö. Tel: (470)81000. Telex: 52301 hivsfc s
*Universitetet i Stockholm [Stockholm U.], 106 91 Stockholm. *1870, 1960* Tel: (8)16-20-00. Telex: 8105199. Cables: university stockholm

F : *math-nat, law, hum, soc.*
TEKNISKA HÖGSKOLAN I STOCKHOLM [Royal I. of Technology], 100 44 Stockholm. *1827, 1876* Tel: (8)7906000. Telex: 14637 iukths F : *techn.*
KAROLINSKA INSTITUTET [Karolinska I.], Box 60400, 104 01 Stockholm. *1810* Tel: (8)340560 F : *med, dent.*
HÖGSKOLAN FÖR LÄRARUTBILDNING I STOCKHOLM, Box 34103, 100 26 Stockholm. Tel: (8)221680
HANDELSHÖGSKOLAN [Stockholm S. of Economics], Box 6501, 113 83 Stockholm. *1909* Tel: (8)7360120
DRAMATISKA INSTITUTET, Box 27090, 102 51 Stockholm. Tel: (8)651100
GRAFISKA INSTITUTET OCH INSTITUTET FÖR HÖGRE KOMMUNIKATIONS-OCH REKLAMUTBILDNING, Box 27094, 102 51 Stockholm. Tel: (8)600224
KONSTFACKSKOLAN, Box 27116, 102 52 Stockholm. Tel: (8)679550
KONSTHÖGSKOLAN, Box 16317, 103 26 Stockholm. *1735* Tel: (8)631190
MUSIKHÖGSKOLAN I STOCKHOLM, Valhallavägen 103–109, 115 31 Stockholm. Tel: (8)631190
DANSHÖGSKOLAN, Box 27043, 102 51 Stockholm. Tel: (8)651600
MUSIKDRAMATISKA SKOLAN I STOCKHOLM, Strandvägen 82, 115 27 Stockholm. Tel: (8)626181
TEATERHÖGSKOLAN I STOCKHOLM, Box 20044, 104 60 Stockholm. Tel: (8)412160
*Universitetet i Umeå [Umeå U.], 901 87 Umeå. Tel: (90)16-50-00. Fax: (90)165488. Telex: 54005 univume s F : *hum, med, dent, soc, math-nat.*
HÖGSKOLAN I LULEÅ [Luleå I. of Tech-

nology], 951 87 Luleå.
Tel: (920)91000. Telex: 80207 centek s
F : *techn.*
HÖGSKOLAN I SUNDSVALL HÄRNÖSAND, Box
860, 851 24 Sundsvall.
Tel: (40)60-154260
HÖGSKOLAN I ÖSTERSUND, Box 373, 831 25
Östersund.
Tel: (63)127680
*Universitetet i Uppsala** [Uppsala U.], Box 256,
751 05 Uppsala.   *1477, 1595*
Tel: (18)155400. Telex: 76024 univups s.
Teletex: 8195007-ich. Telex: 1118853
F : *theo, law, med, hum, soc, nat, phar.*
SVERIGES LANTBRUKSUNIVERSITET [Swedish
U. of Agricultural Sciences], 750 07

Uppsala.   *1978*
Tel: (18)171000
F : *vet, agr. for.*
HÖGSKOLAN I ESKILSTUNA/VÄSTERÅS, Box
11, 721 03 Västerås.
Tel: (21)127920
HÖGSKOLAN I FALUN/BORLÄNGE, Box 2004,
791 02 Falun.
Tel: (23)81900
HÖGSKOLAN I GÄVLE/SANDVIKEN, Box 6052,
800 06 Gävle.
Tel: (46)188360
HÖGSKOLAN I ÖREBRO, Box 923, 701 30
Örebro.
Tel: (19)140100

Svenska Akademiska Rektorskonferensen

The Swedish Rectors' Conference is an informal group comprising the Rectors and Heads of Administration of the 12 universities and colleges with both undergraduate and graduate studies. Two Rectors from the Conference of Rectors of Colleges with only under-graduate studies may also participate as observers.

The purpose of the Conference is to promote exchanges of information and co-operation between universities. It discusses questions of policy and other matters of common interest with the National Board of Universities and Colleges and with the Ministry of Education and maintains relations with other international, regional and national university and academic bodies.

An official of the University whose Rector is currently Chairman of the Conference acts as its Secretary.

La Conférence des Recteurs suédois est un organisme informel comprenant les recteurs et les chefs des services administratifs des douze universités et écoles supérieures offrant des enseignements conduisant au premier diplôme et comportant également des sections pour gradués. Deux recteurs de la Conférence des recteurs d'écoles supérieures ne dispensant que des enseignements conduisant au premier diplôme peuvent également y participer en qualité d'observateurs.

La Conférence a pour but de promouvoir les échanges d'informations et la co-opération entre les universités. Elle débat des problèmes de politique à suivre et d'autres questions d'intérêt commun avec le Conseil national des universités et écoles supérieures et avec le Ministère de l'éducation, et entretient des relations avec d'autres organisations universitaires et académiques internationales, régionales et nationales.

Un responsable de l'université dont le recteur assume actuellement les fonctions de Président de la Conférence en est le Secrétaire.
Chairman: Martin H:son Holmdahl, Rector, Uppsala University.
Secretary: Harald Bohlin.
Uppsala universitet, Box 256, 751 05 Uppsala.
Tel: (18)155400. Fax: (18)1118853. Telex: 76024 univups

Universitets-och högskoleämbetet

The National Board of Universities and Colleges is a government agency responsible for planning, development and information concerning the higher education system of Sweden. The Board, which is subordinate to the Ministry of Education and Cultural Affairs, works independently within the framework of current legislation and instructions. It has a permanent staff of about 220 (full-time equivalents). Its total operating budget amounts to approximately 100 million Swedish Crowns for the fiscal year 1988–1989. This includes means for educational research and development, including university staff development.

The main duties of the Board are concerned with: nationwide planning of higher education and research; central admissions; information and service; and research and development of higher education.

The organizational structure of the agency comprises: the Board of Directors whose members are the Chancellor, who is Chairman, the Deputy Chancellor, who is Vice-Chairman, nine additional members, all appointed by the Government, and two staff representatives; the Chancellor is also head of the permanent staff. The Deputy Chancellor deputises for him.

La Direction de l'Enseignement supérieur et de la Recherche est un organisme gouvernemental,

assumant des responsabilités de planification, de développement et d'information dans le domaine de l'enseignement supérieur en Suède. La Direction, qui est du ressort du Ministère de l'éducation et des affaires culturelles, travaille indépen-damment du Ministère dans le cadre de la législation en vigueur et des circulaires d'application. Elle a un personnel permanent de 220 personnes (en équivalence plein-temps). Son budget total de fonctionnement s'élève à un montant voisin de 100 millions de couronnes suédoises pour l'exercice 1988–1989, y compris les moyens destinés à la recherche et au développement, notamment à l'amélioration de la formation des enseignants universitaires.

Les principales tâches de la Direction portent sur: la planification nationale de l'enseignement supérieur et de la recherche; les admissions aux études; l'information et les services; ainsi que la recherche et le développement dans le domaine de l'enseignement supérieur.

La structure de la Direction comprend: le Conseil d'administration dont les membres sont: le Chancelier, qui préside le Conseil, le Vice-Chancelier, qui est Vice-président, neuf autres membres tous nommés par le gouvernement, et deux représentants du personnel; le Chancelier est aussi chef du personnel permanent. Le Vice-Chancelier le remplace.

Chancellor and Head of the National Board of Universities and Colleges: Gunnar Brodin.
P.O. Box 45501, 10430 Stockholm.
Tel: (8)728-3600

Centralorganisationen SACO/SR

The Swedish Confederation of Professional Associations, founded in 1947, is a confederation of 25 associations having between them a membership of about 300,000 members; this corresponds to approximately 80% of the potential membership. The majority of SACO/SR members are employed in the public sector, but the number in private employment is increasing rapidly.

Under the terms of its constitution, SACO/SR is called upon: 1) to promote the most desirable development in all matters relating to the education and occupational situation of professional workers; and 2) to safeguard the economic and social interests of affiliated groups, and to strive to improve generally their conditions of work.

SACO/SR is often authorized to appoint experts for official committees investigating problems in labour market policy, education, taxation, etc., and its representatives also serve on bodies such as the National Labour Market Board and the National Board of Education. To achieve its objectives, SACO/SR works for the appropriate organization of all professional workers, striving to co-ordinate the efforts of member associations and to represent them in matters of common interest.

La Confédération des Associations professionnelles, fondée en 1947, est une confédération de 25 associations réunissant environ 300.000 membres, ce qui correspond à peu près à 80% du potentiel. La majorité des membres de la SACO/SR travaillent dans le secteur public, mais le nombre de ceux qui sont employés dans le secteur privé augmente rapidement.

Conformément à ses statuts, la SACO/SR doit: 1) promouvoir l'évolution la plus souhaitable dans tous les domaines relatifs à l'éducation et à la situation professionnelle des travailleurs intellectuels; et 2) défendre les intérêts économiques et sociaux des groupes affiliés et s'efforcer d'améliorer en général leurs conditions de travail.

La SACO/SR reçoit souvent mandat pour désigner des experts à des comités officiels étudiant les problèmes qui se posent en matière de politique de main-d'œuvre, d'éducation, de fiscalité, etc . . . et ses représentants siègent au sein d'organismes tels que le Ministère de l'éducation. Pour atteindre ses objectifs, la SACO/SR travaille à la réalisation d'une organisation adéquate de tous les travailleurs intellectuels, en s'efforçant de coordonner les efforts des associations membres et de les représenter pour les questions d'intérêt commun.

President: Jörgen Ullenhag.
Lilla Nygatan 14, Box 2206, 103 15 Stockholm.
Tel: (8)22-52-00. Fax: (8)20-40-49. Teletex: (8)10-52-25

Universitetslärarförbundet — ULF
(IAUPL)
Contact: 18, rue Docteur Roux 75015 Paris (France)
Tel: (33-1)47-83-31-65
Kvinnliga Akademikers Förening i Sverige
(IFUW)
c/o Secretary, Föreningsvägen 13, 18274 Stockholm
Sveriges Förenade Studenkårer — SFS
Björngårdegatan 15, 116 26 Stockholm SO.
Sveriges Förenade Studentkårer — Serviceverksambet — SFS — Resor
Studentbacken 27, 115 40 Stockholm.
Student Catholic Movement in Sweden (Pax Romana)
Linnégatan 79, 114 60 Stockholm.
Academicum Catholicum Sueciae (Pax Romana)
Sibyllegatan 21, Stockholm.
KRISS/scmin Sweden (WSCF)
Götgatan 3, 75222 Uppsala
Tel: (18)12-12-15
Utrikespolitiska Förenengarnas FN-Förbund
(ISMUN)
Gudmundragatan 17, 162 29 Vällingby.

Stockholms Judiska Studentklubb (WUJS)
Contact: 89 Chaussee De Vleurgat, 1050 Brussels (Belgium).
Tel: (02)847-7279. Telex: 20625

*

National Equivalence Information Centre National Swedish Board of Universities and Colleges, P.O. Box 45501, 10430 Stockholm.
Tel: (8)728-3600
Svenska Institutet (Swedish Institute)

Kungsgatan 42, Stockholm 3.
Tel: (8)789-2000. Telex: 10025
Kungliga Skolöverstyrelsen (Ministry of Education)
Stockholm 8.
Tel: (8)763-1000. Fax: (8)723-1192. Telex: 13284
Swedish National Commission for Unesco Ministry of Education and Cultural Affairs, Mynttorget 1, 103 33 Stockholm.
Tel: (8)763-1952 (Chairman). Fax: (8)723-1192. Cables: unescosweden stockholm

SWITZERLAND
SUISSE

UNIVERSITIES AND TECHNICAL UNIVERSITIES —
UNIVERSITES ET UNIVERSITES TECHNIQUES

Universität Basel, Petersplatz, 4051 Basel. (Universitäts-Sekretariat). *1460*
Tél: (61)29-31-11. Télex: 964853 ubib ch
F : théo prot, dr, méd, phil-hist, phil-nat.
Universität Bern, Hochschulstrasse 4, 3012 Bern. *1528, 1834*
Tél: (36)65-81-11. Télex: 912406 uni ch
F : théo évan, théo chré-cath, dr-éco, méd, vét, phil-hist, phil-nat.
*Université de Fribourg, Miséricorde, 1700 Fribourg. (Chancellerie de l'Université). *1889*
Tél: (37)21-91-31
F : théo cath, dr-éco-soc, let, sc.
*Université de Genève, Place de l'Université, 1211 Genève 4. (M. le Secrétaire général). *1559, 1873*
Tél: (22)20-93-33. Télex: 429768 bfmg ch
F : théo prot, let, sc, éco-soc, dr, méd, psyc-sc éd.
E : arc, trad-interp, lang & civilisation françaises.
*Université de Lausanne, Dorigny 1015 Lausanne. *1537, 1890*
Tél: (21)46-11-11. Télex: 455110 unil ch
F : théo prot, dr, méd, let, sc.
E : soc-pol, com, phar, français mod.
Université de Neuchâtel, Avenue du 1er mars 26, 2000 Neuchâtel. (M. le Secrétaire général).

Tél: (38)25-38-51
F : let, sc, dr-éco, théo prot.
E : français mod.
*Universität Zürich, Rämistrasse 71, 8006 Zürich. *1833*
Tél: (1)257-11-11
F : théo prot, dr-pol, méd, vét, phil-hist, phil-nat.
*Ecole polytechnique fédérale de Lausanne, Ecublens, 1015 Lausanne. *1853, 1969*
Tél: (21)47-11-11. Fax: 47-43-80. Télex: 454478 epfl ch. Cables: epfl
D : gé civ, méc, élec, phy, ch, arc, gé rur-géom, math matér.
*Eidgenössische Technische Hochschule Zürich [E. polytechnique fédérale], ETH-Zentrum, 8092 Zürich. *1855*
Tél: (1)256-22-11. Fax: (1)252-01-92. Télex: 823153 ehpk ch
D : gé civ, méc, élec, ch, phar, for, agr, gé rur-géom, math-phy, nat, hum, arc, milit.
Hochschule St. Gallen für Wirtschafts-und Sozialwissenschaften [E. des hautes Etudes économiques et sociales], Dufourstrasse, 50, 9000 St. Gallen. *1899*
Tél: (71)23-31-35
D : éco, adm des aff, dr, techn-nat, sc-cult.

Conférence universitaire suisse (CUS)/ Schweizerische Hochschulkonferenz

La Conférence est un organe institué par une loi fédérale en 1968 dont la tâche principale consiste à réaliser la collaboration des universités entre elles et à organiser leur subventionnement par la Confédération. Sont représentées à la CUS les dix hautes écoles du pays, les neuf collectivités ayant la charge d'une haute école (la Confédération et les huit cantons universitaires) ainsi que diverses instances (Conseil de la science, Fonds national, cantons sans université, étudiants). Le coût de la CUS est supporté à moitié par la Confédération et à moitié par les cantons universitaires.

The Swiss University Conference (SUC), whose main duty is to promote collaboration between the Swiss universities and to coordinate support for them from the Confederation, was established by federal law in 1968. It comprises representatives of the ten universities of the country, of the nine collectivities supporting a university (the Confederation and the eight university cantons) as well as of other bodies (Science Council, National Foundation, non-university cantons, students). The Council receives half its financial support from the Confederation and half from the university cantons.

Président: Hans-Rudolph Striebel.
Secrétaire général: Rolf Deppeler.
Wildhainweg 21, 3012 Berne.
Tél: (31)24-55-33

Conférence des Recteurs

Composée des recteurs de toutes les universités et hautes écoles suisses et d'un délégué permanent par école, la Conférence se réunit trois fois par an au moins pour discuter des questions qui concernent l'ensemble des universités.

Membres: Universités de Bâle, Berne, Fribourg, Genève, Lausanne, Neuchâtel, Zurich; Ecole polytechnique fédérale de Lausanne; Ecole polytechnique fédérale de Zurich; Ecole des hautes Etudes économiques et sociales de St. Gall.

The Rectors' Conference meets at least three times a year to discuss matters of common interest to the universities. It is composed of the rectors of all Swiss universities and institutions of higher education and of one permanent representative of each institution.

Members: Universities of Basle, Bern, Fribourg, Geneva, Lausanne, Neuchâtel, Zürich; Swiss Federal Institute of Technology, Lausanne; Swiss Federal Institute of Technology, Zürich; St-

Gall Graduate School of Economics, Business and Public Administration.
Président: Prof. Jean Guinard.
Secrétariat: Office central universitaire suisse, Sophienstrasse 2, 8032 Zürich.
Tél: (1)47-02-32

Office central universitaire suisse

L'Office est le Secrétariat de la Conférence des Recteurs. Fondé en 1920, l'Office fournit aux étudiants suisses et étrangers les renseignements sur les conditions d'études dans les universités et les instituts de recherche suisses ou étrangers, l'échange de professeurs et d'étudiants entre les universités suisses et entre celles-ci et l'étranger, les bourses et dotations, etc.

The Central Office of the Swiss Universities is the Secretariat of the Rectors' Conference. The Office was founded in 1920 and provides information for Swiss and foreign students on admission requirements of Swiss and foreign universities and research institutions, on the exchange of academic staff and students between Swiss and foreign universities, on scholarships and endowments, etc.

Directeur: Dr. R.L. Nägeli.
Seidenweg 68, 3012 Berne.
Tél: (31)24-23-50

Association suisse des Professeurs d'Université
Présidente: Prof. Dr. Mme I. Zschokke-Gränacher.
Sophienstrasse 2, 8032 Zürich.

Association suisse des femmes universitaires/ Schweizerischer Verband der Akademikerinnen (IFUW)
c/o Secrétaire, Säntisstrasse 16, 8200 Schaffhausen.

Union nationale des Etudiants de Suisse—UNES/ Verband der Schweizerischen Studentenschaften—VSS
Erlachstrasses 9, 3012 Bern.

Schweizerischer Studentenreisedienst—SSR
Leonhardstrasse 19, 8001 Zürich.

Jeunesse Etudiante Catholique Universitaire Suisse—JECU (Pax Romana)
43, Quai Charles-Page, 1205 Genève.

Fédération des Anciens Etudiants suisses (Pax Romana)
Rämistrasse 6, 8001 Zürich.

Mouvement des Etudiants chrétiens en Suisse/ Schweizerische Christliche Studentenbewegung (WSCF)
c/o Kurt Straub, Evangelische Hochschulgemeinde, Auf der Mauer 6, 8001 Zürich.
Tél: (1)251-4410

Union des Etudiants juifs de Suisse (WUJS)
Correspondant: 89 Chaussee De Vleurgat, 1050
Bruxelles (Belgique).
Tél: (2)647-7279. Télex: 20625

*

**Eidgenössiches Department des Innern/
Département fédéral de l'Intérieur** Bundeshaus, Inselgasse, 3003 Bern.
Tél: (31)61-91-11. Fax: (31)8032. Télex: 912890
edi ch

Eidgenössisches Politisches Department/Département politique fédéral
Bundeshaus, 3003 Bern.
Tél: (31)61-21-11. Fax: (31)61-32-37. Télex: 911440 eda ch
Commission nationale suisse pour l'Unesco
Département fédéral des Affaires étrangères, Eigerstrasse 71, 3003 Berne.
Tél: (31)61-35-50. Télex: 911440 eda ch.
Cables: affetra berne pour commission unesco

SYRIAN ARAB REPUBLIC
REPUBLIQUE ARABE SYRIENNE

UNIVERSITIES—UNIVERSITES

*Gami't Dimašq [U. of Damascus], Damascus.
(The Secretary-General). *1903*
Tel: 215100. Telex: 411971 hamak sy
F : *arts, law, eco-com, sc, med, dent, phar, ed,
eng, agr, fa, Isl law, mec-elec.*
I : *agr, sec, ind, eng, dent, com, med.*
S : *nurs.*
*University of Aleppo, Aleppo. *1946, 1960*
Tel: 236132. Telex: 331018 aluniv sy
F : *eng, agr, med, sc, eco-com, arts, dent.*
I : *med, eng, agr, com, heal eng.*
S : *nurs.*

*Gami't Alba'ath [U. of Ba'ath], Homs. *1979*
Tel: 31440. Telex: 44133
F : *arts, eng, sc, ch-pet, eng & vet, dent* (Hama).
I : *eng.*
*Gami't Tichreen [U. of October], Lattakia.
1971
Tel: 36311. Telex: 451084 tiuniv sy
F : *arts, sc, agr, med, eng, mec-elec.*
I : *agr, eng, med, com.*
Higher Institute of Political Science, Damascus.
1976

Council of Higher Education

The Council of Higher Education, replacing the Supreme Council of Universities, was founded in 1975. It is responsible for: a) drawing up plans to implement the policy of the State in matters of higher education; relating higher education to the plans for economic, social and scientific development; and ensuring that its various institutions fulfil their mission and contribute to the achievement of the scientific, social, cultural, economic and national objectives set by the State; b) elaborating higher education policies for all disciplines at all levels; c) drawing up the general policy for scientific research in universities and institutes and directing it towards the solution of the social and economic problems of the region; d) defining the general orientation of training for which each institute of higher education is qualified. This involves, amongst other tasks, the raising of the scientific and technical standards of the personnel in these

institutions, and drawing up methods of application and control; e) setting admission requirements for the universities and institutes; f) co-ordinating matters relating to teaching, degrees, fields of specialization, research, training and production between universities, institutes, faculties and departments and evaluating the work carried out in the different sectors; g) drawing up budgets for the universities and other institutes responsible to the Ministry of Higher Education; h) giving advice concerning problems of education at different levels.

The Council has its seat at Damascus and its President is the Minister of Education.

Members: the presidents of the universities; vice-presidents for scientific affairs and one of the vice-presidents for administrative and student affairs, to be appointed by the Minister; the Dean of the Higher Institute of Political Science; two representatives of the academic staff of the Institutes responsible to the Ministry of Higher

Education and appointed by the Minister for a year; a Vice-Minister from the Ministries of Education, Planning, Higher Education; the directors of scientific research and planning; two representatives of the academic staff union, designated for one year by its Executive Board; two representatives of the National Union of Students, designated by its Executive Board for one year; three experts from the industrial, agricultural, and health sectors, appointed with the approval of the competent Minister; the Secretary-General of the Council, member and rapporteur.

The Council sets up permanent or ad hoc technical committees, comprising members of the Council or other representatives of higher education drawn from the staff of university institutions or the membership of scientific unions, to study problems falling within its competence.

Le Conseil, anciennement connu sous le nom de Conseil supérieur des Universités, a été créé en 1975. Ce Conseil a pour attributions: a) d'établir les plans nécessaires à l'application de la politique de l'enseignement supérieur définie par l'Etat, de lier cet enseignement aux plans de développement économique et social, et au plan du développement scientifique, d'assurer le progrès de cet enseignement, et de veiller à ce que ses différentes institutions remplissent la mission dévolue à chacune d'entre elles, et facilitent la réalisation des objectifs scientifiques, sociaux, culturels, économiques et nationaux de l'Etat, et de contrôler leur exécution; b) de proposer la politique de l'enseignement supérieur dans toutes ses disciplines et tous ses niveaux; c) de proposer la politique générale de la recherche scientifique dans les universités et les instituts et de l'orienter vers le traitement des problèmes sociaux et économiques de la région, et de contrôler l'exécution de cette politique après approbation; d) de définir l'orientation générale de l'entraînement pour lequel chaque institution d'études supérieures est qualifiée, cette orientation prévoyant, entre autres, l'élévation du niveau scientifique et technique du personnel scientifique en exercice dans ces institutions, et de définir les méthodes d'application et son contrôle; e) de définir les principes généraux d'admission dans les Universités et les Instituts; f) de coordonner l'enseignement, les grades scientifiques, les spécialisations, la recherche, la formation et la production, entre les universités, les instituts, les facultés et les sections, et juger de la valeur du travail effectué dans ces différents domaines; g) d'établir les projets du budget

général des universités et des instituts dépendant du Ministère; h) de formuler des avis concernant les problèmes de l'enseignement dans ses différents niveaux.

Le Conseil a son siège à Damas et est placé sous la présidence du ministre.

Membres: les présidents des universités, les vice-présidents des universités pour les problèmes scientifiques et l'un des vice-présidents pour les problèmes administratifs et des étudiants, qui sera désigné par le ministre; le doyen de l'Institut supérieur des Sciences politiques; deux représentants du corps professoral des Instituts qui relèvent du Ministère de l'Enseignement supérieur, nommés par le Ministre pour un an; un vice-ministre de chacun des ministères: de l'éducation, de la planification, de l'enseignement supérieur; le directeur de la recherche scientifique et le directeur de la planification au ministère; deux représentants du syndicat des travailleurs de l'enseignement supérieur, nommés pour un an, par le bureau exécutif du syndicat; deux représentants de l'Union Nationale des Etudiants de Syrie nommés pour un an par le bureau exécutif de l'Union; trois experts travaillant dans les secteurs industriel, agricole, et sanitaire, désignés pour un an par le ministre avec l'accord du ministre compétent et choisis en dehors des institutions d'enseignement supérieur; le secrétaire du Conseil, membre et rapporteur.

Le Conseil constitue des comités techniques permanents ou provisoires pour l'étude des sujets entrant dans ses attributions, et comprend des membres du Conseil ou d'autres membres de l'enseignement supérieur dans les universités et les instituts ou des membres des syndicats des activités scientifiques.

Secretary-General: Khaled Fares.
Immeuble de la Faculté de Pédagogie, Damas.

National Union of Syrian Students—NUSS (IUS)
P.O. Box 3028, Damascus.
Telex: 419199 sy (att. NUSS)
Student Christian Movement (WSCF)
The University Parish, Church of Our Lady of Damascus, Kussur, Damascus.

*

Ministry of Higher Education
Damascus.
Tel: 330-700
Syrian National Commission for Unesco
Ministry of Education, Damascus.
Tel: 444-702. Cables: damas ministère education

TAIWAN
TAIWAN

UNIVERSITIES AND COLLEGES — UNIVERSITES ET COLLEGES

National Institutions — Etablissements nationaux

National Central University, Chung Li, Toaoyuan. (The President).   *1915, 1962*
Tel: (34)427151
C : *li arts, sc, eng, mangt.*

National Cheng Kung University, 1 University Road, Tainan.   *1945, 1956*
Tel: (62)2361111
C : *li arts, sc, eng, bus adm, med.*

National Chengchi University, Mu-cha, Taipei.   *1927, 1954*
Tel: (2)939-8335
C : *li arts, law, com.*

National Chiao Tung University, 1001 Ta-Shueh Road, Hsin Chu.   *1896, 1958*
Tel: (35)712121
C : *eng, sc, mangt.*

National Chung Hsing University, 250 Kuo-kuang Road, Taichung 400.   *1961, 1971*
Tel: (42)873181
C: *law-com, sc-eng, agr, li arts.*

National College of Physical Education and Sports, 250 Wen Hua 1st Road, Kweishan 33333, Taoyuan.   *1987*

National Open University, 172 Chung Cheng Road, Lu Chow, Taipei County.   *1986*
Tel: (2)2829355
D: *hum, bus, soc.*

National Taiwan Normal University, 162 Ho Ping East Road, Sec. 1, Taipei 10610.   *1946*
Tel: (2)3415101
C: *ed, arts, sc, fa app arts.*

National Taiwan University, 1 Roosevelt Road, Sec. 4, Taipei.   *1928, 1945*
Tel: (2)3510231
C : *li arts, sc, law, mangt, med, eng, agr-vet.*

National Tsing Hua University, 101, Sec. 2, Kuangfu Road, Hsinchu City.   *1911, 1955*
tel: (35)714155. Fax: (35)710776
C : *sc, eng, nucl sc, hum-soc.*

National Institute of the Arts, 172 Chung Cheng Road, Lou Chou, Taipei County 247202.   *1982*
Tel: (2)2821331
D: *mus, fa, theat, dance.*

National Taiwan Institute of Technology, 43 Chi-Lung Road, Sec. 4, Taipei.   *1974*
Tel: (2)3413141
ind techn.

National Taiwan College of Marine Science and Technology, 2 Pei-Ning Road, Keelung.   *1953, 1964, 1979*
Tel: (32)622192

National Yang-Ming Medical College, 155 Li-Nung Street, Sec. 2, Shih-Pai, Taipei.   *1975*
Tel: (2)8312300
D : *med, dent, nurs.*

National Kaohsiung Teachers College, 116 Ho-Ping 1st Road, Kaohsiung 8 00.   *1967, 1980*
Tel: (7)7517161
D : *Chinese, math, ed, ch, English, phy, ind ed.*

National Sun Yat-sen University, Hsi-tzu Beach, Kaohsiung, Taipei.   *1924, 1980*
C: *li arts, sc, eng, mangt, mar sc.*

National Taiwan College of Education, Changhua, Taipei.   *1971, 1980*
Tel: (47)232105

Taiwan Provincial Chiayi Teachers College, 151 Lin-sen East Road, Chiayi.   *1957,1966,1987*
D: *ed.*

Taiwan Provincial Hsin-Chu Teachers College, 521 Nan Dah Road, Hsin-chu.   *1940,1965,1987*
D: *ed.*

Taiwan Provincial Hualien Normal College, 123 Hua-Hsi, Hualien.   *1947,1964,1987*
D: *ed.*

Taiwan Provincial Pingtung Normal College, 1 Lin Sen Road, Pingtung.   *1940,1965,1987*
D: *ed.*

Taiwan Provincial Taichung Teachers College, 140 Min-sheng Road, West District Taichung City.   *1923, 1960, 1987*
D: *ed.*

Taiwan Provincial Tainan Teachers College, 17 Su Lin Street, Tainan.   *1898,1962,1987*
D: *ed.*

Taiwan Provincial Taipei Teachers College, 134, Sec. 2, Ho Ping East Road, Taipei.   *1896,1961,1987*

D: *ed.*

Taiwan Provincial Taitung Teachers College, 684, Section 1, Chunghua Road, Taitung.
1948,1967,1987

D: *ed.*

Taipei Municipal Teachers College, 1 Ai Kuo West Road, Taipei.   *1945,1979,1987*

D: *ed.*

Private Institutions — Etablissements privés

Chang Gung Medical College, 5 Fu-shing Street, Kon-Si, Kweishin, Taoyuan.   *1987*
med.

China Medical College, 91 Hsueh Shih Road, Taichung.   *1958*
Tel: (4)2317153
D: *med, phar, nurs.*

Chung Shan Medical and Dental College, No. 113, 2 sec. Tachin Street, Taichung.
1962,1977
Tel: (4)2526190
D : *med, dent, nurs.*

Chung Yuan Christian University, Chung Li, Tao Yuan Hsien.   *1955,1981*
Tel: (34)563171
C : *eng, sc, bus.*

University of Chinese Culture, Yangmingshan, Taipei.   *1962,1980*
Tel: 8610511
C: *li arts, for lang, law, soc, arts, sc, eng, agr, bus.*

Feng Chia University, 100 Wenhua Road, Sit'un, Taichung 400.   *1961,1980*
Tel: (4)2522250
C : *eng, com, sc, mangt.*

Fu Jen Catholic University, 510 Chung Tseng Road, Hsingchuang, Taipei.   *1963*
Tel: (2)9031111
C : *li arts, law, art, for lang, sc-eng, mangt.*
F : *theo.*

Kaohsiung Medical College, 100 Shih-chuan 1st Road, Kaohsiung.   *1954*
Tel: (7)3117820
D : *med, dent, phar, nurs.*

Providence College of Arts and Sciences, 200 Chung Chi Road, Sa Lu, Taichung Hsien.
1954,1963
Tel: 245108

Soochow University, 70 Lin-Hsi Road, Wai-Shuang-Hsi, Shih-lin 11102, Taipei. *1900, 1954*
Tel: (2)8819471
C : *law, arts, sc, for lang-lit, bus.*

Taipei Medical College, 250 Wuhsing Street, Taipei.   *1960*
Tel: (2)7073102
D : *med, dent, phar.*

Tamkang University, 151 Ying-chuan Road, Tamsui, Taipei.   *1950,1980*
Tel: 6212106
S : *li arts, sc, bus, mangt, eng.*

Tatung Institute of Technology, 40 Chungshan N. Road, Sec. 3, Taipei.   *1956, 1963*
Tel: (2)5925252
D : *mec, elec, bus adm, ch, ind des.*

Tunghai University, Taichung.   *1955*
Tel: (42)521121
C : *li arts, sc, eng, mangt, law, agr.*

Also 68 Junior Colleges.

Catholic Students' Association (Pax Romana) 23 Lane 18, Ta-Hsue Road, Tainan City.

Committee for Ministries in Higher Education (WSCF)
Taiwan Presbyterian Church, 89–5 Chang Chun Road, Taipei 104.

*

Ministry of Education
Taipei.
Telex: 10894 chiapu

TANZANIA
TANZANIE

UNIVERSITIES—UNIVERSITES

*University of Dar es Salaam, P.O. Box 35091, Dar es Salaam. (Chief Academic Officer). *1970*
Tel: 49192. Cables: university dar es salaam
F : *arts-soc, law, sc, med, eng, com-mangt.*
I : *Kiswahili res, dev st, res assessment, prod, mar sc.*

Sokoine University of Agriculture, P.O. Box 3000, Morogoro. *1984*
Tel: 3511. Telex: 55308 univmotz. Cables: uniagric, morogoro
F : *agr, for, vet.*
Ce : *continuing ed.*

OTHER INSTITUTIONS—AUTRES INSTITUTIONS
Technical Education—Enseignement technique

Dar es Salaam Technical College, P.O. Box 2958, Dar es Salaam. *1957*
Tel: 28331. Cables: technical
D : *civ eng, elec, mec, electro-telec.*

National Institute of Transport, P.O. Box 705, Dar es Salaam.
Tel: 48328
D : *trans mangt, trans operations, trans eng.*

Professional Education—Enseignement professionnel

Ardhi Institute, P.O. Box 35176, Dar es Salaam. *1974*
Tel: 49112. Cables: ardhichuo
urb & rur plan, surv, estate mangt-valuation, bui eco, arc, publ heal eng.
College of Business Education, P.O. Box 1968, Dar es Salaam. *1965*
Tel: 31056
D : *bus, metrology.*
Co-operative College, P.O. Box 474, Moshi. *1963*
Tel: 2228
D : *acc, mangt-law, pol ed-rur socio, eco-stat, extension ed.*
Institute of Development Management, P.O. Box

1, Morogoro. *1970*
Tel: 2401
publ adm, acc, bus st, comty dev, eco plan.
Institute of Finance Management, P.O. Box 3918, Dar es Salaam. *1972*
Tel: 27171. Cables: insfinance
bank, ins, acc, fin mangt, tax adm.
National Social Welfare Training Institute, P.O. Box 3375, Dar es Salaam.
Tel: 44019
Nyegezi Social Training Institute, P.O. Box 307, Mwanza. *1960*
Tel: 2645. Telex: 46372
D : *acc, mater mangt, jour.*

World University Service (WUS)
c/o Dr. E. Maganya, Inst. of Development Studies, University of Dar es Salaam, P.O. Box 35169, Dar es Salaam.
MUWATA—National Union of Tanzanian Students (IUS)
P.O. Box 19989, Dar es Salaam.
Dar es Salaam University Students' Organization

—DUSO
P.O. Box 35080, Dar es Salaam.
Afro–Shirazi Youth League—ASYL, Student Section
ASYL Headquarters, Zanzibar.
University Catholic Community Council (Pax Romana)
University of Dar es Salaam, P.O. Box 35027,

Dar es Salaam.
Tanzania Student Christian Fellowship (WSCF)
S.L.P. 1454, Dodoma.
Tel: 20445
DUSAUN (ISMUN)
P.O. Box 35037, Dar es Salaam.

*

Ministry of Education
P.O. Box 9121, Dar es Salaam.
Tel: 27903
Unesco National Commission of the United Republic of Tanzania
Jengo la Umoja wa Vijana, Morogoro Road,
P.O. Box 203 84, Dar es Salaam.
Tel: 27211. Cables: tumeunesco dar es salaam

THAILAND
THAILANDE

UNIVERSITIES AND UNIVERSITY INSTITUTIONS— UNIVERSITES ET ETABLISSEMENTS UNIVERSITAIRES

State Institutions—Etablissements d'Etat

Chiang Mai University, Huay Kaew Road, Muang District, Chiang Mai 50002. (The Registrar). *1964*
Tel: 221699. Telex: 43553 unichim th
F : *agr, associated med sc, dent, ed, eng, fa, hum, med, nurs, phar, sc, soc, grad st.*
I : *soc res, heal sc res.*
Ce : *comp serv.*

*Chulalongkorn University, Phyathai Road, Bangkok 10500. *1916*
Tel: 2150876. Telex: 2021f
F : *arc, arts, com-acc, fa-app arts, commun arts, dent, eco, ed, eng, law, med, phar, pol, sc, vet, grad st.*
I : *env res, population st, soc res, heal res, lang, comp serv.*
    INSTITUTE OF ANALYTICAL CHEMISTRY TRAINING, Bangkok 10400.
    THE THAI RED CROSS COLLEGE OF NURSING, Bangkok 10500.

*Kasetsart University, 50 Phaholyothin Road, Bangkok 10900. *1943*
Tel: 5790113. Cables: unikase 10900
F : *agr, eco-bus adm, ed, eng, fish, for, hum, sc, soc, vet, agro-ind, grad st.*
I : *food res-product dev, Kasetsart U. res-dev, comp serv.*
Office : *ext & training.*

Khon Kaen University, Tambon Srithan, Khon Kaen 40000. *1964*
Tel: (043)238755. Telex: 55303 unikhon th
F : *agr, ed, eng, med, nurs, sc, publ heal, hum-*

soc, dent, associated med sc, phar, techn, grad st.
I : *res-dev.*
Ce : *comp serv, instructional res, Esearn cult.*

*King Mongkut's Institute of Technology Chaokuntaharn-Ladkrabang, Chalongkrung Road, Ladkrabang District, Bangkok 10520. *1971*
Tel: 3269157. Telex: 84967 entlakb th
F: *arc, eng, ind ed-sc, agr techn.*
Ce: *comp res & serv.*

*King Mongkut's Institute of Technology North Bangkok, 1518 Pibulsongkram Road, Bang Sue, Bangkok 10800. *1971*
Tel: 281-4204
F: *eng, ind techn, ed-sc.*
I: *techn ed dev.*

*King Mongkut's Institute of Technology Thonburi, Tambon Bangmod, Ratburana, Bangkok 10140. *1971*
F: *eng; ind ed-sc, energ-mater.*
Ce: *sc instruments for standard-ind, res-dev, ASEAN energy, sec.*

Maejo Institute of Agricultural Technology, Sansai-Prao Road, Sansai District, Chiang Mai 50290. *1975*
Tel: (053)244858. Cables: insmajo
F : *agr bus, agr prod.*
Office: *agr res-extension.*

Mahidol University, c/o Siriraj Hospital, Pran Nok Road, Bangkok 10700. *1942*
Tel: 411-5038. Telex: 84770 unidol th. Cables:

umahidol

F : *med (2), phar, dent, trop med, publ heal, med techn, sc, nurs, soc-hum, env-resource st, grad st.*

I : *population soc res, nutr res, lang-cult, res & dev in sc & techn.*

Ce : *comp, anim, primary heal care dev.*

PHRA MONGKUTKLAO COLLEGE OF MEDICINE.

National Institute of Development Administration, Pattana-Samakee Road, Bangkok 10240.   *1966*
Tel: 377-7400. Cables: nida bangkok
Ce : *dev document res, training, inft systems ed, audio vis-publ rel, comp.*
S : *appl stat, bus adm, dev eco, publ adm.*

Prince of Songkhla University, P.O. Box 1, Kohong, Hat Yai 90112, Songkhla.   *1968*
Tel: (074)285800. Telex: 62168 unisong th
   HAT YAI CAMPUS, Tambon Khorhong, Hat Yai, Songkhla 90110.
   F : *dent, eng, med, sc, mangt sc, sc nat resources, phar, nurs, grad st.*
   Ce : *comp.*
   PATTANI CAMPUS, Tambon Roosameelae, Pattani Province 94000.
   F : *ed, hum-soc, sc-techn.*

*Ramkhamhaeng University [Open U.], Ramkhamhaeng Road, Hua Mark, Bangkok 10240.   *1971*
Tel: 3180917
F : *bus adm, eco, ed, hum, law, pol, sc.*

Silpakorn University.   *1943*
   THA PHRA PALACE CAMPUS, Na Phralan Road, Bangkok 10200.
   Tel: 2217760. Cables: unisilp
   F : *archae, arc, decor arts, pnt, graph arts, grad st.*
   Ce: *art, res co-ordinating.*
   SANAMCHANDRA PALACE CAMPUS, Nakhon Pathom Province 73120.
   F : *arts, ed, sc, phar.*

Sri Nakharinwirot University, Soi 23, Sukhumvit Road, Bangkok 10110.   *1974*

Tel: 2580310
   BANGKHEN CAMPUS, Changwattana Road, Bangkhen, Bangkok 10900.
   F : *ed, hum, sc, soc.*
   BANGSAEN CAMPUS, Muang District, Chon Buri Province 20000.
   F : *ed, hum, nurs, phys, sc, soc, grad st.*
   I : *mar sc.*
   MAHA SARAKHAM CAMPUS, Muang District, Maha Sarakham 44000.
   F : *ed, hum, soc, grad st.*
   I : *Northeastern art-cult res, food techn-nutr.*
   PALASUKSA CAMPUS, Rama I Road, Bangkok 10500.
   F : *ed, hum, phys, sc, soc.*
   PATHUMWAN CAMPUS, Henri Dunant Road, Pathumwan District, Bangkok 10500.
   F : *ed, hum, sc, soc.*
   PHITSANULOK CAMPUS, Muang District, Phitsanulok 65000.
   F : *ed, hum, sc, soc, grad st.*
   PRASARNMIT CAMPUS, Soi 23, Sukhumvit Road, Bangkok 10110.
   F : *ed, hum, med, nurs, phys, sc, soc, grad st.*
   I : *behavioural sc res, Southern st, ed-psyc.*
   BANGKOK COLLEGE OF NURSING.
   SONGKHLA CAMPUS, Muang District, Songkhla 90000.
   F : *ed, hum, sc, soc, grad st.*

*Sukhothai Thammathirat Open University, 9/9 Moo 9 Changwatana Road, Pakkred, Nonthaburi 11120.   *1978*
Tel: 5730030. Telex: 72353 unisuko th
S : *hom eco, law, pol, mangt sc, li arts, ed, st, commun arts, eco, heal st, agr coop dev.*

*Thammasat University, Prachan Road, Bangkok 10200.   *1933*
Tel: 221-6111
F : *com-acc, eco, law, li arts, pol, soc adm, jour-mass commun, soc anth, grad st.*
I : *Thai Khadi st, hum res, East Asian st, inft, for ed dev.*

Private Institutions—Etablissements privés

Bangkok University, 40/4 Rama IV Road, Phra Khanong, Bangkok 10110.   *1970*
Tel: 24901-41
F: *acc, bus adm, commun arts, law, eco, grad st.*
D: *English.*

Dhurakijpundit University, 73 Rama VI Road, Phayathai, Bangkok 10400.   *1970*
F: *acc, bus adm, eco, law, hum, grad st.*
D: *English.*

Payap University, 48/5 Huay Kaew Road, P.O.

Box 161, Chiang Mai 50000.   *1974*
Tel: (053)241-255
F: *bus adm, hum, nurs, sc, soc.*

Siam Technical University, 235 Phetkasem Road, Phasicharoen, Bangkok 10160.   *1973*
F: *bus adm, arts, law, eng, eco, grad st.*

Sripatum University, 61 Moo 4 Phaholyothin Road, Bangkaen, Bangkok 10900.   *1972*
F: *law, bus adm, poly, eng, grat st.*

The University of the Thai Chamber of

Commerce, 126/1 Vipavadee Rangsit Road, Samsen Nai, Phayathai, Bangkok 10400. *1970*
F : *acc, bus adm, eco, hum, sc, grad st.*
Ce: *res, Thai cult promotion.*
*Asian Institute of Technology, P.O. Box 2754, Bangkok. (An independent international institution)   *1967*

Tel: 5290041. Telex: 84276 ait th. Cables: ait bangkok
D : *env eng, geotec eng, structural eng-const, agr-food eng, human settlements dev, water resources eng, ind eng-mangt, comp applications, energy techn.*

OTHER INSTITUTIONS—AUTRES INSTITUTIONS

Technical Education—Enseignement technique

Institute of Technology and Vocational Education, 339 Samsen Road, Thewes, Bangkok 10300. (The Registrar).   *1977*
Bangphra Agricultural Campus, Sriracha Province 20210.
Tel: (038)311808
F : *agr.*
Nakorn-Srithammarat Agricultural Campus, Nakorn-Srithammarat 80110.
Tel: (075)411144
F : *agr.*
Chakrapongphuvanart Campus, Wipavadeerangsit Road, Bangkok 10400.
Tel: 2779124
F : *bus adm, hom eco.*
Bangkok Technical Campus, Linchee Road, Tung-Mahamec, Bangkok 10120.

Tel: 2863843
F : *ed, li arts.*
Thewes Campus, 339 Samsen Road, Bangkok 10310.
Tel: 2828737
F : *eng techn.*
Pohchang Campus, Treepatch Road, Bangkok 10120.
Tel: 2214468
F : *fa.*
Dramatic Arts College, Rashini Road, Bangkok 10120.
Tel: 2241408
F : *mus-dram.*

Also 29 Vocational Campuses.

Teacher Training—Formation pédagogique

Ayutthya Teachers' College, Ayutthya 13000.   *1936*
Bansomdet Chao Pheaya Teachers' College, Thonburi, Bangkok 10600.   *1923*
Buriram Teachers' College, Buriram 31000. *1930*
Chachoengsao Teachers' College, Chachoengsao 24000.   *1940*
Chantharakasem Teachers' College, Bangkhen, Bangkok 10900.   *1941*
Chiangmai Teachers' College, Chiangmai 50000.   *1924*
Chiengrai Teachers' College, Chiengrai 57000.   *1973*
Tel: 311713
Kamphaengpet Teachers' College, Kamphaengpet 62000.   *1973*
Kanchanaburi Teachers' College, Kanchanaburi 71000.   *1973*
Lampang Teachers' College, Lampang 52000.   *1972*
Loei Teachers' College, Loei 42000.   *1973*
Mahasarakham Teachers' College, Mahasarakham 44000.   *1930*

Tel: (043)711452
Muban Chombung Teachers' College, Ratchaburli 70150.   *1954*
Nakornpathom Teachers' College, Nakornpathom 73000.   *1934*
Tel: 241019
Nakornratchasima Teachers' College, Nakornratchasima 30000.   *1914*
Tel: 24-21-58
Nakhornsawan Teachers' College, Nakhornsawan 60000.   *1922*
Nakorn Si Thammarat Teachers' College, Nakorn Si Thammarat 80000.   *1957*
Tel: 356544
Phetchabun Teachers' College, Phetchabun 67000.   *1973*
Phetchaburi Teachers' College, Phetchaburi 76000.   *1926*
Phetchaburiwithayalongkorn Teachers' College, Klongluang, Pathumthani 13180.   *1932*
Tel: 5168226. Cables: petchburi T.C. thlnd 13180
Phibunsongkram Teachers' College, Pitsanuloke

65000.   *1923*
Phuket Teachers' College, Phuket 83000.   *1972*
Pranakhorn Teachers' College, Bangkhen,
Bangkok 10900.   *1892*
Ramphaiphanni Teachers' College, Chanthaburi
22000.   *1972*
Sakonnakhon Teachers' College, Sakonnakhon
47000.   *1964*
Songkhla Teachers' College, Songkhla 90000.
                                                1919
Suandusit Teachers' College, Dusit 10300.   *1934*
Tel: 241-0769
Suansunantha Teachers' College, Dusit 10300.
                                                1937
Suratthani Teachers' College, Suratthani 84000.

                                                1973
Surin Teachers' College, Surin 32000.   *1973*
Thepsatri Teachers' College, Lopburi 15000.
                                                1920
Tel: 411029
Thonburi Teachers' College, Thonburi, Bangkok
10600.   *1953*
Ubonratchathani Teachers' College, Ubonratch-
athani 34000.   *1942*
Udonthani Teachers' College, Udonthani 41000.
                                                1923
Uttaradit Teachers' College, Uttaradit 53000.
                                                1936
Yala Teachers' College, Yala 95000.   *1927*
Tel: (073)21-2443

Private Institutions—Etablissements privés

Assumption Business Administration College, 682
Moo 11, Soi Mooban Seri, Bangkapi, Bangkok
10240.   *1972*
Tel: 3141446. Telex: 87468 abac th
F : *bus adm, arts, grad st.*
Ce: *comp, English lang, bus res, inst res.*
Bundit Phitsanulok College, 601 Phraongkhaw
Road, Muang District, Phitsanulok 65000.
                                                1986
F: *law, bus adm.*
Bundit Sakonnakhon College, 50/11 Tambon
Thatnaweng, Muang District, Sakonnakhon
47000.   *1987*
F: *agr.*
Christian College, 124 Silom Road, Bangrak,
Bangkok 10500.   *1983*
Tel: 2832506
F : *nurs.*
Hua-Chiew College, Soi Anantanak-Soi
Nakkasem, Pomprab District, Bangkok 10100.
                                                1981
Tel: 2231280
F : *nurs-midwifery.*
Institute of Social Technology, 43/1111
Raminthra Road, Bangkhen, Bangkok 10220.
                                                1970
F: *bus adm, eco, li arts, grad st.*
Office: *res-dev.*
Kasembundit College, 99/101 Soi Akhanay,
Phatanakarn Road, Bangkok 10250.   *1987*
F: *law, bus adm, eng, commun arts.*
Mission College, 430 Phitsanulok Road, Dusit,
Bangkok 10300.   *1986*
F: *nurs.*
Northeast College, 200 Mitraphab Road, Muang
District, Khon Kaen 40000.   *1988*

F: *bus adm.*
Phakklang College, 932/1 Moo 9, Asia Road,
Tambon Nakhonsawantok, Muang District,
Nakhonsawan 60000.   *1986*
F: *bus adm.*
Rangsit College, Tambon Lakhok, Muang
District, Pathumthani 12000.   *1985*
F: *bus adm, nurs, phys ther, med techn, arts,
phar.*
Saengtham College, 1/20 Moo 4 Phetkasem
Road, Sampran, Nakhon Pathom 73110.   *1975*
F : *div, hum.*
Saint Louis Nursing College, 215 South Sathorn
Road, Yannawa, Bangkok 10120.   *1985*
F: *nurs.*
Siam Bundit College, Ronachaicharynyut Road,
Muang District, Roi Et 45000.   *1985*
F: *bus adm.*
South-East Asia College, 19/1 Phetkasem Road,
Nong-Khaem, Bangkok 10160.   *1973*
F : *bus adm, ind techn, eng, grad st.*
Sri-Esarn College, Maha Sarakam-Kosumpisai
Road, Maha Sarakham 44000.   *1979*
F: *arts, bus adm, sc, law, eco, agr.*
Ce: *cult, res.*
Srisophon College, 103 Sithammasoke Road,
Muang District, Nakhon Si Thammarat 80000.
                                                1984
F : *bus adm, eco.*
Vongchavalitkul College, 199 Moo 6, Tambon
Banko, Nakhorn Ratchasima 30000.   *1984*
F : *bus adm, law, eco.*
Yonok College, 12 Prasanmaitri Road, Muang
District, Laupang 52000.   *1988*
F: *bus adm.*

Thai Association of University Women (IFUW)
9/7 Onnuj Mu 8, Suan Luang, Sukhumvit 77,
Bangkok 10110.

World University Service (WUS)
Faculty of Education, Chulalongkorn University, Bangkok 10500.

The Catholic Graduates Association of Thailand-Newman Club (Pax Romana)
Xavier Hall, 70/9 Rajavithi Road, Victory
Monument, Bangkok.

University Student Catholic Centre (Pax Romana)
Xavier Hall, 70/9 Rajavithi Road, Victory
Monument, Bangkok.

Student Christian Movement of Thailand (WSCF)
328 Phayatai Road, Bangkok 10400.

*

Public Relation Department
Bangkok 10200.
Tel: 281-8821. Telex: 72243 deprela th

Office of the National Culture Commission
Bangkok 10500.
Tel: 214-0048

Ministry of Education
External Relations Division, Bangkok.
Tel: 281-76-44. Cables: minoedu bangkok
10300

Ministry of University Affairs
Bangkok 10400.
Telex: 72610. Fax: (662)2458636

Thailand National Commission for Unesco
External Relations Division, Ministry of
Education, Bangkok 3.
Tel: 281-63-70. Cables: thainatcom education
ministry bangkok

TOGO
TOGO

*Université du Bénin, B.P. 1515, Lomé.
                                        1962, 1970
Tél: 21-30-27. Télex: 5258 ub to
E : adm-carrières jur, éco-gestion, méd, sc, agr,
méc ind, assistants méd, let.
I : éd, techn de sa-biol.

Ecole Africaine et Mauricienne d'Architecture et

d'Urbanisme, B.P. 2067, Lomé.
Tél: 21-62-53. Télex: 5322 mineduc to

Ecole normale supérieure, B.P. 7, Atakpame.
                                        1968
français, anglais, hist, géog, phy, ch, math, nat.

Institut national de la Jeunesse et des Sports, B.P.
7176, Lomé.   *1976*

Mouvement National des Etudiants et Stagiaires
du Togo—MONESTO (IUS)
B.P. 4093, Lomé.
Télex: 5258 (att. monesto)

Association chrétienne des Elèves et Etudiants du
Togo (WSCF)
B.P. 02, Eglise Evangélique, 1, rue Maréchal
Foch, Lomé.
Tél: 21-46-69

*

Ministère de l'Education nationale et de la
Recherche scientifique
B.P. 12175, Lomé.
Tél: 21-39-26. Télex: 5322 minedu to

Commission nationale de la République togolaise
pour l'Unesco
Ministère de l'Education nationale et de la
Recherche scientifique, B.P. 3226, Lomé.
Tél: 21-61-54. Télex: 5322 minedu to

TONGA
TONGA

Senitá Universiti 'o e Pasifiki Tonga [U. of the South Pacific Ce.], P.O. Box 278, Nuku'alofa.
1971
Tel: 21-955
(Attached to U. of the South Pacific, see p. 131).
Va'a Fakalakalaka ki 'uta [I. of Rural Development], Private Bag, Nuku'alofa.   *1981*
Tel: 21-955
(Attached to U. of the South Pacific, see p. 131).

'Atenisi Institute, P.O. Box 220 (or 90), Nuku'alofa.   *1966*
D : *lang, lit, math, phil, soc.*
Kolisi Faiako [Teachers' C.], P.O. Box 123, Nuku'alofa.   *1944, 1986*
Fokololo 'o e Hau [Maritime Polytechnical I.], P.O. Box 485, Nuku'alofa.   *1985*
Tel: 22-667

Ministry of Education
P.O. Box 61, Nuku'alofa.
Tel: 21-511

Tonga National Commission for Unesco Ministry of Education, P.O. Box 61, Nuku'alofa.
Tel: 21-511. Cables: mined nuku'alofa (attention natcom)

TRINIDAD AND TOBAGO
TRINITE ET TOBAGO

*University of the West Indies, St. Augustine Campus. (See also Jamaica p. 235 and Barbados p. 23).
Tel: P.B.X. 66-31359. Telex: 24520 uwiwg

F : *agr, arts-gen st, eng, law, med, nat, soc.*
S : *ed.*
I : *int rel.*

Guild of Undergraduates—GU/TT   (IUS)
University of the West Indies, Faculties of Agriculture and Engineering, St. Augustine.
Telex: 24520 uwi (att. gu/tt)
*
Committee on the Recognition of Degrees (CORD)
National Institute of Higher Education, 20 Victoria Avenue, Port-of-Spain, Trinidad.

Ministry of Education
Alexandra Street 18, St. Clair, Port of Spain, Trinidad.
Tel: 62-22-715
Trinidad and Tobago National Commission for Unesco
Ministry of Education, Alexandra Street 18, St. Clair, Port of Spain, Trinidad.
Tel: 62-22-715. Cables: unescom port of spain

TUNISIA
TUNISIE

UNIVERSITY INSTITUTIONS—
ETABLISSEMENTS UNIVERSITAIRES

*Université des Lettres, des Arts et des Sciences humaines (Tunis I), 29, rue Asdrubel, Lafayette, Tunis 1002.
Tél: (1)788-068
F: hum-soc; let (Manouba).
I: mod lang, press-infor, doc, éd.
Ce: rech éco-soc.

Université des Science, des Techniques et de Médecine (Tunis II), 29, rue Asdrubal, 1002 le Belvédère, Tunis.
Tél: (1)264-577
F: math-phy-nat, méd-phar.
I: art-arc-urb, rech scq-tec; ing, tec (Nabeul).
E: inft, ing, tec; éd (Bizerte).
Ce: calcul.

Université de Droit, d'Economie et de Gestion (Tunis III), B.P. 106, Tunis.
Tél: (1)262-663
F: dr-pol, éco-gest, jur-pol-soc.
I: gest, com-hôtel; com (Carthage).
Ce: rech-publ.

Université de Monastir (Centre), Monastir.
Tél: (3)61-766
F: sc-tec, méd, dent, phar; méd, dr (Sousse); let-hum (Kairouan).
I: ind text (Ksar Helal).
E: ing; éd (Sousse).

Université de Sfax (Sud), Sfax.
Tél: (4)43-828
F: éco-gest, méd, let, dr.
I: tec (Gabès); ind-mines (Gafsa).
E: ing.

Université islamique Ez-Zitouna, Rue Asrubal, Tunis.
Tél: (1)240-834
I: sc relig, théo, prédiction.

Ecole de l'Aviation civile et de la Météorologie, Aérodrome Borj El Amri, Rte. de Medjez El Bab.   1968
Tél: 224-574

Ecole de la Marine Marchande, 12 rue Abd. Ibn Zoubeir, Sousse.   1966
Tél: 032236

Ecole nationale d'Administration, 24, avenue du Docteur Calmette, Mutuelleville, Tunis. 1949

Ecole nationale des Cadres de la Jeunesse, Bir El Bey.   1967
Tél: (1)290-080

Ecole nationale de Médecine vétérinaire, Sidi Thabet.
Tél: (552)200-552460

Ecole normale supérieure d'Education Physique et des Sports, Ksar Saïd, Manouba.
Tél: 223-109

Ecole des Postes et Télécommunications, Route de Raouad, Ariana.   1974
Tél: 762-000

Ecole supérieure d'Agriculture, Mograne.

Ecole supérieure d'Agriculture, Kef.

Ecole supérieure d'Agriculture, Matear, Tunis 7049.
Tél: (2)65-290

Ecole supérieure d'Horticulture, Chott Marriem par Sousse.
Tél: 0369059

Ecole supérieure des Industries alimentaires, 30 rue Alain Savary, Tunis.
Tél: (1)288891

Ecole supérieure des Ingénieurs d'Equipement promotion rurale, Medjez El Bab.
Tél: 70

Institut national agronomique de Tunis, 43, avenue Charles Nicolle, El Menzah, Tunis.
                              1898, 1947, 1963, 1971
Tél: (1)280-950

Institut national de Nutrition et de Technologie alimentaire, 11, rue Aristide Briand, Bab Saadoun, Tunis.   1969
Tél: (1)264-600

Institut national du Travail, Tunis.   1980
Tél: (1)268-105

Institut des Régions Arides, Médenine.
Tél: (5)40661

Institut supérieur d'Animation culturelle, Tunis.

Institut supérieur d'Art dramatique, Tunis.
Tél: (1)780-158

Institut supérieur de Musique, Tunis.

Institut Sylvo-Pastoral, Tabarka.
Tél: (8)44-542

Union générale des Etudiants de Tunisie—UGET
(IUS)
B.P. 492, Tunis.
Association tunisienne «Tourisme et Jeunesse»—
ATTJ
1, avenue de Carthage, Tunis.

*

Ministère de l'Enseignement supérieur et de la
Recherche scientifique
Tunis.
Tél: (1)682-754. Télex: 13870 Minsup tn
Commission nationale tunisienne pour l'Unesco
Ministère de l'Education nationale, 22, rue
d'Angleterre, B.P. 1280, 1000 Tunis.
Tél: (1)258-290. Télex: 13004 mednat tn.
Cables: commission nat tunisienne unesco min
ed nat tun

TURKEY
TURQUIE

UNIVERSITIES AND TECHNICAL UNIVERSITIES—
UNIVERSITES ET UNIVERSITES TECHNIQUES

Akdeniz Üniversitesi, Antalya.   *1982*
Tel: (311)21160
F : *agr, arts-sc, med; eng* (Isparta).
I : *med sc, sc, soc.*
S : *tour-hotel mangt; fish* (Egridir).
C : *voc ed; voc ed, ed* (Burdur); *voc ed*
(Isparta).
Anadolu Üniversitesi, Eskisehir.   *1973, 1982*
Tel: (221)50581. Fax: (221)12026. Telex: 35147
anau tr
F : *arc-eng, arts-sc, eco-adm, ed, med, open ed,
phar.*
I : *med sc, met, sc, soc.*
S : *app fa; fin-acc* (Afyon); *mangt* (Kütahya).
C : *voc ed; voc ed* (Afyon, Bilecik, Bolvadin,
Kütahya).
*Ankara Üniversitesi, Besevler, Ankara.
                                        1946, 1982
Tel: (4)23-43-61. Fax: (4)310-6464. Telex:
42045 irb tr
F : *arg, dent, ed, law, let, med, phar, pol, sc,
theo, vet.*
I : *forensic med, hist of Turkish Republic, med
sc, sc, soc.*
S : *hom eco, jour, para-legal ed.*
C : *voc ed* (Cankiri, Kastamonu, Kirikkale).
*Atatürk Üniversitesi, Erzurum.   *1955, 1982*
Tel: (11)11209. Fax: (11)17140. Telex: 17140
F : *agr, arts-sc, dent, eco-adm, ed, eng, med,
theo; vet* (Kars).
I : *med sc, sc, soc, hist of Turkish Republic.*
S : *nurs.*
C : *voc ed, ed* (Agri, Erzincan); *voc ed*
(Erzincan).

Bilkent Üniversitesi, Bilkent, Ankara.   *1985*
Tel: (4)266-40-40. Fax: (4)223-5345. Telex:
42999 tcsm tr
F : *arts-sc, eng, fa-mus.*
S : *tec sc, for lang.*
*Boğaziçi Üniversitesi, Bebek, Istanbul.
                                      1863, 1971, 1982
Tel: (1)163-15-00. Fax: (1)165-63-57. Telex:
26411 boun tr
F : *arts-sc, eco-adm, ed, eng.*
I : *biomed eng, earthquake res, env sc, sc, soc,
hist of Turkish Republic.*
S : *for lang.*
C : *voc ed.*
*Çukurova Üniversitesi, Adana.   *1973 1982*
Tel: (711)33394. Telex: 62347 cutb tr
F : *agr, arc-eng, arts-sc, eco-adm, ed, med.*
I : *med sc, sc, soc.*
S : *fish; tour-hotel mangt* (Mersin).
C : *ed; voc ed* (Antalya, Ceyhan, Iskenderun,
Mersin, Osmaniye).
Cumhuriyet Üniversitesi, Sivas.   *1973, 1982*
Tel: (477)13023. Fax: (477)15176. Telex: 15167
F : *arts-sc, eng med; agr* (Tokat).
I : *med sc, sc, soc.*
S : *nurs.*
C : *voc ed; voc ed* (Tokat).
*Dicle Üniversitesi, Diyarbakir.   *1973, 1982*
Tel: (831)18725. Fax: (831)13830
F : *arc-eng, arts-sc, dent, ed, law, med; agr*
(Urfa).
I : *med sc, sc, soc.*
C : *ed, voc ed; ed* (Siirt); *voc ed* (Batman,
Urfa).

Dokuz Eylül Üniversitesi, Alsancak, Izmir.
1982
Tel: (51)21-40-80. Fax: (51)22-09-78. Telex: 52889 dbte tr
F : *arc-eng, arts-sc, eco-adm, ed, fa, law, med, theo; eng* (Denizli).
I : *mar sc-techn, sc, soc, hist of Turkish Republic.*
S : *nautical st, mus, para-legal ed; tour-hotel mangt* (Aydin); *bus adm* (Mugla).
C : *ed, voc ed; ed* (Demirci, Denizli).

Ege Üniversitesi, Bornova, Izmir.
1955, 1958, 1982
Tel: (51)18-01-10. Fax: (51)18-28-67
F : *agr, dent, eng, let, med, phar, sc.*
I : *med sc, nucl sc, sc, soc, solar energy.*
S : *fish, jour, mus, nurs.*

Erciyes Üniversitesi, Kayseri. *1978, 1982*
F : *arts-sc, eng, med, soc-adm, theo.*
I : *med hist, med sc, sc, soc.*
S : *tour-hotel mangt* (Nevsehir).
C : *voc ed; voc ed* (Yozgat).

Firat Üniversitesi, Elazig. *1975, 1982*
Tel: (811)17930. Fax: (811)25859. Telex: 64538 efur tr
F : *arts-sc, eng, med, tec ed, vet.*
I : *med sc, sc, sco.*

Gazi Üniversitesi, Besevler, Ankara. *1982*
Tel: (4)13-42-44. Fax: (4)2800099. Telex: 44002 guni tr
F : *arc-eng, arts-sc, dent, eco-adm, ed, med, phar, tec ed, voc ed.*
I : *accident res & prevention, med sc, sc, soc.*
S : *fin, jour, surv-catog; mangt* (Bolu).
C : *art ed, art ed* (for women); *ed, voc ed* (Bolu); *ed* (Kastamonu); *voc ed, ed* (Kirsehir).

*Hacettepe Üniversitesi, Hacettepe, Ankara.
1954, 1967, 1982
Tel: 211-94-42. Telex: 42237 htk tr
HACETTEPE CAMPUS.
F : *dent, med, phar.*
I : *child heal, demographic st, med sc, oncological st, psyc-neurological st.*
S : *hospital adm, med techn, nurs, physio-rehabilitation, soc.*
C : *hom eco, voc ed.*
BEYTEPE CAMPUS.
Telex: 44001 hute tr
F : *eco-adm, eng, ed, fa, let, sc.*
I : *hist of Turkish Republic, nucl sc, sc, soc.*
S : *for lang, mus.*
C : *voc techn.*
ZONGULDAK CAMPUS.
F : *eng.*
C : *voc ed; voc ed* (Eregli).

Inönü Üniversitesi, Malatya. *1975, 1982*
Tel: (821)21871. Telex: 6140
F : *arts-sc, ed, eco-adm.*
I : *sc, soc.*

C : *voc ed; voc ed* (Adiyaman).

*Istanbul Üniversitesi, Beyazit, Istanbul.
1863, 1974, 1923
Tel: (1)522-42-00. Fax: (1)520-5473. Telex: 22062 isur tr
F : *bus adm, dent, eco, eng, for, law, let, med, phar, pol, sc, vet; med* (Cerrahpasa).
I : *acc, bus adm-eco st, cardiology, child heal, forensic med, hist of Turkish Republic, mar sc & techn, med sc, sc, oncological st, soc.*
S : *fish, jour, nurs, para-legal ed, tobacco specialist ed.*

*Istanbul Teknik Üniversitesi, Maslak, Istanbul.
1883, 1944, 1982
Tel: (1)176-30-30. Telex: 28186 itu tr
F : *aerospace sc, arc, arts-sc, bus adm, ch & met eng, civ works, elec-electro, mec, mine, nav arc-mar sc.*
I : *nucl energy, sc, soc.*
S : *mus.*
C : *voc ed* (Düzce, Sakarya).

*Karadeniz Üniversitesi, Trabzon. *1955, 1982*
Tel: (31)169-20. Fax: (31)15781. Telex: 83110 ktu tr
F : *arc-eng, arts-sc, eco-adm, ed, for, med.*
I : *med sc, sc.*
S : *mar sc & techn* (Sürmene).
C : *ed; ed* (Giresun); *voc ed* (Giresun, Gümüshane, Ordu, Rize).

Marmara Üniversitesi, Hüsrev Gerede Caddesi 75, Tesvikiye, Istanbul. *1883, 1908, 1959, 1982*
Tel: (1)528-16-64. Fax: (1)528-16-64. Telex: 311430 oofo tr
F : *arts-sc, dent, eco-adm, ed, fa, law, med, phar, tec ed, theo.*
I : *med sc, sc, soc.*
S : *jour.*
C : *ed.*

Mimar Sinan Üniversitesi, Findikli, Istanbul.
1883, 1927, 1969, 1982
Tel: (1)145-00-00. Fax: (1)511-91-29. Telex: 26439 tstu tr
F : *arc, arts-sc, fa.*
I : *sc, soc.*
S : *mus.*

Ondokuz Mayis Üniversitesi, Samsun. *1975, 1982*
Tel: (361)10146. Fax: (361)19766
F : *agr, arts-sc, ed, med, theo.*
I : *med sc, sc, soc.*
S : *fish* (Sinop).
C : *ed; ed* (Amasya); *voc ed* (Amasya, Corum).

*Orta Dogu Teknik Üniversitesi [Middle East Technical U.], Ankara. *1956, 1959, 1982*
Tel: (4)237-100. Telex: 42761 odtk tr
F : *arc, arts-sc, eco-adm, ed, eng; eng* (Gaziantep).
I : *mar sc, sc, soc.*
S : *for lang.*
C : *voc ed* (Gaziantep, Kahramanmaras).

Selcuk Üniversitesi, Konya.   *1975, 1982*
  Tel: (331)12-09-91. Fax: (33)12-09-98
  F : *agr, arc-eng, arts-sc, ed, law, med, theo, vet.*
  I : *med sc, sc, soc.*
  C : *art ed* (for women), *voc ed; ed* (Nigde); *voc ed* (Nigde).
Trakya Üniversitesi, Edirne.   *1982*
  Tel: (181)122-59. Fax: (181)15867
  F : *arc-eng, arts-sc, med; agr* (Tekirdag).
  I : *med sc, sc, soc.*
  C : *ed, voc ed; ed, voc ed* (Canakkale); *voc ed* (Kirklareli); *voc ed* (Tekirdag).
*Uludag Üniversitesi, Bursa.   *1975, 1982*
  Tel: (241)14-75-50. Fax: (241)48050. Telex: 32225 bunr tr
  F : *agr, arts-sc, eco-adm, ed, eng, med, theo,*

vet; ed, eng (Balikesir).
  I : *med sc, sc, soc.*
  S : *tour-hotel mangt* (Balikesir).
  C : *ed; voc ed* (Balikesir).
Yildiz Üniversitesi, Yildiz, Istanbul.
                          1911, 1925, 1937, 1982
  Tel: (1)161-02-20. Fax: (1)161-42-84. Telex: 26837 ryu tr
  F : *arc, arts-sc, eng; Kocaeli eng* (Izmit).
  I : *sc, soc.*
  C : *voc ed* (Izmit).
Yüzüncü Yil Üniversitesi, Van.   *1982*
  Tel: (611)2305
  F : *arts-sc, vet, agr.*
  I : *soc, sc.*
  C : *ed; voc ed* (Hakkari).

Türk Üniversite Rektörleri Konseyi

The Council of Rectors of Turkish Universities is composed of the rectors of all the universities and those former rectors who are currently members of the Interuniversity Board (an assembly composed of the heads of all Turkish universities and two members elected from the Senate of each university). The President of the Council is elected by the entire membership of the Interuniversity Board for a five-year term. The Council elects two Vice Presidents from among its members for a two-year term and appoints a Secretary General. It appoints representatives to national and international organizations and exercises such functions that it deems necessary for the best interests and co-operation between Turkish universities.

There is also a Conference of Rectors of Turkish Universities, composed of the members of the Council and those Vice Rectors of universities who are currently members of the Inter-university Board. The Conference deals with the co-ordination of academic and other activities between related disciplines in the various Turkish universities. The officers of the Council also serve as officers of the Conference.

Le Conseil des Recteurs des Universités turques se compose des recteurs de toutes les universités ainsi que des anciens recteurs qui sont membres en exercice du Conseil interuniversitaire (assemblée formée des chefs de toutes les universités turques et de deux membres élus au sein du Sénat de chaque université). Le Président du Conseil est élu par la totalité des membres du Conseil interuniversitaire pour cinq ans. Le Conseil élit en son sein deux vice-présidents dont le mandat est de deux ans et nomme un Secrétaire général. Il désigne des représentants auprès des organisations nationales

et internationales et exerce les fonctions qu'il juge nécessaires pour défendre au mieux les intérêts des universités turques et promouvoir leur coopération mutuelle.

Il existe également une Conférence des Recteurs des universités turques, qui se compose des membres du Conseil et de ceux des vice-recteurs qui sont membres en exercice du Conseil inter-universitaire. La Conférence est chargée d'assurer la coordination des activités académiques univer-sitaires et autres entre les disciplines connexes enseignées dans les diverses universités turques. Les responsables du Conseil sont également les responsables de la Conférence.

President: Ihsan Doğnamaci.
Secretary-General: Himmet Umunç.
Yüsek Öğretim Kurulu, Bilkent, Ankara.
  Tel: (4)22-53-16. Telex: 42839

Turk Universiteleri Ögretim Uyeleri Dayanisma Dernegi (IAUPL)
  Contact: 18, rue du Docteur Roux, 75015 Paris (France).
  Tel: (33-1)47-83-31-65
Türk Universiteli Kadinlar Dernegi (Turkish Assocation of University Women) (IFUW)
  Inonu Mahallesi, El Madag Caddesi, 12/1, Harbiye, Istanbul 80209.
Türkiye Milli Taleve Federasyon—TMTF Babiali Cadde 40, Cağoloğlu, Istanbul.
Travel Department
  —see address above—

*

Denklik Bürosu Müsaviri
  Talim Terbiye Dairesi, Milli Egitim Bakanligi, Ankara.

Maarif Vekâleti Dis Münasebetler (Ministry of National Education, Department of Foreign Relations)
Ankara.
Disisleri Bakanligi (Ministry of Foreign Affairs)

Ankara.
Commission nationale turque pour l'Unesco
Göreme Sokak 7, Kavaklidere, Ankara.
Tel: (4)126-58-94. Telex: 46585 unes tr. Cables: unesco ankara

UGANDA
OUGANDA

*Makerere University, P.O. Box 7062, Kampala.
1922, 1949, 1970
Tel: 542803. Telex: 61351 mubsop. Cables: makunika
F : *agr-for, arts, ed, med, sc, soc, law, techn, vet.*
I : *stat-app eco, soc res, ed.*
S : *lib, fa.*
Ce : *continuing ed.*

Uganda College of Commerce, P.O. Box 1337, Kampala. *1964*
Tel: 51202
Uganda Technical College, P.O. Box 7181, Kampala. *1954*
Tel: 65211
Institute of Public Administration, P.O. Box 20131, Lugogo, Kampala. *1969*

Makerere University Academic Staff Association (IAUPL)
Contact: 18 rue du Docteur Roux, 75015 Paris (France).
Tel: (33-1)47-83-31-65
World University Service (WUS)
Makerere University, P.O. Box 1622, Wandegaya, Kampala.
Tel: 42471. Telex: 61351 mubsop uga
National Union of Students in Uganda—NUSU
P.O. Box 16154, Wandegaya, Kampala.
Makerere Students' Guild—MSG (IUS)
Makerere University, P.O. Box 7062, Kampala.

St. Augustine's Society (Pax Romana) Makerere University, c/o St. Augustine Chapel, P.O. Box 7062, Kampala.
Provincial Youth Department (WSCF)
Church of Uganda, P.O. Box 14123, Kampala.
Tel: 70218

*

Ministry of Education
Crested Towers, P.O. Box 4962, Kampala.
Tel: 23-44-40
Uganda National Commission for Unesco
Ministry of Education, Crested Towers, P.O. Box 4962, Kampala.
Tel: 25-97-13. Telex: 61298 educae uga

UNION OF SOVIET SOCIALIST REPUBLICS
UNION DES REPUBLIQUES SOCIALISTES
SOVIETIQUES

UNIVERSITIES — UNIVERSITES

Altajskij Gosudarstvennyj Universitet, Ul. Dimitrova 66, 656099 Barnaul 99, Rossiskaja SFSR. *1973*
Tél: 2-53-80
F : hist-phill, éco, dr, phy-math, ch-biol.

*Azerbajdžanskij Ordena Trudovogo Krasnogo Znameni Gosudarstvennyj Universitet im. S.M. Kirova [U. d'Etat d'Azerbaïdjan S. M. Kirov], Ul. P. Lumumby 23, 370073 Baku, Azerbajdžanskaja SSR. *1920*
Tél: 39-01-86
F : méc-math, math app, phy, ch, biol, hist, phill, géol-géog, dr, ét orntl, bibl, jour.

Baškirskij Gosudarstvennyj Universitet im. 40-letija Oktjabrja, Ul. Frunze 32, 450074 Ufa, Baškirskaja ASSR. *1957*
Tél: 22-63-70
F : hist, phill, phy, math, biol, ch, géog, lang, dr, ét, romane et ger.

*Belorusskij Ordena Trudovogo Krasnogo Znameni Gosudarstvennyj Universitet im. V.I. Lenina, Leninskij prosp, 4, 22080 Minsk, Belorusskaja SSR. *1920*
Tél: 20-94-15
F : phy, méc-math, math app, ch, biol, géog, hist, phill, dr, jour, radio-phy et électro.

Cečeno-Ingušskij Gosudarstvennyj Universitet im. L.N. Tolstogo, Ul. Šeripova 32, 364907 Groznyj Cečeno-Ingušskaja ASSR. *1972*
Tél: 3-40-89
F : phill, hist, éco, biol-ch, géog, phy, math, phill romane et ger, phys.

Celjabinskij Gosudarstvennyj Universitet, Ul Molodogvardecev 706, 454136 Celjabinsk, Rossiskaja SFSR.
Tél: 41-77-79
F : hist-phill, phy-math, ch, éco.

Cernovickij Ordena Trudovogo Krasnogo Znameni Gosudarstvennyj Universitet, Ul. Kocjubinskogo 2, 274012 Cernovcy, Ukrainskaja SSR. *1875*
Tél: 2-56-69
F : phy, math, ch, biol, géog, hist, phill, lang.

Cuvašskij Gosudarstvennyj Universitet im. I.N. Ul'janova, Moskovskij prosp. 15, 428015 Ceboksary, Rossiskaja SFSR. *1969*
Tél: 4-11-67

F : élec, hist-phill, méd, éco, ch, élec ind, phy-math const, const méc.

Dagestanskij Ordena Družby Narodov Gosudarstvennyj Universitet im. V.I. Lenina, Sovetskaja ul. 8, 367025 Mahačkala, Dagestanskaja ASSR. *1957*
Tél: 7-29-50
F : hist, phill, math, ch, biol, lang, phy, éco, dr, com.

Dal'nevostočnyj Gosudarstvennyj Universitet, Ul. Suhanova 8, 690600 Vladivostok Primorskogo Kraja, GSP Rossiskaja SFSR. *1923, 1956*
Tél: 5-76-87
F : hist, dr, phill, phy, math, ch, biol-pédo, géophy, ét orntl.

Dnepropetrovskij Ordena Trudovogo Krasnogo Znameni Gosudarstvennyj Universitet im. 300-letija vossoedinenija Ukrainy s Rossiej, Prosp. Gagarina 72, 320625 Dnepropetrovsk 10, GSP-211 Ukrainskaja SSR. *1919*
Tél: 3-16-71
F : hist, phill, méc-math, phy, techn phy, radio-phy, ch, biol, éco, math app, ped.

Doneckij Gosudarstvennyj Universitet, Universitetskaja ul. 24, 340055 Doneck, Ukrainskaja SSR. *1965*
Tél: 93-30-28
F : hist, phill, lang, phy, math, ch, biol, éco, fin et comp, phill romane et ger, dr.

*Erevanskij Ordena Trudovogo Krasnogo Znameni Gosudarstvennyj Universitet, Ul. Mravjana 1, 375049 Erevan, Armjanskaja SSR. *1920*
Tél: 55-46-29
F : méc-math, math app, phy, ch, biol, hist, phill, éco, dr, géog, géol, lang, radio-phy, phil, ét ontl, éco cyb, socio, phill-lang russes.

Gomel'skij Gosudarstvennyj Universitet, Ul. Sovetskaja 104, 246699 Gomel', Belorusskaja SSR. *1970*
Tél: 57-11-15
F : hist-phill, math, phy, biol, géol, éco, phys.

Gor'kovskij Ordena Trudovogo Krasnogo Znameni Gosudarstvennyj Universitet im. N.I. Lobačevskogo, Prosp. Gagarina 23, 603600 Gor'kij, Rossiskaja SFSR. *1920*

Tél: 65-64-71
F : méc-math, phy, radio-phy, ch, biol, hist-phill, éco ind, calcul numéral et cyb.
Grodnenskij Gosudarstvennyj Universitet, Ul. Ožeško 22, 230023 Grodno, Belorusskaja SSR.
Tél: 7-01-73
F : hist, math, phy, dr, phill.
***Har'kovskij Ordena Trudovogo Krasnogo Znameni i Ordena Druzby Narodov Gosudarstvennyj Universitet im. A.M. Gor'kogo**, Pl. Dzeržinskogo 4, 310077 Har'kov, Ukrainskaja SSR. *1805*
Tél: 45-73-75
F : hist, phill, méc-math, phy, radio-phy, ch, biol, géol-géog, lang, éco, phy-tec.
***Irkutskij Gosudarstvennyj Universitet im. A.A. Zdanova**, Ul. K. Marksa 1, 664003 Irkutsk 3, Rossiskaja SFSR. *1918*
Tél: 4-44-30
F : phy, math, ch, biol-pédo, géol, géog, hist, phill, dr.
Ivanovskij Gosudarstvennyj Universitet im. pervogo v Rossii Ivanovo-Voznesensenskogo Obščegorodskogo soveta rabocih deputatov, Ul. Ermaka 39, 153377 Ivanovo, Rossiskaja SFSR. *1974*
Tél: 4-02-16
F : hist, dr, phill, phill rom-ger, math, phy, bio-ch, éco.
Jakutskij Ordena Družby Narodov Gosudarstvennyj Universitet, Ul. Belinskogo 58, 677891 Jakutsk, Rossiskaja SFSR. *1934*
Tél: 4-38-22
F : hist-phill, phy, math, ing-tec, agr, biol-géog, méd, lang, géol, péd.
Jaroslavskij Gosudarstvennyj Universitet, Sovetskaja ul. 14, Centr, 150000 Jaroslavl', Rossiskaja SFSR. *1970*
Tél: 22-82-10
F : éco, hist-dr, psyc-biol, phy, math.
Kabardino-Balkarskij Ordena Družby Narodov Gosudarstvennyj Universitet, Ul. Cernyševskogo 173, 360004 Nal'čik, Kabardino-Balkarskaja ASSR. *1957*
Tél: 2-52-54
F : hist-phill, phy, math, ing-tec, méd, ch-biol, phys, phill rom-ger, éco-inft.
Kaliningradskij Gosudarstvennyj Universitet, A. Nievskogo ul. 14, 23041 Kaliningrad oblastnoj, Rossiskaja SFSR. *1970*
Tél: 3-49-41
F : hist-phill, phy-math, dr-éco, ch-biol, géog, péd.
Kalininskij Gosudarstvennyj Universitet, Ul. Zeljabova 33, 170013 Kalinin, Rossiskaja SFSR. *1971*
Tél: 3-15-50
F : math, phy, ch-biol, phill, phill romane et ger, hist, éco, dr, math appl.

Kalmyckij Gosudarstvennyj Universitet, Ul. Puškina 11, 358000 Elista, Rossiskaja SFSR. *1970*
Tél: 2-50-60
F : phill, phy-mat, biol, arg, irrig.
Karagandinskij Gosudarstvennyj Universitet, Universitetskaja ul. 28, 470074 Karaganda, Kazahskaja SSR. *1972*
Tél: 74-49-50
F : hist, phill, phy, math, biol, ch éco, dr.
***Kazahskij Ordena Trudovogo Krasnogo Znameni Gosudarstvennyj Universitet im. S.M. Kirova**, Ul. Timirjazeva, 46, 480121 Alma-Ata, Kazahskaja SSr. *1934*
Tél: 62-41-42
F : phy, ch, biol, hist, phill, géog, dr, jour, phil-éco, math, méc-math app.
***Kazanskij Ordena Lenina i Ordena Trudovogo Krasnogo Znameni Gosudarstvennyj Universitet im. V.I. Ul'janova Lenina**, Ul. Lenina 18, 320008 Kazan', Rossiskaja SFSR. *1804*
Tél: 32-88-75
F : méc-math-cyb, phy, ch, biol-pédo, géog, géol, hist, phill, dr.
Kemerovskij Gosudarstvennyj Universitet, Krasnaja ul. 6, 650043 Kemerovo, Rossiskaja SFSR. *1974*
Tél: 23-39-12
F : phill, lang et lit romane-ger, hist, math, phy, ch, biol, éco-dr.
***Kievskij Ordena Lenina i Ordena Oktjabr'skoj Revoljucii Gosudarstvennyj Universitet im. T.G. Sevčenko**, Vladimirskaja ul. 64, 252601 Kiev 17, Ukrainskaja SSR. *1834*
Tél: 266-54-77
F : méc-math, phy, ch, radio-phy, biol, géol, géog, phil, hist, phill, dr, éco, jour, cyb, rel int, phill romane et ger, rel et dr int.
***Kirgizskij Ordena Trudovogo Krasnogo Znameni Gosudarstvennyj Universitet im. 50-letija SSSR**, Ul. Frunze 537, 720024 Frunze 24, Kirgizskaja SSR. *1951*
Tél: 26-26-34
F : ch, méc-math, phy, hist, dr, phill, lang, éco, fin, géog, biol, jour, phill lang russe, phill romane et ger.
***Kišinevskij Ordena Trudovogo Krasnogo Znameni Gosudarstvennyj Universitet im. V.I. Lenina**, Sadovaja ul. 60, 277003 Kišinev, Moldavskaja SSR. *1946*
Tél: 24-00-41. Télex: 163645
F : phill, bibl, hist, dr, ch, math-cyb, phy, biol-pédo, lang, éco, com, jour.
Krasnojarskij Gosudarstvennyj Universitet, Prosp. Svobodnyj 79, 660062 Krasnojarsk 62, Rossiskaja SFSR. *1970*
Tél: 25-45-03
F : dr, math, phy, biol-ch, éco.
Kubanskij Gosudarstvennyj Universitet, Ul.

Karla Libknehta 149, 350751 Krasnodar
Kraevoj GSP, Rossiskaja SFSR.   *1970*
Tél: 33-75-37
F : phill, hist, math, phy, biol, ch, géog, phill
romane et ger, éco, dr, arts.
Kujbyševskij Gosudarstvennyj Universitet, Ul.
Akademika Pavlova 1, 443086 Kujbyšev
oblastnoj 86, Rossiskaja SFSR.
                                           1970
Tél: 34-54-02
F : phill, hist, dr, méc-math, phy, ch-biol.
*Latvijskij Ordena Trudovogo Krasnogo
Znameni Gosudarstvennyj Universitet im.
Petra Stučki, Bul. Rajnisa 19, 226098 Riga,
Latvijskaja SSR.   *1919*
Tél: 22-29-76
F : biol, géog, phy-math, dr, phill, ch, lang, éco,
fin et com, hist-phil, péd.
*Leningradskij Ordena Lenina i Ordena
Trudovogo Krasnogo Znameni Gosudarst-
vennyj Universitet im. A.A. Zdanova, Univer-
sitetskaja nab. 7/9, 199164 Leningrad V-164,
Rossiskaja SFSR.   *1819*
Tél: 218-76-31
F : phy, math-méc, math app, biol-pédo, ch,
géog, géol, hist, dr, phill, phil, éco, ét orntl,
psyc, jour.
D : interp.
L'vovskij Ordena Lenina Gosudarstvennyj
Universitet im. Ivana Franko, Universitetskaja
ul. 1, 290602 L'vov, Ukrainskaja SSR.
                                           1661
Tél: 72-20-68
F : math, méc-math app, biol, ch, géog, géol,
dr, hist, phill, phy, lang, jour, éco.
Marijskij Gosudarstvennyj Universitet, pl.
Lenina 1, 424001 Ioškar-Ola, Marijskaja
ASSR.   *1972*
Tél: 6-20-90
F : hist-phill, phy-math, biol-ch, agr, éco.
Mordovskij Ordena Družby Narodov Gosudarst-
vennyj Universitet im. N.P. Ogareva,
Bol'ševistskaja ul. 68, 430000 Saransk,
Mordovskoj ASSR.   *1957*
Tél: 4-45-63
F : hist-géog, phy, math, ch, biol, élec-atm,
photo-tec-élec, const, méc agr, agr, méd, phill,
éco, lang, éco-agr, dr.
*Moskovskij Ordena Lenina, Ordena Oktjabr
'skoi Revoljucii i Ordena Trudovogo Krasnogo
Znameni Gosudarstvennyj Universitet im.
M.V. Lomonosova, Leninskije Gory, 117234
Moskva V-234, Rossiskaja SFSR.   *1755*
Tél: 139-53-40
F : phy, méc-math, math app-cyb, ch, biol,
pédo, géog, géol, hist, dr, éco, phill, phil, jour,
psyc.
I : ét orntl et africaines.
*Novosibirskij Ordena Trudovogo Krasnogo

Znameni Gosudarstvennyj Universitet im.
Leninskogo Komsomola, Ul. Pirogova 2,
630090 Novosibirsk 90, Rossiskaja SFSR. *1959*
Tél: 35-35-60
F : méc-math, phy, nat, hum, géol-géophy, éco.
Nukusskij Gosudarstvennyj Universitet im. T.G.
Sevčenko, Ul. Universitetskaja 1, 742012
Nukus, Uzbekskaja SSR.
Tél: 2-42-58
F : lang et lit russe, phill, hist-dr, math, phy,
nat-géog, phys, éco-agr, phill romane et ger.
Odesskij Ordena Trudovogo Krasnogo Znameni
Gosudarstvennyj Universitet im. I.I.
Mečnikova, Ul. Petra Velikogo 2, 270057
Odessa, Ukrainskaja SSR.
Tél: 23-58-13
F : phill, hist, phy, géol-géog, biol, ch, dr, phill
romane et ger, méc-math.
Omskij Gosudarstvennyj Universitet, Prosp Mira
55a, 644077 Omsk 77, Rossiskaja SFSR.   *1974*
Tél: 64-17-01
F : hist, math, phy, ch, phill, dr, éco.
Permskij Ordena Trudovogo Krasnogo Znameni
Gosudarstvennyj Universitet im. A.M.
Gor'kogo, Ul. Bukireva 15, 614600 Perm', 22
Rossiskaja SFSR.   *1817*
Tél: 33-38-10
F : phy, méc-math, biol, ch, géol, géog, hist,
phill, dr, éco.
Petrozavodskij Gosudarstvennyj Universitet im.
O.V. Kuusinena, Pr. Lenina 33, 185640 Petro-
zavodsk, Rossiskaja SFSR.   *1940*
Tél: 7-17-91
F : hist-phill, phy-math, agr, méd, techn for,
biol, const, éco, polytec.
*Rostovskij Ordena Trudovogo Krasnogo
Znameni Gosudarstvennyj Universitet im M.A.
Suslova, Ul. Fridriha Engel'sa 105, 344711
Rostov-na-Donu GSP-11, Rossiskaja SFSR.
                                           1915
Tél: 66-32-31
F : phy, ch, biol-pédo, géol-géog, hist, phill, dr,
méc-math, phil, éco.
Samarkandskij Ordena Trudovogo Krasnogo
Znameni Gosudarstvennyj Universitet im.
Ališera Navoi, Bul. Gor'kogo 15, 703004
Samarkand, Uzbekskaja SSR.   *1917, 1933*
Tél: 5-26-26
F : hist, géog, phill, phill romane et ger, math,
phy, ch, biol, math app, dr, ét lit & lang russes.
Saratovskij Ordena Trudovogo Krasnogo
Znameni Gosudarstvennyj Universitet im. N.G.
Cernyševskogo, Astrahanskaja Ul. 83, 410600
Saratov, Rossiskaja SFSR.   *1909*
Tél: 2-16-96
F : phy, méc-math, ch, biol, géog, géol, hist,
phill.
Severo-Osetinskij Gosudarstvennyj Universitet
im. K.L. Hetagurova, Ul. Batutina 46, 362000

Ordžonikidze, Rossiskaja SFSR. *1970*
Tél: 3-98-24
F : phy-math, phill, ch-biol, hist, lang, phys, dr, éco.
Simferopol'skij Gosudarstvennyj Universitet im. M.V. Frunze, Ul. Jaltinskaja 4, 333036
Simferopol', Ukrainskaja SSR. *1972*
Tél: 3-22-80
F : hist, phill, phill romane et ger, géog, nat, phy, math, phys.
Suhumskij Gosudarstvennyj Universitet im. A.M. Gor'kogo, Ul. Cereteli 9, 384900 Suhumi, Abhazskaja ASSR.
Tél: 2-25-98
D : com, dr, phill, lang, hist, math, phy, biol, géog, péd, éco.
Syktyvkarskij Gosudarstvennyj Universitet im. 50-letija SSSR, Oktjabr'skij prosp. 55, 167001 Syktyvkar, Komi ASSR.
Tél: 3-68-20
F : hist, phill, phy-math, ch-bioc, éco.
*Tadžikskij Gosudarstvennyj Universitet im. V.I. Lenina, Prosp. Lenina 17, 734016 Dušanbe, Tadžikskaja SSR. *1948*
Tél: 27-35-17
F : hist, phill tadjik, phy, éco-plan, éco-comp, méc-math, biol, fin, géol, dr, ch, lang et lit russes, lang orntl.
*Tartu State University, Ulikooli 18, 202400 Tartu, Estonskaja SSR. *1632, 1802*
Tél: 3-34-01
F : hist, phill, phy-ch, biol-géog, dr, éco, méd, phys, math.
*Taškentskij Ordena Trudovogo Krasnogo Znameni Gosudarstvennyj Universitet im. V.I. Lenina, Universitetskaja ul. 95, Vuzgorodok, 700095 Taškent, Uzbekskaja SSR. *1920*
Tél: 46-02-24
F : hist, phill, ét orntl, dr, math, math app, phy, ch, biol-pédo, géol, géog, phill romane et ger, jour, lang et lit russes, phil-éco.
*Tbilisskij Ordena Trudovogo Krasnogo Znameni Gosudarstvennyj Universitet, Prosp. Cavčavadze 1, 380028 Tbilisi, Gruzinskaja SSR. *1918*
Tél: 31-47-92
F : hist, phill, dr, éco, éco-plan, ing-éco, géol-géog, méc-math, cyb-math app, biol, ch, phy, phil-psyc, lang et lit ouest-eur, ét orntl, cyb, com.
Tjumenskij Gosudarstvennyj Universitet, Ul. Semakova 10, 652610 Tjumen'3, Rossiskaja SFSR. *1973*
Tél: 6-19-30
F : hist-phill, phill romane et ger, phy, math, ch-biol, éco, géog.
Tomskij Ordena Oktjabr'skoj Revoljucii i Ordena Trudovogo Krasnogo Znameni Gosudarstvennyj Universitet im. V.V.

Kujbyševa, Prosp. Lenina 36, 634010 Tomsk 10, Rossiskaja SFSR. *1888*
Tél: 3-30-60
F : méc-math, math app et cyb, phy, radio-phy, phy tec, ch, biol-pédo, géol-géog, hist, phill, dr, éco.
*Turkmenskij Ordena Trudovogo Krasnogo Znameni Gosudarstvennyj Universitet im. A.M. Gor'kogo, Prosp. Lenina 31, 744014 Ašhabad, Turkmenskaja SSR. *1950*
Tél: 5-11-59
F : phill, géog, hist, phy-math, bio-ch, éco-dr, phill romane et ger, lang et lit russes.
Udmurtskij Gosudarstvennyj Universitet im. 50-letija SSSR, Krasnogerojskaja ul. 71, 426037 Ustinov, Udmurskaja ASSR.
Tél: 75-59-33
F : phill, hist, phy-math, bioch, dr, phill romane et ger, ba, phys.
*Universitet Družby Narodov im. Patrisa Lumumby, Ordžonikidze, Dom 3, Moskva V-302, Rossiskaja SFSR. *1960*
Tél: 234-00-11
F : tec, agr, méd, phy-math-nat, hist-phill, dr-éco.
Ural'skij Ordena Trudovogo Krasnogo Znameni Gosudarstvennyj Universitet im. A.M. Gor'kogo, Prosp. Lenina 51, 620083 Sverdlovsk K-83, Rossiskaja SFSR. *1920*
Tél: 55-73-94
F : math-méc, ch, hist, phill, biol, jour, phy, phil.
Užgorodskij Gosudarstvennyj Universitet, Ul. M. Gor'kogo 46, 294000 Užgorod, Ukrainskaja SSR. *1945*
Tél: 3-42-02
F : hist, phill romane et ger, phy, math, ch, biol, méd, phill.
*Vil'njusskij Ordena Trudovogo Krasnogo Znameni i Ordena Družby Narodov Gosudarstvennyj Universitet im. V. Kapsukasa, Ul. Universiteto 3, 232734 Vil'njus, Litovskaja SSR. *1579, 1803*
Tél: 623-779. Télex: 261128 Va'va
F : phy, math, ch, nat, méd, éco ind, dr, éco cyb-fin, hist, phill, fin, com.
Volgogradskij Gosudarstvennyj Universitet, 2ja Prodol'naja ul. 20, 400062 Volgograd 62, Rossiskaja SFSR.
Tél: 43-81-24
D : lang-lit russes, lang-lit romanes et ger, hist, math, phy.
Voronežskij Ordena Lenina Gosudarstvennyj Universitet im. Leninskogo Komsomola, Universitetskaja pl. 1, 294693 Voronež, Rossiskaja SFSR. *1919*
Tél: 5-29-83
F : hist, phill, phill romane et ger, dr, éco, math, math app-méc, phy, ch, biol-pédo, géol,

géog, jour.
Zaporožskij Gosudarstvennyj Universitet, ul. Žukovskogo 66, 220600 Zaporože, Ukrain-

skaja SSR.
Tél: 64-45-46
F : phill, lang, hist, phy-math, phys.

OTHER INSTITUTIONS (1)—AUTRES INSTITUTIONS (1)

Polytechnical, Industrial, and Factory Institutes— Instituts polytechniques, industriels, et d'entreprise

(Polytechnical)—(Polytechniques)

Azerbajdžanskij Politehničeskij Institut im. C. Il'dryma, Pr. Narimanova 25, 370602 Baku 73, Azerbajdžanskaja SSR.
Tél: 39-13-83
Altajskij Politehničeskij Institut im. I.I. Polzunova, Pr. Lenina 46, 656099 Barnaul 99, Rossiskaja SFSR.
Tél: 5-64-40
Belorusskij Ordena Trudovogo Krasnogo Znameni Politehničeskij Institut, Leninskij Prosp. 65, 220027 Minsk, Belorusskaja SSR.
Tél: 32-40-55
Celjabinskij Politehničeskij Institut im. Leninskogo Komosomola, Pr. Lenina 76, 454044 Celjabinsk 44, Rossiskaja SFSR.
Tél: 39-94-52
Citinskij Politehničeskij Institut, Ul. Kalinina 117, 672076 Cita, Rossiskaja SFSR.
Tél: 3-47-10
Dagestanskij Politehničeskij Institut, Prosp. Kalinina 70, 367024 Mahačkala, Dagestanskaja ASSR.
Tél: 2-39-81
Dal'nevostočnyj Ordena Trudovogo Krasnogo Znameni Politehničeskij Institut im. V.V. Kujbyševa, Puškinskaja ul. 10, Centr, GSP, 690600 Vladivostok, Rossiskaja SFSR.
Tél: 5-38-00
Doneckij Ordena Trudovogo Krasnogo Znameni Politehničeskij Institut, Ul. Artema 58, 340000, Doneck, Ukrainskaja SSR.
Tél: 91-08-89
Erevanskij Ordena Trudovogo Krasnogo Znameni Politehničeskij Institut im. Karla Marksa, Ul. Terjana 105, 375009 Erevan, Armjanskaja SSR.
Tél: 59-85-55

Ferganskij Politehničeskij Institut, Ferganskaja Ul. 86, Kirgili 1, 712022 Fergana, Uzbekskaja SSR.
Tél: 2-13-33
Frunzenskij Politehničeskij Institut, Pr. Mira 66, 720057 Frunze, Kirgizskaja SSR.
Tél: 42-14-62
Gomel'skij Politehničeskij Institut, Prosp. Oktjabrja 48, 246746 Gomel, Belorusskaja SSR.
Tél: 7-09-15
Gor'kovskij Ordena Trudovogo Krasnogo Znameni Politehničeskij Institut im. A.A. Zdanova, Ul. K. Minina 24, 603600 Gor'kij, Rossiskaja SFSR.
Tél: 36-73-43
Gruzinskij Ordena Lenina i Ordena Trudovogo Krasnogo Znameni Politehničeskij Institut im. V.I. Lenina, Ul. Lenina 77, 380075 Tbilisi 75, Gruzinskaja SSR.
Tél: 36-65-05
Habarovskij Politehničeskij Institut, Tihookeanskaja Ul. 136, 660035 Habarovsk Kraevoj, 35 Rossiskaja SFSR.
Tél: 35-85-60
Har'kovskij Ordena Lenina i Ordena Oktjabr'skoj Revoljucii Politehničeskij Institut im. V.I. Lenina, Ul. Frunze 21, 310002 Har'kov 2, Ukrainskaja SSR.
Tél: 47-80-68
Irkutskij Ordena Trudovogo Krasnogo Znameni Politehničeskij Institut, Ul. Lermontova 83, 664028 Irkutsk 28, Rossiskaja SFSR.
Tél: 41-06-52
Jaroslavskij Politehničeskij Institut, Moskovskij Pr 88, 150053 Jaroslavl', Rossiskaja SFSR.
Tél: 44-17-39
Kalininskij Ordena Trudovogo Krasnogo Znameni Politehničeskij Institut, Pervomajs-

---

(1) Based on the classification used by the Ministry of Higher and Specialized Secondary Education, USSR.

(1) Présentées selon las classification utilisée par le Ministère de l'Enseignement supérieur et secondaire spécialisé d'URSS.

kaja nab. 22, 170035 Kalinin 35, Rossiskaja SFSR.
Tél: 4-44-03
Kamskij Politehničeskij Institut, Prosp. Mira 68/19, 423810 Naberežnye Čelny, Rossiskaja SFSR.
Tél: 53-74-49
Karagandinskij Ordena Trudovogo Krasnogo Znameni Politehničeskij Institut, Bul'var Mira 56, 470041 Karaganda, Kazahskaja SSR.
Tél: 54-77-87
Kaunasskij Politehničeskij Institut im. Antanasa Snečkusa, Ul. Donelajcio 73, 233006 Kaunas, Litovskaja SSR.
Tél: 20-26-40
Kazahskij Ordena Trudovogo Krasnogo Znameni Politehničeskij Institut im. V.I. Lenina, I Ul. Stapaeva 22, 480013 Alma-Ata, Kazahskaja SSR.
Tél: 67-69-01
Kievskij Ordena Lenina Politehničeskij Institut im. 50-letija Velikoj Oktjabr'skoi Socialističeskoj Revoljucii, prosp. Pobedy 37, 252056 Kiev, Ukrainskaja SSR.
Tél: 441-93-03
Kirovskij Politehničeskij Institut, Ul. Komuny 36, 610023 Kirov 23, Rossiskaja SFSR.
Tél: 2-65-71
Kišinevskij Politehničeskij Institut im. S.G. Lazo, Prosp. Lenina 168, 277612 Kišinev, Moldavskaja SSR.
Tél: 44-13-00
Komsomol'skij-na-Amure Politehničeskij Institut, Prosp. Lenina 27, 681013 Komsomol'sk-na-Amure Habarovskogo kraja, Rossiskaja SFSR.
Tél: 3-22-53
Krasnodarskij Ordena Trudovogo Krasnogo Znameni Politehničeskij Institut, Krasnaja ul. 135, 350006 Krasnodar 6, Rossiskaja SFSR.
Tél: 55-16-24
Krasnojarskij Politehničeskij Institut, Ul. Kirenskogo 26, 660074 Krasnojarsk 74, Rossiskaja SFSR.
Tél: 5-23-94
Kujbyševskij Ordena Trudovogo Krasnogo Znameni Politehničeskij Institut im. V.V. Kujbyševa, Galaktionovskaja ul. 141, 443010 Kujbyšev obl., Rossiskaja SFSR.
Tél: 32-42-38
Kurskij Politehničeskij Institut, Ul. 50-letija Oktjabrja 94, 305039 Kursk, Rossiskaja SFSR.
Tél: 2-57-43
Kutaisskij Politehničeskij Institut im. N.I. Mushelivšili, Pr. Molodeži 62, 384014 Kutaisi, Gruzinskaja SSR.
Tél: 5-48-74
Kuzbasskij Politehničeskij Institut, Vessennjaja ul. 28, 650026 Kemerovo, 26 Rossiskaja SFSR.

Tél: 23-33-23
*Leningradskij Ordena Lenina Politehnič-eskij Institut im. M.I. Kalinina, Politehnič-eskaja ul. 29, 195251 Leningrad K-251, Rossiskaja SFSR.
Tél: 247-21-31. Télex: 121803 odra
Lipeckij Politehničeskij Institut, Ul. Zegelja 1, 398662 Lipeck, Rossiskaja SFSR.
Tél: 24-13-09
L'vovskij Ordena Lenina Politehničeskij Institut im. Leninskogo Komsomola, Ul. Mira 12, 290646 L'vov, Ukrainskaja SSR.
Tél: 72-47-33
Marijskij Ordena Družby Narodov Politehničeskij Institut im. A.M. Gor'kogo, PL. Lenina 3, 424024 Joškar-Ola, Marijskoj ASSR.
Tél: 9-68-89
Novgorodskij Politehničeskij Institut, Leningradskaja ul. 41, 173003 Novgorod, Rossiskaja SFSR.
Tél: 2-72-44
Novočerkasskij Ordena Trudovogo Krasnogo Znameni Politehničeskij Institut im. Sergo Ordžonikidze, Ul. Prosveščenija 132, 346400 Novočerkassk GSP-1, Rossiskaja SFSR.
Tél: 55-7-79
Novopolockij Politehničeskij Institut im. Leninskogo Komsomola Belorussii, Ul. Blohina 29, 211440 Novopolock, Vitebskoj obl., Belorusskaja SSR.
Tél: 5-21-61
Odesskij Ordena Trudovogo Krasnogo Znameni Politehničeskij Institut, Prosp. T.G. Sevčenko 1, 270044 Odessa, Ukrainskaja SSR.
Tél: 22-19-92
Omskij Politehničeskij Institut, Prosp. Mira 11, 644050 Omsk 50, Rossiskaja SFSR.
Tél: 65-35-37
Orenburgskij Politehničeskij Institut, Prosp. Pobedy 13, 460352 Orenburg, Rossiskaja SFSR.
Tél: 7-67-70
Penzenskij Politehničeskij Institut, Krasnaja ul. 40, 440017 Penza, Rossiskaja SFSR.
Tél: 69-84-12
Permskij Politehničeskij Institut, Komsomol'skij Prosp. 29a, 616600 Perm', GSP-45 Rossiskaja SFSR.
Tél: 32-63-60
Rižskij Ordena Trudovogo Krasnogo Znameni Politehničeskij Institut im. A.Ja. Peljše, Ul. Lenina 1, 226355 Riga, Latvijskaja SSR.
Tél: 22-58-85
Saratovskij Ordena Trudovogo Krasnogo Znameni Politehničeskij Institut, Politehničeskaja ul. 77, 410016 Saratov, 16 Rossiskaja SFSR.
Tél: 25-73-11
Severo-Zapadnyj Zaočnyj Politehničeskij Institut, Ul. Halturina 5, 191065 Leningrad D-

41, Rossiskaja SFSR.
Tél: 312-07-92
Stavropol'skij Politehničeskij Institut, Pr. Kulakova, 2, 355038 Stavropol', Rossiskaja SFSR.
Tél: 6-32-86
Tadžikskij Politehničeskij Institut, Pr. Kujbyséva 10a, 734042 Dušánbe, Tadžikskaja SSR.
Tél: 22-35-11
Tallinskij Ordena Trudovogo Krasnogo Znameni Politehničeskij Institut, Ehitajate tee 5, 200108 Tallinn, Estonskaja SSR.
Tél: 53-21-51
Taškentskij Ordena Družby Narodov Politehničeskij Institut im. A.R. Biruni, Ul. Navoi 13, 700011, GSP, Taškent, Uzbekskaja SSR.
Tél: 41-13-12
Tol'jattinskij Politehničeskij Institut, Belorusskaja Ul. 14, 445002 Tol'jatti, Kubyševskoj obl., Rossiskaja SFSR.
Tél: 23-41-25
Tomskij Ordena Oktjabr'skoj Revoljucii i Ordena Trudovogo Krasnogo Znameni Politehničeskij Institut im. S.M. Kirova, Pr. Lenina 30, 634004 Tomsk 4, Rossiskaja SFSR.
Tél: 99-24-17
Tul'skij Ordena Trudovogo Krasnogo Znameni Politehničeskij Institut, Pr. Lenina 92, 300600 Tula, Rossiskaja SFSR.
Tél: 25-83-62
Turkmenskij Politehničeskij Institut, Ul. Kotovskogo 1, 744025 Ašhabad, 8 Turkmenskaja SSR.
Tél: 9-37-10
Ukrainskij Zaočnyj Politehničeskij Institut im. I.Z. Sokolova, Universitetskaja ul. 16, 310003 Har'kov, Ukrainskaja SSR.
Tél: 22-43-03
Ul'janovskij Politehničeskij Institut, Ul. L'va Tostogo 42, 432700 Ul'janovsk, Rossiskaja SFSR.
Tél: 1-24-83
Ural'skij Ordena Trudovogo Krasnogo Znameni Politehničeskij Institut im. S.M. Kirova, Vtuzgorodok, 620002 Sverdlovsk K2, Rossiskaja SFSR.
Tél: 44-84-74
Vinnickij Politehničeskij Institut, Hmel'nickoe šosse 133, 286021 Vinnica, Ukrainskaja SSR.
Tél: 2-57-18
Vladimirskij Politehničeskij Institut, Ul. Gor'kogo 87, 600026 Vladimir, Rossiskaja SFSR.
Tél: 7-99-79
Volgogradskij Ordena Trudovogo Krasnogo Znameni Politehničeskij Institut, Prosp. im. V.I. Lenina 28, 400066 Volgograd 66, Rossiskaja SFSR.
Tél: 34-22-92

Vologodskij Politehničeskij Institut, Ul. Vorošilova, 3, 160600 Vologda, Rossiskaja SFSR.
Tél: 2-46-45
Voronežskij Politehničeskij Institut, Moskovskij prosp. 14, 394026 Voronež, Rossiskaja SFSR.
Tél: 16-40-67
Vsesojuznyj Ordena Trudovogo Krasnogo Znameni Zaočnyj Politehničeskij Institut, Ul. Pavla Korčagina 22, 129805 Moskva, Rossiskaja SFSR.
Tél: 283-77-58

(Industrial)—(Industriel)

Bratskij Industrial'nyj Institut, Ul. Makarenko 40, 665709 Bratsk, 9, Rossiskaja SFSR.
Tél: 7-22-14
Dneprodzeržinskij Ordena Trudovogo Krasnogo Znameni Industrial'nyj Institut im. Arseničeva, Dneprostroevskaja Ul. 2, 322618 Dneprodzeržinsk, Ukrainskaja SSR.
Tél: 3-21-23
Hersonskij Industrial'nyj Institut, Bereslavskoe šosse 24, 325008 Herson, Ukrainskaja SSR.
Tél: 5-47-11
Kramatorskij Industrial'nyj Institut, Ul. Skadinova 76, 343916 Kramatorsk, Ukrainskaja SSR.
Tél: 5-90-97
Pavlodarskij Industrial'nyj Institut, Ul. Sverdlova 63, 637003 Pavlodar, Kazahskaja SSR.
Tél: 2-76-42
Rudnenskij Industrial'nyj Institut, Ul. 50-let. Oktjabrja, 38, 459120 Rudnyi, Kazahskaja SSR.
Tél: 3-52-53
Sverdlovskij Inženerno-Pedagogičeskij Institut, Ul. Mašinostroitelej 11, 620012 Sverdlovsk.
Tél: 31-04-36
Tjumenskij Industrial'nyj Institut im. Leninskogo Komsomola, Ul. Volodarskogo 38, 625036 Tjumen', Rossiskaja SFSR.
Tél: 6-55-91
Uhtinskij Industrial'nyj Institut, Pervomajskaja ul. 13, 169400 Uhta, Rossiskaja SFSR.
Tél: 5-37-80
Zaporožskij Industrial'nyj Institut, Pr. Lenina 226, 330600 Zaporož'e, Ukrainskaja SSR.
Tél: 2-72-21

(Factory)—(d'Entreprise)

Zavod-Vtuz pri Karagandinskom Metallurgičeskom Kombinate, Pr. Lenina 34, 472300 Temir-Tau, Kazahskaja SSR.
Tél: 3-54-02
Zvod-Vtuz pri Noril'skom Gorno-Metallurgič-

eskom Kombinate im. A.P. Zavenjagina, Ul. 50
let Oktjabrja 7, 663310 Norilsk.
Tél: 6-38-61
Zavod-Vtuz pri proizvodstvennom ob'edinenii
turbinostroenija "Leningradskij Metalličeskij
Zavod", Poljustrovskij prosp. 14, 195108
Leningrad K-108, Rossiskaja SFSR.
Tél: 240-01-54
Zavod-Vtuz pri Moskovskom Dvaždy Ordena

Lenina i Ordena Trudovogo Krasnogo Znameni
Avtomobil'nom Zavode im. I.A. Lihačeva,
Avtozavodskaja ul. 16, 109068 Moskva,
Rossiskaja SFSR.
Tél: 275-52-37
Penzenskij Zavod-Vtuz na pravah filiala
Penzenskogo Politehničeskogo Instituta, Pr.
Baïdukova lo, 440039 Penza, Rossiskaja SFSR.
Tél: 32-63-60

Institutes of Energetics and Electrical Engineering—
Instituts d'Energétique et d'Electricité

Alma-Atinskij Energetičeskij Institut, Ul.
Kosmonavtov 126, 480013 Alma-Ata,
Kazahskaja SSR.
Tél: 67-57-40
Ivanovskij Ordena "Znak početa" Energetičeskij
Institut im. V.I. Lenina, Rabfakovskaja ul. 34,
153548 Ivanovo, Rossiskaja SFSR.
Tél: 48-97-10
Leningradskij Ordena Lenina i Ordena
Oktjabr'skoj Revolucii Elektrotehničeskij
Institut im. V.I. Ul'janova Lenina, Ul. Prof.
Popova 5, 197022 Leningrad P-22, Rossiskaja

SFSR.
Tél: 234-89-05
*Moskovskij Ordena Lenina i Ordena
Oktjabr'skoj Revoljucii Energetičeskij Institut,
Krasnokazarmennaja ul. 14, 105835 GSP
Moskva E-250, Rossiskaja SFSR.
Tél: 362-72-31
Novosibirskij Elektrotehničeskij Institut, Pr.
Karla Marksa 20, 630092 Novosibirsk, Rossis-
kaja SFSR.
Tél: 46-35-87

Institutes of Geology, Mining, Petroleum, and Metallurgical Engineering—
Instituts de Géologie, des Mines, de Pétrochimie et de Métallurgie

(Geology, Mining, and Petroleum
Engineering)—
(Géologie, Mines et Pétrochimie)

Azerbajdžanskij Ordena Trudovogo Krasnogo
Znameni Institut Nefti i Himii im. M. Aziz-
bekova, Pr. Lenina 20, 370601 Baku,
Azerbajdžanskaja SSR.
Tél: 93-83-85
Dnepropetrovskij Ordena Trudovogo Krasnogo
Znameni Gornyj Institut im. Artema, Pr. Karla
Marksa 19, 320600 Dnepropetrovsk, Ukrain-
skaja SSR.
Tél: 45-43-44
Groznenskij Ordena Trudovogo Krasnogo
Znameni Neftjanoj Institut im. Akad, M.D.
Millionščikova, Pl. Revolucii 21, 364902
Groznyj GSP-2, Rossiskaja SFSR.
Tél: 2-21-65
Ivano-Frankovskij Institut Nefti i Gaza,
Karpatskaja Ul. 15, 284018 Ivano-Frankovsk,
Ukrainskaja SSR.
Tél: 4-22-18
Krivorožskij Ordena Trudovogo Krasnogo
Znameni Gornorudnyj Institut, Ul. XXII

Parts'ezda 11, 324030 Krivoj Rog Dnepropet-
rovskoj obl., Ukrainskaja SSR.
Tél: 71-46-04
Leningradskij Ordena Lenina, Ordena
Oktjabr'skoj Revolucii i Ordena Trudovogo
Krasnogo Znameni Gornyj Institut im. G.V.
Plehanova, Vasil'evskij ostrov, 21-ia linija 2,
199026 Leningrad B-26, Rossiskaja SFSR.
Tél: 218-82-01
Moskovskij Ordena Trudovogo Krasnogo
Znameni Geologorazvedočnyj Institut im.
Sergo Ordžonikidze, Korp. Ž Prosp. K. Marksa
18, 103912 Moskva GSP-3, Rossiskaja SFSR.
Tél: 203-21-58
Moskovskij Ordena Trudovogo Krasnogo
Znameni Gornyj Institut, Leninskij prosp. 6,
117049 Moskva M-49, Rossiskaja SFSR.
Tél: 236-95-10
Moskovskij Ordena Oktjabr'skoj Revoljucii i
Ordena Trudovogo Krasnogo Znameni Institut
Nefti i Gaza im. I.M. Gubkina, Leninskij pr. 65,
117296 Moskva B-296, Rossiskaja SFSR.
Tél: 130-92-73
Sverdlovskij Ordena Trudovogo Krasnogo
Znameni Gornyj Institut im. V.V. Vahruševa,

Ul. Kujbyševa 30, 620219 Sverdlovsk, Rossiskaja SFSR.
Tél: 29-31-43
Ufimskij Neftjanoj Institut, Ul. Kosmonavtov 1, 450062 Ufa 62, Baškirskaja SSR.
Tél: 25-24-00

(Metallurgical Engineering)—
(Métallurgie)

Dnepropetrovskij Ordena Trudovogo Krasnogo Znameni Metallurgičeskij Institut im. L.I. Brežneva, Prosp. Gagarina 4, 320095 Dnepropetrovsk, Ukrainskaja SSR.
Tél: 45-31-56
Kommunarskij Gorno-Metallurgičeskij Institut, Pr. Lenina 16, 349104 Kommunarsk Vorošilovgradskoj, obl., Ukrainskaja SSR.
Tél: 2-01-61
Krasnojarskij Ordena Trudovogo Krasnogo Znameni Institut Cvetnyh Metallov im. M.I. Kalinina, Vuzovskij per. 3, 660025 Krasnojarsk 25, Rossiskaja SFSR.
Tél: 34-77-92
Magnitogorskij Ordena Trudovogo Krasnogo Znameni Gorno-Metallurgičeskij Institut im. G.I. Nosova, Pr. V.I. Lenina 38, 455000 Magnitogorsk, Celjabinskoj obl', Rossiskaja SFSR.
Tél: 2-12-87
Moskovskij Ordena Oktjabr'skoj Revoljucii i Ordena Trudovogo Krasnogo Znameni Institut Stali i Splavov, Leninskij pr. 4, 117936-GSP Moskva B-49, Rossiskaja SFSR.
Tél: 236-99-64
Moskovskij Ordena Trudovogo Krasnogo Znameni Večernij Metallurgičeskij Institut, Lefortovskij Val 26, 111250 Moskva E-250, Rossiskaja SFSR.
Tél: 361-13-75
Severo-Kavkazskij Ordena Družby Narodov Gorno-Metallurgičeskij Institut, Ul. Kosmonavta Nikolaeva 44, 362004 Ordžonikidze Severo-Osetinskaja ASSR.
Tél: 3-93-79
Sibirskij Ordena Trudovogo Krasnogo Znameni Metallurgičeskij Institut im. Sergo Ordžonikidze, Props. Kirova 42, 654053 Novo'kuzneck, Kemerovskoj obl., Rossiskaja SFSR.
Tél: 46-47-47
Zdanovskij Metallurgičeskij Institut, Pr. Respubliki 7, 341000 Zdanov, Doneckoj obl., Ukrainskaja SSR.
Tél: 34-30-97

Institutes of Machine and Mechanical Engineering—
Instituts de Construction des Machines et de Mécanique

(Machine, Machine Tool, and Precision Engineering)—
(Machines, Machines-outils et Mécanique de précision)

Brjanskij Ordena "Znak počota" Institut Transportnogo Mašinostroenija, Bulvar 50-let Oktabrja 7, 241035 Brjansk, Rossiskaja SFSR.
Tél: 5-07-59
Iževskij Mehaničeskij Institut, Studenčeskaja ul. 7, 426069 Iževsk, Udmurtskoj ASSR.
Tél: 23-83-50
Kirovogradskij Institut Sel'skohozjajstvennogo Mašinostroenija, Pr. Pravdy 70a, 316017 Kirovograd, Ukrainskaja SSR.
Tél: 9-34-64
Kurganskij Mašinostroitel'nyj Institut, Pl. Lenina, 640669 Kurgan obl., Rossiskaja SFSR.
Tél: 2-34-22
Leningradskij Ordena Trudovogo Krasnogo Znameni Institut Točnoj Mehaniki i Optiki, Sablinskaja ul. 14, 197401 Leningrad, Rossiskaja SFSR.
Tél: 238-43-96
Leningradskij Ordena Lenina i Ordena Krasnogo Znameni Mechaničeskij Institut im. Maršala Sovetskogo Sojuza Ustinova D.F., 1-ja Krasnoarmejskaja ul. 1/21, 198005 Leningrad L-5, Rossiskaja.
Tél: 292-23-47
Mogilevskij Mašinostroitel'nyj Institut, Ul. Lenina 70, 212005 Mogilev, Belorusskaja SSR.
Tél: 5-63-30
Moskovskij Avtomehaničeskij Institut, B. Semenovskaja ul. 38, 105023 Moskva E-23, Rossiskaja SFSR.
Tél: 369-28-32
Moskovskij Institut Elektronnogo Mašinostroenija, B. Vuzovskij per, 3 109028 Moskva, Rossiskaja SFSR.
Tél: 297-90-89
Moskovskij Ordena Trudovogo Krasnogo Znameni Stankoinstrumental'nyj Institut, Vadkovskij per. 3-a, 101472 Moskva GSP

Rossiskaja SFSR.
Tél: 289-43-15
Moskovskoe Ordena Lenina Ordena Oktjabr'skoj Revoljucii i Ordena Trudovogo Krasnogo Znameni Vysšee Tehničeskoe Učilišče im. N.E. Baumana, 2-ja Baumanskaja ul. 5, 107005 Moskva B-5, Rossiskaja SFSR.
Tél: 267-05-41
Rostovskij-na-Donu Ordena Trudovogo Krasnogo Znameni Institut Sel'skohozjajstvennogho Mašinostroenija, Pl. Gagarina 1, 344708 Rostov-na-Donu, Rossiskaja SFSR.
Tél: 38-15-66
Sevastopol'skij Priborostroitel'nyj Institut, Studgorodok, 335053 Sevastopol', Ukrainskaja SSR.
Tél: 24-14-24
Vorošilovgradskij Mašinostroitel'nyj Institut, Kvartal Molodežnij 20a, 348034 Vorošilovgrad, Ukrainskaja SSR.
Tél: 6-23-90
Vsesojuznyj Zaočnyj Mašinostroitel'nyj Institut, Ul. Stromynka 20, 107076 Moskva 5-ja, Rossiskaja SFSR.
Tél: 268-55-19
Zaporožskii Ordena "Znak počota" Mašinostroitel'nyj Institut im. V.J. Cubarja, Ul. Zukovskogo 64, 330063 Zaporož'e, Ukrainskaja SSR.
Tél: 64-25-06

(Chemico-Mechanical Engineering)—
(Génie chimique et mécanique)

Moskovskij Ordena Trudovogo Krasnogo Znameni Institut Himičeskogo Mašinostroenija, Ul. Karla Marksa 21/4, 107884 Moskva B-66, Rossiskaja SFSR.
Tél: 261-49-61
Tambovskij Institut Himičeskogo Mašinostroenija, Leningradskaja Ul. 1, 392620 Tambov, Rossiskaja SFSR.
Tél: 2-10-19

(Shipbuilding Engineering)—
(Construction navale)

Leningradskij Ordena Lenina Korablestroitel'nyj Institut, Locmanskaja ul. 3, 190008 Leningrad F-8, Rossiskaja SFSR.
Tél: 216-22-82
Nikolaevskij Ordena Trudovogo Krasnogo Znameni Korablestroitel'nyj Institut im. Admirala S.O. Makarova, Ul. Geroev Stalingrada 5, 327001 Nikolaev, Ukrainskaja SSR.
Tél: 35-91-48

(Aeronautical Engineering)—
(Génie aéronautique)

Andropovskij Aviacionnyj Tehnologičeskij Institut, Ul. Puškina 53, 152934 Andropov, Rossiskaja SFSR.
Tél: 2-82-07
Har'kovskij Ordena Lenina Aviacionnyj Institut im. N.E. Zukovskogo, Ul. Čkalova 17, 310084 Har'kov 84, Ukrainskaja SSR.
Tél: 44-23-13
Kazanskij Ordena Trudovogo Krasnogo Znameni i Ordena Družby Narodov Aviacionnyj Institut im. A.N. Tupoleva, Ul. Karla Marksa 10, 420084 Kazan', Rossiskaja SFSR.
Tél: 39-71-14
Kujbyševskij Ordena Trudovogo Krasnogo Znameni Aviacionnyj Institut im. Akadamika, S.P. Koroleva, Molodogvardejskaja ul. 151, 443001 Kujbyšev, Rossiskaja SFSR.
Tél: 32-26-06
Leningradskij Institut Aviacionnogo Priborostroenija, Ul. Gercena 67, 190000 Leningrad, Rossiskaja SFSR.
Tél: 312-21-07
Moskovskij Aviacionnyj Tehnologičeskij Institut im. K.E. Ciolkovskogo, Ul. Petrovka 27, 103767 Moskva K-31, Rossiskaja SFSR.
Tél: 221-20-17
Moskovskij Ordena Lenina i Ordena Oktjabr'skoj Revoljucii Aviacionnyj Institut im. Sergo Ordžonikidze, Volokolamskoe Sosse 4, 125871 Moskva A-80, Rossiskaja SFSR.
Tél: 158-13-73
Ufimskij Ordena Lenina Aviacionnyj Institut im. Sergo Ordžonikidze, Ul. Karla Marksa 12, 450025 Ufa 25, Baškirkskaja ASSR.
Tél: 22-63-07

(Printing Technology)—(Imprimerie)

Moskovskij Poligrafičeskij Institut, Ul. Prjanišnikova 2a, 127550 Moskva A8, Rossiskaja SFSR.
Tél: 216-14-70
Ukrainskij Poligrafičeskij Institut im. Ivana Fedorova, Ul. Pidgolosko 19, 290006 L'vov, Ukrainskaja SSR.
Tél: 22-78-62

(Cinematograph Engineering)—
(Techniques cinématographiques)

Leningradskij Institut Kinoinženerov, Ul. Pravdy 13, 191126 Leningrad F-126, Rossiskaja SFSR.
Tél: 215-73-23

Institutes of Electronics, Electrical Equipment and Automation—
Instituts d'Electronique, d'Equipement électrique et d'Automatisation

Har'kovskij Ordena Trudovogo Krasnogo Znameni Institut Radioelektroniki im. Akad, M.K. Jankelja, Pr. Lenina 14, 310141 Har'kov, Ukrainskaja SSR.
Tél: 43-30-53

Moskovskij Ordena Trudovogo Krasnogo Znameni Fisiko-Tehničeskij Institut, Institutskij per. 9, Dolgoprudnyi, 171700 Moskovskaja obl., Rossiskaja SFSR.
Tél: 408-48-00

Moskovskij Ordena Trudovogo Krasnogo Znameni Inženerno-fizičeskij Institut, Kaširskoe šosse 31, 114509 Moskva M-409, Rossiskaja SFSR.
Tél: 324-84-17

Moskovskij Ordena Trudovogo Krasnogo

Znameni Institut Elektronnoj Tehniki, St. Krjukovo Oktjabr'skoj Ž.d., Zelenograd, 103498 Moskva K-498, Rossiskaja SFSR.
Tél: 531-44-41

Moskovskij Institut Radiotehniki Elektroniki i Avtomatiki, Pr. Vernadskogo 78, 117454 Moskva V454, Rossiskaja SFSR.
Tél: 433-04-55

Obninskij Institut Atomnoj Energetiki, Ul. Zolio-Kjuri 1, 249020 Obninsk, Kalužskoj obl., Rossiskaja SFSR.
Tél: 3-81-05

Tomskij Institut Avtomatizirovannyh Sistem Upravlenija i Radioelektroniki, Prosp. Lenina 40, 634050 Tomsk, 50 Rossiskaja SFSR.
Tél: 2-32-27

Institutes of Radio Engineering and Telecommunications—
Instituts de Radio et de Télécommunications

(Radio Engineering)—(Radio)

Minskij Radiotehničeskij Institut, Ul. Petrucja Brovki 6, 220069 Minsk, Belorusskaja SSR.
Tél: 32-32-35

Rjazanskij Radiotehničeskij Institut, Ul. Gagarina 59/1, 390024 Rjazan 24, Rossiskaja SFSR.
Tél: 72-24-45

Taganrogskij Radiotehničeskij Institut im. V.D. Kalmykova, Ul. Cehova 22, 347915 Taganrog 15, Rossiskaja SFSR.
Tél: 6-49-22

(Telecommunications)—(Télécommunications)

Kujbyševskij Elektrotehničeskij Institut Svjazi, Ul. L'va Tolstogo 23, 443099 Kujbyšev obl. 99, Rossiskaja SFSR.
Tél: 33-38-56

Leningradskij Elektrotehničeskij Institut Svjazi im. Prof. M.A. Bonč-Brueviča, Nab. Reki

Mojki 61, 191065 Leningrad D-65, Rossiskaja SFSR.
Tél: 211-60-87

Moskovskij Ordena Trudovogo Krasnogo Znameni Elektrotehničeskij Institut Svjazi, Aviamotornaja ul. 8, 111024 Moskva E-24, Rossiskaja SFSR.
Tél: 274-27-62

Novosibirskij Elektrotehničeskij Institut Svjazi im. N.D. Psurceva, Ul. Kirova 86, 630125 Novosibirsk 8, Rossiskaja SFSR.
Tél: 66-10-38

Odesskij Elektrotehničeskij Institut Svjazi im. A.S. Popova, Ul. Celjuskincev 1/3, 270021 Odessa 20, Ukrainskaja SSR.
Tél: 3-22-44

Taškentskij Elektrotehničeskij Institut Svjazi, Ul. Engel'sa 108, 700000 Taškent, Uzbekskaja SSR.
Tél: 35-09-34

Vsesojuznyj Zaočnyj Elektrotehničeskij Institut Svjazi, U. Narodnogo Opolčnija 32, 123855 Moskva D-423, Rossiskaja SFSR.
Tél: 194-92-65

Institutes of Chemical Engineering—Instituts de Génie chimique

Belorusskij Ordena Trudovogo Krasnogo Znameni Tehnologičeskij Institut im. S.M. Kirova, Ul. Sverdlova 13a, 220630 Minsk, Belorusskaja SSR.

Tél: 22-63-75

Dnepropetrovskij Ordena Trudovogo Krasnogo Znameni Himiko-Tehnologičeskij Institut im. F.E. Dzeržinskogo, Prosp. Gagarina 8, 320640

Dnepropetrovsk, Ukrainskaja SSR.
Tél: 45-32-91
Ivanovskij Ordena Trudovogo Krasnogo Znameni Himiko-Tehnologičeskij Institut, Prosp. F. Engel'sa 7, 153460 Ivanovo, Rossiskaja SFSR.
Tél: 2-92-41
Kazahskij Himiko-Tehnologičeskij Institut, Kommunističeskij prosp. 5, 486018 Cimkent, Kazahskaja SSR.
Tél: 3-64-12
Kazanskij Ordena Trudovogo Krasnogo Znameni Himiko-Tehnologičeskij Institut im. S.M. Kirova, Ul. Karla Marksa 68, 420015 Kazan', Rossiskaja SFSR.
Tél: 32-38-18
Leningradskij Ordena Oktjabr'skoj Revoljucii i Ordena Trudovogo Krasnogo Znameni Tehno-

logičeskij Institut im. Lensoveta, Zagorodnyj prosp. 49, 198013 Leningrad, Rossiskaja SFSR.
Tél: 292-13-12
Moskovskij Ordena Trudovogo Krasnogo Znameni Institut Tonkoj Himičeskoj Tehnologii im. M.V. Lomonosova, prosp. Vernadskogo 86, 117571 Moskva Rossiskaja SFSR.
Tél: 246-64-71
Moskovskij Ordena Lenina i Ordena Trudovogo Krasnogo Znameni Himiko-Tehnologičeskij Institut im. D.I. Mendeleeva, Mijusskaja pl. 9, 125820 GSP Moskva A-47, Rossiskaja SFSR.
Tél: 258-85-20
Voronežskij Tehnologičeskij Institut, Prosp. Revoljucii 19, 394017 Voronež, Rossiskaja SFSR.
Tél: 1-09-16

Institutes of Forestry, Wood, Cellulose and Paper Technology—
Instituts de Sylviculture et Technologie du Bois, de la Cellulose et du Papier

Arhangel'skij Ordena Trudovogo Krasnogo Znameni Lesotehničeskij Institut im. V.V. Kujbyševa, Nab. im. V.I. Lenina 17, 163007 Arhangel'sk, Rossiskaja SFSR.
Tél: 49-159
Brjanskij Ordena Trudovogo Krasnogo Znameni Tehnologičeskij Institut, Ul. Stanke Dimitrova 3, 241037 Brjansk obl., Rossiskaja SFSR.
Tél: 119-12
Leningradskaja Ordena Lenina Lesotehničeskaja Akademija im. S.M. Kirova, Institutskij per. 5, 194018 Leningrad K-18, Rossiskaja SFSR.
Tél: 224-04-41
Leningradskij Ordena Trudovogo Krasnogo Znameni Tehnologičeskij Institut Celjulozno-Bumažnoj Promyšlennosti, Ul. Ivana Cernyh 4, 198092 Leningrad, Rossiskaja SFSR.
Tél: 186-56-39
L'vovskij Lesotehničeskij Institut, Puškina ul. 103, 290032 L'vov, Ukrainskaja SSR.

Tél: 35-24-11
Moskovskij Lesotehničeskij Institut, Pervaja Institutskaja ul. 1, 141001 Mytišči 1, Moskovskaja obl., Rossiskaja SFSR.
Tél: 582-45-78
Sibirskij Ordena Trudovogo Krasnogo Znameni Tehnologičeskij Institut, Prosp. Mira 82, 660649 Krasnojarsk Kraevoj 49, Rossiskaja SFSR.
Tél: 27-99-96
Ural'skij Ordena Trudovogo Krasnogo Znameni Lesotehničeskij Institut im. Leninskogo Komsomola, Sibirskij trakt 37, 620032 Sverdlovsk B-32, Rossiskaja SFSR.
Tél: 24-23-77
Voronežskij Ordena Družby Narodov Lesotehničeskij Institut, Ul. Timirjazeva 8, 394613 Voronež, Rossiskaja SFSR.
Tél: 56-41-08

Institutes of Food Industry—Instituts de l'Industrie alimentaire

(Food Industries)—
(Industrie alimentaire)

Buharskij Tehnologičeskij Institut Piševoj i Legkoj Promyšlenosti, Prosp. Leninskogo Komsomola 15, 705017 Buhara, Uzbekskaja SSR.
Tél: 3-04-02
Džambulskij Tehnologičeskij Institut Legkoj i Piščevoj Promyšlennosti, Kommunističeskaja

Ul. 58, 484030 Džambul, Kazahskaja SSR.
Tél: 4-38-81
Kemerovskij Tehnologičeskij Institut Piščevoj Promyšlennosti, Bul'var Stroitelej 47, 650060 Kemerovo, Rossiskaja SFSR.
Tél: 51-13-43
Kievskij Ordena Trudovogo Krasnogo Znameni Tehnologičeskij Institut Piščevoj Promyšlennosti, Vladimirskaja ul. 68, 252017 Kiev, Ukrainskaja SSR.

Tél: 220-64-00
Kirovabadskij Tehnologičeskij Institut, pos.
Kiraz. Kirovabad, Azerbajdžanskaja SSR.
**Leningradskij Ordena Trudovogo Krasnogo
Znameni Tehnologičeskij Institut Holodil'noj
Promyšlennosti**, Ul. Lomonosova 9, 191002
Leningrad, Rossiskaja SFSR.
Tél: 219-89-36
Mogilevskij Tehnologičeskij Institut, Prosp.
Smidta 3, 212027 Mogilev, Belorusskaja SSR.
Tél: 4-33-30
**Moskovskij Ordena Trudovogo Krasnogo
Znameni Tehnologičeskij Institut Mjasnoj i
Moločnoj Promyšlennosti**, Ul. Talalihina 33,
109818 Moskva Ž-29, Rossiskaja SFSR.
Tél: 271-63-36
**Moskovskij Ordena Trudovogo Krasnogo
Znameni Tehnologičeskij Institut Piščevoj
Promyšlennosti**, Volokolamskoe šosse 11,
125080 Moskva A-80, Rossiskaja SFSR.
Tél: 158-71-84
**Odesskij Tehnologičeskij Institut Piščevoj
Promyšlennosti im. M.V. Lomonosova**, Ul.
Sverdlova 112, 270039 Odessa, Ukrainskaja
SSR.
Tél: 25-32-84
**Odesskij Tehnologičeskij Institut Holodil'noj
Promyšlennosti**, Ul. Petra Velikogo 1/3, 270000
Odessa, Ukrainskaja SSR.
Tél: 23-22-20

**Semipalatinskij Tehnologičeskij Institut Mjasnoj
i Moločnoj Promyšlennosti**, Ul. Glinki 49,
490150 Semipalatinsk, Kazahskaja SSR.
Tél: 5-07-80
Vostočno-Sibirskij Tehnologičeskij Institut, Ul.
Smolina 26, 670000 Ulan-Ude, Burjatskaja
ASSR.
Tél: 53-49
**Vsesojuznyj Zaočnyj Institut Piščevoj Promyšlen-
nosti**, Ul. Čkalova 73, 109803 Moskva Ž-4,
Rossiskaja SFSR.
Tél: 297-51-97

(*Fishery Industries*) —
(*Industrie du Poisson*)

**Astrahanskij Tehničeskij Institut Rybnoj
Promyšlennosti i Hozjajstva**, Ul. Tatiščeva 16,
414025 Astrahan', Rossiskaja SFSR.
Tél: 2-09-02
**Dal'nevostočnyj Tehničeskij Institut Rybnoj
Promyšlennosti i Hozjajstva**, Lugovaja ul. 526,
690636 Vladivostok, Rossiskaja SFSR.
Tél: 9-53-06
**Kaliningradskij Tehničeskij Institut Rybnoj
Promyšlennosti i Hozjajstva**, Sovetskij prosp.
1, 236000 Kaliningrad Oblastnoj, Rossiskaja
SFSR.
Tél: 2-62-91

Institutes of Textile and Light Engineering—
Instituts du Textile et de l'Industrie légère

Blagoveščenskij Tehnologičeskij Institut, 675007
Blagoveščensk Amurskoj obl., Ignat'evskoe
šosse 21, Rossiskaja SFSR.
Tél: 5-41-16
**Dal'nevostocynj Tehnologičeskij Institut
Bytovogo Obsluživanija**, Ul. Gogolja 41,
690600 Vladivostok, Rossiskaja SFSR.
Tél: 5-72-21
**Hmel'nickij Tehnologičeskij Institut Bytovogo
Obsluživanija**, Institutskaja ul. 11, 280016
Hmel'nickij, Ukrainskaja SSR.
Tél: 2-37-55
**Ivanoskij Ordena Trudovogo Krasnogo Znameni
Tekstil'nyj Institut im. M.V. Frunze**, Prosp. F.
Engel'sa 21, 153475 Ivanovo, Rossiskaja
SFSR.
Tél: 4-90-46 ext. 5-73
**Kievskij Tehnologičeskij Institut Legkoj
Promyšlennosti**, Ul. Nemiroviča-Dančenko 2,
252601 Kiev 11, Ukrainskaja SSR.
Tél: 97-75-12
Kostromskoj Ordena Trudovogo Krasnogo

Znameni Tehnologičeskij Institut, Ul. Dzeržin-
skogo 17, 156021 Kostroma, Rossiskaja SFSR.
Tél: 7-79-60
**Leningradskij Ordena Trudovogo Krasnogo
Znameni Institut Tekstil'noj i Legkoj Promyš-
lennosti im. S.M. Kirova**, Ul. Gercena 18,
181065 Leningrad D-65, Rossiskaja SFSR.
Tél: 315-07-47
**Moskovskij Ordena Trudovogo Krasnogo
Znameni Tekstil'nyj Institut im. A.N.
Kosygina**, Kalužskaja ul. 1, 117918 Moskva,
Rossiskaja SFSR.
Tél: 234-28-90
Moskovskij Tehnologičeskij Institut, Glavnaja ul.
99, Pos. Cerkizovo, Puškinskij rajon, 141220
Moskovskaja obl., Rossiskaja SFSR.
Tél: 184-63-03 ext. 4-40
**Moskovskij Ordena Trudovogo Krasnogo
Znameni Tehnologičeskij Institut Legkoj
Promyšlennosti**, Ul. Osipenko 33, 113035
Moskva M35, Rossiskaja SFSR.
Tél: 231-31-48

Omskij Tehnologičeskij Institut Bytovogo Obsluživanija, Krasnogvardeiskaja ul. 9, 640099 Omsk, Rossiskaja SFSR.
Tél: 24-16-93
Sahtinskij Tehnologičeskij Institut Bytovogo Obsluživanija, Ul. Sevčenko 147, 346500 Šahty Rostovsokoj obl., Rossiskaja SFSR.
Tél: 2-71-46
Taškentskij Ordena Družby Narodov Institut Tekstil'noj i Legkoj Promyšlennosti, Ul. Gorbunova 5, 700100 Taškent, Uzbekskaja SSR.
Tél: 53-06-06
Vitebskij Tehnologičeskij Institut Legkoj Promyšlennosti, Moskovskij prosp. 72, 210028 Vitebsk, Belorusskaja SSR.
Tél: 5-72-34
Vsesojuznyj Zaočnyj Institut Tekstil'noj i Legkoj Promyšlennosti, Ul. Narodnogo Opolčenija 38, Korp. 2, 123298 Moskva, Rossiskaja SFSR.
Tél: 943-63-62

Institutes of Architecture and Civil Engineering—
Instituts d'Architecture et du Génie civil

Alma-Atinskij Arhitekturno-Stroitel'nyj Institut, Ul. Obručeva 28, 480123 Alma-Ata, Kazahskaja SSR.
Tél: 49-46-11
Moskovskij Ordena Trudovogo Krasnogo Znameni Arhitekturnyj Institut, Ul. Zdanova 11, 103754-GSP Moskva K-31, Rossiskaja SFSR.
Tél: 228-32-59
Sverdlovskij Arhitekturnjy Institut, Ul. Karla Libknehta 23, 620219 Sverdlovsk GSP-1089, Rossiskaja SFSR.
Tél: 51-80-45

(Civil Engineering)—(Génie civil)

Bakinskij Inženerno-Stroitel'nyj Institut, Ul. Krylova 13, 370073 Baku, Azerbajdžanskaja SSR.
Tél: 38-33-96
Belgorodskij Tehnologičeskij Institut Stroitel'nyj Materialov im. I.A. Grišmanova, Ul. Kostjukova 46, 308012 Belgorod GSP-4, Rossiskaja SFSR.
Tél: 5-41-03
Brestskij Inženerno-Stroitel'nyj Institut, Moskovskaja ul. 267, 220017 Brest, Belorusskaja SSR.
Tél: 2-40-84
Celinogradskij Inženerno-Stroitel'nyj Institut, ul. Ciolkovskogo 2, 473021 Celinograd, Kazahskaja SSR.
Tél: 4-29-53
Dnepropetrovskij Inženerno-Stroitel'nyj Institut, Ul. Cernyševskogo 24-a, 320600 Dnepropetrovsk, Ukrainskaja SSR.
Tél: 46-73-57
Gor'kovskij Ordena Trudovogo Krasnogo Znameni Inženerno-Stroitel'nyj Institut im. V.P. Ckalova, Krasnoflotskaja ul. 65, 603000 Gor'kij, Rossiskaja SFSR.
Tél: 34-02-01

Har'kovskij Institut Inženerov Kommunal'nogo Stroitel'stva, Ul. Revoljucii 12, 310002 Har'kov, Ukrainskaja SSR.
Tél: 47-00-88
Har'kovskij Inženerno-Stroitel'nyj Institut, Sumskaja ul. 40, 310002 Har'kov, Rossiskaja SFSR.
Tél: 40-29-19
Ivanovskij Inženerno-Stroitel'nyj Institut, Krasnych Zor ul., 153547 Ivanovo, Rossiskaja SFSR.
Tél: 2-31-62
Kazanskij Inženerno-Stroitel'nyj Institut, Zelenaja ul. 1, 420043 Kazan'43, Rossiskaja SFSR.
Tél: 37-72-40
Kievskij Ordena Trudovogo Krasnogo Znameni Inženerno-Stroitel'nyj Institut, Vozduhoflotskij prosp. 31, 252180 Kiev, Ukrainskaja SSR.
Tél: 267-71-20
Krasnojarskij Inženerno-Stroitel'nyj Institut, Prosp. Svobodnyj 82, 660062 Krasnojarsk, Rossiskaja SFSR.
Tél: 25-66-69
Kujbyševskij Ordena "Znak pöcota" Inženerno-Stroitel'nyj Institut im. A.I. Miko-jana, Molodogvardeskaja ul. 194, 443644 Kujbyšev obl. Rossiskaja SFSR.
Tél: 33-97-77
Leningradskij Ordena Oktjabr'skoj Revoljucii i Ordena Trudovogo Krasnogo Znameni Inženerno-Stroitel'nyj Institut, 2-ja Krasnoarmejskaja ul. 4, 198005 Leningrad, Rossiskaja SFSR.
Tél: 292-20-26
Makeevskij Inženerno-Stroitel'nyj Institut, pos. Dzeržinskogo, 339023 Makeevka Donečkoj obl., Ukrainskaja SSR.
Tél: 90-29-38
Moskovskij Ordena Trudovogo Krasnogo Znameni Inženerno-Stroitel'nyj Institut im. V.V. Kujbyševa, Jaroslavskoe šosse 26, 127337

Moskva Z-114, Rossiskaja SFSR.
Tél: 183-48-10

Novosibirskij Ordena Trudovogo Krasnogo Znameni Inženerno-Stroitel'nyj Institut im. V.V. Kujbyševa, Leningradskaja ul. 113, 630008 Novosibirsk 8, Rossiskaja SFSR.
Tél: 66-42-95

Odesskij Inženerno-Stroitel'nyj Institut, Ul. Didrihsona 4, 270029 Odessa, Ukrainskaja SSR.
Tél: 23-33-42

Penzenskij Inženerno-Stroitel'nyj Institut, Ul. G. Titova 28, 440028 Penza, Rossiskaja SFSR.
Tél: 62-05-03

Poltavskij Inženerno-Stroitel'nyj Institut, Pervomajskij prosp. 24, 314601 Poltava, Ukrainskaja SSR.
Tél: 7-33-27

Rostovskij Inženerno-Stroitel'nyj Institut, Socialističeskaja ul. 162, 344022 Rostov-na-Donu GSP-2, Rossiskaja SFSR.
Tél: 65-02-05

Samarkandskij Arhitekturno-Stroitel'nyj Institut im. M.U. Ulugbeka, Ul. Ljaljazar 70, 703047 Samarkand 47, Uzbekskaja SSR.
Tél: 3-20-25

Tjumenskij Inženerno-Stroitel'nyj Institut, Ul. Lunarčarskogo 2, 625001 Tjumen, Rossiskaja SFSR.
Tél: 3-45-31

Tomskij Inženerno-Stroitel'nyj Institut, Soljanaja pl. 2, 634003 Tomsk 3, Rossiskaja SFSR.
Tél: 5-39-30

Ust'-Kamenogorskij Stroitel'no-dorožnyj Institut, Studgorodok, 492034 Ust' Kamenogorsk, Kazahskaja SSR.
Tél: 44-63-54

Vil'njusskij Inženerno-Stroitel'nyj Institut, Ul. Sauletekio 11, 232054 Vil'njus, Litovskaja SSR.
Tél: 74-72-52

Volgogradskij Inženerno-Stroitel'nyj Institut, Akademičeskaja ul. 1, 400074 Volgograd, Rossiskaja SFSR.
Tél: 44-13-72

Voronežskij Ordena Trudovogo Krasnogo Znameni Inženerno-Stroitel'nyj Institut, Ul. 20-letija Oktjabrja 84, 394680 Voronež, Rossiskaja SFSR.
Tél: 7-52-68

Vsesojuznyj Zaočnyj Inženerno-Stroitel'nyj Institut, Srednjaja Kalitnikovskaja ul. 30, 109807 Moskva, Rossiskaja SFSR.

Institutes of Surveying and Cartography — Instituts de Géodésie et de Cartographie

Moskovskij Ordena Lenina Institut Inženerov Geodezii, Aerofotos'emki i Kartografi, Gorohovskij per. 4, 103064 Moskva K-64, Rossiskaja SFSR.
Tél: 261-40-44

Novosibirskij Ordena "Znak Početa" Institut Inženerov Geodezii, Aerofotos'emki i Kartografi, ul. Plahotnogo 10, 630108 Novosibirsk 108, Rossiskaja SFSR.
Tél: 43-37-01

Institutes of Hydrology and Meteorology — Instituts d'Hydrologie et de Météorologie

Leningradskij Gidrometeorologičeskij Institut, Malo-Ohtinskij pr. 98, 195196 Leningrad-K196, Rossiskaja SFSR.
Tél: 221-41-63

Odesskij Gidrometeorologičeskij Institut, Ul. Lwowskaja 15, 270016 Odessa, Ukrainskaja SSR.
Tél: 22-49-83

Institutes of Agriculture — Instituts d'Agriculture

(Agriculture) — (Agriculture)

Altajskij Sel'skohozjajstvennyj Institut, Krasnoarmejskij pr. 98, 656099 Barnaul, Rossiskaja SFSR.

Tél: 5-45-35

Andižanskij Institut Hlopkovodstva, Selo Kuigan-jar, Andižanokoro r-na 711520 Andižanskaja obl., Uzbekskaja SSR.
Tél: 4-54-34

Armjanskij Ordena "Znak Početa" Sel' skohozjajstvennyj Institut, Ul. Terjana 74, 375009 Erevan, Armjanskaja SSR.
Tél: 52-45-41

Azerbajdžanskij Ordena "Znak Početa" Sel'skohozjajstvennyj Institut im. S. Agamalily Ogly, Ul. Azizbekova 262, 374700 Kirovabad, Azerbajdžanskaja SSR.
Tél: 2-10-64

Bažkirskij Ordena Trudovogo Krasnogo Znameni Sel'skohozjajstvennyj Institut, Ul. 50-letija Oktjabrja 34, 450089 Ufa Rossiskaja SFSR.
Tél: 22-90-40

Belgorodskij Sel'skohozjajstvennyj Institut, Ul. Vavilova 24, Pos. Majskij, Belgorodskij r-n, 309103 Belgorodskaja obl., Rossiskaja SFSR.
Tél: 204-15

Belocerkovskij Sel'skohozjajstvennyj Institut im. P.L. Pogrebnjaka, M. Svobody 8/1, 256400 Belaja Cerkov Kievskoj obl., Ukrainskaja SSR.
Tél: 5-12-88

Blagoveščenskij Sel'skohozjajstvennyj Institut, Politehničeskaja ul. 86, 675005 Blagoveščensk, Amurskoj obl., Rossiskaja SFSR.
Tél: 2-32-06

Belorusskaja Ordena Oktjabr'skoj Revoljucii i Ordena Trudovogo Krasnogo Znameni Sel'skohozjajstvennaja Akademija, 213410 Gor'ki Mogilevskoj obl., Belorusskaja SSR.
Tél: 2-15-45

Brjanskij Sel'skohozjajstvennyj Institut, pos. Kokino, Vygoničeskij r-n, 243365 Brjanskaja obl., Rossiskaja SFSR.
Tél: 69-37-21

Burjatskij Sel'skohozjajstvennyj Institut, Ul. Puškina 8, 670020 Ulan-Ude, Burjat-skaja ASSR.
Tél: 2-40-11

Celinogradskij Sel'skohozjajstvennyj Institut, Prosp. Pobedy, 116, 473012 Celinograd, Kazahskaja SSR.
Tél: 2-50-56

Cuvaškij Sel'skohozjajstvennyj Institut, Ul. Karla Marksa 29, 428000 Ceboksary, Cuvaškaja SSR.
Tél: 2-23-34

Dagestanskij Ordena Družby Narodov Sel'skohozjajstvennyj Institut, Ul. M. Gadžieva 180, 367032 Mahačkala, Dagestan-skaja ASSR.
Tél: 7-25-25

Dnepropetrovskij Ordena Trudovogo Krasnogo Znameni Sel'skohozjajstvennyj Institut, Ul. Vorošilova 25, 320638 Dnepropetrovsk, Ukrainskaja SSR.
Tél: 44-81-32

Donskoj Ordena Trudovogo Krasnogo Znameni

Sel'skohozjajstvennyj Institut, 346493 St. Persijanovka, Rostovskoj obl., Rossiskaja SFSR.
Tél: 9-36-25

Estonskaja Sel'skohozjajstvennaja Akademija, Ul. Rija 12, 202400 Tartu, Estonskaja SSR.
Tél: 7-55-97

Gor'kovskij Sel'skohozjajstvennyj Institut, Prosp. Gargarina 97, 603078 Gor'kij, Rossi-skaja SFSR.
Tél: 65-34-60

Gorskij Sel'skohozjajstvennyj Institut, Ul. Kirova 37, 362040 Ordžonikidze, Severo Osetinskaja ASSR.
Tél: 3-23-04

Grodnenskij Sel'skohozjajstvennyj Institut, Ul. Terežkovoij 28, 230600 Grodno, Belorusskaja SSR.
Tél: 7-01-68

Gruzinkskij Institut Subtropičeskigo Hozjajstva, Kelasuri, 384904 Suhumi, Gruzinskaja SSR.
Tél: 3-38-69

Gruzinskij Ordena Trudovogo Krasnogo Znameni Sel'skohozjajstvennyj Institut, 13-j Kilometr Voenno-Gruzinskoj Dorogi, 380031 Tbilisi, Digomi Gruzinskaja SSR.
Tél: 51-47-63

Har'kovskij Ordena Trudovogo Krasnogo Znameni Sel'skohozjajstvennyj Institut im. V.V. Dokučaeva, p/o "Kommunist-1", 312131 Har'kov, Ukrainskaja SSR.
Tél: 93-71-46

Hersonskij Ordena Trudovogo Krasnogo Znameni Sel'skohozjajstvennyj Institut im A.D. Cjurupy, Ul. Rosa Luxemburg 23, 325006 Herson 6, Ukrainskaja SSR.
Tél: 2-64-71

Irkutskij Ordena Družby Narodov, Sel'skohoz-jajstvennyj Institut, Pos. Molodežnyj, 664038 Irkutsk, Rossiskaja SFSR.
Tél: 39-13-30

Ivanovskij Sel'skohozjajstvennyj Institut, Sovet-skaja ul. 45, 153467 Ivanovo, Rossiskaja SFSR.
Tél: 2-81-44

Iževskij Sel'skohozjajstvennyj Institut, Ul. Kirova 16, 426018 Iževsk, Udmurtskoj ASSR.
Tél: 3-16-28

Jakutskij Sel'skohozjajstvennyj Institut, Ul. P. Morozova 2, 677891 Jakutsk, Rossiskaja SFSR.
Tél: 2-23-20

Kalininskij Sel'skohozjajstvennyj Institut, p/o Saharovo, 171314 Kalinin, Rossiskaja SFSR.
Tél: 39-92-32

Kamenec-Podol'skij Sel'skohozjajstvennyj Insti-tut, Ul. Sevčenko 13, 281900 Kamenec-Podol'skij Chmielnickoj obl., Ukrainskaja SSR.
Tél: 52-18

Kazahskij Ordena Trudovogo Krasnogo Znameni Sel'skohozjajstvennyj Institut, Prosp. Abaja 8, 480021 Alma-Ata, Kazahskaja SSR.
Tél: 61-30-14

Kazanskij Ordena "Znak Početa" Sel'skohozjajstvennyj Institut im. Gor'kogo, Ul. Karla Marksa 65, 420015 Kazan' 15, Rossiskaja SFSR.
Tél: 2-88-82

Kirgizskij Ordena "Znak Početa" Sel'skohozjajstvennyj Institut im. K.I. Skrjabina, Kommunističeskaja ul. 68, 720453 Frunze, Kirgizskaja SSR.
Tél: 4-54-11

Kirovskij Sel'skohozjajstvennyj Institut, Oktjabr'skij prosp. 133, 610039 Kirov obl., Ukrainskaja SSR.
Tél: 2-97-19

Kišinevskij Ordena Trudovogo Krasnogo Znameni Sel'skohozjajstvennyj Institut im. M.V. Frunze, Ul. Gribova 44, 277049 Kišnev, Moldavskaja SSR.
Tél: 2-14-43

Kostromskoj Sel'skohozjajstvennyj Institut, p/o Karavaevo, 157930 Kostroma, Rossiskaja SFSR.
Tél: 4-12-63

Krasnojarskij Sel'skohozjajstvennyj Institut, Pr. Mira 88, 660607 Krasnojarsk, Rossiskaja SFSR.
Tél: 7-36-09

Krymskij Ordena "Znak Početa" Sel'skohozjajstvennyj Institut im. M.I. Kalinina, Vuzgorodok, 333030 Simferopol' Krymskoj obl., 30, Rossiskaja SFSR.
Tél: 2-72-67

Kubanskij Ordena Trudovogo Krasnogo Znameni Sel'skohozjajstvennyj Institut, Ul. Kalinina 13, 350044 Krasnodar 44, Rossiskaja SFSR.
Tél: 52-31-46

Kujbyševskij Sel'skohozjajstvennyj Institut, Pos. Ustj-Kineljskij 446400 Kinel', Kujbysevskoj obl., Rossiskaja SFSR.

Kurganskij Sel'skohozjajstvennyj Institut, Ul. Kujbyševa 55, 640018 Kurgan obl., Rossiskaja SFSR.
Tél: 2-14-21

Kurskij Sel'skohozjajstvennyj Institut im. Prof. I.I. Ivanova, Ul. Karla Marksa 70, 305034 Kursk, Rossiskaja SFSR.
Tél: 4-12-21

Kustanajskij Sel'skohozjajstvennyj Institut, Ul. Sverdlova 119, 458011 Kustanaj, Kazahskaja SSR.
Tél: 5-12-23

Latvijskaja Ordena Trudovogo Krasnogo Znameni Sel'skohozjajstvennaja Akademija, Ul. Lenina 2, 229600 Elgava, Latvijskaja SSR.

Tél: 2-25-84

Leningradskij Ordena Trudovogo Krasnogo Znameni Sel'skohozjajstvennyj Institut, Leningradskoje šosse 2, 188620 Puškin Leningradskoj obl., Rossiskaja SFSR.
Tél: 290-04-22

Litovskaja Ordena Trudovogo Krasnogo Znameni Sel'skohozjajstvennaja Akademija, 234324 Kaunas, Litovskaja SSR.
Tél: 9-65-02

L'vovskij Sel'skohozjajstvennyj Institut, 292040 Nesterskogo r-na Dubljany, L'vovskoj obl., Ukrainskaja SSR.
Tél: 79-33-45

*Moskovskaja Ordena Lenina i Ordena Trudovogo Krasnogo Znameni Sel'skohozjajstvennaja Akademija im. K.A. Timirjazeva, Ul. Timirjazevskaja 49, 127550 Moskva, Rossiskaja SFSR.
Tél: 216-04-80

Novgorodskij Sel'skohozjajstvennyj Institut, Pskovskaja ul. 3, 173015 Novgorod, Rossiskaja SFSR.
Tél: 7-03-82

Novosibirskij Sel'skohozjajstvennyj Institut, Ul. Dobroljubova 160, 630039 Novosibirsk 39, Rossiskaja SFSR.
Tél: 67-39-22

Odesskij Sel'skohozjajstvennyj Institut, Ul. Sverdlova 99, 270039 Odessa 39, Ukrainskaja SSR.
Tél: 22-37-23

Omskij Ordena Lenina Sel'skohozjajstvennyj Institut im. S.M. Kirova, Sibabovskaja ul. 4, 644008 Omsk 8, Rossiskaja SFSR.
Tél: 22-56-90

Orenburgskij Ordena Trudovogo Krasnogo Znameni Sel'skohozjajstvennyj Institut, Ul. Celjuskincev 18, 460795 Orenburg, Ukrainskaja SSR.
Tél: 7-52-30

Orlovskij Sel'skohozjajstvennyj Institut, Razgradskaja ul. 17, 302033 Orel, Rossiskaja SFSR.
Tél: 6-29-15

Penzenskij Sel'skohozjajstvennyj Institut, Botaničeskaja ul. 30, 440014 Penza, Rossiskaja SFSR.
Tél: 69-08-59

Permskij Gosudarstvennyj Sel'skohozjajstvennyj Institut im. akad. D.N. Prjanišikova, Kommunističeskaja ul. 23, 614600 Perm' GSP-165, Rossiskaja SFSR.
Tél: 32-93-93

Plodoovoščnoj Institut im. I.V. Mičurina, Ul. Internacional-naja 101, 393740 Mičurinsk, Tambovskoj obl., Rossiskaja SFSR.
Tél: 9-01-61

Poltavskij Ordena Trudovogo Krasnogo Znameni

Sel'skohozjajstvennyj Institut, Ul. Skovorody 1/3, 314003 Poltava, Ukrainskaja SSR.
Tél: 7-34-46
Primorskij Sel'skohozjajstvennyj Institut, Bljuhera pr. 44, Primorskogo kraja, 692510 Ussurijsk Kraja 10, Rossiskaja SFSR.
Tél: 2-93-90
Rjazanskij Sel'skohozjajstvennyj Institut im. prof. P.A. Kostyčeva, Ul. Lenina 53, 390000 Rjazan', Rossiskaja SFSR.
Tél: 7-49-64
Samarkandskij Ordena "Znak Početa" Sel'-skohozjajstvennyj Institut im. V.V. Kubjyševa, Ul. Karla Marksa 77, 703003 Samarkand, Uzbekskaja SSR.
Tél: 4-33-20
Saratovskij Sel'skohozjajstvennyj Institut im. Akad. N.I. Vavilova, Pl. Revoljucii 1, 410601 Saratov, Rossiskaja SFSR.
Tél: 2-16-28
Stavropol'skij Ordena Trudovogo Kras-nogo Znameni Sel'skohozjajstvennyj Institut, Zootehničeskij per. 10, 355014 Stavropol', Rossiskaja SFSR.
Tél: 5-18-11
Sverdlovskij Sel'skohozjajstvennyj Institut, Ul. Karla Libknehta 42, 620219 Sverdlovsk GSP-219, Rossiskaja SFSR.
Tél: 51-33-63
Tadžikskij Ordena "Znak Početa" Sel'skohozjaj-stvennyj Institut, Prosp. Lenina 146, 734056 Dušanbe, Tadžikskaja SSR.
Tél: 24-53-41
Taškentskij Ordena Družby Narodov Sel'skohoz-jajstvennyj Institut, Sel'hozinstitut, 700183 Taškent, Uzbekskaja SSR.
Tél: 33-46-85
Tjumenskij Sel'skohozjajstvennyj Institut, Ul. Respubliki 7, 625003 Tjumen', Rossiskaja SFSR.
Tél: 6-16-43
Turkmenskij Ordena "Znak Početa" Sel'-skohoz-jajstvennyj Institut im. M.I. Kalinina, Pervomajskaja Ul. 62, 744000 GSP Ašhabad, Turkmenskaja SSR.
Tél: 4-25-22
Ukrainskaja Ordena Trudovogo Krasnogo Znameni Sel'skohozjajstvennaja Akademija, Ul. Geroev Oborony 15, 252041 Kiev, Ukrain-skaja SSR.
Tél: 63-51-75
Ul'janovskij Sel'skohozjajstvennyj Institut, Bul. Novyj Venec 1, 432601 Ul'janovsk, Rossiskaja SFSR.
Tél: 1-42-72
Umanskij Ordena Trudovogo Krasnogo Znameni Sel'skohozjajstvennyj Institut im. A.M. Gor'kogo, p/o "Sofievka", 258900 Uman', Cerkasskoj obl., Ukrainskaja SSR.

Tél: 5-25-58
Velikolukskij Sel'skohozjajstvennyj Institut, Pl. Lenina 1, 182100 Velikie Luki, Pskovskoj obl., Rossiskaja SFSR.
Tél: 3-26-71
Volgogradskij Sel'skohozjajstvennyj Institut, Institutskaja ul. 8, 400041 Volgograd, Rossi-skaja SFSR.
Tél: 43-08-45
Voronežskij Sel'skohozjajstvennyj Institut im. Akad. D. Glinki, Ul. Mičurina 1, 394612 Voronež 12, Rossiskaja SFSR.
Tél: 6-40-18
Vorošilovgradskij Sel'skohozjajstvennyj Institut, 348008 Vorošilovgrad 8, Ukrainskaja SSR.
Tél: 5-20-40
Vsesojuznyj Ordena "Znak Početa" Sel'-skohoz-jajstvennyj Institut Zaočnogo Obrazovanija, 143900 Balašiha Moskovskoj obl. 8, Rossiskaja SFSR.
Tél: 521-24-56
Zapadno-Kazahstanskij Sel'skohozjajstvennyj Institut, Gorodok SHI, 417025 Ural'sk, Kazahskaja SSR
Tél: 2-19-30
Zitomirskij Sel'skohozjajstvennyj Institut, Ul. 50–letija Oktjabrja 9, 262001 Zitomir, Ukrainskaja SSR.
Tél: 7-44-71

(*Animal Husbandry and Veterinary Science*) — (*Zootechnie et Médecine vétérinaire*)

Alma-Atinskij Ordena Trudovogo Krasnogo Znameni Zooveterinarnyj Institut, Prosp. Abaja 28, 480047 Alma-Ata 28, Kazahskaja SSR.
Tél: 62-78-94
Erevanskij Ordena "Znak Početa" Zootech-ničeskoveterinarnyj Institut, Ul. Nalbandjana 128, 375025 Erevan, Armjanskaja SSR.
Tél: 56-13-42
Gruzinskij Ordena "Znak Početa" Zooveterin-arnyj Učebno-Issledovatel'skij Institut, Krcanisi, 383107 Tbilisi, Gruzinskaja SSR.
Tél: 72-37-52
Har'kovskij Zooveterinarnyj Institut, im. N.M. Borisenko , p/o "Malaja Danilovka", Dergačevskij r-n, 312050 Har'kovskaja obl., Ukrainskaja SSR.
Tél: 32-00-03
Kazanskij Ordena Lenina Veterinarnyj Institut, im. N.E. Baumana, Ul. Sibirskij trakt, 420074 Kazan', Rossiskaja SFSR.
Tél: 4-19-75
Leningradskij Veterinarnyj Institut, Moskovskij prosp. 112, 196006 Leningrad, Rossiskaja

SFSR.
Tél: 298-36-31
Litovskaja Veterinarnaja Akademija, Ul. L.
Adomausko 18, 233022 Kaunas, Litovskaja
SSR.
Tél: 6-03-83
**L'vovskij Ordena Trudovogo Krasnogo Znameni
Zooveterinarnyj Institut**, Pekarskaja ul. 50,
290601 L'vov, Ukrainskaja SSR.
Tél: 72-30-23
**Moskovskaja Ordena Trudovogo Krasnogo
Znameni Veterinarnaja Akademija im. K.I.
Skrjabina**, Ul. Akad. K.I. Skrjabina 23,
109472 Moskva, Rossiskaja SFSR.
Tél: 377-65-01
Omskij Gosudarstvennyj Veterinarnyj Institut,
Oktjabrskaja ul. 92, 644007 Omsk, Rossiskaja
SFSR.
Tél: 22-06-83
Saratovskij Zooveterinarnyj Institut, B.
Sadovaja ul. 220, 410810 Saratov, Rossiskaja
SFSR.
Tél: 2-33-09
Semipalatinskij Zooveterinarnyj Institut, Ul.
Urickogo 17, 490050 Semipalatinsk,
Kazahskaja SSR.
Tél: 2-39-12
Troickij Veterinarnyj Institut, Ul. Gagarina 13,
457100 Troick Celjabinskoj obl., Rossiskaja
SFSR.
Tél: 2-00-10
**Vitebskij Ordena "Znak Početa" Veterinarnyj
Institut im. Oktabr'skoj Revoljucii**, Ul. 1-ja
Dovatora 7/11. 210619 Vitebsk, Belorusskaja
SSR.
Tél: 4-20-43
Vologodskij Moločnyj Institut, p/o Moločnoe,
Ul. Smidta 2, 160901 Vologodskaja obl.,
Rossiskaja SFSR.
Tél: 9-37-30

(Mechanization and Electrification)—
(Mécanisation et Electrification)

**Azovo-Cernomorskij Institut Mechanizacii
Sel'skogo Hozjajstva**, Ul. Lenina 21, 347720
Zernograd, Rostovskoj obl., Rossiskaja SFSR.
Tél: 9-17-43
**Belorusskij Institut Mechanizacii Sel'skogo
Hozjajstva**, Leninskij prosp. 99, 220608 Minsk,
Belorusskaja SSR.
Tél: 64-61-91
**Celjabinskij Ordena Trudovogo Krasnogo
Znameni Institut Mechanizacii Elektrifikacii
Sel'skogo Hozjajstva**, Prosp. Lenina 75, 454080
Celjabinsk, Rossiskaja SFSR.
Tél: 33-13-74

**Har'kovskij Institut Mechanizacii Elektrifikacii
Sel'skogo Hozjajstva**, Artema ul. 44, 310078
Har'kov, Ukrainskaja SSR.
Tél: 22-37-86
**Melitopol'skij Ordena Trudovogo Krasnogo
Znameni Institut Mechanizacii Sel'skogo
Hozjajstva**, Prosp. B. Hmel'nickogo 18, 332315
Melitopol', Zaporožskoj obl., Ukrainskaja
SSR.
Tél: 64-61-91
**Moskovskij Ordena Trudovogo Krasnogo
Znameni Institut Inženerov Sel'skohozjajstven-
nogo Proizvodstva im. V.P. Gorjačkina**,
Timirjazevskaja ul. 58, 127550 Moskva,
Rossiskaja SFSR.
Tél: 216-36-40
**Saratovskij Ordena "Znak Početa" Institut
Mechanizacii Sel'skogo Hozjajstva im. M.I.
Kalinina**, Sovetskaja ul. 60, 410740 Saratov,
Rossiskaja SFSR.
Tél: 2-37-66

(Irrigation and Land Improvement)—
(Irrigation et Aménagement du Sol)

**Džambulskij Gidromelioorativno-Stroitel'nyj
Institut**, Kommunističeskaja ul. 62, 484039
Džambul', Kazahskaja SSR.
Tél: 4-36-51
**Kabardino-Balkarskij Agromeliorativnyj
Institut**, Ul. Tolstogo 185, 360004 Nal'čik
Kabardino-Balkarskaja ASSR.
Tél: 2-23-50
**Moskovskij Ordena Trudovogo Krasnogo
Znameni Gidromeliorativnyj Institut**, Ul.
Prjanišnikova 19, 127550 Moskva Moskovskij,
Rossiskaja SFSR.
Tél: 216-29-62
**Moskovskij Ordena Trudovogo Krasnogo
Znameni Institut Inženerov Zemleustrojstva**,
Ul. Kazakova 15, 103064 Moskva, Rossiskaja
SFSR.
Tél: 261-31-46
**Novočerkasskij Ordena "Znak Početa"
Inženerno-Meliorativnyj Institut**, Puškinskaja
ul. 111, 346409 Novočerkassk, Rossiskaja
SFSR.
Tél: 5-35-33
**Taškentskij Ordena Trudovogo Krasnogo
Znameni Institut Inženerov Irrigacii i Mechan-
izacii Sel'skogo Hozjajstva**, Ul. Kary Nijazova
39, 700000 Taškent, Uzbekskaja SSR.
Tél: 33-46-85
**Ukrainskij Ordena Družby Narodov Institut
Inženerov Vodnogo Hozjajstva**, Leninskja Ul.
11, 266000 Rovno, Ukrainskaja SSR.
Tél: 2-10-86

Institutes of Transport and Telecommunications—
Instituts des Transports et des Télécommunications

(*Rail Transport*)—
(*Transports ferroviaires*)

Alma-Atinskij Institut Inženerov Zeleznodorožnogo Transporta, Ul. Sevčenko 97, 480012 Alma-Ata, Kazahskaja SSR.
Tél: 68-55-07

Belorusskij Institut Inženerov Zeleznodorožnogo Transporta, Ul. Kirova 34, 246653 Gomel', Belorusskaja SSR.
Tél: 21-29-68

Dnepropetrovskij Ordena Trudovogo Krasnogo Znameni Institut Inženerov Zeleznodorožnogo Transporta im. M.I. Kalinina, Ul. Akademika Lazarjana 2, 320629-GSP Dnepropetrovsk 10, Ukrainskaja SSR.
Tél: 3-13-12

Habarovskij Institut Inženerov Zeleznodorožnogo Transporta, Ul. Seryševa 47, 680056 Habarovsk, Rossiskaja SFSR.
Tél: 34-30-76

Har'kovskij Institut Inženerov Zeleznodorožnogo Transporta im. S.M. Kirova, Pl. Fejerbaha 7, 310050 Har'kov, 50 Ukrainskaja SSR.
Tél: 22-22-82

Irkutskij Institut Inženerov Zeleznodorožnogo Transporta, Ul. Cernyševskogo 15, 664074 Irkutsk, Rossiskaja SFSR.
Tél: 6-08-37

Kujbyševskij Institut Inženerov Zeleznodorožnogo Transporta, Pervyj Bezymjannyj per. 18, 443066 Kujbyšev 9, Rossiskaja SFSR.
Tél: 39-49-48

Leningradskij Ordena Lenina i Ordena Oktjabr'skoj Revoljucii Institut Inženerov Zeleznodorožnogo Transporta im. Akademika V.N. Obrazcova, Moskovskij pr. 9, 190031 Leningrad, Rossiskaja SFSR.
Tél: 310-25-21

Moskovskij Ordena Lenina i Ordena Trudovogo Krasnogo Znameni Institut Inženerov Zeleznodorožnogo Transporta, Ul. Obrazcova 15, 103055 Moskva, Rossiskaja SFSR.
Tél: 281-31-77

Novosibirskij Ordena Trudovogo Krasnogo Znameni Institut Inženerov Zeleznodorožnogo Transporta, Ul. Dusi Koval'čuk 191, 630023 Novosibirsk 23, Rossiskaja SFSR.
Tél: 21-75-45

Omskij Institut Inženerov Zeleznodorožnogo Transporta, Pr. Karla Marksa 35, 644010 Omsk, Rossiskaja SFSR.
Tél: 3-42-19

Rostovskij Ordena Trudovogo Krasnogo Znameni Institut Inženerov Zeleznodorožnogo Transporta, Pl. Narodnogo Opolčenija 2, 344017 Rostov-na-Donu 17, Rossiskaja SFSR.
Tél: 31-36-83

Taškenstskij Ordena Trudovogo Krasnogo Znameni Institut Inženerov Zeleznodorožnogo Transporta, Oboronnaja ul. 1, 700045 Taškent L-45, Uzbekskaja SSR.
Tél: 91-14-40

Ural'skij Elektromehaničeskij Institut Inženerov Zeleznodorožnogo Transporta im. Ja.M. Sverdlova, Ul. Kolmogorova 66, 620079 Sverdlovsk 79, Rossiskaja SFSR.
Tél: 58-30-36

Vsesojuznyj Zaočnyj Institut Inženerov Zeleznodorožnogo Transporta, Casovaja ul. 22/2, 125808-GSP-47 Moskva, Rossiskaja SFSR.
Tél: 262-31-32

(*Maritime Transport*)—
(*Transports maritimes*)

Dal'nevostočnoe Vysšee Inženernoe Morskoe Učilišče im. Adm. G.I. Nevel'skogo, Verhnjaja Portovaja ul. 50-a, 690059 Vladivostok 59, Rossiskaja SFSR.
Tél: 2-49-58

Kaliningradskoe Vysšee Inženernoe Morskoe Učilišče, Ul. Molodežnaja 6, 236029 Kaliningrad Oblastnoj, Rossiskaja SFSR.
Tél: 2-72-04

Leningradskoe Ordena Oktjabrjskoj Revoljucii Vysšee Inženernoe Morskoe Učilišče im. Admirala S.O. Makarova, Kosaja Linija 15-a, Vassil'evskij Ostrov, 199026 Leningrad, Rossiskaja SFSR.
Tél: 217-19-34

Murmanskoe Vysšee Inženernoe Morskoe Učilišče im. Leninskogo Komsomola, Sportivnaja ul. 13/6, 183778 Murmansk, Rossiskaja SFSR.
Tél: 6-20-51

Novorossijskoe Vysšee Inženernoe Morskoe Učilišče, Prosp. Lenina 93, 353918 Novorossijsk 18, Rossiskaja SFSR.
Tél: 6-45-45

Odesskij Ordena Trudovogo Krasnogo Znameni Institut Inženerov Morskogo Flota, Ul. Mečnikova 34, 270029 Odessa, Ukrainskaja SSR.
Tél: 3-35-28

Odesskoe Vysšee Inženernoe Morskoe Učilišče im. Leninskogo Komsomola, Ul. Didrihsona 8, 270029 Odessa 29, Ukrainskaja SSR.
Tél: 3-40-88

Petropavlovsk-Kamčatskoe Vysšee Inženernoe Morskoe Učilišče, Ul. Ključevskaja 35, 683023 Petropavlovsk-Kamčatskij.

(Inland Water Transport) —
(Transports fluviaux)

Gor'kovskij Ordena Trudovogo Krasnogo Znameni Institut Inženerov Vodnogo Transporta, Ul. Nesterova 5, 603005 Gor'kij, Rossiskaja SFSR.
Tél: 36-17-56

Leningradskij Ordena Trudovogo Krasnogo Znameni Institut Vodnogo Transporta, Dvinskaja ul. 5/7, 198035 Leningrad, Rossiskaja SFSR.
Tél: 251-12-21

Moskovskij Institut Inženerov Vodnogo Transporta, Ul. Rečnikov 16, 115407 Moskva, Rossiskaja SFSR.
Tél: 116-30-88

Novosibirskij Institut Inženerov Vodnogo Transporta, Ul. Sčetinkina 33, 630099 Novosibirsk, Rossiskaja SFSR.
Tél: 22-64-68

(Civil Aviation) — *(Aviation civile)*

Aktjubinskoe Vysšee Letnoe Učilišče Graždanskoj Aviacii, Ul. Moldagulovoj, 463024 Aktjubinsk, Rossiskaja SFSR.
Tél: 4-07-33

Kievskij Ordena Trudovogo Krasnogo Znameni Institut Inženerov Graždanskoj Aviacii im. 60-letija SSSR, Prosp. Kosmonavta Komorova 1, 252058 Kiev, Ukrainskaja SSR.
Tél: 43-31-41

Kirovogradskoe Vysšee Letnoje Učilišče Graždanskoj Aviacii, Ul. Dobrovoljskogo 1, 316005 Kirovograd Oblastnoj, Ukrainskaja SSR.

Tél: 2-38-64

Moskovskij Institut Inženerov Graždanskoj Aviacii, Kronšstadtskij bul. 20, 125838 Moskva Rossiskaja SFSR.
Tél: 452-59-76

Ordena Lenina Akademija Graždanskoj Aviacii, Ul. Pilotov 38, 196210 Leningrad Rossiskaja SFSR.
Tél: 291-28-43

Rižskij Krasnoznamennyj Institut Inženerov Graždanskoj Aviacii im. Leninskogo Komsomola, Ul. Lomonosova 1, 226019 Riga, Latvijskaja SSR.
Tél: 24-21-97

(Highways Engineering) —
(Ponts et Chaussées)

Har'kovskij Avtomobil'no-Dorožnyj Institut im. Komsomola Ukrainy, Ul. Petrovskogo 25, 310078 Har'kov, Ukrainskaja SSR.
Tél: 42-30-29

Kievskij Avtomobil'no-Dorožnyj Institut im. 60-letija Velikoj Oktjabr'skoj Sočialističeskoj Revoljucii, Ul. Suvorova 1, 252601 Kiev, Ukrainskaja SSR.
Tél: 93-82-03

Moskovskij Ordena Trudovogo Krasnogo Znameni Avtomobil'no-Dorožnyj Institut, Leningradskij prosp. 64, 125319 Moskva A-319, Rossiskaja SFSR.
Tél: 155-01-04

Sibirskij Ordena Trudovogo Krasnogo Znameni Avtomobil'no-Dorožnyj Institut im. V.V. Kujbyševa, Prosp. Mira 5, 644080 Omsk 80, Rossiskaja SFSR.
Tél: 65-98-81

Taškentskij Avtomobil'no-Dorožnyj Institut, Ul. Karla Marksa 32, 700047-GSP Taškent, Uzbekskaja SSR.
Tél: 33-08-27

Institutes of Economics—Instituts de Sciences économiques

(Political Economics) —
(Economie politique)

Alma-Atkinskij Institut Narodnogo Hozjajstva, Ul. Džandosova 55, 480035 Alma-Ata, Kazahskaja SSR.

Ašhabadskij Institut Narodnogo Hozjajstva, Ul. Hudajberdyeva 46, 744004 Ašhabad, Turkmenskaja SSR.

Bakinskij Filial' Leningradskogo Finansovo-Ekonomičeskogo Institut, Ul. Kommanističeskaja 6, 370000 Baku, Azerbadjdžanskaja

SSR.

Belorusskij Ordena Trudovogo Krasnogo Znameni Gosudarstvennyj Institut Narodnogo Hozjajstva im. V.V. Kujbyševa, Partizanskij prosp. 26, 220672 Minsk, 110 Belorusskaja SSR.

Erevanskij Institut Narodnogo Hozjajstva, Ul. Abovjana 52, 375025 Erevan, Armjanskaja SSR.

Gorijskij Ekonomičeskij Institut, Prosp. Čavčavadze 57, 383500 Gori, Georgia SSSR.

Habarovskij Institut Narodnogo Hozjajstva, Ul.

Tihookeanskaja 134, 680049 Habarovsk 35, Rossiskaja SFSR.

Irkutskij Institut Narodnogo Hozjajstva, Ul. V.I. Lenina 11, 664003 Irkutsk 3, Rossiskaja SFSR.

Kievskij Institut Narodnogo Hozjajstva im. D.S. Korotčenko, prosp. Pobeby 54/1, 252057 Kiev, Ukrainskaja SSR.

Kujbyševskij Ordena "Znak Početa" Planovyj Institut, Ul. Sovetskoj Armij 141, 443090 Kujbyšev obl. 90, Rossiskaja SFSR.

Moskovskij Ordena Trudovogo Krasnogo Znameni Institut Narodnogo Hozjajstva im. G.V. Plehanova, Stremjannyj per. 28, 113230 Moskva M-54, Rossiskaja SFSR.

Moskovskij Ordena Trudovogo Krasnogo Znameni Ekonomiko-Statističeskij Institut, Nežinskaja ul. 7, 119517 Moskva G-517, Rossiskaja SFSR.

Novosibirskij Institut Narodnogo Hozjajstva, Ul. Kamenskaja 56, 630070 Novosibirsk 70, Rossiskaja SFSR.

Odesskij Institut Narodnogo Hozjajstva, Ul. Sovetskoj Armii 8, 270100 Odessa, Ukrainskaja SSR.

Rostovskij-na-Donu Ordena "Znak Početa" Institut Narodnogo Hozjajstva, Ul. Fridriha Engle'sa 69, 344708 Rostov-na-Donu, Rossiskaja SFSR.

Saratovskij Ordena "Znak Početa" Ekonomičeskij Institut, Ul. Radiščeva 89, 410760 Saratov, Rossiskaja SFSR.

Sverdlovskij Institut Narodnogo Hozjajstva, Ul. 8 Marta 62, 620001 Sverdlovsk, Rossiskaja SFSR.

Taškentskij Ordena Družby Naradov Institut Narodnogo Hozjajstva, Ul. Almazar 183, 700063 Taškent, 63 Uzbekskaja SSR.

Dal'nevostočnyj Institut Sovetskoj Torgovli, Okeanskij prosp. 19, 690600 Vladivostok, Centr, GSP, Rossiskaja SFSR.

Doneckij Institut Sovetskoj Torgovli, Ul. Sčorsa 31, 340050 Doneck, 50 Ukrainskaja SSR.

Gomel'skij Kooperativnyj Institut, Prosp. Oktjabrja 52a, 246029 Gomel', Belorusskaja SS

Har'kovskij Institut Obščestvennogo Pitanija, Kločovskaja ul. 333, 310051 Har'kov, 51 Ukrainskaja SSR.

Karagandinskij Kooperativnyj Institut, Ul. Akademičeskaja 9, 470017 Karaganda, Kazahskaja SSR.

Kievskij Torgogo-Ekonomičeskij Institut, Ul. Kioto 19, 252156 Kiev, Ukrainskaja SSR.

Leningradskij Ordena Trudovogo Krasnogo Znameni Institut Sovetskoj Torgovli im. F. Engel'sa, Novorossijskaja ul. 50, 194018 Leningrad, Rossiskaja SFSR.

L'vovskij Torgovo-Ekonomičeskij Institut, Ul. Ckalova 10, 290008 L'vov, Ukrainskaja SSR.

Moskovskij Ordena Družby Narodov Kooperativnyj Institut, Ul. Very Vološinoj 12, 14100 Mytišči, Moskva obl., Rossiskaja SFSR.

Novosibirskij Institut Sovetskoj Kooperativnoj Torgovli, Prosp. Karla Marksa 26 630087 Novosibirsk, Rossiskaja SFSR.

Poltavskij Kooperativnyj Institut, Ul. Kovalja 3, 314601 Poltava, Ukrainskaja SSR.

Samarkandskij Ordena Družby Narodov Kooperativnyj Institut im. V.V. Kujbyševa, Kommunističeskaja ul. 41, 703000 Samarkand, Uzbekskaja SSR.

Zaočnyj Institut Sovetskoj Torgovli, Smol'naja ul. 36, 125445 Moskva, Rossiskaja SFSR.

(Engineering Economics) –
(Economie industrielle)

Har'kovskij Inženerno-Ekonomičeskij Institut, Prosp. Lenina 9a, 310141 Har'kov, Ukrainskaja SSR.

Leningradskij Ordena "Znak Početa" Inženerno-Ekonomičeskij Institut im. Pal'miro Tol'jatti, Ul. Marata 27, 191002 Leningrad, Rossiskaja SFSR.

Moskovskij Ordena Trudovogo Krasnogo Znameni Institut Upravlenija im. Sergo Ordžonikidze, Podsosenskij per. 20, 109542 Moskva a, Rossiskaja SFSR.

(Commerce) – (Commerce)

Belgorodskij Kooperativnyj Institut, Sadovaja Ul. 116a, 308023 Belgorod, Rossiskaja SFSR.

(Finance) – (Etudes financières)

Kazanskij Ordena "Znak Početa" Finansovo-Ekonomičeskij Institut im. V.V. Kujbyševa, Ul. Butlerova 4, 420012 Kazan, Rossiskaja SFSR.

Leningradskij Ordena Trudovogo Krasnogo Znameni Finansovo-Ekonomičeskij Institut im. N.A. Voznesenskogo, Kanal Griboedova 30/32, 191023 Leningrad, Rossiskaja SFSR.

Moskovskij Finansovyj Institut, Ul. Kibal'čiča 1, 129848 Moskva I-64, Rossiskaja SFSR.

Ternopol'skij Finansovo-Ekonomičeskij Institut, Pl. Pobedy 3, 282004 Ternopol', Ukrainskaja SSR.

Vsesojuznuj Ordena "Znak Početa" Zaočnyj Finansovo-Ekonomičeskij Institut, Ul. Oleko Dundiča 23, 121108 Moskva G-108, Rossiskaja SFSR.

Institutes of Law—Instituts de Droit

Har'kovskij Ordena Trudovogo Krasnogo Znameni Juridičeskij Institut im. F.E. Dzeržinskogo, Puškinskaja ul. 77, 310024 Har'kov, Ukrainskaja SSR.

Saratovskij Ordena "Znak Početa" Juridičeskij Institut im. D.I. Kurskogo, Ul. Cernyševskogo 104, 410720 Saratov, Rossiskaja SFSR.

Sverdlovskij Ordena Trudovogo Krasnogo Znameni Juridičeskij Institut im. R.A. Rudenko, Ul. Komsomol'skaja 21, 620066 Sverdlovsk GSP-1038, Rossiskaja SFSR.

Vsesojuznyj Juridičeskij Zaočnyj Institut, Starokirocnyj per. 13, 107005 Moskva, Rossiskaja SFSR.

Institutes of Medicine—Instituts de Médecine

(Medicine)—(Médecine)

Aktjubisnkij Gosudarstvennyj Medicinskij Institut, Ul. Lenina 52, 463000 Aktjubinsk, Rossiskaja SFSR.

Alma-Atinskij Ordena Trudovogo Krasnogo Znameni Gosudarstvennyj Medicinskij Institut, Ul. Komsomol'skaja 88, 480012 Alma-Ata, Kazahskaja SSR.

Altajskij Gosudarstvennyj Medicinskij Institut im. Leninskogo Komsomola, Prosp. Lenina 40, 656099 Barnaul, Rossiskaja SFSR.

Andižanskij Gosudarstvennyj Medicinskij Institut im. M.I. Kalinina, Pr. Navoi 136, 710000 Andižan, Uzbekskaja SSR.

Arhangel'skij Ordena Trudovogo Krasnogo Znameni Gosudarstvennyj Medicinskij Institut, Pr. Vinogradova 51, 163061 Arhangel'sk, Rossiskaja SFSR.

Astrahanskij Gosudarstvennyj Medicinskij Institut im. A.V. Lunačarskogo, Ul. Mečnikova 20, 414000 Astrahan', Rossiskaja SFSR.

Azerbajdžanskij Ordena Trudovogo Krasnogo Znameni Gosudarstvennyj Medicinskij Institut im. N. Narimanova, Ul. Bakihanova 23, 370022 Baku 22, Azerbajdžanskaja SSR.

Baškirskij Gosudarstvennyj Medicinskij Institut im. 15-letija VLKSM, Ul. Frunze 47, 450025 Ufa, Rossiskaja SFSR.

Blagoveščenskij Gosudarstvennyj Medicinskij Institut, Ul. Gor'kogo 95, 675006 Blagoveščensk Amurskoj obl., Rossiskaja SFSR.

Celinogradskij Medicinskij Institut, Prosp. Mira 51a, 473013 Celinograd, Kazahskaja SSR.

Celjabinskij Gosudarstvennyj Medicinskij Institut, Ul. Vorovskogo 64, 454092 Celijabinsk, Rossiskaja SFSR.

Cernovickij Gosudarstvennyj Medicinskij Institut, Teatral'naja pl. 2, 274000 Cernovcy, Ukrainskaja SSR.

Citinskij Gosudarstvennyj Medicinskij Institut, Ul. Gor'kogo 39a, 672090 Cita, Rossiskaja SFSR.

Dagestanskij Ordena Družby Narodov Gosudarstvennyj Medicinskij Institut, Pl. Lenina 6, 367025 Mahačkala, Dagestanskaja ASSR.

Dnepropetrovskij Ordena Trudovogo Krasnogo Znameni Medicinskij Institut, Ul. Dzeržinskogo 9, 320044 Dnepropetrovsk, Ukrainskaja SSR.

Doneckij Gosudarstvennyj Medicinskij Institut im. Maksima Gor'kogo, Prosp. Il'iča 16, 340098 Doneck, Ukrainskaja SSR.

Erevanskij Ordena Trudovogo Krasnogo Znameni Gosudarstvennyj Medicinskij Institut, Ul. Kirova 2, 375025 Erevan 25, Armjanskaja SSR.

Gor'kovskij Gosudarstvennyj Medicinskij Institut im. S.M. Kirova, Pl. Minina i Požarskogo 10/1, 603005 Gor'kij, Rossiskaja SFSR.

Grodnenskij Gosudarstvennyj Medicinskij Institut, Ul. Gor'kogo 80, 230015 Grodno, Beloruskaja SSR.

Habarovskij Ordena Trudovogo Krasnogo Znameni Gosudarstvennyj Medicinskij Institut, Ul. Karla Marksa 35, 680000 Habarovsk, Rossiskaja SFSR.

Har'kovskij Medicinskij Institut, Prosp. V.I. Lenina 4, 310022 Har'kov, Ukrainskaja SSR.

Irkutskij Gosudarstvennyj Medicinskij Institut, Ul. Krasnogo Vosstanija 1, 664003 Irkutsk, Rossiskaja SFSR.

Ivano-Frankovskij Medicinskij Institut, Galickaja ul. 2, 284000 Ivano-Frankovsk, Ukrainskaja SSR.

Ivanovskij Gosudarstvennyj Medicinskij Institut im. A.S. Bubnova, Ul. F. Engel'sa 8, 153462 Ivanovo, Rossiskaja SFSR.

Iževskij Ordena Družby Narodov Gosudarstvennyj Medicinskij Institut, Ul. Revoljucionnaja 199, 426034 Iževsk, Udmurtskoj ASSR.

Jaroslavskij Gosudarstvennyj Medicinskij Institut, Revoljucionnaja ul. 5, 150000 Jaroslavl', Rossiskaja SFSR.

Kalininskij Gosudarstvennyj Medicinskij Institut, Sovetskaja ul. 4, 170642 Kalinin, Rossiskaja SFSR.

Karagandisnkij Gosudarstvennyj Medicinskij Institut, Ul. Gogolja 40, 470061 Karaganda, Kazahskaja SSR.

Kaunasskij Medicinskij Institut, Ul. Mickevičjaus 9, 233683 Kaunas, Litovskaja SSR.

Kazanskij Ordena Trudovogo Krasnogo Znameni Gosudarstvennyj Medicinskij Institut im. S.V. Kurašova, Ul. Butlerova 49, 420012 Kazan' 12, Rossiskaja SFSR.

Kemerovskij Gosudarstvennyj Medicinskij Institut, Ul. Vorošilova 22a, 650029 Kemerovo obl., Rossiskaja SFSR.

Kievskij Ordena Trudovogo Krasnogo Znameni Medicinskij Institut im. akad. A.A. Bogomol'ca, Bul. Tarasa Sevčenko 13, 252004 Kiev, Ukrainskaja SSR.

Kirgizskij Gosudarstvennyj Medicinskij Institut, Ul. 50-let Oktjabrja 92, 720061 Frunze, Kirgizskaja SSR.

Kišinevskij Gosudarstvennyj Medicinskij Institut, Prosp. V.I. Lenina 165, 277017 Kišinev, Moldavskaja SSR.

Krasnojarskij Gosudarstvennyj Medicinskij Institut, Ul. Partizana Zeleznjaka 1, 660022 Krasnojarsk, Rossiskaja SFSR.

Krymskij Ordena Trudovogo Krasnogo Znameni Medicinskij Institut, Bul. V.I. Lenina 5/7, 333670 Simferopol', Rossiskaja SFSR.

Kubanskij Gosudarstvennyj Medicinskij Institut im. Krasnoj Armii, Ul. Sedina 4, 350003 Krasnodar, Rossiskaja SFSR.

Kujbyševskij Medicinskij Institut im. D.I. Ul'janova, Capaevskaja ul. 89, 443099 Kujbyšev obl., Rossiskaja SFSR.

Kurskij Gosudarstvennyj Medicinskij Institut, Ul. Karla Marska 3, 305033 Kursk, Rossiskaja SFSR.

1-j Leningradskij Ordena Trudovogo Krasnogo Znameni Medicinskij Institut im. akad. I.P. Pavlova, Ul. L'va Tolstogo 6/8, 197089 Leningrad, Rossiskaja SFSR.

Leningradskij Ordena Trudovogo Krasnogo Znameni Pediatričeskij Medicinskij Institut, Litovskaja ul. 2, 194100 Leningrad K-100, Rossiskaja SFSR.

Leningradskij Sanitarno-Gigieničeskij Medicinskij Institut, Piskarevskij prosp. 47, 195067 Leningrad, Rossiskaja SFSR.

L'vovskij Ordena Družby Narodov Medicinskij Institut, Pekarskaja ul. 69, 290010 L'vov, Ukrainskaja SSR.

Minskij Ordena Trudovogo Krasnogo Znameni Gosudarstvennyj Medicinskij Institut, Prosp. Dzeržinskogo, 220798 Minsk, Belorusskaja SSR.

*1-j Moskovskij Ordena Lenina i Ordena Trudovogo Krasnogo Znameni Medicinskij Institut im. I.M. Sečenova, 2/6 Pirogovskaja ul., 119435 Moskva, Rossiskaja SFSR.

2-j Moskovskij Ordena Lenina Gosudarstvennyj Medicinskij Institut im. N.I. Pirogova, Ul. Ostrovitjanova 1, 117437 Moskva, Rossiskaja SFSR.

Novosibirskij Medicinskij Institut, Krasnyj prosp. 52, 630091 Novosibirsk, Rossiskaja SFSR.

Odesskij Medicinskij Institut im. N.I. Pirogova, Narimana Narimanova, per. 2, 270100 Odessa, Ukrainskaja SSR.

Omskij Ordena Trudovogo Krasnogo Znameni Gosudarstvennyj Medicinskij Institut im. M.I. Kalinina, Ul. V.I. Lenina 12, 644099 Omsk, Rossiskaja SFSR.

Orenburgskij Gosudarstvennyj Medicinskij Institut, Sovetskaja ul. 6, 460834 Orenburg, Rossiskaja SFSR.

Permskij Gosudarstvennyj Medicinskij Institut, Ul. Kujbyševa 39, 614600 Perm', GSP 186, Rossiskaja SFSR.

Rižskij Medicinskij Institut, Bul. Padom'ju 12, 226352 Riga GSP, Latvijskaja SSR.

Rjazanskij Medicinskij Institut im. akad. I.P. Pavlova, Ul. Majakovskogo 105, 390000 Rjazan, Rossiskaja SFSR.

Rostovskij Ordena Družby Narodov Medicinskij Institut, Nahičevanskij per. 29, 344718 Rostovna-Donu, Rossiskaja SFSR.

Samarkandskij Ordena Družby Narodov Gosudarstvennyj Medicinskij Institut im. akad. I.P. Pavlova, Ul. Frunze 18, 703000 Samarkand, Uzbekskaja SSR.

Saratovskij Ordena Trudovogo Krasnogo Znameni Gosudarstvennyj Medicinskij Institut, Ul. 20-Letija VLKSM 112, 410601 Saratov, Rossiskaja SFSR.

Semipalatinskij Gosudarstvennyj Medicinskij Institut, Ul. Sovetskaja 103, 490050 Semipalatinsk, Kazashskaja SSR.

Severo-Osetinskij Gosudarstvennyj Medicinskij Institut, Puškinskaja ul. 10, 362025 Ordžonikidze, Rossiskaja SFSR.

Smolenskij Gosudarstvennyj Medicinskij Institut, Ul. Glinki 3, 214000 Smolensk, Rossiskaja SFSR.

Sredneaziatskij Medicinskij Pediatričeskij Institut, Ul. Cermet 103, 700140 Taškent, Uzbekskaja SSR.

Stavropol'skij Gosudarstvennyj Medicinskij Institut, Ul. Mira 310, 355024 Stavropol' Kraevoj, Rossiskaja SFSR.

Sverdlovskij Ordena Trudovogo Krasnogo Znameni Gosudarstvennyj Medicinskij Institut, Ul. Repina 3, 620119 Sverdlovsk, Rossiskaja SFSR.

Tadžikskij Gosudarstvennyj Medicinskij Institut im. Abuali Ibn-Siny (Avicenny), Prosp. V.I. Lenina 139, 734003 Dušanbe, Tadžikskaja SSR.

Taškentskij Ordena Trudovogo Krasnogo Znameni Gosudarstvennyj Medicinskij Institut,

Ul. Karla Marksa 103, 700033 Taškent, Uzbekskaja SSR.

Tbilisskij Ordena Trudovogo Krasnogo Znameni Gosudarstvennyj Medicinskij Institut, Prosp. V. Pšavela 33, 380077 Tbilisi 77, Gruzinskaja SSR.

Ternopol'skij Medicinskij Institut, Pl. Svobody 6, 282001 Ternopol', Ukrainskaja SSR.

Tjumenskij Gosudarstvennyj Medicinskij Institut, Odesskaja ul. 52, 625023 Tjumen', Rossiskaja SFSR.

Tomskij Ordena Trudovogo Krasnogo Znameni Gosudarstvennyj Medicinskij Institut, Moskovskij trakt 2, 634050 Tomsk, Rossiskaja SFSR.

Turkmenskij Ordena Družby Narodov Gosudarstvennyj Medicinskij Institut, Ul. Saumjana 58, 744000 Ašhabad GSP-19, Turkmenskaja SSR.

Ustinovskij Ordena Družby Narodov Gosudarstvennyj Medicinskij Institut, Revoljucionnaja ul. 199, 426034 Ustinov, Rossiskaja SFSR.

Vinnickij Ordena "Znak Početa" Medicinskij Institut im. N.I. Pirogova, Ul. Pirogova 54, 286018 Vinnica, Ukrainskaja SSR.

Vitebskij Ordena Družby Narodov Medicinskij Institut, Prosp. Frunze 27, 210023 Vitebsk, Belorusskaja SSR.

Vladivostokskij Medicinskij Institut, Pr. Ostrjakova 2, 690600 Vladivostok, Rossiskaja SFSR.

Volgogradskij Medicinskij Institut, Pl. Pavših Borcov 1, 400066 Volgograd, Rossiskaja SFSR.

Voronežskij Gosudarstvennyj Medicinskij Institut im. N.N. Burdenko, Studenčeskaja ul. 10, 394622 Voronež, Rossiskaja SFSR.

Vorošilovgradskij Medicinskij Institut, Ul. 50-let Oborony Luganska, 348045 Vorošilovgrad, Ukrainskaja SSR.

Zaporožskij Medicinskij Institut, Ul. Majakovskogo 26, 330074 Zaporože, Ukrainskaja SSR.

(Dentistry) — (Stomatologie)

Moskovskij Ordena Trudovogo Krasnogo Znameni Medicinskij Stomatologičeskij Institut im. N.A. Semaško, Delegatskaja ul. 20, 103473 Moskva, Rossiskaja SFSR.

Poltavskij Medicinskij-Stomatologičeskij Institut, Ul. Sevčenko 23, 314024 Poltava, Ukrainskaja SSR.

(Pharmacy) — (Pharmacie)

Habarovskij Gosudarstvennyj Farmacevtičeskij Institut, Ul. K. Marksa 30, 680000 Habarovsk, Rossiskaja SFSR.

Har'kovskij Farmacevtičeskij Institut, Ul. Puškinskaja 53, 310024 Har'kov 24, Ukrainskaja SSR.

Leningradskij Himiko-Farmacevtičeskij Institut, Ul. Professora Popova 14, 197022 Leningrad, Rossiskaja SFSR.

Permskij Farmacevtičeskij Institut, Ul. V.I. Lenina 48, 614600 Perm', GSP-277, Rossiskaja SFSR.

Pjatigorskij Farmacevtičeskij Institut, Prosp. Kalinina 11, 357533 Pjatigorsk, Stavropol'-skogo kraja, Rossiskaja SFSR.

Taškentskij Farmacevtičeskij Institut, Ul. Kafanowa 35, 700015 Taškent, Uzbekskaja SSR.

Conservatories and Institutes of Dramatic and Fine Arts —
Conservatoires et Instituts des Beaux-Arts et d'Art dramatique

Alma-Atinskaja Gosudarstvennaja Konservatorija im. Kurmangazy, ul. Kirova 136, 480091 Alma-Ata, Kazahskaja SSR.

Astrahanskaja Gosudarstvennaja Konservatorija, Sovetskaja ul. 23, 414000 Astrahan', Rossiskaja SFSR.

Azerbajdžanskaja Ordena Trudovogo Krasnogo Znameni Gosudarstvennaja Konservatorija im. Uz. Gadžibekova, Ul. G. Dimitrova 98, 370014 Baku, Azerbajdžanskaja SSR.

Belorusskaja Ordena Družby Narodov Gosudarstvennaja Konservatorija im. A.V. Lunačarskogo, Internacional'naja Ul. 30, 220303 Minsk, Belorusskaja SSR.

Dal'nevostočnyj Pedagogičeskij Institut, Iskusstv, Ul. 1 Maja 3, 690600 Vladivostok,

Rossiskaja SFSR.

Doneckij Gosudarstvennyj Muzykal'no-Pedagogičeskij Institut, Ul. Artema 44, 340086 Doneck, Ukrainskaja SSR.

Erevanskaja Ordena Trudovogo Krasnogo Znameni Gosudarstvennaja Konservatorija im. Komitasa, Ul. Sajat-Novy 1a, 375009 Erevan 9, Armjanskaja SSR.

Gor'kovskaja Gosudarstvennaja Konservatorija im. M.I. Glinki, Ul. Piskunova 40, 603600 Gor'kij, Rossiskaja SFSR.

Gosudarstvennaja Konservatorija Latvijskoj SSR im. Ja. Vitola, Ul. Krišjana Barona 1, 226050 Riga, Latvijskaja SSR.

Gosudarstvennaja Ordena Družby Narodov Konservatorija Litovskoj SSR, Prosp. Lenina

42, 232600 Vil'njus, Litovskaja SSR.
Gosudarstvennyj Muzykal'no-Pedagogičeskij Institut im. Gnesinyh, Ul. Vorovskogo 30/36 121069 Moskva G-69, Rossiskaja SFSR.
Har'kovskij Gosudarstvennyj Institut Iskusstv im. I.P. Kotljarevskogo, Pl. Soretskoj Ukrainy 11/13, 310003 Har'kov, Ukrainskaja SSR.
Kazanskaja Gosudarstvennaja Konservatorija, B. Krasnaja Ul. 38, 420015 Kazan' 15, Rossiskaja SFSR.
Kievskaja Ordena Lenina Gosudarstvennaja Konservatorija im. P.I. Cajkovskogo, Ul. Karla Marksa 1/3, 252001 Kiev, Ukrainskaja SSR.
Kirgizskij Gosudarstvennyj Institut Iskusstv im. B. Bejšenalievoj, Ul. Džantoševa 115, 720460 Frunze 5, Kirgizskaja SSR.
Krasnojarskij Gosudarstvennyj Institut Iskusstv, Prosp. Mira 98, 660049 Krasnojarsk, Rossiskaja SFSR.
Leningradskaja Ordena Lenina Gosudarstvennaja Konservatorija im. N.A. Rimskogo-Korsakova, Teatral'naja pl. 3, 190000 Centr, Leningrad, Rossiskaja SFSR.
L'vovskaja Gosudarstvennaja Konservatorija im. N.V. Lysenko, Ul. Bojko 5, 290005 L'vov, Ukrainskaja SSR.
Moldavskaja Gosudarstvennaja Konservatorija, Sadovaja ul. 87, 277014 Kišinev, Moldavskaja SSR.
Moldavskij Gosudarstvennyj Institut Iskusstv, Ul. Sadovaja 85, 227014 Kišinev, Moldavskaja SSR.
Moskovskaja Dvaždy Ordena Lenina Gosudarstvennaja Konservatorija im. P.I. Cajkovskogo, Ul. Gercena 13, 103009 Moskva K-9, Rossiskaja SFSR.

Novosibirskaja Gosudarstvennaja Konservatorija im. M.I. Glinki, Sovetskaja Ul. 31, 630099 Novosibirsk 99, Rossiskaja SFSR.
Odesskaja Gosudarstvennaja Konservatorija im. A.V. Neždanovoj, Ul. Ostrovidova 63, 270000 Odessa, Ukrainskaja SSR.
Rostovskij Muzykal'no-Pedagogičeskij Institut, Budennovskij prosp. 23, 344007 Rostov-na-Donu, Rossiskaja SFSR.
Saratovskaja Gosudarstvennaja Konservatorija im. L.V. Sobinova, Prosp, Kirova 1, 410730 Saratov, Rossiskaja SFSR.
Tadžikskij Gosudarstvennyj Institut Iskusstv im. M. Tursyn-zade, Ul. Ždanova 73a, 734032 Dušanbe, Tadžikskaja SSR.
Tallinskaja Gosudarstvennaja Konservatorija, Bul'var Vabaduše 130, 200015 Tallin, Estonskaja SSR.
Taškentskaja Gosudarstvennaja Konservatorija im. M. Ašrafi, Puškinskaja ul. 31, 700000 Taškent, Uzbeskaja SSR.
Tbilisskaja Gosudarstvennaja Konservatorija im. V. Saradžišvili, Ul. Griboedova 8, 380004 Tbilisi 4, Gruzinskaja SSR.
Turkmenskij Gosudarstvennyj Pedagogičeskij Institut Iskusstv, Prosp. V.I. Lenina 3, 744007 Ašhabad, Turkmenskaja SSR.
Uflimskij Gosudarstvennyj Institut Iskusstv, Ul. Lenina 14, 450093 Ufa, Rossiskaja SFSR.
Ural'skaja Ordena Trudovogo Krasnogo Znameni Gosudarstvennaja Konservatorija im. M.P. Musorgskogo, Prosp. Lenina 26, 620014 Sverdlovsk, Rossiskaja SFSR.
Voronežskij Gosudarstvennyj Institut Iskusstv, Berezovaja Rošča 54, 394043 Voronež, Rossiskaja SFSR.

Institutes of Dramatic Art and Cinematography—
Instituts d'Art dramatique et cinématographique

Azerbajdžanskij Gosudarstvennyj Institut Iskusstv im. M.A. Alieva, Ul. Karganova 13, 370000 Baku, Azerbajdžanskaja SSR.
Alma-Atinskij Gosudarstvennyj Teatral'no-Hudožestvennyj Institut, Sovetskaja ul. 28, 480100 Alma-Ata, Kazahskaja SSR.
Belorusskij Gosudarstvennyj Teatral'no-Hudožestvennyj Institut, Leninskij prosp. 81, 220012 Minsk, Belorusskaja SSR.
Gosudarstvennyj Ordena Trudovogo Krasnogo Znameni i Ordena Družby Narodov Institut Teatral'nogo Iskusstva im. A.V. Lunačarskogo, Sobinovskij per. 6, 103009 Moskva K-9, Rossiskaja SFSR.
Gruzinskij Gosudarstvennyj Teatral'nyj Institut im. S. Rustaveli, Prosp. Rustaveli 17, 380004

Tbilisi, Gruzinskaja SSR.
Gosudarstvennyj Institut Teatral'nogo Iskusstva im. I.K. Karpenko-Karogo, Ul. Jaroslavov Val 40, 252034 Kiev, Ukrainskaja SSR.
Leningradskij Gosudarstvennyj Institut Teatra, Muzyki Kinematografii im. N.K. Cerkasova, Mohovaja ul. 34, 191028 Leningrad, Rossiskaja SFSR.
Skola-Studija (vuz) im. V.I. Nemiroviča-Dančenko pri MHAT SSSR im. M. Gor'kogo, ul. Gor'kogo 6, str. 7, 103009 Moskva K-9, Rossiskaja SFSR.
Sverdlovskij Gosudarstvennyj Teatraljnyj Institüt, Ul. Kitibknehta 38, 620151 Sverdlovsk, Rossiskaja SFSR.
Taškentskij Gosudarstvennyj Teatral'no-

Hudožestvennyj Institut im. A.N. Ostrovskogo, Ul. Germana Lopatina 77, 700031 Taškent 31, Uzbekskaja SSR.
Teatral'noe Učilišče (vuz) im. M.S. Sčepkina pri Gosudarstvennom Ordena Lenina i Ordena Oktjabr'skoj Revoljucii Akademičeskom Malom Teatre SSSR, Pušečnaja ul. 2/6, 103012 Moskva, Rossiskaja SFSR.
Teatral'noe Učilišče (vuz) im. B.V. Sčukina pri Gosudarstvennom Ordena Lenina i Ordena Trudovogo Krasnogo Znameni Teatre im. E.

Vahtangova, Ul. Vahtangova 12a, 121002 Moskva G-2, Rossiskaja SFSR.
Teatral'noe Učilišče (vuz) pri Jaroslavskom Gosudarstvennom Akademičeskom Teatre im. F.G. Volkova, Pervomajskaja ul. 43, 150000 Jaroslavl', Rossiskaja SFSR.
Vsesojuznyj Ordena Trudovogo Krasnogo Znameni Gosudarstvennyj Institut Kinematografii, Ul. Vil'gel'ma Pika 3, 129226 Moskva 1-226, Rossiskaja SFSR.

Institutes of Fine and Applied Arts —
Instituts des Beaux-Arts et Arts appliqués

(Fine and Applied Arts) —
(Beaux-Arts et Arts appliqués)

Gosudarstvennaja Akademija Hudožestv Latvijskoj SSR im. Teodora Zal'kalna, Bul'var Kommunarov 13, 226185 Riga GSP, Latvijskaja SSR.
Gosudarstvennyj Hudožestvennyj Institut Litovskoj SSR, Ul. Tiesos 6, 232600 Vil'njus, Litovskaja SSR.
Gosudarstvennyj Hudožestvennyj Institut Estonskoj SSR, Tartuskoe šosse 1, 200104 Tallin, Estonskaja SSR.
Erevanskij Gosudarstvennyj Hudožestvenno-Teatral'nyj Institut, Ul. Isaakjana 36, 375009 Erevan, Armjanskaja SSR.
Har'kovskij Gosudarstvennyj Hudožestvenno-Promyšlennyj Institut, Krasnoznamennaja ul. 8, 310002 Har'kov, Ukrainskaja SSR.
Kievskij Gosudarstvennyj Hudožestvennyj Institut, Ul. Smirnova-Lastočkina 20, 252053 Kiev, Ukrainskaja SSR.
Krasnojarskij Gosudarstvennyj Hudožestvennyj Institut, pr. Mira 98, 660049 Krasnojarsk, Rossiskaja SFSR.
Ordena Trudovogo Krasnogo Znameni Institut Zivopisi, Skul'ptury i Arhitektury im. I.E.

Repina, Universitetskaja nab. 17, 199034 Leningrad V-34, Rossiskaja SFSR.
L'vovskij Gosudarstvennyj Institut Prikladnogo i Dekorativnogo Iskusstva, Ul. Gončarova 38, 290011 L'vov, Ukrainskaja SSR.
Moskovskij Gosudarstvennyj Institut Živopisi, Skulptury i Hudožestvennoj Pedagogiki, Suščevskij val 73, Kor 2, 129272 Moskva, Rossiskaja SFSR.
Moskovskij Ordena Trudovogo Krasnogo Znameni Gosudarstvennyj Hudožestvennyj Institut im. V.I. Surikova, Tovariščeckij nep. 30, 109004 Moskva Z-4, Rossiskaja SFSR.
Tbilisskaja Ordena Trudovogo Krasnogo Znameni Gosudarstvennaja Akademija Hudožestv, Ul. Griboedova 22, 380008 Tbilisi, Gruzinskaja SSR.

(Architecture and Industrial Art) —
(Architecture et Arts industriels)

Leningradskoe Vysšee Hudožestvennopromyšlennoe Učilišče im. V.I. Muhinoj, Soljanoj per. 13, 192028 Leningrad, Rossiskaja SFSR.
Moskovskoe Vysšee Hudožestvennopromyšlennoe Učilišče, Volokolamskoe šosse 9, 125080 Moskva, Rossiskaja SFSR.

Pedagogical Institutes — Instituts pédagogiques

*Moskovskij Ordena Lenina i Ordena Trudovogo Krasnogo Znameni Gosudarstvennyj Pedagogičeskij Institut im. V.I. Lenina, Pirogovskaja ul. 1, 119435 Moskva, Rossiskaja SFSR.
Also 187 other institutes of education and 21 institutes of physical education.

*Moskovskij Ordena Družby Narodov Gosudarstvennyj Pedagogičeskij Institut Inostrannyh Jazykov im. Morisa Toreza, Metrostroevskaja ul. 38, 119034 Moskva G-34, Rossiskaja SFSR.
Also 11 other institutes of foreign languages and 18 institutes of cultural, literary and historical studies.

Sovet Rektorov Vysših Učebnyh Zavadenii SSSR.
Les Conseils de recteurs des universités et
autres établissements d'enseignement supérieur
ont été créés en 1972–73 dans les grands centres
d'enseignement supérieur d'Union soviétique,
afin de coordonner les activités des divers établissements, de recueillir et de diffuser les
expériences positives acquises dans l'organisation du processus d'enseignement, d'améliorer
la qualité de la formation, des études et de la
recherche ainsi que la qualification du personnel
enseignant.

On compte plus de 80 Conseils qui regroupent
environ 90% des établissements d'enseignement
supérieur du pays, ainsi qu'un nombre important
de facultés ou de filiales situées dans d'autres
villes que leur institution-mère.

Outre les chefs d'établissement, les Conseils
comportent des étudiants et des enseignants, des
représentants des entreprises et des organisations
du secteur industriel, agricole, scientifique et
culturel et des représentants responsables des
organes locaux du gouvernement et des organisations sociales. Ainsi se trouve assurée la liaison
entre les établissements d'enseignement
supérieur et les secteurs les plus importants de la
vie économique et sociale. Un large ensemble
d'organisations sociales ou autres intéressées au
développement de l'éducation participent
également aux activités des Conseils.

Les Conseils de recteurs travaillent sous la
direction immédiate du Comité d'Etat pour
l'Enseignement public de l'URSS. Ils ont pour
tâches principales de: mettre au point des
mesures en vue de la mise en oeuvre par les
établissements d'enseignement supérieur des
décisions des organes responsables de l'Etat
concernant le développement et l'amélioration
de l'enseignement supérieur dans le pays;
élaborer des propositions et mesures en vue du
développement de l'enseignement supérieur
dans les différentes régions économiques;
organiser des échanges d'expériences et l'analyse
en commun du travail de formation des établissements d'enseignement supérieur; introduire des
méthodes novatrices et de nouvelles techniques
d'enseignement et d'administration dans le
processus d'éducation; organiser des activités
favorisant la formation culturelle, idéologique et
politique des étudiants, ainsi que l'amélioration
de l'enseignement dans les sciences sociales et
humaines; coordonner les travaux entrepris dans
les établissements d'enseignement supérieur
sur les problèmes scientifiques complexes et
développer la participation des étudiants à la
recherche; unifier les efforts des établissements
d'enseignement supérieur en vue de l'amélioration de la qualification du personnel enseignant;
renforcer la coopération entre les établissements

d'enseignement supérieur et les entreprises ou
organisations concernant les stages des étudiants
dans la production et le placement des diplômés
dans les différentes branches de l'économie
nationale; coordonner les activités d'orientation
professionnelle et de préparation des jeunes à
l'entrée dans l'enseignement supérieur ainsi que
l'accès des nouveaux étudiants aux divers établissements; mettre au point des mesures en vue
d'améliorer les conditions de vie et d'habitation
des étudiants, ainsi que les services culturels,
médicaux et sportifs des établissements
d'enseignement supérieur; unifier les efforts des
établissements d'enseignement supérieur en vue
de la création de facilités et d'équipements
communs.

Grâce au travail pratique accompli par les
Conseils de recteurs, le rythme de développement de l'enseignement supérieur a pu être
accéléré et le niveau général des activités des
institutions universitaires a pu être élevé. Enfin,
un dispositif d'amélioration de la qualification
des responsables de l'enseignement supérieur a
été créé et fonctionne de manière satisfaisante.

Les Conseils de recteurs organisent systémat-
iquement la coopération entre les établissements
par des réunions scientifiques, des séminaires,
des colloques, des expositions, des concours
entre les étu-diants dans les différents domaines
d'études et de recherche, etc. ... Une série
d'institutions et d'équipements communs ont été
créés sous leur direction: centres d'informatique,
bibliothèques scientifiques, services de santé
pour les étudiants, hôpitaux et centres de
médecine préventive, installations sportives,
stades, cités universitaires, clubs, etc. ...

Les activités des Conseils de recteurs permettent d'améliorer la qualité de la formation des
étudiants, conformément aux exigences du
progrès social et du développement de la science
et de la technique. Elles favorisent la promotion
culturelle de la jeunesse soviétique et assurent un
lien permanent entre les établissements
d'enseignement supérieur et la société.

*The Councils of Rectors of Universities and
other institutions of higher education were set up
between 1972 and 1973 in the major centres of
higher education in the Soviet Union. Their object
is: to co-ordinate the activities of institutions of
higher education; to gather and disseminate
positive experience gained in the organization of
the teaching process; to improve education and
training and study and research activities; and also
to improve the qualifications of teaching staff.*

*There are more than 80 Councils and these
cover approximately 90% of the institutions of
higher education in the country, as well as a
significant number of branches and faculties of
university institutions situated in other towns.*

In addition to the heads of institutions of higher education, the Councils include students and members of academic staff; representatives of enterprises and organizations and of different sectors of industry, agriculture, science and culture; and responsible officials of local organs of government departments and social organizations. This makes it possible to maintain mutual relationships between the institutions of higher education and the most important sectors of social and economic life. A wide range of social and other organizations interested in the development of education is also associated with the work of the Councils of Rectors.

The Councils of Rectors function under the immediate direction of the Union-Republic State Committee for Public Education of the USSR. Their main tasks are: to draw up measures for institutions of higher education to give effect to decisions taken by governing organs of the State for the development and improvement of higher education in the country; to draw up measures and proposals for the further development of higher education in the country; to organize exchanges of experience and the study of the work of institutions of higher education in training specialists; to introduce progressive methods and new techniques of teaching and administration into the educational process; to develop measures favouring the cultural and the ideological and political training of students and the improvement of the teaching of the human and social sciences; to co-ordinate work on complex scientific problems being carried out in institutions of higher education and to develop student participation in research; to consolidate the efforts of institutions of higher education to improve the qualifications of academic staff; to strengthen relations between institutions of higher education and enterprises and organizations in matters concerning student participation in productive work and in the placement of graduates and to study the use of young graduates in different branches of the national economy; to co-ordinate the work of professional orientation and the organization of the preparation of young people for study in institutions of higher education, and to co-ordinate the intake of new students; to draw up measures for improving student living conditions, cultural and medical services and mass sports facilities in institutions of higher education; and to consolidate the efforts of institutions of higher education to develop and strengthen common inter-institutional material and study facilities.

The practical work of the Councils of Rectors has led to a more rapid development of higher education, the general level of activities of university institutions has been raised and a scheme for improving the qualifications of senior staff responsible for the direction of institutions of higher education has been set up and is functioning successfully.

The Councils of Rectors systematically promote a variety of inter-institutional activities—scientific and methodological and theoretical meetings, seminars, symposia, exhibitions, competitions for students in different fields of study and research, etc. Under their direction, undertakings of inter-institutional significance have been set up including computer centres, scientific libraries, student health centres, hospitals and preventative health centres, sports centres, stadia, student campuses, and clubs.

The activities of the Councils of Rectors make possible an improvement in the quality of training of graduates to meet the demands of social progress and the development of science and technology. They further the broad cultural training of Soviet youth and ensure a permanent link between institutions of higher education and society.

Comité d'Etat pour l'Enseignement public de l'URSS, Lusinovskaja ul. 51, 113093 Moskva, Rossiskaja SFSR.

Profsoiuz Rabotnikov Prosveščenija Vysšei Skoly i Naučnyh Učreždenij SSSR
Le Syndicat de l'Enseignement et de la Science de l'URSS réunit le personnel des institutions d'enseignement supérieur, des instituts de recherche et des autres établissements d'enseignement de tout le pays.

The Educational and Scientific Workers' Union groups members of staff of institutions of higher education, of research institutes and of other educational establishments throughout the country.
Président: Rimm Papilov.
Leninskij prosp. 42, Moskva, SSSR.

Department of Ecclesiastical Foreign Affairs (WSCF)
Russian Orthodox Church, Ryleev 18/2, Moskva 634, Rossiskaja SFSR.
Student Council of the USSR
Bogdan Khmelnitsky 7/8, Moskva, Rossiskaja SFSR.
Télex: 411855 (attn. SC/USSR)
SPUTNIK International Youth Tourist Bureau for the USSR
Lebiagiy per. 4, Moskva G-19, Rossiskaja SFSR.

*

Comité d'Etat pour l'Enseignement public de l'URSS
Lusinovskaja ul. 51, 113093 Moskva, Rossiskaja SFSR.

Ministère de l'Education populaire de la RSS de Biélorussie
Ul. Sovietskaja 9, 220010 Minsk, Belorusskaja SSR.
Ministère de l'Enseignement supérieur et second-aire spécialisé, RSS d'Ukraine
Ul. Krethtatik, 252001 Kiev, Ukrainskaja SSR.
Commission nationale de l'Union des Républiques socialistes soviétiques pour l'Unesco
Ministère des Affaires étrangères de l'URSS, Prospekt Kalinina 9, Moskva G-19, Rossiskaja SFSR.

Tél: 290-08-53. Télex: 411587. Cables: unesco-com Moscow
Commission nationale de la République socialiste soviétique de Biélorussie pour l'Unesco
Bul' Lenin 8, Minsk, Belorusskaja SSR.
Tél: 22-29-22. Cables: unescocom minsk
Commission nationale de la République socialiste soviétique d'Ukraine pour l'Unesco
Ul. Karla Liebknechta 15, Kiev, Ukrainskaja SSR.
Tél: 293-4233. Cables: unescocom kiev

UNITED ARAB EMIRATES
EMIRATS ARABES UNIS

*The United Arab Emirates University, P.O. Box 15551, Al-Ain.   *1976*
Tel: (3)642500. Fax: (3)645277. Telex: 33521 jameah em

F : *arts, sc, ed, adm-pol, law-Sharia, eng, agr, med-heal sc.*
Ce : *lang.*

Ministry of Education and Youth
Abu Dhabi.
Tel: 343933

United Arab Emirates National Commission for Unesco
Ministry of Education and Youth, Abu Dhabi.
Tel: (3)343933. Telex: 22581 tarbia em

UNITED KINGDOM
ROYAUME-UNI

UNIVERSITIES AND UNIVERSITY COLLEGES—
UNIVERSITES ET COLLEGES UNIVERSITAIRES

University of Aberdeen, Aberdeen, Scotland AB9 1FX. (The Secretary).   *1495*
Tel: (224)272000. Fax: (224)487048. Telex: 73458 uniabn g. Cables: aberdeen university
F : *art-soc, sc, law, med, div.*

Aston University, Aston Triangle, Birmingham, England B4 7ET. (The Secretary).   *1895, 1966*
F : *eng, sc, soc, mangt.*

University of Bath, Claverton Down, Bath, England BA2 7AY. (The Registrar and Secretary).   *1894, 1966*
Tel: (225)826826. Fax: (225)62508 (group 3). Telex: 449097 uobath g
S : *arc & bui-eng, biol, ch eng, ch, ed, elec, eng, hum-soc, mangt, mater, math, mod lang, phar, phy.*

Queen's University of Belfast, Belfast, N. Ireland BT7 1NN. (The Secretary).
                                            1845, 1908
Tel: (232)245133. Fax: (232)247895. Telex: 74487 qubadm g. Cables: university, belfast, northern ireland
F : *arts, sc, law, med-dent, theo, agr-food sc, eco-soc, ed, eng.*

University of Birmingham, P.O. Box 363, Birmingham, England B15 2TT. (The Secretary).   *1880, 1900*
Tel: (21)4721301. Fax: (21)4714691. Telex: 338938 spsphy g
F : *arts, ed, sc-eng, law, med-dent, com-soc.*

University of Bradford, Richmond Road, Bradford, England BD7 1DP. (The Registrar).
                                            1957, 1966
Tel: (274)733466. Fax: (274)726365. Telex: 51309 unibfd g. Cables: unibfd g
B of st : *eng, life sc, phys, soc.*

*University of Bristol, Senate House, Bristol, England BS8 1TH. (The Registrar and Secretary).   *1876, 1909*
Tel: (272)303030. Fax: (272)732657. Telex: 455938 bsuniv g. Cables: university, bristol bs8 ith
F : *arts, sc, law, med, eng, soc, ed.*

Brunel University, Kingston Lane, Uxbridge, Middlesex, England UB8 3PH. (The Secretary General).   *1957, 1966*
Tel: (395)74000. Telex: 261173 g
S : *biol, ch, eng, soc, math st, mater.*

D : *cyb, ed, phy.*

University of Buckingham, Buckingham, England MK18 1EG. (The Registrar and Secretary).   *1973*
Tel: (280)814080
S: *acc-fin mangt, biol-soc, eco, Eur st, hist-pol-English lit, law, pol-eco-law.*

*University of Cambridge, The Old Schools, Cambridge, England CB2 1TN. (The Registrary).   *XIIIc.*
Tel: (223)332200. Fax: (223)332332. Telex: 81240 camspl g
F : *arc-hist of arts, class, div, English, mod & medie lang, mus, orntl st, eco-pol, ed, hist, law, phil, eng, geog-geol, math, phy-ch, archaeanth, biol "A" (bot-zoo), biol "B" (anatbioch-pathology), med.*

CHRIST'S COLLEGE.	*1448, 1505*
Tel: (223)334900	
CHURCHILL COLLEGE.	*1960*
Tel: (223)336000	
CLARE COLLEGE.	*1326*
Tel: (223)358681	
CLARE HALL.	*1966*
Tel: (223)332360	
CORPUS CHRISTI COLLEGE.	*1352*
Tel: (223)338000	
DARWIN COLLEGE.	*1964*
Tel: (223)335660	
DOWNING COLLEGE.	*1800*
Tel: (223)334800	
EMMANUEL COLLEGE.	*1584*
Tel: (223)334200	
FITZWILLIAM COLLEGE.	*1869, 1966*
Tel: (223)332000	
GIRTON COLLEGE.	*1869, 1924*
Tel: (223)338999	
GONVILLE AND CAIUS COLLEGE.	
	1348, 1558
Tel: (223)332400	
HOMERTON COLLEGE.	*1895, 1977*
Tel: (223)245931	
HUGHES HALL.	*1885, 1968*
Tel: (223)334893	
JESUS COLLEGE.	*1496*
Tel: (223)68611	
KING'S COLLEGE.	*1441*
Tel: (223)350411	

LUCY CAVENDISH COLLEGIATE SOCIETY. *1965*
Tel: (223)332190
MAGDALENE COLLEGE. *1542*
Tel: (223)332100
NEW HALL. *1954*
Tel: (223)351721
NEWNHAM COLLEGE. *1871, 1917*
Tel: (223)335700
PEMBROKE COLLEGE. *1347*
Tel: (223)338100
PETERHOUSE. *1284*
Tel: (223)338200
QUEEN'S COLLEGE. *1448, 1465*
Tel: (223)335511
ROBINSON COLLEGE. *1977*
Tel: (223)311431
ST. CATHERINE'S COLLEGE. *1473*
Tel: (223)338300
ST. EDMUND'S COLLEGE. *1896, 1965, 1975*
Tel: (223)350398
ST. JOHN'S COLLEGE. *1511*
Tel: (223)338600
SELWYN COLLEGE. *1882*
Tel: (223)335846
SIDNEY SUSSEX COLLEGE. *1596*
Tel: (223)338800
TRINITY COLLEGE. *1546*
Tel: (223)338400
TRINITY HALL. *1350*
Tel: (223)352500
WOLFSON COLLEGE. *1965, 1977*
Tel: (223)335900

City University, St. John Street, London, England EC1V 4PB. (The Secretary). *1891, 1966*
Tel: (1)2534399. Fax: (1)2500837. Telex: 263896
app sc, eng, mangt, soc.

Cranfield Institute of Technology, Cranfield, Bedford, England MK43 0AL. (The General Secretary).
Tel: (234)750111. Fax: (234)751806. Telex: 825072 citech g
F : *agr eng, food prod & rur land use, eng, mangt-adm, manufacturing techn & prod, mangt, sc-techn.*

*University of Dundee, Dundee, Scotland DD1 4HN. (The Secretary). *1881, 1967*
Tel: (382)23181. Fax: (382)201604. Telex: 76293. Cables: dundee university
F : *eng-app sc, law, med, sc, arts-soc, env st.*

University of Durham, Old Shire Hall, Durham, England DH1 3HP. (The Registrar and Secretary). *1832*
Tel: (91)3742000. Fax: (91)3743740. Telex: 537351 durlib g
F : *div, arts, sc, ed, law, mus, soc.*

University of East Anglia, Norwich, England NR4 7TJ. (The Registrar and Secretary). *1964*

Tel: (603)56161. Fax: (603)58553. Telex: 975197. Cables: ueanor norwich
S : *English-Am st, Eur st, soc, biol, ch, math-phy, env sc, fa-mus, dev st, comp st, law.*

University of Edinburgh, Old College, South Bridge, Edinburgh, Scotland EH8 9YL. (The Secretary). *1583*
Tel: (31)6671011. Telex: 727442 unived g
F : *arts, sc, law, med-dent, div, mus, soc, vet.*

*University of Essex, Wivenhoe Park, Colchester, Essex, England CO4 3SQ. (The Registrar). *1961*
Tel: (206)873333. Fax: (206)873598. Telex: 98440 unilib g
S : *comparative st, phy, soc, math st.*

University of Exeter, Northcote House, The Queen's Drive, Exeter, England EX4 4QJ. (The Academic Registrar and Secretary). *1922, 1955*
Tel: (392)263263. Telex: 42894
F : *arts, sc, law, soc, app sc, ed.*

University of Glasgow, Glasgow, Scotland G12 8QQ. (The Secretary). *1451*
Tel: (41)3398855. Telex: 777070 unigla
F : *arts, sc, law, med-dent, div, eng, vet, soc.*

*Heriot-Watt University, Riccarton, Edinburgh, Scotland EH14 4AS. (The Secretary). *1821, 1966*
Tel: (31)4495111. Fax: (31)4495153
F : *eng, eco-soc, sc, env st.*

*University of Hull, Hull, England HU6 7RX. (The Registrar). *1927, 1954*
Tel: (482)46311. Telex: 52530
F : *arts, sc, soc, law.*

University of Keele, Keele, Staffordshire, England ST5 5BG. (The Registrar). *1949, 1962*
Tel: (782)621111. Fax: (782)613847. Telex: 36113 unklib g
B of st : *hum, nat, soc.*

University of Kent at Canterbury, The Registry, Canterbury, Kent, England CT2 7NZ. (The Registrar and Secretary). *1964*
Tel: (227)764000. Fax: (227)459025. Telex: 965449 ukclib g
F : *hum, nat, soc.*

University of Lancaster, University House, Bailrigg, Lancaster, England LA1 4YW. (The Secretary). *1964*
Tel: (524)65201. Fax: (524)63806. Telex: 65111
B of st : *nat, math, techn-bus, soc-hist-phil, lang-lit-area st, ed.*

University of Leeds, Leeds, England LS2 9JT. (The Registrar). *1884, 1904*
Tel: (532)431751. Fax: (532)420090. Telex: 556473 unilds g
F : *arts, sc, law, med-dent, eco-soc, app sc, ed.*

*University of Leicester, University Road, Leicester, England LE1 7RH. (The Registrar). *1918, 1957*

Tel: (533)522522. Fax: (533)522200. Telex: 341198

F : *arts, sc, soc, law, med.*

*University of Liverpool, P.O. Box 147, Liverpool, England L69 3BX. (The Registrar).
                                          1881, 1903

Tel: (51)7096022. Fax: (51)7086502. Telex: 627095 unilpl g

F : *arts, sc, law, med-dent, eng, vet, soc-env st.*

*University of London, Senate House, Malet Street, London, England WC1E 7HU. (The Principal).   *1836*

Tel: (1)6368000. Fax: (1)6360373. Telex: 269400 senlib g

F : *theo, arts, laws, mus, med, sc, eng, eco, ed.*

Schools of the
University of London

BIRKBECK COLLEGE, Malet Street, London, England WC1E 7HX. (The Secretary and Clerk to the Governors).   *1823, 1926*
Tel: (1)580-6622
F : *arts, sc, eco.*

THE BRITISH POSTGRADUATE MEDICAL FEDERATION, 33 Millman Street, London, England WC1N 3EJ. (The Secretary). *1945*
Tel: (1)831-6222
F : *med.*

CHARING CROSS AND WESTMINSTER MEDICAL SCHOOL, The Reynolds Building, St. Dunstan's Road, London, England W6 8RP. (The Secretary).   *1818, 1834*
Tel: (1)748-2040
F : *med.*

HEYTHORP COLLEGE, 11-13 Cavendish Square, London, England W1M 0AN. (The Secretary and Registrar).   *1926, 1971*
Tel: (1)580-6941
F : *theo, arts.*

IMPERIAL COLLEGE OF SCIENCE AND TECHNOLOGY, South Kensington, London, England SW7 2AZ. (The Registrar).   *1907*
Tel: (1)589-5111. Fax: (1)5847596. Telex: 261503
F : *sc, eng, eco.*

INSTITUTE OF EDUCATION, 20 Bedford Way, London, England WC1H 0AL. (The Secretary).   *1902*
Tel: (1)6361500

KING'S COLLEGE LONDON, Strand, London, England WC2R 2LS. (The Registrar).
                          1829, 1891, 1908, 1966
Tel: (1)836-5454. Fax: (1)836-1799
F : *theo, arts, laws, mus, med, sc, eng, ed.*

THE LONDON HOSPITAL MEDICAL COLLEGE, Turner Street, London, England E1 2AD. (The Secretary).   *1785, 1900*
Tel: (1)377-7000. Fax: (1)377-7677
F : *med.*

THE LONDON SCHOOL OF ECONOMICS AND POLITICAL SCIENCE, Houghton Street, London, England WC2A 2AE. (The Secretary).   *1895*
Tel: (1)405-7686. Fax: (1)4057686 (ext. 2190). Telex: 24655 blpes g
F : *arts, laws, sc, eco.*

LONDON SCHOOL OF HYGIENE AND TROPICAL MEDICINE, Keppel Street, Gower Street, London, England WC1E 7HT. (The Secretary).   *1924*
Tel: (1)636-8636. Telex: 8953474
F : *med, sc.*

QUEEN MARY COLLEGE, Mile End Road, London, England E1 4NS. (The Registrar).
                          1887, 1915
Tel: (1)980-4811. Fax: (1)981-7517. Telex: 893750. Easylink: 19019285
F : *arts, laws, sc, eng, eco.*

ROYAL FREE HOSPITAL SCHOOL OF MEDICINE, Rowland Hill Street, London, England NW3 2PF. (The Secretary).   *1874*
Tel: (1)794-0500
F : *med.*

ROYAL HOLLOWAY AND BEDFORD NEW COLLEGE, Egham Hill, Egham, Surrey, England TW20 0EX. (The Registrar).
                          1849, 1886, 1909
Tel: (784)34455. Fax: (784)37520. Telex: 935504 (library)
F : *arts, mus, sc, eco.*

ROYAL POSTGRADUATE MEDICAL SCHOOL, Hammersmith Hospital, Du Cane Road, London, England W12 0HS. (The Secretary).   *1931*
Tel: (1)743-2030
F : *med.*

THE ROYAL VETERINARY COLLEGE, Royal College Street, Camden Town, London, England NW1 0TU. (The Secretary). *1791*
Tel: (1)387-2898
F : *med.*

ST. BARTHOLOMEW'S HOSPITAL MEDICAL COLLEGE, West Smithfield, London, England EC1A 7BE. (The Secretary).   *1662*
Tel: (1)606-7404
F : *med.*

ST. GEORGE'S HOSPITAL MEDICAL SCHOOL, Cranmer Terrace, Tooting, London, England SW17 0RE. (The Secretary). *1751*
Tel: (1)672-9944
F : *med.*

ST. MARY'S HOSPITAL MEDICAL SCHOOL, Norfolk Place, Paddington, London, England W2 1PG. (The Secretary).   *1854*
Tel: (1)723-1252. Fax: (1)724-7345
F : *med.*

SCHOOL OF ORIENTAL AND AFRICAN STUDIES, Malet Street, London, England

WC1E 7HP. (The Secretary). *1916*
Tel: (1)637-2388. Telex: 896616 sendit g.
Cables: soasul london
F : *arts, laws, mus, sc, eco.*

THE SCHOOL OF PHARMACY, 29-39 Brunswick
Square, London, England WC1N 1AX.
(The Clerk to the Council and Secretary).
1842, 1952
Tel: (1)837-7651
F : *med, sc.*

UNITED MEDICAL AND DENTAL SCHOOLS OF
GUY'S AND ST. THOMAS'S HOSPITALS,
Lambeth Palace Road, London, England
SE1 7EH. (The Secretary).
XVIII c. & XIII c., 1982
Tel: (1)928-9292
F : *med.*

UNIVERSITY COLLEGE LONDON, Gower
Street, London, England WC1E 6BT. (The
Secretary). *1826, 1907*
Tel: (1)387-7050
F : *arts, laws, med, sc, eng, eco.*
I: *arc.*

WESTFIELD COLLEGE, Kidderpore Avenue,
Hampstead, London, England NW3 7ST.
(The Registrar). *1882, 1933*
Tel: (1)435-7141
F : *arts.*

WYE COLLEGE, Wye, Ashford, Kent, Eng-
land TN25 5AH. (The Secretary).
1893, 1948
Tel: (233)812401. Telex: 96118 anzeec g.
Cables: college, wye
F : *sc (agr & hort).*

Institutes of the
University of London

BRITISH INSTITUTE IN PARIS, 11, rue de Con-
stantine, 75007 Paris, France. (The London
Secretary: Senate House, Malet Street,
London, England WC1E 7HU).
1927, 1969
Tel: (33-1)4555-7199 (Paris). (1)636-8000
(London)

COURTAULD INSTITUTE OF ART, Somerset
House, Strand, London WC2R 0RN. (The
Registrar and Secretary). *1932*
Tel: (1)872-0220

INSTITUTE OF ADVANCED LEGAL STUDIES, 17
Russell Square, London, England WC1B
5DR. (The Secretary). *1947*
Tel: (1)637-1731

INSTITUTE OF CLASSICAL STUDIES, 31-34
Gordon Square, London, England WC1H
0PY. (The Secretary). *1953*
Tel: (1)387-7696

INSTITUTE OF COMMONWEALTH STUDIES, 27-
28 Russell Square, London, England

WC1B 5DS. (The Secretary). *1949*
Tel: (1)580-5876

INSTITUTE OF GERMANIC STUDIES, 29 Russell
Square, London, England WC1B 5DP.
(The Deputy Director). *1950*
Tel: (1)580-2711. Cables: germanic insti-
tute, russell square, london

INSTITUTE OF HISTORICAL RESEARCH, Senate
House, Malet Street, London, England
WC1E 7HU. (The Secretary and Librar-
ian). *1921*
Tel: (1)636-0272

INSTITUTE OF LATIN AMERICAN STUDIES, 31
Tavistock Square, London, England
WC1H 9HA. (The Secretary). *1965*
Tel: (1)387-5671

INSTITUTE OF UNITED STATES STUDIES, 31
Tavistock Square, London, England
WC1H 9EZ. (The Secretary). *1965*
Tel: (1)387-5534

SCHOOL OF SLAVONIC AND EAST EUROPEAN
STUDIES, Senate House, Malet Street,
London, England WC1E 7HU. (The Regis-
trar). *1915, 1932*
Tel: (1)637-4934

WARBURG INSTITUTE, Woburn Square,
London, England WC1H 0AB. (The Secre-
tary and Registrar). *1944*
Tel: (1)580-9663

Institutes having Recognized Teachers

GOLDSMITHS' COLLEGE, Lewisham Way,
New Cross, London, England SE14 6NW.
Tel: (1)692-7171

JEWS' COLLEGE, 44A Albert Road, London,
England NW4 2SJ.
Tel: (1)203-6427

LONDON BUSINESS SCHOOL, Sussex Place,
Regent's Park, London, England NW1 4SA
1965
Tel: (1)262-5050

ROYAL ACADEMY OF MUSIC, Marylebone
Road, London, England NW1 5HT.
Tel: (1)935-5461

ROYAL COLLEGE OF MUSIC, Prince Consort
Road, London, England SW7 2BS. *1883*
Tel: (1)589-3643

TRINITY COLLEGE OF MUSIC, Mandeville
Place, London, England W1M 6AQ.
Tel: (1)935-5773

Loughborough University of Technology, Loughborough, England LE11 3TU. (The Registrar).
1952, 1966
Tel: (509)263171. Fax: (509)231983. Telex:
34319. Cables: technology, loughborough
S : *eng, human-env st, pure-app sc, ed st.*

University of Manchester, Manchester, England
M13 9PL. (The Registrar). *1851, 1880*
Tel: (61)275-2000

F : *arts, sc, law, med-dent, theo, eco-soc, ed, mus, techn, bus adm.*

University of Manchester Institute of Science and Technology, P.O. Box 88, Sackville Street, Manchester, England M60 1QD. (The Secretary and Registrar).   *1902, 1956*
Tel: (61)236-3311. Fax: (61)228-7040. Telex: 666094. Cables: technology manchester
(Faculty of Technology in the University of Manchester).

University of Newcastle upon Tyne, Newcastle upon Tyne, England NE1 7RU. (The Registrar).   *XIX c., 1963*
Tel: (91)232-8511. Fax: (91)281-8057. Telex: 53654 uninew g. Cables: university newcastle upon tyne
F : *arts, sc, law, med-dent, eco-soc, ed, agr, eng.*

University of Nottingham, University Park, Nottingham, England NG7 2RD. (The Registrar).
                                            1881, 1948
Tel: (602)506101. Fax: (602)588138. Telex: 37346 uninot g. Cables: university nottingham
F : *arts, pure sc, agr, app sc, ed, law-soc, med.*

Open University, Walton Hall, Milton Keynes, England MK7 6AA. (The Secretary).   *1969*
Tel: (908)74066. Fax: (908)653744. Telex: 825061. Cables: openuniv walton
F : *arts, ed st, math, sc, soc, techn.*
I : *ed techn.*

*University of Oxford, University Offices, Wellington Square, Oxford, England OX1 2JD. (The Registrar).   *XII c.*
Tel: (865)270000. Cables: university offices oxford
F : *theo, law, med, hum, anth-geog, biol-agr, English, mod hist medie & mod lang, mus, orntl st, phy, math, psyc, physiological sc, soc.*

ALL SOULS COLLEGE.   *1438*
  Tel: (865)279379
BALLIOL COLLEGE.   *1263–68*
  Tel: (865)277777
BRASENOSE COLLEGE.   *1509*
  Tel: (865)277830
CAMPION HALL.   *1896, 1918*
  Tel: (865)240861
CHRIST CHURCH.   *1546*
  Tel: (865)276150
CORPUS CHRISTI COLLEGE.   *1517*
  Tel: (865)276700
EXETER COLLEGE.   *1314*
  Tel: (865)279600
GREEN COLLEGE.   *1979*
  Tel: (865)274700
GREYFRIARS.   *1910, 1957*
HERTFORD COLLEGE.   *1740, 1874*
  Tel: (865)279400
JESUS COLLEGE.   *1571*
  Tel: (865)279700
KEBLE COLLEGE.   *1868, 1870*

Tel: (865)272727
LADY MARGARET HALL.   *1878, 1926*
  Tel: (865)274300
LINACRE COLLEGE.   *1962*
  Tel: (865)271650
LINCOLN COLLEGE.   *1427*
  Tel: (865)279800
MAGDALEN COLLEGE.   *1458*
  Tel: (865)276000
MANSFIELD COLLEGE.   *1886, 1955*
  Tel: (865)270999
MERTON COLLEGE.   *1264*
  Tel: (865)276310
NEW COLLEGE.   *1379*
  Tel: (865)248451
NUFFIELD COLLEGE.   *1937, 1958*
  Tel: (865)278500
ORIEL COLLEGE.   *1326*
  Tel: (865)27655
PEMBROKE COLLEGE.   *1624*
  Tel: (865)276444
THE QUEEN'S COLLEGE.   *1340*
  Tel: (865)279120
REGENT'S PARK COLLEGE.   *1810, 1957*
  Tel: (865)59887
ST. ANNE'S COLLEGE.   *1879, 1952*
  Tel: (865)274800
ST. ANTHONY'S COLLEGE.   *1950*
  Tel: (865)59651
ST. BENET'S HALL.   *1897, 1918*
  Tel: (865)515006
ST. CATHERINE'S COLLEGE.   *1962*
  Tel: (865)249541
ST. CROSS COLLEGE.   *1965*
  Tel: (865)278490
ST. EDMUND HALL.   *c. 1278*
  Tel: (865)279000
ST. HILDA'S COLLEGE.   *1893, 1926*
  Tel: (865)276884
ST. HUGH'S COLLEGE.   *1886, 1926*
  Tel: (865)274900
ST. JOHN'S COLLEGE.   *1555*
  Tel: (865)277300
ST. PETER'S COLLEGE.   *1929, 1961*
  Tel: (865)278900
SOMERVILLE COLLEGE.   *1879, 1926*
  Tel: (865)270600
TRINITY COLLEGE.   *1554-55*
  Tel: (865)279900
UNIVERSITY COLLEGE.   *1249*
  Tel: (865)276602
WADHAM COLLEGE.   *1612*
  Tel: (865)277900
WOLFSON COLLEGE.   *1966*
  Tel: (865)274100
WORCESTER COLLEGE.   *1283, 1714*
  Tel: (865)278300
*University of Reading, Whiteknights, P.O. Box 217, Reading, England RG6 2AH. (The Regis-

trar). *1892, 1926*
Tel: (734)875123. Telex: 847813
F : *sc, agr-food, let-soc, urb-reg st.*

Royal College of Art, Kensington Gore, London, England SW7 2EU. (The Registrar).
1837, 1967
Tel: (1)584-5020. Fax: (1)225-1487
fa, graph des, ind des (all postgraduate).

University of St. Andrews, College Gate, North Street, St. Andrews, Scotland KY16 9AJ. (The Registrar and Secretary). *1410*
Tel: (334)76161. Telex: 76213. Cables: university st. andrews
F : *arts, div, sc.*

University of Salford, Salford, England M5 4WT. (The Registrar). *1896, 1967*
Tel: (61)736-5843. Fax: (61)737-0880. Telex: 668680
F : *sc, soc, eng.*

*University of Sheffield, Sheffield, England S10 2TN. (The Registrar and Secretary).
1897, 1905
Tel: (742)768555. Fax: (742)739826 Group 3. Telex: 547216 ugshef g. Cables: university sheffield
F : *arts, pure sc, law, med-dent, soc, eng, arc, mater tec, ed, lib.*

University of Southampton, Highfield, Southampton, England SO9 5NH. (The Secretary and Registrar). *1902, 1952*
Tel: (703)559122. Fax: (703)559308. Telex: 47661. Cables: university southampton
F : *arts, sc, law, soc, ed, eng-app sc, med, math st.*

University of Stirling, Stirling, Scotland FK9 4LA. (The Secretary). *1967*
Tel: (786)73171. Fax: (786)63000. Telex: 77557 stuniv g. Cables: stirling university
arts, soc, sc, ed.

University of Strathclyde, Royal College Building, 204 George Street, Glasgow, Scotland G1 1XW. (The Registrar). *1796, 1964*
Tel: (41)552-4400. Fax: (41)552-0775. Telex: 77472
S : *math-phy-comp sc, ch-mater sc, mec & ch eng-nav arc, civ-mining, eng-app geol, elec-electro eng, arc-bui sc-plan, biol sc, arts-soc sc, bus-adm, phar sc.*

University of Surrey, Guildford, Surrey, England GU2 5XH. (The Secretary). *1891, 1966*
Tel: (483)571281. Fax: (483)300803. Telex: 859331
F : *biol-ch, eng, hum, math-phy.*

University of Sussex, Sussex House, Falmer, Brighton, England BN1 9RH. (The Registrar and Secretary). *1961*
Tel: (273)606755. Fax: (273)678335. Telex:

877159 unisex. Cables: university brighton
S : *African & Asian st, app sc, biol, cultural & comty st, eng-app sc, English & Am st, Eur st, math-phy, molecular sc, soc.*

University of Ulster, University House, Cromore Road, Coleraine, Co. Londonderry, N. Ireland BT52 1SA. (The Secretary). *1965, 1970, 1984*
Tel: (265)4141. Fax: (265)57528. Telex: 747597
F : *art-des, bus-mangt, ed, hum, sc, soc-heal sc, techn.*

University of Wales, University Registry, King Edward VII Avenue, Cathays Park, Cardiff, Wales CF1 3NS. (The Registrar). *1893*
Tel: (222)382656. Cables: university registry cardiff
F : *law, med, theo, arc, ed, mus, rur sc, techn.*

UNIVERSITY COLLEGE OF WALES, Aberystwyth, Dyfed, Wales SY23 2AX. (The Registrar). *1872*
Tel: (970)3177. Fax: (970)612774. Telex: 35181
F : *arts, sc-rur sc, law, ed, mus, eco-soc.*

UNIVERSITY COLLEGE OF NORTH WALES, Bangor, Gwynedd, Wales LL57 2DG. (The Secretary and Registrar). *1884*
Tel: (248)351151. Telex: 61100. Cables: unicol bangor
F : *arts, sc, theo.*

ST. DAVID'S UNIVERSITY COLLEGE, Lampeter, Dyfed, Wales SA48 7ED. (The Registrar and Secretary). *1882, 1971*
Tel: (570)422351. Telex: 48475
arts, theo.

UNIVERSITY COLLEGE OF SWANSEA, Singleton Park, Swansea, Wales SA2 8PP. (The Registrar). *1920*
Tel: (792)205678. Fax: (792)295618. Telex: 48358
F : *arts, sc, app sc, eco-soc.*

UNIVERSITY OF WALES COLLEGE OF CARDIFF, Heath Park, Cardiff, Wales CF4 4XN.

UNIVERSITY OF WALES COLLEGE OF MEDICINE, Heath Park, Cardiff, Wales CF4 4XN. (The Registrar). *1931*
Tel: (222)755944. Telex: 498696
med-dent.

*University of Warwick, Coventry, England CV4 7AL. (The Secretary and Registrar). *1965*
Tel: (203)523523. Fax: (203)461606. Telex: 317472
F : *arts, ed st, soc st, sc.*

University of York, Heslington, York, England YO1 5DD. (The Registrar). *1963*
Tel: (904)430000. Fax: (904)415185. Telex: 57933 yorkul. Cables: university york
arts, ed, nat, soc.

OTHER INSTITUTIONS—AUTRES INSTITUTIONS

Polytechnics—Polytechniques

City of Birmingham Polytechnic, Perry Barr, Birmingham, England B42 2SU.
Tel: (21)356-6911. Telex: 33409 cbpoly g

Brighton Polytechnic, Lewes Road, Moulsecoomb, Brighton, England BN2 4AT.
Tel: (273)693655. Fax: (273)688917

Bristol Polytechnic, Coldharbour Lane, Frenchay, Bristol, England BS16 1QY.
Tel: (272)656261

The Polytechnic of Central London, 309 Regent Street, London, England W1R 8AL.
Tel: (1)580-2020

City of London Polytechnic, 31 Jewry Street, London, England EC3N 2EY.
Tel: (1)283-1030

Coventry (Lanchester) Polytechnic, Priory Street, Coventry, England CV1 5FB.
Tel: (203)24166. Fax: (203)258597

The Hatfield Polytechnic, P.O. Box 109, College Lane, Hatfield, Herts, England AL10 9AB.
Tel: (7072)79000. Fax: (7072)79670. Telex: 262413 hertis g

Huddersfield Polytechnic, Queensgate, Huddersfield, England HD1 3DH.
Tel: (484)22288. Fax: (484)516151

Kingston Polytechnic, Penrhyn Road, Kingston-upon-Thames, Surrey, England KT1 2EE.
Tel: (1)549-1366

Lancashire Polytechnic, Corporation Street, Preston, England PR1 2TQ.
Tel: (772)22141

Leeds Polytechnic, Calverley Street, Leeds, England LS1 3HE.
Tel: (532)463000. Fax: (532)425733

Leicester Polytechnic, P.O. Box 143, Leicester, England LE1 9BH.
Tel: (533)551551. Fax: (533)550307

Liverpool Polytechnic, Rodney House, 70 Mount Pleasant, Liverpool, England L3 5UX.
Tel: (51)207-3581

Manchester Polytechnic, Lower Ormond Street, All Saints, Manchester, England M15 6BH.
Tel: (61)228-6171. Fax: (61)236-7383. Telex: 667915 pollib g

*Middlesex Polytechnic, 114 Chase Side, London, England N14 5PN.
Tel: (1)886-6599. Fax: (1)202-6545. Telex: 8954762 midpol g

Newcastle upon Tyne Polytechnic, Ellison Building, Ellison Place, Newcastle upon Tyne, England NE1 8ST.
Tel: (632)326002. Fax: (91)235-8017. Telex: 53519 newpol g

Polytechnic of East London, Longbridge Road, Dagenham, Essex, England RM8 2AS.
Tel: (1)590-7722. Fax: (1)5907-7222

The Polytechnic of North London, Holloway Road, London, England N7 8DB.
Tel: (1)607-2789. Fax: (1)700-4272

North Staffordshire Polytechnic, College Road, Stoke on Trent, Stafford, England ST4 2DE.
Tel: (782)45531

Oxford Polytechnic, Headington, Oxford, England OX3 0BP.
Tel: (865)64772. Fax: (865)819073

Plymouth Polytechnic, Drake Circus, Plymouth, England PL4 8AA.
Tel: (752)21312. Fax: (752)222792. Telex: 45423 pplrc g

Portsmouth Polytechnic, Ravelin House, Museum Road, Portsmouth, England PO1 2QQ.
Tel: (705)827681

Sheffield City Polytechnic, Pond Street, Sheffield, England S1 1WB.
Tel: (742)20911. Fax: (742)758019. Telex: 54680 shpoly g

Polytechnic of the South Bank, Borough Road, London, England SE1 0AA.
Tel: (1)928-8989

Sunderland Polytechnic, Langham Tower, Ryhope Road, Sunderland, England SR2 7EF.
Tel: (783)76231. Fax: (91)565-4864. Telex: 537339 seeds g

Teesside Polytechnic, Borough Road, Middlesborough, Cleveland, England TS1 3BA.
Tel: (642)218121. Fax: (642)226822. Telex: 587537 teplib g

Thames Polytechnic, Wellington Street, Woolwich, London, England SE18 6PF.
Tel: (1)854-2030. Fax: (1)316-5491

Trent Polytechnic, City Centre Side, Burton Street, Nottingham, England NG1 4BU.
Tel: (602)418248. Fax: (602)414024. Telex: 377534 polnot g

The Polytechnic of Wales, Llantwit Road, Treforest Pontypridd, Mid-Glamorgan, Wales CF37 7DL.
Tel: (443)405133. Fax: (443)480558

The Polytechnic-Wolverhampton, The Molineux, Molineux Street, Wolverhampton, England WV1 7SB.
Tel: (902)710652

Approximately 500 other Colleges of Education, Technology and Further Education.
Environ 500 autres collèges d'éducation, techniques et d'éducation post-secondaire.

Central Institutions (Scotland) – Institutions centrales (Ecosse)

Robert Gordon's Institute of Technology, Schoolhill, Aberdeen, Scotland AB9 1FR.
Tel: (224)633611. Fax: (224)642003
Paisley College of Technology, High Street, Paisley, Renfrewshire, Scotland PA1 2BE.
Tel: (41)887-1241. Fax: (41)8870812
Scottish College of Textiles, Netherdale, Galashiels, Selkirkshire, Scotland TD1 3HF.
Tel: (896)3351. Fax: (896)58965
The Duncan of Jordanstone College of Art, Perth Road, Dundee, Scotland DD1 4HT.
Tel: (382)23261
Dundee College of Technology, 40 Bell Street, Dundee, Scotland DD1 1HG.
Tel: (382)27225. Fax: (382)200782
Edinburgh College of Art, Lauriston Place, Edinburgh, Scotland EH3 9DF.
Tel: (31)229-9311. Fax: (31)2290089
Glasgow College of Technology, Cowcaddens Road, Glasgow, Scotland G4 0BA.
Tel: (41)332-7090. Telex: 779341
Glasgow School of Art, 167 Renfrew Street, Glasgow, Scotland G3 6RQ.

Tel: (41)332-9797. Fax: (41)3323506
Napier College of Commerce and Technology, 219 Colinton Road, Edinburgh, Scotland EH14 1DJ.
Tel: (31)444-2266
Queen Margaret College, 36 Clerwood Terrace, Edinburgh, Scotland EH12 8TS.
Tel: (31)339-8111. Fax: (31)3396697
The Queen's College, Glasgow, 1 Park Drive, Glasgow, Scotland G3 6LP.
Tel: (41)334-8141
The Royal Scottish Academy of Music and Drama, St. George's Place, Glasgow, Scotland G2 1BS.
Tel: (41)332-4101. Fax: (41)3328901
Leith Nautical College, 24 Milton Road East, Edinburgh, Scotland EH15 2PP.
Telex: 72594 nautec g

54 other Colleges of Technology and Further Education.
54 autres collèges techniques et d'enseignement post-secondaire.

Agricultural Colleges – Collèges d'Agriculture

East of Scotland College of Agriculture, West Mains Road, Edinburgh, Scotland, EH9 3JG.
Tel: (31)667-1041
Writtle Agriculture College, Writtle, Chelmsford, England, CM1 3RR.
Tel: (245)420705
Harper Adams Agricultural College, Newport, Shropshire, England TF10 8NB.
Lancashire College of Agriculture and Horticulture, Myerscough Hall, Bilsborrow, Preston, Lancashire, England PR3 0RY.
Tel: (995)40611
North of Scotland College of Agriculture, 581 King Street, Aberdeen, Scotland, AB9 1UD.
Tel: (224)480291
Gloucestershire College of Agriculture, Hartpury House, Hartpury, Gloucester, England.
Seale-Hayne College, Newton Abbot, Devon,

England TQ12 6NQ.
Tel: (626)52523
Shuttleworth Agricultural College, Old Warden Park, Biggleswade, Bedfordshire, England SG18 9DX.
Tel: 76727
Welsh Agricultural College, Llanbadarn Fawr, Aberystwyth, Wales.
West of Scotland Agricultural College, Auchincruive, Nr. Ayr, Scotland KA6 5HW.
Tel: (292)520331
Loughry College of Agriculture and Food Technology, Cookstown, Co. Tyrone, N. Ireland BT80 9AA.
Greenmount College of Agriculture and Horticulture, Antrim, N. Ireland BT41 4PU.
Enniskillen Agricultural College, Enniskillen, Co. Fermanagh, N. Ireland.

Committee of Vice-Chancellors and Principals

The Committee of Vice-Chancellors and Principals of the Universities of the United Kingdom, first established in 1918, originated in occasional meetings of the academic heads of universities convened for special purposes. The Committee is a consultative and advisory body. It considers matters of common interest to universities and is not restricted to topics specifically referred to it. The Committee consists of the Vice-Chancellors of the universities in England and Wales and the Principals of the universities in Scotland which are in receipt of grants through the University Grants Committee, the Vice-

Chancellors of the two universities in Northern Ireland, certain additional members from the universities of London, Manchester, and Wales, and the Vice-Chancellors of The Open University, Cranfield Institute of Technology and the University of Buckingham. The decisions of the Committee do not bind the universities, but, by its consultative activities and the nature of its membership, the Committee holds an influential position in university affairs. All major university matters are kept under regular review by the Committee supported by its general purposes committee, its four standing committees— concerned respectively with matters of finance and development, academic affairs, staff and student affairs, international university affairs— and by a number of specialist sub-committees.

The Committee has been instrumental in the establishment of several delegate bodies, representative of the universities, to undertake specific tasks. These include the Universities' Central Council on Admissions, the Standing Conference on University Entrance, and the Universities' Committee on Non-Teaching Staffs.

The Chairman of the Committee is elected annually.

Le Comité des vice-chanceliers et principaux des universités du Royaume-Uni, créé en 1918, doit ses origines à une série de réunions occasionnelles de chefs d'université convoquées à des fins particulières. Organisme consultatif, le Comité examine les questions d'intérêt commun aux universités et n'est pas tenu de se limiter aux sujets qui lui sont explicitement soumis. Il se compose des vice-chanceliers des universités d'Angleterre et du Pays de Galles, des principaux des universités d'Ecosse, bénéficiaires des fonds du Comité des crédits universitaires, des vice-chanceliers des deux universités de l'Irlande du Nord, ainsi que d'un certain nombre de membres supplémentaires des universités de Londres, de Manchester et du Pays de Galles, et des vice-chanceliers de l'Open University, Cranfield Institute of Technology et de l'University of Buckingham. Les décisions du Comité ne lient pas les universités mais, de par ses activités consultatives et sa composition, le Comité exerce une influence considérable sur les affaires universitaires. Le Comité étudie en permanence les principales questions universitaires avec le concours de son comité des objectifs généraux, de ses quatre comités permanents s'occupant respectivement des affaires financières et du développement, des problèmes académiques, des questions intéressant le personnel enseignant et les étudiants et des relations universitaires internationales, et d'un certain nombre de sous-comités formés de spécialistes.

Le Comité a contribué à la création de plusieurs organismes représentatifs des universités et

chargés de tâches précises, notamment le Conseil central des universités sur les admissions, la Conférence permanente sur l'entrée dans les universités et le Comité du personnel non enseignant des universités.

Le Président du Comité est élu tous les ans.

Chairman (1989–90): Sir Edward Parkes, Vice-Chancellor, University of Leeds.
Secretary General: Tom Burgner.
29 Tavistock Square, London WC1H 9EZ.
Tel: (1)387-9231

Universities Funding Council

The Universities Funding Council, replacing the University Grants Committee, was established by the Education Reform Act 1988 to administer funds made available by the Secretary of State for Education and Science for the support of teaching, research and other activities connected with them in the universities. The Council is empowered to keep under review activities eligible for funding and to perform the functions laid down in the Statute.

Le Conseil chargé du financement des universités, qui remplace le Comité des Crédits Universitaires, a été créé en vertu de la loi sur l'Education de 1988 avec pour mission d'administrer les fonds mis à disposition par le Secrétaire d'Etat pour l'éducation et la science pour soutenir l'enseignement, la recherche et les autres activités connexes se déroulant dans les universités. Le Conseil est habilité à examiner les activités susceptibles de recevoir un financement et à s'acquitter des fonctions stipulés dans les Statuts.

Chairman: Lord Chilver.
Chief Executive: Sir Peter Swinnerton-Dyer.
Secretary: N.T. Hardyman.
14 Park Crescent, London W1N 4DH.
Tel: (1)636-7799. Fax: (1)631-4227

The Universities Central Council on Admissions

The Universities Central Council on Admissions (UCCA) was set up by the universities of the United Kingdom in 1961. The UCCA office receives applications for admission to full-time first degree courses at all the universities and university colleges in the United Kingdom; decisions on such applications are made by the universities themselves and transmitted through the UCCA office.

The Council, which consists of representatives of all participating universities, publishes annual reports and statistical supplements about university applications. Its work is financed mainly by contributions from member universities and partly by fees charged to all applicants. It is a registered company, limited by guarantee, and has the status of an educational charity.

Le Conseil central des universités pour les admissions a été créé par les universités du Royaume-Uni en 1961. Il reçoit les demandes d'admission en première année pour tous les programmes à plein temps dans toutes les universités et collèges universitaires du Royaume-Uni; les décisions sur ces demandes sont prises par les universités elles-mêmes et transmises par l'intermédiaire des bureaux du Conseil.

Le Conseil se compose de représentants de toutes les universités participantes; il publie des rapports annuels et des suppléments statistiques sur les demandes d'admissions aux universités. Ses activités sont principalement financées par les contributions des universités membres, le reste provenant des droits acquittés par tous les candidats. C'est une société dûment enregistrée, limitée par une garantie, et qui bénéficie du statut d'oeuvre de bienfaisance à caractère éducatif.

Chairman: Dr. D. Harrison, Vice-Chancellor, University of Exeter.

General Secretary: P.A. Oakley.

P.O. Box 28, Cheltenham, Glos. GL50 1HY.

Tel: (242)222444

Council for National Academic Awards (CNAA)

The Council is a self-governing body established by Royal Charter in September 1964. It has powers granted by its charter to award degrees and other academic qualifications, comparable in standards with those granted by United Kingdom universities, to students who complete approved courses of study or research in establishments which do not have the power to award their own degrees. CNAA degrees are now offered in more than 160 subjects ranging from architecture to zoology, and are conducted in more than 130 educational establishments. The CNAA is now the largest degree awarding body in the United Kingdom and about one-third of all students who are studying for a degree in the United Kingdom attend CNAA-approved courses.

The Chairman and twenty-five members of the Council are appointed by the Secretaries of State for Education and Science and for Scotland for a period of three years. The Chief Officer is the one executive member of the Council. The Chairmen of the main Committees of Council, if not otherwise appointed, are *ex officio* members of the Council, which may itself appoint up to three co-optive members. The Council is advised on academic policy by its ten main committees, eight of which are concerned with groups of related disciplines, namely (i) Art and Design; (ii) Arts and Humanities; (iii) the Built Environment; (iv) Business and Management; (v) Engineering; (vi) Science; (vii) Social Sciences; (viii) Teacher Education. There are also Committees for Academic and Institutional Policy and for Scotland. The membership of each of these is determined by Council and is reviewed every three or four years.

The assessment of courses and research degree applications submitted to the Council is carried out by some seventy Subject Boards and Specialist Panels, under authority delegated to them by Council and the Committees to which they are responsible. The number and composition of the Subject Boards responsible to each Committee are determined by the Committee and normally renewed every three years. The membership of each Subject Board or Panel normally comprises teachers from universities and from the polytechnics and other colleges associated with the Council, members from industry, commerce or other private organizations and independent practitioners in the field. The special groups set up by the Committee for Teacher Education to consider each submission for a Bachelor of Education course also include practising school teachers. Each Board or Panel is responsible to the relevant Committee for ensuring that the provisions of Statute 8(5) of the Council's Charter and Statutes are fulfilled.

This Statute states: "Each Committee shall, subject to the provisions of the Rules, exercise and be responsible to the Council for the following functions: (a) ensuring that the Degrees, Diplomas, Certificates and other academic awards and distinctions granted and conferred by the Council in the subjects assigned to the Committee are comparable in standards to awards granted and conferred by universities; (b) approval of courses of study in the subjects assigned to the Committee after having had regard to (i) the standard of work in the subject of a course at the establishment at which it is being pursued and the facilities available thereat for that course; (ii) the curriculum and syllabus of a course; (iii) the qualifications of the teachers conducting a course; (iv) any arrangements for practical training and experience in connection with a course; (v) the standards required for admission to a course; and (vi) the arrangements for conducting examinations in the subjects assigned to the Committee and for the appointment of external examiners to act with the teaching staff of the establishment."

Approval of a course of study or research is subject to the appropriate regulations of Council which include, *inter alia*, (i) Principles and Regulations for the Award of the Council's First Degrees and Diploma of Higher Education (1979); (ii) Principles and Regulations for Taught Courses leading to the Award of Master's Degrees and Postgraduate Diplomas (1985); (iii) Regulations for the Award of the Council's Degrees of Master of Philosophy and Doctor of

Philosophy (1983); (iv) Regulations and Conditions for the Award of Higher Doctorates (1980).

Le 'Council for National Academic Awards' est un organisme autonome créé par Charte royale en septembre 1964. Il peut, aux termes de la charte qui le régit, délivrer des grades et d'autres diplômes d'un niveau comparable à celui des universités du Royaume-Uni à des étudiants qui achèvent des programmes d'études ou de recherche officiellement reconnus dans des établissements non habilités à conférer leurs propres diplômes.

Le Conseil confère actuellement des grades dans plus de 160 disciplines, allant de l'architecture à la zoologie, et qui sont enseignées dans plus de 130 établissements d'enseignement. Le Conseil est actuellement l'organisme le plus grand du Royaume-Uni pour l'octroi de grades et environ un tiers de tous les étudiants qui étudient dans le but d'obtenir un grade au Royaume-Uni assistent à des cours agréés par le Conseil.

Le Président et les vingt-cinq membres du Conseil sont nommés pour trois ans par le Secrétaire d'Etat pour l'éducation et la science et le Secrétaire d'Etat pour l'Ecosse. Le «Chief Officer» (directeur) est le seul agent d'exécution qui soit en même temps membre du Conseil. Les Présidents des principaux Comités du Conseil sont, s'ils n'y ont pas été nommés, membres de droit du Conseil, qui peut lui-même nommer jusqu'à trois membres cooptés. Le Conseil bénéficie, en ce qui concerne la politique d'enseignement, du concours de ses dix principaux comités, huit d'entre eux s'occupant de disciplines connexes, c'est-à-dire: (i) l'art et les arts graphiques; (ii) les lettres et les sciences humaines; (iii) l'environnement architectural; (iv) les sciences commerciales et les sciences de la gestion; (v) les sciences de l'ingénieur; (vi) les sciences; (vii) les sciences sociales; (viii) la formation pédagogique. Le Conseil dispose également de Comités pour les institutions et pour l'Ecosse, et est conseillé, en matière de politique générale, par le Comité de la politique d'enseignement. La composition de chacun de ces Comités est fixée par le Conseil et est réexaminée tous les trois ou quatre ans.

Quelque soixante-dix Commissions et Comités d'experts chargés de disciplines particulières, qui se sont vu déléguer des pouvoirs par le Conseil et les Comités devant lesquels ils sont responsables, procèdent à l'évaluation des cours et des demandes de diplômes de recherche qui sont soumis au Conseil. Le nombre et la composition des Commissions chargées des disciplines particulières sont fixés par chaque Comité; la composition en est normalement renouvelée tous les trois ans. Chaque Commission ou Groupe chargé d'une discipline comprend généralement parmi ses membres des enseignants des universités, des «Polytechniques» et d'autres collèges associés au Conseil, des membres de l'industrie, du commerce ou d'autres organismes, ainsi que des praticiens exerçant à titre indépendant dans ces domaines. Les Groupes spéciaux créées par le Comité pour la formation pédagogique, qui examinent les dossiers de tous les étudiants désirant suivre un cours conduisant au «Bachelor of Education» (B.Ed.), comprennent également parmi leurs membres des enseignants en exercice. Chaque Commission ou Comité d'experts est responsable devant son Comité du respect des dispositions de l'Article 8(5) de la Charte et des Statuts du Conseil.

Cet Article stipule que «chaque comité, sous réserve des dispositions du Règlement, exerce les fonctions suivantes dont il est responsable devant le Conseil: (a) veiller à ce que les grades, les diplômes, les certificats et autres titres académiques conférés par le Conseil dans les domaines dont le Comité est responsable soient d'un niveau comparable à celui des titres conférés par les universités; (b) approuver les programmes d'études dans les disciplines dont le Comité est responsable, après avoir pris en considération (i) le niveau de l'établissement en ce qui concerne les études dans une discipline donnée, et les facilités offertes pour celles-ci; (ii) le programme du cours; (iii) les qualifications des enseignants assurant le cours; (iv) toutes dispositions prises en vue de l'acquisition d'une formation et d'une expérience pratiques ayant rapport au cours; (v) le niveau requis pour l'admission au cours; et (vi) les dispositions relatives au déroulement des examens dans les disciplines relevant de la compétence du Comité, ainsi qu'à la nomination d'examinateurs venant de l'extérieur appelés à se joindre au corps enseignant de l'établissement».

Les programmes de formation ou de recherche sont approuvés dans la mesure où ils sont conformes aux divers règlements du Conseil qui comprennent notamment (i) Règlements et conditions de délivrance des premiers grades du Conseil, ainsi que du diplôme d'enseignement supérieur du Conseil (1979); (ii) Principes et Règlements des études enseignées sanctionnées par les grades de «Master» et diplômes d'études avancées (1985); (iii) Règlements concernant les grades de «Master of Philosophy» et de «Doctor of Philosophy» conférés par le Conseil (1983); (iv) Règlements concernant la collation des doctorats dits supérieurs (1980).

Chairman: Sir Brian Nicholson.
Chief Executive: Dr. M. Frazer.
344/354 Gray's Inn Road, London WC1X 8BP.
 Tel: (1)278–4411.

The Committee of Directors of Polytechnics (CDP)

Between 1969 and 1973, thirty groupings of well-established institutions of higher education in England and Wales were formally designated as Polytechnics. They constitute comprehensive academic communities within the polytechnics and colleges sector of higher education. Their broadly-based curricula span business and social studies, engineering, science and technology, art and design, the humanities and teacher education at postgraduate, undergraduate, diploma and certificate levels. The full-time and sandwich courses attract students from the whole of the UK and from overseas, while part-time courses are also available to serve local and regional needs. The Polytechnics thus offer distinctive educational opportunities which are alternative and complementary to those of the Universities, and are characterized by a dual concern for vocational relevance and high academic achievement. For first degree and postgraduate work (including research), polytechnics are accredited for validation purposes by the Council for National Academic Awards, a body required by its Charter to maintain standards equivalent to those of the Universities.

In 1987/88 almost 170,000 students were enrolled on full-time and sandwich courses in the Polytechnics, of whom rather more than 75% are studying for qualifications at or above first degree level. In addition, 85,000 students were following part-time courses extending throughout the academic year, and a further 90,000 were enrolled on post-experience short courses of a professional or vocational nature.

The Committee of Directors of Polytechnics (CDP) was formally established in April 1970. The Directors of all 30 Polytechnics are full members and associate membership is extended to representatives of analogous institutions in Scotland and of the two Polytechnics in Hong Kong.

The key purposes of the CDP are to provide a forum for the discussion of matters of common concern to Polytechnics and to contribute to the evolution of policy for the development of this sector of higher education. In keeping with this role, the Committee seeks to ensure full polytechnic representation in the national and international consideration of higher education. The CDP itself presents evidence on major issues to parliamentary and other national committees enquiring into educational matters, and regularly meets representatives from central and local government and from other bodies with an interest in higher education.

A supporting framework of semi-specialized Standing Committees has been evolved to keep broad areas of interest under review, and working groups are set up to make detailed recommendations on specific topics.

In addition to occasional publications on a range of subjects, the CDP publishes annually the *Polytechnic Courses Handbook* which provides comparative information on all full-time and sandwich advanced courses offered by polytechnics, and a rapid-reference leaflet *The Polytechnics*. A twice-yearly publication *Focus on Polytechnics* is distributed to schools and colleges. The CDP also issues an annual Statistical Report on the First Destination and Employment of Polytechnic First Degree and HND Students.

Par regroupement d'établissements d'enseignement supérieur reconnus d'Angleterre et du Pays de Galles, trente institutions d'enseignement supérieur officiellement désignées sous le terme de «Polytechnics» ont été créées de 1969 à 1973. Elles constituent des communautés académiques polyvalentes dans le secteur qu'occupent, au sein de l'enseignement supérieur, les «Polytechnics» et les collèges. Le large éventail de leurs programmes comprend les sciences économiques et commerciales, les sciences de l'ingénieur, les sciences sociales, la science et la technologie, l'art et les arts graphiques, les lettres et sciences humaines, et la formation pédagogique aux niveaux tant postgradué qu'à celui des premiers cycles, des diplômes et des certificats. Cours à plein temps et cours et stages alternés attirent aussi bien des étudiants de toutes les parties du Royaume-Uni que des étudiants étrangers; des cours à temps partiel sont également organisés pour répondre aux besoins locaux. Les «Polytechnics» offrent ainsi des formations à la fois différentes et complémentaires de celles des universités. Leur double caractéristique est de rechercher tant l'utilité professionnelle que la qualité intellectuelle de la formation. Pour les travaux menant à un premier diplôme et ceux de niveau post-gradué (y compris la recherche), les «Polytechnics» ont obtenu l'accréditation, à des fins de reconnaissance, du Council for National Academic Awards, organisme dont la Charte exige qu'il octroie des diplômes et des qualifications de même niveau que celui des universités.

En 1987/88, les «Polytechnics» comptaient près de 170.000 étudiants à plein temps ou à des cours et stages alternés; plus de 75% d'entre eux se préparaient en vue d'une qualification se situant soit au niveau du premier grade, soit au-delà. En outre, 85.000 étudiants suivaient des cours à temps partiel durant toute l'année universitaire, 90.000 étaient inscrits à de brefs cours de recyclage professionnel.

Le Comité des Directeurs de Polytechniques (CDP) a été officiellement constitué en avril 1970.

Les Directeurs des trente «Polytechnics» sont membres titulaires, et la qualité de membre associé est accordée aux représentants des institutions analogues d'Ecosse et des deux «Polytechnics» de Hong-Kong.

Les principaux objectifs du CDP sont de fournir un cadre de discussion pour les problèmes d'intérêt commun aux «Polytechnics» et de contribuer à l'évolution de la politique en vue du développement de ce secteur de l'enseignement supérieur. En tenant ce rôle, le Comité cherche à assurer une représentation adéquate des 'Polytechnics' dans le domaine de l'enseignement supérieur, aux niveaux tant national qu'international. Le CDP lui-même soumet des dossiers aux comités parlementaires et aux autres comités nationaux effectuant des enquêtes sur des problèmes éducatifs; il se réunit régulièrement avec des représentants du gouvernement à l'échelon central et régional et des membres d'autres organismes s'occupant d'enseignement supérieur.

Un ensemble de Comités permanents semi-spécialisés a été constitué pour passer en revue les principaux domaines d'intérêt, et des groupes de travail ont été créés pour formuler des recommandations détaillées sur des sujets déterminés.

Outre les publications de périodicité non régulière qu'il fait paraître sur un grand nombre de sujets divers, le CDP public chaque année le guide des cours des 'Polytechnics'; cette publication contient les renseignements nécessaires sur tous les cours à plein temps et tous les cours et stages alternés organisés par ces établissements, ainsi qu'une brochure intituleé The Polytechnics, présentée sous un format permettant de la consulter très rapidement. Une publication semestrielle intitulée «Focus on Polytechnics» est diffusée auprès des écoles et collèges. Le CDP édite également un Rapport statistique annuel sur le premier emploi des étudiants des «Polytechnics» titulaires d'un Premier Grade Universitaire ou d'un Higher National Diploma (HND).

Chairman (1988–90): Professor G.T. Fowler, Rector, Polytechnic of East London.
Secretary: Dr. M.S. Lewis.
Kirkman House, 12-14 Whitfield Street, London W1P 6AX.
Tel: (1)637-9939. Fax: (1)436-4966

The Polytechnics and Colleges Funding Council (PCFC)

The PCFC was established as a result of the 1988 Education Act to oversee the sector of higher education formerly controlled by local authorities. The Council consists of 15 members appointed by the Secretary of State for Education and Science, and meets 5 times a year. The PCFC distributes over £1 billion of public funds in England each year to all the polytechnics, the largest colleges of higher education and a number of specialist colleges. It also funds certain higher education courses in further education colleges. In April 1989, the PCFC sector comprised 84 institutions serving nearly 350,000 students – considerably more than the universities. The PCFC also advises the Secretary of State on the Funding of higher education. For this it has established Programme Advisory Groups to review provision in nine subject areas. It also establishes ad hoc committees of inquiry on particular issues.

Le Conseil chargé du financement des «Polytechnics» et des «Colleges» (PCFC) a été créé à la suite de la loi sur l'éducation de 1988, avec pour objet de superviser le secteur de l'enseignement supérieur anciennement placé sous la direction des autorités régionales. Le Conseil se compose de quinze membres nommés par le Secrétaire d'Etat pour l'éducation et la science et se réunit cinq fois par an. Le PCFC répartit annuellement en Angleterre des fonds publics s'élevant à plus d'un milliard de livres sterling entre tous les «Polytechnics», les «colleges» d'enseignement supérieur les plus importants et un certain nombre de «colleges» spécialisés. Il finance également certains enseignements de niveau supérieur dans des instituts d'éducation permanente. En avril 1989, le secteur couvert par le PCFC comprenait quatre-vingt quatre institutions répondant aux besoins de près de 350.000 étudiants – sensiblement plus que les universités. Le PCFC conseille également le Secrétaire d'Etat en ce qui concerne le financement de l'enseignement supérieur. Il a, à cet effet, créé des Comités consultatifs de programmes chargés d'étudier les questions de financement dans neuf domaines précis. Il constitue également des commissions d'enquête temporaires pour l'étude de problèmes particuliers.

Chairman: Sir Ron Dearing.
Chief Executive: William Stubbs.
Metropolis House, 22 Perry Street, London W1P 9FF.
Tel: (1)637-1132. Fax: (1)436-4320

The British Council

The British Council was established in 1934 to promote a wider knowledge of Britain and of the English language abroad and to develop closer cultural relations with other countries. Its work embraces culture in its widest sense and includes education, science, medicine, the arts and every kind of social and intellectual interchange. The Council received its Royal Charter in 1940. It is represented in 82 overseas countries.

The Council is the principal agent of Her Majesty's Government for cultural conventions

with twenty-three countries. It also has responsibilities in the implementation of intergovernmental educational, scientific and cultural programmes agreed with East European countries. Work in support of the teaching of English abroad is one of the Council's main activities. The Council's general policy is to cooperate with ministries of education overseas in the training of local teachers of English, and in advising on syllabuses, textbooks and multimedia learning resources. Education in its broadest sense forms the largest element in the Council's general cultural work. Representatives normally act as education advisers (sometimes as cultural attachés) to British embassies and high commissions, and in the Third World have considerable responsibilities as agents for the Overseas Development Administration (ODA) in the field of educational aid. Assistance is also given in collaboration with international development agencies such as the World Bank. Council staff both at home and abroad include specialists in a whole range of educational and scientific activities and they maintain close contact with those working in teacher education, curriculum development, university interchange, educational technology and science teaching and research. In addition, the Council recruits for a variety of posts in overseas universities, colleges, schools and in ministries of education; assists British-type schools; conducts British examinations where appropriate; and provides information and advice on all aspects of British educational life. Council educational and scientific work overseas is supported by specialist departments in headquarters which provide consultancy and resource services. There are also highly developed facilities in educational technology with resources for advisory work and training and materials production. The Council sponsors tours and exhibitions to demonstrate British achievements in the field of drama, dance, music and the fine arts.

The Council runs or is associated with 116 reference or lending libraries in the countries in which it is represented and, as ODA's agent, manages the Low Priced Book Scheme which is designed to provide tertiary level textbooks and books on the teaching and learning of English for students in certain developing countries at greatly reduced prices. It also helps to promote the use of British publications overseas by organizing exhibitions of books and periodicals.

The British Council promotes educational, youth, and other exchanges with overseas countries primarily by sponsoring visits in both directions. It sends British specialists abroad on short advisory visits and recruits British teachers for service in overseas universities and schools. It arranges and supports academic interchanges between Britain and other countries. It also acts for many foreign governments in publicizing their scholarships and organizing selection boards.

It offers a number of scholarships for study in Britain to postgraduate students, and others from Commonwealth and foreign countries. It administers on behalf of various United Nations specialized agencies a number of United Nations Fellowships programmes, including those involving postgraduate study; similarly it administers on behalf of the Overseas Development Administration training awards under H.M.G.'s technical co-operation programmes.

The Council maintains offices in Britain, mainly in university cities, to provide services for professional visitors and students.

Publications include: British Book News (monthly); Higher Education in the United Kingdom (alternative years); How to Live in Britain, a handbook for students (annually); Overseas Students in Britain (annually); Scholarships Abroad (annually); and a wide range of free and priced publications on the learning and teaching of English.

Le Conseil britannique a été créé en 1934 afin de promouvoir à l'étranger la connaissance de la Grande-Bretagne et de la langue anglaise et d'établir d'étroites relations culturelles avec d'autres pays. Ses activités sont d'ordre culturel au sens le plus large et portent sur l'éducation, la science, la médecine, les lettres et les arts et toutes sortes d'échanges de caractère social et intellectuel. Il a reçu une Charte royale en 1940. Il est représenté dans 82 pays étrangers.

Le Conseil est le principal instrument du gouvernement de Sa Majesté pour l'application des accords culturels avec vingt-trois pays. Il contribue également à la mise en œuvre de programmes éducatifs et culturels intergouvernementaux établis en accord avec les pays d'Europe de l'Est. L'une des principales activités du Conseil consiste à promouvoir l'enseignement de l'anglais à l'étranger. Sa politique est de coopérer avec les ministres de l'éducation des pays étrangers en vue de la formation d'enseignants d'anglais nationaux de ces pays, et il donne des avis sur les programmes, les manuels et les matériels pédagogiques «multi-media». L'éducation au sens le plus large constitue l'élément essentiel des activités culturelles générales du Conseil. Ses représentants à l'étranger servent fréquemment de conseillers en matière d'éducation (quelquefois d'attachés culturels) auprès des ambassades et hautes commissions britanniques, et assument, dans les pays du Tiers-Monde, d'importantes fonctions en tant que représentants de l'Administration du Développement Outre-Mer dans le domaine de l'aide à l'éducation. Le Conseil octroie également une

assistance, en collaboration avec des organis-ations s'occupant de développement international, telles que la Banque Mondiale. Le personnel du Conseil tant en Grande-Bretagne qu'à l'étranger comprend des spécialistes de toute une gamme d'acti-vités éducatives et scientifiques, qui entre-tiennent d'étroites relations avec les personnes s'occupant de formation pédagogique, d'amélior-ation des programmes, d'échanges universitaires, de technologie éducative et d'enseignement et de recherche scientifique. Le Conseil s'occupe de recrutement pour divers postes dans des univer-sités, collèges, écoles et ministères de l'éducation étrangers, apporte son concours à des écoles de type britannique; fait, le cas échéant, passer des examens britanniques; et fournit des informations et des avis sur tous les aspects de l'enseignement en Grande-Bretagne. Les activités éducatives et scientifiques du Conseil à l'étranger sont soutenues par des départements spécialisés installés au siège et qui fournissent des services consultatifs et logis-tiques. Le Conseil dispose aussi d'un équipement très perfectionné en technologie de l'éducation permettant de fournir des services consultatifs, de dispenser une formation et de mettre au point des matériels. Il patronne des tournées et des exposi-tions qui présentent les meilleures réalisations britanniques dans le domaine du théâtre, de la danse, de la musique et des beaux-arts.

Le Conseil dirige ou est associé à 116 biblio-thèques de référence ou de prêt dans les pays où il est représenté. Il gère en outre, en tant que représentant du Ministère du Développement Outre-Mer, le Programme de vente de livres à prix réduit, qui permet aux étudiants de certains pays en voie de développement d'acquérir, pour un prix sensiblement plus bas, des livres et manuels d'apprentissage et d'enseignement de l'anglais au niveau post-secondaire. Il contribue également à promouvoir à l'étranger l'utilisation des publica-tions britanniques, en organisant des expositions de livres et de périodiques.

Le Conseil britannique stimule les échanges éducatifs, de jeunes, ou autres, avec les pays étrangers, notamment en patronnant des visites dans les deux sens. Il envoie des spécialistes britanniques à l'étranger pour de brèves missions consultatives et recrute des enseignants britan-niques pour les universités et écoles d'outre-mer. Il organise et soutient les échanges universitaires entre la Grande-Bretagne et les autres pays. Il assure également des services à de nombreux gouvernements étrangers en annonçant les bour-ses offertes par eux et en organisant des comités de sélection.

Il offre un certain nombre de bourses d'études en Grande-Bretagne aux étudiants avancés du Commonwealth et des pays étrangers. Il admin-istre, pour le compte de diverses institutions spécialisées des Nations Unies, une série de programmes de bourses des Nations Unies, y compris dans le domaine des études avancées; il administre également, pour le compte de l'Admin-istration du Développement Outre-Mer, des bourses de formation accordées au titre des pro-grammes de coopération technique du gouverne-ment britannique.

Le Conseil entretient des bureaux en Grande-Bretagne, principalement dans les villes universit-aires, afin d'assurer des services aux universitaires et aux étudiants en visite.

Parmi les publications figurent: British Book News (mensuelle); Higher Education in the United Kingdom (tous les deux ans); How to Live in Britain, a handbook for students (annuelle); Overseas Students in Britain (annuelle); Scholar-ships Abroad (annuelle); et une vaste gamme de publications gratuites et payantes sur l'apprentis-sage et l'enseignement de l'anglais.

Director-General: Richard Francis.
10 Spring Gardens, London SW1A 2BN.
Tel: (1)930-8466. Fax: (1)839-6347. Telex: 8952201

Carnegie Trust for the Universities of Scotland

The annual income of the Trust is about £819,000 which is devoted to the improvement and expansion of the universities of Scotland and the extension of opportunities for postgraduate study and research, and to assisting Scottish students in the payment of unversity fees.

Les revenus annuels du Fonds Carnegie pour les universités d'Ecosse se montent à environ £819.000, qui sont consacrés à l'amélioration et au développement des universités d'Ecosse, à l'extension du dispositif d'études avancées et de recherche et à l'assistance des étudiants écossais dans le paiement de leurs droits d'études.

Secretary and Treasurer: Prof. J.T. Coppock.
Merchant's Hall, 22 Hanover Street, Edinburgh EH2 2EN, Scotland.

Fulbright Commission (United States—United Kingdom Educational Commission)

Established by agreements between the United Kingdom and the United States Govern-ments in 1948, 1965 and 1971 as a binational Commission of seven British and seven Ameri-can members, the Commission administers the Fulbright programme of Educational Visits and Exchanges in the United Kingdom. It offers scholarships to American graduate students for research and study, and awards to American scholars for lecturing or advanced research in Britain. Similarly, grants are made to British lecturers and research scholars to visit the U.S.A. covering round-trip travel between a scholar's home in Britain and the host institution in

America (closing dates for application: March, for those travelling 1 June–31 July; May, for those travelling in August). For British postgraduate students grants cover maintenance for an academic year, and round-trip travel (closing date: 28 October).

The Commission funds a Higher Education Links programme, jointly with the British Council, enabling a direct exchange of faculty for teaching purposes or collaborative research (closing date: 31 October). Fellowship awards are available to both U.S. and U.K. citizens in specialist fields such as the Arts, the Professions, Academic Administration, Research Libraries, Business and Industry. The Commission houses an Educational Advisory Service which provides counselling for students who wish to study in the U.S.A. and also acts as a general source of information on the U.S. education system.

Créée en vertu d'accords conclus entre les gouvernements du Royaume-Uni et des Etats-Unis en 1948, 1965 et 1971, la Commission d'éducation Etats-Unis-Royaume-Uni est un organisme binational formé de sept membres britanniques et de sept membres américains; elle administre le programme Fulbright d'échanges et de séjours éducatifs au Royaume-Uni. Elle octroie des bourses aux étudiants américains avancés désireux de poursuivre des études ou des recherches, et fournit des subventions aux enseignants et chercheurs américains en visite au Royaume-Uni. Des crédits couvrant le voyage aller et retour entre le lieu de résidence du chercheur et l'institution qui l'accueille en Amérique sont, de la même manière, accordés aux enseignants et chercheurs britanniques en visite (dates limites de dépôt des demandes: mars, pour ceux qui voyagent entre le 1er juin et le 31 juillet; mai, pour ceux qui voyagent en août). Les subventions versées aux étudiants britanniques avancés comprennent l'octroi d'une bourse pendant une année académique, et couvrent les frais de voyage aller et retour (date limite du dépôt de la demande: 28 octobre).

La Commission finance, conjointement avec le Conseil britannique, un programme de coopération dans l'enseignement supérieur, qui permet d'organiser directement des échanges d'enseignants à des fins soit d'enseignement, soit de recherches conjointes (date limite: 31 octobre). Des bourses universitaires sont offertes aux spécialistes américains et britanniques dans le domaine des lettres, des professions libérales, d l'administration universitaire, des bibliothèques de recherche, des affaires et de l'industrie. La Commission comprend un Service-conseil en éducation qui renseigne les étudiants désirant étudier aux Etats-Unis, et sert également d'office central d'information sur le système d'éducation aux Etats-Unis.

Executive Director: John E. Franklin.

6 Porter Street, London W1M 2HR.
Tel: (1)486-7697

The Commonwealth Foundation

The Foundation was established in 1966 and registered as a charity in English law, following a decision by Commonwealth Heads of Government at their meeting in London in 1965, to promote closer professional co-operation within the Commonwealth. In February 1983, the Foundation was reconstituted as an international organization, retaining the objects, autonomous character and organizational arrangements in broadly the same terms as approved earlier, with expanded terms of reference. The Foundation is funded by its Member Governments. The target income is currently £1.61 million.

It makes grants for attendance at small conferences and workshops and for study visits and training attachments within the Commonwealth; provides financial support to Commonwealth professional associations and professional centres; funds short-term fellowship schemes in co-operation with other organizations to promote Commonwealth understanding, mid-career training and health, the media and culture; and makes grants to facilitate the flow of professional information through the distribution of publications.

In pursuance of its enlarged mandate from Commonwealth Heads of Government, the Foundation has been promoting better understanding of the work carried out by the non-governmental organizations and encouraging the strengthening of information links through facilitating the establishment of Commonwealth NGO liaison units in each Commonwealth country.

La Fondation du Commonwealth a été créée en 1966 et enregistrée en tant qu'institution bénévole dans le droit anglais, après la décision prise, lors de leur réunion de Londres en 1965, par les chefs de gouvernement des pays du Commonwealth, de promouvoir le renforcement de la cooperation entre les professionnels au sein du Commonwealth. En février 1983, la Fondation a été transformée en organisation internationale: elle conserve ses objectifs, son autonomie et sa structure dans des conditions à peu près semblables à celles approuvées antérieurement, mais dispose d'un mandat élargi. La Fondation est financée par les gouvernements membres. Le montant prévu, en ce qui concerne ses recettes, est actuellement de 1,61 million de livres sterling.

Elle accorde des subventions pour la participation à de petites conférences et réunions ainsi que pour des séjours d'études et des détachements au sein du Commonwealth, destinés à fournir des compléments de formation; verse des contributions financières aux associations professionnelles

et aux centres professionnels du Commonwealth; octroie, en coopération avec d'autres organisations, des bourses à court terme en vue de promouvoir la coopération, la formation en cours de carrière, la santé, les moyens de communication de masse et la culture au sein du Commonwealth; elle accorde des subventions destinées à stimuler la circulation d'informations professionnelles par la diffusion de publications.

En vertu du mandat élargi que lui ont conféré les chefs de gouvernement des pays du Commonwealth, la Fondation oeuvre pour une meilleure compréhension des tâches accomplies par les organisations non gouvernementales et favorise le renforcement des relations en matière d'information en facilitant la création d'unités de liaison Commonwealth ONG dans chaque pays du Commonwealth.

Director: 'Inoke F. Faletau.
Marlborough House, Pall Mall, London SW1Y 5HY.
Tel: (1)930-3783. Fax: (1)930-0827. Telex: 27678 comsec

Association of University Teachers (AUT) (IAUPL)

The objects of the Association of University Teachers, which was founded in June 1919, are "the advancement of university education and research, the regulation of relations between university teachers and their employers, the promotion of common action by university teachers and the safeguarding of the interests of the members". Membership is open to all full-time University Teachers, Research Workers, Academic Library Staff, and Senior Administrative Staff in the United Kingdom. The Association is essentially a Trade Union with branches in every university and university college in England, Wales, Scotland and Northern Ireland; in addition there are some Attached Members in certain recognized institutions and Corresponding Members in overseas University institutions. The Local Associations send representatives to a Central Council which meets twice a year; its business and that of its Executive Committee is to initiate and co-ordinate general policy and to secure the considered opinion of members on matters of general academic and professional concern. Reports are prepared on such matters, which, after consideration by the Local Associations and final approval by Council, are made available to the general public and presented in interested quarters as the views of the Association. Its Bulletin is published ten times a year and is distributed to members only.

The Association has continually worked for mutual understanding and the exchange of views

with the universities of other countries, and held its first International Universities Conference at Oxford in 1934, followed by other conferences at various centres in Europe until the outbreak of war.

L'objet de l'Association des enseignants des universités, qui a été fondée en juin 1919, est: 'l'avancement de l'enseignement et de la recherche universitaires, la régulation des relations entre les enseignants des universités et leurs patrons, la promotion de l'action commune des enseignants des universités et la sauvegarde des intérêts de ses membres'. Elle est ouverte à tous les enseignants et chercheurs à plein temps des universités du Royaume-Uni, ainsi qu'au personnel des bibliothèques universitaires, et aux cadres administratifs. L'Association a la forme d'un Syndicat avec des sections, qui existent dans chaque université et collège universitaire d'Angleterre, du Pays de Galles, d'Ecosse et d'Irlande du Nord; en outre elle compte des membres affiliés dans certaines institutions reconnues et des membres correspondants dans les institutions universitaires d'outre-mer. Les associations locales délèguent des représentants à un Conseil central qui se réunit deux fois par an; la tâche du Conseil et de son Comité exécutif est de coordonner et de formuler la politique générale de l'organisation et de solliciter l'avis des membres sur les questions touchant à la profession ou plus généralement à l'université. Des rapports sont rédigés sur ces questions, qui, après avoir été examinés par les associations locales et définitivement approuvés par le Conseil, sont mis à la disposition du public et présentés dans les milieux intéressés comme représentant le point de vue de l'Association. Celle-ci publie dix fois par an un Bulletin qui est exclusivement réservé à ses membres.

L'Association s'est toujours efforcée de promouvoir la compréhension mutuelle et l'échange d'idées avec les universités d'autres pays et a tenu sa première conférence universitaire internationale à Oxford en 1934, qui fut suivie d'autres conférences dans différents centres européens jusqu'au commencement de la guerre.

General Secretary: Diana Warwick.
United House, 1 Pembridge Road, London W11 3HJ.
Tel: (1)221 4370

Association of Polytechnic Teachers (APT)

The objects of the Association, which was founded in 1973, are: "The representation and promotion of the interests of Polytechnic teachers in all professional and employment matters". Membership is open to all Polytechnic teachers, Research Staff, Academic Related Staff and Senior Administrative Staff in the 31

Polytechnics. The Association is both a professional association and a trade union, representing the interests of its members.

The APT is a federated organization based upon 8 Local Associations in the individual Polytechnics. A National Council at which the general policy of the Association is determined meets twice a year. The execution of this policy is the responsibility of the Executive Committee which produces discussion documents which form the bases for publications of the Association.

The APT works for closer co-operation between the Polytechnics and Universities in Great Britain and Northern Ireland and for the establishment of closer links with university institutions internationally.

The Association has recently extended its objectives and its membership to include lecturers in major institutes of higher education.

The APT also holds specialist conferences and publishes a monthly Bulletin.

Les objectifs de l'Association des Enseignants des "Polytechnics", créée en 1973, sont: "la représentation et la défense des intérêts des enseignants des 'Polytechnics' dans les domaines de la profession et de l'emploi". Elle est ouverte à tous les ensei-gnants des "Polytechnics", ainsi qu'aux chercheurs, au personnel académique auxiliaire et aux cadres administratifs de ces trente-et-une institutions. Organisation professionnelle, l'Association est aussi un syndicat, et représente les intérêts de ses membres.

L'APT est une organisation de type fédéral s'appuyant sur 8 Associations locales existant dans chacun des "Polytechnics". Un Conseil national se tient deux fois par an, qui définit la politique générale de l'Association. Le Comité exécutif est chargé d'en assurer la mise en oeuvre. Le Comité prépare en outre des documents de discussion servant de base aux publications de l'Association.

L'APT oeuvre en vue du développement de la coopération entre les "Polytechnics" et les universités de Grande-Bretagne et d'Irlande du Nord, et en vue de l'établissement de liens plus étroits avec les autres institutions universitaires au plan international.

L'Association a récemment élargi ses objectifs et permet l'admission à la qualité de membre d'enseignants d'autres institutions importantes d'enseignement supérieur.

L'APT organise aussi des conférences de spécialistes et publie un Bulletin mensuel.

National Secretary: Dr. B.E. Davison.
Chief Executive: Maureen Douglass.
Caxton Chambers, 81 Albert Road, Southsea, Hampshire PO5 2SG.
Tel: (705) 818625

The Society for Research into Higher Education Ltd.

The Society was set up in 1964 to encourage and co-ordinate research and development into all forms of higher education. It does this in a number of ways, but principally by publicizing findings, by providing ways in which those findings can be discussed and by providing a means by which researchers can get in touch with one another. *Abstracts* of articles and books on research and development in higher education are published three times a year. The *Bulletin* appears about every six weeks and carries information on the Society's meetings, courses and conferences organized by its members, and items of general interest. There is an annual conference in December at which research findings are discussed. The papers are published later.

There are six regional branches. Their programmes provide a useful way of bringing together not only research workers, but other people in colleges and universities who would like to keep abreast of current developments in research into higher education. The Society has a number of small working parties studying particular aspects of research in higher education and their work is intended to result in publications.

The Society has a growing number of members overseas, among colleges, universities and libraries, as well as a regular exchange of publications and information with educational institutions abroad. The International Committee was established to foster contacts with overseas researchers and their work. The *International Newsletter* now appears twice a year (March and November).

The Society publishes, through the imprint SRHE & NFER-Nelson, monographs on aspects of research and development of specialist and general interest. It also sponsors a journal *Studies in Higher Education*. The Society's income is derived from subscriptions and sales of publications, with occasional grants from other bodies toward the cost of organizing conferences or specific publications. Recently, the Society has received grants from the Leverhulme Trust, the Gulbenkian Foundation and the British Government's Department of Education and Science to conduct a Study of the Future of Higher Education in Britain. The Study was directed by Professor Gareth Williams and Dr. Tessa Blackstone. The 11 volumes are available from SRHE & NFER-Nelson, Windsor SL4 1DF. Telephone: 58961.

La Société pour la recherche sur l'enseignement supérieur a été créée en 1964 pour promouvoir et coordonner la recherche et le développement sur

l'enseignement supérieur sous toutes ses formes. Elle accomplit cette tâche de diverses manières, mais surtout en diffusant les résultats, en facilitant l'organisation de débats sur ces résultats, et en offrant aux chercheurs des possibilités d'entrer en contact les uns avec les autres. Elle publie trois fois par an des résumés d'articles et de livres consacrés à la recherche et au développement en matière d'enseignement supérieur. La Société fait paraître toutes les six semaines un bulletin contenant des informations sur ses réunions, les cours et conférences organisés par ses membres, et des articles d'intérêt général. Elle tient chaque année en décembre une conférence qui fait le point des résultats de la recherche: elle publie ultérieurement les communications qui y ont été présentées.

La Société compte six bureaux régionaux. Leurs programmes offrent d'utiles possibilités de rencontre non seulement aux chercheurs, mais aussi aux membres des collèges et des universités qui souhaitent se tenir au courant de l'évolution de la recherche sur l'enseignement supérieur. La Société a également constitué divers petits groupes de travail pour étudier des aspects particuliers de la recherche sur l'enseignement supérieur et il est prévu d'en publier les travaux.

La Société compte un nombre croissant de membres à l'étranger, dans les collèges, les universités et les bibliothèques, et elle procède à des échanges réguliers de publications et d'informations avec des institutions d'enseignement étrangères. Un International Committee (Comité international) a été créé pour favoriser le développement des contacts avec les chercheurs étrangers et une meilleure connaissance de leurs travaux. L'International Newsletter est maintenant publié deux fois par an (en mars et en novembre).

La Société publie, par l'intermédiaire de la maison d'édition SRHE & NFER-Nelson, des monographies portant sur des aspects de la recherche et du développement qui présentent un intérêt non seulement pour les spécialistes mais aussi pour le public en général. Elle patronne également la publication du périodique Studies in Higher Education. Les recettes de la Société proviennent des abonnements et ventes de publications, mais elle reçoit parfois des sommes d'autres organismes à titre de contribution aux frais d'organisation de certaines conférences ou de production de certaines publications. Récemment, la Société a reçu des subventions du Leverhulme Trust, de la Fondation Gulbenkian et du Département pour l'éducation et la science du Gouvernement britannique pour réaliser une étude sur l'avenir de l'enseignement supérieur en Grande-Bretagne. L'étude était dirigée par le Professeur Gareth Williams et Mme Tessa Blackstone. Les onze volumes sont disponibles chez SRHE & NFER-Nelson, Windsor SL4 1DF.

Téléphone: 58961
Administration: Rowland Eustace.
c/o University of Surrey, Guildford, Surrey GU2 5XH.
Tel: (483) 39003

The Central Bureau

The Central Bureau was established in 1948 by the British Government to act as the national information office and co-ordinating unit for every type of educational visit and exchange. Its main task is the enrichment of the British educational system through international contact and co-operation; in-service training abroad for teachers, administrators, inspectors and advisers; the appointment of foreign language teaching assistants abroad; the placement of students and graduates in training positions in industry and commerce in the UK and abroad; the linking of all types of educational establishments and local education authorities with counterparts abroad; the organization of binational and international meetings, conferences, seminars and courses; the disbursement of information on all forms of educational visits and exchanges; and the publication of authoritative guides on international education. The Bureau is responsible to the Department of Education and Science, the Scottish Education Department, the Department of Education for Northern Ireland, and the Welsh Office Education Department, and also acts in an advisory capacity to other agencies and governments.

The Central Bureau produce the following guides offering opportunities for paid and voluntary work in the UK and overseas: *Working Holidays*. The comprehensive and authoritative annual guide to thousands of short-term paid and voluntary jobs in Britain and overseas. Price £7.45 (inclusive of postage for each publication) (U.K.); *Volunteer Work*. A comprehensive directory of organizations recruiting volunteers for long-term projects in Britain and in 153 countries worldwide. Price £3.55 (U.K.); *Home from Home*. A comprehensive guide to 80 reputable organizations arranging homestays, term stays and exchanges in Britain and 40 other countries in Europe and around the world. Price £3.95 (U.K.); *Study Holidays*. A guide to language courses arranged all over Europe, published in August 1988. Price £5.10 (U.K.); *Young Visitors to Britain*. A clear and authoritative pocket guide providing comprehensive and up-to-date information for young foreigners living, studying, holidaying or working in Britain. Price £2.45 (U.K.).

These guides provide invaluable information for school-leavers, those taking a year between, graduates, the unemployed, and anyone looking

for a challenge. They are obtainable from book-shops or from the Central Bureau.

Créé par le Gouvernement britannique en 1948, le Bureau central sert d'office national d'informa-tion et d'organisme de coordination pour tous les types de visites et échanges éducatifs. Il a essentiel-lement pour tâche d'enrichir le système éducatif britannique par la coopération et les contacts internationaux; la formation en cours de carrière à l'étranger, pour les enseignants, les administra-teurs, les inspecteurs et les conseillers en matière d'éducation; la nomination à l'étranger d'assist-ants d'enseignement de langues étrangères; le placement en situation de formation des étudiants et des diplômés dans l'industrie et le commerce au Royaume-Uni et à l'étranger; la liaison de tous les types d'établissements éducatifs et des autorités éducatives locales, avec leurs homologues à l'étranger; l'organisation de réunions, confér-ences, séminaires et cours impliquant deux ou plusieurs pays; la diffusion d'informations sur toutes les formes de visites et échanges éducatifs; la publication de répertoires dignes de foi sur l'éducation internationale. Le Bureau relève du Département de l'Education et de la Science, du Département écossais pour l'Education, du Département de l'Education pour l'Irlande du Nord, et du Département gallois pour l'éducation; il assure en outre des services consultatifs à d'autres gouvernements et institutions.

Le Bureau central prépare et publie, en langue anglaise, les guides ci-après qui indiquent les possibilités de séjour au Royaume-Uni et outre-mer, à titre bénévole ou contre rémunération: "Working Holidays", guide annuel détaillé comportant des renseignements dignes de foi sur des milliers d'activités de courte durée exercées au Royaume-Uni et outre-mer, en échange d'un salaire ou à titre bénévole. Prix: £7,45 (y compris les frais de port pour chaque publication) (Royaume-Uni); "Volunteer Work", répertoire détaillé des organisations recrutant des volontaires pour des projets déterminés en Grande-Bretagne et dans cent cinquante-trois pays du monde; Prix: £3,55 (Royaume-Uni); 'Home from Home', guide détaillé de 80 organisations de bonne réputation organisant des séjours avec accueil en famille, des séjours d'un trimestre et des échanges en Grande-Bretagne et dans 40 autres pays d'Europe et du monde. Prix: £3,95 (Royaume-Uni); 'Study Holidays', guide des cours de langues organisés dans toute l'Europe, à paraître en août 1988. Prix: £5,10 (Royaume-Uni); 'Young Visitors to Britain', guide de poche clair et fiable contenant des informations détaillées et à jour; destiné aux jeunes étrangers vivant, étudiant, travaillant ou en vacances en Grande-Bretagne. Prix: £2,45 (Royaume-Uni).

Ces guides fournissent de précieuses inform-ations pour: les jeunes sortant de l'enseignement secondaire; ceux qui font une pause d'un an avant d'entreprendre d'autres études; les diplômés; les sans emploi; et toute personne à la recherche d'une activité constituant en quelque sorte un défi. On peut se les procurer en librairie, ou en s'adressant au Bureau central.

Director: A.H. Male.
Seymour Mews House, Seymour Mews, London W1H 9PE.
Tel: (1) 486-5101. Telex: 21368 cbevex g;
3 Bruntsfield Crescent, Edinburgh EH10 4HD, Scotland.
Tel: (31) 447-8024;
and 16 Malone Road, Belfast BT9 5BN, Northern Ireland.
Tel: (232) 664418/9

Voluntary Service Overseas (VSO)

VSO is an independant charity which supports development initiatives which work towards more equal distribution of resources and greater access to land, capital, health care, skills, tech-nology and education.

Skilled and experienced people are recruited in response to requests from over 40 countries in Africa, Asia, the Pacific and the Caribbean. Salary, based on local rates of pay and accom-modation are provided by the organization or community that makes the request; other costs are met by VSO. VSO workers assist in the development of Third World countries by passing on their skills in the fields of education, agricul-ture, health, technical trades, crafts, engineer-ing, business and social development.

Le Service volontaire outre-mer (VSO) est une organisation indépendante de bienfaisance; il a pour mission de soutenir les initiatives en matière de développement qui visent à une répartition plus équitable des ressources et à un accès plus large à la terre, aux capitaux, aux soins médicaux, au savoir-faire, à la technologie et à l'éducation.

Les candidats possédant des compétences et de l'expérience sont recrutés à la suite de demandes émanant de plus de 40 pays d'Afrique, d'Asie, du Pacifique et des Caraïbes. Le salaire, basé sur les taux de rémunération locaux et le logement, sont fournis par l'organisation ou la communauté effectuant la demande; le VSO prend en charge les autres frais.

Les volontaires du VSO aident au dévelop-pement des pays du Tiers-Monde en transmettant leur savoir-faire dans les domaines de l'éducation, de l'agriculture, de la santé, des métiers tech-niques, de l'artisanat, du génie, du développement social et de la gestion d'entreprise.

Director: Neil McIntosh.
317-325 Putney Bridge Road, London SW15.
Tel: (1) 235-5191

British Federation of University Women (IFUW)
Crosby Hall, Cheyne Walk, London SW3 5BA.
World University Service (WUS)
20/21 Compton Terrace, London N1 2UN.
Tel: (1)226-6747. Telex: 265451 monref g
National Union of Students of the U.K.
461 Holloway Road, London N7 6LJ.
The Newman Society (Pax Romana)
18 Divis Drive, BT11 8AA, N. Ireland.
Catholic Student Council (Pax Romana)
Aston University Students' Union, Gosta
Green, Birmingham.
Newman Association of Great Britain (Pax
Romana)
30 Baker Street, London W1M 2DS.
Christian Education Movement (WSCF)
Pages Lane, London N10 1PR.
Tel: (1) 444-8383
British Student Christian Movement (WSCF)
186 St. Paul's Road, Balsall Heath, Birmingham B12 8LZ.
Tel: (21) 440-3000
United Nations Association—Youth Council
(ISMUN)

3 Whitehall Court, London SW1A 2EL.
Union of Jewish Students (WUJS)
Contact: 89 Chaussee De Vleurgat, 1050 Brussels (Belgium).
Tel: (2) 647-7279. Telex: 20625

*

National Academic Recognition Information Centre (NARIC)
The British Council, 10 Spring Gardens, London SW1 2BN.
Tel: (1)930-8466. Fax: (1)839-6347. Telex: 8952201
Foreign and Commonwealth Office
Downing Street, London S.W.1
Fax: (1) 270-3094
Department of Education and Science
Elizabeth House, York Road, London SE1 7PH.
Tel: (1)934-9033. Telex: 23171
Overseas Development Administration
Eland House, Stag Place, London SW1E 5DH.
Tel: (1)273 3000. Fax: (1) 213-6749

UNITED STATES OF AMERICA
ETATS-UNIS D'AMERIQUE

UNIVERSITIES, COLLEGES AND
TECHNICAL INSTITUTIONS (1)—
UNIVERSITES, COLLEGES, ET ECOLES TECHNIQUES (1)

Institutions awarding doctorates—Institutions délivrant un doctorat

*Adelphi University, Garden City, New York
11530.   *1896*
Tel: (516)663-1120
C : *arts-sc.*
S : *nurs, soc w, bus adm, ed.*
Alfred University, Alfred, New York 14802.
                                                    1836
Tel: (607)871-2111
C : *li arts, nurs, bus adm, cer, eng, art ed.*

NEW YORK STATE COLLEGE OF CERAMICS AT
ALFRED UNIVERSITY MAIN, Alfred, New
York 14802.   *1900*
American Conservatory of Music, Chicago,
Illinois 60602.   *1886*
Tel: (312)263-4161
S : *mus.*
The American University, Washington, D.C.
20016.   *1893*

---

(1) Based on a classification proposed by the U.S. Department of Education, Washington, D.C.
(1) D'après un classement proposé par l'U.S. Department of Education, Washington, D.C.

Tel: (202)885-1000
C : *arts-sc, law, ed, commun.*
S : *bus adm, gov-publ adm, int serv, nurs, justice.*

Andrews University, Berrien Springs, Michigan 49104. *1874*
Tel: (616)471-3307
C : *arts-sc, techn, diet.*
S : *theo, bus, ed.*

Arizona State University, Tempe, Arizona 85287. *1885*
Tel: (602)965-9011. Fax: (602)9652011. Telex: 1561058 asu ut. Easylink: 62015316
C : *li arts, arc, eng, bus adm, ed, eng sc, law, nurs, fa, publ prog.*
S : *soc serv adm.*

Ashland College, Ashland, Ohio 44805. *1878*
Tel: (419)289-4142
C : *arts-sc-ed, nurs, bus adm.*
D : *sc.*

Atlanta University, 223 Chestnut Street S.W., Atlanta, Georgia 30314. *1865, 1872*
Tel: (404)681-0251
S : *arts-sc, bus adm, ed, lib serv, soc w.*

Auburn University, Auburn, Alabama 36849–3501. *1856*
Tel: (205)826-4000. Fax: (205)8217675. Telex: 5106002392 auburn fishery
C : *arts-sc, arc-fa, ed, eng, hom eco, phar, vet, bus, nurs, for, sc-math.*

Ball State University, Muncie, Indiana 47306. *1918*
Tel: (317)289-1241
C : *arc, bus, ed, fa-app arts, arts-sc.*

Baylor University, Waco, Texas 76798. *1845*
Tel: (817)755-1011
C : *arts-sc.*
S : *bus, ed, law, mus, nurs, dent.*
Ce : *med.*

Biola University, La Mirada, California 90639–0001. *1908*
Tel: (213)944-0351
C : *arts-sc-ed, psyc, intercult st, nurs, mus.*

Bob Jones University, Greenville, South Carolina 29614. *1927*
Tel: (803)242-5100
S: *arts-sc, fa, ed, appl st, bus adm, relig.*

*Boston College, University Heights, Chestnut Hill, Massachusetts 02167. *1863*
Tel: (616)552-8000
C : *arts-sc.*
S : *ed, law, nurs, soc w, mangt.*

*Boston University, 121 Bay State Road, Boston, Massachusetts 02215. *1839*
Tel: (617)353-2000. Fax: (617)3539393. Telex: 4990042 bu astronomy
C : *li arts, bus adm, eng, heal professions.*
S : *ed, fa-app arts, nurs, soc w, publ commun, law, med, theo, dent.*

Bowling Green State University, Bowling Green, Ohio 43403. *1910*
Tel: (419)372-2531
C : *arts-sc, bus adm, ed, mus, heal serv, mass commun.*
S : *art, jour, mus, speech commun, techn.*

*Brandeis University, 415 South Street, Waltham, Massachusetts 02254. *1948*
Tel: (617)736-2000
C : *arts-sc, soc.*

Brigham Young University, Provo, Utah 84602. *1875*
Tel: (801)378-4511
C : *biol-agr sc, bus, ed, fam living, fa-commun, gen st, nurs, phys, soc, eng sc-techn, physical sc-math, relig instruction.*
S : *lib-infor sc, mangt, law.*

Brown University, Providence, Rhode Island 02912. *1764*
Tel: (401)863-1000. Telex: 952095 brntlxctr pvd
C : *arts-sc, med, eng. comp.*

*Bryn Mawr College, Bryn Mawr, Pennsylvania 19010. *1880, 1885*
Tel: (215)645-5000
S : *arts-sc, soc w-res, ed.*

California Institute of Integral Studies, 765 Ashbury Street, San Francisco, California 94117. *1968*
Tel: (415)753-6100
S : *arts-sc, bus, eng, behavioral sc.*

*California Institute of Technology, 1201 East California Boulevard, Pasadena, California 91125. *1891*
Tel: (818)356-6811. Fax: (818)4498676. Telex: 188192 caltech psd
D : *eng-app sc, geol sc, phy-math-astr.*

California State University:
CALIFORNIA STATE UNIVERSITY—LOS ANGELES, 5151 State University Drive, Los Angeles, California 90032. *1947*
Tel: (213)224-0111. Telex: 887377 csulbf ud
S : *let-sc, bus-eco, ed, eng, fa-app arts, soc, heal-hum.*

SAN DIEGO STATE UNIVERSITY, San Diego, California 92182. *1897*
C : *arts, sc.*
S : *bus adm, ed, eng, soc w, fa, heal-hum.*

SAN FRANCISCO STATE UNIVERSITY, 1600 Holloway Avenue, San Francisco, California 94132. *1899*
S : *behavioral-soc, bus, creative arts, ed, heal-phys-recr, hum, sc, ethnic st.*

Caribbean Center for Advanced Studies, Apartado 41246 Manillas Station, Santurce, Puerto Rico 00940. *1966*
Tel: (809)725-2586
S : *arts-sc.*

*Carnegie-Mellon University, 5000 Forbes Avenue, Pittsburgh, Pennsylvania 15213. *1900*

Tel: (412)268-2000. Fax: (412)2682860. Telex: 5106013951 software eng
C : *hum-soc, fa, bus, arc, mus.*
S : *ind adm, urb & publ aff.*
I : *techn, eng.*

Case Western Reserve University, 2040 Adelbert Road, Cleveland, Ohio 44106.   *1826*
Tel: (216)368-2000. Fax: (216)3685088. Telex: 882849 case
S : *app soc, dent, sc-eng, law, lib, mangt, med, nurs.*
I : *techn.*

*Catholic University of America, 620 Michigan Avenue, Northeast Washington, D.C. 20064.   *1887*
Tel: (202)635-5000
C : *arts-sc, lib-infor, phil.*
S : *eng-arc, law, mus, nurs, soc w, relig st.*

Central Michigan University, Warrimer Hall, Mount Pleasant, Michigan 48859.   *1892*
Tel: (517)774-3131. Telex: 887422 cmu bkstore ud
S : *arts-sc, bus-adm, fa-app arts, ed, heal-phys-recr.*

*The City University of New York, 535 E. 80th Street, New York, New York 10021.
Tel: (212)794-5555. Fax: (212)5351040
    CUNY Bernard Baruch College, 17 Lexington Avenue, New York, New York 10010.   *1919*
    S : *li arts-sc, bus, ed.*
    CUNY Brooklyn College, Bedford Avenue and Avenue H, Brooklyn, New York 11210.   *1930*
    S : *li arts, ed, sc.*
    CUNY City College, New York, New York 10031.   *1847*
    C: *arts-ed.*
    S: *ed, eng, arc, hum, soc, sc, nurs.*
    CUNY College of Staten Island, Staten Island, New York 10301.   *1955*
    C: *arts-sc.*
    CUNY Graduate School and University Center, 33 West 42nd Street, New York, New York 10036.   *1961*
    S : *li arts-sc.*
    D : *li arts-sc.*
    CUNY John Jay College of Criminal Justice, New York, New York 10019.
                    1964, 1965
    F : *li arts, prof st.*
    CUNY Lehman College, Bedford Park Boulevard West, Bronx, New York 10468.
                    1931
    P : *li arts.*
    C : *ed, nat, soc, nurs.*

Claremont Graduate School, 150 East 10th Street, Claremont, California 91711.   *1925*
Tel: (714)621-8000

C : *arts-sc.*

Clark University, 950 Main Street, Worcester, Massachusetts 01610.   *1887*
Tel: (617)793-7711
C : *arts-sc-ed.*

Clarkson University, Potsdam, New York, 13676.   *1896*
Tel: (315)268-6400
S : *arts-sc, eng, mangt.*

Clayton University, 7710 Carondelet Street, St. Louis, Missouri 63105.   *1972*

Clemson University, 201 Sikes Hall, Clemson, South Carolina 29634.   *1889*
Tel: (803)656-3311. Telex: 981694 clemson sc
C : *li arts, agr, sc, eng, for-recr resources, arc, ed, nurs, com-ind.*

Cleveland State University, Euclid Avenue at East 24th Street, Cleveland, Ohio 44115. *1964*
Tel: (216)687-2000. Telex: 8104218252 csu clv
C : *arts-sc, bus adm, ed, eng, law, urb aff.*

College of St. Thomas, 2115 Summit Avenue, St. Paul, Minnesota 55105.   *1885*
C: *ed, mangt, bus, theo.*

College of William and Mary, The, Williamsburg, Virginia 23185.   *1693*
Tel: (804)253-4600
F : *arts-sc.*
S : *bus adm, ed, law, mar sc.*

Colorado School of Mines, 1500 Illinois, Golden, Colorado 80401.   *1869*
Tel: (303)273-3000. Fax: (303)2733283. Telex: ITT 4938824 csm ui
C : *mining eng.*

Colorado State University, Fort Collins, Colorado 80523.   *1870*
Tel: (303)491-1101. Telex: 452014 ciim isard
C : *hum-soc, agr sc, bus, eng, for-natural resources, hom eco, vet-biomed sc.*

*Columbia University, 116 Street and Broadway, New York, New York 10027.   *1754*
Tel: (212)280-1754. Fax: (212)2801754. Telex: 220094 colu ur
C : *gen st, int aff, nurs.*
S : *arc, arts-sc, bus, dental-oral surg, eng-app sc, jour, law, lib serv, publ heal, soc w.*
F : *med.*
    Barnard College, 606 West 120th Street, New York, New York 10027.   *1889*
    Tel: (212)280-5262
    arts-sc-ed.
    Columbia University Teachers' College, 525 West 121st Street, New York, New York 10027.   *1887*
    arts-sc-ed.

Cornell University, Ithaca, New York 14853.
    Cornell University Endowed Colleges, Ithaca, New York 14853.   *1865*
    Tel: (607)255-1000. Fax: (607)255-7116. Telex: 6713054 corneluw. Easylink:

62619660 esl ud
C : *arts-sc, arc-art-plan, eng, ed.*
S : *bus-publ adm, hotel adm, law.*
CORNELL UNIVERSITY MEDICAL CENTER, 1300 York Avenue, New York, New York, 10021. *1898*
C : *med, nurs, med sc.*
CORNELL UNIVERSITY STATUTORY COL-LEGES, Ithaca, New York 14853. *1865*
C : *arts-sc, ed, agr, hum ecology, vet.*
S : *ind lab rel.*
Creighton University, 2500 California Street, Omaha, Nebraska 68178–0001. *1878*
Tel: (402)280-2703. Fax: (402)2802244. Telex: 438119 creighton
C : *arts-sc, bus adm, ed.*
S : *dent, law, med, phar, nurs.*
*Dartmouth College, Hanover, New Hampshire 03755. *1769*
Tel: (603)646-1110.
F : *arts-sc.*
S : *bus adm, eng, med.*
De Paul University, 25 East Jackson Boulevard, Chicago, Illinois 60604. *1898*
Tel: (312)341-8300. Telex: 206917 ud
C : *arts-sc, com, law, arc, dram.*
S : *ed, mus.*
Drake University, 25th and University Avenue, Des Moines, Iowa 50311. *1881*
Tel: (515)271-2011
C : *li arts, bus & publ adm, ed, fa, phar, heal sc.*
S : *jour, law.*
Drew University, Madison Avenue, Madison, New Jersey 07940. *1866, 1867*
Tel: (201)377-3000
C : *arts-sc.*
S : *theo.*
Drexel University, 32 and Chestnut Streets, Philadelphia, Pennsylvania 19104. *1891*
Tel: (215)895-2000
C : *hum-soc, infor sc, eng, bus adm, sc, ed.*
S : *lib.*
Duke University, Durham, North Carolina 27706. *1838*
Tel: (919)684-2323. Fax: (919)6845959
C : *arts-sc, ed.*
S : *eng, for, law, medical-allied ed, nurs, theo, bus.*
Duquesne University of the Holy Ghost, 600 Forbes Avenue, Pittsburgh, Pennsylvania 15282. *1878*
Tel: (412)434-6000. Fax: (412)4346294
C : *arts-sc.*
S : *bus adm, ed, law, mus, nurs, phar.*
East Carolina University, East Fifth Street, Greenville, North Carolina 27834. *1907*
Tel: (919)757-6131
C: *arts-sc.*
S: *bus, ed, art, hom eco, nurs, mus, med, allied*

heal profession, techn.
East Tennessee State University, Johnson City, Tennessee 37614–0002. *1911*
Tel: (615)929-4112. Telex: 557353 etsubkstr joci
C : *arts-sc, bus adm-eco, ed, heal, med, app sc-techn*
East Texas State University, East Texas Station, Commerce, Texas 75428. *1889*
Tel: (214)886-5000
S : *li-fa, arts-sc, bus adm, sc-techn, ed.*
Emory University, 1380 South Oxford Road, N.E., Atlanta, Georgia 30322. *1836*
Tel: (404)727-6123. Telex: 8107518512 emery medlib
S : *arts-sc, bus, dent, law, med, nurs, theo.*
Fairleigh Dickinson University.
TEANECK CAMPUS, 1000 River Road, Teaneck, New Jersey 07666. *1954*
C : *li arts, bus adm, sc-eng, ed.*
S : *dent.*
Florida Agricultural and Mechanical University, Tallahassee, Florida 32307. *1887*
Tel: (904)599-3000
S: *arts-sc, gen st, hum-soc, ed, nurs, phar, sc-techn, arc, bus-ind, jour.*
Florida Atlantic University, 500 Northwest 20th Street, Boca Raton, Florida 33431–0991. *1961*
Tel: (305)393-3000. Fax: (407)3948829
S : *arts-sc, bus, eng, mus, soc, ed, hum.*
Florida Institute of Technology, 150 W. University Boulevard, Melbourne, Florida 32901–6988. *1958*
Tel: (305)768-8030. Telex: 9103509068 fit iver
C : *sc-eng, ed, mangt-hum.*
S : *aero, psyc.*
I : *med.*
Florida International University, Tamiami Trail, Miami, Florida 33199. *1965*
Tel: (305)554-2000
S: *sc, bus, diet, eng, ed, nurs, hospital mangt, publ aff-soc serv, int aff.*
*Florida State University, Tallahassee, Florida 32306. *1851*
Tel: (904)644-2525. Telex: 5106000494 isu ocean. Easylink: 62018155 esl ud
S : *bus, law, lib, mus, nurs, sc, commun, theat, crim, ed, eng, hom eco, soc w, vis arts.*
*Fordham University, Fordham Road, Bronx, New York 10458. *1841*
Tel: (212)579-2000. Fax: (212)9772662
C : *arts-sc.*
S : *bus adm, ed, law, soc serv, relig ed.*
Gallaudet University, 800 Florida Avenue, N.E., Washington D.C. 20002. *1864*
Tel: (202)651-5051
C : *arts-sc-ed (for deaf students).*
S : *commun, ed.*
George Mason University, 4400 University Drive,

Fairfax, Virginia 22030.   *1957*
Tel: (703)323-2000. Fax: (703)3232630
C: *arts-sc, law.*
S: *bus adm.*

*George Washington University, The, 800
Florida Avenue, N.E., Washington, D.C.
20052.   *1821*
Tel: (202)5051
C : *arts-sc, ed.*
S : *eng-app sc, govt-bus adm, med, publ-int aff.*
Ce : *law.*

*Georgetown University, 37 and 0 Street, N.W.,
Washington, D.C. 20057.   *1789*
Tel: (202)625-0100. Telex: 4972232 fgin. Easy-
link: 62005070 esl ud
C : *arts-sc, lang-ling.*
S : *bus adm, law, med, nurs, for serv.*

Georgia Institute of Technology, 225 North
Avenue, Northwest Atlanta, Georgia 30332.
                                             1885
Tel: (404)894-2000. Fax: (404)8943120. Telex:
542507 gtrc oca atl
C : *eng, arc, ind mangt, sc, li st.*

Georgia State University, University Plaza,
Atlanta, Georgia 30303.   *1913*
Tel: (404)658-2000
S : *arts-sc, bus adm, ed, allied heal sc, law, publ
& urb aff.*

Glassboro State College, Route 322, Glassboro,
New Jersey 08028.   *1923*
Tel: (609)863-5000
C: *li arts, prof st, fa-performing arts, bus adm.*

Golden Gate University, 536 Mission Street, San
Francisco, California 94105.   *1901*
Tel: (415)442-7000. Telex: 6502754174 mci un
C : *arts-sc.*
S : *law, bus.*

Gonzaga University, East 502 Boone Avenue,
Spokane, Washington 99258.   *1887*
Tel: (509)328-4220. Easylink: 62020543 esl ud
C: *arts-sc.*
S: *bus adm, ed, eng, law.*

Grambling State University, Grambling, Louis-
iana 71245.   *1901*
Tel: (318)247-3811
C: *arts-sc, ed-occp, nurs, sc-techn.*

Hamline University, St. Paul, Minnesota 55104-
1284.   *1854*
Tel: (612)641-2800
C: *arts-sc.*
S: *law.*

*Harvard University, Cambridge, Massachusetts
02138.   *1636*
Tel: (617)495-1000. Fax: (617)4952678. Telex:
325660 las pau. Easylink: 62901858 esl ud
F : *arts-sc.*
S : *bus adm, dent, des-arc, ed, law, publ heal,
div, med, govt.*

Hofstra University, Hempstead, Long Island,

New York 11550.   *1935*
Tel: (516)560-6600
C : *arts-sc.*
S : *bus, ed, law, lib.*

*Howard University, 2400 6th Street N.W.,
Washington, D.C. 20059.   *1867*
Tel: (202)636-6100. Telex: 892327 hubs wsh.
Easylink: 62020594 esl ud
C : *li arts, dent, fa, phar, allied heal sc.*
S : *eng, arc-city plan, law, med, soc w, nurs, ed,
commun, bus-publ adm, div.*

Idaho State University, 741 South 7th Avenue,
Campus, Box 8310, Pocatello, Idaho 83209–
0009.   *1901*
Tel: (208)236-2475. Telex: 9109971093 isucsc
S : *li arts, bus ed, phar, heal professions, eng,
ed, voc ed.*

Illinois Institute of Technology, 3300 South
Federal Street, Chicago, Illinois 60616.   *1892*
Tel: (312)567-3001
S : *sc-let, eng, law, arc-des, li arts, bus adm.*

Illinois State University, North and School
Streets, Normal, Illinois 61761.   *1857*
Tel: (309)438-2111
C : *arts-sc-ed, fa, app sc-techn, bus, ed.*

Indiana State University, Terre Haute, Indiana
47809.   *1865*
Tel: (812)237-6311
C : *arts-sc, heal-phys-recr, nurs, bus, ed, techn.*

*Indiana University at Bloomington, Bryan Hall
100, Bloomington, Indiana 47405.   *1820*
Tel: (812)332-0211. Fax: (812)3355678. Telex:
272279 indiana u blom. Cables: indvers
C : *arts-sc.*
S : *bus, ed, heal-phys, law, mus, lib, publ env
aff, jour.*

INDIANA UNIVERSITY—PURDUE UNIVERSITY
AT INDIANAPOLIS, 355 North Lansing,
Indianapolis 46202.   *1969*
S : *med, dent, nurs, law, soc serv, art, li arts,
phys, eng-techn, sc, ed, bus, optom, publ &
env aff.*

Indiana University of Pennsylvania, Indiana,
Pennsylvania 15705.   *1875*
Tel: (412)357-2100
S : *nat-math, soc-sc-hum, bus, ed, fa, heal serv,
hom eco.*

***Iowa State University of Science and Tech-
nology**, Ames, Iowa 50011.   *1858*
Tel: (515)294-4357. Easylink: 62011719 esl ud
C : *agr, eng, hom eco, sc-hum, vet, ed, des, bus
ed, des.*

John Hopkins University, The, Baltimore,
Maryland 21218.   *1876*
Telex: 264170 jhu ur
F : *arts-sc, med.*
S : *hyg-publ heal, int st, nurs, eng.*
L : *app phy.*

Kansas State University, Anderson Hall, Man-

hattan, Kansas 66506.   *1863*
Tel: (913)532-6011. Telex: 5106000752 ksu grains
C : *arts-sc, agr, arc-des, ed, eng, hom eco, vet, bus adm.*
Kent State University, Kent, Ohio 44242.   *1910*
Tel: (216)672-3000
C : *arts-sc, bus adm, ed, fa-prof arts.*
S : *lib, heal-phys-recr, nurs.*
D : *arc, hom eco, jour, mus, techn.*
Lamar University, 4400 M.L. King, Jr. Parkway, P.O. Box 10001-LUS, Beaumont, Texas 77710.
                                          1923
Tel: (409)880-7011. Fax: (409)8802309
C : *heal serv.*
S : *arts, sc, bus, ed, eng, fa-app arts, sc, tec arts.*
Lehigh University, Bethlehem, Pennsylvania 18015.   *1865*
Tel: (215)758-3000. Telex: 7106601086 lehigh univ ud
C : *arts-sc, bus-eco, eng, physical sc.*
S : *ed.*
Lewis and Clark College, 0615 South West Palatine Hill, Portland, Oregon 97219.   *1867*
Tel: (503)244-6161. Easylink: 62006021
C: *arts-sc.*
S: *law.*
Loma Linda University, Loma Linda, California 92350.   *1905*
Tel: (714)824-4300. Telex: 676482 intlh loml
S : *arts-sc, dent, allied heal professions, med, nurs, ed, vet.*
Long Island University, Greenvale, New York 11548.   *1954*
   Long Island University Brooklyn Campus, Brooklyn, New York 11201–9926.   *1926*
   C : *arts-sc, phar-heal sc.*
   S : *bus.*
Louisiana State University and Agricultural and Mechanical College, Baton Rouge, Louisiana 7003.   *1855*
Tel: (504)388-3202. Telex: 5109933414 isu btr. Easylink: 62049359 esl ud
C : *arts-sc, eng, agr, bus adm, ed, env des, vet.*
S : *soc welfare, mus, lib, hom eco, jour.*
   Louisiana State University Medical Center, 1440 Canal Street, Suite 1510, New Orleans, Louisiana 70112–2784.   *1931*
   med, nurs, dent, allied heal professions.
Louisiana Tech University, Box 3178, Tech Station, Ruston, Louisiana 71272.   *1894*
Tel: (318)257-3060. Telex: 467673 Patec ci. Easylink: 62150520 esl ud
S : *art-sc, bus adm, ed, eng, hom eco, life sc.*
Loyola University of Chicago, 820 North Michigan Avenue, Chicago, Illinois 60611.   *1870*
Tel: (312)670-3000. Easylink: 62012684 esl ud
C : *arts-sc.*

S : *bus adm, dent, law, med, nurs, soc w, ed.*
Loyola University in New Orleans, 6363 Saint Charles Avenue, New Orleans, Louisiana 70118.   *1912*
Tel: (504)865-3240
C: *arts-sc, bus adm, mus, law.*
Marquette University, 615 North 11th Street, Milwaukee, Wisconsin 53233.   *1864*
Tel: (414)224-7250. Telex: 7101110506 pms 056 xxesh
C : *li arts, bus adm, eng, jour, nurs, med techn.*
S : *dent, law, ed.*
*Massachusetts Institute of Technology, 77 Massachusetts Avenue, Cambridge, Massachusetts 02139.   *1861*
Tel: (617)253-1000. Telex: 174194 mit com
S : *arc plan, eng, hum-soc, mangt, soc.*
Medical College of Wisconsin, The, P.O. Box 26509, 8701 Watertown Plank Road, Milwaukee, Wisconsin 53226.   *1913*
Tel: (414)257-8296
S : *arts-sc, nurs.*
Medical University of South Carolina, Charleston, South Carolina 29425.   *1824*
Tel: (803)792-2300
C: *med, dent, allied heal sc.*
S: *nurs, phar.*
Memphis State University (Tennessee State University System), Memphis, Tennessee 38152.
                                          1912
Tel: (901)454-2040. Telex: 53915 msu bookstr mfs
C : *arts-sc, bus, ed, eng, commun, fa.*
S : *law.*
Miami University, East High Street, Oxford, Ohio 45056.   *1809*
Tel: (513)529-1809
C : *arts-sc.*
S : *appl sc, bus adm, fa.*
*Michigan State University, East Lansing, Michigan 48824–1046.   *1855*
Tel: (517)355-1855. Telex: 5106019207 natsupcyclab
C : *arts-sc, arts-let, bus, ed, eng, int st, osteopathy, med, nat, soc sc, vet, hum med, agr, nurs, urb aff.*
Michigan Technological University, Houghton, Michigan 49931.   *1885*
Tel: (906)487-1885
C : *eng-bus adm, for, sc-arts, ed.*
Middle Tennessee State University (Tennessee State University System), Murfreesboro, Tennessee 37132.   *1911*
Tel: (615)898-2300. Telex: 989661 mtsu bkstor ud. Easylink: 62022623 esl ud
S : *li arts, ed, basic app sc, bus-eco.*
Middlebury College, Old Chapel Building, Middlebury, Vermont 05753.   *1800*
Tel: (802)388-3711. Telex: 353249 midd coll ud

C : sc, hum.

S : lang.

Mississippi State University, Mississippi State, Mississippi 39762.   *1878*
Tel: (601)325-2323. Fax: (601)3253560. Easylink: 62007813 esl ud

C : arts-sc, bus-ind, ed, eng, agr-hom eco, arc, vet.

Montana State University (Montana University System), Bozeman, Montana 59717.   *1893*
Tel: (406)994-0211

C : let-sc, agr, ed, eng, arts, arc.

S : hom eco, nurs, bus.

National College of Education, 2840 Sheridan Road, Evanston, Illinois 60201.   *1886*
Tel: (312)256-5150

C: arts-sc-ed.

National University, 4141 Camino Del Rio South, San Diego, California 92108.   *1971*
Tel: (800)NAT-UNIV. Telex: 797684 natuniv

C : arts-sc, ed, mangt.

D : bus, law.

New Jersey Institute of Technology, Newark, New Jersey 07102.   *1881*
Tel: (201)596-3000. Telex: 5106012452 ud

C : eng, arc.

New Mexico Institute of Mining and Technology, Campus Station, Socorro, New Mexico 87801.
                                                            1889

Tel: (505)835-5011

I : teacher ed.

Ce : pet recovery res.

Bureau : mine-mineral resources.

New Mexico State University, Box 3004, Las Cruces, New Mexico 88003.   *1888*
Tel: (505)646-0111. Telex: 9109830549 nmsu cip Pacs. Easy link: 62003991 esl ud

C : arts-sc, agr-hom eco, bus adm-eco, ed, eng, hum & commun serv.

New School for Social Research, 66 West 12th Street, New York, New York 10011.   *1919*
Tel: (212)741-5600. Telex: 291192 psns ur

S : arts-sc.

*New York University, Washington Square, New York, New York 10012.   *1831*
Tel: (914)993-4000. Fax: (212)6747858. Telex: 235128 nyu ur. Cables: ny univer new york. Easylink: 62953009 esl ud

C : arts-sc, dent.

S : arts, ed, law, bus-publ adm, soc w, med.

North Carolina State University, Raleigh, Raleigh, North Carolina 27695.   *1862*
Tel: (919)737-2011

S: li arts, agr-life sc, des, ed, eng, for, recr, hum-soc serv, tex, vet.

North Dakota State University of Agriculture and Applied Science, 1301 12th Avenue North, Fargo, North Dakota 58105.   *1890*
Tel: (701)237-8011

C : agr, eng, hom eco, phar, hum-soc.

North Texas State University, Denton, Texas 762 03-3737.   *1890*
Tel: (817)565-2000

C : arts-sc, bus adm, ed, lib–infor sc.

S : hom eco, mus.

Northeast Louisiana University, 700 University Avenue, Monroe, Louisiana 71209–0001. *1931*
Tel: (318)342-2011

S : li arts, bus adm, ed, phar-heal sc, pure-app sc.

*Northeastern University, 360 Huntington Avenue, Boston, Massachusetts 02115-5095.
                                                            1898
Tel: (617)437-2000. Fax: (617)3261709. Telex: 948664 nuintcoop bsn. Easylink: 62048873 esl ud

C : li arts, bus adm, ed, eng, nurs, phar-heal professions, law, comp.

Northern Arizona University, NAU Box 4084, Flagstaff, Arizona 86011.   *1899*
Tel: (602)523-9011

C : arts-sc, bus, creative arts, eng-techn, ed.

S : app sc-techn, for, behavioral sc, heal prof.

Northern Illinois University, DeKalb, Illinois 60115.   *1899*
Tel: (815)753-8000. Fax: (815)7530198. Telex: 981417 niu telecomm ud

C : li arts-sc, law, bus, ed, fa-vis-performing arts.

Northwestern University, 633 Clark Street, Evanston, Illinois 60208.   *1851*
Tel: (312)491-3741. Telex: 5106019269 nucisst evn ug

C : arts-sc.

S : dent, ed, jour, law, med, mus, speech, mangt.

I : techn.

Nova University, 3301 College Avenue, Fort Lauderdale, Florida 33314.   *1964*
Tel: (305)475-7300. Easylink: 62030850 esl ud

C : arts-sc.

Oakland University, Rochester, Michigan 48309-4401.   *1957*
Tel: (313)370-2100

S : arts-sc, eng, ed, eco, nurs.

The Ohio State University, 190 North Oval Mail, Columbus, Ohio 43210-1358.   *1870*
Tel: (614)292-6446. Telex: 245334 ubs col. Easylink: 62712183 esl ud

C : arts-sc, agr, bio sc, adm sc, det, ed, eng, law, med, phar, soc w, vet.

S : nurs, mus, jour, arc, hom eco, nat resources, heal-phys-recr.

*Ohio University, Athens, Ohio 45710.   *1804*
Tel: (614)593-1000. Fax: (614)5934229. Telex: 8102392992 ohio univ ahen

C : arts-sc, bus adm, ed, fa, hom eco.

S : jour, mus, nurs, soc w.

Oklahoma State University, Main Campus, Stillwater, Oklahoma 74078.   *1890, 1891*
Tel: (405)624-5000. Telex: 160274 osu ut
C : *arts-sc, agr, bus adm, ed, eng, hom eco, vet, tec.*

Old Dominion University, 5215 Old Hampton Boulevard, Norfolk, Virginia 23529.   *1930*
Tel: (804)440-3000. Telex: 823428 old dom nfk
S : *sc-heal, bus adm, ed, eng.*

Oral Roberts University, 7777 South Lewis, Tulsa, Oklahoma 74171.   *1965*
Tel: (918)495-6528
C: *arts-sc-ed, nurs, bus, law, dent, med.*

Oregon Graduate Center for Study and Research, 19600 N.W. Von Neuman, Beaverton, Oregon 97006.   *1963*
Tel: (503)690-1121
C : *li arts.*

Oregon Health Sciences University, Portland, Oregon 97201.   *1974*
Tel: (503)225-8311. Fax: (503)2795241. Easy link: 62023796 esl ud
S: *med, nurs.*

Oregon State University, Corvallis, Oregon 97331.   *1850, 1865*
Tel: (503)754-0123. Telex: 5105960682 osu covs. Easy link: 62929202 esl ud
S : *agr, bus, ed, eng, for, hom eco, phar, sc, li arts, oceanog, vet.*

Pace University, One Pace Plaza, New York, New York 10038.   *1906*
Tel: (212)488-1200
S : *arts-sc, bus, ed, nurs, law.*

PACE UNIVERSITY—WHITE PLAINS CAMPUS, 78 North Broadway, White Plains, New York 10603.   *1923*
C : *arts-sc-ed, law, bus.*

PACE UNIVERSITY—PLEASANTVILLE-BRIAR-CLIFF CAMPUS, 861 Bedford Road, Pleasantville, New York 10570.   *1963*
Telex: 6713263 pace
C : *arts-sc.*
S : *nurs.*

Pacific University, Forest Grove, Oregon 97116.   *1849*
Tel: (503)357-6151
C: *arts-sc, optom.*
S: *psyc.*

*The Pennsylvania State University, System Administration, 201 Old Main, University Park, Pennsylvania 16802.   *1855*
Tel: (814)865-4700. Telex: 5106703532 pn st bs adm
C : *agr, art-arc, bus adm, earth-mineral sc, ed, eng, heal-phys-recr, hum dev, li arts, sc.*

PENNSYLVANIA UNIVERSITY HERSHEY MEDICAL CENTER, 500 University Drive, Hershey, Pennsylvania 17033.   *1964*
PENNSYLVANIA UNIVERSITY CAPITOL

CAMPUS, Route 230, Middletown, Pennsylvania 17057.   *1966*
C : *art-sc-ed.*

Pepperdine University, 24255 Pacific Coast Highway, Malibu, California 90265.   *1937*
Tel: (213)456-4000. Telex: 3725839 pepper u malibu. Easy link: 62930345 esl ud
C : *arts-sc.*
S : *law, bus, ed, psyc.*

Pepperdine University, Los Angeles, California 90034.   *1937*
Tel: (213)390-4087
C: *arts-sc.*
S: *mangt-bus.*

Phillips University, University Station, Enid, Oklahoma 73701.   *1906*
Tel: (405)237-4433
C : *arts-sc.*

*Polytechnic University, Brooklyn Campus, 333 Jay Street, Brooklyn, New York 11201.   *1854*
Tel: (718)643-5000
I : *eng, arts-sc.*

POLYTECHNIC UNIVERSITY, FARMINGDALE CAMPUS, Route 110, Farmingdale, New York 11735.   *1854*
Tel: (516)454-5150
C: *arts-sc.*

Ponce School of Medicine, University Street, P.O. Box 7004, Ponce, Puerto Rico 00732–7004.   *1976*
Tel: (809)840-2519
S : *med.*

Portland State University, 724 S.W. Harrison, P.O. Box 751, Portland, Oregon 97207.   *1946*
Tel: (503)229-4433
C : *arts-let, urb aff, performing arts.*
D : *heal-phys-recr.*
S : *bus adm, ed, soc w, eng.*

Princeton University, Princeton, New Jersey 08544.   *1746*
Tel: (609)452-3000. Fax: (609)4526218. Telex: 4991258 tiger. Easylink: 62010854 esl ud
arts-sc.
S : *arc, eng.*

Providence College, Eaton Street and River Avenue, Providence, Rhode Island 02918.   *1917*
Tel: (401)865-2413
C : *arts-sc-ed.*

*Purdue University, West Lafayette, Indiana 47907.   *1869*
Tel: (317)494-2145. Fax: (317)4946609. Telex: 4930593 pherlui. Easylink: 62005934 esl ud
S : *hum-soc, techn, sc, hom eco, ind mangt, vet, eng, agr, phar-pharmaceutical sc.*

Rensselaer Polytechnic Institute, 110 8th Street, Troy, New York 12180-3590.   *1824*
Tel: (518)266-6611. Fax: (518)2766003. Telex: 6716050 rpitrou

S : *arc, eng, hum-soc, mangt, sc.*

Rice University, P.O. Box 1892, Houston, Texas 77251   *1891*
Tel: (713)527-4036. Fax: (713)5224117. Telex: 556457 space phys hou
C : *hum-soc.*
S : *arc, mus, eng, adm.*

The Rockefeller University, 1230 York Avenue, New York, New York 10021–6399.   *1901*
Tel: (212)570-8000. Telex: 7105814156 nn rus nyk
C : *sc-let-psyc.*

Rutgers, The State University of New Jersey, New Brunswick, New Jersey 08903.   *1766*
Tel: (201)932-1766. Fax: (201)9323407. Easylink: 62043811 esl ud
C : *arts-sc, phar, eng.*
S : *lib sc, ed, soc w, app psyc, creative arts.*

RUTGERS, THE STATE UNIVERSITY OF NEW JERSEY, NEW BRUNSWICK CAMPUS, New Brunswick, New Jersey 08903.   *1766*
C : *arts-sc, eng, phar, infor-lib, nurs.*
S: *app & prof psyc, law, ed, soc w, mangt, arts.*

RUTGERS, THE STATE UNIVERSITY OF NEW JERSEY NEWARK CAMPUS, Newark, New Jersey 07102.   *1892*
Tel: (201)648-1766
C : *arts-sc, nurs.*
S : *law, bus adm, crim justice, mangt.*

St. John's University, Grand Central and Utopia Parkways, Jamaica, New York 11439.   *1870*
Tel: (718)990-6161
C : *arts-sc, bus adm, phar, allied heal professions.*
S : *human serv, law.*

Saint Louis University, 221 North Grand Boulevard, St. Louis, Missouri 63103.   *1818*
Tel: (314)658-2474. Fax: (314)6583874. Telex: 550132 stl univ stl. Easylink: 62002060 esl ud
S : *arts-sc, med, law, bus-adm, soc serv, nurs.*

St. Mary's Seminary and University, 5400 Roland Avenue, Baltimore, Maryland 21210.   *1791*
Tel: (301)323-3200
C : *arts-sc.*
S : *theo.*
I : *theo.*

Sam Houston State University, Sam Houston Avenue, Huntsville, Texas 77341.   *1879*
Tel: (409)294-1111
S : *arts-sc, bus adm, ed, crim justice.*

Santa Clara University, Santa Clara, California 95053.   *1851*
Tel: (408)554-4000
S: *bus, eng, law, arts-sc.*

Saybrook Institute, 1772 Vallejo Street, San Francisco, California 94117.   *1970*
Tel: (415)441-5034

S : *arts-sc.*

Seattle University, 12th and E. Columbia, Seattle, Washington 98122.   *1891*
Tel: (206)626-6200
C : *arts-sc.*
S : *bus, ed, sc-eng, nurs.*

Seton Hall University, 400 South Orange Avenue, South Orange, New Jersey 07079.   *1856*
Tel: (201)761-9000. Fax: (201)7619432. Telex: 139167 emp st comm
C : *arts-sc.*
S : *bus-adm, ed, nurs.*
NEWARK CAMPUS.
S : *law.*

Simmons College, 300 The Fenway, Boston, Massachusetts 02115.   *1899*
Tel: (617)738-2000
C : *arts-sc.*
S : *lib sc, soc, w, hum.*

Smith College, Northampton, Massachusetts 01063.   *1871*
Tel: (413)584-2700
C : *arts-sc.*
S : *soc w.*

South Dakota School of Mines and Technology, 500 E. St. Joseph, Rapid City, South Dakota 57701.   *1885*
Tel: (605)394-2511. Fax: (615)3946131. Easy link: 62860379 esl ud
D : *eng.*
I : *atmospheric sc.*

South Dakota State University, Box 2201, Brookings, South Dakota 57007-2298.   *1881*
Tel: (605)688-4151
C : *arts-sc, agr-bio sc, eng, hom eco, phar, nurs, ed.*

*Southern Illinois University at Carbondale, Carbondale, Illinois 62901.   *1869*
Tel: (618)453-2121. Telex: 9106686894 sdsu bkng. Easylink: 62017444 esl ud
C : *li arts-sc, ed.*
S : *agr, bus adm, commun-fa, human resources, eng-techn, law, med.*

Southern Illinois University at Edwardsville, Edwardsville, Illinois 62026–1001.   *1957*
Tel: (618)692-2000
C : *bus, ed, fa, hum, sc-techn, soc, nurs.*
S : *dental med, eng.*

Southern Methodist University, Dallas, Texas 75275.   *1911*
Tel: (214)692-2000. Telex: 5106017197 smu geo ug
S : *hum-sc, arts, bus adm, law, theo, eng-app sc.*

Southern University and Agricultural and Mechanical College, P.O. Box 9614, Southern Branch Post Office, Baton Rouge, Louisiana 70813.   *1880*
Tel: (504)771-5020. Easylink: 62048398 esl ud

C: *arts-sc, agr, bus, ed, eng, sc.*
Ce: *law.*
S: *nurs, acc, arc.*

Spalding University, 851 S. Fourth Street, Louisville, Kentucky 40203.   *1814*
Tel: (502)585-9911
C: *arts-sc-ed, nurs, bus, soc.*

Springfield College, 263 Alden Street, Springfield, Massachusetts 01109.   *1885*
Tel: (413)787-3000. Fax: (413)7883342
D : *arts-sc, ed, heal-phys-recr.*

*Stanford University, Stanford, California 94305–1684.   *1885*
Tel: (415)723-2300. Fax: (415)7230010. Telex: 348402 stanf stnu. Easylink: 62033575
S : *bus, earth sc, ed, eng, hum-sc, law, med.*

State University of New York System (SUNY), State University Plaza, Albany, New York:
Tel: (518)443-5313. Easylink: 62437800 esl ud

STATE UNIVERSITY OF NEW YORK AT ALBANY, 1400 Washington Avenue, Albany, New York 12222.   *1844*
Tel: (518)442-5571
C : *arts-sc, hum-fa, sc-math.*
S : *bus, criminal justice, ed, lib, publ aff, soc-behavioral sc, soc welfare.*

STATE UNIVERSITY OF NEW YORK AT BINGHAMTON, Vestal Parkway East, Binghamton, New York 13901.   *1946*
Tel: (607)777-2000
C : *arts-sc, ed, phys.*
S : *nurs, techn, mangt, eng.*

STATE UNIVERSITY OF NEW YORK AT BUFFALO, Main Campus, Capen Hall, Buffalo, New York 14260.   *1846*
Tel: (716)831-2000
F : *arts-let, eng-app sc, law.*
S : *law, lib st, soc w, arc-env, des, mangt, math, soc-nat.*

STATE UNIVERSITY OF NEW YORK HEALTH SCIENCES CENTER AT BUFFALO, 3435 Main Street, Buffalo, New York 14214.   *1846*
Tel: (716)831-2000
S : *nurs, dent, phar, med, heal professions.*

STATE UNIVERSITY OF NEW YORK AT STONY BROOK, Main Campus, Stony Brook, New York 11794.   *1957*
Tel: (516)246-5000. Telex: 5102287767 sunnyadmin stlk
C : *soc & behavioral sc, fa, hum, sc, math, eng.*
S : *med, dent, soc w, ed, nurs, heal professions.*

STATE UNIVERSITY OF NEW YORK HEALTH SCIENCES CENTER AT STONY BROOK, Stony Brook, New York 11794.   *1970*
S : *med, nurs, dent, soc welfare.*

STATE UNIVERSITY OF NEW YORK HEALTH SCIENCE CENTER AT BROOKLYN, 450 Clarkson Avenue, Brooklyn, New York 11203.   *1860*
Tel: (718)270-4000
C : *nurs, heal professions.*

STATE UNIVERSITY OF NEW YORK HEALTH SCIENCE CENTER AT SYRACUSE, 155 Elizabeth Blackwell, Syracuse, New York 13210.   *1834*
Tel: (315)473-4570. Telex: 7105410555 sunycesf syr
C : *med, heal professions.*

STATE UNIVERSITY OF NEW YORK COLLEGE OF ENVIRONMENTAL SCIENCE AND FORESTRY, Syracuse, New York 13210.   *1911*
Tel: (315)470-6644
for, land arc, eng.

STATE UNIVERSITY OF NEW YORK COLLEGE OF OPTOMETRY, 100 East 24th Street, New York 10001.   *1971*
Tel: (212)420-5100

Stephen F. Austin State University, 1936 North Street, Nacogdoches, Texas 75962.   *1921*
Tel: (409)568-2011
S : *li arts, ed, fa, for, bus, app art, sc, math.*

*Stevens Institute of Technology, Castle Point, Hoboken, New Jersey 07030.   *1870*
Tel: (201)420-5105. Telex: 132366 steven ipo.
Easy link: 62958246 esl ud
I : *sc-eng.*

*Syracuse University, Syracuse, New York 13244.   *1870*
Tel: (315)423-3611. Telex: 131659 syr uni eng
C : *arts-sc, vis-performing arts, hum dev, law, nurs, eng, arc, soc w, publ commun, lib sc, ed.*
S : *mangt.*

*Temple University, Broad and Montgomery Streets, Philadelphia, Pennsylvania 19122.   *1888*
Tel: (215)787-7000. Easy link: 62017754 esl ud
C : *li arts, ed, heal professions, mus, heal-phys-recr.*
S : *art, bus adm, commun-theatre, dent, law, med, nur, phar, soc adm, eng techn.*

Tennessee State University, 3500 Centennial Boulevard, Nashville, Tennessee 37203.   *1912*
Tel: (615)320-3214
S: *arts-sc, agr-hom eco, ed, eng-techn, bus, allied heal professions, nurs.*

Tennessee Technological University, Dixie Avenue and McGee Boulevard, Cookeville, Tennessee 38505.   *1915*
Tel: (615)372-3223
C : *arts-sc, ed, eng.*
S : *agr, hom eco, bus adm, nurs.*

Tennessee Temple University, 1815 Union Avenue, Chattanooga, Tennessee 37404.   *1946*
Tel: (615)493-4100
C: *arts-sc.*

Texas A & I University, Santa Gertrudes, Kingsville, Texas 78363. *1917, 1925*
Tel: (512)595-2111
S : *arts-sc, agr, bus adm, teacher ed, eng.*

Texas A & M University, College Station, Texas 77843–1246. *1876*
Tel: (409)845-3211. Easy link: 62024237 esl ud
C : *li arts-ed, agr, eng, geo sc, sc, vet, med.*
S : *arc, bus adm.*

Texas Christian University, 2800 South University Drive, Fort Worth, Texas 76129. *1873*
Tel: (817)921-7793. Easy link: 62028475 esl ud
C : *arts-sc, nurs.*
S : *bus, ed, fa, mangt infor.*

Texas Southern University, 3100 Cleburne Street, Houston, Texas 77004. *1947*
Tel: (713)527-7011
C : *arts-sc, techn, commun.*
S : *mangt, law, phar, behavioral sc.*

Texas Tech University, Lubbock, Texas 79409–4349. *1923*
Tel: (806)742-2011. Fax: (806)7432218. Telex: 5106012483 tiec tx tech
S : *arts-sc, agr sc, bus adm, ed, eng, hom eco, law.*

　TEXAS TECH UNIVERSITY HEALTH SCIENCES CENTER, Lubbock, Texas 79430. *1969*
　S: *allied heal, med, nurs.*

Texas Woman's University, Box 23925 TWU Station, Denton, Texas 76204. *1901*
Tel: (817)898-2000
C : *arts-sc, ed, fa, heal-phys recr, nurs, nutr-tex dev.*
S : *lib sc, occp & physio.*

*****Tufts University**, Medford, Massachusetts 02155. *1852*
Tel: (617)628-5000. Telex: 928182 tuftex. Easy link: 62027469 esl ud
F : *arts-sc.*
C : *li arts, eng.*
S : *dent, dipl, law, med, vet, nutr.*

*****Tulane University of Louisiana**, 6823 St. Charles Avenue, New Orleans, Louisiana 70118. *1834*
Tel: (504)865-5000. Fax: (504)5877417. Telex: 9102405092 camrn proj. Easy link: 62046540 esl ud
C : *arts-sc.*
S : *arc, bus, eng, law, med, publ heal-trop med, soc w.*

Tuskegee University, Tuskegee Institute, Alabama 36088. *1881*
Tel: (205)727-8011
C: *arts-sc, ed, agr, arc, hom eco, phys, soc w, voc ed, vet, nurs.*
S: *agr, ed, eng, hom eco-food adm, ind, nurs, phys, vet, med, arc, bus, soc w.*

United States International University, 10455 Pomerador Road, San Diego, California 92126. *1952*

Tel: (619)693-4534
C : *arts-sc.*
S : *bus adm, ed, performing-vis arts, hum behavior.*

The University of Akron, 1810 Harvard Boulevard, Akron, Ohio 44325. *1870*
Tel: (513)278-5817. Telex: ITT 4931678 uakrnui
C: *arts-sc, bus adm, ed, eng, app arts, law, nurs, techn.*

University of Alabama, University Boulevard, Alabama 35486–1498. *1831*
Tel: (205)348-6010
C : *arts-sc, ed, eng.*
S : *com-bus adm, comty heal sc, hom eco, law, nurs, soc w, commun, lib serv, com.*

University of Alabama in Birmingham, University Station, Birmingham, Alabama 35294. *1966*
Tel: (205)934-4011. Telex: WUT 59817 uab bhm
S : *bus, dent, ed, eng, hum, med, nat-math, nurs, publ-allied heal, soc-behavioral sc, opt.*

University of Alabama in Huntsville, Huntsville, Alabama 35899. *1950*
Tel: (205)895-6295
S : *primary medical care, sc-eng, math-nat.*
D : *hum-behavioral sc, nurs-allied sc, adm sc.*

University of Alaska, Fairbanks, Alaska 99775. *1917*
Tel: (907)474-7521
C : *arts-env sc, mangt ed, mine ind, eng, agr-land res mangt, hum-rur dev, mar sc.*

　UNIVERSITY OF ALASKA ANCHORAGE CAMPUS, 3211 Providence Drive, Anchorage, Alaska 99508. *1976*
　Tel: (907)786-1800
　C: *arts-sc.*
　S: *bus-publ adm, ed, nurs.*
　D: *eng.*

University of Arizona, Tucson, Arizona 85721. *1885*
Tel: (602)626-3237. Telex: 1561161 medlib ut
C : *li arts, agr, arc, bus-publ adm, ed, eng, fa, law, med, mine, nurs, phar, earth sc, behavioral sc.*

University of Arkansas at Fayetteville, Administration Building, Maple Street, Fayetteville, Arkansas 72701. *1871, 1872*
Tel: (501)575-2000. Fax: (501)5755502. Telex: 314000 uaf intlag progr. Easy link: 62021499 esl ud
C : *arts-sc, agr, arc, bus adm, ed, eng, law, nurs, hum rel, infor.*

　UNIVERSITY OF ARKANSAS MEDICAL SCIENCES CAMPUS, 4301 West Markham, Little Rock, Arkansas 72205. *1879*
　Tel: (501)661-5454
　C : *med, nurs, phar, soc, serv.*

University of Bridgeport, 380 University Avenue, Bridgeport, Connecticut 06601.   *1927*
Tel: (203)576-4000. Telex: 643572 ub bpt
C: *arts-sc, bus adm, eng, heal sc, fa, hum, law.*
*University of California, 2200 University Avenue, Berkeley, California 94720.
Tel: (415)642-6000
   *UNIVERSITY OF CALIFORNIA—BERKELEY, Berkeley, California 94720.   *1868*
   Tel: (415)642-6000. Fax: (415)6428082. Telex: 9103667945 uc space berk. Easylink: 62907238 esl ud
   C: *eng, env des, let-sc, nat resources.*
   S: *bus adm, ed, law, lib, optom, publ heal, soc welfare, jour, ch, publ policy.*
   *UNIVERSITY OF CALIFORNIA—DAVIS, Davis, California 95616.   *1905*
   Tel: (916)752-1011. Telex: 9105310785 uc davis. Easylink: 62108620 esl ud
   C: *agr, let-sc, eng, law, env st.*
   S: *med, vet.*
   UNIVERSITY OF CALIFORNIA—HASTINGS COLLEGE OF LAW, 200 McAllister Street, San Francisco, California 94102–4978.
                                       1878
   Tel: (415)565-4600
   S: *law.*
   UNIVERSITY OF CALIFORNIA—IRVINE, Campus Drive, Irvine, California 92717.
                                       1965
   Tel: (714)856-6345. Telex: 5106000638 uci soc sci
   C: *hum, fa, med, soc, mangt.*
   S: *eng, adm, biol sc, mangt.*
   *UNIVERSITY OF CALIFORNIA—LOS ANGELES, 405 Hilgard Avenue, Los Angeles, California 90024.   *1919*
   Tel: (213)825-4321. Fax: (213)2068460. Telex: 9103427597 ucla isa. Easy link: 62611580 esl ud
   C: *eng, fa, let-sc.*
   S: *arc, mangt, dent, ed, law, lib serv, med, nurs, publ heal, soc welfare.*
   UNIVERSITY OF CALIFORNIA—RIVERSIDE, 900 University Avenue, Riverside, California 92521–4009.   *1954*
   Tel: (714)787-1012
   C: *let-sc, hum-soc.*
   S: *nat-agr sc, ed, mangt.*
   UNIVERSITY OF CALIFORNIA—SAN DIEGO, La Jolla, California 92093.   *1912*
   Tel: (619)534-2230
   C: *arts-sc, med, eng.*
   *UNIVERSITY OF CALIFORNIA—SAN FRANCISCO, Third Avenue and Parnassus, San Francisco, California 94143.   *1864*
   Tel: (415)476-9000. Telex: 261539 deanur. Easy link: 62933060 esl ud
   S: *dent, med, nurs, phar.*

   *UNIVERSITY OF CALIFORNIA—SANTA BARBARA, Santa Barbara, California 93106.   *1898*
   Tel: (805)961-2311. Fax: (805)9614445
   C: *eng, let-sc, arts-sc, ed.*
   UNIVERSITY OF CALIFORNIA—SANTA CRUZ, Santa Cruz, California 95064.   *1962*
   Tel: (408)429-4008
   D: *hum, nat, soc, mar sc, arts-sc.*
University of Central Florida, P.O. Box 25000, Orlando, Florida 32816.   *1963*
Tel: (305)275-2000. Telex: 567425 ucfbookstr orl
S: *arts-sc, ed, bus, eng, nurs, heal.*
The University of Chicago, 5801 S. Ellis Avenue, Chicago, Illinois 60637.   *1891*
Tel: (312)702-1234. Telex: 282131 univchgo. Easy link: 62947707 esl ud
D: *biol sc, hum, physical sc, soc.*
S: *bus, div, ed, law, lib, med, soc serv adm.*
University of Cincinnati, Clifton Avenue, Cincinnati, Ohio 45221.   *1819*
Tel: (513)475-8000. Telex: TWX 8104612417 ocu m cin. Easylink: 62025181 esl ud
C: *arts-sc, bus adm, des-arc-art, ed, eng, law, med, mus, nurs-heal, phar.*
*University of Colorado at Boulder, Boulder, Colorado 80309.   *1876*
Tel: (303)492-0111. Telex: TWX 9109403441 lasp univ colo
C: *arts-sc, law, eng, env des, bus, phar, jour, mus, ed.*
   UNIVERSITY OF COLORADO AT COLORADO SPRINGS, 1420 Austin Bluffs Parkway, Colorado Springs, Colorado 80933–7150.
                                       1965
   Tel: (303)593-3000
   arts-sc, bus, ed, eng, publ aff.
   UNIVERSITY OF COLORADO AT DENVER, 1100 14th, Denver, Colorado 80202.   *1912*
   Tel: (303)556-2800
   arts-sc, mus, env des, bus, ed, eng, publ aff.
   UNIVERSITY OF COLORADO HEALTH SCIENCES CENTER, 4200 East 9th Avenue, Denver, Colorado 80262.   *1883*
   Tel: (303)399-1211. Telex: 317252 cu med ud
   S: *dent, nurs, med, counseling.*
University of Connecticut, Storrs, Connecticut 06268.   *1881*
Tel: (203)486-2337. Telex: WUT 994484 uconn coop stor
C: *arts-sc, agr, allied heal-nat resources.*
S: *bus adm, ed, eng, fa, hom eco, law, nurs, phar, soc w.*
Ce: *med, dent med.*
   UNIVERSITY OF CONNECTICUT HEALTH CENTER, Farmington, Connecticut 06032.
                                       1961

Tel: (203)674-2808
S: *dent.*

University of Dallas, 1845 East Northgate, University of Dallas Station, Irving, Texas 75062.   *1956*
Tel: (214)721-5000
C : *arts-sc-ed.*
S: *mangt.*

University of Dayton, 300 College Park Avenue, Dayton, Ohio 45469.   *1850*
Tel: (513)229-0123. Easylink: 62805649 esl ud
C : *arts-sc.*
S : *bus adm, ed, eng, law.*

University of Delaware, Newark, Delaware 19716.   *1833*
Tel: (302)451-2000. Telex: 709985 ccm univdel ud. Easylink: 62035616 esl ud
C : *arts-sc, agr sc, bus-eco, ed, eng, hom eco, nurs, phys-recr, urb aff, mar, hum resources.*

University of Denver, University Park, Denver, Colorado 80208.   *1864*
Tel: (303)871-2000. Telex: 160298 udenver ut
C : *arts-sc, bus adm, law.*
S : *lib, soc w, mus, nurs, int, ed.*

University of Detroit, 4001 West McNichols Road, Detroit, Michigan 48221.   *1877*
Tel: (313)927-1000
C : *li arts, bus adm, eng-sc.*
S : *arc, dent, law, ed.*

University of Dubuque, 2000 University Avenue, Dubuque, Iowa 52001.   *1852*
Tel: (319)589-3000
C: *li arts.*
S: *theo.*

University of Evansville, 1800 Lincoln Avenue, Evansville, Indiana 47702-0329.   *1854*
Tel: (812)477-6241. Telex: 8103530525 meadag evs
C: *arts-sc, fa.*
S: *bus adm, ed, eng-app sc, nurs.*

University of Florida, 233 Tigert Hall, Gainsville, Florida 32611.   *1853*
Tel: (904)392-3261. Telex: 704921 aaie ud. Easylink: 62034606 esl ud
S : *sc, anaesthesia, law, nurs, phar, eng, agr, for, bus, jour, med, ed, vet, dent, arc.*

The University of Georgia, Athens, Georgia 30602.   *1785*
Tel: (404)542-3030. Easylink: 62820466 esl ud
C : *arts-sc, agr, bus adm, ed, env des.*
D : *heal-phys.*
S : *for, hom eco, jour law, phar, soc w, vet.*

University of Hartford, 200 Bloomfield Avenue, West Hartford, Connecticut 06117.   *1877*
Tel: (203)243-4100. Telex: 9102505313 u of h ug
C : *arts-sc, mus.*
S : *art, bus-publ adm, ed, eng, techn.*

*University of Hawaii at Manoa, 2500 Campus Road, Honolulu, Hawaii 96822.   *1907*

Tel: (808)948-8855
C : *arts-sc, bus adm, ed, eng, trop agr, travel mangt.*
S : *lib, med, nurs, publ heal, soc w, law, arc.*

University of Health Sciences-The Chicago Medical School, 3333 Green Bay Road North, Chicago, Illinois 60064.   *1912*
Tel: (312)578-3000
S: *med, heal sc.*

University of Houston, 4800 Calhoun Boulevard, Houston, Texas 77004.   *1927*
Tel: (713)749-1011.   Telex: 5101005878 5101005878 esl uc. Easylink: 62768212 esl ud
C : *arts-sc, ed, phar, bus adm, eng, techn, arc, hotel & restaurant mangt, hum, nat, optom, soc.*
S : *commun, mus, soc w.*
Ce: *law.*

University of Idaho, Moscow, Idaho 83843. *1889*
Tel: (208)885-6424. Telex: 5107760923 ui cid mocw
C : *let-sc, agr, bus-eco, ed, eng, law, mine, for, art-arc.*

*University of Illinois at Urbana-Champaign, Urbana, Illinois 61801.   *1867*
Tel: (217)333-1000. Telex: 5106007653 ui law ud. Easy link: 62942369 esl ud
C : *arts-sc, law, vet, eng, agr, com-bus adm, fine-app arts, app life st, commun, ed, aviation, soc w, labor ind.*
S : *soc w, lib.*
I : *env st.*

UNIVERSITY OF ILLINOIS AT CHICAGO, P.O. Box 4348, Chicago, Illinois 60680.   *1865*
Tel: (312)996-3000. Telex: 270362 u of i cgo war
C : *med, dent, ed, phar, arts-sc, eng, bus adm, soc.*
S : *publ heal.*

*University of Iowa, Iowa City, Iowa 52242.
                                                                         1847
Tel: (319)335-3500. Fax: (319)3350381. Telex: 5106011952 5106011952 esl ui
C : *li arts, bus adm, dent, ed, eng, law, med, nurs, phar.*

University of Judaism, 15600 Mulholland Drive, Los Angeles, California 90077.   *1947*
Tel: (213)476-9777
C: *arts-sc.*

University of Kansas, Lawrence, Kansas 66045.
                                                                         1864
Tel: (913)864-2700. Telex: WUT 535004 dept phys astr. Easylink: 62805859 esl ud
C : *arts-sc.*
S : *bus, ed, eng, arc-urb des, soc welfare, fa, jour, law, phar.*

UNIVERSITY OF KANSAS MEDICAL CENTER, Kansas City, Kansas 66103.   *1905*
Tel: (913)588-5000
S: *allied heal professions, med, nurs.*

University of Kentucky, 206 Administration Building, Lexington, Kentucky 40506. *1865* Tel: (606)257-9000. Telex: 204009 uk commsvc lex. Easylink: 62953355 esl ud
C : *arts-sc, agr, bus eco, dent, ed, eng, law, med, nurs, phar, fa, commun.*
S : *soc professions, arc, hom eco, lib.*

University of La Verne, 1950 3rd Street, La Verne, California 91750. *1891* Tel: (714)593-3511
C : *arts-sc, law.*
S: *bus-eco.*

University of Louisville, 2301 South 3rd Street, Louisville, Kentucky 40292. *1798* Tel: (502)588-5555
C : *arts-sc.*
S : *bus, dent, ed, eng, law, med, mus, soc w.*

University of Lowell, One University Avenue, Lowell, Massachusetts 01854. *1894* Tel: (617)452-5000. Telex: 7103436461 ulcar lowe. Easylink: 62948108 esl ud
C : *li arts, eng, mangt sc, pure-allied sc, mus, heal professions, ed.*

*University of Maine, Orono, Maine 04469. Tel: (207)581-1410
C: *arts-sc, bus adm, ed, for resources, life sc & agr.*
S: *law.*

UNIVERSITY OF SOUTHERN MAINE, 96 Falmouth Street, Portland, Maine 04103. *1878* Tel: (207)780-4141
C : *arts-sc.*
S : *law, nurs, bus-eco, ed.*

University of Maryland, Adelphi, Maryland 20783.
Tel: (301)853-3601. Telex: 5106010426 u md cen adm uq

UNIVERSITY OF MARYLAND COLLEGE PARK CAMPUS, College Park, Maryland 20742. *1856* Tel: (301)454-3311. Fax: (301)4541572. Telex: 5101005296 u of md l ud. Easy link: 62929200 esl ud
C : *agr, arc, bus-mangt, ed, eng, hum, ecology, lib-infor serv, phys-recr-heal, jour, publ aff.*

UNIVERSITY OF MARYLAND BALTIMORE PROFESSIONAL SCHOOLS, 520 West Redwood Street, Baltimore, Maryland 21201. *1807* Tel: (301)528-6975. Telex: 898156 autopsy um. Easylink: 62362580 esl ud
S : *phar, soc w, nurs, dent, law, med, commun, plan.*

UNIVERSITY OF MARYLAND—EASTERN SHORE, Princess Anne, Maryland 21853. *1886* Tel: (301)651-2200. Telex: 898237 univ md estnsh

li arts.

UNIVERSITY OF MARYLAND GRADUATE SCHOOL, Baltimore, Maryland 21228.

*University of Massachusetts, Amherst, Massachusetts 01003. *1863* Tel: (413)545-0111. Telex: 948633 camp ctr htl
S : *agr, bus adm, eng, heal sc, phys, ed, med, mangt.*
F : *hum-fa, soc-behavioral sc, food-nat resources.*
D : *hom eco, nurs, vet-anim sc, mus-dance, land-arc-reg plan.*

UNIVERSITY OF MASSACHUSETTS AT BOSTON, Harbor Campus, Boston, Massachusetts 02125. *1965* Tel: (617)929-7000
C : *li arts, mangt, nurs.*

UNIVERSITY OF MASSACHUSETTS MEDICAL CENTER AT WORCESTER, Worcester, Massachusetts 01605. *1962* Tel: (617)856-2266
S: *med.*

University of Medicine and Dentistry of New Jersey, Newark, New Jersey 07103. *1954* Tel: (201)454-4000

University of Miami, University Station, Coral Gables, Florida 33124. *1925* Tel: (305)284-2211. Fax: (305)3619306. Telex: 256644 mar depur. Easylink: 62488920 esl ud
S : *li arts, sc, arc, bus, eng, law, med, nurs, mar sc.*

University of Michigan, Ann Arbor, Michigan 48109. *1817* Tel: (313)764-1817. Fax: (313)9367787. Telex: 4993064 u of m aa. Easylink: 62837898 esl ud
C : *lit sc-arts, eng, arc-urb plan, phar, law.*
S : *nat resources, mus, med, nurs, dent, bus adm, soc w, publ heal, ed, lib sc, art.*

University of Minnesota, Twin Cities Campus, 100 Church Street Southeast, Minneapolis, Minnesota 55455. *1851* Tel: (612)625-5000. Telex: 9102503489 u of m me mps uq. Easylink: 62023179 esl ud
C : *li arts, vet, agr, hom eco, ed, for, phar.*
S : *law, med, nurs, dent, publ heal, mangt.*
I : *techn.*

University of Mississippi, University, Mississippi 38677. *1844* Tel: (601)232-7211. Easylink: 62028978 esl ud
C : *li arts.*
S : *bus adm, ed, eng, law, phar.*

UNIVERSITY OF MISSISSIPPI MEDICAL CENTER, Jackson, Mississippi 39216. *1955* Tel: (601)984-1100
S: *allied heal professions, dent, med, nurs.*

*University of Missouri, University Hall, Columbia, Missouri 65211.
Tel: (314)882-2011. Telex: WUT 434199 murr coma. Easy link: 62580470 esl ud

UNIVERSITY OF MISSOURI—COLUMBIA, Colombia, Missouri 65211. *1839*
Tel: (314)882-2121
C : *arts-sc, law, med, nurs, vet, eng, agr, for, hom eco, bus-publ adm, jour, ed.*
S : *lib-infor serv, publ-comty serv.*

UNIVERSITY OF MISSOURI—KANSAS CITY, 5100 Rockhill Road, Kansas City, Missouri 64110. *1929*
Tel: (816)276-1000. Telex: 42284 umkc bkstr ksc. Easylink: 62019355 esl ud
C : *arts-sc, law, med, dent, adm, phar, ed.*
Conservatory : *mus.*

UNIVERSITY OF MISSOURI—ROLLA, Rolla, Missouri 65401–0249. *1870*
Tel: (314)341-4111
C : *arts-sc.*
S : *eng.*

UNIVERSITY OF MISSOURI—SAINT LOUIS, 8001 Natural Bridge Road, Saint Louis, Missouri 63121. *1963*
Tel: (314)553-5000. Telex: 4948232 naussstl. Easylink: 62029014 esl ud
C : *arts-sc.*
S : *bus ed, optom, nurs.*

University of Montana, Missoula, Montana 59812. *1893*
Tel: (406)243-0211
C : *arts-sc.*
S : *bus adm, ed, fa, for, jour, phar, law.*

*University of Nebraska, 3835 Holdrege, Lincoln, Nebraska 68583.
Tel: (402)472-2111. Telex: 5101002759 u of nob info

UNIVERSITY OF NEBRASKA-LINCOLN, 14th & R. Streets, Lincoln, Nebraska 68588. *1869*
Tel: (402)472-7211. Telex: 438087 un intprg
C : *arts-sc, agr, hom eco, bus adm, dent, ed, arc, law, eng-techn.*
S : *jour.*

UNIVERSITY OF NEBRASKA MEDICAL CENTER, 42nd and Dewey, Omaha, Nebraska 68105. *1869*
Tel: (402)5594353. Easylink: 62961153 esl ud
C : *nurs, phar, med, allied heal professions.*

UNIVERSITY OF NEBRASKA AT OMAHA, 60th and Dodge Street, Omaha, Nebraska 68182. *1908*
Tel: (402)554-2200
C : *fa, ed, bus adm, arts-sc.*

University of Nevada, 405 Marsh Avenue, Reno, Nevada 89557.
Tel: (702)784-4901. Telex: 9102505931 u of nevada. Easylink: 62775557 esl ud

UNIVERSITY OF NEVADA—LAS VEGAS, 4505 S. Maryland Parkway, Las Vegas, Nevada 89154. *1957*
Tel: (702)739-3011

C : *arts-let, sc-math, bus-eco, ed, allied heal professions, hotel adm.*

UNIVERSITY OF NEVADA—RENO, Reno, Nevada 89557–0095. *1874*
Tel: (702)784-4636. Telex: 9103806050 nvu lib reno
C : *arts-sc, agr, bus, adm, ed, eng.*
S : *nurs, med, hom eco.*

University of New England, 11 Hillsbeach Road, Biddeford, Maine 04005. *1939*
Tel: (207)283-0171
C: *arts-sc, osteopathic med.*
S: *lifelong ed.*

University of New Hampshire, Durham, New Hampshire 03824. *1866*
Tel: (603)862-1234. Telex: 950030 unh phys dura
C : *li arts, eng-physical sc, agr.*
S : *bus-eco, heal st, app sc.*

University of New Haven, 300 Orange Avenue, West Haven, Connecticut 06516. *1920*
Tel: (203)932-7000
S: *arts-sc, bus adm, eng, hotel adm.*

University of New Mexico, Albuquerque, New Mexico 87131. *1889*
Tel: (505)277-0111. Easylink: 62912200 esl ud
C : *arts-sc, bus adm, ed, eng, fa, nurs, phar, arc-plan.*
S : *law, med.*

University of New Orleans, Lake Front, New Orleans, Louisiana 70148. *1956*
Tel: (504)286-6000
D: *li arts, bus adm, ed, eng, sc.*

*University of North Carolina, Box 2688, Chapel Hill, North Carolina 27514.
Tel: (919)962-1000. Easy link: 62002555 esl ud

UNIVERSITY OF NORTH CAROLINA AT CHAPEL HILL, Chapel Hill, North Carolina 27514. *1789*
Tel: (919)962-1000
C : *arts-sc, law, nurs, dent, bus adm, soc w, phar, jour, lib sc, publ heal, ed, med.*

UNIVERSITY OF NORTH CAROLINA AT GREENSBORO, 1000 Spring Garden Street, Greensboro, North Carolina 27412. *1891*
Tel: (919)334-5000
C : *arts-sc, ed, hom eco, mus, nurs, bus-eco, heal-phys-recr.*

University of North Dakota, Grand Forks, North Dakota 58202. *1883*
Tel: (701)777-2011. Telex: 332537 underc. Easylink: 62049688 esl ud
C : *arts-sc, bus-publ adm, ed, eng, nurs.*
S : *law, med, fa, hum resources dev.*

University of Northern Colorado, Greeley, Colorado 80639. *1890*
Tel: (303)351-1890. Easylink: 62689290 esl ud
C : *ed, arts-sc.*
S : *vis-performing arts, bus, heal-phys-recr,*

nurs, ind techn-hom eco, lib.
*University of Notre Dame du Lac, Notre Dame, Indiana 46556.   *1842*
Tel: (219)239-5000. Fax: (219)2396712. Telex: 469669 notre dame a. Easylink: 62131650 esl ud
C : *arts-let, bus adm, eng, law, sc, theo, mus, art, arc.*
University of Oklahoma, 600 Parrington Oval, Norman, Oklahoma 73069.   *1890*
Tel: (405)325-0311. Telex: 9108306521 ou purch norm
C : *arts-sc, bus adm, ed, eng, fa, law, li st, env des.*
   UNIVERSITY OF OKLAHOMA HEALTH SCIENCES CENTER, Oklahoma City, Oklahoma 73190.
University of Oregon, Eugene, Oregon 97403–1226.   *1876*
Tel: (503)686-3111. Telex: 5105970354 u of o lib eug u
C : *li arts.*
S : *arc-allied arts, bus adm, ed, heal-phys-recr, jour, law, mus.*
University of the Pacific, 3601 Pacific Avenue, Stockton, California 95211.   *1851*
Tel: (209)946-2011
C : *arts-sc.*
S : *dent, med, ed, eng, law, mus, phar.*
*University of Pennsylvania, 34th and Spruce Streets, Philadelphia, Pennsylvania 19104.
                                          1740
Tel: (215)898-5000. Telex: TWX 7106700328 u of pa pha. Easylink: 62912193 esl ud
C : *arts-sc.*
S : *commun, dent, ed, fa, eng, bus, law, med, nurs, soc w, vet.*
*University of Pittsburgh, 4200 5th Avenue, Pittsburgh, Pennsylvania 15260–0001.   *1787*
Tel: (412)624-4141. Fax: (412)6485911. Telex: 199126 university pgh. Easylink: 62824479 esl ud
C : *ed, eng, gen st, law, lib-infor sc, publ heal, heal related professions, soc w, dental med, nurs, phar.*
S : *bus, med.*
F : *arts-sc.*
*University of Puerto Rico Rio Piedras, Ponce de Leon Avenue, Rio Piedras, Puerto Rico 00931.
                                          1903
Tel: (809)764-0000
C : *gen st, law, bus adm, phar, ed, hum.*
S : *arc, publ, publ heal, soc, commun.*
   UNIVERSITY OF PUERTO RICO MAYAGUEZ CAMPUS, College Station, Mayaguez, Puerto Rico 00709.   *1911*
   Tel: (809)834-4040
   C : *arts-sc-eng-agr, bus adm.*
   UNIVERSITY OF PUERTO RICO MEDICAL

SCIENCES CAMPUS, GPO Box 5067, San Juan, Puerto Rico 00936.   *1950*
Tel: (809)758-2525
C: *allied heal professions.*
S: *bio-med, dent, med, nurs, phar, publ heal.*
The University of Rhode Island, 22 Davis Hall, Lower College Road, Kingston, Rhode Island 02881–0806.   *1892*
Tel: (401)792-1000. Telex: 6814185 uribookstore. Easylink: 62926791 esl ud
C : *arts-sc, bus adm, eng, nurs, phar, hum serv.*
S : *lib.*
University of Rochester, Rochester, New York 14627.   *1850*
Tel: (716)275-2121. Telex: 823081 uno uf
C : *arts-sc, ed, eng-appl sc, hum dev.*
S : *med-dent, mus, mangt, nurs.*
University of Saint Thomas, 3812 Montrose, Houston, Texas 77006.   *1947*
Tel: (713)522-7911
S : *arts-sc, nurs, bus, ed, int st.*
University of San Diego, Alcala Park, San Diego, California 92110.   *1949*
Tel: (619)260-4600
C: *arts-sc.*
S: *bus adm, ed, law, nurs.*
*University of San Francisco, 2130 Fulton Street, Ignation Heights, San Francisco, California 94117–1080.   *1855*
Tel: (415)666-6886. Telex: 9103722298 usfenroll
C : *arts-sc, bus adm.*
S : *nurs, law, ed.*
University of South Alabama, 307 University Boulevard, Mobile, Alabama 36688.   *1964*
Tel: (205)460-6101. Telex: 505408 usabooks mbl
C : *arts-sc-ed, bus mangt st, eng.*
S : *nurs, allied heal st.*
*University of South Carolina at Columbia, Columbia, South Carolina 29208.
Tel: (803)777-7000. Telex: 9102501347 usc esri ng. Easylink: 62047486 esl ud
   UNIVERSITY OF SOUTH CAROLINA AT COLUMBIA, Columbia, South Carolina 29208.
                                          1801
   Tel: (803)777-7000
   C : *hum-soc, law, phar, ed, eng, bus adm, jour, nurs, soc w, lib, publ heal.*
   S : *med.*
University of South Dakota, 414 East Clark Street, Vermillion, South Dakota 57069. *1862*
Tel: (605)677-5011. Easylink: 62860888 esl ud
C : *arts-sc, bus, ed, fa, law.*
University of South Florida, 4202 Fowler Avenue, Tampa, Florida 33620.   *1956*
Tel: (813)974-2011. Easylink: 62044092 esl ud
S : *bus, jour, eng, lib, med, nurs, sc.*

*University of Southern California, University Park, Los Angeles, California 90089.   *1880*
Tel: (213)743-2311. Fax: (213)7474176. Telex: 4720490 usc isa. Easylink: 62012417 esl ud
C : *let-arts-sc.*
S : *arc-fa, bus adm, dent, ed, eng, law, fa, lib sc, med, mus, phar, performing arts, soc w, heal related professions, publ adm, commun.*
I : *mar-coastal st, systems mangt.*

University of Southern Mississippi, Southern Station, Box 5001, Hattiesburg, Mississippi 39406–5001.   *1910*
Tel: (601)266-4111. Telex: 469229 usm a
C : *li arts, heat-phys-recr, sc-techn.*
S : *bus adm, ed-psyc, fa, nurs, soc w, lib serv, hom eco.*

University of Southwestern Louisiana, East University Avenue, Lafayette, Louisiana 70504.   *1898*
Tel: (318)231-6000
C : *arts-hum-behavioral sc, agr, com, ed, eng, nurs, biol-math-physical sc, bus ed.*

University of Tennessee, Cumberland Avenue, Knoxville, Tennessee 37996.   *1794*
Tel: (615)974-2591. Telex: 557461 utsupbkst kxv. Easylink: 62047591 esl ud
C : *li arts, vet, soc w, agr, arc, bus adm, commun, ed, eng, hom eco, law, nurs.*
  UNIVERSITY OF TENNESSEE AT MEMPHIS, 800 Madison Avenue, Memphis, Tennessee 38163.   *1911*
  Tel: (901)577-4000
  C: *allied heal sc, dent, nurs, phar.*
  S: *med sc, med.*
  UNIVERSITY OF TENNESSEE-OAK RIDGE, Oak Ridge, Tennessee 37830.
  S: *biomed sc.*
  UNIVERSITY OF TENNESSEE SPACE INSTITUTE, Tullahoma, Tennessee 37388.

University of Texas, 601 Colorado Street, Austin, Texas 78701.
Tel: (512)499-4201. Telex: 910240181 univ coop east uq. Easy link: 62031434 esl ud
  UNIVERSITY OF TEXAS AT ARLINGTON, 800 South Cooper Street, Arlington, Texas 76019–0125.   *1895*
  Tel: (817)273-2011. Fax: (817)2733392. Telex: 5106012493 tiec tx arlton
  S : *bus, eng, li arts, sc, soc w, arc, nurs.*
  I : *urb st.*
  UNIVERSITY OF TEXAS AT AUSTIN, University Station, Austin, Texas 78712.   *1883*
  Tel: (512)471-3434. Telex: 5106002119 u tex arl aus
  C: *bus adm, ed, eng, fa, phar, nat, nurs, soc-behavioral sc.*
  S : *arc, commun, law, lib, soc w, publ aff.*
  UNIVERSITY OF TEXAS AT DALLAS, P.O. Box 830 688, Richardson, Texas 75080–0688.

1969
  Tel: (214)690-2111
  C : *arts-hum, mangt-adm, nat-math, soc, ed, hum dev.*
  UNIVERSITY OF TEXAS AT EL PASO, El Paso, Texas 79968–0512.   *1913*
  Tel: (915)747-5000. Telex: 5106012490 tiec txelpaso
  C : *bus adm, ed, eng, li arts, nurs, sc.*
  UNIVERSITY OF TEXAS HEALTH SCIENCE CENTER AT DALLAS, 5323 Harry Hines Boulevard, Dallas, Texas 75235.   *1972*
  Tel: (214)688-3401
  S: *allied heal professions, biomed sc, med.*
  UNIVERSITY OF TEXAS HEALTH SCIENCE CENTER AT HOUSTON, P.O. Box 20036, Houston, Texas 77225.   *1943*
  Tel: (713)7924875
  S: *allied heal sc, biomed sc, dent hyg, dent, med, nurs, publ heal.*
  UNIVERSITY OF TEXAS HEALTH SCIENCE CENTER AT SAN ANTONIO, 7703 Floyd Curl Drive, San Antonio, Texas 78284.   *1976*
  Tel: (512)567-7000. Easylink: 62912195 esl ud
  S: *allied heal sc, biomed sc, dent, med, nurs.*
  UNIVERSITY OF TEXAS MEDICAL BRANCH AT GALVESTON, Galveston, Texas 77550. *1891*
  Tel: (409)761-1011. Telex: 765485 ut med br gal
  S: *allied heal sc, biomed sc, med, nurs.*

University of The South, Sewanee, Tennessee 37375-4013.   *1860*
Tel: (615)598-5931
C: *arts-sc, phys.*
S: *theo.*

University of Toledo, 2801 W. Bancroft Street, Toledo, Ohio 43606.   *1872*
Tel: (419)537-2696. Telex: 8104421633 u of t lib
C :*arts-sc, bus adm, ed, eng, law, phar, techn.*

University of Tulsa, 600 South College Avenue, Tulsa, Oklahoma 74104.   *1894*
Tel: (918)592-6000. Telex: 49753 infosvc tu tul. Easylink: 62926725 esl ud
C : *arts-sc, bus adm, ed, eng-phy, soc, nurs.*
S : *law.*

University of Utah, Salt Lake City, Utah 84112.   *1850*
Tel: (801)581-7200. Telex: 3789459 univ utah slc. Easy link: 62018500 esl ud
C : *hum, bus, ed, eng, fa, law, med, mine-miner ind, nurs, phar, heal-phys-recr, arc, sc, soc-behavioral sc.*
S : *soc w.*

University of Vermont and State Agriculture College, Burlington, Vermont 05405–0160.   *1791*
Tel: (802)656-3480. Telex: 954629 uvmbokstr bul. Easylink: 62003678 esl ud

C : *arts-sc, agr-hom eco, nurs, eng-math-bus adm, nat resources, ed-soc serv.*
*University of Virginia, Charlottesville, Virginia 22906. *1819*
Tel: (804)924-0311. Telex: 9102500352 facartsci uq. Easy link: 62031780 esl ud
C : *arts-sc.*
S : *arc, bus adm, ed, eng-app sc, law, med, nurs.*
University of Washington, Seattle, Washington 98195. *1861*
Tel: (206)543-2100. Fax: (206)5439285. Telex: 4979696 uw ui. Easylink: 62003057 esl ud
C : *arts-sc, arc-urb plan, ed, ocean fish, phar, for.*
S : *bus adm, dent, eng, law, med, nurs, soc w, publ heal.*
University of West Florida, 11000 University Parkway, Pensacola, Florida 32514. *1963*
Tel: (904)474-2000
S: *sc, mus, nurs, arts-sc.*
University of West Los Angeles, 12201 Washington Place, Los Angeles, California 90066. *1966*
Tel: (213)313-1011
University of Wisconsin, 500 Lincoln Drive, Madison, Wisconsin 53706.
Tel: (608)262-1234
    UNIVERSITY OF WISCONSIN-MADISON, Wisconsin 53706. *1849*
    Tel: (608)262-1234. Fax: (608)2620123. Telex: 265452 uofwisc mds. Easy link: 62762820 esl ud
    C : *let-sc, agr, eng, allied heal, fam resources.*
    S : *bus, ed, law, med, nurs, phar, soc w, lib, jour, nat resources, vet, env st, mus.*
    UNIVERSITY OF WISCONSIN-MILWAUKEE, P.O. Box 413, Milwaukee, Wisconsin 53201. *1956*
    Tel: (414)963-4444. Telex: 5106017841 purch uwmil. Easylink: 62001447 esl ud
    C : *let-sc, eng-app sc.*
    S : *arc-urb, bus adm, ed, fa, lib-infor sc, nurs, soc welfare, allied heal professions.*
University of Wyoming, Box 3434 University Station, Laramie, Wyoming 82071. *1886*
Tel: (307)766-1121. Telex: 9103808784 atmos
C : *arts-sc, agr, ed, eng, law, nurs, heal sc, human med.*
Utah State University, Logan, Utah 84322. *1888*
Tel: (801)750-1000. Telex: 3789426 utahstateu logan
C : *hum-arts-soc, agr, bus, ed, eng, fam life, nat resources, sc.*
Valdosta State College, North Patterson, Valdosta, Georgia 31698. *1906*
Tel: (912)247-3335
C: *arts-sc.*
D: *nurs, fa, aerospace st.*
S: *ed, bus adm.*

Valparaiso University, Valparaiso, Indiana 46383. *1859*
Tel: (219)464-5000. Easylink: 62048380 esl ud
C: *arts-sc, bus adm, eng, nurs.*
S: *law.*
Vanderbilt University, Nashville, Tennessee 37240. *1873*
Tel: (615)322-7311. Fax: (615)3435555. Telex: 554323 vu book st nas.
C : *arts-sc, ed.*
S : *eng, law, med, nurs, theo, mangt.*
Villanova University, Villanova, Pennsylvania 19085. *1842*
Tel: (215)645-4500
C : *li arts-sc, com-fin, eng, nurs.*
S : *law.*
Virginia Commonwealth University, 901 W. Franklin Street, Richmond, Virginia 23284–0001. *1838*
Tel: (804)257-0100
C : *allied heal prof, arts-sc, bus, dent, ed, med, nurs, phar, soc w, art, commun-publ aff.*
Virginia Polytechnic Institute and State University, Blacksburg, Virginia 24061. *1872*
Tel: (703)961-6000. Telex: 9103331861 vpi bks ud
C : *arts-sc, agr-life sc, arc, bus, eng, ed, vet.*
Wake Forest University, Reynolda Station, Winston-Salem, North Carolina 27109. *1834*
Tel: (919)761-5000. Fax: (919)7611145. Easylink: 62894145 esl ud
C : *arts-sc, bus-acct.*
S : *law, med, mangt.*
Washington and Lee University, Lexington, Virginia 24450. *1749*
Tel: (703)463-8400
C: *arts-sc, com.*
S: *law.*
Washington State University, Pullman, Washington 99164. *1892*
Tel: (509)335-3564. Telex: 5107741099 coll ag pman
C : *agr, eco-bus, ed, eng, hom eco, phar, vet, nurs.*
D : *sc, soc.*
*Washington University, Lindell and Skinner, St. Louis, Missouri 63130. *1853*
Tel: (314)889-5000. Easylink: 62912198 esl ud
C : *arts-sc.*
S : *arc, bus, dent, eng, fa, law, med, soc w.*
*Wayne State University, 5050 Cass Avenue, Detroit, Michigan 48202. *1868*
Tel: (313)577-2424
C : *li arts, ed, eng, nurs, phar, allied heal, heal phys.*
S : *bus adm, law, med, soc w.*
Wesleyan University, Middletown, Connecticut 06457. *1831*
Tel: (203)347-9411

C : *arts-sc.*

West Georgia College, Carrollton, Georgia 30118-0001. *1933*
Tel: (404)834-1311
C: *arts-sc, bus, ed.*

West Virginia College of Graduate Studies, Institute, West Virginia 25112. *1972*
Tel: (304)768-9711
C: *ed, behavioral sc, bus-mangt, eng-sc.*

West Virginia University, Morgantown, West Virginia 26506. *1867*
Tel: (304)293-0111. Easylink: 62039683 esl ud
C : *arts-sc, agr-for, eng, hum res-ed, mus, bus eco.*
S : *dent, jour, law, med, mineral-energy resources, nurs, phar, phys, soc w.*
Ce : *creative arts.*

Western Michigan University, Kalamazoo, Michigan 49008–3899. *1903*
Tel: (616)383-0960. Telex: 6877099 west mich univ. Easylink: 62025184 esl ud
S : *arts-sc, app sc, bus, ed, fa, heal-human serv, eng.*

Western New England College, 1215 Wilbraham Road, Springfield, Massachusetts 01119-2684. *1919*
Tel: (413)782-3111
C: *arts-sc.*
S: *bus adm, eng, law, higher ed.*

Western Oregon State College, 345 North Monmouth Avenue, Monmouth, Oregon 97361-1394. *1856*
Tel: (503)838-1220
C: *arts-sc-ed.*

Western State University College of Law Orange County, 111 N. State College Boulevard, Fullerton, California 92631. *1966*
Tel: (714)738-1000
C: *law.*

Western State University College of Law of San Diego, 1333 Front Street, San Diego, California 92110. *1969*

Tel: (619)297-9700
C: *law.*

The Wichita State University, Wichita, Kansas 67208. *1895*
Tel: (316)689-3456. Easylink: 62049832 esl ud
S : *arts-sc, heal, fa, ed, eng, bus adm.*

Widener University, 14th and Chestnut Streets, Chester, Pennsylvania 19013. *1821*
Tel: (215)499-4000
C: *arts-sc, mangt, app sc, eng, nurs, hotel mangt.*

Williamette University, 900 State Street, Salem, Oregon 97301. *1842*
Tel: (503)370-6300
C: *li arts, adm.*
S: *law.*

Worcester Polytechnic Institute, 100 Institute Road, Worcester, Massachusetts 01609. *1865*
Tel: (617)793-5000. Easylink: 62036736 esl ud
I : *eng-sc.*

The Wright Institute—Berkeley, 2728 Durant Avenue, Berkeley, California 94704. *1974*
Tel: (415)841-9230
S : *arts-sc.*

Wright State University, Colonel Glenn Highway, Dayton, Ohio 45435. *1964*
Tel: (513)873-3333
C: *li arts, psyc.*
S: *bus-adm, ed, sc-eng, nurs, med, mus, soc w.*

Yale University, New Haven, Connecticut 06520. *1701*
Tel: (203)436-0300. Fax: (203)4320948. Telex: 9102502359 yale estm europe. Easylink: 62040792 esl ud
C : *arts-sc, nurs, mangt.*
S : *art-arc, dram, for, law, med, mus, div.*

Yeshiva University, 500 West 185th Street, New York, New York 10033–3299. *1886*
Tel: (212)960-5400
C : *arts-sc, med.*
S : *soc w, law, hebrew st.*

Institutions with Graduate Schools and with or without Professional Schools—

Institutions avec sections pour gradués et dotées éventuellement d'écoles professionnelles

Abilene Christian University, 1600 Campus Court, Abilene, Texas 79699. *1906*
Tel: (915)674-2000. Easylink: 62023923 esl ud
C : *arts-sc-ed, bus, fa, nat-appl sc.*

Adams State College, Alamosa, Colorado 81102. *1921*
Tel: (303)589-7121
D : *arts-sc-ed.*

Adrian College, 110 South Madison Street, Adrian, Michigan 49221–2575. *1859*
Tel: (517)265-5161
C : *arts-sc-ed.*

Alabama Agricultural and Mechanical University, Normal, Alabama 35762. *1875*
Tel: (205)859-7011. Telex: 9102405482 bama il ud

S : *arts-sc, bus, techn, ed, agr-hom eco.*

Alabama State University, 915 South Jackson Street, Montgomery, Alabama 36195. *1874*
Tel: (205)293-4100
S : *arts-sc, bus adm, mus.*
D : *comp.*

Alaska Pacific University, 4101 University Drive, Anchorage, Alaska 99508. *1959*
Tel: (907)561-1266

Albany State College, 504 College Drive, Albany, Georgia 31705. *1903*
Tel: (912)439-4600
C: *arts-sc.*

Alcorn State University, Lorman, Mississippi 39096–9998. *1871*
Tel: (601)877-3711. Fax: (601)8773885
D : *arts-sc, ed, bus, agr, nurs.*

Allegheny College, N. Main, Meadville, Pennsylvania 16335. *1815*
Tel: (814)724-3100
C : *arts-sc.*

Allentown College of Saint Francis de Sales, Station Avenue, Center Valley, Pennsylvania 18034. *1962*
Tel: (215)282-1100
C: *arts-sc-ed.*

Amber University, 1700 Eastgate Drive, Garland, Texas 75041. *1971*
Tel: (214)279-6511. Easylink: 62757388 esl ud
bus-mangt, comp-infor.

American College, 270 Bryn Mawr Avenue, Bryn Mawr, Pennsylvania 19010. *1927*
Tel: (215)896-4500
S : *arts-sc.*

American Graduate School of International Management, Thunderbird Campus, Glendale, Arizona 85306. *1946*
Tel: (602)978-7011
S : *personnel st, com.*

American International College, 170 Wilbraham, Springfield, Massachusetts 01109. *1885*
Tel: (413)737-7000
S : *arts-sc-bus, adm, ed, psyc, nurs.*

American Technological University, P.O. Box 1416, U.S. Highway 190 West, Killeen, Texas 76540–1416. *1973*
Tel: (817)526-1150
C : *arts-sc.*

Anderson University, 1100 East 5th Street, Anderson, Indiana 46012-3462. *1917*
Tel: (317)649-9071
C: *arts-sc.*
S: *theo, arts-cult-relig, theor & app sc.*

Angelo State University, 2601 West Avenue N., San Angelo, Texas 76909. *1928*
Tel: (915)942-2041
C : *li-sc-ed.*

Anna Maria College, Paxton, Massachusetts 01612–1198. *1946*

C : *arts-sc-ed.*

Antioch University-Antioch College, Livermore Street, Yellow Springs, Ohio 45387. *1852*
Tel: (513)767-7331
C : *arts-sc-ed.*
S : *law.*

Appalachian State University, Boone, North Carolina 28608. *1899*
Tel: (704)262-2000. Telex: 888370 app state univ
C : *arts-sc, bus, fa-app arts, ed.*

Aquinas College, 1607 Robinson Road, Grand Rapids, Michigan 49506. *1886*
Tel: (616)459-8281
C : *arts-sc.*

Arkansas State University, P.O. Box 10, State University, Arkansas 72467. *1909*
Tel: (501)972-3030
S : *arts-sc, bus, ed, eng, app sc, fa, nurs, commun, continuing ed.*

Arkansas Technical University, Russellville, Arkansas 72801. *1909*
Tel: (501)968-0389
C : *arts-sc, ed, systems sc, physical sc.*

Armstrong State College, 11935 Abercorn Street, Savannah, Georgia 31406. *1935*
Tel: (912)927-5211. Telex: 804732 asc book sav
C : *arts-sc-ed, commun, heal sc.*

Art Center College of Design, 1700 Lida Street, Pasadena, California 91103–1999. *1930*
Tel: (818)584-5000. Telex: 6711486 artce uw
C : *arts-sc.*

Assumption College, 500 Salisbury Street, Worcester, Massachusetts 01609–1296. *1904*
Tel: (617)752-5615
C : *arts-sc.*

The Athenaeum of Ohio, The, 6616 Beechmont Avenue, Cincinnati, Ohio 45230. *1829*
Tel: (513)231-2223
C : *li arts.*

Auburn University:
AUBURN UNIVERSITY AT MONTGOMERY, Atlanta Highway, Montgomery, Alabama 36183-0401.
Tel: (205)279-3000
li arts, bus, ed, nurs, sc.

Augsburg College, 731 21st Avenue South, Minneapolis, Minnesota 55454. *1869*
Tel: (612)330-1000
C: *arts-sc.*

Augusta College, 2500 Walton Way, Augusta, Georgia 30910. *1925*
Tel: (404)737-1401
C : *arts-sc-ed, bus.*

Augustana College, 639 38th Street, Rock Island, Illinois 61201. *1860*
Tel: (309)794-7000
C : *arts-sc.*

Augustana College, Sioux Falls 29th Summit,

Sioux Falls, South Dakota 57197.   *1860*
Tel: (605)336-0770. Easylink: 62902671 esl ud
C : *arts-sc.*
Aurora University, 347 South Gladstone, Aurora, Illinois 60507.   *1893*
Tel: (312)892-6431. Fax: (312)8929286
C: *arts-sc.*
S: *bus, soc w, nurs-heal.*
Austin College, 900 North Grand Avenue, Sherman, Texas 75090.   *1849*
Tel: (214)892-9101
C : *hum, sc, soc.*
Austin Peay State University, College Street, Clarksville, Tennessee 37040.   *1927, 1929*
Tel: (615)7011
D : *arts-sc, bus, ed-human serv.*
Averett College, 420 West Main Street, Danville, Virginia 24541.   *1859*
Tel: (804)793-7811
C: *arts-sc.*
Avila College, Kansas City, Missouri 64145-9990.   *1916*
C: *arts-sc.*
Azusa Pacific College, Highway 66 at Citrus Avenue, Azusa, California 91702.   *1899*
Tel: (818)969-3434
D : *arts-sc, ed, nurs, mus, behavioral sc, theo.*
Baker University, Baldwin City, Kansas 66006.   *1858*
Tel: (913)594-6451
C : *arts-sc.*
Baldwin-Wallace College, 275 Eastland Road, Berea, Ohio 44017.   *1845*
Tel: (216)826-2900
C : *arts-sc.*
Baltimore Hebrew College, 5800 Park Heights Avenue, Baltimore, Maryland 21215.   *1919*
Tel: (301)578-6900. Easy link: 62939441 esl ud
S: *grad st.*
Baptist Bible College, 628 East Kearney, Springfield, Missouri 65803.   *1950*
Tel: (417)869-9611
Baptist Bible College of Pennsylvania, 538 Venard Road, Clarks Summit, Pennsylvania 18411.   *1932*
Tel: (717)587-1172
ed-theo.
Baptist College at Charleston, P.O. Box 10087, Charleston, South Carolina 29411.   *1960*
Tel: (803)797-4011
C: *arts-sc.*
Bard College, Annandale-on-Hudson, New York 12504.   *1860*
Tel: (914)758-6822
C: *arts-sc.*
Barry University, 11300 N.E. 2nd Avenue, Miami, Florida 33161.   *1940*
Tel: (305)758-3392. Telex: 6811310 barryuw
C : *arts-sc, bus, commun.*

S : *nurs, soc w, ed.*
Bayamon Central University, Box 1725, Bayamon, Puerto Rico 00621.   *1970*
Tel: (809)786-3030
C: *hum, sc, ed, bus adm, phys, nurs.*
Beaver College, Easton and Church Roads, Glenside, Pennsylvania 19038.   *1853*
Tel: (215)572-2900
C : *arts-sc.*
Bellarmine College, 2001 Newburg Road, Louisville, Kentucky 40205.   *1950*
Tel: (502)452-8211
C : *arts-sc, bus, nurs.*
Belmont College, Nashville, Tennessee 37203.   *1951*
Tel: (615)385-7001
C: *arts-sc.*
Beloit College, Beloit, Wisconsin 53511.   *1846*
Tel: (608)365-3391
C : *arts-sc.*
Bemidji State University, Bemidji, Minnesota 56601.   *1913*
Tel: (218)755-2000. Easylink: 62860174 esl ud
D : *hum, ed, behavioral sc, bus-ind, fa, phys, sc-math.*
Bennington College, Bennington, Vermont 05201.   *1925*
Tel: (802)442-5401
C : *arts-sc.*
Berry College, Mount Berry Station, Rome, Georgia 30149.   *1902*
Tel: (404)232-5374
C : *arts-sc.*
Bethel College, 1101 West McKinley Avenue, Mishawaka, Indiana 46545.   *1947*
Tel: (219)259-8511
C: *arts-sc.*
Birmingham-Southern College, 800 8th Avenue West, Birmingham, Alabama 35254.   *1856*
Tel: (205)226-4600
C: *arts-sc.*
Black Hills State College, 1200 University Street, Spearfish, South Dakota 57783.   *1883*
Tel: (605)642-6011. Easylink: 62860176 esl ud
C : *arts-sc.*
Bloomsburg University of Pennsylvania, Bloomsburg, Pennsylvania 17815–1301.   *1839*
Tel: (717)389-4000
C : *arts-sc, bus.*
Boise State University, 1210 University Drive, Boise, Idaho 83725.   *1932*
Tel: (208)385-1202
C : *arts-sc-ed-occp, bus, heal sc.*
Boston Conservatory, Boston, Massachusetts 02215.   *1867*
C: *arts-sc.*
D: *dance, mus, theat.*
Bowie State College, Jericho Park Road, Bowie, Maryland 20715.   *1865*

Tel: (301)464-3000
C : *arts-sc.*
Bradley University, 1501 West Bradley Avenue, Peoria, Illinois 61625.   *1897*
Tel: (309)676-7611. Fax: (309)6772827
C : *arts-sc, bus adm, ed, eng-techn, commun, fa, heal sc, lib.*
Brenau College, One Centennial Circle, Gainesville, Georgia 30501.   *1878*
Tel: (404)534-6100
C : *arts-sc.*
Bridgewater State College, Bridgewater, Massachusetts 02324.   *1840*
Tel: (617)697-1200
C : *arts-sc.*
Bristol College, Bristol College P.O. Box 757, Bristol, Tennessee 37621-0757.   *1895*
Tel: (615)968-1442
bus (grad).
Bucknell University, Lewisburg, Pennsylvania 17837.   *1846*
Tel: (717)523-1271. Fax: (717)5245781
C : *arts-sc, eng.*
Butler University, 4600 Sunset Avenue, Indianapolis, Indiana 46208.   *1855*
Tel: (317)283-8000
C : *li arts, bus adm, ed, phar, fa.*
Cabrini College, Eagle and King of Prussia Roads, Radnor, Pennsylvania 19087.   *1957*
Tel: (215)687-2100
C: *arts-sc.*
California Baptist College, 8432 Magnolia Avenue, Riverside, California 92504.   *1950*
Tel: (714)689-5771
C: *arts-sc.*
California Lutheran University, 60 West Olsen Road, Thousand Oaks, California 91360.   *1959*
Tel: (805)492-2411
C : *arts-sc.*
California State University:
CALIFORNIA STATE COLLEGE-BAKERSFIELD, 9001 Stockdale Highway, Bakersfield, California 93311-1099.   *1965*
Tel: (805)2011
C : *arts-sc-ed, bus adm.*
CALIFORNIA STATE UNIVERSITY-DOMINGUEZ HILLS, 1000 East Victoria Street, Carson, California 90747.   *1960*
Tel: (213)516-3300
C : *ed, hum-fa, soc, mangt.*
CALIFORNIA STATE UNIVERSITY-SAN BERNARDINO, 5500 State Parkway, San Bernardino, California 92407.   *1960*
Tel: (714)887-7201
S : *soc, ed, adm, nat, hum, soc-behavioral sc.*
CALIFORNIA STATE UNIVERSITY-STANILAUS, 800 W. Monte Vista, Turlock, California 95380.   *1957*

Tel: (209)667-3122
C : *arts-sc-ed, bus adm.*
CALIFORNIA STATE POLYTECHNIC UNIVERSITY-POMONA, 3801 West Temple Avenue, Pomona, California 91768.   *1938*
Tel: (714)869-7659
S : *arts, agr, eng, env-des.*
CALIFORNIA STATE UNIVERSITY-CHICO, Chico, California 95929.   *1887*
Tel: (916)895-6116. Easylink: 62022665 esl ud
S : *behavioral sc-soc, fa, nat, commun.*
D : *agr-hom eco, bus, ed, app sc, heal-hum serv.*
CALIFORNIA STATE UNIVERSITY-FRESNO, Shaw and Maple Avenues, Fresno, California 93740–0001.   *1911*
Tel: (209)294-4240. Telex: 5106001919 csuf ag. Easylink: 62025757 esl ud
C : *hum-sc-ed-occp, agr sc, eng, soc w, nat, bus, heal professions, soc, arts, hum.*
CALIFORNIA STATE UNIVERSITY-FULLERTON, 800 North State College Boulevard, Fullerton, California 92634.   *1957*
Tel: (714)773-2011. Telex: 5102506691 calstatefllrtn ug
S : *hum-soc, bus adm-eco, ed, eng-math-sc, hum dev, arts, eng.*
CALIFORNIA STATE UNIVERSITY-HAYWARD, Hayward, California 94542.   *1957*
Tel: (415)881-3000
C : *arts-sc.*
S : *bus-eco, ed, soc.*
*CALIFORNIA STATE UNIVERSITY-LONG BEACH, 1250 Bellflower Boulevard, Long Beach, California 90840.   *1948, 1949*
S : *hum, ed, soc-behavioral sc, eng, fa, app arts-sc, bus adm.*
CALIFORNIA STATE UNIVERSITY-NORTHRIDGE, 18111 Nordhoff Street, Northridge, California 91330.   *1958*
Tel: (818)885-3700
S : *bus adm-eco, ed, eng, prof st-commun, hum, arts, sc-math, soc-behavioral st, comp.*
*CALIFORNIA STATE UNIVERSITY-SACRAMENTO, 6000 J. Street, Sacramento, California 95819–2694.   *1947*
Tel: (916)278-6011
S : *arts-sc, bus adm, ed, eng, soc w, comp.*
D : *heal-phys-recr, nurs.*
CALIFORNIA POLYTECHNIC STATE UNIVERSITY-SAN LUIS OBISPO, San Luis Obispo, California 93407.   *1901*
Tel: (805)546-0111. Fax: (805)5461171
D : *agr-natural resources, hum dev-ed, soc, bus, arts-hum, sc-math, art, env des, ed, eng.*
HUMBOLDT STATE UNIVERSITY, 130 Siemens Hall, Arcata, California 95521.   *1913*
Tel: (707)826-3011

S : *natural resources, eco-bus, hum-creative arts, soc-behavioral sc.*
D : *heal-phys.*
SAN JOSE STATE UNIVERSITY, One Washington Square, San Jose, California 95192.
1857
Tel: (408)277-3228. Telex: 171171 ud
C : *hum-arts, app sc-arts, bus, ed, eng, sc, soc w, soc.*
SONOMA STATE UNIVERSITY, 1801 East Cotati Avenue, Rohnert Park, California 94928.   *1960*
Tel: (707)664-2880
C : *hum, nat, soc.*

California University of Pennsylvania, Third Street, California, Pennsylvania 15419.   *1852*
Tel: (412)938-4000
C : *arts-sc-ed, sc-techn.*

Calvin College, Grand Rapids, Michigan 49506.
1876
Tel: (616)957-6000
C : *arts-sc-ed, math, soc, lang, lit.*

Cambridge College, Institute of Open Education, 6 Story Street, Cambridge, Massachusetts 02138.   *1971*
Tel: (617)492-5108
ed (graduate).

Campbell University, Buies Creek, North Carolina 27506.   *1887*
Tel: (919)893-4111
C : *arts-sc.*
S : *law, bus.*

Canisius College, 2001 Main Street, Buffalo, New York 14208.   *1870*
Tel: (716)883-7000. Easylink: 62955232 esl ud
C : *arts-sc.*
S : *bus adm.*

Capital University, 2199 East Main Street, Columbus, Ohio 43209.   *1850*
Tel: (614)236-6011
C : *arts-sc, nurs.*
S : *law, mus.*

Cardinal Stritch College, 6801 North Yates Road, Milwaukee, Wisconsin 53217.   *1937*
Tel: (414)352-5400. Fax: (414)3517516
C : *arts-sc.*

Carlow College, 333 5th Avenue, Pittsburgh, Pennsylvania 15213.   *1929*
Tel: (412)578-6059
C: *arts-sc.*

Carthage College, 2001 Alford Drive, Kenosha, Wisconsin 53141.   *1847*
Tel: (414)552-8500
C : *arts-sc.*

Castleton State College, Castleton, Vermont 05735.   *1787*
Tel: (802)468-5611. Easylink: 62461330 esl ud
C : *arts-sc.*

Catholic University of Puerto Rico, Las Americas Avenue, Station 6, Ponce, Puerto Rico 00731.
1948
Tel: (809)844-4150
C : *arts-hum, ed, bus adm, sc.*
S : *law.*

Centenary College of Louisiana, 2911 Centenary Boulevard, Shreveport, Louisiana 71134–0188.   *1825*
Tel: (318)869-5011
C : *arts-sc.*

Central Baptist College, 1501 College Avenue, CBC Station, Conway, Arkansas 73032.
Tel: (501)329-6872

Central Connecticut State University, 1615 Stanley Street, New Britain, Connecticut 06050.   *1849*
Tel: (203)827-7305. Telex: 9102505958 ccsu ct
S : *arts-sc, bus, techn.*

Central Missouri State University, Warrensburg, Missouri 64093.   *1871*
Tel: (816)429-4111. Telex: 434001 cmsu wrsb
S : *arts-sc, bus-eco ed, app sc-techn.*

Central State University, 100 North University Drive, Edmond, Oklahoma 73034.   *1890*
Tel: (405)341-2980
S : *li arts, ed, bus, math-sc, arts-sc, spe arts-sc.*

Central Washington University, Ellensburg, Washington 98926.   *1890*
Tel: (509)963-1111. Telex: 5106017719 central wa un ug
C : *arts-sc, bus-eco.*

Chadron State College, Tenth and Main, Chadron, Nebraska 69337.   *1911*
Tel: (308)432-4451. Easylink: 62009587 esl ud
S : *arts-sc.*

Chaminade University of Honolulu, 3140 Waialae Avenue, Honolulu, Hawaii 96816–1578.   *1955*
Tel: (808)735-4711. Easy link: 62662760 esl ud
C : *arts-sc, bus adm.*

Chapman College, 333 North Glassell Street, Orange, California 92666.   *1861*
Tel: (714)997-6710. Easy link: 62027160 esl ud
C : *arts-sc.*

Chestnut Hill College, German Town and Northwestern Avenues, Philadelphia, Pennsylvania 19118.   *1924*
Tel: (215)248-7000
C: *arts-sc-ed.*

Cheyney University of Pennsylvania, Cheyney, Pennsylvania 19319.   *1837*
Tel: (215)399-2000
C : *arts-sc-ed-tec-app sc.*

Chicago State University, 9500 South King Drive Avenue, Chicago, Illinois 60628.   *1867*
Tel: (312)995-2000
C : *arts-sc-ed, bus adm, nurs, allied heal professions.*

Cincinnati Bible College, 2700 Glenway Avenue, Cincinnati, Ohio 45204.   *1924*

Tel: (513)244-8100
theo.
The Citadel, Charleston, South Carolina 29409.
                                                    1842
Tel: (803)892-5000
C: *arts-sc.*
City University, 6661 Northup Way, Bellevue,
Washington 98008.   *1973*
Tel: (206)643-2000
bus-com, data proceing, heal professions,
comp-infor.
*The City University of New York:
   CUNY HUNTER COLLEGE, 695 Park Avenue,
   New York, New York 10021.   *1870*
   Tel: (212)772-4000. Telex: 5106001645 hunt
   col
   C : *hum-arts.*
   S : *soc w, nurs, heal sc.*
   D : *ed.*
   CUNY QUEENS COLLEGE, 63-30 Kissena
   Boulevard, Flushing, New York 11367.
                                                    1937
   Tel: (718)520-7323. Telex: 9102500567 qns
   col lib nyk. Easy link: 62036778 esl ud
   C : *gen st, math-nat, teacher ed, arts, soc.*
Clarion University of Pennsylvania, Clarion,
Pennsylvania 16214.   *1867*
Tel: (814)226-2000
C : *arts, commun, lib, bus adm, hum, nurs, ed-*
hum serv.
Clarke College, 1550 Clarke Drive, Dubuque,
Iowa 52001.   *1843*
Tel: (319)588-6300
C : *arts-sc.*
Cleveland College of Jewish Studies, 26500
Shaker Boulevard, Beachwood, Ohio 44122.
                                                    1963
Tel: (216)464-4050
li arts-ed.
Coleman College, 7380 Parkway Drive, La Mesa,
California 92041.   *1963*
Tel: (619)465-3990
S: *arts-sc.*
Colgate University, Hamilton, New York 13346.
                                                    1919
Tel: (315)824-1000
C : *arts-sc.*
College of Boca Raton, 3601 North Military Trail,
Boca Raton, Florida 33431.   *1963*
Tel: (305)994-0770
arts, bus.
College of Charleston, 66 George Street, Charles-
ton, South Carolina 29424.   *1770*
Tel: (803)792-5500
C : *arts-sc.*
College of Great Falls, 1301 30th Street South,
Great Falls, Montana 59405.   *1932*
Tel: (406)761-8810
C: *arts-sc-ed.*

College of the Holy Cross, College Street,
Worcester, Massachusetts 01610.   *1843*
Tel: (617)793-2011
C : *arts-sc.*
The College of Idaho, 2112 Cleveland Boulevard,
Caldwell, Idaho 83605–9990.   *1891*
Tel: (208)459-5011
C : *arts-sc.*
College Misericordia, Lake Street, Dallas,
Pennsylvania 18612.   *1924*
Tel: (717)675-2181
C : *arts-sc-ed.*
College of Mount St. Joseph, Mount St. Joseph,
Ohio 45051.   *1906, 1920*
Tel: (513)244-4200
C : *arts-sc.*
College of New Rochelle, Castle Place, Rochelle,
New York 10801.   *1904*
Tel: (914)632-5300
S : *arts-sc, new resources, nurs.*
College of Notre Dame, 1500 Ralston Avenue,
Belmont, California 94002.   *1868*
Tel: (415)593-1601
C : *li arts.*
College of Notre Dame of Maryland, 4701 North
Charles Street, Baltimore, Maryland 21210.
                                       1873
Tel: (301)435-0100
C : *arts-sc.*
College of St. Catherine, 2004 Randolph Avenue,
St. Paul, Minnesota 55105.   *1905*
Tel: (612)690-6525
C : *arts-sc.*
College of St. Francis, 500 Wilcox Street, Joliet,
Illinois 6045.   *1920*
Tel: (815)740-3360
C : *arts-sc.*
College of St. Joseph, Clement Road, Rutland,
Vermont 05701.   *1954*
Tel: (802)773-5900
C : *arts-sc-ed, bus.*
College of St. Rose, 432 Western Avenue,
Albany, New York 12203.   *1920*
Tel: (518)454-5111
C : *arts-sc.*
College of St. Scholastica, 1200 Kenwood
Avenue, Duluth, Minnesota 55811.   *1912*
Tel: (218)723-6000
C : *arts-sc.*
College of St. Thomas, 2115 Summit Avenue, St.
Paul, Minnesota 55105.   *1885*
Tel: (612)647-5600
C : *ed, mangt, bus, theo.*
College of Santa Fe, St. Michael's Drive, Santa
Fe, New Mexico 87501.   *1947*
Tel: (505)473-6011
C: *arts-sc-ed.*
Colorado College, Colorado Springs, Colorado
80903.   *1874*

Tel: (303)473-2233
S : *arts-sc.*
Columbia College, 600 South Michigan Avenue, Chicago, Illinois 60605.   *1890*
Tel: (312)663-1600
C: *arts-sc.*
Columbia College, 1301 Columbia College Drive, Columbia, South Carolina 29203.   *1854*
Tel: (803)786-3012
C: *arts-sc*
Columbus College, Algonquin Drive, Columbus, Georgia 31993–2399.   *1958*
Tel: (404)568-2001. Easylink: 62023123 esl ud
D : *arts-sc, bus-eco, sc, ed.*
Concordia College, 7400 Augusta, River Forest, Illinois 60305–1499.   *1864*
Tel: (312)771-8300
S : *arts-sc, teacher ed.*
Concordia Teachers' College, 900 North Columbia Avenue, Seward, Nebraska 68434.   *1894*
Tel: (402)643-3651
C: *ed.*
Connecticut College, 270 Mohegan Avenue, New London, Connecticut 06320.   *1911*
Tel: (203)447-1911
C : *arts-sc.*
Converse College, 580 E. Main, Spartanburg, South Carolina 29301.   *1889*
Tel: (803)596-9000
C : *arts-sc.*
S : *mus.*
The Cooper Union, Cooper Square, New York, New York 10003.   *1859*
Tel: (212)254-6300
C : *art, arc, eng.*
Coppin State College, 2500 West North Avenue, Baltimore, Maryland 21216.   *1900*
Tel: (301)383-4500
S : *arts-sc-ed, nurs.*
Corpus Christi State University, 6300 Ocean Drive, Corpus Christi, Texas 78412.
Tel: (512)991-6810. Fax: (512)991-6810
C: *arts-hum, bus adm, ed, sc-techn.*
Criswell College for Biblical Studies, 525 North Ervay, Dallas, Texas 75201.   *1970*
Tel: (214)954-0012
Cumberland College, Williamsburg, Kentucky 40769.   *1889*
Tel: (606)549-2200
C: *arts-sc.*
Curry College, 1071 Blue Hill Avenue, Milton, Massachusetts 02186.   *1879*
Tel: (617)333-0500. Easylink: 62958046 esl ud
C: *arts-sc.*
Dallas Baptist University, 7777 West Kiest Boulevard, Dallas, Texas 75211-0601.   *1965*
Tel: (214)331-8311
C: *arts-sc.*
David Lipscomb College, Granny White Pyke,

Nashville, Tennessee 37203-6001.   *1891*
Tel: (615)385-3855
C: *arts-sc.*
Delaware State College, 1200 North DuPont Highway, Dover, Delaware 19901.   *1891*
Tel: (302)736-4901
C: *arts-sc.*
Delta State University, Highway 8 West, Cleveland, Mississippi 38732.   *1924*
Tel: (601)846-4000
C : *arts-sc, ed, bus, nurs.*
DePauw University, South Locust Street, Greencastle, Indiana 46135.   *1837*
Tel: (317)658-4800
C : *arts-sc.*
Dominican College of San Rafael, 1520 Grand Avenue, San Rafael, California 94901.   *1889*
Tel: (415)457-4440
C : *arts-sc.*
Dowling College, Idle Hour Boulevard, Oakdale, Long Island, New York 11769.   *1959*
Tel: (516)589-6100
C : *arts-sc.*
Drury College, 900 North Benton, Springfield, Missouri 65802.   *1873*
Tel: (417)865-8731
C : *arts-sc.*
D'Youville College, 320 Porter Avenue, Buffalo, New York 14201.   *1908*
Tel: (716)881-3200
C: *arts-sc.*
D: *nurs.*
Earlham College, 701 National Road West, Richmond, Indiana 47374.   *1847*
Tel: (317)983-1200
C : *arts-sc.*
S : *relig.*
East Central University, Ada, Oklahoma 74820.
                                             1909
Tel: (405)332-8000
C : *arts-sc, ed, nurs.*
East Stroudsburg University of Pennsylvania, East Stroudsburg, Pennsylvania 18301.   *1893*
Tel: (717)424-3211
C : *arts-sc-ed, sc, heal sc, phys.*
East Texas State University:
  EAST TEXAS STATE UNIVERSITY AT TEXARKANA, 2600 North Robison Road, Texarkana, Texas 75505.   *1971*
  Tel: (214)838-6514
  D: *adm, arts-sc, teaching.*
Eastern College, Fairview Drive, St. Davids, Pennsylvania 19087.   *1952*
Tel: (215)341-5810
C: *arts-sc.*
Eastern Connecticut State University, 83 Windham Street, Williamtie, Connecticut 06226.
                                             1889
Tel: (203)456-2231

C : *arts-sc, personnel adm.*

Eastern Illinois University, Lincoln Street, Charleston, Illinois 61920.   *1895*
Tel: (217)581-2223
C : *arts-sc.*
S : *ed, bus, heal-phys-recr, app sc.*

Eastern Kentucky University, Lancaster Avenue, Richmond, Kentucky 40475–0931.
                                                  1906
Tel: (606)622-0111
C : *arts-sc, app arts-techn, bus, ed, allied heal-nurs, law enforcement, nat-math, hum, phys.*

Eastern Michigan University, Ypsilanti, Michigan 48197.   *1849*
Tel: (313)487-1849. Easylink: 62025185 esl ud
C : *arts-sc.*
D : *ind-techn, ed, bus, mus, nurs, heal-phys-recr.*

Eastern Montana College, 1500 North 30th Street, Billings, Montana 59101.   *1927*
Tel: (406)657-2011. Fax: (406)6572037
C : *arts-sc-ed, bus, eco.*

Eastern Nazarene College, 20 East Elm Avenue, Quincy, Massachusetts 02170.   *1918*
Tel: (617)773-6350
C : *arts-sc.*

Eastern New Mexico University, Portales, New Mexico 88130.   *1934*
Tel: (505)562-1011
C : *arts-sc, bus, ed-techn, fa.*

Eastern Oregon State College, 8th and K, La Grande, Oregon 97850.   *1929*
Tel: (503)963-1393
C : *arts-sc.*

Eastern Washington University, Cheney, Washington 99004.   *1882*
Tel: (509)359-2371. Fax: (509)359456
C : *let-sc.*
S : *fa, bus adm, hum, learning dev, soc w, math-techn.*
D : *heal sc.*

Edgewood College, 855 Woodrow, Madison, Wisconsin 53711.   *1927*
Tel: (608)257-4861
C: *arts-sc-ed.*

Edinboro University of Pennsylvania, Edinboro, Pennsylvania 16444.   *1857*
Tel: (814)732-2000
C : *arts-sc.*

Elmira College, Park Place, Elmira, New York 14901–2099.   *1855*
Tel: (607)734-3911
C : *nurs, bus, fa.*

Elon College, 101 Haggard Avenue, Elon College, North Carolina 27244-2010.   *1889*
Tel: (919)584-9711
C: *arts-sc.*

Embry-Riddle Aeronautical University, Daytona Beach, Florida 32014.   *1926*

Tel: (800)222-3728
C : *aeronautical st, aviation techn, eng.*

Emerson College, 100 Beacon Street, Boston, Massachusetts 02116–1596.   *1880*
Tel: (617)578-8500
C : *arts-sc.*

Emmanuel College, 400 The Fenway, Boston, Massachusetts 02115.   *1919*
Tel: (617)735-9760
C : *arts-sc.*

Emporia State University, 1300 Commercial, Emporia, Kansas 66801.   *1863*
Tel: (316)343-1200. Easylink: 62956691 esl ud
C : *arts-sc-ed-psyc, lib, bus.*

The Evergreen State College, Olympia, Washington 98505.   *1967*
Tel: (206)866-6000
S : *arts-sc.*

Fairfield University, North Benson Road, Fairfield, Connecticut 06430.   *1942*
Tel: (203)254-4000
C : *arts-sc, nurs, commun, bus.*

Fairleigh Dickinson University:
   MADISON CAMPUS, 285 Madison Avenue, Madison, New Jersey 07940.   *1958*
   Tel: (201)593-8500. Easylink: 62019885 esl ud
   C: *arts-sc, bus adm.*
   RUTHERFORD CAMPUS, West Passaic and Montross Avenues, Rutherford, New Jersey 07070.   *1942*
   Tel: (201)460-5000
   C: *arts-sc, bus adm.*

Fashion Institute of Technology, 227 West 27th Street, New York, New York 10001.   *1944*
Tel: (212)760-7675. Easylink: 62250110 esl ud
D: *bus-techn, li arts.*

Fayetteville State University, 1000 Marchinson Road, Fayetteville, North Carolina 28301.
                                                  1867
Tel: (919)486-1111. Easylink: 62024519 esl ud
C: *arts-sc.*
S: *ed.*

Ferris State College, 901 South State Street, Big Rapids, Michigan 49307.   *1884*
Tel: (616)796-0461. Fax: (616)592-2662
C: *gen ed, ed, phar, tec-app arts, bus, heal, sc-arts, optom, nurs.*

*Fisk University, 1000 17th Avenue N., Nashville, Tennessee 37203.   *1866*
Tel: (615)329-8500
C : *arts-sc.*

Fitchburg State College, 160 Pearl Street, Fitchburg, Massachusetts 01420.   *1894*
Tel: (617)345-2151
C : *arts-sc.*

Florida Southern College, 111 Lake Hollingsworth Drive, Lakeland, Florida 33802.   *1885*
Tel: (813)680-4111

C: *arts-sc.*

Fontbonne College, 6800 Wydown Boulevard, St. Louis, Missouri 63105. *1917*
Tel: (314)862-3456
C : *arts-sc.*

Fort Hayes State University, Hayes, Kansas 67601–4099. *1902*
Tel: (913)628-4000
F : *li arts-ed, nurs, bus.*

Fort Valley State College, 805 State College Drive, Fort Valley, Georgia 31030. *1895*
Tel: (912)825-6211
C : *arts-sc, agr, hom eco.*

Framingham State College, 100 State Street, Framingham, Massachusetts 01701. *1839*
Tel: (617)620-1220

Francis Marion College, P.O. Box F-7500, Florence, South Carolina 29501. *1970*
Tel: (803)661-1362
C : *arts-sc.*

Franciscan School of Theology, 1712 Euclid Avenue, Berkeley, California 94709. *1968*
Tel: (415)848-5232

Franciscan University of Steubenville, Franciscan Way, Steubenville, Ohio 43952. *1946*
Tel: (614)283-3771
nurs.

Franklin and Marshall College, P.O. Box 3003, Lancaster, Pennsylvania 17604. *1787*
Tel: (717)291-3911
C : *arts-sc.*

Free Will Baptist Bible College, 3606 West End Avenue, Nashville, Tennessee 37205. *1942*
Tel: (615)383-1340. Easylink: 62011171 esl ud
bus-com, commun, fa, theo.

Fresno Pacific College, 1717 S. Chestnut Avenue, Fresno, California 93702. *1944*
Tel: (209)251-7194
S : *arts-sc.*

Friends University, 2100 University, Wichita, Kansas 67213. *1898*
Tel: (316)261-5800
C: *arts-sc.*

Frostburg State College, College Avenue, Frostburg, Maryland 21532. *1898*
Tel: (301)689-4000
C : *arts-sc, teacher ed.*

Furman University, Poinsett Highway, Greenville, South Carolina 29613. *1826*
Tel: (803)294-2000
C : *arts-sc.*

Gannon University, University Square, Erie, Pennsylvania 16541. *1933*
Tel: (814)871-7000
C : *hum-sc, bus adm, sc-eng, ed.*

Gardner-Webb College, Boiling Springs, North Carolina 28017. *1905*
Tel: (704)434-2361
C: *arts-sc-ed, nurs, bus adm.*

Georgetown College, Jackson Street, Georgetown, Kentucky 40324. *1829*
Tel: (502)863-8011
C : *arts-sc.*

Georgia College, West Hancock Street, Milledgeville, Georgia 31061. *1889*
Tel: (912)453-5350
C : *arts-sc.*

Georgia Southern College, Statesboro, Georgia 30460–8033. *1906*
Tel: (912)681-5611
C : *arts-sc-ed, bus, heal, phys, nurs, techn.*

Georgia Southwestern College, Americus, Georgia 31709. *1906*
Tel: (912)928-1279
C : *arts-sc-ed.*

Georgian Court College, Lakewood Avenue, Lakewood, New Jersey 08701. *1908*
Tel: (201)364-2200
C : *arts-sc.*

Goddard College, Plainfield, Vermont 05667. *1938*
Tel: (802)454-8311
C : *arts-sc.*

Goucher College, Dulaney Valley Road, Townson, Maryland 21204. *1885*
Tel: (301)337-6000
C : *arts-sc.*

Governors State University, Stunkel Road, Park Forest, Illinois 60466. *1969*
Tel: (312)534-5000
C : *arts-sc, ed, bus, hum, heal professions.*

Grand Rapids Baptist College, 1001 East Betline N.E., Grand Rapids, Michigan 49505. *1941*
Tel: (616)949-5300. Easylink: 62958191 esl ud
C : *arts-sc, theo.*

Grand Valley State College, Allendale, Michigan 49401. *1960*
Tel: (616)895-6611. Telex: 9102406080 gavsc allendale
C : *arts-sc-ed, hum, sc, math, soc serv, bus.*

Gratz College, 10th Street and Tabor Road, Philadelphia, Pennsylvania 19141. *1895*
Tel: (215)329-3363
S : *li arts.*

Gwynedd-Mercy College, Sumneytown Pike, Gwynedd Valley, Pennsylvania 19437. *1948*
Tel: (215)646-7300
C: *arts-sc.*

Hampton University, Hampton, Virginia 23668. *1868*
Tel: (804)727-5000
S : *ed, nurs, app sc, bus.*
D : *arts-sc.*

Hardin-Simmons University, 2200 Hickory, Abilene, Texas 79698. *1891*
Tel: (915)677-7281. Easy link: 62006164 esl ud
D : *arts-sc, ed, relig, eco-bus adm, theo.*
S : *mus, nurs.*

Harding University, Searcy, Arkansas 72143.
1924
Tel: (501)268-6161
C : *arts-sc-ed, bus.*
   HARDING UNIVERSITY GRADUATE SCHOOL
OF RELIGION, 1000 Cherry Road, Memphis,
Tennessee 38117.   *1958*
Tel: (901)761-1353
Hartford Graduate Center, 275 Windsor Street,
Hartford, Connecticut 06120.   *1955*
Tel: (203)548-2400
C : *arts-sc.*
Harvey Mudd College, 12th and Columbia,
Claremount, California 91711.   *1955*
Tel: (714)621-8120
C : *arts-sc.*
Hawaii Pacific College, 1188 Fort Street,
Honolulu, Hawaii 96813.   *1965*
Tel: (800)544-0200
C: *arts-sc.*
Hebrew College, 43 Hawes Street, Brookline,
Massachusetts 02146.   *1921*
Tel: (617)232-8710
C : *arts-sc.*
Henderson State University, Arkadelphia,
Arkansas 71923.   *1890*
Tel: (501)246-5511
C : *li arts.*
S : *fa, sc-math, bus, ed.*
Heritage College, Route 3, Box 3540, Toppenish,
Washington 98948.   *1907*
Tel: (509)865-2244
S : *arts-sc.*
Hollins College, Roanoke, Virginia 24020.   *1842*
Tel: (703)362-6000
C : *arts-sc.*
Holy Apostles College, 33 Prospect Hill Road,
Cromwell, Connecticut 06416.   *1956*
Tel: (203)635-5311
theo.
Holy Names College, 3500 Mountain Boulevard,
Oakland, California 94619–9989.   *1868*
Tel: (415)436-0111
C : *arts-sc.*
Hood College, Rosemont Avenue, Frederick,
Maryland 21701.   *1893*
Tel: (301)663-3131
C : *arts-sc.*
Houston Baptist University, 7502 Fondren Road,
Houston, Texas 77074.   *1960*
Tel: (713)774-7661
C : *arts-sc-ed, bus, nurs, fa, soc w, hum.*
Huntington College, 2803 College Avenue,
Huntington, Indiana 46750.   *1897*
Tel: (219)356-6000
C : *arts-sc.*
Illinois Benedictine College, 5700 College Road,
Lisle, Illinois 60532–0960.   *1887*
Tel: (312)960-1500. Fax: (312)960-1126

C : *arts-sc.*
Immaculata College, Immaculata, Pennsylvania
19345-0901.   *1920*
Tel: (215)647-4400
C: *arts-sc.*
Incarnate Word College, 4301 Broadway, San
Antonio, Texas 78209.   *1881*
Tel: (512)828-1261
C : *arts-sc.*
*Indiana University:
   INDIANA UNIVERSITY AT KOKOMO, 2300
South Washington Street, Kokomo,
Indiana 46901.   *1945*
Tel: (317)453-2000
D: *bus, ed, nurs, li st.*
   INDIANA UNIVERSITY NORTHWEST, 3400
Broadway, Gary, Indiana 46408.   *1921*
Tel: (219)980-6500
S: *arts-sc, bus, ed, nurs, allied heal sc.*
   INDIANA UNIVERSITY AT SOUTH BEND, 1700
Mishawaka Avenue, South Bend, Indiana
46634.   *1940*
D: *arts-sc, bus-eco, ed, mus, dental nurs.*
   INDIANA UNIVERSITY SOUTHEAST, 4201
Grant Line Road, New Albany, Indiana
47150.   *1941*
Tel: (813)945-2731
D: *arts-sc-ed, hum, nat, soc, bus, nurs,
techn, ed.*
   INDIANA UNIVERSITY-PURDUE UNIVERSITY
AT FORT WAYNE, 2101 Coliseum Boulevard
East, Fort Wayne, Indiana 46805.   *1964*
Tel: (219)482-5121. Fax: (219)4816880
C: *arts-let, techn-eng, nurs, sc-hum.*
Inter-American University of Puerto Rico,
Galileo Street, Jardines Metropolitanos, Rio
Piedras 00927.
Tel: (809)766-1912
   INTER-AMERICAN UNIVERSITY OF PUERTO
RICO METROPOLITAN CAMPUS, Francisco
Sein St. and Road Number 1, Km. 16.3, Rio
Piedras, Puerto Rico 00919.   *1960*
Tel: (809)751-8000
C : *arts-sc-ed, eco, nurs, sc-techn, behav-
ioral sc, hum, med, techn.*
   INTER-AMERICAN UNIVERSITY OF PUERTO
RICO, SAN GERMAN CAMPUS, P.O. BOX
5100, San German, Puerto Rico 00753.
1912
Tel: (809)892-1095
C : *arts-sc.*
Iona College, 715 North Avenue, New Rochelle,
New York 10801–1890.   *1940*
Tel: (914)636-2000
C : *arts-sc, bus adm.*
Ithaca College, Ithaca, New York 14850.   *1892*
Tel: (607)274-3013. Telex: 131386 ithaca coll
D : *bus adm.*
S : *heal-phys-recr, hum, allied heal professions,*

commun.

Jackson State University, 1440 J.R. Lynch Street, Jackson, Mississippi 39217.   *1877*
Tel: (601)968-2121
D : *li arts, ed-techn st, bus-eco.*

Jacksonville State University, Jacksonville, Alabama 36265.   *1883*
Tel: (205)231-5781
S : *li st, ed, bus eco, math-sc, hum, nurs, mus, fa.*

Jacksonville University, 2800 University Boulevard N., Jacksonville, Florida 32211.   *1934*
Tel: (904)744-3950
C : *arts-sc, fa, bus adm, ed, mus, commun, nurs.*

James Madison University, Harrisonburg, Virginia 22807.   *1908*
Tel: (703)568-6211. Easylink: 62978505 esl ud
S : *arts-sc-ed, bus, fa, nurs.*

Jersey City State College, 2039 Kennedy Boulevard, Jersey City, New Jersey 07305–1597.
1927
Tel: (201)547-6000
C : *arts sc-ed.*
Ce : *media-techn.*

Jesuit School of Theology at Berkeley, 1735 LeRoy Avenue, Berkeley, California 94709.
1934
Tel: (415)841-8804
S: *theo, li arts, mangt.*

John Carroll University, 20700 North Park Boulevard, Cleveland, Ohio 44118.   *1886*
Tel: (216)397-1886
C : *arts-sc.*
S : *bus.*

John F. Kennedy University, 12 Ahrindard, Orinda, California 94563.   *1964*
Tel: (415)254-0200
S : *gen st, law, mangt, prof psyc, li arts.*

Johnson State College, Johnson, Vermont 05656.
1828
Tel: (802)635-2356
C : *arts-sc-ed, hum, math, sc, heal, arts, bus, eco.*

Kean College of New Jersey, Morris Avenue, Union, New Jersey 07083.   *1855*
Tel: (201)527-2000
C : *arts-sc-ed, hum, soc, math, sc, heal.*

Kearney State College, 905 West 25th Street, Kearney, Nebraska 68849–0601.   *1903*
Tel: (308)236-8441
C : *ed, fa-hum, bus-techn, nat-soc.*

Keene State College, 229 Main Street, Keene, New Hampshire 03431–4183.   *1909*
Tel: (603)352-1909
C : *arts-sc-ed, prof st, hum.*

Kennesaw College, P.O. Box 444, Marietta, Georgia 30061.   *1963*
Tel: (404)429-2700

C: *arts-sc-ed, bus, sc, behavioral sc, allied heal professions.*

Kentucky State University, East Main Street, Frankfort, Kentucky 40601.   *1886, 1926*
Tel: (502)227-6000
C : *arts-sc, app sc, bus, leadership.*

Kutztown University of Pennsylvania, Kutztown, Pennsylvania 19530.   *1866, 1926*
Tel: (215)683-4000
D : *arts-sc, ed, vis & performing arts.*

La Grange College, 601 Broad Street, La Grange, Georgia 30240.   *1831*
Tel: (404)882-2911
C : *arts-sc.*

La Salle University, 20th Street and Olney Avenue, Philadelphia, Pennsylvania 19141.
1863
Tel: (215)951-1000
S : *arts-sc, bus adm, relig, ed, biling.*

Lake Erie College, 391 W. Washington Street, Painesville, Ohio 44077.   *1856*
Tel: (216)352-3361
C : *arts-sc.*

Lake Forest College, Lake Forest, Illinois 60045.
1857
Tel: (312)234-3100. Fax: (312)234-7170
LAKE FOREST GRADUATE SCHOOL OF MANAGEMENT.   *1946*
Tel: (312)234-5005

Lake Superior State College, 1000 College Drive, Sault Sainte Marie, Michigan 49783-9981. *1946*
Tel: (906)635-2315. Easylink: 62020505 esl ud
C : *arts-sc-ed.*

Lander College, Stanley Avenue, Greenwood, South Carolina 29646.   *1872*
Tel: (803)229-8307
C : *arts-sc.*

Laredo State University, West End Laredo Street, Laredo, Texas 78040.   *1969*
Tel: (512)722-8001
C : *arts-sc.*
D: *bus adm, ed-psyc.*

Lenoir-Rhyne College, Box 7163, Hickory, North Carolina 28603.   *1891*
Tel: (704)328-1741
C : *arts-sc.*

Lewis University, Route 53, Romeoville, Illinois 60441.   *1932*
Tel: (815)838-0500
C : *arts-sc-ed-occup, bus, nurs.*

Liberty University, 3765 Candlers Mountain Road, Lynchburg, Virginia 24506.   *1971*
Tel: (804)582-2000
C: *arts-sc.*

Lincoln Christian College, 100 Campus View Drive, Lincoln, Illinois 62656.   *1944*
Tel: (217)732-3168
bus-ed-let-theo.

Lincoln Memorial University, Route 25E.,

Harrogate, Tennessee 37752-0901. *1897*
Tel: (615)869-3611
C: *arts-sc-ed-occp, fa, nurs, hum, bus adm, behavioral sc, app sc, comp.*
Lincoln University, Old Route 1, Lincoln University, Pennsylvania 19352. *1854*
Tel: (215)932-8300
C: *arts-sc.*
Lincoln University, 820 Chestnut, Jefferson City, Missouri 65101. *1866*
Tel: (314)681-5000. Telex: 5106015934 inter linc
C : *arts-sc-ed, bus-eco, app sc-techn.*
Lindenwood Colleges, 1st Capitol Highway and Kings Highway, St. Charles, Missouri 63301. *1827*
Tel: (314)946-6912
C : *arts-sc.*
Linfield College, McMinnville, Oregon 97128–6894. *1849*
Tel: (503)472-4121
S : *arts-sc-ed.*
Livingston University, Station One, Livingston, Alabama 35470. *1835*
Tel: (205)652-9661
S : *ed, bus, li arts.*
Lock Haven University of Pennsylvania, Lock Haven, Pennsylvania 17745. *1870*
Tel: (717)893-2011
C: *arts-sc-ed, phys, heal-recr.*
Long Island University:
  LONG ISLAND UNIVERSITY, SOUTHAMPTON CAMPUS, Montauk Highway, Southampton, New York 11968. *1963*
  Tel: (516)283-4000
  C: *arts-sc-ed.*
  LONG ISLAND UNIVERSITY, C.W. POST CAMPUS, Northern Boulevard, Brookville, New York 11548. *1954*
  Tel: (516)299-0200
  C: *arts-sc-ed.*
Longwood College, Farmville, Virginia 23901. *1839*
Tel: (804) 392-9291
C : *arts-sc.*
Loras College, 1450 Alta Vista Street, Dubuque, Iowa 52004-0178. *1839*
Tel: (319) 588-7100
C : *arts-sc.*
Louisiana State University
  LOUISIANA STATE UNIVERSITY IN SHREVEPORT, 8515 Youree Drive, Shreveport, Louisiana 71115. *1965*
  Tel: (318)797-5000
  D : *li arts, ed, sc, bus adm.*
Loyola College in Maryland, 4501 North Charles Street, Baltimore, Maryland 21210. *1852*
Tel: (301) 323-1010
C : *arts-sc-ed, bus.*

Loyola Marymount University, Loyola Boulevard at West 8th Street, Los Angeles, California 90045. *1911*
Tel: (213) 642-2700
C : *arts-sc, bus adm, sc-eng, fa-commun arts.*
S : *law.*
D : *ed.*
Lynchburg College, Lynchburg, Virginia 24501. *1903*
Tel: (804) 522-8100
C : *arts-sc, bus.*
Lyndon State College, Lyndonville, Vermont 05851. *1911*
Tel: (802) 626-9371
C : *arts-sc.*
Madonna College, 36600 Schoolcraft Road, Livonia, Michigan 48150-1173. *1947*
Tel: (313) 591-5000
C : *arts-sc.*
Maharishi International University, Route 1, Fairfield, Iowa 52556. *1971*
Tel: (515) 472-5031. Telex: 286515 miuop ur
C : *arts-sc.*
Maine Maritime Academy, Castine, Maine 04421. *1941*
Tel: (207) 326-4311
C : *eng.*
Manchester College, 604 College Avenue, North Manchester, Indiana 46962. *1889*
Tel: (219) 982-2141
C : *arts-sc.*
Manhattan College, Manhattan College Parkway Riverdale, New York 10471. *1853*
Tel: (212) 920-0100
S : *arts-sc-ed, bus, eng, hum serv, gen st.*
Manhattanville College, Purchase Street, Purchase, New York 10577. *1841*
Tel: (914) 694-2200
C : *arts-sc.*
Mankato State University, Mankato, Minnesota 56001. *1866*
Tel: (507) 389-6767. Easylink: 62835877 esl ud
D : *arts-hum, bus, ed, heal-phys, nurs, nat, math-hom-eco, soc-behavioral sc.*
Mansfield University of Pennsylvania, Mansfield, Pennsylvania 16933. *1857*
Tel: (717) 662-4000
C : *arts-sc.*
Marietta College, 215 5th Street, Marietta, Ohio 45750. *1834*
Tel: (614) 373-4643
C : *arts-sc.*
Marion College, 4201 South Washington Street, Marion, Indiana 46952. *1920*
Tel: (317) 674-6901
C : *arts-sc.*
Marist College, 83 North Road, Poughkeepsie, New York 12601. *1946*
Tel: (914) 471-3240

C : *arts-sc.*

Marlboro College, Marlboro, Vermont 05344.
                                                    1946
Tel: (802) 257-4333
C : *arts-sc.*

Marshall University, 3rd Avenue and Hall Greer
Boulevard, Huntington, West Virginia 25701.
                                                    1837
Tel: (304) 696-3160. Easylink: 620 19765 esl ud
C : *arts-sc.*
S : *bus-app sc, med, nurs.*

Mary Washington College, 1301 College Avenue,
Frederickburg, Virginia 22401.   *1908*
Tel: (703) 899-4100
C : *arts-sc.*

Marycrest College, 1607 West 12th Street,
Davenport, Iowa 52804.   *1939*
Tel: (319) 326-9512
C : *arts-sc.*

Marygrove College, 8425 W. McNichols Road,
Detroit, Michigan 48221–2599.
                                                    1910
Tel: (313) 862-8000
C : *arts-sc.*

Marylhurst College, Marylhurst, Oregon 97036-
0261.   *1893*
Tel: (503) 636-8141
C : *arts-sc, mangt, rel, ed.*
D : *mus, art.*

Marymount University, 2807 North Glebe Road,
Arlington, Virginia 22207.   *1950*
Tel: (703) 522-5600
C : *arts-sc.*

Maryville College St. Louis, 13550 Conway
Road, St. Louis, Missouri 63141.   *1872*
Tel: (314) 576-9300
C : *arts-sc.*

Marywood College, 2300 Adams Avenue,
Scranton, Pennsylvania 18509–1598.   *1915*
Tel: (717) 348-6211
C : *arts-sc.*
S : *soc w.*

Massachusetts College of Arts, 621 Huntington
Avenue, Boston, Massachusetts 02115.   *1873*
Tel: (617) 232-1555

McNeese State University, 4100 Ryan Street,
Lake Charles, Louisiana 70609.   *1938*
Tel: (318) 437-5500. Easylink: 628 85683 esl ud
S : *bus, ed, art, hum, sc, techn-eng.*

Mercer University, 1400 Coleman Avenue,
Macon, Georgia 31207.   *1833*
Tel: (912) 744-2700
C : *li arts.*
S : *law, med, bus-eco.*

  Mercer University in Atlanta, 3001
  Mercer University Drive, Atlanta, Georgia
  30341.   *1960*
  Tel: (404) 688-6291
  arts-sc, bus-eco.

Mercy College, 555 Broadway, Dobbs Ferry,
New York 10522.   *1950*
Tel: (914) 693-4500
C : *arts-sc.*

Mercy College of Detroit, 8200 West Outer Drive,
Detroit, Michigan 48219.   *1941*
Tel: (313) 592-6000
C : *arts-sc-ed, hum, math, nurs, allied heal
professions, soc.*

Mercyhurst College, 501 East 38th Street, Erie,
Pennsylvania 16546.   *1926*
Tel: (814) 825-0200
C : *arts-sc-ed.*

Meredith College, 3800 Hillsborough Street,
Raleigh, North Carolina 27607-5298.   *1891*
Tel: (919) 829-8600
C : *arts-sc.*

Metropolitan State College, 1006 11th Street,
Denver, Colorado 80204.   *1963*
Tel: (303) 556-3019. Easylink: 620 15282 esl ud
S : *bus, math, eng techn, li arts, sc-techn, prof st*
Ce : *ed.*

Miami Christian College, 2300 Northwest 135th
Street, Miami, Florida 33167.   *1949*
Tel: (305) 685-7431
arts-sc, theo.

Midwestern State University, 3400 Taft Boule-
vard, Wichita Falls, Texas 76308.   *1922*
Tel: (817) 692-6611
S : *li arts.*

Millersville University of Pennsylvania, Millers-
ville, Pennsylvania 17551.   *1854*
Tel: (717) 872-3011
C : *hum-ed, soc.*

Mills College, Oakland, California 94613.   *1852*
Tel: (415) 430-2255
C : *arts-sc-ed.*

Millsaps College, Jackson, Mississippi 39210-
0001.   *1890, 1892*
Tel: (601) 354-5201
C : *arts-sc-ed-occp.*

Milwaukee School of Engineering, 342 North
Water Street, P.O. Box 644, Milwaukee,
Wisconsin 53201.   *1903*
Tel: (800) 558-4653
C : *eng.*

Minot State College, Minot, 11th Avenue North
West, North Dakota 58701.   *1913*
Tel: (701) 857-3000
C : *arts-sc.*

Mississippi College, College Street, Clinton,
Mississippi 39058.   *1826*
Tel: (601) 925-3300
C : *arts-sc.*
S : *ed, nurs, law, bus adm.*

Mississippi University for Women, College
Street, Columbus, Mississippi 39701.   *1884*
Tel: (601) 329-4750
C : *arts-sc, hom eco, ed, nurs, fa-performing*

arts, sc-math, bus-eco, hum, commun, heal-
phys-rec.
Mississippi Valley State University, Itta Bena,
Mississippi 38941. *1946*
Tel: (601) 254-9041
D : arts-sc, ed, bus, sc-techn.
Mobile College, Mobile, Alabama 36613. *1961*
C : arts-sc.
Monmouth College, Cedar Avenue, West Long
Branch, New Jersey 07764. *1933*
Tel: (201) 571-3400
C : arts-sc, hum-soc, sc, bus.
**Montana College of Mineral Science and Tech-
nology**, Butte, Montana 59701. *1893*
Tel: (406) 496-4101
C : mine, ind eng, arts-sc.
Montclair State College, Valley Road and
Normal Avenue, Upper Montclair, New Jersey
07043. *1908*
Tel: (201) 893-4000. Telex: 133542 m s c bs mclr
S : hum, math-sc, prof arts-sc, fa-performing
arts, bus adm.
Monterey Institute of International Studies, 421
Van Buren Street, Monterey, California 93940.
1955
Tel: (408) 649-3113
C : arts-sc, int bus, lang-hum.
Moody Bible Institute, 820 North La Salle Street,
Chicago, Illinois 60610. *1886*
Tel: (312) 329-4000. Telex: 703394 moody net
ud
Moorhead State University, 1104 7th Avenue
South, Moorhead, Minnesota 56560–9980.
1885
Tel: (218) 236-2011. Easylink: 628 60254 esl ud
F : math-nat, arts-hum, bus-ind.
Moravian College, Main Street and Elizabeth
Avenue, Bethlehem, Pennsylvania 18018.
1742
Tel: (215) 861-1300. Easylink: 620 22646 esl ud
C : arts-sc.
Morehead State University, University Boule-
vard, Morehead, Kentucky 40351. *1922*
Tel: (606) 783-2221
S : arts-sc, bus-eco.
Morgan State University, Cold Spring La-Hillen
Road, Baltimore, Maryland 21239. *1867*
Tel: (301) 444-3333
C : arts-sc.
S : bus-mangt.
Morningside College, 1501 Morningside Avenue,
Sioux City, Iowa 51106. *1893*
Tel: (712) 274-5000. Telex: 5106016956 morn-
ingside
C : arts-sc.
*****Mount Holyoke College**, South Hadley, Massa-
chusetts 01075–1496. *1837*
Tel: (413) 538-2000. Telex: 6716465 mh esh
C : arts-sc-ed.

Mount Marty College, 1105 West 8th, Yankton,
South Dakota 57078. *1936*
Tel: (605) 668-1515
C : arts.
Mount Mary College, 2900 Menomonee River
Parkway, Milwaukee, Wisconsin 53222. *1913*
Tel: (414) 258-4810
C : arts-sc.
Mount St. Mary's College, Emittsburg, Maryland
21727. *1808*
Tel: (301) 447-6122
S : theo.
Mount Saint Mary's College, 12001 Chalon
Road, Los Angeles, California 90049. *1925*
Tel: (213) 476-2237
C : arts-sc.
Mount St. Mary College, 330 Powell Avenue,
Newburgh, New York 12550. *1930*
Tel: (914) 561-0800
C : arts-sc.
Multnomah School of the Bible, 8435 Northeast
Glisan Street, Portland, Oregon 97220. *1936*
Tel: (503) 255-0332
theo.
Mundelein College, 6363 Sheridan Road,
Chicago, Illinois 60660. *1929*
Tel: (312) 262-8100
C : arts-sc.
Murray State University, 15th and Main,
Murray, Kentucky 42071–3305. *1922*
Tel: (502) 762-3011. Fax: (502) 7624270
C : creative expression, publ aff, humanistic st.
S : arts-sc ed, ind-techn, bus.
The Naropa Institute, 2130 Arapoe Avenue,
Boulder, Colorado 80302–9989. *1974*
Tel: (303) 444-0202
arts-sc.
Nashotah House, Nashotah, Wisconsin 53058.
1842
Tel: (414) 646-3371
S : theo, arts-sc.
Nazareth College in Kalamazoo, 3333 Gu Road,
Kalamazoo, Michigan 49001. *1924*
Tel: (616) 349-4200
C : arts-sc.
Nazareth College of Rochester, 4245 East
Avenue, Rochester, New York 14610. *1924*
Tel: (716) 586-2525
C : arts-sc.
Neumann College, Convent Road, Aston,
Pennsylvania 19014. *1965*
Tel: (215) 459-0905
S : li arts.
New College of California, 777 Valencia Street,
San Francisco, California 94102. *1971*
Tel: (415) 626-1694
C : arts-sc, law, hum.
New England College, Proctor Square, Henniker,
New Hampshire 03242. *1946*

Tel: (603) 428-2232
C : *arts-sc, eng.*
New Mexico Highlands University, Las Vegas, New Mexico 87701.   *1893*
Tel: (505) 425-7511
C : *arts-sc.*
New York Institute of Technology, Wheatley Road, Old Westbury, New York 11568–0170.
                                        1955
Tel: (516) 686-7516
C : *eng-techn, ed, arc-arts, bus-mangt, hum, labor & ind rel, nat, hum resources.*
Niagara University, Niagara University, New York 14109.   *1856*
Tel: (716) 285-1212
C : *arts-sc, bus adm, nurs.*
S : *ed.*
Nicholls State University, Highway 1, P.O. Box 2168, Thibodaux, Louisiana 70310.   *1948*
Tel: (504) 446-8111. Telex: 9102503719 nichols ud
C : *arts-sc, ed, bus adm, life sc-techn.*
Norfolk State University, 2401 Corprew Avenue, Norfolk, Virginia 23504.   *1935*
Tel: (804) 623-8600
C : *arts-sc-ed-occp, soc w, techn, bus, heal, soc.*
North Adams State College, Church Street, North Adams, Massachusetts 01247.   *1894*
Tel: (413) 664-4511
C : *arts-sc.*
North Carolina Agricultural and Technical State University, 1601 East Market Street, Greensboro, North Carolina 27411.   *1891*
Tel: (919) 334-7500. Telex: 5106007089 intlag pro ncat
C : *arts-sc.*
S : *agr, bus-eco, ed, eng, nurs, techn.*
North Carolina Central University, 1801 Fayetteville Street, Durham, North Carolina 27707.
                                        1910
Tel: (919) 683-6100
C : *arts-sc.*
S : *bus, law, lib-infor*
North Carolina School of the Arts, 200 Waughtown Street, Winston-Salem, North Carolina 27117.   *1963*
Tel: (919) 784-7170
S : *des-production, drama, mus.*
North Central College, 30 North Brainard Street, Naperville, Illinois 60566.   *1861*
Tel: (312) 420-3400
C : *arts-sc.*
North Georgia College, Dahlonega, Georgia 30597.   *1873*
Tel: (404) 864-3391
C : *arts-sc.*
Northeast Missouri State University, Kirksville, Missouri 63501.   *1867*
Tel: (816) 785-4000

C : *arts-sc.*
Northeastern Illinois University, 5500 North St. Louis Avenue, Chicago, Illinois 60625.   *1961*
Tel: (312) 583-4050
C : *arts-sc-ed, bus, mus, phys.*
Northeastern State University, Tahlequah, Oklahoma 74464.   *1846*
Tel: (918) 456-5511
C : *arts-sc, opt om.*
Northern Kentucky University, Louie B. Nunn Drive, Highland Heights, Kentucky 41076.
                                        1968
Tel: (606) 572-5100
C : *arts-sc, bus, prof st, law.*
Northern Michigan University, 610 Cohodas Administrative Center, Marquette, Michigan 49855.   *1899*
Tel: (906) 227-1000. Fax: (902) 2272722. Easylink: 62033056 esl ud
S : *arts-sc, bus, ed, nurs.*
Northern Montana College, P.O. Box 751, Havre, Montana 59501.   *1929*
Tel: (406) 265-3221
C : *arts-sc-ed, techn & prof st.*
Northern State College, Aberdeen, South Dakota 57401.   *1901*
Tel: (605) 622-3011. Easylink: 62860276 esl ud
C : *arts-sc-ed, bus, fa.*
Northrop University, 5800 West Arbor Vitae Street, Los Angeles, California 90045.   *1942*
Tel: (213) 337-4407
C : *eng, comp, arts-sc.*
S : *law, aero-space eng.*
Northwest Christian College, 828 East 11th Avenue, Eugene, Oregon 97401.   *1895*
Tel: (503) 343-1641
C : *arts-sc.*
Northwest Missouri State University, Maryville, Missouri 64468.   *1905*
Tel: (816) 582-1212
C : *arts-sc.*
Northwest Nazarene College, 623 Holly Street, Nampa, Idaho 83651.   *1913*
Tel: (208) 467-8011
C : *arts-sc.*
Northwestern Oklahoma State University, Oklahoma Boulevard, Alva, Oklahoma 73717.
                                        1897
Tel: (405) 327-1700
C : *arts-sc.*
Northwestern State University of Louisiana, College Avenue, Natchitoches, Louisiana 71497.
                                        1884
Tel: (318) 357-6011
S : *li arts, bus, ed, nurs sc-tech.*
Norwich University, Northfield, Vermont 05663.
                                        1819
Tel: (802) 485-2000
    VERMONT COLLEGE CAMPUS, College Street,

Montpelier, Vermont 05602.   *1834*
Tel: (802) 229-0522
C : *arts-sc.*

Notre Dame College, 2321 Elm Street, Manchester, New Hampshire 03104.   *1950*
Tel: (603) 669-4298
C : *arts-sc.*

Nyack College, South Boulevard, Nyack, New York 10960–9987.   *1882*
Tel: (914) 358-1710
C : *arts-sc, theo.*

Oberlin College, Oberlin, Ohio 44074.   *1833*
Tel: (216) 775-8400
C : *arts-sc.*
Conservatory : *mus.*

Occidental College, 1600 Campus Road, Los Angeles, California 90041.   *1887*
Tel: (213) 259-2700
C : *arts-sc.*

Oglethorpe University, 4484 Peachtree Road, N.E., Atlanta, Georgia 30319.   *1835*
Tel: (404) 261-1441
C : *arts-sc.*

Ohio University:
  OHIO UNIVERSITY, LANCASTER, Lancaster, Ohio 43130.   *1968*
  Tel: (614) 654-6711

Oklahoma City University, 2501 North Blackwelder, Oklahoma City, Oklahoma 73106.
          1901
Tel: (405) 521-5032. Fax: (405) 521-5172
C : *arts-sc.*
S : *sc, law.*

Olivet College, Olivet, Michigan 49076–9990.
          1844
Tel: (616) 749-7000
C : *arts-sc-ed.*

Olivet Nazarene College, Kankakee, Illinois 60901.   *1907*
Tel: (815) 939-5011
C : *arts-sc.*

Ouachita Baptist University, 410 Ouachita Street, Arkadelphia, Arkansas 71923.   *1886*
Tel: (501) 246-4531. Easylink: 62032071 esl ud
C : *arts-sc.*
S : *mus.*

Our Lady of Holy Cross College, 4123 Woodland Drive, New Orleans, Louisiana 70114.   *1922*
Tel: (504) 394-7744
S : *arts-sc.*

Our Lady of the Lake University, 411 S.W. 24th Street, San Antonio, Texas 78285.   *1911*
Tel: (512) 434-6711
C : *arts-sc.*
S : *ed, soc w, clin st, bus adm.*

Pacific Christian College, 2500 East Nutwood Avenue, Fullerton, California 92631.   *1928*
Tel: (714) 879-3901
C : *arts-sc.*

Pacific Lutheran University, South 121st and Park Avenue, Tacoma, Washington 98447.
          1890
Tel: (206) 531-6900
C : *arts-sc.*
S : *bus adm, ed, fa, nurs, phys.*

Pacific Oaks College, 5 Westmoreland Place, Pasadena, California 91103.   *1951*
Tel: (818) 795-9161
S : *arts-sc.*

Pacific Union College, Angwin, California 94508.
          1882
Tel: (707)965-6311. Fax: (707) 9656371
D : *arts-sc.*

Pan American University, 1201 West University Drive, Edinburg, Texas 78539.   *1927*
Tel: (512) 381-2011
  C : *hum, sc-math, ed, bus adm, soc, mus, phys, nurs ed.*

Park College, 8700 River Park Drive, Parkville, Missouri 64152.   *1875*
Tel: (816) 741-2000
C : *arts-sc.*

The Pennsylvania State University:
  THE PENNSYLVANIA STATE UNIVERSITY AT ERIE, BEHREND COLLEGE, Station Road, Erie, Pennsylvania 16563.   *1926*
  Tel: (814) 898-6000
  S : *bus.*

  PENNSYLVANIA STATE UNIVERSITY KING OF PRUSSIA CENTER FOR GRADUATE STUDIES AND CONTINUING EDUCATION, 650 South Henderson Road, King of Prussia, Pennsylvania 19406.   *1963*
  Tel: (215) 265-7640

Peru State College, Peru, Nebraska 68421.   *1867*
Tel: (402) 872-3815
C : *arts-sc.*

Philadelphia College of Textiles and Science, Schoolhouse Lane and Henry Avenue, Philadelphia, Pennsylvania 19144.   *1884*
Tel: (215) 951-2700
C : *arts-sc.*

Pittsburg State University, Pittsburg, Kansas 66762.   *1903*
Tel: (316) 231-7000
S : *arts-sc-ed, techn, bus-eco, app sc.*

Plymouth State College, (University of New Hampshire System), Plymouth, New Hampshire 03264.   *1871*
Tel: (603) 536-1550
C : *arts-sc-ed.*

Point Loma Nazarene College, 3900 Lomaland Road, San Diego, California 92106–2899.
          1902
Tel: (619) 221-2200
C : *arts-sc.*

Point Park College, 201 Wood Street, Pittsburgh, Pennsylvania 15222.   *1960*

Tel: (412) 392-3860. Telex: 314426 point park col

C : *arts-sc.*

Polytechnic University, Westchester Campus, Hawthorne, New York 10532.
Tel: (914) 347-6934
S : *grad.*

Prairie View Agricultural and Mechanical University, Prairie View, Texas 77446.   *1876*
Tel: (409) 857-3311
C : *agr, eng, hom eco, ind ed, nurs, bus, ed.*

Pratt Institute, 200 Wylloughby Avenue, Brooklyn, New York 11205.   *1887*
Tel: (718) 636-3600
S : *art-des, arc, eng, lib-infor sc, arts-sc.*

Purdue University:
PURDUE UNIVERSITY CALUMET, 2233 171st Street, Hammond, Indiana 46323.   *1943*
Tel: (219) 844-0520. Fax: (219) 989-2581
S : *hum-soc-ed, eng, techn, sc-nurs.*

PURDUE UNIVERSITY NORTH CENTRAL CAMPUS, Westville, Indiana 46391.   *1943*
Tel: (219) 785-254
arts-sc-ed, math, phy, bioch, nurs, soc, eng.

Queens College, 1900 Selwyn Avenue, Charlotte, North Carolina 28274-0001.   *1857*
Tel: (704) 332-7121. Easylink: 62025524 esl ud
C : *arts-sc.*

Quincy College, 1800 College Avenue, Quincy, Illinois 62301.   *1859*
Tel: (217) 222-8020
C : *arts-sc.*

Quinnipiac College, Mount Carmel Avenue, Hamden, Connecticut 06518.   *1929*
Tel: (203) 288-5251
C : *li arts, bus, nat, prof training.*

Radford University, Radford University Station, Radford, Virginia 24142.   *1910*
Tel: (703) 731-5000
C : *arts-sc-ed, bus-prof st, fa, nurs.*

Reed College, 3203 S.E. Woodstock Boulevard, Portland, Oregon 97202.   *1909*
Tel: (503) 771-1112. Telex: 4947538 reed lib ptl
C : *arts-sc.*

Regis College, West 50th Avenue and Lowell Boulevard, Denver, Colorado 80221-1099.   *1877*
Tel: (303) 458-4100
C : *arts-sc.*

Rhode Island College, 600 Mount Pleasant Avenue, Providence, Rhode Island 02908.   *1854*
Tel: (401) 456-8000. Easylink: 6279107 esl ud
S : *arts-sc, hum, ed, soc w.*

Rhode Island School of Design, 2 College Street, Providence, Rhode Island 02903.   *1877*
Tel: (401) 331-3511
D : *arc, art-des, fa, li arts, museum.*

Rider College, 2083 Lawrenville Road, Law-

renceville, New Jersey 08648.   *1865*
Tel: (609) 896-5000
S : *li arts-sc, bus adm, ed.*

Rivier College, 420 Main Street, Nashua, New Hampshire 03060.   *1933*
Tel: (603) 888-1311
C : *arts-sc-ed.*

Robert Morris College, Narrows Run Road, Coraopolis, Pennsylvania 15108.   *1921*
Tel: (412) 262-8200
C : *arts-sc-ed, bus adm.*

Rochester Institute of Technology, 1 Lamb Memorial Drive, Rochester, New York 14623.   *1829*
Tel: (716) 475-2400. Telex: 709337 ritroc ud
C : *eng, bus, fa-app arts, sc, app sc.*
I : *techn, graph arts-photography.*

Rockford College, 5050 East State Street, Rockford, Illinois 61108–2393.   *1847*
Tel: (815) 226-4060
C : *arts-sc.*

Rockhurst College, 5225 Troost Avenue, Kansas City, Missouri 64110.   *1910*
Tel: (816) 926-4150
C : *arts-sc.*

Rollins College, Winter Park, Florida 32789–4499.   *1885*
Tel: (305) 646-2000
C : *arts-sc, bus.*

Roosevelt University, 430 South Michigan Avenue, Chicago, Illinois 60605–1394.   *1945*
Tel: (312) 341-3500
D : *labor ed.*

Rosary College, 7900 West Division Street, River Foreset, Illinois 60305.   *1901*
Tel: (312) 366-2400
C : *arts-sc, lib.*

Rose-Hulman Institute of Technology, 5500 Wabash Avenue, Terre-Haute, Indiana 47803.   *1874*
Tel: (812) 877-1511

Russell Sage College, 45 Ferry Street, Troy, New York 12180.   *1916*
Tel: (518) 270-2000
C : *arts-sc.*

Rutgers, The State University of New Jersey:
RUTGERS, THE STATE UNIVERSITY OF NEW JERSEY CAMDEN CAMPUS, 406 Penn, Camden, New Jersey 08102.   *1927*
Tel: (609) 757-1766
C : *arts-sc, law.*

Sacred Heart University, P.O. Box 6460, Bridgeport, Connecticut 06606-0460.   *1963*
Tel: (203) 371-7999
C : *arts-sc, bus adm, hum, soc, math.*

Saginaw Valley State College, 2250 Pierce Road, University Center, Michigan 48710.   *1963*
Tel: (517) 790-4000
C : *arts-sc.*

S : *bus, mangt, ed.*
D : *eng techn, nurs, publ serv.*
St. Ambrose University, 518 West Locust Street, Davenport, Iowa 52803.   *1882*
Tel: (319) 383-8888
C : *arts-sc, bus, eng.*
St. Bonaventure University, Route 417, St. Bonaventure, New York 14778.   *1858*
Tel: (716) 375-2000
S : *arts-sc, bus adm, ed.*
St. Cloud State University, 207 Administrative Services Building, St. Cloud, Minnesota 56301.
                                                            1869
Tel: (612) 255-3151. Easylink: 62860391 esl ud
C : *bus, ed, sc-techn, soc, fa-hum.*
St. Edward's University, 3001 S. Congress Avenue, Austin, Texas 78704.   *1885*
Tel: (512) 448-8400
C : *arts-sc.*
Saint Francis College, 2701 Spring Street, Fort Wayne, Indiana 46808.   *1890*
Tel: (219) 432-3551
C : *arts-sc.*
St. Francis College, Loretto, Pennsylvania 15940.
                                                            1847
Tel: (814) 472-7000
C : *arts-sc.*
St. John's College, P.O. Box 1671, Annapolis, Maryland 21404.   *1694*
Tel: (301) 263-2371
C : *arts-sc.*
St. John's College, Santa Fe, New Mexico 87501.
                                                            1964
Tel: (505) 982-3691
C : *arts-sc.*
St. John Fisher College, 3690 East Avenue, Rochester, New York 14618.   *1948*
Tel: (716) 385-8000
C : *arts-sc, ed, mangt.*
St. John's University, Collegeville, Minnesota 56321.   *1857*
C : *arts-sc.*
St. Joseph College, 1678 Asylum Avenue, West Hartford, Connecticut 06117.   *1932*
Tel: (203) 232-4571
C : *arts-sc.*
St. Joseph's College, Rensselaer, Indiana 47978–0408.   *1889*
Tel: (219) 866-7111
C : *arts-sc.*
St. Joseph's University, 5600 City Avenue, Philadelphia, Pennsylvania 19131.   *1851*
Tel: (215) 879-7300
C : *arts-sc, bus adm.*
St. Lawrence University, Canton, New York 13617.   *1856*
Tel: (315) 379-5011. Easylink: 62960839 esl ud
C : *arts-sc.*
St. Martin's College, 700 College Street, S.E.,

Lacey, Washington 98503.   *1895*
Tel: (206) 491-4700
C : *arts-sc.*
St.-Mary-of-the-Woods College, St.-Mary-of-the-Woods, Indiana 47876.   *1840*
Tel: (812) 535-5151
C : *arts-sc.*
St. Mary's College, Winona, Minnesota 55987.
                                                            1912
Tel: (507) 452-4430. Telex: 9102504644 smc ug
C : *arts-sc.*
St. Mary's College of California, Moraga, California 94575.   *1863*
Tel: (415) 376-4411
S : *li arts, bus, ed, theo, nurs, paralegal.*
St. Mary's University of San Antonio, One Camino Sante Marie, San Antonio, Texas 78284.   *1852*
Tel: (512) 436-3011
S : *arts-sc, bus adm, law, sc, eng, techn, hum.*
St. Michael's College, College Parkway, Winooski, Vermont 05404.   *1903*
Tel: (802) 655-2000. Telex: 5102990013 vtsmc wino
C : *arts-sc.*
St. Peter's College, 2641 Kennedy Boulevard, Jersey City, New Jersey 07306.   *1872*
Tel: (201) 333-4400
C : *arts-sc-ed, nurs.*
St. Thomas University, 16400 N.W. 32nd Avenue, Miami, Florida 33054.   *1962*
Tel: (305) 625-6000
C : *arts-sc.*
St. Thomas Aquinas College, Route 340, Sparkhill, New York 10976.   *1958*
Tel: (914) 359–9500
C : *arts-sc-ed, hum, nat, soc, bus.*
St. Xavier College, 3700 West 103rd Street, Chicago, Illinois 60655.   *1847*
Tel: (312) 779-3300
C : *arts-sc-ed.*
S : *nurs.*
Salem College, Pennsylvania Avenue, Salem, West Virginia 26426.   *1888*
Tel: (304) 782-5011
C : *arts-sc.*
Salem State College, 352 Lafayette Street, Salem, Massachusetts 01970.   *1854*
Tel: (617) 745-0556
C : *arts-sc.*
Salisbury State College, Camden Avenue, Salisbury, Maryland 21801.   *1925*
Tel: (301) 543-6000
C : *arts-sc.*
Salve Regina The Newport College, Ochre Point Avenue, Newport, Rhode Island 02840. *1934*
Tel: (401) 847-6650
C : *arts-sc.*
Samford University, 800 Lakeshore Drive,

Birmingham, Alabama 35229.   *1841*
Tel: (205) 870-2718. Telex: 888743 samforol u
ud
C : *arts-sc.*
S : *bus, ed, phar, law, nurs.*
D : *mus.*
San Jose State University, One Washington
Square, San Jose, California 95192.   *1857*
Tel: (408) 277-3228. Telex: 171171 ud
C : *arts-sc.*
S : *app arts-sc, bus, ed, eng, sc, soc, soc w.*
Sangamon State University, Shepherd Road,
Springfield, Illinois 62708.   *1969*
Tel: (217) 786-6600. Easylink: 62036593 esl ud
C : *arts-sc, mangt, hum serv, pol, heal.*
Sarah Lawrence College, Bronxville, New York
10708.   *1926*
Tel: (914) 337-6700
C : *arts-sc.*
Savannah State College, P.O. Box 20449,
Savannah, Georgia 31404.   *1890*
Tel: (912) 356-2240
D : *arts-sc, bus, hum, soc.*
Scaritt Graduate School, 1008 19th Avenue S.,
Nashville, Tennessee 37203–4466.   *1892*
Tel: (615) 327-2700
C : *arts-sc, theo.*
School for International Training, Kipling Road,
Brattleboro, Vermont 05301.   *1964*
Tel: (802) 257-7751. Easylink: 620 49809 esl ud
C : *arts-sc.*
Seattle Pacific University, West and West
Bertona 3rd Avenue Seattle, Washington
98119.   *1891*
Tel: (206) 281-2050
S : *hum, ed, relig, mus, heal sc, math, phys, bus,
soc-behavioral sc, fa.*
Shenandoah College—Conservatory of Music,
Millwood Pyke, Winchester, Virginia 22601.
                                        1875
Tel: (703) 665-4500
C : *arts-sc-ed, mus.*
Shippensburg University of Pennsylvania, Ship-
pensburg, Pennsylvania 17257.   *1871*
Tel: (717) 532-9121
C : *arts-sc-ed.*
S : *ed, bus, soc, hum serv.*
Siena Heights College, 1247 East Siena Heights
Drive, Adrian, Michigan 49221–1796.   *1919*
Tel: (517) 263-0731
C : *arts-sc.*
Simpson College, 701 North C. Street, Indianola,
Iowa 50125–1299.   *1860*
Tel: (515) 961-6251
C : *arts-sc.*
Simpson College, 801 Silver Avenue, San Fran-
cisco, California 94134.   *1921*
Tel: (415) 334-7400
C : *arts-sc.*

Sioux Falls College, 1501 South Prairie Avenue,
Sioux Falls, South Dakota 57105-1699.   *1883*
Tel: (605) 331-5000. Easylink: 62835914 esl ud
C : *arts-sc-ed.*
Slippery Rock University of Pennsylvania, Slip-
pery Rock, Pennsylvania 16057–9989.   *1889*
Tel: (412) 794-2510
S : *arts-sc.*
South Carolina State College, Orangeburg, South
Carolina 29117.   *1896*
Tel: (803) 536-7000
S : *arts-sc, hom eco, ed, ind ed-eng techn, bus.*
Southeast Missouri State University, 900 Normal
Avenue, Cape Girardeau, Missouri 63701.
                                        1873
Tel: (314) 651-2000
C : *ed, bus, hum, behavioral sc, publ adm, soc,
sc-techn.*
Southeastern Bible College, 2901 Paisnee
Avenue, Birmingham, Alabama 35256–2699.
                                        1935
Tel: (205) 251-2311
S : *mus, chr ed, arts-sc, elementary & secondary
ed.*
Southeastern Louisiana University, P.O. Box
490, University Station, Hammond, Louisiana
70402.   *1925*
Tel: (800) 222-7358
C : *hum, sc-techn, ed, bus, nurs.*
Southeastern Massachusetts University, Old
Westport Road, North Dartmouth, Massa-
chusetts 02747.   *1895*
Tel: (617) 999-8000
C : *arts-sc, bus-ind, eng, fa-app arts, nurs.*
Southeastern Oklahoma State University, Station
A, Durant, Oklahoma 74701.   *1909*
Tel: (405) 924-0121
C : *behavioral st, bus, li arts.*
Southeastern University, 501 Eye Street S.W.,
Washington, D.C. 20024.   *1879*
Tel: (202) 488-8162
S : *arts-sc.*
Southern Arkansas University, Magnolia,
Arkansas 71753.   *1909*
Tel: (501) 234-4000
D : *bus-com, ed, fa, nat, soc, techn, li arts,
performing arts, prof.*
Southern California College, 55 Fair Drive, Costa
Mesa, California 92626.   *1920*
Tel: (714) 556-3610
C : *arts-sc.*
Southern College of Technology, 1112 Clay
Street, Marietta, Georgia 30060.   *1948*
Tel: (404) 424-7230
C : *arts-sc.*
Southern Connecticut State University, 501
Crescent Road, New Haven, Connecticut
06515–0901.   *1893*
Tel: (203) 397-4276. Easylink: 620 31629 els ud

C : *arts-sc-ed.*

D : *lib, bus, nurs, soc w.*

Southern Nazarene University, 6729 Northwest 39th Expressway, Bethany, Oklahoma 73008.
1899

Tel: (405) 789-6400

C : *arts-sc, ministry-hum, soc st, sc-heal.*

S : *bus, ed, nurs, mus.*

Southern Oregon State College, 1250 Siskiyou Boulevard, Ashland, Oregon 97520.   *1926*

Tel: (503) 482-3311. Fax: (503) 482 6445

C : *arts-sc.*

Southern University and Agricultural and Mechanical College System:

  SOUTHERN UNIVERSITY IN NEW ORLEANS, 6400 Press Drive, New Orleans, Louisiana 70126.   *1956*

  Tel: (504) 282-4401

  arts-sc.

Southern Utah State College, 351 West Center, Cedar City, Utah 84720.   *1897*

Tel: (801) 586-7700. Fax: (801) 586-7934

C : *arts-let, bus-techn, ed, sc.*

Southwest Missouri State University, 901 South National, Springfield, Missouri 65804.   *1906*

Tel: (417) 836-5000. Fax: (417) 8364538. Telex: 434371 smsubook spg

S : *arts-hum, ed, sc-techn, bus, psyc, heal & app sc, sc-math.*

Southwest Texas State University, University Station, San Marcos, Texas 78666–4615.   *1899*

Tel: (512) 245-2111

S : *li-fa, app arts, ed, sc, bus, heal, techn, commun.*

Southwestern Oklahoma State University, Weatherford, Oklahoma 73096.   *1901*

Tel: (405) 772-6611

D : *arts-sc, ed, bus, heal sc.*

Spertus College of Judaica, 618 South Michigan Avenue, Chicago, Illinois 60605.   *1925*

Tel: (312) 922-9012

for lang, theo, publ affairs.

Spring Hill College, 4000 Dauphin Street, Mobile, Alabama 36608.   *1830*

Tel: (205) 460-2121

C : *arts-sc.*

State University of New York:

  COLLEGE AT BROCKPORT, Brockport, New York 14420.   *1867*

  Tel: (716) 395-2211

  C : *li st, soc professions.*

  Ce : *arts.*

  COLLEGE AT BUFFALO, 1300 Elmwood Avenue, Buffalo, New York 14222.   *1867*

  Tel: (716) 878-4000

  C : *arts-hum, app prof st, nat-soc.*

  COLLEGE AT CORTLAND, P.O. Box 2000, Cortland, New York 13045.   *1866*

  Tel: (607) 753-2011

D : *arts-sc, ed, prof st.*

COLLEGE AT FREDONIA, Central Avenue, Fredonia, New York 14063.   *1867*

Tel: (716) 673-3111

C : *arts-sc-ed, hum, nat, soc.*

COLLEGE AT GENESEO, Geneseo, New York 14454.   *1867*

Tel: (716) 245-5211

C : *arts-sc.*

COLLEGE AT NEW PALTZ, New Paltz, New York 12561.   *1823*

Tel: (914) 257-2121

C : *arts-sc-ed, fa-performing arts.*

COLLEGE AT ONEONTA, Oneonta, New York 13820.   *1887*

Tel: (607) 431-3500

C : *li st.*

COLLEGE AT OSWEGO, Oswego, New York 13126.   *1861*

Tel: (315) 341-2500

C : *arts-sc, prof st.*

COLLEGE AT PLATTSBURGH, Plattsburgh, New York 12901.   *1889*

Tel: (518) 564-2000

S : *arts-sc, gen & prof st.*

COLLEGE AT POTSDAM, Pierrepont Avenue, Potsdam, New York 13676.   *1816*

Tel: (315) 267-2000

C : *arts-sc, mus, prof st.*

COLLEGE AT PURCHASE, Purchase, New York 10577.   *1967*

Tel: (914) 253-5000

C : *dance, vis arts, mus, theat, let-sc.*

EMPIRE STATE COLLEGE, Saratoga Springs, New York 12866.   *1971*

Tel: (518) 587-2100

C : *arts-sc.*

MARITIME COLLEGE, Fort Schuyler, Bronx, New York 10465.   *1874*

Tel: (212) 409-7200

C : *arts-sc.*

Stetson University, 421 North Woodland Boulevard, Deland, Florida 32720.   *1883*

Tel: (904) 734-4121

S : *sc, law, mus, bus.*

Suffolk University, Boston, Masschusetts 02114.
1906

C : *arts-sc, bus adm.*

S : *law.*

Sul Ross State University, Alpine, Texas 79832.
1917

Tel: (915) 837-8011

D : *li arts, sc, ed, fa, bus adm, range anim sc.*

Swarthmore College, Chester Road and College Avenue, Swarthmore, Pennsylvania 19081.
1864

Tel: (215) 328-8000

S : *arts-sc.*

Syracuse University:

UTICA COLLEGE OF SYRACUSE UNIVERSITY, 1600 Burrstone Road, Utica, New York 13502.   *1946*
Tel: (315) 792-3144
C : *arts-ac.*

Tarleton State University, Tarleton Station, Stephenville, Texas 76402.   *1899*
Tel: (817) 968-9000
S : *arts-sc, agr, bus, ed.*

Temple University:
TEMPLE UNIVERSITY, AMBLER CAMPUS, Ambler, Pennsylvania 19002.   *1910*
Tel: (215) 283-1200
C : *arts-sc.*

Texas Wesleyan College, 1201 Wesleyan, P.O. Box 50010, Forth Worth, Texas 76105.   *1891*
Tel: (817) 534-0251
C : *arts-sc-ed, bus, fa, hum.*

Thomas College, West River Road, Waterville, Maine 04901.   *1894*
Tel: (207) 873-0771
C : *hum-sc, bus.*

Towson State University, Towsontown Boulevard and Osler Drive, Baltimore, Maryland 21204.   *1866*
Tel: (301) 321-2000
C : *arts-let-commun, ed, nat-math, app sc, fa, allied heal professions, phys.*

Trenton State College, Hillwood Lakes, CN4700, Trenton, New Jersey 08650.   *1855*
Tel: (609) 771-1855
C : *arts-sc-ed.*
D : *bus, ind ed-techn, nurs.*

Trevecca Nazarene College, 333 Murfreesboro Road, Nashville, Tennessee 37203-4411. *1901*
Tel: (615) 248-1200
C : *arts-sc-ed.*

Trinity College, 300 Summit Street, Hartford, Connecticut 06106.   *1823*
Tel: (203) 527-3151
C : *arts-sc.*

Trinity College, Michigan Avenue and Franklin Street, N.E., Washington, D.C. 20017. *1897*
Tel: (202) 939-5000
C : *arts-sc.*

Trinity University, 715 Stadium Drive, San Antonio, Texas 78284.   *1869*
Tel: (512) 736-8401
C : *hum, ed, sc-math-eng, art, soc-behavioral sc.*
S : *bus-mangt.*

Troy State University, University Avenue, Troy, Alabama 36082.   *1887*
Tel: (205) 566-3000. Telex: 9103805032 troy state
C : *arts-sc-ed, bus, jour, nurs.*
TROY STATE UNIVERSITY AT DOTHAN-FORT RUCKER, 227 North Foster Street, Dothan, Alabama 36301–6947.   *1965*

Tel: (205) 792-8783
arts-sc.
TROY STATE UNIVERSITY AT MONTGOMERY, 231 Montgomery Street, Montgomery, Alabama 36195–5701.   *1965*
Tel: (205) 834-1400. Telex: 9103507474 troy state
arts-sc.

Union College, College Street, Barbourville, Kentucky 40906.   *1879*
Tel: (606) 546-4151
C : *arts-sc-ed.*

Union College, Union Street, Schenectady. New York 12308.   *1795*
Tel: (518) 370-6000
D : *eng, arts.*

United States Sports Academy, Daphine, Alabama 36526.   *1972*
Tel: (205) 626-3303
S : *sports mangt, spec med, fitness mangt, coaching.*

Universitad Del Turabo, Apartado 3030, Caguas, Puerto Rico 00625.   *1972*
Tel: (809) 744-8791
S : *arts-sc.*

University of Alaska:
UNIVERSITY OF ALASKA JUNEAU, 11120 Glacier Highway, Juneau, Alaska 99801.   *1956*
Tel: (907) 789-2101. Easylink: 620 45293 els ud
D : *gen st, fish sc, bus, ed.*

University of Arkansas:
UNIVERSITY OF ARKANSAS AT LITTLE ROCK, 2801 South University Avenue, Little Rock, Arkansas 72204.   *1927*
Tel: (501) 569-3000
C : *bus adm, ed, fa, li arts, sc.*
S : *soc w, law, eng, com.*

University of Baltimore, 1420 North Charles Street, Baltimore, Maryland 21201.   *1925*
Tel: (301) 625-3000. Easylink: 620 05286 esl ud
C : *li arts.*
S : *law, bus.*

University of Central Arkansas, Conway, Arkansas 72032.   *1907*
Tel: (501) 329-2931
C : *sc-hum, ed, bus adm, fa-app arts-sc.*

University of Charleston, 2300 Maccorkle Avenue SE, Charleston, West Virginia 25304–1099.   *1887*
Tel: (304) 357-4713
C : *arts-sc, heal sc, bus, des.*

University of Connecticut:
UNIVERSITY OF CONNECTICUT AT STAMFORD, Stamford, Connecticut 06903.   *1951*
Tel: (203) 322-3466
arts-sc.

University of the District of Columbia, 4200

Connecticut Avenue N.W., Washington, D.C. 20008. *1976*
Tel: (202) 282-7300
C : *arts-sc, ed, fa, eng, physical sc.*
S : *eng techn, mangt, agr-nat resources.*

University of Guam, Uog Station, Mangilao, Guam 96913. *1952*
Tel: (671) 734-2177
C : *arts-sc-ed, agr, bus-publ adm.*

University of Houston:
UNIVERSITY OF HOUSTON AT CLEAR LAKE, 2700 Bay Area Boulevard, Houston, Texas 77058. *1971*
Tel: (713) 488-7170
S : *bus, publ adm.*
UNIVERSITY OF HOUSTON VICTORIA, 2302C Red River, Victoria, Texas 77901. *1973*
Tel: (512) 576-3151
C : *arts-sc-ed, bus.*

University of Indianapolis, 1400 East Hanna Avenue, Indianapolis, Indiana 46227. *1902*
Tel: (317) 788-3368
C : *arts-sc.*
S : *ed, nurs.*

University of Mary, 7500 University Drive, Bismarck, North Dakota 58501. *1959*
Tel: (701) 255-7500
C : *arts-sc, nurs, law, med.*

University of Mary Hardin-Baylor, Box 399, UMHB Station, Belton, Texas 76513. *1845*
Tel: (817) 939-5811
C : *arts-sc-ed, fa, bus, nurs.*

University of Michigan:
UNIVERSITY OF MICHIGAN—DEARBORN, 4901 Evergreen Road, Dearborn, Michigan 48128. *1959*
Tel: (313) 593-5000. Easylink: 629 42245 esl ud
C: *arts-sc-let.*
S : *mangt, eng, ed.*
UNIVERSITY OF MICHIGAN—FLINT, Flint, Michigan 48502-2186. *1956*
Tel: (313) 762-3000. Easylink: 620 12682 esl ud
C : *arts-sc-ed.*
F : *mangt, nurs.*

University of Minnesota:
UNIVERSITY OF MINNESOTA AT DULUTH, 10 University Drive, Duluth, Minnesota 55812. *1947*
Tel: (218) 726-8000
C : *let-sc, ed, sc-eng.*
S : *med, soc dev, bus-eco, fa.*

University of Montevallo, Montevallo, Alabama 35115. *1896*
Tel: (205) 665-6030
C : *arts-sc, bus, ed, fa.*

University of North Alabama, Wesleyan Avenue, Florence, Alabama 35632–0001. *1872*

Tel: (205) 766-4100
C : *arts-sc, ed, nurs, bus.*

University of North Carolina:
APPALACHIAN STATE UNIVERSITY, Boone, North Carolina 28608. *1899*
Tel: (704) 262-2000
C : *arts-sc, bus, fa-app arts, ed.*
FAYETTEVILLE STATE UNIVERSITY, Murchinson Road, Fayetteville, North Carolina 28301. *1867*
Tel: (919) 486-1111
S : *arts-sc-ed, bus, eco, hum dev, hum, fa, soc-behavioral sc, physical sc.*
NORTH CAROLINA AGRICULTURAL AND TECHNICAL STATE UNIVERSITY, 1601 East Market Street, Greensboro, North Carolina 27411. *1891*
Tel: (919) 334-7500
S : *agr, ed, arts-sc, eng, nurs, bus-eco.*
D : *ind ed-tech.*
NORTH CAROLINA CENTRAL UNIVERSITY, 1801 Fayetteville Street, Durham, North Carolina 27701. *1910*
Tel: (919) 683-6100
C : *arts-sc.*
S : *law, lib, bus.*
NORTH CAROLINA SCHOOL OF THE ARTS, 200 Waughton Street, Winston-Salem, North Carolina 27117–2189. *1963*
Tel: (919) 784-7170
C : *li arts, sc, mus, dance, drama, des.*
PEMBROKE STATE UNIVERSITY, Pembroke, North Carolina 28372. *1887*
Tel: (919) 521-4214
C : *arts-sc.*
UNIVERSITY OF NORTH CAROLINA AT ASHEVILLE, One University Heights, Asheville, North Carolina 28804–3299. *1927*
Tel: (704) 251-6600
C : *arts-sc.*
UNIVERSITY OF NORTH CAROLINA AT CHARLOTTE, Charlotte, North Carolina 28223. *1946*
Tel: (704) 547-2000
C : *arc, arts-sc, bus adm, ed, eng, nurs.*
UNIVERSITY OF NORTH CAROLINA AT WILMINGTON, 601 South College Road, Wilmington, North Carolina 28403. *1947*
Tel: (919) 395-3000
C : *arts-sc.*
S : *bus adm, ed, nurs.*
WESTERN CAROLINA UNIVERSITY, Cullowhee, North Carolina 28723. *1889*
Tel: (704) 227-7211
S : *arts-sc, bus, ed-psyc, nurs, heal sc, techn-app sc.*

University of North Florida, 4567 St. Johns Bluff Road, South Jacksonville, Florida 32216. *1965*
Tel: (904) 646-2624

S : *sc, nurs, bus, ed.*

University of Northern Iowa, Cedar Falls, Iowa 50614.   *1876*
Tel: (319) 273-2311
C : *bus-behavioral sc, ed, hum-fa, nat, mus, heal-phys, physical sc.*

University of Phoenix, 2525 N. 3rd Street, Phoenix, Arizona 85004.   *1976*
Tel: (602) 258-3666
C : *arts-sc, nurs.*

University of Portland, 5000 N. Willamette Boulevard, Portland, Oregon 97203–5798.
                                                           1901
Tel: (503) 283-7911
C : *arts-sc.*
S : *bus, ed, eng, nurs.*

University of Puerto Rico:
UNIVERSITY OF PUERTO RICO MEDICAL SCIENCES CAMPUS, GPO Box 5067, San Jaun, Puerto Rico 00936.   *1950*
Tel: (809) 758-2525

University of Puget Sound, 1500 North Warner, Tacoma, Washington, 98416.   *1888*
Tel: (206) 756-3201. Easylink: 620 22764 esl ud
C : *arts-sc.*
S : *law.*

University of Redlands, 1200 East Colton Avenue, P.O. Box 3080, Redlands, California 92373.   *1907*
Tel: (714) 793-2121
C : *arts-sc.*

University of Richmond, University of Richmond, Virginia 23173–1903.   *1830*
Tel: (804) 289-8000
S : *bus adm, law.*

University of St. Thomas, 8312 Montrose Boulevard, Houston, Texas 77006.   *1947*
Tel: (713) 522-7911
C : *arts-sc-ed.*
S : *theo, nurs.*

University of Scranton, Linden and Monroe, Scranton, Pennsylvania 18510.   *1888*
Tel: (717) 961-7400
C : *arts-sc.*
S : *mangt.*

University of Southern Colorado, 2200 Bonforte Boulevard, Pueblo, Colorado 81001.   *1933*
Tel: (303) 549-2100
C : *arts-sc, mus, fa, eng.*

University of Southern Indiana, 8600 University Boulevard, Evansville, Indiana 47712.   *1965*
Tel: (812) 464-8600. Telex: 278453 usi bkstr
D : *allied heal professions, bus, ed, eng techn, hum, sc-math, soc.*

University of Tampa, 401 West Kennedy Boulevard, Tampa, Florida 33606–1490.
                                                           1931
Tel: (813) 253-3333
C : *arts-sc.*

University of Tennessee:
UNIVERSITY OF TENNESSEE AT CHATTANOOGA, 615 McCallie Avenue, Chattanooga, Tennessee 37402.   *1886*
Tel: (615) 755-4111. Telex: 558494 utbookstor cta. Easylink: 620 47076 esl ud
C : *arts-sc, bus adm, ed, eng, nurs.*
UNIVERSITY OF TENNESSEE AT MARTIN, Martin, Tennessee 38238–5009.   *1927*
Tel: (901) 587-7000
S : *li arts, agr, bus adm, ed, hom eco, eng-eng techn.*

University of Texas:
UNIVERSITY OF TEXAS OF THE PERMIAN (D) BASIN, 4901 East University, Odessa, Texas 79762.   *1969*
Tel: (915) 367-2011
C : *arts-sc, eng.*
UNIVERSITY OF TEXAS AT SAN ANTONIO, San Antonio, Texas 78285.   *1969*
Tel: (512) 691-4011
C : *soc, bus, fa, math, arts-hum.*
UNIVERSITY OF TEXAS AT TYLER, 3900 University Boulevard, Tyler, Texas 75701.
                                                           1971
Tel: (214) 566-1471
C : *arts-sc, ed, bus, sc-math.*

University of the Virgin Islands, Charlotte Amalie Saint Thomas, Virgin Islands 00802.
                                                           1962
Tel: (809) 776-9200
C : *arts-sc.*

University of Wisconsin:
UNIVERSITY OF WISCONSIN—EAU CLAIRE, 105 Garfield Avenue, Eau Claire, Wisconsin 54701.   *1916*
Tel: (715) 836-2637
S : *arts-sc, bus, ed, nurs.*
UNIVERSITY OF WISCONSIN—GREEN BAY, 2420 Nicolet Drive, Green Bay, Wisconsin 54301–7001.   *1965*
Tel: (414) 465-2000
C : *arts-sc.*
UNIVERSITY OF WISCONSIN—LA CROSSE, 1725 State Street, La Crosse, Wisconsin 54601.   *1909*
Tel: (608) 785-8000
C : *arts-sc-ed, heal-phys-recr, bus adm.*
UNIVERSITY OF WISCONSIN—OSHKOSH, 800 Algama Boulevard, Oshkosh, Wisconsin 54901.   *1871*
Tel: (414) 424-0202
S : *bus adm, ed, let-sc, nurs.*
UNIVERSITY OF WISCONSIN—PARKSIDE, BOX 2000, Kenosha, Wisconsin 53141–2000.
                                                           1965
Tel: (414) 553-2345
S : *fa, mangt sc, ed, eng, sc, hum, bus adm, behavioral sc.*

UNIVERSITY OF WISCONSIN—PLATTEVILLE, 1 University Plaza, Platteville, Wisconsin 53818–9998.   *1866*
Tel: (608) 342-1101
S : *arts-sc, agr, bus-ind-commun, ed, eng.*

UNIVERSITY OF WISCONSIN—RIVER FALLS, River Falls, Wisconsin 54022.   *1874*
Tel: (715) 425-3911
C : *arts-sc, agr, ed.*

UNIVERSITY OF WISCONSIN—STEVENS POINT, 2100 Main Street, Stevens Point, Wisconsin 54481.   *1894*
Tel: (715) 346-4242. Telex: 163429 uwsp li
C : *let-sc, ed, fa, nat resources, bus, hom eco, commun.*

UNIVERSITY OF WISCONSIN—STOUT, Meno monie, Wisconsin 54751.   *1893*
Tel: (715) 232-1122
C : *li st, ed, hom eco, ind techn.*

UNIVERSITY OF WISCONSIN—SUPERIOR, 1800 Grand Avenue, Superior, Wisconsin 54880–2898.   *1893*
Tel: (715) 394-8101
C : *arts-sc-ed, fa, bus-eco, hum, soc, sc-math.*

UNIVERSITY OF WISCONSIN—WHITEWATER, 800 West Main Street, Whitewater, Wisconsin 53190.   *1868*
Tel: (414) 472-1234
S : *let-sc, bus-eco, ed, arts.*

Upsala College, 345 Prospect Street, East Orange, New Jersey 07019.   *1893*
Tel: (201) 266-7000
C : *arts-sc.*

Ursuline College, 2550 Lander Road, Pepper Pike, Ohio 44124.   *1871*
Tel: (216) 449-4200
C : *arts-sc, nurs.*

Vassar College, Raymond Avenue, Poughkeep-sie, New York 12601.   *1861*
Tel: (914) 452-7000
C : *arts-sc.*

Virginia State University, Petersburg, Virginia 23803.   *1882*
Tel: (804) 520-5000. Telex: 5106009276 vsu intl ug
S : *arts-sc, ed, bus, sc-techn, agr, hum.*

Wagner College, 631 Howard Avenue, Staten Island, New York 10301.   *1883*
Tel: (212) 390-3100
C : *arts-sc.*

Walla Walla College, College Place, Washington 99324.   *1892*
Tel: (509) 527-2615
C : *arts-sc.*
S : *nurs, theo, eng.*

Walsh College, 2020 Easton Street, N.W., Canton, Ohio 44720.   *1958*
Tel: (216) 499-7090

C : *arts-sc.*

Warner Pacific College, 2219 S.E. 68th Avenue, Portland, Oregon 97215–4099.   *1937*
Tel: (503) 775-4366
C : *arts-sc.*

Warren Wilson College, Warren Wilson Road, Swannanoa, North Carolina 28778–2099. *1894*
Tel: (704) 298-3325
C : *arts-sc.*

Washburn University of Topeka, 17th and Col-lege Streets, Topeka, Kansas 66621.   *1865*
Tel: (913) 295-6300
C : *arts-sc-ed.*
S : *law, bus, nurs, hom eco.*

Washington Bible College, 6511 Princess Garden Parkway, Lanham, Maryland 20706.   *1938*
Tel: (301) 552-1400

Washington College, Washington Avenue, Chestertown, Maryland 21620.   *1782*
Tel: (301) 778-2800
C : *arts-sc.*

Washington and Jefferson College, Washington, Pennsylvania 15301.   *1781*
Tel: (412) 223-6006
C : *arts-sc-ed.*

Wayland Baptist University, 1900 West 7th Street, Plainview, Texas 79072.   *1908*
Tel: (806) 296-5521
S : *arts-sc.*

Wayne State College, Wayne, Nebraska 68787.
                                                    1909
Tel: (402) 375-2200
C : *arts-sc.*

Waynesburg College, 51 West College Street, Waynesburg, Pennsylvania 15370.   *1849*
Tel: (412) 627-8191
C : *arts-sc.*

Weber College, P.O. Box 96, Babson Park, Florida 33827.   *1927*
Tel: (813) 638-1431
C : *arts-sc.*

Weber State College, 3750 Harrison Boulevard, Ogden, Utah 84408.   *1889*
Tel: (801) 6236-6140
S : *arts-sc, bus, ed, heal sc, soc, hum, techn.*

Webster University, 470 East Lookwood Avenue, Saint Louis, Missouri 63119–3914.
                                                    1915
Tel: (314) 968-6900. Telex: 6715247 webu uw
C : *arts-sc.*

Wells College, Aurora, New York 13026–0500.
                                                    1868
Tel: (315) 364-3209
C : *arts-sc.*

Wesley College, P.O. Box 70, Florence, Missis-sippi 39073–0070.   *1972*
Tel: (601) 845-2265
C : *arts-sc.*

West Chester University of Pennsylvania, Uni-

versity Avenue and High Street, West Chester, Pennsylvania 19383. *1871*
Tel: (215) 436-1000
C : *arts-let.*
S : *mus, heal-phys, ed, bus.*

West Coast University, 440 South Shatto Place, Los Angeles, California 90020. *1909*
Tel: (213) 487-4433
C : *arts-sc, eng, bus.*

West Georgia College, Carrolton, Georgia 30118. *1933*
C : *arts-sc, bus, ed.*

West Texas State University, Canyon, Texas 79016. *1909*
Tel: (806) 656-0111. Telex: 5106012485 tiec w tx st
C : *arts-sc-ed.*
S : *bus, agr, nurs, fa.*

West Virginia Institute of Technology, Montgomery, West Virginia 25136. *1895*
Tel: (404) 834-1311
C : *arts-sc, eng.*

West Virginia Wesleyan College, Meade Street and College Avenue, Buckhannon, West Virginia 26201. *1890*
Tel: (304) 473-8000
C : *arts-sc.*

Western Carolina University, Cullowhee, North Carolina 28723. *1889*
Tel: (706) 227-7211. Fax: (704) 2277327. Telex: 4946590 wcarunv
C : *arts-sc.*
S : *appl sc-techn, bus, ed-psyc, nurs-heal sc.*

Western Connecticut State University, 181 White Street, Danbury, Connecticut 06810. *1903*
Tel: (203) 797-4297
C : *arts-sc-ed, bus, publ adm.*

Western Illinois University, 312 Sherman Hall, Macomb, Illinois 61455. *1899*
Tel: (309)298-1185. Telex: 9102544881 intlpgwiu macm
S : *arts-sc, app sc, bus, ed, heal-phys-recr, fa.*

Western International University, 10202 N. 19th Avenue, Phoenix, Arizona 85021. *1978*
Tel: (602) 943-2311
C : *arts-sc, bus, gen st.*

Western Kentucky University, Bowling Green, Kentucky 42101. *1922*
Tel: (502) 745-0111. Telex: 9102405738 wku bowl
C : *arts-hum, ed, sc-techn, bus, publ adm.*

Western Maryland College, College Hill, Westminster, Maryland 21157–4390. *1867*
Tel: (301) 848-7000
C : *arts-sc-ed.*

Western New Mexico University, College Avenue, Silver City, New Mexico 88061. *1893*
Tel: (505) 538-6238

C : *arts-sc-ed, bus, soc, sc-math.*

Western State College of Colorado, College Heights, Gunnison, Colorado 81230. *1911*
Tel: (303) 943-3035
C : *arts-sc.*

Western Washington University, 516 High Street, Bellingham, Washington 98225. *1893*
Tel: (206) 676-3000. Fax: (206) 6763044
C : *arts-sc, env st, bus-eco, ed, fa.*

Westfield State College, Western Avenue, Westfield, Massachusetts 01086. *1838*
Tel: (413) 568-3311
C : *arts-sc, human resources.*

Westminster College, South Market Street, New Wilmington, Pennsylvania 16172. *1852*
Tel: (412) 946-8761
C : *arts-sc.*

Westminster College, 1840 South 13th East, Salt Lake City, Utah 84105. *1875*
Tel: (801) 488-4298
C : *arts-sc, bus, nurs, prof st, heal.*

Westminster Choir College, Hamilton Avenue at Walnut Lane, Princeton, New Jersey 08540. *1926*
Tel: (609) 921-7100
C : *arts-sc.*

Wheaton College, 501 East Seminary, Wheaton, Illinois 60187. *1860*
Tel: (312) 260–5000. Telex: 984467 whtn coll
C : *arts-sc.*
Conservatory : *mus.*

Wheeling Jesuit College, 316 Washington Avenue, Wheeling, West Virginia 26003. *1954*
Tel: (304) 243-2000
C : *arts-sc.*

Whittier College, 13406 E. Philadelphia Street, P.O. Box 634, Whittier, California 90608. *1887*
Tel: (213) 693-0771
C : *arts-sc, law.*

Whitworth College, West 300 Hawthorne Road, Spokane, Washington 99251. *1890*
Tel: (509) 466-1000
S : *arts-sc.*

Wilkes College, 184 South River Street, Wilkes-Barre, Pennsylvania 18766. *1933*
Tel: (717) 824-4651
C : *arts-sc-ed, heal sc.*

William Carey College, Tuscan Avenue, Hattiesburg, Mississippi 39401. *1906*
Tel: (601) 582-5051
S : *arts-sc, nurs, mus, bus.*

William Paterson College of New Jersey, 300 Pompton Road, Wayne, New Jersey 07470. *1855*
Tel: (201) 595-2000
S : *arts-commun, ed, hum, mangt, sc, soc.*

Williams College, Main Street, Williamstown, Massachusetts 01267. *1793*
Tel: (413) 597-3131. Telex: 469735 economics

ci
C : *arts-sc.*

Wilmington College, 320 Dupont Highway, New Castle, Delaware 19720. *1967*
Tel: (302) 328-9401
C : *arts-sc, behavioral & app sc.*

Wingate College, Wingate, North Carolina 28174. *1895*
Tel: (704) 233-8000. Telex: 753023 wingate ud
C : *arts-sc.*

Winona State University, 8th and Johnston Streets, Winona, Minnesota 55987. *1858*
Tel: (507) 457-5000. Easylink: 62860939 esl ud
C : *arts-sc-ed, bus, nat-app sc, nurs.*

Winthrop College, 701 Oakland Avenue, Rock Hill, South Carolina 29733. *1886*
Tel: (803) 323-2201
C : *arts-sc.*
S : *bus adm, ed, hom eco, mus, sc.*

Wisconsin Conservatory of Music, 1584 North Prospect Avenue, Milwaukee, Wisconsin 53202-2394. *1899*
Tel: (414) 276-4350
S : *arts-sc, mus.*

Wittenberg University, P.O. Box 702, Springfield, Ohio 45501. *1845*
Tel: (513) 327-7916
C : *arts-sc.*

Woodbury University, 1027 Wilshire Boulevard, Los Angeles, California 90017. *1884*
Tel: (213) 482-8491
C : *arts-sc.*

Worcester State College, 486 Chandler Street, Worcester, Massachusetts 01602-2597. *1874*
Tel: (617) 752-7700
C : *arts-sc.*

Xavier University of Louisiana, 7325 Palmetto Street, New Orleans, Louisiana 70125. *1915*
Tel: (504) 486-7411
C : *arts-sc, phar.*

Xavier University, 3800 Victoria Parkway, Victory Parkway, Cincinnati, Ohio 45207-1096. *1831*
Tel: (513) 745-3000
C : *arts-sc, bus adm.*

York College of Pennsylvania, Country Club Road, York, Pennsylvania 17403-3426. *1787*
Tel: (717) 846-7788
C : *arts-sc.*

Youngstown State University, 410 Wick Avenue, Youngstown, Ohio 44555. *1908*
Tel: (216) 742-3000
C : *arts-sc.*
S : *bus adm, ed, eng, fa-performing arts, app sc-techn.*

Institutions without Graduate Schools and with or without Professional Schools—

Institutions sans sections pour gradués, mais avec éventuellement des écoles professionnelles

Academy of the New Church, P.O. Box 278, Bryn Athyn, Pennsylvania 19009-0278. *1876*
Tel: (215) 947-4200
C : *arts-sc.*
S : *theo.*

Agnes Scott College, East College Avenue, Decatur, Georgia 30030. *1889*
Tel: (404) 371-6430
C : *arts-sc.*

Alaska Bible College, Box 289, Glennallen, Alaska 99588. *1966*
Tel: (907) 822-3201
S : *arts-sc.*

Albertus Magnus College, 700 Prospect Street, New Haven, Connecticut 06511. *1925*
Tel: (203) 773-8550
C : *arts-sc.*

Albion College, 611 East Porter Street, Albion, Michigan 49224-1899. *1835*
Tel: (517) 629-5511
C : *arts-sc.*

Albright College, Box 15234, Reading, Pennsyl-

vania 19612. *1856*
Tel: (215) 921-2381
C : *arts-sc.*

Alderson-Broaddus College, Philippi, West Virginia 26416. *1871*
Tel: (304) 457-1700
C : *arts-sc.*

Alice Lloyd College, Pippa Passes, Kentucky 41844. *1923*
Tel: (606) 368-2101
C : *arts-sc.*

Allen University, 1530 Harden Street, Columbia, South Carolina 29204. *1870*
Tel: (803) 254-4165
C : *arts-sc.*

Alma College, 614 West Superior Street, Alma, Michigan 48801. *1886*
Tel: (517) 463-7111
C : *arts-sc.*

Alvernia College, Reading, Pennsylvania 19607. *1958*
Tel: (215) 777-5411

C : *arts-sc.*

Alverno College, 3401 South 39 Street, Milwaukee, Wisconsin 53215–4020.   *1887*
Tel: (414) 647-3999
C : *arts-sc, nurs, behavioral sc, fa, commun, arts-hum, nat.*

American College of Puerto Rico, Box 2037, Bayamon, Puerto Rico 00619.   *1963*
Tel: (809) 786-0090
S : *arts-sc.*

American Indian Bible College, 10020 North 15th Avenue, Phoenix, Arizona 85021.   *1957*
Tel: (602) 944-3335
Theo.

American Islamic College, Chicago, Illinois 60613.   *1981*
Tel: (312) 281-4700
arts.

Amherst College, Amherst, Massachusetts 01002.   *1821*
Tel: (413) 542-2000
C : *arts-sc.*

Antillian College, Box 118, Mayaguez, Puerto Rico 00709–0118.   *1957*
Tel: (809) 834-9595
C : *arts-sc, ed.*

Appalachian Bible College, Bradley, West Virginia 25818.   *1950*
Tel: (304) 877-6428
theo.

Arizona College of the Bible, 2045 West Northern Avenue, Phoenix, Arizona 85021.   *1971*
Tel: (602)995-2670
ed-theo.

Arkansas Baptist College, 1600 Bishop Street, Little Rock, Arkansas 72202.   *1884*
Tel: (501) 374-7856
C : *arts-sc.*

Arkansas College, P.O. Box 2317, 2300 Highland Road, Batesville, Arkansas 72501.   *1872*
Tel: (501) 793-9813
C : *arts-sc-ed-occp, heal, hum.*

Arlington Baptist College, 3001 West Division, Arlington, Texas 76012.   *1939*
Tel: (817) 461-8741
ed, theo.

Asbury College, 201 North Lexington Avenue, Wilmore, Kentucky 40390.   *1890*
Tel: (606) 858-3511
C : *arts-sc.*

Athens State College, 301 Beaty Street, Athens, Alabama 35611.   *1822*
Tel: (205) 232-1802
C : *arts-sc.*

Atlanta Christian College, 2605 Ben Hill Road, East Point, Georgia 30344.   *1937*
Tel: (404) 761-8861
C : *arts-sc.*

Atlantic Christian College, West Lee Street,

Wilson, North Carolina 27893.   *1902*
Tel: (919) 237-3161
C : *arts-sc.*

Atlantic Union College, South Lancaster, Massachusetts 01561.   *1882*
Tel: (617) 365-4561
C : *arts-sc.*

Baltimore Hebrew College, 5800 Park Heights Avenue, Baltimore, Maryland 21215.   *1919*
Tel: (301) 578-6900. Easylink: 629 39441 els ud
ed, lang, relig, phil.

Baptist Bible Institute, 1306 College Drive, Graceville, Florida 32440.   *1943*
Tel: (904) 263-3261
theo.

Barat College, 700 East Westleigh Road, Lake Forest, Illinois 60045.   *1858*
Tel: (312) 234-3000
C : *arts-sc.*

Barber-Scotia College, 145 Cabarrus Avenue, Concord, North Carolina 28025.   *1867*
Tel: (704) 786-5171
C : *arts-sc.*

Bartlesville Wesleyan College, 2201 Silverlake Road, Bartlesville, Oklahoma 74006–6299.
        1910
Tel: (918) 333-6151
C : *arts-sc, ed, fa, math-sc, hum.*

Bates College, Lewiston, Maine 04240.   *1855*
Tel: (207) 786-6255
C : *arts-sc.*

Belhaven College, 1500 Peachtree Street, Jackson, Mississippi 39202.   *1883*
Tel: (601) 968-5928
C : *arts-sc-ed.*

Bellevue College, Galvin Road at Harvell Drive, Bellevue, Nebraska 68005–3098.   *1965*
Tel: (402) 291-8100
C : *arts-sc.*

Belmont Abbey College, Belmont, North Carolina 28012.   *1876*
Tel: (704) 825-3711
C : *arts-sc.*

Benedict College, Harden and Blanding Streets, Columbia, South Carolina 29204.   *1870*
Tel: (803) 256-4220
C : *arts-sc.*

Benedictine College, 2nd and Division, Atchison, Kansas 66002.   *1858*
Tel: (913) 367-5340
C : *arts-sc.*

Bennett College, 900 East Washington Street, Greensboro, North Carolina 27401–3239.
        1873
Tel: (919) 273-4431
C : *arts-sc-ed, hum, soc.*

Berea College, Berea, Kentucky 40404.   *1855*
Tel: (606) 986-9341
C : *arts-sc.*

Bethany Bible College, 800 Bethany Drive, Santa Cruz, California 95066.   *1919*
Tel: (408) 438-3800
S : *arts-sc.*

Bethany College, Lindsborg, Kansas 67456. *1881*
Tel: (913) 227-3311
C : *arts-sc.*

Bethany College, Bethany, West Virginia 26032–9989.   *1840*
Tel: (304) 829-7000
C : *arts-sc.*

Bethel College, 300 East 27th Street, P.O. Box Drawer B, North Newton, Kansas 67117. *1887*
Tel: (316) 283-2500
C : *arts-sc.*

Bethel College, McKenzie, Tennessee 38201.
                                                                    1842
Tel: (901) 352-5321
C : *arts-sc.*

Bethel College, 3900 Bethel Drive, St. Paul, Minnesota 55112.   *1871*
Tel: (612) 638-6400
C : *arts-sc.*

Bethune-Cookman College, 640 2nd Avenue, Daytona Beach, Florida 32015.   *1904*
Tel: (904) 255-1401
C : *arts-sc-ed, hum, math, soc, bus.*

Blackburn College, 700 College Avenue, Carlinville, Illinois 62626.   *1857*
Tel: (217) 854-3231
C : *arts-sc.*

Bloomfield College, 1 Park Place, Bloomfield, New Jersey 07003.   *1868*
Tel: (201) 748-9000
C : *arts-sc.*

Blue Mountain College, P.O. Box 338, Blue Mountain, Mississippi 38610.   *1873*
Tel: (601) 685-4771
C : *arts-sc.*

Bluefield College, Bluefield, Virginia 24605. *1920*
Tel: (304) 327-7137
C : *arts-sc.*

Bluefield State College, 900 Pulaski Street, Bluefield, West Virginia 24701.   *1895*
Tel: (304) 325-7102
C : *arts-sc.*

Bluffton College, College Avenue, Bluffton, Ohio 45817.   *1899*
Tel: (419) 358-8015
C : *arts-sc.*

Boise Bible College, 8695 Marigold Street, Boise, Idaho 83714.   *1945*
Tel: (208) 376-7731
theo.

Boricua College, 3755 Broadway, New York, New York 10032.   *1974*
Tel: (212) 694-1000
arts-sc.

Bowdoin College, Brunswick, Maine 04011. *1794*

Tel: (207) 725-3000
C : *arts-sc.*

Bradford College, 320 South Main Street, Bradford, Massachusetts 01830.   *1803*
Tel: (617) 372-7161
C : *arts-sc.*

Brescia College, 120 West 7th Street, Owensboro, Kentucky 42301.   *1950*
Tel: (502) 685-3131
C : *arts-sc.*

Brewton-Packer College, Mt. Vernon, Georgia 30445.   *1904*
Tel: (912) 583-2241
C : *arts-sc.*

Briar Cliff College, 3303 Rebecca Street, Sioux City, Iowa 51104.   *1929*
Tel: (712) 279-5321
C : *arts-sc, ed.*

Bridgeport Engineering Institute, P.O. Box 6459, Bridgeport, Connecticut 06606–9990.   *1924*
Tel: (203) 372-4395
C : *eng, sc, li arts.*

Bridgewater College, Bridgewater, Virginia 22812.   *1880*
Tel: (703) 828-2501
C : *arts-sc.*

Brigham Young University:
HAWAII CAMPUS, 550220 Kulanui Street, Laie Oahu 96762.   *1955*
Tel: (808) 293-3211. Telex: 4993759 byutelcom
D : *lang arts, ed, behavioral sc-soc, bus fa, math-nat-techn.*

Bryan College, Box 7000, Dayton, Tennessee 37321–7000.   *1930*
Tel: (615) 775-2041
C : *arts-sc.*

Buena Vista College, Storm Lake, Iowa 50588.
                                                                    1891
Tel: (712) 749-2103
C : *arts-sc.*

Burlington College, 95 North Avenue, Burlington, Vermont 05401–8477.   *1972*
Tel: (802) 862-9616
S : *arts-sc.*

Caldwell College, Ryerson Avenue, Caldwell, New Jersey 07006.   *1939*
Tel: (201) 228-4424
C : *arts-sc.*

California Maritime Academy, P.O. Box 1392, Vallejo, California 94590.   *1929*
Tel: (707) 648-4222
D : *marine eng, gen st, voc ed, nautical ind techn.*

Calumet College of St. Joseph, 2400 New York Avenue, Whiting, Indiana 46394.   *1951*
Tel: (219) 473-7770
C : *arts-sc.*

Calvary Bible College, 15800 Calvary Road,

Kansas City, Missouri 64147.   *1932*
Tel: (816)322-0110
Cameron University, 2800 Gore Boulevard, Lawton, Oklahoma 73505.   *1909*
Tel: (405) 248–2200
C : *arts-sc-ed, bus, fa, lang, math, app sc, soc, nat-heal.*
Campbellsville College, 200 College Street, West, Campbellsville, Kentucky 42718.   *1906*
Tel: (502) 465-8158
C : *arts-sc.*
Capitol Institute of Technology, 13301 Springfield Road, Laurel, Maryland 20708.   *1932*
Tel: (301) 953-3200
C : *eng, elec, gen st, math-sc, comp.*
Caribbean University College, Box 493, Bayamon, Puerto Rico 00619.   *1969*
Tel: (809) 780-0070
C : *arts-sc.*
Carleton College, 1 North College Street, Northfield, Minnesota 55057.   *1866*
Tel: (507) 663-4000. Telex: 9102504390 carleton ug
C : *arts-sc.*
Carrol College, Helena, Montana 59625.   *1909*
Tel: (406) 442-3450. Fax: (406) 4433964
C : *arts-sc.*
Carroll College, 100 Northeast Avenue, Waukesha, Wisconsin 53186.   *1846*
Tel: (414) 547-1211
C : *arts-sc.*
Carson-Newman College, Russell Avenue, Jefferson City, Tennessee 37760.   *1851*
Tel: (615) 475-9061
C : *arts-sc-ed, hum, bus-eco, soc, mus, sc-math, relig, nurs, phys, heal-recr.*
Catawba College, West Innes Street, Salisbury, North Carolina 28144-2488.   *1851*
Tel: (704) 637-4466
C : *arts-sc-ed.*
Cathedral College of the Immaculate Conception, 7200 Douglaston Parkway, Doulgaston, New York 11632.   *1914*
Tel: (718) 631-4600
C : *arts-sc.*
Cedar Crest College, College Drive and Hamilton Street, Allentown, Pennsylvania 18104.   *1867*
Tel: (215) 437-4471
C : *arts-sc.*
Cedarville College, 251 North Main Street, Box 601, Cedarville, Ohio 45314–0601.   *1887*
Tel: (513) 766-2211
C : *arts-sc.*
Centenary College, 400 Jefferson Street, Hackettstown, New Jersey 07840.   *1867*
Tel: (201) 852-1400
C : *arts-sc.*
Center for Advanced Studies on Puerto Rico and

the Caribbean, Cristo Street # 52, P.O. Box S-4467, Old San Juan, Puerto Rico 00904.   *1976*
Tel: (809) 723-4481
S : *arts-sc.*
Central Bible College, 3000 North Grant Avenue, Springfield, Missouri 65803.   *1922*
Tel: (417) 833-2551
theo.
Central Christian College of the Bible, P.O. Box 70, Moberly, Missouri 65270.   *1957*
Tel: (816) 263-3900
theo.
Central Methodist College, 441 Central Methodist College, Church Street, Fayette, Missouri 65248.   *1853*
Tel: (816) 248-3391
C : *arts-sc.*
Central New England College of Technology, 768 Main Street, Worcester, Massachusetts 01610.   *1971*
Tel: (617) 755-4314
D : *eng, techn, comp.*
Central State University, Wilberforce, Ohio 45384.   *1887*
Tel: (216) 777-315. Easylink: 620 25183 esl ud
C : *arts-sc, ed.*
Central University of Iowa, 812 University, Pella, Iowa 50219.   *1853*
Tel: (515) 628-4151
C : *arts-sc-ed.*
Central Wesleyan College, Central, South Carolina 29630–1020.   *1906*
Tel: (803) 639-2453
C : *arts-sc.*
Centre College of Kentucky, West Walnut Street, Danville, Kentucky 40422.   *1819*
Tel: (606) 236-5211
C : *arts-sc.*
Chatham College, Woodland Road, Pittsburgh, Pennsylvania 15232.   *1869*
Tel: (412) 365-1100. Easylink: 627 78580 esl ud
C : *arts-sc.*
Christ-College-Irvine, 1530 Concordia, Irvine, California 92715.   *1972*
Tel: (714) 854-8002
C : *arts-sc.*
Christendom College, Front Royal, Virginia 22630.   *1977*
Tel: (703) 636-2908
Arts-sc.
Christian Brothers College, 650 East Parkway South, Memphis, Tennessee 38104.   *1871*
Tel: (901) 278-0100
C : *arts-sc-ed, bus adm, eng, math.*
Christian Heritage College, 2100 Greenfield Drive, El Cajon, California 92021.   *1970*
Tel: (619) 440-3043
C : *arts-sc-ed.*
Christopher Newport College, 50 Shoe Lane,

Newport News, Virginia 23606.
Tel: (804) 599-7000
C : *arts-sc-ed, bus-eco, soc, let-nat.*

Circleville Bible College, Box 458, Circleville, Ohio 43113. *1948*
Tel: (614) 474-8896
theo.

The City University of New York:

CUNY York College, 94-20 Guy R. Brewer Boulevard, Jamaica, New York 11451. *1966, 1967*
Tel: (718) 262-2000
C : *arts-sc-ed.*

CUNY Medgar Evers College, 1150 Carroll Street, Brooklyn, New York 11225. *1969*
Tel: (718) 735-1750
C : *arts-sc-ed, math, phys, hum, bus, heal.*

CUNY New York City Technical College, 300 Jay Street, Brooklyn, New York 11201.
Tel: (718) 643-4900
C : *arts-sc.*

Claflin College, College Avenue, N.E., Orangeburg, South Carolina 29115. *1869*
Tel: (803) 534-2710
C : *arts-sc.*

Claremont McKenna College, 500 East 9th Street, Claremont, California 91711. *1946*
Tel: (714) 621-8000
C : *arts-sc.*

Clark College, 240 Chestnut Street, S.W., Atlanta, Georgia 30314. *1879*
Tel: (404) 681-3080
C : *arts-sc.*

Clearwater Christian College, Clearwater, Florida 34619. *1966*
Tel: (813) 726-1153
D : *ed, theo, lit, fa, bus, math, comp, psyc.*

Coe College, 1220 First Avenue, N.E.,Cedar Rapids, Iowa 52402. *1851*
Tel: (319) 399-8000
C : *arts-sc.*

Cogswell College, 10420 Bubb Road, Cupertino, California 95014. *1887*
Tel: (408) 252-5550
C : *arts-sc.*

Cogswell College North, 10626 Northeast 37th Circle, Kirkland, Washington 98033. *1979*
Tel: (206) 822-3137
C : *arts-sc.*

Coker College, College Avenue, Hartsville, South Carolina 29550. *1908*
Tel: (803) 332-1381
C : *arts-sc, mus.*

Colby College, Mayflower Hill Drive, Waterville, Maine 04901. *1813*
Tel: (207) 872-3000
C : *arts-sc.*

Colby-Sawyer College, New London, New Hampshire 03257. *1837*
Tel: (603) 526-2010
C : *arts-sc.*

College of the Atlantic, Eden Street, Bar Harbor, Maine 04609. *1969*
Tel: (207) 288-5015
C : *arts-sc.*

College of Mount St. Vincent, Riverdale Avenue and West 263rd Street, Riverdale, New York 10471. *1847*
Tel: (212) 549-8000
C : *arts-sc.*

College of Our Lady of the Elms, 291 Springfield Street, Chicopee, Massachusetts 01013. *1928*
Tel: (413) 598-8351
C : *arts-sc.*

College of St. Benedict, 37 South College Avenue, St. Joseph, Minnesota 56374. *1913*
Tel: (612) 363-5308
C : *arts-sc.*

College of St. Elizabeth, Convent Station, New Jersey 07961. *1899*
Tel: (201) 539-1600
C : *arts-sc, theo.*

College of St. Mary, 1901 South 72nd Street, Omaha, Nebraska 68124. *1923*
Tel: (402) 399-2400
C : *arts-sc.*

College of St. Teresa, 1130 West Broadway, Winoma, Minnesota 55987. *1907*
Tel: (507) 454-2930
C : *arts-sc.*

College of the Southwest, Lovington Highway, Hobbs, New Mexico 88240–9986. *1956*
Tel: (505) 392-7237
C : *arts-sc.*

College of Wooster, Wooster, Ohio 44691. *1866*
Tel: (216) 263-2000
C : *arts-sc.*

Colorado Christian College, 180 South Garrison, Denver, Colorado 80226. *1914*
Tel: (303) 238-5386
arts-sc-theo.

Colorado Technical College, 655 Elkton Drive, Colorado Springs, Colorado 80907. *1965*
Tel: (303) 598-0200
D : *gen st, electronics, life sc, hum, soc st, eng, solar, math, comp, ind mangt.*

Columbia Christian College, 9101 East Burnside, Portland, Oregon 97216–1515. *1949*
Tel: (503) 255-7060
C : *arts-sc.*

Columbia College, 10th and Roger Streets, Columbia, Missouri 65216. *1851*
Tel: (314) 875-8700
C : *arts-sc.*

Columbia College, 925 North La Brea Avenue, Hollywood, California 90038. *1952*

Tel: (213) 851-0550
C: *arts-sc.*

Columbia Union College, 7600 Flower Avenue, Takoma Park, Maryland 20912.   *1904*
Tel: (301) 270-9200
C: *arts-sc.*

Concord College, Athens, West Virginia 24712.
                                                              1872
Tel: (304) 384-3115
C: *arts-sc.*

Concordia College, 4090 Geddes Road, Ann Arbor, Michigan 48105–2797.   *1962*
Tel: (313) 995-7300
C: *arts-sc.*

Concordia College, 171 White Plains Road, Bronxville, New York 10708–9990.   *1881*
Tel: (914) 337-9300
C: *arts-sc.*

Concordia College Wisconsin, 12800 North Lake Shore Drive, Mequon, Wisconsin 53092.   *1881*
Tel: (414) 243-5700
C: *arts-sc.*

Concordia College, Moorhead, Minnesota 56560.
                                                              1891
Tel: (218) 299-3000. Telex: 9102500321 concordia moor uc. Easylink: 628 60193 esl ud
C: *arts-sc.*

Concordia College, Hamline and Marshall Avenues, St. Paul, Minnesota 55104.   *1893*
Tel: (612) 641-8278
C: *arts-sc-ed.*

Concordia College, 2811 N.E. Holman Street, Portland, Oregon 97211.   *1905*
Tel: (503) 288-9371
arts.

Concordia Lutheran College, 3400 Interstate 35N., Austin, Texas 78705.   *1926*
Tel: (512) 452-7661
C: *arts-sc-ed, bus, theo.*

Cornell College, Mount Vernon, Iowa 52314.
                                                              1853
Tel: (319) 895-8811
C: *arts-sc.*

Cornish College of the Arts, 710 East Roy, Seattle, Washington 98102–4696.   *1915*
Tel: (206) 323-1400
S: *arts-sc.*

Covenant College, Scenic Highway, Lookout Mountain, Georgia 30750.   *1955*
Tel: (404) 820-1560
C: *arts-sc.*

Culver-Stockton College, College Hill, Canton, Missouri 63435–9989.   *1853*
Tel: (314) 288-5221
C: *arts-sc.*

Cumberland University, Lebanon, Tennessee 37087.   *1842*
Tel: (615) 444-2562
arts.

Daemen College, 4380 Main Street, Amherst, New York 14226.   *1947*
Tel: (716) 839-3600
C: *arts-sc-ed.*

Dakota State College, North Washington Avenue, Madison, South Dakota 57042.   *1881*
Tel: (605) 256-5111. Fax: (605) 2565136. Easylink: 620 11182 els ud
C: *arts-sc.*

Dakota Wesleyan University, Mitchell, South Dakota 57301–9983.   *1885*
Tel: (605) 996-6511
C: *arts-sc.*

Dallas Christian College, 2700 Christian Parkway, Dallas, Texas 75234.   *1950*
Tel: (214) 241-3371
ed-theo.

Dana College, 2848 College Drive, Blair, Nebraska 68008.   *1884*
Tel: (402) 426-9000
C: *arts-sc.*

Daniel Webster College, University Drive, Nashua, New Hampshire 03063.   *1965*
Tel: (603) 883-3356
C: *arts-sc.*

Davidson College, Davidson, North Carolina 28036.   *1837*
Tel: (704) 892-2000
C: *arts.*

Davis and Elkins College, Sycamore Street, Elkins, West Virginia 26241.   *1904*
Tel: (304) 636-1900
C: *arts-sc-occp.*

Defiance College, 701 North Clinton Street, Defiance, Ohio 43512.   *1850*
Tel: (419) 784-4010
C: *arts-sc.*

Delaware Valley College of Science and Agriculture, Route 202, Doylestown, Pennsylvania 18901.   *1896*
Tel: (215) 345-1500
C: *sc-agr-bus adm.*

Denison University, Granville, Ohio 43023. *1831*
Tel: (614) 587-0810
C: *arts-sc.*

DeVry Institute of Technology, 12801 Crossroads Parkway, City of Industry, California 91744.
                                                              1983
Tel: (213) 699-9927

DeVry Institute of Technology, 250 North Arcadia Avenue, Decatour, Georgia 30030.
                                                              1969
Tel: (404) 292-7900

DeVry Institute of Technology, 3300 North Campbell Avenue, Chicago, Illinois 60618.
                                                              1931
Tel: (312) 929-8500

DeVry Institute of Technology, 2000 South Finley Road, Lombard, Illinois 60148.   *1982*

Tel: (312) 953-1300

DeVry Institute of Technology, 11224 Holmes Road, Kansas City, Missouri 64131.   *1931*
Tel: (816) 941-0430

DeVry Institute of Technology, 1350 Alum Creek Drive, Columbus, Ohio 43209.   *1952*
Tel: (614) 253-7291

DeVry Institute of Technology, 4250 Beltline Road, Irving, Texas 75038.   *1969*
Tel: (214) 258-6767
C : *eng.*

DeVry Institute of Technology, 2149 West Dunlop Avenue, Phoenix, Arizona 85021.
          1967
Tel: (602) 870-9222

Dickinson College, Carlisle, Pennsylvania 17013–2896.   *1773*
Tel: (717) 243-5121
C : *arts-sc.*

Dickinson State University, Dickinson, North Dakota 58601–4896.   *1918*
Tel: (701) 227-2507
C : *arts-sc-occp.*

Dillard University, 2601 Gentilly Boulevard, New Orleans, Louisiana 70122–3097.   *1869*
Tel: (504) 283-8822
D : *hum, nat, soc, ed, mus, nurs, bus adm.*

Doane College, Crete, Nebraska 68333.   *1872*
Tel: (402) 826-2161
C : *arts-sc.*

Dominican College of Blauvelt, 10 Western Highway, Orangeburg, New York 10962.   *1952*
Tel: (914) 359-7800
C : *arts-sc.*

Don Bosco College, Swartswood Road, Newton, New Jersey 07860.   *1928*
Tel: (201) 383-3900
C : *arts-sc.*

Dordt College, 498 4th Avenue Northeast, Sioux Center, Iowa 51250.   *1955*
Tel: (712) 722-3771
C : *arts-sc.*

East Coast Bible College, 6900 Wilkinson Boulevard, Charlotte, North Carolina 28214.   *1976*
Tel: (704) 394-2307
ed-theo.

East Texas Baptist University, 1209 North Grove Street, Marshall, Texas 75670.   *1912*
Tel: (214) 935-7963
C : *arts-sc.*

Eastern Christian College, P.O. Box 629, Bel Air, Maryland 21014.   *1960*
Tel: (301) 734-9727
theo.

Eastern Mennonite College, Harrisonburg, Virginia 22801.   *1917*
Tel: (703) 433-2771
C : *arts-sc.*

East-West University, 816 South Michigan Avenue, Chicago, Illinois 60605.   *1978*
Tel: (312) 939-0111
S : *arts-sc, bus, eng.*

Eckerd College, 4200 54th Avenue, St. Petersburg, Florida 33733.   *1958*
Tel: (813) 867-1166
C : *arts-sc.*

Edward Waters College, 1658 Kings Road, Jacksonville, Florida 32209.   *1866*
Tel: (904) 354-3030
C : *arts-sc-ed.*

Electronic Data Processing College of Puerto Rico, Munoz Rivera 555, Hato Rey, Puerto Rico 00918.   *1968*
Tel: (809) 896-2137
S : *arts-sc.*

Elizabeth City State University, Parkview Drive, Elizabeth City, North Carolina 27909.   *1891*
Tel: (919) 335-3230. Easylink: 620 24524 esl ud *arts.*

Elizabethtown College, College Avenue, Elizabethtown, Pennsylvania 17022.   *1899*
Tel: (717) 367-1151
C : *arts-sc.*

Elmhurst College, 190 Prospect, Elmhurst, Illinois 60126.   *1871*
Tel: (312) 279-4100
C : *arts-sc.*

Emmanuel College School of Christian Ministries, P.O. Box 129, Franklin Springs, Georgia 30639.   *1973*
Tel: (404) 245-7226
theo.

Emmaus Bible College, 2570 Ashbury Road, Dubuque, Iowa 52001.   *1942*
Tel: (319) 588-8000

Emory & Henry College, Ambrister Drive, Emory, Virginia 24327.   *1836*
Tel: (703) 944-3121
C : *arts-sc.*

Erskine College, Due West, South Carolina 29639.   *1839*
Tel: (803) 379-2131
C : *arts-sc.*

Eugene Bible College, 2155 Bailey Hill Road, Eugene, Oregon 97405.   *1925*
Tel: (503) 485-1780
theo.

Eureka College, 300 East College Avenue, Eureka, Illinois 61530.   *1855*
Tel: (309) 467-3721
C : *arts-sc.*

Evangel College, 1111 North Glenstone, Springfield, Missouri 65802.   *1955*
Tel: (417) 865-2811
C : *arts-sc.*

Fairmont State College, Locust Avenue, Fairmont, West Virginia 26554.   *1865*
Tel: (304) 367-4000

C : *arts-sc.*

Faulkner University, 5345 Atlanta Highway, Montgomery, Alabama 36193.   *1942*
Tel: (205) 272-5820
C : *arts-sc.*

Felician College, 260 South Main Street, Lodi, New Jersey 07644.   *1942*
Tel: (201) 778-1190
C : *arts-sc-ed, nurs.*

Ferrum College, Box 22, Ferrum, Virginia 24088.   *1913*
Tel: (703) 365-2121
C : *arts-sc-ed.*

Findlay College, 1000 North Main Street, Findlay, Ohio 45840.   *1882*
Tel: (419) 422-8313. Telex: 5101011958 findlay clg ud
C : *arts-sc.*

Flagler College, P.O. Box 1027, Saint Augustine, Florida 32085.   *1968*
Tel: (904) 829-6481
C : *arts-sc.*

Flaming Rainbow University, 419 North 2nd Street, Downing Street, Tahleguah, Oklahoma 74960.   *1971*
Tel: (918) 696-3644
C : *arts-sc.*

Florida Bible College, 1701 North Peinciana Boulevard, Kissimmee, Florida 32758.   *1962*
Tel: (305) 933-4500
ed-theo.

Florida Christian College, P.O. Box 1579, Kissimmee, Florida 32742.   *1975*
Tel: (305) 847-8966
phil-theo.

Florida Memorial College, 15800 Northwest 42nd Avenue, Miami, Florida 33054.   *1879*
Tel: (305) 625-4141
C : *arts-sc-ed, bus adm, math, hum, soc.*

Fort Lewis College, Durango, Colorado 81301.   *1911*
Tel: (303) 247-7010
S : *arts-sc-ed, bus adm.*

Fort Wayne Bible College, 1025 West Rudisill Boulevard, Fort Wayne, Indiana 46807.   *1904*
Tel: (219) 456-2111
arts-sc-theo.

Franklin College of Indiana, 501 East Monroe Street, Franklin, Indiana 46131.   *1834*
Tel: (317) 736-8441
C : *arts-sc.*

Franklin Pierce College, College Road, Rindge, New Hampshire 03461.   *1962*
Tel: (603) 899-5111
C : *arts-sc.*

Franklin University, 201 South Grant Avenue, Columbus, Ohio 43215.   *1902*
Tel: (614) 224-6237. Fax: (614) 4610957
C : *arts-sc, techn, eng, bus.*

Freed-Hardeman College, 158 East Main Street, Henderson, Tennessee 38340.   *1869*
Tel: (901) 989-6000
C : *arts-sc-ed, soc w.*

Friends Bible College, P.O. Box 288, Haviland, Kansas 67059.   *1917*
Tel: (316) 862-5252
arts-sc-theo.

Friends World College, Plover Lane, Huntington, New York 11743.   *1965*
Tel: (516) 549-5000
C : *arts-sc.*

Geneva College, College Avenue and 32nd Street, Beaver Falls, Pennsylvania 15010.   *1848*
Tel: (412) 846-5100
C : *arts-sc.*

George Fox College, Newberg, Oregon 97132.   *1891*
Tel: (503) 538-8383
C : *arts-sc, mus.*

Gettysburg College, North Washington Street, Gettysburg, Pennsylvania 17325–1486.   *1832*
Tel: (717) 337-6000
C : *arts-sc.*

Glenville State College, 200 High Street, Glenville, West Virginia 26351–9990.   *1872*
Tel: (304) 462-7361
C : *arts-sc-ed.*

God's Bible School and College, 1810 Young Street, Cicinnati, Ohio 45210.   *1900*
Tel: (513) 721-7944
ed-arts-sc-theo.

Goldey Beacom College, 4701 Limestone Road, Wilmington, Delaware 19808–0551.   *1886*
Tel: (302) 998-8814
C : *arts-sc.*

Gordon College, 255 Grapevine Road, Wenham, Massachusetts 01984.   *1889*
Tel: (617) 927-2300
C : *arts-sc.*

Goshen College, 1700 South Main Street, Goshen, Indiana 46526.   *1894*
Tel: (219) 533-3161. Easylink: 620 11224 esl ud
C : *arts-sc-ed, soc w, nurs.*

Grace Bible College, P.O. Box 910, Grand Rapids, Michigan 49509.   *1945*
Tel: (616) 538-2330
Theo.

Grace College of the Bible, 1515 South 10th Street, Omaha, Nebraska 68108.   *1943*
Tel: (402) 449-2831

Graceland College, Lamoni, Iowa 50140.   *1895*
Tel: (515) 784-5000
C : *arts-sc.*

Grand Canyon College, 3300 West Camelback Road, Phoenix, Arizona 85017.   *1949*
Tel: (602) 249-3300
C : *arts-sc.*

Grand View College, 1200 Grandview Avenue,

Des Moines, Iowa 50316. *1896*
Tel: (515) 263-2800
C : *li arts.*

Great Lakes Bible College, Box 40060, Lansing, Michigan 48901. *1949*
Tel: (517) 321-0242
ed, theo.

Green Mountain College, 16 College Street, Poultney, Vermont 05764. *1834*
Tel: (802) 287-9313
C : *arts-sc.*

Greensboro College, 815 West Market Street, Greensboro, North Carolina 27401–1875. *1838*
Tel: (919) 272-7102
C : *arts-sc.*

Greenville College, 315 East College Avenue, Greenville, Illinois 62246–0159. *1892*
Tel: (618) 664-1840
C : *arts-sc.*

Grinnell College, P.O. Box 805, Grinnell, Iowa 50112–0810. *1846*
Tel: (515) 236-2500
C : *arts-sc.*

Grove City College, Grove City, Pennsylvania 16127. *1876*
Tel: (412) 458-6600
C : *arts-sc.*

Guilford College, 5800 West Friendly Avenue, Greensboro, North Carolina 27410. *1837*
Tel: (919) 292-5511
C : *arts-sc.*

Gustavus Adolphus College, St. Peter, Minnesota 56082. *1862*
Tel: (507) 931-8000
C : *arts-sc.*

Hamilton College, Clinton, New York 13323. *1812*
Tel: (315) 859-4011
C : *arts-sc.*

Hampden-Sydney College, Hampden-Sydney, Virginia 23943. *1776*
Tel: (804) 223-4381
C : *arts-sc.*

Hampshire College, West Street, Amherst, Massachusetts 01002. *1965*
Tel: (413) 549-4600
C : *arts-sc.*

Hannibal-Lagrange College, 2800 Palmyra Road, Hannibal, Missouri 63401. *1858*
Tel: (314) 221-3675
C : *arts.*

Hanover College, Hanover, Indiana 47243. *1827*
Tel: (812) 866-2151
C : *arts-sc.*

Hartwick College, West Street, Oneonta, New York 13820. *1928*
Tel: (607) 432-4200
C : *arts-sc.*

Hastings College, 7th Street and Turner Avenue, Hastings, Nebraska 68901. *1882*
Tel: (402) 463-2402
C : *arts-sc.*

Haverford College, Haverford, Pennsylvania 19041–1392. *1833*
Tel: (215) 896-1350
C : *arts-sc.*

Hawaii Loa College, 45-045 Kamehameha Highway, Kaneohe, Hawaii 96744. *1963*
Tel: (808) 235-3641
C : *arts-sc, eng.*

Hawthorne College, Antrim, New Hampshire 03440. *1962*
Tel: (603) 588-6341
S : *arts-sc.*

Heidelberg College, 310 East Market Street, Tiffin, Ohio 44883. *1850*
Tel: (419) 448-2000. Telex: 241519 heid berg tifn. Easylink: 620 44719 esl ud
C : *arts-sc-ed.*

Hendrix College, Conway, Arkansas 72032. *1884*
Tel: (501) 329-6811
C : *arts-sc.*

High Point College, 933 Montlieu Avenue, High Point, North Carolina 27262. *1924*
Tel: (919) 841-9000
C : *arts-sc.*

Hillsdale College, 33 East College, Hillsdale, Michigan 49242. *1844*
Tel: (517) 437-7341
C : *arts-sc.*

Hillsdale Free Will Baptist College, P.O. Box 7208, Moore, Oklahoma 73153. *1959*
Tel: (405) 794-6661
arts.

Hiram College, Hiram, Ohio 44234. *1850*
Tel: (216) 569-3211. Telex: 9103805429 hiram college
C : *arts-sc.*

Hobart College,337 Pulteney Street, Geneva, New York 14456. *1822*
Tel: (315) 789-5500
C : *arts-sc.*

Hobe Sound Bible College, P.O. Box 1065, Hobe Sound, Florida 33455. *1960*
Tel: (305) 546-5534
ed-theo.

Holy Family College, Grant and Frankford Avenues, Philadelphia, Pennsylvania 19114. *1954*
Tel: (215) 637-7700
C : *arts-sc.*

Hope College, 137 East 12th Street, Holland, Michigan 49423. *1866*
Tel: (616) 392-5111
C : *arts-sc, nat, hum, soc.*

Houghton College, Houghton, New York 14744. *1883*

Tel: (716) 567-2211
C : arts-sc.
Howard Payne University, 1000 Fisk Avenue, Brownwood, Texas 76801.   *1889*
Tel: (915) 646-2502
C : arts-sc.
Huntingdon College, 1500 East Fairview Avenue, Montgomery, Alabama 36194–6201.   *1854*
Tel: (205) 365-0511
C : arts-sc.
Huron College, Huron, South Dakota 57350.
                                            1883
Tel: (605) 352-8721
C : arts-sc, nurs.
Huston–Tillotson College, 1820 East 8th Street, Austin, Texas 78702.   *1876*
Tel: (512) 476-7421
C : arts-sc.
Illinois College, 1101 West College Avenue, Jacksonville, Illinois 62650–2299.   *1829*
Tel: (217) 245-7126
C : arts-sc.
Illinois Wesleyan University, 210 East University Street, Bloomington, Illinois 61712.   *1850*
Tel: (309) 556-3131
C : hum, ed, bus-eco, soc.
S : nurs, art, mus, dram, sc.
Indiana Institute of Technology, 1600 East Washington Boulevard, Fort Wayne, Indiana 46803–1297.   *1930*
Tel: (219) 422-5561
I : sc-eng, bus-art, arts-sc.
Indiana University:
   INDIANA UNIVERSITY EAST, 2325 Chester Boulevard, Richmond, Indiana 47374.
                                            1971
   Tel: (317) 966-8261
   D : behavioral sc-soc, bus-techn, hum, nurs, sc-math.
Inter-American University of Puerto Rico:
   AGUADILLA REGIONAL COLLEGE.   *1957*
   Tel: (809) 891-0925
   ARECIBO REGIONAL COLLEGE.   *1957*
   Tel: (809) 878-5475
   S : nurs.
   BARRANQUITAS REGIONAL COLLEGE.   *1957*
   Tel: (809) 857-2585
   FAJARDA REGIONAL COLLEGE.   *1965*
   Tel: (809) 863-2390
International Bible College, P.O. Box IBC, Florence, Alabama 35630.   *1971*
Tel: (205) 766-6616
theo.
Iowa Wesleyan College, North Main, Mount Pleasant, Iowa 52641.   *1842*
Tel: (319) 385-8021
C : arts-sc.
Jamestown College, Jamestown, North Dakota 58401–3401.   *1883*

Tel: (701) 253-2333. Telex: 9103808869
C : arts-sc.
Jarvis Christian College, U.S. Highway 80, Hawkins, Texas 75765.   *1912*
Tel: (214) 769-2174
C : arts-sc.
John Brown University, Siloam Springs, Arkansas 72761.   *1919*
Tel: (501) 524-3131
C : arts-sc-ed.
John Wesley College, 2314 North Centennial, High Point, North Carolina 27260.   *1932*
Tel: (919) 889-2262
ed-psyc-theo.
Johnson Bible College, Knoxville, Tennessee 37998.   *1893*
Tel: (615) 573-4517
ed-mus-theo.
Johnson Cay. Smith University, 100 Beatties Ford Road, Charlotte, North Carolina 28216.
                                            1867
Tel: (704) 378-1000
C : arts-sc.
Jordan College, Cedar Springs, Michigan 49319.
                                            1967
Tel: (616) 696-1180
C : arts-sc.
Judson College, 1151 North State Street, Elgin, Illinois 60120.   *1963*
Tel: (312) 695-2500
C : arts-sc.
Judson College, Marion, Alabama 36756.   *1838*
Tel: (205) 683-6161
C : arts-sc.
Juniata College, 1700 Moore Street, Huntingdon, Pennsylvania 16652.   *1876*
Tel: (814) 643-4310
C : arts-sc.
Kalamazoo College, 1200 Academy Street, Kalamazoo, Michigan 49007.   *1833*
Tel: (616) 383-8400
C : arts-sc.
Kansas Newman College, 3100 McCormick Avenue, Wichita, Kansas 67213.   *1933*
Tel: (316) 942-4291
C : arts-sc.
Kansas Wesleyan, 100 East Claflin, Salina, Kansas 67401.   *1885*
Tel: (913) 827-5541
C : arts-sc.
Kendall College, 2408 Orrington Avenue, Evanston, Illinois 60201.   *1934*
Tel: (312)
C : arts-sc.
Kentucky Christian College, Grayson, Kentucky 41143–1199.   *1919*
Tel: (606) 474-6613
C : arts-sc.
Kentucky Wesleyan College, 3000 Frederica

Street, Owensboro, Kentucky 42301. *1860*
Tel: (502) 926-3111
C : *arts-sc.*

Kenyon College, Gambier, Ohio 43022–9623.
1824
Tel: (614) 427-2244
C : *arts-sc.*

Keuka College, Keuka Park, New York 14478.
1890
Tel: (315) 536-4411
C : *arts-sc.*

King College, East State Street, Bristol, Tennessee 37620. *1867*
Tel: (615) 968-1187
C : *arts-sc.*

King's College, Loge Road, Briarcliff Manor, New York 10510. *1938*
Tel: (914) 941-7200
C : *arts-sc.*

King's College, 133 North River Street, Wilkes-Barre, Pennsylvania 18711. *1946*
Tel: (717) 826-5900
C : *arts-sc.*

Knox College, Galesburg, Illinois 61401. *1837*
Tel: (309) 343-0112
C : *arts-sc.*

Knoxville College, 901 College Street, N.W., Knoxville, Tennessee 31291. *1875*
Tel: (615) 524-6511
C : *arts-sc.*

Lafayette College, Easton, Pennsylvania 18042–1798. *1826*
Tel: (215) 250-5000
C : *arts-sc-eng.*

Lakeland College, P.O. Box 359, Sheboygan, Wisconsin 53081. *1862*
Tel: (414) 565-2111
C : *arts-sc-ed.*

Lambuth College, Lambuth Boulevard, Jackson, Tennessee 38301. *1843*
Tel: (901) 427-1500
C : *arts-sc.*

Lancaster Bible College, 901 Eden Road, Lancaster, Pennsylvania 17601. *1933*
Tel: (717) 569-7071
ed-theo.

Lane College, 545 Lane Avenue, Jackson, Tennessee 38301. *1882, 1895*
Tel: (901) 424-4600
C : *arts-sc-ed.*

Langston University, Langston, Oklahoma 73050. *1897*
Tel: (405) 466-2231. Easylink: 620 09383 esl ud
C : *arts-sc-ed, bus, app sc, hom eco, allied heal professions, mus.*

Lawrence Institute of Technology, 21000 West Ten Mile Road, Southfield, Michigan 48075–1058. *1932*
Tel: (313) 356-0200

S : *arc, eng, bus-ind, mangt, arts-sc, associated st, art.*

Lawrence University, P.O. Box 599, Appleton, Wisconsin 54912. *1847*
Tel: (414) 739-3681
C : *li arts.*
Conservatory : *mus.*

Lebanon Valley College, Annville, Pennsylvania 17003. *1866*
Tel: (717) 867-6100
C : *arts-sc.*

Lee College, Ecoee Street, Cleveland, Tennessee 37311. *1918*
Tel: (615) 472-2111
C : *arts-sc.*

Le Moyne College, Le Moyne Heights, Syracuse, New York 13214. *1946*
Tel: (212) 752-1530
D : *arts-sc.*

Le Moyne-Owen College, 807 Walker Avenue, Memphis, Tennessee 38126. *1862*
Tel: (901) 774-9090
C : *arts-sc.*

Le Tourneau College, 2300 South Mobberly Avenue, Longview, Texas 75607. *1946*
Tel: (214) 753-0231. Easylink: 620 06181 esl ud
C : *arts-sc.*

Lewis Clark State College, 8th Avenue and 6th Street, Lewiston, Idaho 83501. *1893*
Tel: (208) 746-2341
C : *arts-sc, voc ed, prof st, ed.*

Life Bible College, 1100 Glendale Boulevard, Los Angeles, California 90026. *1925*
Tel: (213) 413-1234
theo.

Limestone College, 1115 College Drive, Gaffney, South Carolina 29340. *1845*
Tel: (803) 489-7151
C : *arts-sc.*

Lindsey Wilson College, Columbia, Kentucky 42728. *1903*
Tel: (502) 384-2126
C : *arts-sc.*

Livingstone College, 701 West Monroe Street, Salisbury, North Carolina 28144. *1879*
Tel: (704) 633-7960
C : *arts-sc.*

Loretto Heights College, 3001 South Federal Boulevard, Denver, Colorado 80236. *1918*
Tel: (303) 936-8441
C : *arts-sc.*

Louisiana College, 1140 College Drive, Pineville, Louisiana 71359. *1906*
Tel: (318) 487-7011
C : *arts-sc.*

Lourdes College, 6832 Convent Boulevard, Sylvania, Ohio 43560. *1958*
Tel: (419) 885-3211
C : *arts-sc.*

Lubbock Christian College, 5601 West 19th Street, Lubbock, Texas 79407.   *1957*
Tel: (806) 792-3221
C : *arts-sc-ed.*

Luther College, Decorah, Iowa 52101.   *1861*
Tel: (319) 387-1287
C : *arts-sc.*

Lutheran Bible Institute of Seattle, Providence Heights, Issaquah, Washington 98027.   *1944*
Tel: (206) 392-0400
theo.

Lycoming College, 700 College Place, Williamsport, Pennsylvania 17701-5192.   *1812*
Tel: (717) 321-4000
C : *arts-sc.*

McKendree College, 701 College Road, Lebanon, Illinois 62254-9990.   *1828*
Tel: (618) 537-4481
C : *arts-sc.*

McMurry College, 14th and Sayles, Abilene, Texas 79697.   *1923*
Tel: (915) 691-6200
C : *arts-sc.*

MacMurray College, 447 East College Avenue, Jacksonville, Illinois 62650.   *1846*
Tel: (217) 245-6151
C : *arts-sc.*

McPherson College, 1600 East Euclid Street, P.O. Box 1402, McPherson, Kansas 67460.   *1887*
Tel: (316) 241-0731
C : *arts-sc.*

Macalester College, 1600 Grand Avenue, St. Paul, Minnesota 55105.   *1874*
Tel: (612) 696-6000
C : *arts-sc.*

Mallinckrodt College, 1041 Ridge Road, Wilmette, Illinois 60091.   *1918*
Tel: (312) 256-1094
S : *arts-sc.*

Malone College, 75 25th Street, N.W., Canton, Ohio 44709.   *1892*
Tel: (216) 489-0800
C : *arts-sc.*

Manhattan Christian College, 1407 Anderson, Manhattan, Kansas 66502.   *1927*
Tel: (913) 539-3571
C : *arts-sc.*

Marian College, 3200 Cold Spring Road, Indianapolis, Indiana 46222.   *1851*
Tel: (317) 929-0213
C : *arts-sc.*

Marian College of Fond du Lac, 45 South National Avenue, Fond du Lac, Wisconsin 54935-4699.   *1936*
Tel: (414) 921-3900
C : *arts-sc-ed, bus, nurs, soc w, theo.*

Mars Hill College, Mars Hill, North Carolina 28754.   *1856*

Tel: (704) 689-1111
C : *arts-sc-ed, allied heal professions, soc w.*

Martin Center College, 3553 North College Avenue, Indianapolis, Indiana 46205.   *1977*
Tel: (317) 923-5349
arts-sc.

Mary Baldwin College, Frederick and New Streets, Staunton, Virginia 24401.   *1842*
Tel: (703) 887-7000
C : *arts-sc.*

Marymount College of Kansas, Iron Avenue and Marymount Road, Salina, Kansas 67401.   *1922*
Tel: (913) 825-2101
C : *arts-sc-ed, bus adm, fa, nurs, psyc, relig, phys.*

Marymount College, Tarrytown, New York 10591.   *1908*
Tel: (914) 631-3200
C : *arts-sc-ed.*

Marymount Manhattan College, 221 East 71st Street, New York, New York 10021.   *1936*
Tel: (212) 517-0400
C : *arts-sc, lifelong ed.*

Maryville College, Maryville, Tennessee 37801.   *1819*
Tel: (615) 982-6412
C : *arts-sc.*

Massachusetts Maritime Academy, P.O. Box D, Buzzards Bay, Massachusetts 02532.   *1891*
Tel: (617) 759-5761. Telex: 5101012536 oiti ma usa
C : *arts-sc.*

Master's College, 21726 West Placerita Canyon Road, Newhall, California 91322.   *1927*
Tel: (805) 259-3540
arts.

Mayville State University, 330 3rd Street, Mayville, North Dakota 58257.   *1889*
Tel: (701) 786-2301. Telex: 384386 mys mavl ud
C : *arts-sc.*

Medaille College, 18 Agassiz Circle, Buffalo, New York 14214.   *1875*
Tel: (716) 884-3281
S : *arts-sc, ed.*

Merrimack College, North Andover, Massachusetts 01845.   *1947*
Tel: (617) 683-7111
C : *arts-sc-ed, bus adm, soc, hum, eng.*

Mesa College, P.O. Box 2647, Grand Junction, Colorado 81502.   *1925*
Tel: (303) 248-1020
S : *bus-allied heal, ind-techn, hum-fa, soc-behavioral sc, nat-math, nurs, ed.*

Messiah College, Grantham, Pennsylvania 17027.   *1909*
Tel: (717) 766-2511
C : *arts-sc.*

Methodist College, 5400 Ramsey Street, Fayetteville, North Carolina 28301–1499.   *1956*

Tel: (919) 488-7110
C : *arts-sc.*

Metropolitan State College, 1006 11th Street, Denver, Colorado 80204.   *1964*
Tel: (303) 556-3019. Easylink: 620 15282 esl ud
S : *bus, math, eng techn, li arts, sc-techn, prof st.*
Ce : *ed.*

Michigan Christian College, 800 West Avon Road, Rochester, Michigan 48063.   *1959*
Tel: (313) 651-5800
arts.

Mid-American Bible College, 3500 Southwest 119th Street, Oklahoma City, Oklahoma 73170.   *1953*
Tel: (405) 691-3881
arts-sc-theo.

Mid-American Nazarene College, 2030 College Way, P.O. Box 1776, Olathe, Kansas 66061–1776.   *1966*
Tel: (913) 782-3750
C : *arts-sc.*

Mid-Continent Baptist Bible College, P.O. Box 1, Mayfield, Kentucky 42066–0357.   *1949*
Tel: (502) 247-8521
theo.

Midland Lutheran College, 900 North Clarkson, Fremont, Nebraska 68025–4395.   *1883*
Tel: (402) 721-5480
C : *arts-sc.*

Miles Colleges, Birmingham, Alabama 35208.
                                                        1905
Tel: (205) 923-2771
C : *arts-sc.*

Milligan College, Milligan College, Tennessee 37682.   *1866*
Tel: (615) 929-0116
C : *arts-sc.*

Millikin University, 1184 West Main Street, Decatur, Illinois 62522.   *1901*
Tel: (217) 424-6211
C : *arts-sc, fa.*
S : *bus-ind mangt, nurs.*

Minnesota Bible College, 920 Mayowood Road Southwest, Rochester, Minnesota 55902. *1913*
Tel: (507) 288-4563
theo.

Missouri Baptist College, 12542 Conway Road, Saint Louis, Missouri 63141–8698.   *1963*
Tel: (314) 434-1115
C : *arts-sc.*

Missouri Southern State College, Newmand and Duquesne Roads, Joplin, Missouri 64801. *1937*
Tel: (417) 624-8100
C : *techn.*
D : *arts-sc, ed, psyc, bus adm.*

Missouri Valley College, 500 East College, Marshall, Missouri 65340.   *1888*
Tel: (816) 886-6924
C : *arts-sc.*

Missouri Western State College, 4525 Downs Drive, Saint Joseph, Missouri 64507–2294.
                                                        1915
Tel: (816) 271-4200
C : *li arts-sc, ed-app sc, prof st.*

Molloy College, 1000 Hempstead Avenue, Rockville Centre, New York 11570.   *1955*
Tel: (516) 678-5000
C : *arts-sc.*

Monmouth College, 700 East Broadway, Monmouth, Illinois 61462.   *1853*
Tel: (309) 457-2311. Fax: (309) 7347500
C : *arts-sc.*

Montreat-Anderson College, Montreat, North Carolina 28757.   *1916*
Tel: (704) 669-8011
C : *arts-sc.*

Moody Bible Institute, 820 North LaSalle Drive, Chicago, Illinois 60610.   *1886*
Tel: (312) 329-4261
eng-theo.

Morehouse College, 830 Westview Drive, S.W., Atlanta, Georgia 30314.   *1867*
Tel: (404) 752-1500
C : *arts-sc.*
S : *med.*

Morris Brown College, 634 Martin L. King, Jr. Drive, Atlanta, Georgia 30314.   *1881*
Tel: (404) 525-7831
C : *arts-sc.*

Morris College, North Main Street, Sumter, South Carolina 29150.   *1908*
Tel: (803) 775-9371
C : *arts-sc.*

Mount Ida College, 777 Dedham Street, Newton Centre, Massachusetts 02159.   *1899*
Tel: (617) 969-7000
C : *arts-sc.*

Mount Mercy College, 1330 Elmhurst Drive, N.E., Cedar Rapids, Iowa 52402.   *1928*
Tel: (319) 363-8213
C : *arts-sc.*

Mount Olive College, Mount Olive, North Carolina 28365.   *1951*
Tel: (919) 658-2502
C : *arts-sc.*

Mount Saint Clare College, 400 N. Bluff Boulevard, Clinton, Iowa 52732.   *1928*
Tel: (319) 242-4023
C : *arts-sc, bus adm.*

Mount Senario College, 1000 College Avenue, Ladysmith, Wisconsin 54848.   *1962*
Tel: (715) 532-5511
C : *arts-sc.*

Mount Union College, 1972 Clark Avenue, Alliance, Ohio 44601.   *1846*
Tel: (216) 821-5320
C : *arts-sc.*

Mount Vernon College, 2100 Foxhall Road,

N.W., Washington, D.C. 20007.   *1875*
Tel: (202) 331-0400
C : *arts-sc.*

Mount Vernon Nazarene College, 800 Martinsburg Road, Mount Vernon, Ohio 43050. *1966*
Tel: (614) 397-1244. Easylink: 628 17314 esl ud
C : *arts-sc.*

Muhlenberg College, 24th and Chew Streets, Allentown, Pennsylvania 18104.   *1848*
Tel: (215) 821-3100
C : *arts-sc.*

Muskingum College, College Drive, New Concord, Ohio 43762–1199.   *1837*
Tel: (614) 826-8211
C : *arts-sc, mus.*

NAES College, 2838 West Peterson, Chicago, Illinois 60659.   *1974*
Tel: (312) 761-5000
arts.

Nazarene Bible College, P.O. Box 17549, Colorado Springs, Colorado 80935.   *1964*
Tel: (303) 596-5110
theo.

Nebraska Christian College, 1800 Syracuse, Norfolk, Nebraska 68701.   *1945*
Tel: (402) 371-5960
C : *arts-sc.*

Nebraska Wesleyan University, 5000 St. Paul Avenue, Lincoln, Nebraska 68504.   *1887*
Tel: (402) 466-2371
C : *arts-sc.*

Newberry College, 2100 College, Newberry, South Carolina 29108.   *1856*
Tel: (803) 276-5010
C : *arts-sc.*

North Carolina Wesleyan College, 3400 Wesleyan Boulevard, Rocky Mount, North Carolina 27807–8630.   *1956*
Tel: (919) 977-7171
C : *arts-sc.*

North Central Bible College, 910 Elliot Avenue South, Minneapolis, Minnesota 55404. *1930*
Tel: (612) 332-3491
arts-sc-theo.

Northeastern Bible College, 12 Oak Lane, Essex Fells, New Jersey 07021.   *1950*
Tel: (201) 226-1076
ed-theo.

North Park College and Theological Seminary, 5125 North Spaulding Avenue, Chicago, Illinois 60625.   *1891*
Tel: (312) 583-2700
C : *arts-sc.*

Northland College, 1411 Ellis Avenue, Ashland, Wisconsin 54806-3999.   *1892*
Tel: (715) 682-4531
C : *arts-sc.*

Northwest College, P.O. Box 579, Kirkland, Washington 98033.   *1934*

Tel: (206) 822-8266
ed-theo.

Northwest College of the Assemblies of God, P.O. Box 579, Kirkland, Washington 98033.   *1934*
Tel: (206) 822-8266
C : *arts-sc.*

Northwestern College, 101 9th Street, Orange City, Iowa 51041.   *1882*
Tel: (712) 737-4821
C : *arts-sc.*

Northwestern College, 3003 North Snelling Avenue, Roseville, Minnesota 55113.   *1902*
Tel: (612) 5100
C : *arts-sc.*

Northwood Institute, 3225 Cook Road, Midland, Michigan 48640.   *1959*
Tel: (517) 631-1600
C : *arts-sc.*

Notre Dame College of Ohio, 4545 College road, Cleveland, Ohio 44121.   *1922*
Tel: (216) 381-1680
C : *arts-sc.*

Oakwood College, Oakwood Road, Huntsville, Alabama 35896.   *1896, 1917*
Tel: (205) 837-1630
C : *arts-sc.*

Oglala Lakota College, Box 351, Kyle, South Dakota 57752.   *1970*
Tel: (605) 455-2321
C : *arts-sc.*

Ohio Dominican College, 1216 Sunbury Road, Columbus, Ohio 43219.   *1911, 1913*
Tel: (614) 253-2741
C : *arts-sc.*

Ohio Northern University, 525 South Main Street, Ada, Ohio 45810.   *1871*
Tel: (419) 772-2000
C : *arts-sc-ed-eng-phar-law, bus adm.*

Ohio State University:
   Lima Campus, 4240 Campus Drive, Lima, Ohio 45804.   *1960*
   Tel: (419) 228-2641
   Mansfield Campus, 1680 University Drive, Mansfield, Ohio 44906.   *1958*
   Tel: (419) 755-4011. Fax: (419) 7554332
   Marion Campus, 1465 Mount Vernon Avenue, Marion, Ohio 43302.   *1957*
   Tel: (614) 389-2361
   Newark Campus, University Drive, Newark, Ohio 43055.   *1957*
   Tel: (614) 366-3321

Ohio University:
   Ohio University-Belmont, 45425 National Road, St. Clairsville, Ohio 43950.   *1957*
   Tel: (614) 695-1720
   Ohio University-Chillicothe, 571 West 5th Street, P.O. Box 629, Chillicothe, Ohio 45601.   *1946*
   Tel: (614) 775-9500

OHIO UNIVERSITY-IRONTON, Ironton, Ohio
45638. *1956*
Tel: (614) 533-4600
OHIO UNIVERSITY-PORTSMOUTH, RESIDENT
CREDIT CENTER, Portsmouth, Ohio 45662.
1975
Tel: (614) 353-8218
OHIO UNIVERSITY-ZANESVILLE, 1425
Newark Road, Zanesville, Ohio 43701.
1946
Tel: (614) 453-0762
Ohio Valley College, College Parkway, Parkers-
burg, West Virginia 26101. *1960*
Tel: (304) 485-7384
Ohio Wesleyan University, Sandusky Street,
Delaware, Ohio 43015. *1842, 1844*
Tel: (614) 369-4431. Telex: 246653 bkstr dewr
C : *arts-sc, nurs.*
Oklahoma Baptist University, 500 West Univer-
sity, Shawnee, Oklahoma 74801. *1910*
Tel: (405) 275-2850
C : *arts-sc-ed-fa, bus, nurs, Chris serv.*
Oklahoma Christian College, Route 1, Box 141,
Oklahoma City, Oklahoma 73111. *1950*
Tel: (405) 478-1661
C : *arts-sc.*
Oklahoma Panhandle State University, Good-
well, Oklahoma 73939. *1909*
C : *arts-sc.*
Oregon Institute of Technology, Campus Drive,
Klamath Falls, Oregon 97601–8801. *1946*
Tel: (503) 882-6321
C : *arts-sc, eng techn, allied heal techn, ind
techn, bus.*
Ottawa University, 10th and Cedar Streets,
Ottawa, Kansas 66067. *1865*
Tel: (913) 242-5200
C : *arts-sc.*
Otterbein College, College and Grove Streets,
Westerville, Ohio 43081. *1847*
Tel: (614) 890-3000
arts.
Ozark Christian College, 1111 North Main
Street, Joplin, Missouri 64801. *1942*
Tel: (417) 624-2518
theo.
Pacific Coast Baptist Bible College, 1100 South
Valley Center, San Dimas California 91773.
1967
Tel: (714) 599-6843
arts-sc-theo.
Paine College, 1235 15th Street, Augusta,
Georgia 30910–2799. *1882*
Tel: (404) 722-4471
C : *arts-sc.*
Palm Beach Atlantic College, 1101 South Olive
Avenue, West Palm Beach, Florida 33401.
1968
Tel: (305) 833-8592

C : *arts-sc.*
Patten College, 2433 Coolidge Avenue, Oakland,
California 94601. *1945*
Tel: (415) 533-8300
C : *arts-sc.*
Paul Quinn College, 1020 Elm Street, Waco,
Texas 76704. *1872*
Tel: (817) 753-6415
C : *arts-sc.*
Pfeiffer College, Misenheimer, North Carolina
28109–0960. *1885*
Tel: (704) 463-7343
C : *arts-sc.*
Philadelphia College of Bible, Langhorn Manor,
Langhorne, Pennsylvania 19047. *1913*
Tel: (215) 752-5915
Philander Smith College, 812 West 13th Street,
Little Rock, Arkansas 72202. *1877*
Tel: (501) 375-9845
C : *arts-sc.*
Piedmont Bible College, 716 Franklin Street,
Winston-Salem, North Carolina 27101. *1845*
Tel: (919) 725-8344
ed, theo.
Piedmont College, 165 Central Avenue,
Demorest, Georgia 30535. *1897*
Tel: (404) 778-8301
C : *arts-sc.*
Pikeville College, Sycamore Street, Pikeville,
Kentucky 41501–1194. *1889*
Tel: (606) 432-9200
C : *arts-sc.*
Pillsbury Baptist Bible College, 315 South Grove,
Owatonna, Minnesota 55060. *1957*
Tel: (507) 451-2710
arts-sc-theo.
Pine Manor College, 400 Heath Street, Chestnut
Hill, Massachusetts 02167. *1911*
Tel: (617) 731-7000
C : *arts-sc.*
Pitzer College, 1150 North Mills Avenue,
Claremont, California 91711. *1963*
Tel: (714) 621-8000
C : *arts-sc.*
Pomona College, 333 North College Way, Clare-
mont, California 91711. *1887*
Tel: (714) 621-8000
C : *arts-sc.*
Presbyterian College, South Broad Street,
Clinton, South Carolina 29325. *1880*
Tel: (803) 833-2820
C : *arts-sc.*
Prescott College, 220 Grove Avenue, Prescott,
Arizona 86301. *1966*
Tel: (602) 778-2090
C : *arts-sc.*
Principia College, Elsah, Illinois 62028. *1898*
Tel: (618) 374-2131
C : *arts-sc.*

Pugat Sound Christian College, 410 Fourth Avenue North, Edmonds, Washington 98020.
1950
Tel: (206) 775-8686
theo.

Ramapo College of New Jersey, 505 Ramapo Valley Road, Mahwah, New Jersey 07430.
1969
Tel: (201) 529-7500
S : *app-theoretical sc, Am st, contemporary arts, env st, intercultural st, soc, hum, bus adm, ed.*

Randolph-Macon College, Ashland, Virginia 23005.
1830
Tel: (804) 752-7305
C : *arts-sc.*

Randolph-Macon Women's College, 2500 Rivermont Avenue, Lynchburg, Virginia 24503.
1891
Tel: (804) 846-7392
C : *arts-sc.*

Reformed Bible College, 1869 Robinson Road Southeast, Grand Rapids, Michigan 49506.
1939
Tel: (616) 458-0404
theo.

Regis College, Weston, Massachusetts 02193.
1927
Tel: (617) 893-1820
C : *arts-sc.*

Rhodes College, 2000 North Parkway, Memphis, Tennessee 38112.
1848
Tel: (901) 726-3000
Arts.

Rio Grande College and Community College, 1 Atwood Drive, Rio Grande, Ohio 45674. *1876*
Tel: (614) 245-5353
C : *arts-sc.*

Ripon College, 300 Seward Street, P.O. Box 248, Ripon, Wisconsin 54971–0248.
1851
Tel: (414) 748-8115
C : *arts-sc.*

Roanoke Bible College, P.O. Box 387, Elizabeth City, North Carolina 27909.
1948
Tel: (919) 338-5191
theo.

Roanoke College, Salem, Virginia 24153.   *1842*
Tel: (703) 389-2351
C : *arts-sc.*

Roberts Wesleyan College, 2301 Westside Drive, Rochester, New York 14624.
1866
Tel: (716) 594-9471
C : *arts-sc.*

Rocky Mountain College, 1511 Poly Drive, Billings, Montana 59102.
1878
Tel: (406) 657-1000
C : *arts-sc.*

Roger Williams College, Ferry Road, Bristol, Rhode Island 02809.
1948
Tel: (401) 253-1040

C : *arts-sc.*

Rosemont College, Rosemont, Pennsylvania 19010.
1921
Tel: (215) 527-0200
C : *arts-sc.*

Rust College, 7 Rust Avenue, Holly Springs, Mississippi 38635.
1866
Tel: (601) 252-4661
C : *arts-sc.*

Saint Alphonsus College, 1762 Mapleton Avenue, Suffield, Connecticut 06078.
1963
Tel: (203) 668-7393
C : *arts-sc.*

St. Andrews Presbyterian College, Laurinburg, North Carolina 28352.
1958
Tel: (919) 276-3652
C : *arts-sc.*

St. Anselm College, Manchester, New Hampshire 03102.
1889
Tel: (603) 669-1030
C : *arts-sc-nurs.*

St. Augustine's College, 1315 Oakwood Avenue, Raleigh, North Carolina 27611.
1867
Tel: (919) 828-4451
C : *arts-sc.*

St. Francis College, 180 Remsen Street, Brooklyn, New York 11201.
1850
Tel: (718) 522-2300
C : *arts-sc.*

St. Joseph's College, P.O. Box 7009, Mountain View, California 94039.
1878
Tel: (415) 967-9501
C : *arts-sc.*

St. Joseph's College, Whites Bridge Road, North Windham, Maine 04062.
1912
Tel: (207) 892-6766
C : *arts-sc.*

St. Joseph's College, 245 Clinton Avenue, Brooklyn, New York 11205.
1916
Tel: (718) 636-6800
C : *arts-sc, gen st.*

St. Joseph's College Suffolk Campus, 155 Roe Boulevard, Patchogue, New York 11772.
1916
C : *arts-sc.*

Saint Leo College, Route 52, Saint Leo, Florida 33574.
1889
Tel: (904) 588-8283
C : *arts-sc.*

St. Louis Christian College, 1360 Grandview Drive, Florissant, Missouri 63033.
1956
Tel: (314) 837-6777
theo.

Saint Louis University:
Parks College of Saint Louis University, Cahokia, Illinois 62206.
1927
Tel: (618) 337-7500
C : *arts-sc.*

St. Mary College, 4100 South 4th Street Traffic-

way Leavenworth, Kansas 66048.   *1923*
Tel: (913) 682-5151
C : *arts-sc.*

St. Mary's College, Notre Dame, Indiana 46556.
          1844
Tel: (219) 284-4000
C : *arts-sc.*

Saint Mary's College of Maryland, Saint Mary's
City, Maryland 20686.   *1839*
Tel: (301) 862-0200
D : *hum, human dev, sc-math, soc, arts-sc, ed.*

Saint Mary's College, Orchard Lake and
Commerce Roads, Orchard Lake, Michigan
48033.   *1885*
Tel: (313) 682-1885
C : *arts-sc.*

St. Mary of the Plains College, 240 San Jose
Drive, Dodge City, Kansas 67801.   *1952*
Tel: (316) 225-4171
C : *arts-sc.*

St. Norbert College, De Pere, Wisconsin 54115.
          1898
Tel: (414) 337-3165
C : *arts-sc.*

St. Olaf College, Northfield, Minnesota 55057.
          1874
Tel: (507) 663-3032. Easylink: 62835910 esl ud
C : *arts-sc.*

St. Paul Bible College, Bible College, Minnesota
55375.   *1916*
Tel: (612) 446-1411
arts-sc-theo.

Saint Paul's College, 406 Windsor Avenue,
Lawrenceville, Virginia 23868–1299.   *1888*
Tel: (804) 848-3111
C : *arts-sc.*

St. Vincent College, Latrobe, Pennsylvania
15650.   *1846*
Tel: (412) 539-9761. Easylink: 620 09333 esl ud
C : *arts-sc, ed.*

Salem College, South Church Street, Winston-
Salem, North Carolina 27108.   *1772*
Tel: (919) 721-2600
C : *arts-sc, mus.*

San Jose Bible College, 790 South 12th Street,
P.O. Box 1090, San Jose, California 95018.
          1939
Tel: (408) 293-9058
ed-theo.

School of the Ozarks, Point Lookout, Missouri
65726–0017.   *1906*
Tel: (417) 334-6411
C : *arts-sc.*

Schreiner College, Highway 27, Kerrville, Texas
78028.   *1928*
Tel: (512) 896-5411
arts.

Scripps College, 1030 North Columbia, Claremont, California 91711.   *1926*

Tel: (714) 621-8000
C : *arts-sc.*

Selma University, Selma, Alabama 36701.   *1878*
Tel: (205) 872-2533
C : *arts-sc, theo.*

Seton Hill College, Seton Hill Drive, Greensburg,
Pennsylvania 15601.   *1883*
Tel: (412) 834-2200
C : *arts-sc-ed.*

Shaw University, 118 East South Street, Raleigh,
North Carolina 27611.   *1865*
Tel: (919) 755-4800
C : *arts-sc.*

Sheldon Jackson College, 801 Lincoln, Sitka,
Alaska 99835.   *1878*
Tel: (907) 747-3666
C : *arts-sc.*

Shepherd College, Shepherdstown, West Vir-
ginia 25443.   *1871*
Tel: (304) 876-2511
C : *arts-sc-ed.*

Shimer College, P.O. Box A500, Waukegon,
Illinois 60079.   *1853*
Tel: (312) 623-8400
C : *arts-sc.*

Shorter College, Rome, Georgia 30161.   *1873*
Tel: (404) 291-2121
C : *arts-sc.*

Siena College, Route 9, Loudonville, New York
12211.   *1937*
Tel: (518) 783-2300
D : *arts-sc.*

Sierra Nevada College, Incline Village, Nevada
89450–4269.   *1969*
Tel: (702) 831-1314
C : *arts-sc.*

Silver Lake College, 2406 South Alverno Road,
Manitowoc, Wisconsin 54220.   *1869*
Tel: (414) 684-6691
C : *arts-sc.*

Simon's Rock of Bard College, Alford Road,
Great Barrington, Massachusetts 01230.   *1964*
Tel: (413) 528-0771
C : *arts-sc.*

Sinte Gleska College, Box 490, Rosebud, South
Dakota 57570.   *1970*
Tel: (605) 747-2263
S : *arts-sc-ed.*

Skidmore College, North Broadway, Saratoga
Springs, New York 12866–0851.   *1922*
Tel: (518) 584-5000
C : *arts-sc-ed, nurs.*

Sojowner-Douglass College, 500 North Carolina
Street, Baltimore, Maryland 21205.   *1980*
Tel: (301) 276-0306
arts.

Southeastern Baptist College, 4229 Highway 15th
North, Laurel, Mississippi 39440.   *1955*
Tel: (601) 426-6346

theo.

Southeastern College of the Assemblies of God, 1000 Longfellow Boulevard, Lakeland, Florida 33801.   *1935*
Tel: (813) 665-4404
arts-sc-theo.

Southern Baptist College, Walnut Ridge, Arkansas 72476.   *1941*
Tel: (501) 886-6741
C : *arts-sc.*

Southern College of Seventh-Day Adventists, P.O. Box 370, Collegedale, Tennessee 37315.
                                                          1892
Tel: (615) 238-2111
C : *arts-sc.*

Southern Vermont College, Monument Road, Bennington, Vermont 05201.   *1926*
Tel: (802) 442-5427
C : *arts-sc.*

Southwest Baptist University, 1601 South Springfield, Bolivar, Missouri 65613.   *1878*
Tel: (417) 326-5281
C : *arts-sc.*

Southwest State University, Marshall, Minnesota 56258.   *1963*
Tel: (507) 537-7021. Easylink: 628 60389 esl ud
C : *arts-sc-ed, bus, hum, soc.*

Southwestern Adventist College, Keene, Texas 76059.   *1893*
Tel: (817) 645-3921
C : *arts-sc.*

Southwestern Assemblies of God College, 1200 Sycamore, Waxahachie, Texas 75165.   *1927*
Tel: (214) 937-4010
S : *arts-sc.*

Southwestern Christian College, P.O. Box 10, Terrell, Texas 75160.   *1949*
Tel: (214) 563-3341
eng-ed-theo.

Southwestern College, 2625 East Cactus Road, Phoenix, Arizona 85032.   *1960*
Tel: (602) 992-6101
ed-theo.

Southwestern College, Winfield, Kansas 67156.
                                                          1885
Tel: (316) 221-4150
C : *arts-sc, mus.*

Southwestern College of Christian Ministries, P.O. Box 340, Bethany, Oklahoma 73008.
                                                          1946
Tel: (405) 789-7661
theo.

Southwestern University, University Avenue, Georgetown, Texas 78627–0770.   *1840*
Tel: (512) 863-6511. Telex: 9103501677 s w university
C : *arts-sc.*
S : *fa.*

Spelman College, 350 Spelman Lane, Southwest,

Atlanta, Georgia 30314.   *1881*
Tel: (404) 681-3643
C : *arts-sc, advanced st.*

Spring Arbor College, 106 East Main, Spring Arbor, Michigan 49283.   *1873*
Tel: (517) 750-1200
C : *arts-sc.*

Spring Garden College, 7500 Germantown Avenue, Philadelphia, Pennsylvania 19119.
                                                          1851
Tel: (215) 248-7900
C : *arts-sc.*

State University of New York:
    COLLEGE OLD WESTBURY, Box 210, Old Westbury, New York 11568.   *1967*
    Tel: (516) 876-3000
    C : *arts-sc-ed, hum, bus, phys-recr.*
    COLLEGE OF AGRICULTURE AND TECHNOLOGY AT COBLESKILL, Cobleskill, New York 12043.   *1916*
    Tel: (518) 234-5011
    COLLEGE OF TECHNOLOGY AT FARMINGDALE, Farmingdale, New York 11735. *1912*
    Tel: (516) 420-2000
    C : *arts-sc.*
    S : *bus, eng techn, hum-heal sc.*

Stephens College, Columbia, Missouri 65215-0001.   *1833*
Tel: (314) 442-2211
C : *arts-sc-ed.*

Sterling College, Sterling, Kansas 67579.   *1887*
Tel: (316) 278-2173
C : *arts-sc.*

Stillman College, P.O. Drawer 1430, Tuscaloosa, Alabama 35403.   *1876*
Tel: (205) 349-4240
C : *arts-sc.*

Stockton State College, Pomora, New Jersey 08240.   *1969*
Tel: (609) 652-1776
C : *arts-hum, nat-math, soc-behavioral sc, ed, sc-math, prof st.*

Stonehill College, 320 Washington Street, North Easton, Massachusetts 02357.   *1948*
Tel: (617) 238-1081
C : *arts-sc.*

Susquehanna University, University Avenue, Selinsgrove, Pennsylvania 17870–9989.   *1858*
Tel: (717) 374-0101
C : *arts-sc-ed, fa, bus.*

Sweet Briar College, Sweet Briar, Virginia 24595.
                                                          1901
Tel: (804) 381-6100
C : *arts-sc.*

Tabor College, 400 South Jefferson, Hillsboro, Kansas 67063.   *1908*
Tel: (316) 947-3121
C : *arts-sc.*

Talladega College, 627 West Battle Street, Talla-

dega, Alabama 35160.   *1867*
Tel: (205) 362-0206
C : *arts-sc.*

Tarkio College, Tarkio, Missouri 64491.   *1883*
Tel: (816) 736-4131
D : *arts-sc.*

Taylor University, Reade Avenue, Upland, Indiana 46989.   *1846*
Tel: (317) 998-2751
C : *arts-sc-ed, mus.*

Tennessee Wesleyan College, P.O. Box 40, College Street, Athens, Tennessee 37303.   *1857*
Tel: (615) 745-7504
C : *arts-sc.*

Texas A & M University at Galveston, 51st on Pelican Island, P.O. Box 1675, Galveston, Texas 77553.   *1971*
Tel: (409) 740-4415
C : *eng.*

Texas College, 2404 North Grand Avenue, Tyler, Texas 75702.   *1894*
Tel: (214) 593-8311
C : *arts-sc.*
D : *ed.*

Texas Lutheran College, 1000 West Court Street, Seguin, Texas 78155.   *1891*
Tel: (512) 370-4161
C : *arts-sc.*

Thiel College, 75 College Avenue, Greenville, Pennsylvania 16125.   *1866*
Tel: (412) 588-7700
C : *arts-sc.*

Thomas A. Edison State College, 101 West State Street, CN545, Trenton, New Jersey 08625.
                                          1972
Tel: (609) 984-1100
C : *arts-sc.*

Thomas Aquinas College, 10000 North Ojai Road, San Paula, California 93060.   *1969*
Tel: (805) 525-4417
C : *arts-sc.*

Thomas More College, Crestview Hills, Kentucky 41017.   *1921*
Tel: (606) 341-5800
C : *arts-sc.*

Toccoa Falls College, Toccoa Falls, Georgia 30598.   *1907*
Tel: (404) 886-6831
C : *arts-sc.*

Tougaloo College, Tougaloo, Mississippi 39174.
                                          1869
Tel: (601) 956-4941
C : *arts-sc.*

Touro College, 30 West 44th Street, New York, New York 10036.   *1970*
Tel: (212) 575-0190
C : *arts-sc.*
S : *law, Jewish st, gen st.*

Transylvania University, 300 North Broadway,

Lexington, Kentucky 40508.   *1780*
Tel: (606) 233-8120
C : *arts-sc.*

Tri-State University, South Darling Street, Angola, Indiana 46703.   *1884*
Tel: (219) 665-3141
C : *bus adm-eng, arts-sc.*

Trinity Bible College, 50 South 6th, Ellendale, North Dakota 58436.   *1948*
Tel: (701) 349-3621

Trinity Christian College, 6601 West College Drive, Palos Heights, Illinois 60463.   *1956*
Tel: (312) 597-3000. Easylink: 629 85736 esl ud
C : *arts-sc-ed.*

Trinity College, 208 Colchester Avenue, Burlington, Vermont 05401.   *1925*
Tel: (802) 658-0337. Easylink: 629 05061 esl ud
C : *arts-sc.*

Trinity College, 2077 Half Day Road, Deerfield, Illinois 60015–1284.   *1897*
Tel: (312) 948-8980
C : *arts-sc.*

Tusculum College, P.O. Box 49, Greenville, Tennessee 37743–9997.   *1794*
Tel: (615) 638-1111
C : *arts-sc.*

Union College, 3800 South 48th Street, Lincoln, Nebraska 68506.   *1891*
Tel: (402) 488-2331
C : *arts-sc.*

Union University, Highway 45 By-Pass, Jackson, Tennessee 38303.   *1825*
Tel: (901) 668-1818
S : *arts-sc, mus.*

United States Coast Guard Academy, New London, Connecticut 06320.   *1876*
Tel: (203) 444-8275
C : *eng-sc.*

United States Merchant Maritime Academy, Steamboat Road, Kings Point, New York 11024.   *1943*
Tel: (516) 482-8200
C : *mar eng.*

Unity College, RR78, Quaker Hill Road, Unity, Maine 04988.   *1966*
Tel: (207) 948-3131
C : *arts-sc, soc, hum, vis st, env.*

Universidad Metropolitana, Rio Pedras, Puerto Rico 00928.   *1980*
Tel: (809) 766-1717
C : *arts-sc.*

Universidad Politécnica de Puerto Rico, Hato Rey, Puerto Rico 00919.   *1974*
Tel: (809) 754-8000
C : *arts-sc.*

University of Arkansas:
    UNIVERSITY OF ARKANSAS AT MONTICELLO, Box 3596, Monticello, Arkansas 71655.
                                          1909

Tel: (501) 367-6811
C : *arts-sc.*
UNIVERSITY OF ARKANSAS AT PINE BLUFF, North Cedar Street, Pine Bluff, Arkansas 71601.   *1873*
Tel: (501) 541-6500

University of Connecticut:
UNIVERSITY OF CONNECTICUT AT AVERY POINT, Groton, Connecticut 06340.   *1967*
Tel: (203) 446-1020
arts-sc.
UNIVERSITY OF CONNECTICUT AT HARTFORD, 200 Bloomfield Avenue, West Hartford, Connecticut 06117.   *1946*
Tel: (203) 243-4100. Telex: 883997 ips intl
arts-sc.
UNIVERSITY OF CONNECTICUT AT WATERBURY, Waterbury, Connecticut 06710. *1946*
Tel: (203) 757-1231
arts-sc.

University of Hawaii at Hilo, Hilo, Hawaii 96720.
                                                     1947
Tel: (808) 961-9311
C : *arts-sc, agr.*

University of Hawaii-West Oahu College, 96-043 Ike, Pearl City, Hawaii 96782.   *1976*
Tel: (808) 456-5921
S : *arts-sc.*

University of Houston:
UNIVERSITY OF HOUSTON DOWNTOWN, One Main Street, Houston, Texas 77002.   *1974*
Tel: (713) 221-8000
C : *arts-sc.*

University of Maine:
UNIVERSITY OF MAINE AT AUGUSTA, University Heights, Augusta, Maine 04330.   *1965*
Tel: (207) 622-7131
C : *arts-sc.*
UNIVERSITY OF MAINE AT FARMINGTON, 86 Main Street, Farmington, Maine 04938.
                                                     1864
Tel: (207) 778-3501
C : *arts-hum.*
UNIVERSITY OF MAINE AT FORT KENT, 25 Pleasant Street, Fort Kent, Maine 04743–1292.   *1878*
Tel: (207) 834-3162
C : *arts-sc.*
UNIVERSITY OF MAINE AT MACHIAS, O'Brien Avenue, Machias, Maine 04654.   *1909*
Tel: (207) 255-3313
C : *arts-sc.*
UNIVERSITY OF MAINE AT PRESQUE ISLE, 181 Main, Presque Isle, Maine 04769.   *1903*
Tel: (207) 764-0311
arts-sc.

University of Maryland:
UNIVERSITY OF MARYLAND BALTIMORE COUNTY CAMPUS, 5401 Wilkens Avenue,

Catonsville, Maryland 21228.   *1963*
Tel: (301) 455-1000. Easylink: 620 09736 esl ud
C : *arts.*
UNIVERSITY OF MARYLAND UNIVERSITY COLLEGE, University Boulevard at Adelphi Road, College Park, Maryland 20742. *1947*
Tel: (301) 985-7000. Easylink: 629 29200 esl ud
C : *arts-sc.*

University of Minnesota:
UNIVERSITY OF MINNESOTA AT MORRIS, Morris, Minnesota 56267.   *1959*
Tel: (612) 589-2211. Easylink: 628 60901 els ud
D : *ed, sc-math, soc, hum.*

University of North Carolina:
ELIZABETH CITY STATE UNIVERSITY, Parkview Drive, Elizabeth City, North Carolina 27909.   *1891*
Tel: (919) 335-3230
C : *arts-sc.*
WINSTON-SALEM STATE UNIVERSITY, Winston-Salem, North Carolina 27110.
                                                     1892
Tel: (919) 761-2011
C : *arts-sc.*
S : *nurs.*

University of the Ozarks, 415 College Avenue, Clarksville, Arkansas 72830–2880.   *1834*
Tel: (501) 754-3839
C : *arts-sc.*

University of Pittsburgh:
UNIVERSITY OF PITTSBURGH AT BRADFORD, Campus Drive, Bradford, Pennsylvania 16701.   *1963*
Tel: (814) 362-3801
arts.
UNIVERSITY OF PITTSBURGH AT GREENSBURG, Greensburg, Pennsylvania 15601.
                                                     1963
Tel: (412) 837-7040
arts.
UNIVERSITY OF PITTSBURGH AT JOHNSTOWN, Johnstown, Pennsylvania 15904.   *1927*
Tel: (412) 266-9661
arts-sc.

University of Puerto Rico:
UNIVERSITY OF PUERTO RICO CAYEY UNIVERSITY COLLEGE, Barcelo Avenue, Cayey, Puerto Rico 00633.   *1967*
Tel: (809) 738-2161
C : *arts-sc.*
UNIVERSITY OF PUERTO RICO HUMACHAO UNIVERSITY COLLEGE, CUH Station, Box 428, Humacao, Puerto Rico 00661.   *1962*
Tel: (809) 852-2525
C : *hum, bus adm, nurs, soc w.*
UNIVERSITY OF PUERTO RICO, ARECIBO

TECHNOLOGICAL UNIVERSITY COLLEGE, Call Box A-1806, Arecibo, Puerto Rico 00613. *1967*
Tel: (809) 878-2830
C : *arts-sc.*

UNIVERSITY OF PUERTO RICO, BAYAMÓN TECHNOLOGICAL UNIVERSITY COLLEGE, Bayamón, Puerto Rico 00619. *1971*
Tel: (809) 786-2885

UNIVERSITY OF PUERTO RICO, PONCE TECHNOLOGICAL UNIVERSITY COLLEGE, Ponce, Puerto Rico 00732. *1970*
Tel: (809) 844-8181

University of Science and Arts of Oklahoma, Chickasha, Oklahoma 73018. *1908*
Tel: (405) 224-3140
C : *arts-sc-ed.*

University of the State of New York, Regents College Degrees, Cultural Education Center, Room 5D45, Albany, New York 12230. *1970*
Tel: (518) 474-3703
arts-sc.

University of South Carolina:

UNIVERSITY OF SOUTH CAROLINA AT AIKEN, 171 University Parkway, Aiken, South Carolina 29801. *1961*
Tel: (803) 648-6851
C : *arts-sc.*

UNIVERSITY OF SOUTH CAROLINA – COASTAL CAROLINA COLLEGE, P.O. Box 1954, Conway, South Carolina 29526. *1959*
Tel: (803) 347-3161
comp.

UNIVERSITY OF SOUTH CAROLINA AT SPARTANBURG, Spartanburg, South Carolina 29303. *1967*
Tel: (803) 578-1800
C : *arts-sc-ed, hum, bus, nurs.*

University of Virginia:

UNIVERSITY OF VIRGINIA CLINCH VALLEY COLLEGE, College Avenue, Wise, Virginia 24293. *1954*
Tel: (703) 328-2431
C : *arts-sc.*

Upper Iowa University, Box 1857, Fayette, Iowa 52142. *1857*
Tel: (319) 425-5200
C : *arts-sc.*

Urbana University, College Way, Urbana, Ohio 43078–9988. *1850*
Tel: (513) 652-1301
C : *arts-sc.*

Ursinus College, Collegeville, Pennsylvania 19426. *1869*
Tel: (215) 489-4111
C : *arts-sc.*

Valley City State University, Valley City, North Dakota 58072. *1889*
Tel: (701) 845-7100

C : *arts-sc.*

Valley Forge Christian College, Charlestown Road, Phoenixville, Pennsylvania 19460. *1938*
Tel: (215) 935-0450
C : *arts-sc.*

Vennard College, University Park, Iowa 52595. *1910*
Tel: (515) 673-8391
C : *arts-sc.*

Villa Julie College, Stevenson, Maryland 21153. *1952*
Tel: (301) 486-7000
C : *arts-sc.*

Villa Maria College, 2551 West Lake Road, Erie, Pennsylvania 16505. *1925*
Tel: (814) 838-1966
C : *arts-sc.*

Virginia Intermont College, Moore and Harmeling Streets, Bristol, Virginia 24201. *1884*
Tel: (703) 669-6101
C : *arts-sc.*

Virginia Union University, 1500 North Lombardy Street, Richmond, Virginia 23220. *1865*
Tel: (804) 257-5846
C : *arts-sc.*
S : *relig, bus adm.*

Virginia Wesleyan College, Wesleyan Drive, Norfolk, Virginia 23502. *1961*
Tel: (804) 461-3232
C : *arts-sc.*

Viterbo College, 815 South 9th Street, La Crosse, Wisconsin 54601. *1890*
Tel: (608) 784-0040
C : *arts-sc.*

Voorhees College, Voorhees Road, Denmark, South Carolina 29042. *1897*
Tel: (803) 793-3351
C : *arts-sc.*

Wabash College, 301 West Wabash, Crawfordsville, Indiana 47933. *1832*
Tel: (317) 362-1400
C : *arts-sc.*

Walsh College, 2020 Easton Street, N.W., Canton, Ohio 44720. *1958*
Tel: (216) 499-7090
C : *arts-sc.*

Warner Southern College, 5301 Highway 27 South, Lake Wales, Florida 33853. *1968*
Tel: (813) 638-426
C : *arts-sc-ed, hum, soc, theo, sc.*

Warren Wilson College, Warren Wilson Road, Swannanoa, North Carolina 28778–2099. *1894*
Tel: (704) 298-3325
C : *arts-sc.*

Wartburg College, 222 9th Street Northwest, Waverly, Iowa 50677. *1852*
Tel: (319) 352-8200. Telex: 592866 wartburg wg ud
C : *arts-sc.*

Wayland Baptist University, 1900 West 7th Street, Plainview, Texas 79072.   *1908*
Tel: (806) 296-5521
S : *arts-sc.*

Waynesburg College, 51 West College Street, Waynesburg, Pennsylvania 15370.   *1849*
Tel: (412) 627-8191
C : *arts-sc.*

Webb Institute of Naval Architecture, Crescent Beach Road, Glen Cove, New York 11542.
1889
Tel: (516) 671-2213
I : *nav arc, marine eng.*

Wellesley College, Wellesley, Massachusetts 02181.   *1875*
Tel: (617) 235-0320
C : *arts-sc.*

Wentworth Institute of Technology, 550 Huntington Avenue, Boston, Massachusetts 02115.
1904
Tel: (617) 442-9010
C : *eng, arts-sc, aero, des.*

Wesley College, 450 North State Street, Dover, Delaware 19901.   *1873*
Tel: (302) 736-2400
C : *arts-sc.*

Wesley College, P.O. Box 70, Florence, Mississippi 39073.   *1972*
Tel: (601) 845-2265
theo.

Wesleyan College, 4760 Forsyth Road, Macon, Georgia 31297–4299.   *1836*
Tel: (912) 477-1110
C : *arts-sc.*

West Coast Christian College, 6901 North Maple Avenue, Fresno, California 93710.   *1949*
Tel: (209) 299-7201
C : *arts-sc.*

West Liberty State College, West Liberty, West Virginia 26074.   *1837*
Tel: (304) 336-5000
C : *arts-sc-ed-occp, bus-eco, nat, sc, fa, hum, phys, psyc, heal.*

West Virginia State College, Institute, West Virginia 25112.   *1891*
Tel: (304) 766-3000
C : *arts-sc-ed, ind techn, bus adm, soc, mus, phys.*

Westbrook College, 716 Stevens Avenue, Portland, Maine 04103.   *1831*
Tel: (207) 797-7261
C : *arts-sc.*

Western Baptist College, 5000 Deer Park Drive, S.E., Salem, Oregon 97301.   *1935*
Tel: (503) 581-8600
C : *arts-sc.*

Westmar College, Le Mars, Iowa 51031.   *1890*
Tel: (712) 546-7081
C : *arts-sc.*

Westminster College, Fulton, Missouri 65251.
1851
Tel: (314) 642-3361
C : *arts-sc.*

Westmont College, 955 La Paz Road, Santa Barbara, California 93108.   *1940*
Tel: (805) 969-5051
C : *arts-sc.*

Wheaton College, Norton, Massachusetts 02766.
1834
Tel: (617) 285-7722. Telex: 984467 whtn coll
C : *arts-sc, bus.*

Whitman College, 345 Boyer Avenue, Walla Walla, Washington 99362.   *1859*
Tel: (509) 527-5111
C : *arts-sc.*

Wilberforce University, Wilberforce, Ohio 45384.   *1856*
Tel: (513) 376-2911
C : *arts-sc.*

Wiley College, 711 Rosborough Spring Road, Marshall, Texas 75670.   *1873*
Tel: (214) 938-8341
C : *arts-sc.*

William Jewell College, Liberty, Missouri 64068.
1849
Tel: (816) 781-7700
C : *arts-sc-ed, nurs.*

William Penn College, Oskaloosa, Iowa 52577.
1873
Tel: (515) 673-8311
C : *arts-sc.*

William Smith College, Geneva, New York 14456.   *1908*
Tel: (315) 789-5500
C : *arts-sc.*

William Tyndale College, 35700 West 12 Mile Road, Farmington Falls, Michigan 48018. *1945*
Tel: (313) 553-7200
arts.

William Woods College, Fulton, Missouri 65251.
1870
Tel: (314) 642-2251
C : *arts-sc.*

Wilmington College, Pyle Center, Box 1185, Wilmington, Ohio 45177.   *1870*
Tel: (513) 382-6661
C : *arts-sc.*

Wilson College, Philadelphia Avenue, Chambersburg, Pennsylvania 17201–9986.
1869
Tel: (717) 264-4141
C : *arts-sc.*

Winston-Salem State University, Winston-Salem, North Carolina 27110.   *1892*
Tel: (919) 761-2011. Easylink: 620 49289 esl ud
arts-sc.

Wisconsin Lutheran College, Milwaukee, Wisconsin 53226.   *1973*

Tel: (414) 774-8620
C : *arts-sc.*
Wofford College, 429 North Church Street, Spartanburg, South Carolina 29301.   *1854*
Tel: (803) 585-4821
C : *arts-sc.*

World College West, 101 South San Antonio Road, P.O. Box 3060, San Rafael, California 94912.   *1971*
Tel: (707) 765-4500
C : *arts-sc, hum serv.*

Independent Professional Schools—
Ecoles professionnelles indépendantes

Academy of Art College, 540 Powell Street, San Francisco, California 94108.   *1929*
Tel: (415) 673-4200
C : *arts, interior & graph des, photography.*
Albany College of Pharmacy, 106 New Scotland Avenue, Albany, New York 12208.   *1881*
Tel: (518) 445-7211
C : *phar.*
Albany Law School of Union University, 80 New Scotland Avenue, Albany, New York 12208.
1851
Tel: (518) 445-2311
S : *law.*
Albany Medical College, 47 New Scotland Avenue, Albany, New York 12208.   *1939*
Tel: (518) 445-5582
S : *med.*
Alfred Adler Institute, 618 South Michigan Avenue, Chicago, Illinois.   *1952*
Tel: (312) 294-7100
psyc.
American Conservatory Theatre, 450 Geary Street, San Francisco, California 94102.   *1969*
Tel: (415) 771-3880
dram.
American Film Institute, Los Angeles, California 90027.   *1969*
Tel: (213) 856-7600
cinema.
Armstrong University, 2222 Harold Way, Berkeley, California 94704.   *1918*
Tel: (415) 848-2500
S : *bus adm, law, ed.*
Arthur D. Little Management Education Institute, 35 Acorn Park, Cambridge, Massachusetts 02140.   *1973*
Tel: (617) 864-5770
Babson College, Babson Park, Wellesley, Massachusetts 02157–0901.   *1919*
Tel: (617) 235-1200
C : *bus adm, ed.*
Bank Street College of Education, 610 West 112 Street, New York, New York 10025.   *1916*
Tel: (212) 663-7200
C : *ed, adm.*
Baylor College of Dentistry, 3302 Gaston Avenue, Dallas, Texas 75246.   *1905*

Tel: (214) 828-8100
C : *dent, dent hyg.*
Baylor College of Medicine, One Baylor Plaza, Texas Medical Center, Houston, Texas 77030.
1903
Tel: (713) 799-4951. Fax: (713) 7901275. Telex: 797908 ismet hou. Easylink: 620 24057 els ud
C : *med, ed.*
Bentley College, Beaver and Forest Streets, Waltham, Massachusetts 02254.   *1917*
Tel: (617) 891-2000. Telex: 9102400945 bentley adm ug
C : *bus, arts-sc.*
Brooklyn Law School, 250 Joralemon Street, Brooklyn, New York 11201.   *1901*
Tel: (718) 625-2200
S : *law.*
Brooks Institute of Photography, 801 Alston Road, Santa Barbara, California 93018.   *1945*
Tel: (805) 966-3888
Bryant College, 450 Douglas Pike, Smithfield, Rhode Island 02917.   *1863*
Tel: (401) 232-6000
C : *bus adm.*
California College of Arts and Crafts, 5212 Broadway, Oakland, California 94618.   *1907*
Tel: (415) 653-8118
S : *arc, des, fa.*
California College of Podiatric Medicine, 1210 Scott Street, San Francisco, California 94115.
1914
Tel: (415) 563-8070
C : *podiatry, adm.*
California Family Study Center, 4404 Riverside Drive, Burbank, California 91505.   *1971*
Tel: (818) 843-0711
California Institute of the Arts, 24700 McBean Parkway, Valencia, California 91355.   *1961*
Tel: (805) 255-1050
S : *art-des, dance, film-video, mus, theat.*
California School of Professional Psychology, 1900 Addison Street, Berkeley, California 94704.
Tel: (415) 548-5415
CALIFORNIA SCHOOL OF PROFESSIONAL PSYCHOLOGY AT FRESNO, 1350 M. Street, Fresno, California 93721.   *1969*

Tel: (209) 486-8420
S : *psyc.*
CALIFORNIA SCHOOL OF PROFESSIONAL PSYCHOLOGY AT LOS ANGELES, 2235 Beverly Boulevard, Los Angeles, California 90004. *1969*
Tel: (213) 483-7034
S : *psyc.*
CALIFORNIA SCHOOL OF PROFESSIONAL PSYCHOLOGY AT SAN DIEGO, 16212 Ferris Square, San Diego, California 92121. *1969*
Tel: (619) 452-1664
S : *psyc.*

California Western School of Law, 350 Cedar Street, San Diego, California 92101. *1958*
Tel: (619) 239-0391
C : *law.*

Center for Humanistic Studies, Detroit, Michigan 48202. *1980*
Tel: (313) 875-7440

Chicago College of Osteopathic Medicine, 5200 Ellis Avenue, Chicago, Illinois 60615. *1900*
Tel: (312) 947-3000
C : *osteopathy.*

Chicago School of Professional Psychology, 806 South Plymouth Court, Chicago, Illinois 60605. *1979*
Tel: (312) 786-9443
C : *psyc.*

Cincinnati College of Mortuary Science, 2220 Victory Parkway, Cincinnati, Ohio 45206. *1882*
Tel: (513) 861-3240

The City University of New York:
MOUNT SINAI SCHOOL OF MEDICINE, One Gustav L. Levy Place, New York, N.Y. 10029. *1963*
Tel: (212) 650-6696
S : *med, biol sc.*

Cleary College, 2170 Washtenaw Avenue, Ypsilanti, Michigan 48197. *1883*
Tel: (313) 483-4400
C : *bus, arts-sc.*

Cleveland Chiropractic College, 590 North Vermont Avenyue, Los Angeles, California 90004. *1911*
Tel: (213) 660-6166
C : *chiropractic.*

Cleveland Chiropratic College, 6401 Rockhill Road, Kansas City, Missouri 64131. *1922*
Tel: (816) 333-8230

Cleveland Institute of Art, 11141 East Boulevard, Cleveland, Ohio 44106. *1882*
Tel: (216) 421-4322

Cleveland Institute of Music, 11021 East Boulevard, Cleveland, Ohio 44106. *1920*
Tel: (216) 791-5165

College of Aeronautics, La Guardia Airport, Flushing, New York 11371. *1932*

Tel: (718) 429-6600
College for Developmental Studies, 563 North Alfred Street, Los Angeles, California 90048. *1963*
Tel: (213) 852-1321

College for Human Services, 345 Hudson Street, New York, New York 10014. *1964*
Tel: (212) 989-2002
soc.

College of Insurance, 101 Murray Street, New York, New York 10007. *1947*
Tel: (212) 962-4111
C : *act-ins, ed.*

College of Osteopathic Medicine of the Pacific, College Plaza, Pomona, California 91766. *1975*
Tel: (714) 623-6116

Columbus College of Art and Design, 47 North Washington Avenue, Columbus, Ohio 43215. *1879*
Tel: (614) 224-9101

Conservatory of Music of Puerto Rico, G.P.O. 41227 Minillas Station, Santurce, Puerto Rico 00940–1227. *1959*
Tel: (809) 751-0160
S : *mus.*

Conway School of Landscape Design, Conway, Massachusetts 01341. *1972*
Tel: (413) 369-4044

Corcoran School of Art, 17th and New York Avenue N.W., Washington D.C. 20006. *1890*
Tel: (202) 628-9484

Cranbrook Academy of Art, 500 Lone Pine Road, P.O. Box 801, Bloomfield Hills, Michigan 48013. *1932*
Tel: (318) 645-3303

Davenport College of Business, 415 East Fulton Street, Grand Rapids, Michigan 49503. *1866*
Tel: (616) 451-3511

Deaconess College of Nursing, 6150 Oakland Avenue, St. Louis, Missouri 63139. *1889*
Tel: (314) 768-3041

Detroit College of Business, 4801 Dakman Boulevard, Dearborn, Michigan 48126. *1962*
Tel: (313) 582-6983
C : *bus.*

Detroit College of Law, 130 East Elizabeth Street, Detroit, Michigan 48201. *1891*
Tel: (313) 965-0150
C : *law.*

Dickinson School of Law, 150 South College Street, Carlisle, Pennsylvania 17013–2899. *1834*
Tel: (717) 243-4611. Fax: (717) 2434443
S : *law.*

Dr. Martin Luther College, College Heights, Ulm. Minnesota 56073. *1884*
Tel: (507) 354-8221
C : *ed, arts-sc.*

Dyke College, 112 Prospect Avenue, Cleveland,

Ohio 44115.   *1848*
Tel: (216) 696-9000
C : *bus, ed.*
Eastern Virginia Medical School, 385 Mobray
Arch, Box 1980, Norfolk, Virginia 23501. *1964*
Tel: (804) 446-5600. Telex: 9102409699 conrad
rsln ug
Fielding Institute, 2112 Santa Barbara Street,
Santa Barbara, California 93101.   *1974*
Tel: (805) 687-1099
C : *psyc, ed.*
Forest Institute of Professional Psychology, 1717
Round Road, Des Plaines, Illinois 60616. *1979*
Tel: (312) 635-4175
psyc.
Fort Lauderdale College, 1401 East Broward
Boulevard, Fort Lauderdale, Florida 33301.
                                                 1940
Tel: (305) 462-3761
C : *bus, arts-sc.*
GMI Engineering and Management Institute,
1700 West 3rd Avenue, Flint, Michigan 48502.
                                                 1919
Tel: (313) 762-9500
I : *eng.*
Grantham College of Engineering, P.O. Box 539,
10570 Humbolt Street, Los Alamitos, Califor-
nia 90720.   *1951*
Tel: (213) 493-4421
Griffin College, 2005 5th Avenue, Seattle, Wash-
ington 98121.   *1909*
Tel: (206) 624-7154
bus.
Hahnemann University, Broad and Vine Streets,
Philadelphia, Pennsylvania 19102–1192. *1848*
Tel: (215) 448-7000. Fax: (215) 4888108
C : *med, radiologic techn, nurs, allied heal*
professions, med.
Harrington Institute of Interior Design, 410 South
Michigan Avenue, Chicago, Illinois 60605.
                                                 1931
Tel: (312) 939-4975
Harris-Stowe State College, 3026 Laclede
Avenue, Missouri 63103.   *1857*
Tel: (314) 533-3366
C : *ed, math-sc, hum.*
Humphreys College, 6650 Inglewood Avenue,
Stockston, California 95207.   *1896*
Tel: (209) 478-0800
law.
Husson College, One College Circle, Bangor,
Maine 04401.   *1898*
Tel: (207) 947-1121
C : *bus, ed, nurs.*
Illinois College of Optometry, 3241 South Michi-
gan Avenue, Chicago, Illinois 60616.   *1872*
Tel: (312) 225-1700. Easylink: 620 08586 esl ud
C : *optom, sx.*
Illinois School of Professional Psychology, 220

South State/1 Quincy Court, Chicago, Illinois
60604.   *1976*
Tel: (312) 341-6500
S : *psyc.*
Institite of Paper Chemistry, 1043 East South
River Drive, P.O. Box 1039, Appleton, Wis-
consin 54912–1039.   *1929*
Tel: (414) 734-9251. Fax: (414) 7383448. Telex:
469289 papchemaple ci
I : *eng.*
ITT Technical Institutes:
    4919 Coldwater Road, Fort Wayne, Indiana
    462825.   *1967*
    Tel: (219) 484-4107
    9511 Angola Court, Indianapolis, Indiana
    46268.   *1966*
    Tel: (317) 875-8640
    10822 Southeast Bush Street, Portland,
    Oregon 97266.   *1971*
    Tel: (503) 760-5690
    C : *arts-sc.*
John Marshall Law School, 315 South Plymouth
Court, Chicago, Illinois 60604.   *1899*
Tel: (312) 427-2737
S : *law.*
Johnson and Wales College, 8 Abbott Park Road,
Providence, Rhode Island 02903–3776.   *1914*
Tel: (401) 456-1000
C : *bus, culinary arts, mangt.*
Jones College, 5353 Arlington Expressway, Jack-
sonville, Florida 32211–5588.   *1918*
Tel: (904) 743-1122
C : *bus.*
    ORLANDO COLLEGE, 5500 Diplomat Circle,
    Orlando, Florida 38126.   *1918*
    S : *bus.*
Juilliard School, Lincoln Center, New York,
New York 10023.   *1905*
Tel: (212) 799-5000
mus, performing arts.
Kansas City Art Institute, Kansas City, Missouri
64111.   *1885*
Tel: (816) 561-4852
Keller Graduate School of Management, 10 South
Riverside Plaza, Chicago, Illinois 60606. *1973*
Tel: (312) 454-0880
Kirksville College of Osteopathic Medicine, 800
West Jefferson, Kirksville, Missouri 63501.
                                                 1892
Tel: (816) 626-2121
C : *osteopathy.*
Laboratory Institute of Merchandising, 12 East
53rd Street, New York, New York 10022. *1939*
Tel: (212) 752-1530
Lesley College, 29 Everett Street, Cambridge,
Massachusetts 02238.   *1909*
Tel: (617) 868-9600
C : *ed, psyc, arts-hum, sc.*
Life Chiropractic College, Marietta, Georgia

30060.   *1974*
Tel: (404) 424-0554. Easylink: 629 12799 esl ud
Life Chiropractic College-West, San Lorenzo,
California 94580.   *1976*
Tel: (415) 276-9013
C : *chiropractic.*

Logan College of Chiropractic, P.O. Box 100,
Chesterfield, Missouri 63017.   *1935*
Tel: (314) 227-2100
S : *chiropractic.*

Los Angeles College of Chiropractic, 16200 East
Amber Valley Drive, Whittier, California
90604.   *1911*
Tel: (213) 947-8755
C : *chiropractic*

Manhattan School of Music, 120 Claremont
Avenue, New York, New York 10027.   *1917*
Tel: (212) 749-2802
S : *mus.*

Mannes College of Music, 150 West 85th Street,
New York, New York 10024.   *1916*
Tel: (212) 580-0210
mus.

Maryland Institute, College of Art, 1300 Mount
Royal Avenue, Baltimore, Maryland 21217.
                                           1826
Tel: (301) 669-9200
art.

**Massachusetts College of Pharmacy and Allied
Health Sciences**, 179 Longwood Avenue,
Boston, Massachusetts 02115.   *1923*
Tel: (617) 732-2800
C : *phar.*

Massachusetts School of Professional Psychology,
322 Sprague Street, Dedham, Massachusetts
022026.   *1974*
Tel: (617) 329-6777
psyc.

Mayo Medical School, 200 First Street, S.W.,
Rochester, Minnesota 55905.   *1971*
Tel: (507) 284-3671. Easylink: 629 12176 esl ud.
C : *med, rad.*

Medical College of Georgia, Administration
Building, Room 170, Augusta, Georgia 30912.
                                           1828
Tel: (404) 828-2201
S : *med, dent, nurs, allied heal sc.*

Medical College of Ohio, 3000 Arlington Avenue,
Caller Service 10008, Toledo, Ohio 43699–
0008.   *1964*
Tel: (419) 381-4172
C : *med, rad, nurs, allied heal sc.*

Medical College of Pennsylvania, 3300 Henley
Avenue, Philadelphia, Pennsylvania 19129.
                                           1850
Tel: (215) 842-6000
C : *med, rad.*

Medical University of South Carolina, 171 Ashley
Avenue, Charleston, South Carolina 29425.

                                           1824
Tel: (803) 792-2211. Easylink: 625 48100 esl ud
S : *nurs, phar.*

Meharry Medical College, 1005 18th Avenue N.,
Nashville, Tennessee 37208.   *1876*
Tel: (615) 327-6111
C : *dent, med, allied heal professions.*

Memphis College of Art, Overton Park,
Memphis, Tennessee 38112.   *1936*
Tel: (901) 324-8208
art.

Menlo College, 1000 El Camino Real, Menlo
Park, California 94025.   *1927*
Tel: (415) 323-6141
C : *bus adm, let-sc.*

Mennonite College of Nursing, 804 North East
Street, Bloomington, Illinois 61701.   *1983*
Tel: (309) 829-0715
nurs.

Milwaukee Institute of Art and Design, 342 North
Water Street, Milwaukee, Wisconsin 53202.
                                           1974
Tel: (414)276-7889
S : *art.*

Minneapolis College of Art and Design, 133 East
25th Street, Minneapolis, Minnesota 55404.
                                           1886
Tel: (612) 870-3161
art-des.

Moore College of Art, 20th and the Parkway,
Philadelphia, Pennsylvania 19103.   *1844*
Tel: (215) 568-4515
Art.

National College, 321 Kansas City Street, P.O.
Box 1780, Rapid City, South Dakota 57701.
                                           1941
Tel: (605) 394-4998
C : *bus, ed.*

National College of Chiropractic, 200 East
Roosevelt Road, Lombard, Illinois 60148–
6118.   *1906*
Tel: (312) 629-2000
C : *chiropractic.*

New England College of Optometry, 424 Beacon
Street, Boston, Massachusetts 02115.   *1894*
Tel: (617) 266-2030
C : *optom.*

New England Conservatory of Music, 290 Huntington Avenue, Boston, Massachusetts 02115.
                                           1867
Tel: (617) 262-1120
mus.

New England School of Law, Boston, Massachu-
setts 02116.   *1908*
Tel: (617) 262-1120
C : *law.*

New Hampshire College, 2500 North River Road,
Manchester, New Hampshire 03104.   *1932*
Tel: (603) 668-2211. Telex: 7102200616

nhcollege man. Easylink: 620 46598 esl ud
C : *bus, hum serv.*
New York Chiropractic College, P.O. Box 167, Glen Head, New York 11545. *1919*
Tel: (516) 626-2700
C : *chiropractic.*
New York College of Podiatric Medicine, 53 East 124th Street, New York, New York 10035.
1911
Tel: (212) 427-8400
S : *podiatry.*
New York Law School, 57 Worth Street, New York, New York 10013. *1891*
Tel: (212) 966-3500
S : *law.*
New York Medical College, Valhalla, New York 10595–1690. *1860*
Tel: (914) 993-4000
C : *med, medical sc, heal sc.*
New York School of Interior Design, 155 East 56th Street, New York, New York, 10022. *1916*
Tel: (212) 753-5365
S : *int des.*
Nichols College, Dudley Hill, Dudley, Massachusetts 01570. *1931*
Tel: (617) 943-1560
C : bus adm, arts-sc.
Northeastern Ohio Universities, College of Medicine, 4209 State Route 44, P.O. Box 95, Rootstown, Ohio 44272–0095. *1973*
Tel: (216) 325-2511
C : *med, sc.*
Northwestern College of Chiropractic, 2501 West 84th Street, Bloomington, Minnesota 55431.
1941
Tel: (612) 888-4777
C : *chiropractic.*
Ohio College of Podiatric Medicine, 10515 Carnegie Avenue, Cleveland, Ohio 44106.
1916
Tel: (216) 231-3300
C : *podiatric.*
Oklahoma College of Osteopathic Medicine and Surgery, P.O. Box 2280, 111 West 17th Street, Tulsa, Oklahoma 74107. *1972*
Tel: (918) 582-1972
C : *osteopathy.*
O'More College of Design, 423 South Margin Street, Franklin, Tennessee 37064. *1970*
Tel: (615) 794-4254
C : *des.*
Orlando College, 5500–5800 Diplomat Circle, Orlando, Florida 32810. *1918*
Tel: (305) 628-5870
C : *bus.*
Otis Art Institute of Parson's School of Design, 2401 Wilshire Boulevard, Los Angeles, California 90057. *1911*
Tel: (213) 257-0505

C : *arts.*
Pacific Graduate School of Psychology, 431 Burgess Drive, Palo Alto, California 94025.
1975
Tel: (415) 321-1895
C : *psyc.*
Pacific Northwest College of Art, Oregon Art Institute, 1219 Southwest Park Avenue, Portland, Oregon 97205. *1909*
Tel: (503) 226-4391
C : *art.*
Paier College of Art, Inc., 6 Prospect Court, Hamde, Connecticut 06511. *1946*
Tel: (203) 777-3851
C : *art.*
Palmer College of Chiropractic, 1000 Bradley Street, Davenport, Iowa 52803. *1895*
Tel: (319) 326-9600
C : *chiropractic.*
Palmer College of Chiropractic – West, Sunnyvale, California 94087. *1978*
Tel: (408) 244-8907
C : *chiropractic.*
Pasadena College of Chiropractic, 8420 Beverly Road, Pico River, California 90660. *1973*
Tel: (213) 692-0331
C : *chiropractic.*
Pennsylvania College of Optometry, 1200 West Godfrey Avenue, Philadelphia, Pennsylvania 19141. *1919*
Tel: (215) 276-6260
C : *optom.*
Pennsylvania College of Podiatric Medicine, 8th and Race Streets, Philadelphia, Pennsylvania 19107. *1960*
Tel: (215) 629-0300
C : *podiatry.*
Philadelphia College of the Arts, Broad and Pine Streets, Philadelphia, Pennsylvania 19102.
1876
Tel: (215) 875-4800
C : *vis & performing arts.*
Philadelphia College of Osteopathic Medicine, 4150 City Avenue, Philadelphia, Pennsylvania 19131. *1898*
Tel: (215) 581-6370. Fax: (215) 4733674
C : *osteopathy.*
Philadelphia College of Pharmacy and Science, Philadelphia, Pennsylvania 19104. *1821*
C : *phar, sc.*
Portland School of Art, 97 Spring Street, Portland, Maine 04101. *1882*
Tel: (207) 775-3052
S : *art.*
Post College, 800 Country Club Road, Waterbury, Connecticut 06708. *1890*
Tel: (203) 755-0121
C : *bus, arts-sc.*
Research College of Nursing, 5225 Troast

Avenue, Kansas City, Missouri 64132.   *1980*
Tel: (816) 276-4000
C : *nurs.*

Ringling School of Art and Design, 1191 27th
Street, Sarasota, Florida 33580.   *1931*
Tel: (813) 355-9771
C : *li arts.*

Rush University, 1653 West Congress Parkway,
Chicago, Illinois 60612.   *1837, 1969*
Tel: (312) 942-7100
C : *med, nurs, heal sc.*

St. Louis College of Pharmacy, 4588 Parkview
Place, St. Louis, Missouri 63110.   *1864, 1865*
Tel: (314) 367-8700
C : *phar.*

St. Louis Conservatory of Music, 560 Trinity, St.
Louis, Missouri 63130.   *1923*
Tel: (314) 863-3033
mus.

Samuel Merritt College of Nursing, 370 Haw-
thorne Avenue, Oakland, California 94609.
                                        1909
Tel: (415) 420-6076
C : *nurs.*

San Francisco Art Institute, 800 Chestnut Street,
San Francisco, California 94133.   *1871*
Tel: (415) 771-7020
C : *art.*

San Francisco Conservatory of Music, 1201
Ortega Street, San Francisco, California 94122.
                                        1917
Tel: (415) 564-8086
mus.

Savannah College of Art and Design, 342 Bull
Street, Savannah, Georgia 31401.   *1976*
Tel: (912) 238-2487
S : *art-des.*

School of the Art Institute of Chicago, Columbus
Drive and Jackson Boulevard, Chicago, Illinois
60603.   *1866*
Tel: (312) 443-3700
S : *art.*

School of the Associated Arts, 344 Summit Street,
St. Paul, Minnesota 55102.   *1924*
Tel: (612) 224-3416
art.

School of the Museum of Fine Arts, 230 The
Fenway, Boston, Massachusetts 02715.   *1948*
Tel: (617) 267-1218
S : *fa.*

School of Visual Arts, 209 East 23rd Street, New
York, New York 10010.   *1947*
Tel: (212) 679-7350
C : *vis-arts.*

Sherman College of Straight Chiropratic, Spar-
tanburg, South Carolina 29304.   *1973*
Tel: (803) 578-8770
C : *chiropractic.*

South Texas College of Law, 1303 San Jacinto

Street, Houston, Texas 77002.   *1923*
Tel: (713) 659-8040
C : *law.*

Southern California College of Optometry, 2575
Yorbor Linda Boulevard, Fullerton, California
92631.   *1904*
Tel: (714) 870-7226
C : *optom.*

Southern California Institute of Architecture,
1800 Berkeley Street, Santa Monica, California
90404.   *1972*
Tel: (213) 829-3482
S : *arch.*

Southern College of Optometry, 1245 Madison
Avenue, Memphis, Tennessee 38104.   *1932*
Tel: (901) 725-0180
C : *optom.*

Southwestern University School of Law, 675
South Westmoreland Avenue, Los Angeles,
California 90005.   *1911*
Tel: (213) 738-6731
C : *law.*

Strayer College, 1100 Vermont Avenue, N.W.,
Washington, D.C. 20005.   *1904*
Tel: (202) 467-6966
C : *bus, arts-sc.*

Swain School of Design, 388 County Street, New
Bedford, Massachusetts 02740.   *1881*
Tel: (617) 997-7831
S : *des.*

Tampa College, 3319 West Hillsborough
Avenue, Tampa, Florida 33614.   *1890*
Tel: (813) 879-6000
C : *bus, arts-sc.*

Texas Chiropractic College, 5912 Spencer High-
way, Pasadera, Texas 77505.   *1908*
Tel: (713) 487-1170
C : *chiropractic.*

Texas College of Osteopathic Medicine, Camp
Bowie at Montgomery, Fort Worth, Texas
76107.   *1966*
Tel: (817) 735-2000
C : *osteopathy.*

Thomas M. Cooley Law School, 217 South
Capitol Avenue, P.O. Box 13038, Lancing,
Michigan 48901.   *1972*
Tel: (517) 371-5140
C : *law.*

*Thomas Jefferson University, 11th and Walnut
Streets, Philadelphia, Pennsylvania 19107.
                                        1824
Tel: (215) 928-6000. Fax: (215) 928-7642
C : *med, allied heal sc, nurs.*

Tiffin University, 155 Miami Street, Tiffin, Ohio
44883.   *1888*
Tel: (419) 447-6442
C : *bus, arts-sc.*

**Union for Experimenting Colleges and Univer-
sities**, 632 Vine Street, Suite 1010, Cincinnati,

Ohio 45202. *1964*
Tel: (513) 621-6444
Universidad Central del Caribea Escuela de Medicina de Cayey, José R. Oliver Street, Hato Rey, Puerto Rico 00633. *1976*
Tel: (809) 738-2330
C : *med.*
University of Health Sciences-Chicago Medical School, 3333 Green Bay Road, North Chicago, Illinois 60064. *1912*
Tel: (312) 578-3000
S : *med, heal sc.*
University of Health Sciences, 2105 Independence Boulevard, Kansas City, Missouri 64124. *1916*
Tel: (816) 283-2000
C : *osteopathy.*
Vander Cook College of Music, 3209 South Michigan Avenue, Chicago, Illinois 60616. *1909*
Tel: (312) 225-6288
C : *mus.*
Vermont Law School, South Royalton, Vermont 05068. *1972*
Tel: (902) 763-8303
C : *law, env law.*
Walsh College of Accountancy and Business Administration, 3838 Livernois Road, Troy, P.O. Box 7006, Michigan 48607–7006. *1922*
Tel: (313) 689-8282
C : *bus, ed.*
West Suburban College of Nursing, Erie at

Austin, Oak Park, Illinois 60302. *1914*
Tel: (312) 383-6200
S : *nurs.*
West Virginia School of Osteopathic Medicine, 400 North Lee Street, Greenbrier, West Virginia 24901. *1974*
Tel: (304) 645-6270
C : *osteopathy.*
Western Montana College, 710 South Atlantic Street, Dillon, Montana 59725. *1893*
Tel: (406) 683-7011
S : *ed.*
Western States Chiropractic College, 2900 N.E. 132nd Avenue, Portland, Oregon 97230. *1907*
Tel: (503) 256-3180
C : *chiropractic.*
Westminster Choir College, Hamilton Avenue at Walnut Lane, Princeton, New Jersey 08540. *1926*
Tel: (609) 921-7100
Wheelock College, 200 The Riverway, Boston, Massachusetts 02215. *1888*
Tel: (617) 734-5200
C : *ed.*
William Mitchell College of Law, 875 Summit Avenue, St. Paul, Minnesota 55105. *1900*
Tel: (612) 227-9171
C : *law.*
Wright Institute, 2728 Durant Avenue, Berkeley, California 94704. *1969*
Tel: (415) 841-9230
C : *psyc, arts-sc.*

American Association of Community and Junior Colleges

The Association was established in 1920 to stimulate the professional development of its members and to promote the growth of community, technical, and junior colleges. Membership currently includes 1,039 community, technical, and junior colleges, 185 individual members, and 124 educational associates. A Board of Directors is responsible for establishing Association policy. National conventions are held annually. The president is the chief operating officer. A system of councils and task forces was created to bring about greater participation in the affairs of this national organization.

As the only professional organization of this level of higher education, the Association also serves as liaison between its members and other institutions and association.

Publications: Community and Junior College Journal (8 times a year); AACJC Letter (weekly); AACJC Annual Guide to Community, Technical, and Junior Colleges; AACJC Membership Directory; The Neglected Majority;

Management by One-Liners; Building Communities: A Vision for a New Century, etc.

L'Association américaine des "community and junior colleges" a été créée en 1920 afin de promouvoir la qualité professionnelle de ses membres et d'encourager la croissance des "community, technical and junior colleges". Elle groupe actuellement 1,039 collèges, 185 membres pédagogiques et 120 membres associés. Un conseil d'administration définit et dirige les activités de l'Association. Les assemblées se réunissent annuellement à l'échelon national. Le président est directeur exécutif. Un ensemble de conseils et groupes de travail a été créé pour permettre une participation accrue aux affaires de cette organisation nationale.

Etant la seule organisation professionnelle à ce niveau de l'enseignement supérieur, l'Association assure la liaison entre ses membres et d'autres institutions et associations.

Publications: Community and Junior College Journal (huit numéros par an); AACJC Letter (hebdomadaire); AACJC Annual Guide to Community, Technical, and Junior Colleges;

AACJC Membership Directory; The Neglected Majority; Management by One-Liners; Building Communities: A Vision for a New Century, etc.
President: Dale Parnell.
1 Dupont Circle, N.W., Suite 410, Washington, D.C. 20036.
Tel: (202) 293-7050

American Association of State Colleges and Universities

The Association (AASCU), established in 1961, comprises some 372 institutions of higher education located throughout the U.S. and reaching to the territories of Guam and the Virgin Islands. AASCU also includes 33 state systems of state colleges and universities represented by their chief executive officers. With a combined enrolment of approximately two and one-half million, AASCU members educate one out of five of all baccalaureate degree students in the United States. They have a commitment to quality education for the future and to globalizing the perspectives of their students and faculty through co-operation in international development activities and through the international exchange of faculty and students.

Since its inception in 1961, AASCU has expanded its programmes in direct response to the diverse needs of its members. Presently it provides members analyses of federal programmes and legislation and arranges for the views of the membership to be presented for consideration in legislation and policy-making. AASCU assists institutions to respond to the changing demands of the environment by providing opportunities for professional development and materials on topics such as programmes for new student clientele, resource allocation, future planning and programme evaluation. As a lead association in urban programmes, AASCU offers members new opportunities to increase their expertise in dealing with urban concerns and to form partnerships with local governments. In addition to the programmatic focuses of AASCU, it serves as a general information resource for its members and as a forum that they can use to communicate with each other and with external groups and the general public.

While institutions are represented in AASCU by their president and chancellors, programmes are designed to serve other key institutional components such as chief academic officers, international programme officers, research and grants directors, public information officers and the administrators of urban affairs and agricultural programmes. As a part of its 25th Anniversary Celebration in 1986, the AASCU Board of Directors commissioned a National Commission on the Role and Future of State Colleges and Universities, chaired by former U.S. Secretary of Education Terrel H. Bell. The National Commission, composed of 22 corporate, education and government officials throughout the United States, released its final report to the AASCU membership at the Annual Meeting of the Association, November 9–12, 1986 in Phoenix, Arizona. Issues studied by the National Commission included governance, leadership, financing higher education, access and equity, curriculum and educational mission, and teacher education concerns.

AASCU is a member-directed organization, and its policies are set at the annual meeting each fall. The Board of Directors conducts AASCU's business at quarterly meetings. Committees meet as needed to supervise current programmes, and discuss possible new directors for programmes in their subject areas such as environmental education, career education, rural development, and academic and student personnel. Funded primarily by membership dues, AASCU also receives some foundation and government grants and contracts for particular projects.

Under the guidance of a committee of 24 AASCU presidents, the AASCU Office of International Programs (OIP) is the mechanism used to assist its institutions in planning and developing their international role and responsibilities. It also serves as a catalyst for the improvement of international studies in AASCU institutions and represents the international interests of AASCU with outside agencies and organizations. Each AASCU member has designated an International Education Advisor on campus who acts as a liaison with AASCU in Washington, D.C. The work of this Office of International Programs can be divided into three priority areas: 1) the strengthening of the international-intercultural dimension on campus through workshops, consultations, studies, publications, seminars, and faculty development institutes; 2) the involvement of the AASCU institutional resource base in international development through consulting missions, feasibility studies, and the development of linkages between AASCU institutions and agencies in other nations; 3) the influencing of the policies and priorities of a number of U.S. federal agencies as well as private and international agencies.

AASCU is also one of the charter members of CICHE (Consortium for International Cooperation in Higher Education) through which five major educational associations committed to international education co-operate with specific emphasis on international development services and linkages with other countries.

The Office of International Programs pub-

lishes a bimonthly publication, *International Memo*, which provides its members with current information on campus activities, current government policies and legislation, OIP programmes and other associations or agencies programmes in international affairs. The *International Memo* is part of the larger *Memo to the President* which contains news of higher education as well as activities of the Association and its member institutions.

Créée en 1961, l'Association des collèges et universités d'état (AASCU) compte environ 372 institutions d'enseignement supérieur réparties sur tout le territoire des Etats-Unis, et allant jusqu'à Guam et aux Iles Vierges. L'AASCU comprend aussi trente-trois systèmes de collèges et universités d'état représentés par leurs principaux responsables exécutifs. Les institutions membres de l'AASCU, qui ont des effectifs globaux d'environ deux millions et demi d'étudiants, assurent la formation d'un cinquième de tous les étudiants des Etats-Unis préparant un baccalaureate. Les institutions qui la composent s'engagent à dispenser un enseignement de qualité ouvert sur l'avenir et à élargir les perspectives de leurs étudiants et de leurs enseignants en les faisant participer à des activités de coopération internationale et en organisant des échanges internationaux d'enseignants et d'étudiants.

Depuis sa création en 1961, l'AASCU a considérablement développé ses programmes en réponse directe à la variété des besoins de ses membres. Elle fournit actuellement à ses membres des analyses de la législation et des programmes fédéraux et oeuvre pour que ses membres puissent faire connaître leurs points de vue, et ainsi influer sur la législation et l'élaboration de la politique. L'AASCU aide les institutions à répondre à l'évolution des besoins de leur environnement en offrant des possibilités de perfectionnement sur le plan professionnel et en fournissant de la documentation sur des questions telles que les programmes destinés aux nouvelles clientèles étudiantes, l'affectation des ressources, la planification des activités futures et l'évaluation des programmes. Association de pointe en matière de programmes urbains, l'AASCU offre à ses membres de nouvelles possibilités d'accroître leurs connaissances dans le domaine urbain, et de nouer des liens de coopération avec les administrations locales. En plus de ses activités en matière de programmes, l'AASCU constitue pour ses membres un centre général d'information et un forum leur offrant la possibilité de communiquer entre eux ainsi qu'avec les organismes extérieurs et le grand public.

Bien que les institutions soient représentées à l'AASCU par leurs présidents et chanceliers, les programmes visent également à répondre aux besoins de leurs autres éléments essentiels tels que les principaux responsables des études, les responsables des programmes internationaux, les directeurs de la recherche et des crédits, les chargés de l'information du public, et les administrateurs des programmes annexes en matière de santé, d'urbanisme et d'agriculture. Dans le cadre du vingt-cinquième anniversaire en 1986, le Conseil d'administration de l'AASCU a nommé une Commission nationale chargée d'étudier le rôle et l'avenir des "colleges" et des universités d'état. Elle est présidée par l'ancien Secrétaire d'Etat américain à l'Education, Terrel H. Bell. La Commission Nationale, qui comprend 22 personnalités officielles provenant des milieux d'affaires, de l'enseignement et gouvernementaux des Etats-Unis, a rendu public son rapport final aux membres de l'AASCU à la Conférence annuelle qui se tiendra du 9 au 12 novembre 1986 à Phoenix en Arizona. La Commission nationale a étudié les problèmes de gestion, de direction, de financement, d'accès et d'égalité des chances dans l'enseignement supérieur, des programmes et de la mission éducative, ainsi que de la formation pédagogique.

L'AASCU est une organisation dirigée par ses membres et ses orientations sont fixées lors de la réunion annuelle qui se tient chaque automne. Le Conseil d'administration, qui se réunit chaque trimestre, assure la direction des affaires de l'AASCU. Des comités se réunissent, le cas échéant, pour contrôler les programmes en cours, et débattre des orientations nouvelles pouvant être données aux programmes existant dans leurs domaines spécifiques, tels que l'éducation relative à l'environnement, l'enseignement à finalité plus spécifiquement professionnelle, le développement rural, et le personnel enseignant et les étudiants. Principalement financée par les cotisations des membres, l'AASCU reçoit aussi des subventions accordées par des fondations et par les pouvoirs publics et accepte des contrats pour des projets déterminés.

C'est par son Office des Programmes internationaux (OIP), placé sous la direction d'un comité formé de 24 présidents membres de l'AASCU, que l'AASCU aide ses institutions à définir et à développer leur fonction et leurs tâches internationales. Il joue également un rôle de catalyseur pour l'amélioration des études internationales dans les institutions de l'AASCU et représente les intérêts internationaux de l'AASCU auprès des institutions et organisations extérieures. Chaque institution de l'AASCU désigne un Conseiller pour l'éducation internationale, qui assure une liaison avec le siège de l'AASCU à Washington D.C. Les travaux de l'Office des Programmes internationaux se situent dans les trois domaines prioritaires suivants: 1) le

renforcement de la dimension internationale et interculturelle à l'université (ateliers, consultations, études, publications, séminaires, et instituts de formation pédagogique.); 2) la participation des services de l'AASCU à des activités dans le domaine du développement international grâce à des missions de consultation, à des études concernant les possibilités de réalisation pratique des activités, et au développement des liens entre les institutions de l'AASCU et les organisations d'autres nations; 3) l'infléchissement des politiques et des priorités d'un certain nombre d'institutions fédérales des Etats-Unis, ainsi que d'institutions privées et internationales.

L'AASCU est également l'un des membres fondateurs du CICHE (Consortium for International Co-operation in Higher Education) (Consortium de la coopération internationale en matière d'enseignement supérieur) grâce auquel cinq grandes associations éducatives axées sur l'éducation internationale coopèrent plus spécialement dans le domaine des services en matière de développement international et des liens avec les autres pays.

L'Office des Programmes internationaux publie une publication bi-mensuelle, International Memo, qui fournit aux membres des informations d'actualité sur les activités des universités, la politique et la législation des gouvernements, les programmes de l'OIP et les programmes d'autres associations ou institutions dans le domaine international. L'International Memo fait partie du périodique intitulé Memo to the President, qui contient des informations d'actualité sur l'enseignement supérieur ainsi que sur les activités de l'Association et de ses institutions membres.

President: Allan W. Ostar

1 Dupont Circle, Suite 700 Washington, D.C. 20036.

Tel: (202) 293-7070

American Council on Education

The American Council on Education (ACE), composed of 1434 institutions of higher learning and national and 151 regional education associations, is the major nongovernmental body in the United States concerned with postsecondary education. A nonprofit, private organization, the Council reflects a characteristic of U.S. higher education, a system without national control, comprising a large number of autonomous colleges, universities, and other units. In its voluntary capacity, the Council convenes leaders of educational institutions and associations for co-operative effort to improve educational standards, policies, services, and procedures.

The Council's Washington-based staff of 200 also: a) issue guidelines that serve as models for the nation's campuses to follow in adapting to a changing world, and regularly provide research data and other information to policy makers to assist them in their day-to-day deliberations; b) work with campus chief executives, senior administrators, and faculty in their challenging roles and conduct national and regional conferences, seminars, and workshops to promote more effective leadership and management skills. The Council is concerned with equity issues affecting women and minorities in higher education, especially to senior administrative positions, and operates national identification and training programmes to assist in these endeavours. In addition the Council, through its Higher Education and the Handicapped Resource Centre, offers technical assistance on access for handicapped students; c) serve as an advocate for adult learners in a variety of ways, from administering nationally the GED high school equivalency exam to providing college credit recommendations for courses taught outside the traditional campus classroom by corporations and the military; d) foster linkages with business, labour, and government and act as a facilitator in bringing these groups together with academe to seek solutions to such diverse problems as America's declining position in global markets to retraining the work force; and e) help shape international education policy at the federal level and work with the nation's campuses and higher education groups on issues affecting colleges and universities around the world. The Council administers the Senior Fulbright Scholar Program through the Council for International Exchange of Scholars.

The Council regularly convenes such groups as the Washington Education Secretariat, a forum for thirty higher education associations to discuss education issues of national importance; the Association Council for Policy Analysis and Research, a forum for the discussion, planning and execution of both short and long-range research projects affecting higher education; and the Action Committee for Higher Education, which serves as the public affairs arm of higher education's efforts nationally on student aid funding issues. The Council provides informational services, and through its publications programme makes available to educators and the general public widely used handbooks, informational reports, and volumes of critical analyses of social and educational problems. A publications catalogue and brochures descriptive of Council activities are available on request.

Le Conseil américain pour l'éducation (ACE), formé de 1434 établissements d'enseignement supérieur et associations régionales d'éducation, est le 151 principal organisme non gouvernemental des Etats-Unis s'occupant d'enseignement

post-secondaire. Organisation privée à but non lucratif, le Conseil reflète une caractéristique majeure de l'enseignement supérieur des Etats-Unis, système qui fonctionne sans contrôle central et comprend un grand nombre de collèges, universités, et autres organes autonomes. Le Conseil est en mesure de réunir, à titre bénévole, des responsables d'institutions et d'associations d'éducation en vue d'une action commune visant à améliorer les niveaux, la politique et les méthodes d'enseignement.

Le personnel du Conseil, composé de 200 personnes travaillant à Washington, a aussi pour activités: a) de publier des recommandations qui servent de modèles à suivre aux campus à travers tout le pays en vue de s'adapter à l'évolution mondiale, et de fournir régulièrement des données de recherches et d'autres informations aux responsables chargés de l'orientation pour les aider dans leurs délibérations quotidiennes; b) de collaborer avec les principaux dirigeants, les administrateurs et les enseignants des campus dans leur rôle difficile d'organisation de conférences nationales et régionales, de séminaires, ainsi que d'ateliers destinés à promouvoir une meilleure efficacité des compétences de gestionnaire et de directeur. Le Conseil s'intéresse aux problèmes d'égalité des chances qui affectent les femmes et les minorités dans l'enseignement supérieur, spécialement de leur progression dans les postes administratifs importants. Il organise des programmes d'intégration et de formation pour les aider à réaliser ces projets. En outre, le Conseil, grâce à son Centre de l'Enseignement Supérieur et pour l'Aide aux Handicapés, offre une assistance technique aux étudiants handicapés pour leur accès à l'université; c) de défendre les intérêts des étudiants adultes de multiples façons, ce qui peut aller de l'organisation au plan national de l'examen d'équivalence des études secondaires GED aux lettres de recommandation accréditant les unités de valeur acquises hors du campus traditionnel, dans des entreprises ou dans le cadre de l'armée; d) d'encourager les liens entre les entreprises, les milieux professionnels et le gouvernement, également de servir d'intermédiaire entre ces groupes et le personnel enseignant pour trouver des solutions à des problèmes aussi variés que le déclin de l'Amérique sur les marchés mondiaux et la reconversion de la population active; e) d'aider à structurer une politique internationale de l'éducation au niveau fédéral et de travailler avec les universités du pays et les autres établissements d'enseignement supérieur sur les problèmes qui les affectent dans le monde entier. Le Conseil administre le Programme des Bourses d'études avancées Fullbright grâce à le Conseil pour les Echanges Internationaux de Boursiers.

Le Conseil rénuit régulièrement des groupes tels

que: le Secrétariat de l'Enseignement Supérieur de Washington, forum rassemblant 30 associations d'enseignement supérieur pour discuter les problèmes de l'enseignement d'importance nationale; le Conseil de l'Association pour l'Analyse et la Recherche de politiques d'orientation, une tribune de discussion, de planification et de réalisation des projets à long et à court terme concernant l'enseignement supérieur; enfin le Comité d'Action pour l'Enseignement Supérieur qui sert d'instrument des affaires publiques pour les efforts sur le plan national visant à régler les problèmes de l'aide financière aux étudiants. Le Conseil fournit des services d'information et, par son programme de publications, met au service des éducateurs et du public des répertoires largement utilisés, des rapports d'information et des analyses critiques sur des problèmes sociaux ou éducatifs. Un catalogue des publications et des brochures décrivant les activités du Conseil sont disponibles sur demande.

President: Robert H. Atwell.
1 Dupont Circle, Suite 800, Washington, D.C. 20036.
Tel: (202) 939-9310

Association of American Colleges

The Association was founded in 1915 and has as its mission the encouragement and support of liberal education at all of the nation's colleges and universities. Its purpose as defined by its constitution is "To enhance and promote humane and liberating learning and to strengthen institutions of higher education as settings for humane and liberating learning."

The Association is a voluntary, non-profit organization with a present membership of 615 public and private colleges and universities, research and comprehensive, large and small, two-year and four-year, church-related and secular. AAC membership breaks down as follows: 50% of all the public and private research universities in the United States; 50% of the doctorate-granting colleges and universities; 36% of the comprehensive colleges and universities; 38% of the liberal arts colleges; 3% of the two-year colleges, and 4% of the professional and other specialized schools.

Publications: Liberal Education (five times a year from 1987); Integrity in the College Curriculum; A New Vitality for General Education; miscellaneous monographs.

Fondée en 1915, l'Association des collèges américains a pour mission de favoriser et de soutenir les arts libéraux dans tous les collèges et universités du pays. Aux termes de ses statuts, son objet est de "cultiver et promouvoir une formation

humaine et libératrice et de renforcer les institutions d'enseignement supérieur en tant que foyers d'acquisition d'une telle formation".

L'Association est un organisme bénévole, sans but lucratif, qui compte actuellement parmi ses membres 615 universités et collèges, publics et privés, grands et petits, faisant de la recherche et dispensant tous les enseignements, confessionnels et laïques avec des cursus de deux et quatre ans. Les membres de l'AAC représentent 50% de toutes aux universités aux Etats-Unis, publiques et privées, faisant de la recherche; 50% de tous les collèges et universités conférant un doctorate; 36% des collèges et universités dispensant tous les enseignements; 38% des collèges d'arts libéraux; 3% des collèges dispensant un enseignement de deux ans, et 4% des écoles professionnelles et autres écoles spécialisées.

Publications: "Liberal Education" (cinq fois par an à partir de 1987); "Integrity in the College Curriculum"; "A New Vitality for General Education"; diverses monographies.
President: John W. Chandler
1818 R Street, N.W., Washington, D.C. 20009.
Tel: (202) 387-3760

Association of American Universities

Established in 1900, the Association (AAU) currently consists of 54 American and 2 Canadian universities, half public institutions and half private, with pre-eminent programmes in graduate and professional education and scholarly research. The Washington staff of the AAU works with the membership to provide information, develop policies, and co-ordinate activities in the federal relations area.

The semi-annual general meetings of the Association provide a forum for heads of member institutions to exchange information and ideas on major questions of common interest. Specific activities are coordinated through committees covering such issues as graduate education, scientific research, health policy, and library support.

The Association of Graduate Schools (AGS), an affiliate of the AAU, is composed of the graduate deans of AAU member institutions. The AGS meets once annually just prior to the AAU's Fall meeting.

L'Association des universités américaines (AAU), établie en 1900, se compose actuellement de 54 universités des Etats-Unis et de 2 universités canadiennes, dont la moitié sont du secteur public et l'autre du secteur privé, et qui se signalent par la haute qualité tant de leurs programmes d'études avancées et professionnelles que de leur recherche. Le personnel de l'AAU à Washington travaille,

conjointement avec les membres, pour fournir des informations, mettre au point des politiques, et coordonner les activités dans le domaine des relations avec le gouvernement fédéral.

Les réunions semestrielles de l'Association fournissent aux chefs des institutions membres l'occasion d'échanger des informations et des idées sur des problèmes majeurs d'intérêt commun. Des comités coordonnent les activités dans un certain nombre de domaines spécifiques tels que l'enseignement au niveau postgradué, la recherche scientifique, la politique de santé, et l'aide aux bibliothèques.

L'"Association of Graduate Schools" (AGS), association affiliée à l'AAU, est formée des doyens chargés des études postgraduées des institutions membres de l'AAU. L'AGS se réunit une fois par an juste avant la réunion d'automne de l'AAU.
President: Robert M. Rosenzweig.
Chairman: Harold T. Shapiro, President, University of Princeton.
One Dupont Circle, Suite 730, Washington, D.C. 20036.
Tel: (202) 466-5030

National Association of State Universities and Land-Grant Colleges

Founded in 1887, this is the oldest organization of colleges and universities in the United States. Of its membership of 149 colleges and universities, 72 are land-grant institutions whose establishment was aided by the famous "Land-Grant Acts" of 1862 and 1890, under which the Congress of the United States offered to aid each State in making higher education in a broad range of subject matter widely available.

The other major state universities which are members of the Association have various origins, many of them based on the "seminary grants" made to the States by the Ordinance of 1787, or in the acts of admission of the various States to the Union.

Members of the Association enrol about 2.7 million students in U.S. higher education, but give about 60% of all advanced degrees at the doctoral level. The Association is concerned both with the unique responsibilities of land-grant institutions as a national system, and with co-operation among members on the problems of complex, publicly controlled universities in general. The governing body is a Senate in which all members are represented. Internal structure includes a division of Agriculture; a division of Urban Affairs; a Marine Division; a division of International Affairs; a Council of Presidents; Councils of Academic Affairs, Business Affairs, Extension, Research Policy and Graduate

Education, Student Affairs, and University Relations; Commissions on Art and Sciences, Education for the Engineering Professions, Veterinary Medicine, Home Economics and Education for the Teaching Professions. An Executive Committee functions between annual conventions.

Fondée en 1887, l'Association des universités d'état et des "Land-Grant Colleges" est la plus ancienne organisation de collèges et d'universités des Etats-Unis. Sur les 149 universités et collèges qui la composent, 72 sont des institutions à "dotation foncière" dont la création fut favorisée par le fameux "Land-Grant Acts" de 1862 et 1890, aux termes duquel le Congrès des Etats-Unis s'engageait à aider chaque état à assurer largement l'enseignement supérieur dans toute une série de disciplines.

Les autres grandes universités d'état faisant partie de l'Association ont des origines diverses, beaucoup devant leur existence aux "seminary grants" consentis aux états par l'Ordonnance de 1787, ou par les divers actes d'admission des états à l'Union.

Les membres de l'Association comptent à peu près 2.7 million étudiants inscrits dans l'enseignement supérieur américain, mais confèrent environ 60% de tous les grades avancés, au niveau du doctorat. L'Association se préoccupe tant des responsabilités originales des institutions de type "Land-Grant" à l'échelon national que de la coopération de ses membres concernant les problèmes des grandes universités publiques en général. Son organe directeur est le Sénat, au sein duquel tous les membres sont représentés. Parmi ses structures internes, elle comporte une division de l'agriculture; une division de l'urbanisme; une division de sciences marines; une division des affaires internationales; un conseil des présidents; des conseils sur les affaires académiques, sur les affaires financières, sur l'éducation des adultes et sur la politique en matière de recherche, l'enseignement au niveau postgradué, les questions étudiantes, et les relations universitaires; des commissions sur les arts et les sciences, à la médecine vétérinaire, à la profession d'ingénieur, à l'économie domestique et aux professions de l'enseignement. Un Comité exécutif fonctionne entre les réunions annuelles.

President: Robert L. Clodius

1 Dupont Circle, N.W., Suite 710, Washington, D.C. 20036.

Tel: (202) 778-0818

Council on International Education Exchange

The Council on International Education Exchange is a non-profit, private organization of approximately 180 academic institutions (colleges, universities and secondary schools) and 30 national organizations in North America and abroad which conduct student exchange programmes. The organization was established in 1947 to provide technical assistance to student exchange programmes, arrange transportation, secure facilities, conduct orientation and distribute information. Prior to 1967 it was known as the Council on Student Travel.

In its capacity as a member of the Student Air Travel Association – an organization of recognized student travel bureaux – the Council is now involved in the operation of an extensive network of low-cost student air charter transportation throughout Europe and to points in Asia, the Middle East, Africa and America. The Council arranges year-round transatlantic and transpacific transportation for educational groups and individual students and teachers.

As a member of the International Student Travel Confederation (ISTC) – formed to coordinate the services offered by national student travel bureaux and other organizations – the Council is authorized to issue the International Student Identity Card (ISIC). The ISIC entitles the holder to transportation reductions worldwide and to benefit from the number of discounts and facilities open to the student traveller throughout the world.

The Council also maintains an extensive information service which includes publications on accommodations, tour programmes and travel to and within the United States.

The Council's publications also include an annual *Student Travel Catalog*, which outlines the Council's student work, study and travel services for U.S. students going abroad; and four major paperbacks which are revised biennially, *Work Study, Travel Abroad: The Whole World Handbook, The Teenager's Guide to Study, Travel and Adventure Abroad* are published by St. Martin's Press and *Where to Stay: U.S.A.*, a guide to low-cost accommodation in the United States (454 pages) is published by Frommer/Pasmantier. *Volunteer! The Comprehensive Guide to Voluntary Service in the U.S. and Abroad* is published by the Council and the Commission on Voluntary Service and Action.

The Council sponsors reciprocal student work exchange programmes in Costa Rica, France, Germany, Ireland, Jamaica, New Zealand, and the United Kingdom. It conducts workshops for administrators and directors of overseas study programmes to consider problems in the field of educational exchange and has published a guide to the evaluation of these programmes.

In co-operation with member institutions, the Council administers several study programmes abroad for U.S. students, including a secondary school exchange between the U.S. and Austria,

Costa Rica, France, Germany, Israel, Italy, Japan, Spain, the United Kingdom, USSR, and Venezuela; summer, semester, and academic year language programmes in China; language study at centres in France, Spain, and the Dominican Republic; a film study programme in Paris; semester programme in Indonesian language and culture in Java; summer programme in tropical biology in Costa Rica; international business study in China, Japan, and Spain. Summer programmes in the U.S. and Europe are offered to Japanese students, secondary school teachers of English and young Japanese bankers and business men. Similar travel programmes in Japan are conducted for Americans.

In addition to its head office in New York and branch offices throughout the U.S., the Council maintains offices in Paris, Bonn, Rome, Madrid, London, Tokyo, and Kyoto which provide services to universities and organizations in Europe and Japan respectively.

Le Conseil pour les échanges éducatifs internationaux est une organisation privée sans but lucratif regroupant environ 180 institutions universitaires (collèges, universités et écoles secondaires) et 30 organisations nationales situées en Amérique du Nord et à l'étranger et mettant en œuvre les programmes d'échanges d'étudiants. Cette organisation a été créée en 1947 pour fournir une aide technique aux programmes d'échanges d'étudiants, organiser les transports, assurer diverses facilités, orienter et informer. Elle était connue jusqu'en 1967 sous le nom de "Council on Student Travel".

En tant que membre du Student Air Travel Association—une association de bureaux de voyage agréés pour étudiants—ce Conseil s'occupe maintenant de la gestion d'un vaste réseau de transport à bas prix pour étudiants et par "charter" dans toute l'Europe jusqu'en Asie, au Moyen-Orient, en Afrique et en Amérique. Le Conseil organise toute l'année des voyages transatlantiques et transpacifiques de groupes ou individuels, à l'intention des étudiants et des enseignants.

En tant que membre de l'"International Student Travel Confederation" (ISTC)—habilitée à coordonner les services offerts par les bureaux nationaux de voyage agréés pour étudiants et d'autres organisations—le Conseil a le pouvoir de délivrer les cartes d'identité internationales d'étudiant (ISIC). L'ISIC donne, pour ses détenteurs, droit à des réductions dans le domaine des transports qui sont valables dans le monde entier et permet de bénéficier d'un certain nombre de réductions et de facilités à la disposition des étudiants voyageant dans le monde entier.

Le Conseil assure également un vaste service d'informations qui édite des publications sur les facilités d'hébergement, des programmes d'excursions et de voyage en direction et à l'intérieur des Etats-Unis.

Les publications du Conseil comportent notamment un "Student Travel Catalog" (annuel) qui fournit des informations sur le travail, les études et les voyages organisés à l'intention des étudiants des Etats-Unis se rendant à l'étranger; et quatre volumes brochés importants qui sont révisés tous les deux ans. Work, Study, Travel Abroad: The Whole World Handbook, the Teenager's Guide to Study, Travel and Adventure Abroad *sont publiés par la maison d'édition St. Martin et* Where to Stay: USA, *un guide des facilités d'hébergement bon marché existant aux Etats-Unis (454 pages), est édité par Frommer et Pasmantier.* Volunteer! The Comprehensive Guide to Voluntary Service in the U.S. and Abroad *est publié par le Conseil et la Commission pour le Service Volontaire.*

Le Conseil organise des programmes d'échanges réciproques de travaux d'étudiants au Costa Rica, en France, en Allemagne, en Irelande, en Jamaïque, en Nouvelle-Zélande, et au Royaume-Uni. Il organise des journées d'étude pour les directeurs et les administrateurs de programmes d'études à l'étranger afin d'étudier les problèmes que posent ces programmes et a publié un guide sur la manière d'en évaluer les résultats.

En coopération avec les institutions membres, le Conseil gère plusieurs programmes d'études à l'étranger organisés à l'intention des étudiants des Etats-Unis et comportant des échanges scolaires entre les Etats-Unis et l'Autriche, le Costa Rica, la France, l'Allemagne, l'Israël, l'Italie, le Japon, l'Espagne, le Royaume-Uni, l'Union soviétique et le Venezuela; des cours de langues en Chine durant un été, un semestre ou une année académique entière; des cours de langues dans divers centres de France, d'Espagne et de la République dominicaine; un programme d'études cinématographiques à Paris; un programme d'un semestre à Java sur la langue et la culture indonésiennes; un programme d'été au Costa Rica en biologie tropicale; des cours de commerce international en Chine, au Japon et en Espagne. Des programmes d'été aux Etats-Unis et en Europe sont organisés à l'intention des étudiants, des enseignants du secondaire et des jeunes banquiers et hommes d'affaires japonais. Des programmes de voyages similaires sont organisés au Japon pour les étudiants américains.

Outre de son siège de New York et ses succursales dans tous les Etats-Unis, le Conseil a des bureaux à Paris, Bonn, Rome, Madrid, Londres, Tokyo, et Kyoto, qui assurent des services aux universités et organisations d'Europe et du Japon.
President-Executive Director: Jack Egle

205 East 42nd Street, New York, New York 10017.
Tel: (212) 661-1414. Fax: (212) 972-3231.
Telex: 423227. Cables: costudents

Institute of International Education (IIE)

Founded in 1919, the Institute, which is the largest U.S. educational exchange agency, is a private non-profit organization. It builds international understanding—and furthers international development—between the U.S. and 152 other nations and territories.

IIE administers grants which assist some 7,700 foreign nationals annually to study in the U.S. Applications are made through selection committees all over the world. IIE places foreign students at appropriate U.S. academic institutions and provides them with orientation and intensive English language training, academic guidance, and supervision. Over half of the 5,000 foreign university students IIE serves annually are participants in the U.S. Government's Fulbright Fellowship Program. Others are assisted by Unesco, the Ford Foundation, corporations, foreign governments, and other agencies.

IIE organizes a competition for approximately 600 grants for graduate study abroad for U.S. students each year. These awards include Fulbright Fellowships as well as grants made by foreign governments, universities, foundations, corporations and other donors. IIE also selects outstanding young American performers to participate in international music competitions every year. The Institutes Arts International Program provides technical assistance and consulting services to members, other artists, and non-profit organizations seeking to develop international opportunities for performances and exhibits.

Approximately 800 mid-career professionals and distinguished leaders and specialists from other nations come to the U.S. each year through two IIE-administered programmes. Sponsored by the U.S. Information Agency: the International Visitor Program and the Hubert H. Humphrey North-South Fellowship Program. The visitors pursue individually arranged itineraries in their professional fields or participate in group programmes organized around issues such as energy development or urban policy. They are offered opportunities to learn about the U.S. while pursuing their professional development. Humphrey Fellows—about 150 of them annually—are mid-career professionals who combine non-degree university course work with professional affiliations and special seminars.

IIE also arranges specialized short-term non-degree study, training, and professional development programmes for some 2,000 foreign professionals, technicians, and other specialists annually, largely in development-related fields. Sponsors include governments, corporations, foundations, and international organizations.

IIE provides financial and personnel services for 1200 scientific and administrative personnel on technical co-operation projects overseas. Chief among these projects are 20 International Agricultural Research Institutes, the "Green Revolution" centres which have made possible great increases in food production in the developing world through agricultural research.

Through its New York headquarters, six regional offices, overseas offices on two continents and representatives in many countries, IIE provides information on higher education in the U.S. and abroad to well over 200,000 individuals each year. Professional services are provided to 600 colleges and universities which are Educational Associates of IIE. These services include biennial seminars and other special meetings, all IIE publications, and an Educational Associate Newletter.

IIE publishes comprehensive reference directories and informational brochures for U.S. students planning study abroad and foreign students planning study in the U.S. IIE publications also include *Open Doors*, a report on the Institute's annual census of foreign students in the U.S. IIE also conducts research on policy issues in international educational exchange and publishes the findings. The statistical reports *Open Doors* and *Profiles* provide data and analysis based on the Institute's annual census of foreign students in the United States.

Fondé en 1919, l'Institut de l'éducation internationale (IIE), qui est la plus importante institution des Etats-Unis s'occupant d'échanges éducatifs, est une organisation privée à but non lucratif. Elle a objet de promouvoir la compréhension internationale et de favoriser le développement international en organisant des échanges entre les Etats-Unis et cent-cinquante-deux nations et territoires.

L'IIE administre des bourses qui permettent à environ sept mille sept cents ressortissants étrangers par an de venir étudier aux Etats-Unis. Les demandes sont examinées par des comités de sélection répartis dans le monde entier. L'Institut place les étudiants étrangers dans les établissements américains appropriés, leur assure des services d'orientation et une formation linguistique intensive, et leur dispense des conseils pour les études. Plus de la moitié des étudiants cinq mille bénéficient des bourses Fulbright étrangers dont s'occupe l'IIE chaque année octroyées par le gouvernement des Etats-Unis, et les autres de bourses offertes par l'Unesco, la Fondation Ford, des sociétés, des gouvernements étrangers et d'autres institutions.

L'IIE organise un concours pour l'attribution d'environ six cents bourses donnant chaque année à des diplômés américains la possibilité de poursuivre des études avancées à l'étranger. Il s'agit de bourses Fulbright ainsi que de bourses offertes par des gouvernements étrangers, des universités, des fondations, des sociétés et d'autres donateurs. L'IIE sélectionne également de jeunes artistes américains de premier plan en vue de les faire participer chaque année à des concours musicaux de classe internationale. L'Arts International Program de l'IIE octroie une assistance technique et des services consultatifs aux membres, à des artistes, aux organisations à but non lucratif qui s'efforcent de développer à l'échelon international les possibilités existant dans le domaine des représentations et des expositions.

Environ huit cents professionnels ayant effectué la moitié de leur carrière viennent chaque année aux Etats-Unis grâce à deux programmes administrés par l'IIE et patronnés par l'U.S. Information Agency; l'International Visitor Program, et le Programme Hubert H. Humphrey North-South de Bourses. Les "Visitors" suivent des programmes individuels dans leurs domaines professionnels respectifs, ou participent à des programmes de groupe organisés sur des questions telles que le développement des ressources énergétiques ou la politique urbaine. Ils ont ainsi la possibilité d'apprendre à connaître les Etats-Unis tout en poursuivant leur développement professionnel. Les boursiers du Program Humphrey, dont le nombre est d'environ cent-cinquante chaque année, sont des professionnels qui ont effectué la moitié de leur carrière et suivent des enseignements universitaires non sanctionnés par un diplôme, tout en poursuivant leurs activités professionnelles et en assistant à des séminaires particuliers.

L'IIe organise également chaque année, à l'intention d'environ deux mille professionnels, techniciens et autres spécialistes étrangers travaillant en majorité dans de domaine du développement ou dans des secteurs voisins, des enseignements spécialisés de courte durée, non sanctionnés par la délivrance d'un diplôme, des cours de formation et des programmes de perfectionnement professionnel. Au nombre des organismes finançant ces activités figurent des gouvernements, des sociétés, des fondations et des organisations internationales.

L'IIE assure des services financiers et de personnel à mille deux cents scientifiques et membres du personnel administratif pour des projets de coopération technique à l'étranger. Au nombre de ces projets figurent en priorité vingt Instituts internationaux de recherche agronimique et les Centres de la "Révolution Verte" qui ont permis, par la recherche agronomique, d'accroître de façon considérable la production alimentaire dans les pays en voie de développement.

Grâce à son siège de New York, à ses six bureaux régionaux, à ceux d'outre-mer répartis dans deux continents et à ses représentants dans de nombreux pays, l'IIE renseigne annuellement plus de 200.000 personnes sur l'enseignement supérieur aux Etats-Unis et à l'étranger. Des services d'ordre professionnel sont assurés aux six cent collèges et universités qui sont devenus des associés de l'IIE. Ces services comportent notamment l'organisation et la tenue de séminaires biennaux et d'autres réunions spéciales, le service de toutes les publications de l'IIE, et la publication d'une Educationa Associate Newsletter.

L'IIE publie des répertoires et ouvrages de référence et des brochures d'information visant à aider les étudiants des Etats-Unis à préparer leurs études à l'étranger et les étudiants étrangers à préparer leurs études aux Etats-Unis. Les publications de l'IIE comprennent également Open Doors, qui est un rapport statistique annuel de l'IIE sur les étudiants étrangers aux Etats-Unis. L'IIE dirige également des recherches sur les diverses options offertes en matière d'échanges éducatifs internationaux et en publie les conclusions. Les rapports statistiques intitulés Open Doors et Profiles contiennent des données et une analyse fondées sur le recensement annuel qu'effectue l'Institut sur les étudiants étrangers aux Etats-Unis.

President: Dr. Richard M. Krasno
809 United Nations Plaza, New York, N.Y. 10017.
Tel: (212) 984-5365. Fax: (212) 984-5452.
Telex: trt 175977. Cables: intered

Council on Postsecondary Accreditation

Founded in January 1975, the Council is a voluntary national non-profit organization. Its major purpose is to support, co-ordinate, and improve all non-governmental accrediting activities at the postsecondary level. The Council incorporates the purposes and responsibilities of two previously existing bodies: the Federation of Regional Accrediting Commissions of Higher Education and the National Commission on Accrediting. It receives support from some 6000 accredited institutions of postsecondary education and has accorded recognition to fifty-four national, regional, and specialized accrediting bodies with which it works closely.

There are two types of educational accreditation: "institutional" and "specialized". The former applies to an entire institution, the latter normally to evaluations of a particular college or school within a university or even a single discipline. Some accrediting bodies are primarily "specialized" dealing with higher education in a

single discipline or field or professional training. The procedures used by each type of accrediting group are similar and the evaluations and decisions they make are considered to be equally valid but not necessarily synonymous.

Among its aims and purposes the Council sets out to: review the accrediting practices of its recognized bodies and ensure the integrity and consistency of their policies and procedures; promote the interests of the educational consumer; develop policies and procedures for co-ordinating accrediting activities; promote or conduct research to improve methods and techniques of accrediting; represent postsecondary accreditation before governmental bodies when directed to do so; conduct an information programme on the accrediting process; and prepare and distribute a list of recognized accrediting agencies.

Le Conseil d'accréditation postsecondaire est une organisation nationale à but non lucratif et bénévole. Son objet principal est d'animer, de coordonner et d'améliorer toutes les activités non gouvernementales d'accréditation au niveau postsecondaire. Le Conseil a repris les objectifs et les fonctions de deux organismes antérieurs: la Fédération des Commissions régionales d'accréditation de l'enseignement supérieur et la Commission nationale d'accréditation. Il bénéficie du concours d'environ six mille établissements accrédités d'enseignement postsecondaire et a donné sa sanction à cinquante-quatre organismes nationaux, régionaux et spécialisés d'accréditation, avec lesquels il collabore étroitement.

Il y a deux types d'accréditation: l'accréditation "institutionnelle" et l'accréditation "spécialisée". La première s'applique à un établissement dans son ensemble et la seconde porte sur un collège ou une école particulière au sein d'une université, ou même sur une seule discipline. Certains organismes d'accréditation sont avant tout "spécialisés" et s'occupent de l'enseignement supérieur d'une discipline ou d'un domaine de formation professionnelle particulière. Les méthodes utilisées par chacun de ces types d'organismes sont semblables et les évaluations auxquelles ils procèdent et les décisions qu'ils sont amenés à prendre sont considérées comme également valables, même si elles ne sont pas nécessairement identiques.

Les principales attributions du Conseil sont les suivantes: examiner les pratiques des organismes qu'il a reconnus en matière d'accréditation afin d'assurer l'intégrité et la cohérence politique de leurs méthodes; promouvoir les intérêts des usagers de l'enseignement; mettre au point des politiques et des mécanismes de coordination en matière d'accréditation; promouvoir ou effectuer des recherches visant à l'amélioration des méthodes et des techniques d'accréditation; représenter, le cas échéant, les organismes d'accréditation postsecondaires auprès des organismes gouvernementaux; mettre en oeuvre un programme d'information sur les procédures d'accréditation; et établir et diffuser une liste des organismes d'accréditation reconnus.

President: Thurston E. Manning.
One Dupont Circle, N.W., Suite 305 Washington, D.C. 20036.
Tel: (202) 452-1433

The Carnegie Foundation for the Advancement of Teaching

Founded by Andrew Carnegie in 1905 and Chartered by Act of the Congress of the United States in 1906, the Foundation has the advancement of higher education as its major function. Together with The Carnegie Corporation of New York, it provided support for the Carnegie Commission on Higher Education from 1967 to 1974 and then, in 1974, created the Carnegie Council on Policy Studies in Higher Education. The Council ceased to exist at the end of 1979 and the Foundation assumed direct responsibilities for independent reviews and analysis of education and its needs and contributions in relation to the nation's social concerns and purposes.

La Fondation, qui a été créée par Andrew Carnegie en 1905 et a reçu en 1906 une charte en vertu d'une loi du Congrès des Etats-Unis, a pour fonction principale de développer l'enseignement supérieur. Elle a, de même que la Carnegie Corporation de New York, apporté de 1967 à 1974 un soutien à la Commission Carnegie sur l'enseignement supérieur et a ensuite créé en 1974 le Conseil Carnegie pour l'étude des politiques en matière d'enseignement supérieur. Depuis que ce Conseil a cessé d'exister à la fin 1979, la Fondation procède, sous sa responsabilité directe, à des études et analyses indépendantes sur l'enseignement, sur ses besoins, et la contribution qu'il peut apporter pour résoudre, dans le domaine social, les problèmes et atteindre les objectifs de la nation.

President: Ernest Boyer.
Vice-President: Vito Perrone.
Vice-President, General Services: Verne A. Stadtman.
Secretary and Treasurer: Jean Van Gorden.
5 Ivy Lane, Princeton, New Jersey 08540.
Tel: (609) 452-1780

National Education Association of the United States

The purpose of the Association is to elevate the character and advance the interests of the

profession of teaching and to promote the cause of education in the United States.

Active membership is available to anyone actively engaged in educational work of a professional nature if he has an earned bachelors' or higher degree, or holds a regular vocational or technical certificate. Educational Support membership is available to any employee of a school district, college or university, or other institution devoted primarily to educational work who is not eligible for Active membership. Associate membership is available to any person interested in advancing the cause of education but who are not eligible for active membership.

L'objet de l'Association nationale des Etats-Unis pour l'éducation est de rehausser le caractère et de défendre les intérêts de la profession enseignante aux Etats-Unis et d'y promouvoir la cause de l'éducation.

Membres actifs: toutes les personnes dont la profession consiste à s'occuper activement d'éducation et qui justifient d'un grade de "bachelor", d'un diplôme supérieur, ou d'un certificat ordinaire dans le domaine technique ou professionnel; membres de soutien éducatif: toute personne employée dans une école, un "college" ou une université, ou tout autre établissement à caractère essentiellement éducatif qui ne peut devenir membre actif; membres associés: les personnes désirant promouvoir la cause de l'éducation mais ne remplissant pas les conditions requises pour être reconnues comme membres actifs.

President: Mary H. Futrell.

Executive Secretary: Don Cameron.

1201 16th Street, N.W., Washington, D.C. 20036.

Tel: (202) 822-7002

Peace Corps

The Peace Corps was founded in March 1961. An agency of the federal government, it is a source of skilled individuals requested by developing nations to share their knowledge and experience at the grass-roots level, so that the citizens of those nations may better meet their basic human needs. Several universities and private educational research institutions co-operate with the agency by helping train its volunteers for service abroad.

By the end of 1988, the Peace Corps expects to have over 6,000 volunteers serving in 65 countries. More than 120,000 Americans have served since the agency's foundation. The Peace Corps operates under Congressional authorization. It has three goals as stipulated in the Peace Corps Act: to help countries meet their need for trained manpower; to promote an understanding of Americans abroad; and to help Americans understand the peoples of other countries.

Most volunteers serve abroad for two years. To prepare volunteers to perform well in another culture, they are trained for approximately three months. Volunteers are trained in the countries to which they are assigned, although some assignments require more extensive training, often conducted in the U.S.

Most volunteers have college backgrounds, and the Peace Corps recruits heavily among people with trade skills and agricultural backgrounds. The agency has 16 regional recruiting offices across the country. Faculty members or administrators at various schools act as liaisons, helping recruiters set up their visits to the campuses.

The combination of service and work abroad has been recognized by several schools as a unique education experience. An increasing number provide credit for Peace Corps service when combined with postgraduate studies.

About 30 per cent of the volunteers work in educational programmes, many of them in teacher training institutes. Since the agency was founded more volunteers have been in education than in any other programme. Other major areas of volunteer assignment include food production, water conservation, forestry, engineering and health and nutrition.

Peace Corps headquarters is in Washington D.C., but each host country operation has staff in the field to plan programmes and support volunteers. Many host country nationals are on these staffs. The agency's budget for the 1988 fiscal year was $146.2 million.

Le Peace Corps, qui a été fondé en 1961, est une institution du gouvernement fédéral, elle constitue un réservoir de spécialistes qualifiés où puisent les nations en voie de développement lorsqu'elles leur font appel pour venir partager leurs connaissances et mettre en commun leur expérience au niveau le plus concret, celui de la base, de façon à permettre aux citoyens de ces nations de mieux faire face à leurs besoins essentiels. Plusieurs universités et institutions privées de recherches sur l'éducation coopèrent avec l'organisation en aidant à former ses volontaires pour le service à l'étranger.

Avant fin 1988, le Peace corps pense disposer de plus de 6.000 volontaires servant dans 65 pays. Plus de 120.000 Américains ont servi comme volontaires depuis la fondation de l'organisation. Le Peace Corps exerce ses activités en vertu de l'autorisation qui lui a été donnée par le Congrès. Ses trois objectifs stipulés dans le "Peace Corps Act" sont: aider les pays à faire face à leurs besoins en matière de cadres, favoriser la compréhension de l'Amérique à l'étranger, et aider les Américains à comprendre les peuples d'autres pays.

La plupart des volontaires sert à l'étranger pendant deux ans. Pour les préparer à bien

remplir leur tâche dans une culture différente, ils reçoivent une formation d'une durée approximative de trois mois. Les volontaires sont formés dans les pays où ils sont affectés, bien que certaines affectations exigent une formation plus approfondie qui est souvent dispensée aux Etats-Unis.

La plupart des volontaires aient une formation de niveau supérieur, et le Peace Corps recrute largement dans les milieux agricoles et artisanaux. L'organisation dispose de 16 offices régionaux de recrutement dans tout le pays. Les membres du corps enseignant ou les administrateurs des diverses écoles assurent la liaison, en aidant les responsables du recrutement à organiser leurs visites de "campus".

Plusieurs écoles considèrent cette association du service et du travail à l'étranger comme une expérience unique dans le domaine de l'éducation. Un nombre croissant d'entre elles accordent un avantage aux étudiants pour le service dans le Peace Corps s'il est associé à des études avancées.

Environ 30 pour cent de tous les volontaires travaillent à des programmes éducatifs, un grand nombre dans des instituts de formation pédagogique. Depuis la fondation de l'organisation, l'enseignement est la tâche principale à laquelle s'emploient les volontaires. Les autres grands secteurs où sont affectés les volontaires sont la production alimentaire, la protection des eaux, les études forestières, les sciences de l'ingénieur, la santé et la nutrition.

Le siège du Peace Corps est à Washington, D.C., mais chaque opération nationale dispose sur place d'un personnel distinct pour planifier les programmes et s'occuper des volontaires. De nombreux ressortissants des pays d'accueil font partie de ces effectifs de personnel. Le budget de l'organisation, pour l'exercice fiscal 1988, s'élevait à 146.2 millions de dollars.

The Director
806 Connecticut Avenue, N.W., Washington, D.C. 20526.
Tel: (202) 254-5010

African-American Institute

The African-American Institute (AAI) was formed in the mid-1950s with the dual goal of assisting the development of the new African nations and improving mutual understanding between Africa and America. AAI works closely with governments and universities both in Africa and the United States.

More than 10,000 Africans have benefited from training and educational opportunities under one or more of AAI's programmes. Fields of study for African students have been those that Africans have designated as high priority, development-related areas.

Assistance with the training of staff for the African universities and the training of professionals in fields directly related to the African countries' economic development priorities is provided under the African Graduate Fellowship Programme which receives nominations for study at the Master's and Ph.D. level. The Institute has also helped African universities recruit staff. In co-operation with the Starr Foundation, AAI is also offering awards for Master's degree study in Actuarial Science. Candidates for this programme come from selected African countries to study at institutions in the U.S.

AAI's responsiveness to Africa's changing needs is exemplified by the number of programmes it has undertaken in recent years to aid southern Africans. The Southern African Student Programme provides two-year scholarships for qualified candidates from minority-ruled countries to pursue specialized or Master's degree training. Under another AAI programme, study grants are made available to refugees from minority-ruled countries in southern Africa who wish to study in African universities and postsecondary vocational technical institutions.

AAI's newest programme, The Human Resources Development Programme, for candidates from the former Portuguese colonies of Angola, Mozambique, Guinea-Bissau, Cape Verde, São Tomé and Principe is also providing development-related training grants for post-secondary study in Africa or the U.S., as well as in Brazil.

AAI recognizes the importance of high-level manpower training, as do the independent nations of Africa. In future years, in order to expand its involvement in African development, AAI will also become increasingly involved in fields that will help spread the benefits of development to the majority of Africans. AAI's first step in this direction was to publish a comprehensive survey of non-formal education programmes in Africa. AAI has published a small volume of case studies in African community development and a report of a donor agencies' meeting in April 1974 on rural development in Africa. The trend in AAI's development programme will be away from broad responses to general problems and toward more highly-focused efforts dealing with smaller components of specific development problems.

AAI's American information programme has also entered new fields. The Institute's Africa Policy Information Center gathers and disseminates statements of policy alternatives and factual material on important current issues in U.S.—African relations. Non-partisan itself, AAI also helps to organize workshops and conferences in

which various groups and individuals can probe positions in depth and come into contact with new points of view.

Other activities to inform Americans about Africa include short-term training and supply and development of materials to American school teachers interested in teaching about Africa. AAI's Educators to Africa Association offers African travel opportunities to American teachers, students and other interested groups. Other AAI activities include arranging U.S. visits for African educators, professionals and government leaders, and a variety of other informational programmes involving both African and American participation.

AAI is a private, non-profit organization under a Board of Trustees. It acts as a contractor to the U.S. Government's Agency for International Development and to the Bureau of Eduational and Cultural Affairs of the Department of State. AAI also receives foundations and corporate support, as well as a variety of individual contributions.

Publications: Africa Report (bimonthly); African Update; South Africa/Namibia Update.

L'Institut afro-américain (AAI) a été créé vers 1955 avec pour double objectif d'aider au développement des nouvelles nations africaines et d'accroître la compréhension mutuelle entre l'Afrique et l'Amérique. L'AAI travaille en étroite relation avec les gouvernements et les universités d'Afrique et des Etats-Unis.

Plus de 10.000 Africains ont bénéficié des possibilités de formation offertes par l'AAI dans le cadre d'un, ou de plusieur, de ses programmes. Les domaines d'études choisis pour ces programmes ont trait au développement et correspondent aux priorités établies par les Africains eux-mêmes. L'Institut apporte son aide à la formation des enseignants pour les universités africaines et des spécialistes des domaines directement liés au développement économique dans le cadre du Programme africain de bourses pour diplômés, qui reçoit directement des universités les listes de candidats aux études au niveau du "Master's degree" et du "Ph.D.". L'Institut aide également les universités africaines à recruter du personnel. L'AAI offre en outre, en collaboration avec la Fondation Starr, des subventions pour des études en sciences actuaires au niveau du "Master's degree". Les candidats intéressés par ce programme, qui sont originaires de certains pays d'Afrique, vont étudier dans des institutions des Etats-Unis.

Le nombre de programmes entrepris ces dernières années en faveur des Africains du Sud prouve combien l'AAI se veut attentif aux besoins changeants de l'Afrique. Dans le cadre de son Programme pour les étudiants d'Afrique du Sud,

l'AAI octroie aux candidats originaires des pays gouvernés par des minorités et possédant les qualifications voulues des bourses de deux ans destinées à leur permettre d'acquérir une formation spécialisée ou au niveau du "Master's degree". En vertu d'un autre programme de l'AAI, des bourses d'études sont offertes aux réfugiés originaires de pays d'Afrique du Sud gouvernés par des minorités qui souhaitent étudier dans des universités et des institutions postsecondaires de formation professionnelle et/ou technique africaines.

Aux termes du dernier en date de ses programmes, le Programme de développement des ressources humaines, l'AAI octroie également aux candidats originaires des anciennes colonies portugaises que sont l'Angola, le Mozambique, la Guinée-Bissau, le Cap Vert, São Tomé et l'Ile du Prince des subventions leur permettant d'acquérir en Afrique ou aux Etats-Unis, ainsi qu'au Brésil, une formation en matière de développement.

L'AAI reconnaît l'importance de la formation de cadres supérieurs, comme le font les nations indépendantes d'Afrique. Dans les années à venir, afin d'accroître sa contribution au développement africain, l'AAI s'intéressera de plus en plus à des domaines permettant de faire bénéficier la majorité des Africains des avantages du développement. La première mesure prise par l'AAI en ce sens a été de publier une étude détaillée sur les programmes d'enseignement extra-scolaire en Afrique. L'AAI a publié un petit volume d'études de cas sur le développement communautaire en Afrique, ainsi qu'un rapport sur une réunion d'organismes donateurs tenue en avril 1974 sur le développement rural en Afrique. Le programme de développement de l'AAI cessera progressivement d'apporter des réponses de caractère général à des pro-blèmes généraux pour s'orienter vers des efforts plus concentrés portant sur des éléments plus restreints de problèmes spécifiques de développement.

Le programme d'information américain de l'AAI aborde également de nouveaux domaines. Le Centre d'information de l'Institut sur la politique africaine rassemble et diffuse des communiqués sur diverses orientations possibles et des informations concrètes sur d'importantes questions d'actualité dans les relations américano-africaines. Organisation non-partisane, l'AAI aide également à organiser des sessions d'études et des conférences permettant à divers groupes et particuliers de procéder à des échanges de vues approfondis et de se trouver en présence de points de vue nouveaux.

Au nombre des autres activités destinées à informer les Américains sur l'Afrique figurent la formation à court terme et la fourniture de matériel didactique aux instituteurs et professeurs

américains désirant dispenser un enseignement sur l'Afrique. L'Association de l'AAI "Educateurs pour l'Afrique" offre des facilités de voyage en Afrique aux enseignants et aux étudiants américains, ainsi qu'à d'autres groupes d'intéressés. Les activités de l'AAI comportent aussi l'organisation de séjours aux Etats-Unis pour des éducateurs, des membres des professions et des personnalités gouvernementales africaines, ainsi qu'une gamme très variée d'autres programmes d'information où sont associés Africains et Américains.

L'AAI est une organisation privée, à but non lucratif, dirigée par un Conseil d'administration. Elle travaille sous contrat avec l'Agence américaine pour le développement international et avec le Bureau des affaires éducatives et culturelles du Département d'Etat. L'AAI reçoit également une aide des fondations et des sociétés, ainsi que diverses contributions de particuliers.

Publications: Africa Report (bimestriel); African Update; South Africa/Namibia Update.
Chairman, Board of Trustees: Dana S. Creel, Vice-Chairman, Rockefeller Brothers' Fund.
President: William R. Cotter.
Executive Vice-President: Walter C. Carrington.
833 United Nations Plaza, New York, N.Y. 10017.
Telex: 666565 aframny

United States Department of Education

The Department of Education was established on 4 May 1980. Under the Department of Education Organization Act (Public Law 96–88), education programmes and those which fund rehabilitative services for the handicapped which were formerly administered by the Department of Health Education and Welfare were transferred to the new Department of Education. Most of these programmes had been situated within the Department of Health, Education, and Welfare's Division of Education comprised of an Office of the Assistant Secretary for Education and an Office of Education. Education-related programmes from the National Science Foundation and the Departments of Labor, Justice, and Housing and Urban Development became a part of the new Department of Education, too. Additionally, the legislation called for the transfer of the Department of Defense Overseas Dependents Schools within three years of the establishment of the Department of Education. However, this transfer was repealed 8 November 1985.

In addition to a Secretary and an Under Secretary, legislation established offices headed by Assistant Secretaries overseeing some 150 programmes for elementary and secondary education, postsecondary education, vocational and adult education, and rehabilitative services, educational research and improvement, and civil rights. Also authorized were a general counsel and an inspector general as were offices to administer bilingual programmes, to represent nonpublic education, and to provide planning, budget, management, legislation and public affairs functions.

The Act also created an Intergovernmental Advisory Council on Education, representing educators, parents, students and the public to advise the Secretary of Education and the President on the impact of federal policies on state and local education, agencies and institutions.

A long standing committee, the Federal Interagency Committee on Education, was reauthorized in the Act. Its purpose is to assure effective co-ordination of policies and administrative practices among all executive branch agencies that have education-related programmes.

The Department of Education was enacted to: strengthen the federal commitment to ensure access to equal educational opportunity for every individual; supplement and complement the efforts of states, local school systems and other instrumentalities of the states, the private sector, public and private educational institutions, public and private nonprofit educational research institutions, community-based organizations, parents, and students to improve the quality of education; encourage the increased involvement of the public, parents, and students in federal education programmes; promote improvements in the quality and usefulness of education through federally supported research, evaluations, and sharing of information; improve the co-ordination of federal education programmes; improve the management and efficiency of federal education activities, especially with respect to the process, procedures, and administrative structures for the dispersal of federal funds; and increase the accountability of federal education programmes to the President, the Congress, and the public.

When the Continental Congress drew up the Constitution in 1787, education was not included in the functions assigned to the federal government. Education became one of the many public obligations left to the states under the Tenth Amendment. States, in turn, have delegated much of their authority to local school districts. Congress strongly reaffirmed state and community control of education – now almost two centuries old in Public Law 96–88: "The establishment of the Department of Education shall not diminish the responsibility for education which is reserved to the states and local school systems and other instrumentalities of the states." The Department of Education has no

line authority over chief state school officers, local school boards, or superintendents.

In keeping with its goals, the present administration has sought to: 1) reduce the federal role in educational policymaking which should be left to state and local governments; 2) reduce the complexity and quantity of federal education grant-in-aid programmes; and 3) reduce federal expenditure for education. Much progress has been made and has thus had a significant impact on federal policy related to education. For example, Department of Education programmes now support less than 7 per cent (all federal support is 8.7 per cent) of the total expenditure for education.

As of 31 May 1988, there were 3,180 Department of Education employees located in the Department of Education headquarters in Washington, D.C. and approximately 1,500 employees in 10 regional offices located in major cities across the nation.

Le Département de l'éducation a été créé en date du 4 mai 1980. En vertu de la Loi portant création du Département de l'éducation (Loi d'intérêt public 96–88), les programmes d'éducation et de financement des services de rééducation pour les handicapés, qui étaient auparavant administrés par le Département de la Santé, de l'Education et des Affaires sociales, sont désormais du ressort du nouveau Département de l'Education. La plupart de ces programmes figuraient dans les activités de la Division de l'Education du Département de la Santé, de l'Education et des Affaires sociales, laquelle comprenait le Bureau de Secrétaire adjoint pour l'Education et l'Office de l'Education. Les programmes relatifs à l'éducation émanant de la Fondation nationale pour la Science et des Départements de la Main-d'Oeuvre, de la Justice et du Logement et du Développement urbain ont également été intégrés au nouveau Département de l'Education. La législation prévoit en outre, dans les trois années suivant la création du Département de l'Education, le rattachement au nouvel organe du Département des écoles d'outre-mer dépendant du Ministère de la Défense. Ce rattachement a, néanmoins, été annulé le 8 novembre 1985.

Outre les fonctions de Secrétaire et de Sous-Secrétaire, la législation a créé des offices dirigés par les Secrétaires adjoints qui veillent à la mise en oeuvre d'environ cent-cinquante programmes concernant l'enseignement primaire et secondaire, l'enseignement postsecondaire, l'enseignement professionnel et l'éducation des adultes, l'enseignement spécial pour handicapés et les services de rééducation, la recherche éducative et l'amélioration des programmes, et les droits civiques. Elle a également autorisé la nomination d'un conseil général ainsi que la création d'offices

chargés d'administrer les programmes bilingues, de représenter l'enseignement non public et d'assumer des fonctions dans les domaines de la planification, du budget, de la gestion, de la législation et des affaires publiques.

La Loi a aussi créé un Conseil consultatif intergouvernemental, qui représente les éducateurs, les parents, les étudiants et le public, et est chargé de conseiller le Secrétaire de l'Education et le Président des Etats-Unis sur les répercussions qu'ont les politiques fédérales sur les organismes et institutions dépendant des Etats ou des autorités régionales.

La Loi rétablit un ancien comité intitulé le Comité fédéral inter-institutionnel pour l'éducation. Son but est d'assurer une véritable coordination des politiques et des pratiques administratives de toutes les institutions du pouvoir exécutif qui ont des programmes concernant l'éducation.

Aux termes de la Loi, le Département de l'Education doit: renforcer l'action du pouvoir fédéral en vue d'assurer à tous les citoyens l'égalité des chances en matière d'éducation; unir ses efforts à ceux des Etats, des systèmes d'écoles dépendant des autorités régionales, des autres organes compétents des Etats, du secteur privé, des institutions éducatives publiques et privées, des institutions de recherche éducative à but non lucratif des secteurs public et privé, des organisations communautaires, des parents et des étudiants pour améliorer la qualité de l'éducation; encourager une participation accrue du public, des parents et des étudiants aux programmes d'éducation du gouvernement fédéral; promouvoir l'amélioration de la qualité et de l'efficacité de l'éducation bénéficiant d'un soutien du pouvoir fédéral grâce à des recherches, à des évaluations et à la diffusion de l'information; améliorer la coordination des programmes d'éducation du gouvernement fédéral; améliorer la gestion et l'efficacité des activités du pouvoir fédéral en matière d'éducation, en ce qui concerne plus particulièrement le système, les modalités et les structures administratives de répartition des crédits fédéraux; et accroître l'importance que revêtent pour le Président, le Congrès et le public les programmes fédéraux en matière d'éducation.

Lorsque le Congrès continental a élaboré la Constitution en 1787, l'éducation ne figurait pas parmi les fonctions réservées au gouvernement fédéral. L'éducation est devenue l'une des nombreuses obligations publiques incombant aux Etats en vertu du Dixième Amendement. Les Etats ont à leur tour délégué une bonne partie de leur pouvoir aux circonscriptions régionales en matière d'éducation. Le Congrès a, dans la Loi d'intérêt public 96–88, nettement réaffirmé que l'éducation reste, comme depuis presque deux siècles, la compétence des Etats et des com-

munautés: "La création du Département de l'Education ne diminue pas la responsabilité en matière d'éducation, qui demeure réservée aux Etats, aux systèmes d'écoles dépendant des autorités régionales et aux autres organes compétents des Etats." Le Département de l'Education ne détient pas d'autorité directe sur les principaux responsables des écoles des Etats, ni sur les conseils des écoles régionales, ni sur les directeurs.

Fidèle à ses objectifs, l'Administration actuelle n'a cessé et ne cesse de s'efforcer 1) de diminuer le rôle du pouvoir fédéral dans l'élaboration de la politique de l'éducation, tâche qui doit être réservée aux gouvernements des Etats et aux autorités locales; 2) de restreindre le nombre des programmes d'aide fédérale à l'éducation prenant la forme de subventions et d'en réduire la complexité; 3) et de comprimer les dépenses engagées par le pouvoir fédéral pour l'éducation. Des progrès considérables ont été réalisés, ce qui a des répercussions importantes sur la politique fédérale en matière d'éducation. A titre d'exemple, le pourcentage que représente maintenant le soutien des programmes du Département de l'Education ne correspond qu'à 7% de la totalité des dépenses engagées au titre de l'éducation (l'aide du secteur fédéral est elle de 8,7%).

Au 31 mai 1988, trois mille cent quatre-vingts employés du Département de l'Education travaillaient à son siège de Washington, D.C. et environ 1.500 autres employés dans dix bureaux régionaux situés dans des grandes villes de tous les Etats-Unis.

The Secretary of Education, U.S. Department of Education, 400 Maryland Avenue, S.W., FOB-6, Washington, D.C. 20202.
Tel: (202) 732-3000

Other Organizations

The following list of national and regional organizations has been prepared on the basis of information published by the U.S. Office of Education, and following consultation with the American Council on Education.

La liste suivante d'organisations nationales et régionales a été établie d'après les informations publiées par l'"U.S. Office of Education", et après consultation avec l'"American Council on Education".

Accreditation Board for Engineering and Technology●
Executive Director: David R. Reyes-Guerra.
345 E. 47th Street, New York, New York 10017.
Tel: (212) 705-7685

Accrediting Bureau of Health Education Schools●
Administrator: Hugh A. Woosley.
Oak Manor Offices, 29089 U.S. 20 West, Elkhart, Indiana 46514.
Tel: (219) 293-0124

Accrediting Commission on Education for Health Services Administration●
Executive Secretary: Sherril B. Gelmon.
1911 N. Fort Myer Drive, Arlington, Virginia 22209.
Tel: (703) 524-0511

Accrediting Council on Education in Journalism and Mass Communication●
Executive Director: Susanne Shaw.
School of Journalism, University of Kansas, Stauffer-Flint Hall, Lawrence, Kansas 66045.
Tel: (913) 864-3973

Agricultural Communications in Education
Co-ordinator: Don N. Collins.
c/o Resource Washington, Inc., 655 15th Street, N.W., Suite 300, 20005 Washington, D.C.

American Anthropological Association
Executive Director: Edward J. Lehman.
1703 New Hampshire Avenue, N.W., Washington, D.C. 20009.

American Assembly of Collegiate Schools of Business●
Executive Vice-President: William K. Laidlaw, Jr.
605 Old Ballas Road, Suite 220, St. Louis, Missouri 63141.
Tel: (314) 872-8481

American Association for the Advancement of Science
Executive Officer: Alvin W. Trivelpiece.
1333 H Street, N.W., Washington, D.C. 20005.
Tel: (202) 26-6400

American Association of Bible Colleges●
Executive Director: Randall E. Bell.
P.O. Box 1523, Fayetteville, Arkansas 72701.
Tel: (501) 521-8164

American Association of Colleges for Teacher Education
Executive Secretary: David G. Imig.
One Dupont Circle, Suite 610, N.W., Washing-

---

(1) Organizations marked ● are recognized accrediting bodies.
(1) Les organismes suivis du signe ● sont des organismes «d'accréditation» reconnus.

ton, D.C. 20036.
Tel: (202) 293-2450

American Association of Colleges of Pharmacy
Executive Director: Carl E. Trinca.
1426 Prince Street, Alexandria, Virginia 22314

American Association of Collegiate Registrars and Admissions Officers
Executive Secretary: J. Douglas Conner.
One Dupont Circle, Suite 330, Washington, D.C. 20036.
Tel: (202) 293-9161

American Association of Dental Schools
Executive Director: Richard D. Mumma, Jr.
1625 Massachusetts Avenue, N.W., Suite 300, Washington, D.C. 20036.

American Association of Colleges of Osteopathic Medicine
Executive Director: Sherry R. Arnstein.
6110 Executive Boulevard, Suite 405, Rockville, Maryland 20852.

American Association for Counseling and Development●
Executive Director: Carol L. Bobby
5999 Stevenson Avenue, Alexandria, Virginia 22304.
Tel: (703) 823-9800 (Ext. 301)

American Association for Higher Education
President: Russell Edgerton.
One Dupont Circle, Suite 600, Washington, D.C. 20036.
Tel: (202) 293-6440

American Association of University Professors
Secretary-General: Ernest Benjamin.
1012-4th Street, N.W., Suite 500, Washington, D.C. 20005.
Tel: (202) 737-5906

American Association of University Women (see p. 564)

American Bar Association●
Executive Director: Thomas H. Gonser.
750 Lake Shore Drive, Chicago, Illinois 60617.

American Board of Funeral Service Education
Executive Director: Gordon Bigelow.
23 Crestwood Road, Cumberland, Maine 04021.
Tel: (207) 829-5715

American Chemical Society●
Executive Director: John K. Crum.
1155 16th Street, N.W., Washington, D.C. 20036.
Tel: 202) 872-4589

American College Health Association
Executive Director: Stephen K. Blom.
15879 Crabbs Branch Way, Rockville, Maryland 20855.

American Conference of Academic Deans
Chairman: Carl B. Straub.
1818 R. Street, N.W., Washington, D.C. 20009.

Tel: (202) 387-3760

American Council for Construction Engineering●
Executive Vice President: Robert M. Dillon.
1015 15th Street, N.W., Suite 700, Washington, D.C. 20005.
Tel: (202) 347-5075

American Council of Learned Societies
President: Stanley N. Katz.
228 East 45th Street, New York, New York 10017.

American Council on Pharmaceutical Education●
Executive Director: Daniel A. Nona.
311 West Superior Street, Chicago, Illinois 60610.
Tel: (312) 664-35755

American Dental Association
Secretary: Mario V. Santangelo.
211 East Chicago Avenue, Chigaco, Illinois 60611.
Tel: (312) 440-2719

American Dietetic Association●
Assistant Executive Director: Barbara Bobeng.
Division of Education and Research, 216 West Jackson Boulevard, Chicago, Illinois 60606.
Tel: (312) 899-4870

American Economic Association
Secretary: C. Elton Hinshaw.
1313 21st Avenue, South Nashville, Tennessee 37212.

American Educational Research Association
Executive Officer: William J. Russell.
1230 17th Street, N.W., Washington, D.C. 20036.
Tel: (202) 223-9485

American Historical Association
Executive Director: Samuel R. Gammon.
400 "A" Street, S.E., Washington, D.C. 20003.
Tel: (202) 544-2422

American Home Economics Association●
Director of Accreditation: Bonnie Rader.
Office of Professional Education, AHEA, 2010 Massachusetts Avenue, N.W., Washington, D.C. 20036.
Tel: (202) 862-8355

American Institute of Biological Sciences
Executive Director: Charles M. Chambers.
1401 Wilson Boulevard, Arlington, Virginia 22209.
Tel: (202) 628-1500

American Library Association●
Accreditation Officer: June Lester.
50 East Huron Street, Chicago, Illinois 60611.
Tel: (312) 944-6780

American Mathematical Society
Executive Director: William Le Veque.
P.O. Box 6248, Providence, Rhode Island 02940.

Tel: (401) 272-9500

American Medical Association, Committee on Allied Health Education and Accreditation●
Director: John J. Fauser.
535 North Dearborn Street, Chicago, Illinois 60610.
Tel: (312) 645-4660

American Medical Association●
535 Dearborn Street, Chicago, Illinois 60610.
Tel: (312) 645-4660

American Optometric Association●
Manager: Joyce Urbeck.
Council on Optometric Education, 243 N. Lindbergh Boulevard, Saint Louis, Missouri 63141.
Tel: (314) 991-4100

American Osteopathic Association●
Director: Douglas Ward.
142 East Ontario Street, Chicago, Illinois 60611.
Tel: (312) 280-5842

American Personnel and Guidance Association
Executive Director: Patrick J. McDonough.
5999 Stevenson Avenue, Alexandria, Virginia 22304.

American Philosophical Association
Executive Secretary: David H. Hoekema.
University of Delaware, Newark, Delaware 19711.

American Physical Society
Executive Secretary: W.W. Havens, Jr.
335 East 45th Street, New York, New York 10017.

American Physical Therapy Association●
Director of Accreditation: Virginia Nieland.
Department of Educational Affairs, Transpotomas Plaza, 1111 North Fairfax Street, Alexandria, Virginia 22314.
Tel: (703) 684-2782

American Podiatric Medical Association●
Director: Jay Levrio.
Council on Podiatry Education, 9312 Old Georgetown Road, Bethseda, Maryland 20814.
Tel: (301) 571-8200

American Political Science Association
Executive Director: Catherine Rudder.
1527 New Hampshire Avenue, N.W., Washington, D.C. 20036.
Tel: (202) 483-2512

American Psychological Association●
Director of Accreditation: Paul D. Nelson.
1200-17th Street, N.W., Washington, D.C. 20036.
Tel: (202) 955-7671

American Society of Journalism School Administrators
(see: **Accrediting Council on Educational Journalism**)

American Society for Engineering Education
Executive Director: W. Edward Lear.
Eleven Dupont Circle, Suite 200, Washington, D.C. 20036.
Tel: (202) 298-7080

American Society of Landscape Architects●
Director of Education: Karen L.a. aNiles.
1733 Connecticut Avenue, N.W., Washington, D.C. 20009.
Tel: (202) 466-7730

American Sociological Association
Executive Officer: William V. D'Antonio.
1722 N Street, N.W., Washington, D.C. 20036.
Tel: (202) 833-3410

American Speech-Language Hearing Association●
Director: Billie Ackerman.
Standards and Ethics Division, 10801 Rockville Pike, Rockville, Maryland 20852.
Tel: (301) 897-5700

American Studies Association
Executive Secretary: Roberta K. Gladowski.
4025 Chestnut Street, University of Pennsylvania, Philadelphia, Pennsylvania 19104.

American Theater Association
Executive Director: Jack Morrison.
1000 Vermont Avenue, N.W., Washington, D.C. 20005.

American Veterinary Medical Association●
Director: Edward R. Ames.
930 N. Meacham Road, Schaumburg, Illinois 60196.
Tel: (312) 858-8070

Association of American Geographers
Educational Affairs Director: Salvatore J. Natoli.
1710 Sixteenth Street, N.W., Washington, D.C. 20009.

Association of American Law Schools●
Executive Director: Betsy Levin.
One Dupont Circle, Suite 370, Washington, D.C. 20036.
Tel: (202) 296-8851

Association of American Library Schools
Secretary: Janet C. Phillips.
Park Lane, State College, Pennsylvania 16801.

Association of American Medical Colleges
President: Robert G. Petersdorf.
One Dupont Circle, Suite 200, Washington, D.C. 20036.
Tel: (202) 828-0400

Association of Catholic Colleges and Universities
President: Sr. Alice Gallin.
One Dupont Circle, Suite 770, Washington, D.C. 20036.
Tel: (202) 457-0650

Association for Clinical Pastoral Education, Inc.●
Executive Director: Rev. Charles E. Hall, Jr.

475 Riverside Drive, New York, N.Y. 10027.
Association of College and University Housing Officers
Manager: Rhea Down Smith.
101 Curl Drive, Suite 140, Columbus, Ohio 43210.
Tel: (614) 292-0099
Association of Collegiate Schools of Architecture
Executive Director: Richard McCommons.
1735 New York Avenue, N.W., Washington, D.C. 20036.
Tel: (202) 785-2324
Association of Continuing Higher Education
Executive Vice-President: William D. Barton.
451 Communication Building, University of Tennessee, Knoxville, Tennessee 37916.
Association of Governing Boards of Universities and Colleges
President: Robert L. Gale.
One Dupont Circle, Suite 400, Washington, D.C. 20036.
Tel: (202) 296-8400
Association of Independent Colleges and Schools●
Executive Director: James M. Phillips.
Accrediting Commission, AICS, One Dupont Circle, Suite 350, Washington, D.C. 20036.
Tel: (202) 659-2460
Association of Jesuit Colleges and Universities
President: Rev. William McInnes, S.J.
1424 16th Street, N.W., Suite 300, Washington, D.C. 20036.
Tel: (202) 667-3889
Executive Director: John G. Lorenz.
1527 New Hampshire Avenue, N.W., Washington, D.C. 20036.
Association of Theological Schools in the United States and Canada
Executive Director: Leon Pacala.
42 East National Road, Vandalia, Ohio 45377 0130.
Tel: (513) 898-4654
Association of University Summer Sessions
Recorder: Leslie Coyne.
Summer Sessions, Indiana University, Bloomington, Indiana 47401.
Tel: (812) 335-5048
College Board
President: Donald Stewart.
45 Columbus Avenue., New York, New York 10023-6992.
Tel: (212) 713-8000
Commission on Dental Education● American Dental Association●
Secretary: Mario V. Santangelo.
211 East Chicago Avenue, Chicago, Illinois 60611.
Tel: (312) 440-2719
Council on Accreditation of Nurse Anesthesia

Educational Programs●
Director of Accreditation: Doris A. Stoll.
216 Higgins Road, Pack Ridge, Illinois 60068.
Tel: (312) 692-7050
Council for Advancement and Support of Education
President: Gary Quehl.
11 Dupont Circle, Suite 400, Washington, D.C. 20036.
Tel: (202) 328-5900
The Council on Chiropractic Education●
Executive Vice President: Ralph G. Miller.
3209 Ingersoll Avenue, Des Moines, Iowa 50312.
Tel: (515) 255-2184
Council on Education for Public Health●
Executive Director: Patricia P. Evans.
1015–15th Street, N.W., Suite 403, Washington, D.C. 20005.
Tel: (202) 789-1030
Council for Financial Aid to Education
President: John R. Haire.
680 Fifth Avenue, New York, New York 10019.
Council of Graduate Schools in the United States
President: Jules B. LaPidus.
One Dupont Circle, Suite 430, Washington, D.C. 20036.
Tel: (202) 223-3791
Council of Independent Colleges
President (Acting): Allen P. Splete.
One Dupont Circle, Suite 320, Washington, D.C. 20036.
Tel: (202) 466-7230
Council on Rehabilitation Education●
Executive Director: Charline McGrath.
185 North Wabash Street, Room 1617, Chicago, Illinois 60601.
Tel: (312) 346-6027
Council on Social Work Education●
Director: Nancy Randolph.
1744 R Street, N.W., Washington, D.C. 20036.
Tel: (202) 667-2300
Educational Testing Service
President: Gregory R. Anrig.
Princeton, New Jersey, 08540.
Foundation for Interior Design Education Research●
322 Eighth Avenue, Room 1501, New York, New York 10001.
Tel: (212) 929-8366
Liaison Committee on Medical Education●
Secretary: Harry S. Jonas.
Council on Medical Education, 535 North Dearborn Street, Chicago, Illinois 60610.
Tel: (312) 645-4933
Linguistic Society of America
Associate Secretary: Margaret W. Reynolds.
1325 18th Street, N.W., Washington, D.C.

20036-6501.
Tel: (202) 835-1714
Middle States Association of Colleges and Secondary Schools●
Executive Director: Howard L. Simmon.
3624 University City Science Center, Philadelphia, Pennsylvania 19104.
Tel: (215) 662-5606
Modern Language Association
Executive Director: Phyllis Franklin. 10 Astor Place, New York, New York 10003.
Tel: (212) 475-9500
National Architectural Accrediting Board●
Executive Director: John Maudlin-Jeronimo.
1735 New York Avenue, N.W., Washington, D.C. 20006.
Tel: (202) 783-2007
National Association of College Admissions Counsellors
Executive Director: Frank E. Burtnett.
1800 Diagonal Road, Suite K30, Alexandria, Virginia 22314.
National Association of College and University Attorneys
Executive Director: Phillip M. Grier.
One Dupont Circle, Suite 620, Washington, D.C. 20036.
Tel: (202) 883-8390
National Association of College and University Business Officers
Executive Vice-President: Caspar Harris.
One Dupont Circle, Suite 500, Washington, D.C. 20036.
Tel: (202) 861-2500
National Association of College and University Chaplains and Directors of Religious Life
President: Barbara A.B. Patterson.
Emory University, Atlanta Georgia 30322.
National Association of Collegiate Deans, Registrars, and Admission Officers
Executive Secretary: Helen Mayes.
917 Dorsett Avenue, Albany, Georgia 31701.
National Association of Educational Buyers
Executive Vice-President: Neil Markee.
180 Froehlick Farm, Woodbury, New York 11797.
Tel: (516) 921-7100
National Association for Equal Opportunity in Higher Education
President: Samuel L. Myers.
2243 Wisconsin Avenue, Washington, D.C. 20007.
National Association of Foreign Student Affairs (NAFSA)
Executive Vice-President: John Reichard.
1860 19th Street, N.W., Washington, D.C. 20009.
Tel: (202) 462-4811
National Association of Independent Colleges and

Universities
President: Richard F. Rosser.
122C Street, N.W., Suite 750, Washington, D.C. 20036.
Tel: (202) 383-5950
National Association for Industrial Technology
Executive Director: Harvey A. Pearson.
University of Florida, P.O. Box 17074, Jacksonville, Florida 32216.
National Association of Schools of Art and Design●
Executive Director: Samuel Hope.
11250 Roger Bacon Drive, No. 5, Reston, Virginia 22090.
Tel: (703) 437-0700
National Association of Schools of Music●
Executive Director: Samuel Hope.
11250 Roger Bacon Drive, No. 5, Reston, Virginia 22090.
Tel: (703) 437-0700
National Association of Schools of Public Affairs and Administration●
Executive Director: Alfred M. Zuck.
1120 G. Street, N.W., Suite 520, Washington, D.C. 20005.
Tel: (202) 628-8965
National Association of Student Personnel Administrators
Executive Director: Elizabeth M. Nuff.
1700 18th Street, N.W., Suite 301, Washington, D.C. 20009-2508.
Tel: (202) 265-7500
National Association of Trade and Technical Schools●
Executive Secretary: Dorothy Coyne Fenwick.
2251 Wisconsin Avenue, Suite 200, Washington, D.C. 20001.
Tel: (202) 333-1021
National Association of University Women
President: Carrie A. Haynes.
1205, W. 80th Street, Los Angeles, California 90044.
National Association of Women Deans, Administrators, and Counselors (a Department of the National Education Association)
Executive Director: Patricia Rueckel.
1625 I Street, N.W., Suite 624A, Washington, D.C. 20006.
National Council for Accreditation of Teacher Education●
Director: Richard C. Kunkel.
2029 K. Street, Suite 500, Washington, D.C. 20006.
Tel: (202) 466-7496
National Home Study Council●
Executive Secretary: William A. Fowler.
Accrediting Commission, NHSC, 1601 Eighteenth Street, N.W., Washington, D.C. 20009.

Tel: (202) 234-5100
National League for Nursing, Inc.●
Vice-President for Education and Accreditation Services: Patricia Moccia.
10 Columbus Circle, New York, New York 10019.
Tel: 212) 582-1022
National Recreation and Park Association●
Professional Services Director: Donald D. Henkel.
3101 Park Center Drive, Alexandria, Virginia 22302.
Tel: (703) 820-4940.
National University Continuing Education Association
Executive Director: Kay J. Kohl.
One Dupont Circle, Suite 420, Washington, D.C. 20036.
Tel: (202) 659-3130
Near East College Association, Inc.
Administrative Director: Walter Prosser.
850 Third Avenue, 18th Floor, New York, New York 10022.
New England Association of Schools and Colleges●
Director: Charles M. Cook.
15 High Street, The Sanborn House, Winchester, Massachusetts 01890.
Tel: (617) 729-6762
New England Board of Higher Education
Executive Director: John C. Hoy.
45 Temple Place, Boston, Massachusetts 02111.
Tel: (617) 357-9620
North Central Association of Colleges and Schools●
Director: A. Thrash.
Commission on Institutions of Higher Education, 159 N. Dearborn Street, 6th Floor, Chicago, Illinois 60601.
Tel: (312) 263-0456
Northwest Association of Schools and Colleges●
Executive Director: James F. Bemis.
37003 University Way N.E., Seattle, Washington, 98105.
Tel: (206) 543-0195
Social Science Research Council
President: Frederic E. Wakeman, Jr.
605 Third Avenue, New York, New York 10016.
Tel: (212) 661-0280
Society of American Foresters●
Associate Director: Gregory Smith.
5400 Grosvenor Ln., Washington, D.C. 20014.
Tel: (301) 897-8720
Society for Values in Higher Education (formerly National Council on Religion in Higher Education)
Director: David C. Smith.

409 Prospect Street, New Haven, Connecticut 06510.
Southern Association of Colleges and Schools●
Executive Director: James T. Rogers.
1866 Southern Lane, Decatur, Georgia 30033-4097.
Tel: (404) 329-6500
Southern Regional Education Board
President: Winfred L. Godwin.
592-10th Street, N.W., Atlanta, Georgia 30318-5790.
Tel: (404) 875-9211
Speech Communication Association
Executive Secretary: William Work.
5105 Backlick Road No. E., Annandale, Virginia 22003.
Tel: (703) 750-0534
Western Association of Schools and Colleges●
Executive Director: Stephen S. Weiner.
c/o Mills College, Box 9990, Oakland, California 94613.
Tel: (415) 632-5000
Western Interstate Commission for Higher Education
Executive Director: Phillip Sirotkin.
Post Office Drawer P, Boulder, Colorado 80302.
Tel: (303) 497-0200

*

American Association of University Women (IFUW)
2401 Virginia Avenue, N.W., Washington, D.C. 20037.
United States National Student Association— USNSA
2115 S Street, N.W., Washington, D.C. 20008.
United States National Student Travel Association —USNSTA
70 Fifth Avenue, New York, N.Y. 10011.
Council on International Educational Exchange —CIEE (see p. 553).
American Graduate and Professional Commission (Pax Romana)
Queens College, Flushing, N.Y. 11367.
Phi Kappa Theta—Alumni Fraternity (Pax Romana)
c/o Edward Kirchner.
31 Chesterfield Road, Stanford, Connecticut 06902.
Student Christian Federation (WSCF)
2311 Bowditch Avenue, Berkeley, California 94704.
Tel: (416) 848-1157
Youth and Students for World Peace and Environmental Protection (ISMUN)
505 S. 45th Street, Philadelphia, Pa. 19143.
"Network" (WUJS)
15 East 26th Street, New York, N.Y. 10010.

Contact: 89 Chausee De Vleugat, 1050 Brussels (Belgium)
Tel: (2) 647-7279. Telex: 20625

*

Office of Postsecondary Education
Assistant Secretary: C. Ronald Kimberling.
United States Department of Education, 7th and D Streets, Washington, DC 20202.
Tel: (202) 732-3547
Higher Education Management Services
Director: Richard L. Fairley.
Office of Postsecondary Education, United States Department of Education, 7th and D streets, Washington, DC 20202.
Tel: (202) 245-2592
Higher Education Management Services
Chief of Eligibility: Leslie W. Ross.

Office of Postsecondary Education, United States Department of Education, Washington, DC 20202.
Tel: (202) 245-8082
Higher Education Institutional Eligibility Branch
Acting Chief: Lois Moore.
Division of Eligibility and Certification, Office of Postsecondary Education, United States Department of Education, 400 Maryland Avenue, SW., Washington, DC 20202.
Tel: (202) 732-3465.
The Associate Direction for Educational and Cultural Affairs
International Communication Agency, Washington, D.C. 20547.
United States Department of Education
(See p. 561).

URUGUAY
URUGUAY

*Universidad Mayor de la República, Avenida 18 de Julio 1824, Montevideo. (Sr. Secretario general).   *1849*
Tél: (2) 409201. Télex: 26519 udelar uy.
Cables: udelar
F : agr, arc, éco-adm, dr-soc, hum-sc, ing-arp, méd, dent, ch-phar, vét.
E : inf, serv soc, ba, bibl.
Universidad del Trabajo de Uruguay, Calle San Salvador 1674, Montevideo.   *1942*
Tél: (2) 45094

D : arg, gé ind, arts app, com-adm, éd voc, plan éd, rech éd.
Egalement 8 instituts affiliés.
Universidad Católica Damaso Antonio Larrañaga, Larrañaga, Montevideo.   *1985*
Tél: (2) 803515
Instituto de Estudios Superiores, Constituyente 1711, Montevideo.   *1930*
D : phill, pho, mus, géog, paléo, géol, méd clima, math.
E : éd.

Asociación de Mujeres Tituladas en la Universidad del Uruguay (IFUW)
Calle Pedro F. Barro 1070, Pocitos, Montevideo.
Servicio Universitario Mundial (WUS)
18 de Julio 841, Escritorio 702, Montevideo.
Tél: (2) 921042
Federación de Estudiantes Universitarios del Uruguay—FEUU (IUS)
Arenal Grande 1422, Montevideo.
Movimiento Intelectuales Católicos—MIIC (Pax Romana)
c/o Archevêque de Montevideo, Arzobispado, Calle Treinta y Tres 1368, Montevideo.
Asociación de Estudiantes y Profesionales

Católicos (Pax Romana)
Avenida Rivera 2336–40, Montevideo.
Unión de Jovenes Uruguayos pro Naciones Unidas (ISMUN)
26 ap 202, Montevideo.
World Union of Jewish Students (WUJS)
Correspondant: 89 chaussee De Vleurgat, 1050 Brussels (Belgium).
Tél: (2) 647-7279. Télex: 20625

*

Ministerio de la Educación y la Culture
Montevideo.
Tél: (2) 950103. Fax: (2) 809397. Télex: 22280 uy

Comisión Nacional del Uruguay para la Unesco
Ministerio de Educación y la Cultura, Montevideo.

Tél: (2) 959292. Télex: 6682 (mec uy 23133).
Cables: comision unesco diplomacio montevideo

VENEZUELA
VENEZUELA

UNIVERSITIES — UNIVERSITES

*Universidad de los Andes, Avenida 3, Mérida, Estado Mérida. *1810*
Tél: (74) 520011. Télex: 74137 ulamve
F : dr, méd, phar, dent, ing, for, hum-éd, éco, sc, arc.
E : dr, méd, inf, phar, nutr-diét, bioch, dent, gé civ, élec, arc, gé for, géog, éd; éd (San Cristóbal); agr, éd, gé civ, ind, adm des aff (Trujillo); let, hist, éco, adm des aff.

*Universidad de Carabobo, Avenida Bolívar 125–139, Valencia, Estado Carabobo. *1892*
Tél: (41) 215044. Télex: 41478
F : éco-soc, dr, ing, méd.
E : adm com-comp, rel ind, éco, éd, dr, élec, gé civ, gé ind, méc, méd, bioch, inf, dent.

Universidad Católica Andrés Bello, La Vega, Montalbán, Caracas. *1953*
Tél: (2) 442-95-11
F : éco-soc, dr, hum-let, ing.
E : éco, adm com-comp, soc, dr, phil, éd, commun soc, psyc, let, gé civ, gé ind.

Universidad Católica del Táchira, Apartado 366, San Cristóbal, Estado Táchira. *1962, 1982*
F : dr, éco-soc, hum-éd, relig st.

Universidad Católica «Cecilio Acosta», Urb. La Paz, Etapa II, Edif, Sede Instituto "Niños Cantores del Zulia", Apartado 1841, Maracaibo. *1983*
F : éd-commun, hum-soc, ba.
E : éd, commun soc, phil, arts plast.

*Universidad Central de Venezuela, Ciudad Universitaria, Los Chaguaramos, Caracas 105. *1721*
Tél: (2) 61-98-11
F : agr, acr-urb, sc, vét, dr, soc-éco, phar, hum, éd, ing, méd, dent.
E : agr, acr, biol, phy, math-inft, ch, vét, dr, éco, adm-comp, stat-act, ét int, commun soc, lang mod, pol-adm, anth-socio, trav soc, phar, let, éd, phil, géog, hist, bibl, psyc, gé civ, ch, pét, méc, élec, géol-mine-mét, méd (2), bioch,

sa publ, dent, diét; agr, vét (Maracay).

*Universidad Centro Occidental «Lisandro Alvaredo», Carrera 19 Entre Calles 8 y 9, Edif. Antiguo Hotel Nueva Segovia, Barquisimeto, Estado Lara. *1962*
Tél: (51) 513551
E : adm-comp, agr, vét, méd, math, inft, gé civ.

Universidad José María Vargas, Avenida Sucre Torre Sur, Los Dos Caminos, Caracas. *1983*
F : adm, arc-arts plast, éd, ing.

*Universidad Metropolitana, Distribuidor Autopista a Guarenas (La Urbina), Apartado postal 76.819, Caracas 107. *1970*
Tél: (2) 241-48-33
F : éco-soc, sc-arts, ing.
E : adm, méc, élec, gé ch, gé civ, gé des systèmes, math, lang mod, éd.

Universidad Nacional Abierta de Venezuela [National Open U.], Avenida Gamboa 18, San Bernardino, Caracas 101.
Tél: (2) 574-13-22. Télex: 2611
math, gé civ, gé ind, gé des systèmes, éd, adm.

Universidad Nacional Experimental de la Costa Oriental del Largo de Maracaibo, Maracaibo, Estado Zulia. *1982*

Universidad Nacional Experimental «Francisco de Miranda», Edif. "Don Angel", Prolongación Avenida Los Medanos, Coro.
Tél: (68) 519732
gé civ, gé ind, méd, anth, infor.

Universidad Nacional Experimental de Guayana, Edif. Seguros Orinoco Altavista, Puerto Ordaz, Estado Bolívar. *1982*
F : ing, éd, rel ind.

Universidad Nacional Experimental de Los Llanos Centrales «Romulo Gallegos», San Juan de Los Morros, Estado Guarico.
Tél: (46) 37668
agr, sa.

Universidad Nacional Experimental de Los Llanos Occidentales «Ezequiel Zamora», Alto

Barinas, Apartado 19, Estado Barinas. *1975*
Tél: (73) 41201. Télex: 73171
gé agr, gé agro-ind, dév, conservation, éco agr,
zoo, adm rég, plan rég.
Universidad Nacional Experimental «Rafael María Baralt», Calle El Rosario, Cabimas-Dtt., Bolívar (Estado Zulia).
éd, soc.
Universidad Nacional Experimental del Táchira, Paramillo, San Cristóbal, Estado Táchira.
Tél: (76) 59056. Télex: 76196
gé ind, méc, gé agr, zoo.
*Universidad de Oriente, Apartado 245, Cerro Colorado, Cumaná. *1958*
Tél: (93) 23366
E : gé agr, zoo (Monagas); géol-mine, méd (Bolívar); comp, ing, tec (Anzoategui); soc, agr-mar (Nueva Esparta); adm, sc, éd, soc (Sucre).
Universidad Pedogógica Libertador, Edif. Ministerio de Educación, Caracas. *1983*
Universidad Rafael Urdaneta, Urb. Cataclaro, Calle 52, No. 5−205 Esq., Avenida 11D, Maracaibo, Estado Zulia.
Tél: (61) 71601
F : ing, zoo, pol-adm.
E : élec, ch, zoo, pol-adm publ.
Universidad Santa María, Avenida Paez, Frente Plaza Madariaga, El Paraíso, Caracas. *1953*

Tél: (2) 41-55-96
F : dr, phar.
E : éco, adm-comp, dr, phar, gé civ.
Universidad Simón Bolívar, Apartado postal 80659, Caracas 1080. *1967*
Tél: (2) 962-1101. Télex: 21910 sub ve
élec, méc, math, ch, arc-urb, inft, électro; tec, tour, adm transp, adm des douanes (Litoral).
*Universidad Simón Rodríguez, Avenida Jose María Vargas, Edf. Torre El Colegio, Urb. Santa Fé Norte, Caracas.
Tél: (2) 979-10-22. Télex: 21910
éd, soc, ing.
Universidad del Sur del Lago, Maracaibo, Estado Zulia. *1982*
agr, mar sc, éd.
Universidad Tecnológica del Centro, Valencia, Estado Carabobo. *1981*
Tél: (45) 718088
F : eng, adm.
*Universidad del Zulia, Apartado postal 526, Maracaibo, Estado Zulia. *1891*
Tél: (61) 512077. Télex: 62172
F : agr, arc, vét, dr, éco-soc, hum-éd, ing, méd, dent.
E : math, gé ind, gé agr, arc, vét, dr, éco, adm com-comp (2), éd, let, jour, phil, gé civ, ch, géol, pét, méc, bibl, méd, bioch, inf, nutr-diét, dent; éd, soc (Cabimas); éd, soc (Punto Fijo).

OTHER INSTITUTIONS—AUTRES INSTITUTIONS

Technical Education—Enseignement technique

Instituto Universitario Politécnico, Parque Tecnológico Corpahuaico, Barquisimeto, Estado Lara. *1962*
Tél: (51) 420022. Télex: 52421 iupb ve
Instituto Universitario Politécnico «Luis Caballero Mejías», Avenida Principal de la Yaguara, Caracas.
Tél: (2) 49-89-17
Instituto Universitario Politécnico de Las Fuerzas Armadas, Sede Principal en El Edificio de la Comandancia General de la Aviación, La Carlota, Caracas.
Tél: (2) 355022
Instituto Universitario Politécnico Experimental de Guayana, Ciudad Guayana, Puerto Orda 3, Estado Bolívar. *1971*
Tél: (86) 22-18-93
Instituto Universitario de Tecnología de la Región Capital, 8 Carretera Panamericana, Caracas 107. *1971*
Tél: (2) 69-18-81
Instituto Universitario de Tecnología 'Antonio

José de Sucre', Avenida Principal Cruce Con 4a. Transversal, Urbanización La Castellana, Caracas. *1972*
Tél: (2) 32-20-24
Instituto Universitario de Tecnología de Administración y Hacienda Pública, Avenida Urdaneta Esq., Las Ibarras, Edif. Central, Caracas.
Tél: (2) 81-89-82
Instituto Universitario de Tecnología "Rodolfo Loero Arismendi", Avenida Caurimare, Colinas de Bello Monte 2424, Caracas.
Tél: 59338
Instituto Universitario de Tecnología de Coro, Parque Los Orumos, Coro, Estado Falcón.
1971
Instituto Universitario de Tecnología de Cumaná, Km. 4, Carretera Cumanacoa, Cumaná, Estado Sucre. *1971*
Tél: (93) 62091. Télex: 93165
Instituto Universitario de Tecnología de Ejido, Via Marzano Bajo, Ejido, Estado Mérida. *1981*

Instituto Universitario de Tecnología de El Tigre, Carretera El Tigre, Via Ciudad Bolívar, El Tigre, Estado Anzoategui. *1977*

Instituto Universitario de Tecnología Isaac Newton, Avenida Constitución Edif. Alayon Plaza, Manacay, Estado Araguay. *1983*

Instituto Universitario de Tecnología de Los Llanos, Valle de La Pascua Urb, Guamachal, Estado Guarico.
Télex: 49603 iutip ve

Instituto Universitario de Tecnología de La Victoria, Zona Industrial Soco, Avenida Ricaurte Frente a Maviplanca, La Victoria, Estado Aragua. *1971*
Tél: (44) 24723. Télex: 44130

Instituto Universitario de Tecnología del Mar, Fundación La Salle, Punta de Piedras, Margarita, Estado Nuova Esparta. *1977*

Instituto Universitario de Tecnología Pto. Cabello, Avenida Bolívar 31–7 Rancho Grande, Puerto Cabello, Estado Carabobo. *1976*

Instituto Universitario de Tecnología Agro-

Industrial, Parque Exposición Teotime De Pablos, San Cristóbal, Estado Táchira. *1971*
Tél: (76) 26290

Instituto Universitario de Tecnología, Avenida Alberto Ravell, Cruce Con Avenida José Antonio Paez, San Felipe, Estado Yaracuy. *1974*

Instituto Universitario de Tecnología Industrial, Local del Colegio La Salle, Avenida La Salle Urbanización Guaparo, Valencia, Estado Carabobo. *1978*

Instituto Universitario de Tecnología Industrial, Colegio Tirso de Molina, San Bernardino, Caracas. *1978*

Instituto Universitario de Tecnología de Valencia, Urb. El Trigal, Calle Gual. 92–98, Valencia, Estado Carabovo. *1976*

Instituto Universitario de Tecnología Venezuela, Avenida Universidad Edif. La Metropolitana, Caracas. *1983*

Instituto Universitario de Tecnología del Estado Trujillo, Avenida Caracas Edif. "El Tiempo" Local 3, Valera, Estado Trujillo. *1978*

Professional Education–Ensignement professionel

Colegio Universitario «Fermín Toro», Carrera 29 No. 20–24, Barquisimeto, Estado Lara.
Tél: (51) 510304
éd, soc.

Colegio Universitario Jean Piaget, Avenida Principal, Qta. La Lomita Urbanización Los Guayabitos, Baruta.
psycopéd.

Colegio Universitario de Cabimas, La Estrella, Sector Amparo 117, Cabimas, Estado Zulia.

Colegio Universitario de Caracas, Avenida Libertador Cruce con Calle Caicara, Urb. Los Cedros, Caracas.
Tél: (2) 72-29-29
adm, éd.

Colegio Universitario Francisco de Mirandas, Mijares a Jesuitas, Caracas.
Tél: (2) 81-43-51
adm, éd.

Colegio Universitario INAPSI, Avenida El Bosque Quinta "Malalita", La Florida, Caracas.
éd.

Colegio Universitario Monseñor de Talavera, Avenida Principal de la Castellana, Cruce en Los Granados, La Castellana, Caracas.
Tél: (2) 32-13-11
éd, techn.

Colegio Universitario de Rehabilitación, Calle La Guayanita, Bella Vista, El Pescozon, Caracas 102.

Tél: (2) 49-47-60
thér.

Colegio Universitario de Carúpano, Valle de Canchunchu, Via El Pilar, Carúpano, Estado Sucre.
adm, éd.

Colegio Universitario de la Región Capital, Avenida Los Pinos, Los Teques, Estado Miranda.
Tél: (32) 42539
adm éd.

Colegio Universitario de Maracaibo, Urb. La Floresta, Apartado 1878, Maracaibo, Estado Zulia.
Tél: (61) 54-99-96
adm, éd.

Colegio Universitario "Rafael Belloso Chacín", Calle 77 esquina Avenida 3H, Maracaibo, Estado Zulia. *1982*
Tél: (61) 91-12-52

Colegio Universitario de Psicopedagogía, Avenida San Gabriel No. 45, Urb. El Avila, Caracas.
Tél: (2) 74-19-94

Colegio Universitario de Banca y Finanzas, Edf. Insbanca, Mijares a Santa Capilla, Caracas. *1978*

Instituto Universitario Jesús E. Lossada, Edif. Sede Del IUJEL, Calle 78, 17–129, Maracaibo, Estado Zulia. *1982*

Instituto Universitario de Mercadotecnia,

Edificio Cediaz, Planta Principal, Avenida Casanova, Caracas.

Instituto Universitario «Nueva Esparta», Reducto a Glorieta 73, Caracas.
inft, ing, tour.

Instituto de Nuevas Profesiones, Avenida Romulo Gallegos, Caracas.
Tél: (2) 74-57-78
tour, com int, publicité.

Instituto Universitario de Relaciones Públicas, Altagracia Mijares, Edificio Edoval, Primer Piso, Caracas.

Tél: (2) 81-82-35

Instituto Universitario de Seguros, IESA, Avenida Los Chaguaramos, La Florida, Caracas. *1972*

Instituto Universitario Tecnológico de Seguridad Industrial, Apartado 2242, Los Angeles, Via San Diego, Valencia, Estado Carabobo. *1979*
Tél: (41) 37-73-53

Instituto Universitario YMCA «Lope Mendoza», Avenida Guicaipuro, San Bernardino, Caracas. *1983*

Teacher Training—Formation pédagogique

Instituto Universitario Pedagógico Experimental, Avenida Vargas, Barquisimeto, Estado Lara.
1959
Tél: (51) 411800

Instituto Universitario 'Avepane', Avenida San Juan Bosco 57–15, Entre Avenida 9 y 10, Altimira, Caracas. *1972*
Tél: (2) 61-76-51

Instituto Universitario Pedagógico, Avenida Páez El Paraíso, Caracas. *1936*
Tél: (2) 41-61-31

Instituto Universitario Pedagógico del Este, Calle 8, La Urbina, Prolongación Avenida Romulo Gallegos, Caracas.

Instituto Universitario Pedagógico «Monseñor Rafael Arías Blanco», Sector UD-5, Detrás del

Bloque 23, La Hacienda, Caricuao, Caracas.

Instituto Venezolano de Audición y Lenguaje, Calle Araure con Cuchivero, Urb. El Marqués, Caracas. *1972*
Tél: (2) 33-63-77

Instituto Universitario Pedagógico Experimental, Avenida Principal Las Delicias, Antiguo Parque Ferial, Maracay, Estado Aragua. *1971*
Tél: (43) 411361

Instituto Universitario Pedagógico Experimental «J.M. Siso Martínez», Caracas. *1976*

Instituto Universitario Pedagógico Experimental, Carretera Sur, Urbanización Juancó, Maturín, Estado Monagas. *1971*
Tél: (91) 39895

Consejo Nacional de Universidades

Le Conseil national des universités est présidé par le Ministre de l'éducation et comprend les recteurs des universités d'Etat et privées, trois professeurs et trois étudiants représentant respectivement les universités non expérimentales, les universités nationales expérimentales, les universités privées, deux professeurs élus parmi les membres du Congrès de la République et un représentant du Conseil national des recherches scientifiques et technologiques. Le Secrétaire du Conseil, le directeur du Bureau de planification du secteur universitaire, un représentant du Ministre de l'économie et des finances et un doyen pour chaque université nationale ou privée font également partie du Conseil, avec droit de parole.

Le Conseil national des universités a notamment pour fonctions: de définir l'orientation et les grandes lignes de développement du système universitaire conformément aux besoins du pays; d'examiner des modèles d'organisation universitaire et de recommander l'adoption de ceux

répondant le mieux aux besoins du pays; de coordonner et d'harmoniser les activités des différentes universités; de définir les critères pour la création, la suppression, la modification et le fonctionnement des facultés, écoles, instituts ou autres sections analogues des universités; de proposer au pouvoir exécutif national des règlements concernant la reconnaissance et les équivalences des titres et diplômes; de déterminer périodiquement les objectifs à atteindre dans la formation des ressources humaines de niveau supérieur; d'exiger de chaque université nationale la présentation d'un budget-programme; de veiller à la bonne gestion des budgets des universités nationales; de veiller au respect, dans chacune des universités, des dispositions de la Loi et des normes et résolutions qu'il appartiendra au Conseil d'édicter, dans le cadre de ses attributions.

Le Conseil est doté d'un Secrétariat permanent et bénéficie du concours du Bureau de planification du secteur universitaire, qui lui sert de bureau technique.

The National Universities Council is chaired by the Minister of Education and comprises: the Rectors of the State and private universities; three professors and three students representing respectively the national non-experimental universities, the national experimental universities and the private universities; two professors elected from among the members of the Congress of the Republic; and one representative from the National Council for Scientific and Technological Research. The Secretary of the Council, the Director of the Office of University Planning, a representative of the Minister of Economics and Finance, and a Dean from each national or private university are also members of the Council with speaking rights.

The functions of the National Universities Council are: to define policy and guidelines for the development of the university system in accordance with the country's needs; to examine models of university organization and recommend the adoption of those which best meet the needs of the country; to coordinate and harmonize the activities of the various universities; to define criteria for the creation, abolition, modification and operation of faculties, schools, institutes and other university departments; to propose to the government regulations for the recognition and equivalence of degrees and diplomas; periodically to decide on aims to be achieved in the training of human resources at the level of higher education; to require every national university to present a budget and programme; to supervise the good management of the budgets of the national universities; and to ensure that all universities respect the provisions of the law and the standard and requirements set by the Council in the exercise of its competencies.

The Council has a permanent Secretariat and enjoys the active assistance of the Office for University Planning, which serves it as a technical bureau.

Directeur: Ruth Lerner.
Avenida Urdaneta, Edif. Bco Italo, Caracas.
Télex: 26513 opsu vc

Movimiento Nacional de Intelectuales Católicos (Pax Romana)
c/o P.José Miguel Munarriz S.J., Avenida Cristóbal Rosas 16, (Santa Mónica), Caracas 104.

Movimiento Cristiano Caleb (WSCF)
Apartado de Correos 1025, Barquisimeto, Estado Lara.

World Union of Jewish Students (WUJS)
Correspondant: 89 Chaussee De Vleurgat, 1050 Brussels (Belgium).
Tél: (2) 647-7279. Télex: 20625

*

Ministerio de Educación
Caracas.
Tél: (2) 562-5444. Télex: 21943 min ed

Comisión Nacional Venezolana de coopération con la Unesco
Ministerio de Relaciones Exteriores, Caracas 1010.
Tél: (2) 81-81-74. Télex: 22721. Cables: corusion unesco exteriores caracas

SOCIALIST REPUBLIC OF VIET NAM
REPUBLIQUE SOCIALISTE DU VIET NAM

UNIVERSITIES—UNIVERSITES

*Trùong Dai hoc Tông hop Hànôi [U. de Hanôi], 23 boulevard Lê-thauh-Tôn, Hànôi, (M. le Secrétaire général).
Tél: 44615
F : math, phy, ch, biol, let, hist, géol-géog.

*Viên Dai hoc Hô Chí Minh ville [U. d'Hô Chí Minh ville], 3 Công-Trùong Chiên Si, Hô Chí Minh ville.   1917, 1957
Tél: 90396
F : let-hum, sc exactes-nat.

*Viên Dai hoc Huê [U. de Hué], 3 Lê-Loi, Huê, Thua-Thiên.   1957
Tél: 2256
F : let, dr-éco, sc.

Trùong Dai hoc Cân-Thó [U. of Cân-Thó], rue de 30 Thang 4, Cân-Thó (Han Giang Province).
Tél: 20237
F: math-phy, ch-biol, let, lang étr, hist-geóg, agr, alim, élev-vét, pêch, éco agr, méd, hydrotec.

Truòng Dai hoc Bách Khoa Hànôi [Technical U. of Hanoi], Hànôi.   1956
Tél: 52771
F : bât, élec, électro, ch ind, alim, mét, thermodynamiques ind, gé tex, adm entrep, phy-mat.

Truòng Dai hoc Bách Khoa Thành pho Hô Chí Minh ville [Technical U. of Hô Chí Minh ville], 268, rue Lý Thuòng Kiêt, Q.10, Thành phó Hô Chí Minh ville.   1957, 1976
F : méc, élec, ch, thermodynamiques app, hydrotec, gé civ, géol.

Dai hoc y Hànôi [U. des Sciences de la Santé], Rue Trung tu, Secteur Dong Da, Hànôi.
                              1902, 1963, 1986
Tél: 43790

Truòng Dai hoc su Pham Ky Thuat [U. péd. de Technologie], 1 Hoang Dieu, Thu Duc, Hô Chí Minh ville.   1962, 1972
Tél: 98641

OTHER INSTITUTIONS—AUTRES INSTITUTIONS

Technical Education—Enseignment technique

Trùong Cao dang My thuât công nghiêp [E. sup. des Arts Industriels], Hànôi.   1966

Trùong Dai hoc Giao thông vân tai [E. sup. de Communications et de Transports] Hànôi.
                                      1960
Tél: 43311
F : méc, trans, const, adm entrep.

Trùong Dai hoc Xây dung [E. sup. de Constructions], Hànôi.   1966
F : const de bât, hyd et const ports-ponts et chaussées, arc, adm entrep.

Trùong Dai hoc Thuy loi [E. sup. d'Hydraulique], Hànôi.   1959

Tél: 2201
F : hyd agr, hydro-élec.

Trùong Dai hoc Mo và Dia chât [E. sup. des Mines et de Géologie], Hànôi.   1966
F : mine, géol, géod.

Trùong Dai hoc Co diên [E. sup. de Mécanique et d'Electricité], Hànôi.

Trùong Dai hoc Công nghiêp nhe [E. sup. d'Industrie légère], Hànôi.

Ecole supérieure polytechnique, Da Nang.

Ecole supérieure de Formation des Techniciens et Chercheurs, Dalat.

Professional Education—Ensignement professionnel

Trùong Dai hoc Nông nghiêp I [E. sup. d'Agriculture I], Hànôi.   1956
F : cult alim & ind, élev, vét, méc agr, élec agr.

Trùong Dai hoc Nông nghiêp II [E. sup. d'Agriculture II], Hànôi.
F : cult alim & ind, élev, vét.

Trùong Cao dang My thuât [E. sup. des Beaux-Arts], Hànôi.   *1957*
F : pnt, arts décor, sculp.

Trùong Can bô Thuong nghiêp Trung uong [E. sup. de Commerce], Hànôi.   *1965*
D : éco de com, produits de com, art culinaire.

Trùong Can bô ngoai thuong [E. sup. de Commerce extérieur], Hànôi.

Trùong Dai hoc Kinh te Kê hoach [E. sup. d'Economie et de Planification], Hànôi.   *1958*
F : éco ind, éco agr, éco du trav, plan, stat, march-matér.

Trùong Can bô-Tài chinh kê toan ngân hàng Trung uong [E. sup. des Finances, de Comptabilité et de Banque], Hànôi.   *1963*
F : fin, comp, banque.

Trùong Cao dong Am nhac [E. sup. de Musique], Hànôi.   *1962*
Tél: 54900

Trùong Dai hoc Duoc khoa Hànôi [E. sup. de Pharmacie], Hànôi.   *1965*
Tél: 54539

Trùong Dai hoc Thuy san [E. sup. de Pisciculture], Hànôi.   *1966*
F : pêch, pisc, méc.

Trùong Dai hoc Lâm nghiêp [E. sup. de Sylviculture], Hànôi.   *1961*

Ecole supérieure d'Agriculture, 45 Cuong-Dê, Hô Chí Minh ville.   *1959, 1968*
E : agr, for-élev.
D : pêch, péd (agr).

Ecole supérieure d'Architecture, Hô Chí Minh ville.

Ecole supérieure de Médecine-Pharmacie, Hô Chí Minh ville.

Ecole supérieure de Médecine, Huê.

Ecole supérieure de Formation des Cadres, Tay Nguyen.

Teacher Training—Formation pedagogique

Trùong Dai hoc Su pham 1 Hànôi [E. sup. de Pédagogie 1 Hànôi], Hànôi.   *1956*
F : let, hist, géog, psyc-péd, math, phys, ch, biol, techn agr, techn ind, phil marxiste et éd idéologique.

Trùong Dai hoc Su pham 2 Hànôi [E. sup. de Pédagogie 2 Hànôi], Hànôi.
F : let, géog, math, phys.

Trùong Dai hoc Su pham Viêt Bac [E. sup. de Pédagogie Viêt Bac], Viêt Bac.   *1966*
F : let, hist, géog, math, phys, ch, biol, techn agr.

Trùong Dai hoc Su pham Vinh [E. sup. de Pédagogie Vinh], Vinh.   *1959*
F : let, hist, math, phys, ch, biol, techn agr.

Trùong Dai hoc Su pham Ngoai ngu [E. normale supérieure de Langues étrangères], Hànôi.

F : russe, chinois, anglais, français.

Trùong Dai hoc Su pham thanh phô Hô Chí Minh [E. sup. de Pédagogie ville Hô Chí Minh], Hô Chí Minh ville.
F : let, hist, géog, math, phys, ch, biol, lang étr (anglais, français, russe).

Trùong Dai hoc Su pham Huê [E. sup. de Pédagogie Huê], Huê.
F : let, hist, géog, math, phys, ch, biol, lang étr (anglais, français, russe).

Trùong Cán bô Thê duc Thê thao trung uong [E. sup. de Culture physique et de Sports], Bac ninh.   *1962*

Trùong Dai hoc Ngoai ngu [E. sup. de Langues étrangères], Hànôi.
Tél: 43269
F : russe, chinois, anglais, français.

Union nationale des Etudiants du Viet Nam—UNEV (IUS)
64 Ba Trieu, Hànôi.

Syndicat des Enseignants vietnamiens Hànôi.

Mouvement des Intellectuels catholiques du Viet Nam (Pax Romana)
289 Hai Bà Trung, Hô Chí Minh ville.

Confédération des Etudiants catholiques du Viet Nam (Pax Romana)
43 Nguyên-Thông, Hô Chí Minh ville.

Ministère de l'Education
Hànôi.

Commission nationale vietnamienne pour l'Unesco
10 Lê Phung Hiêu, Hànôi.
Tél: 55441. Cables: ubaunesco hanoi

*

WESTERN SAMOA
SAMOA OCCIDENTAL

National University of Samoa/Iuniveste aoao Samoa í Sisifo (The Co-ordinator), Private Bag, National University, Apia.

Western Samoa Technical Institute, c/o Department of Education, P.O. Box 201, Apia.

School of Agriculture, Alafua Campus, University of South Pacific, P.O. Box 890, Apia. *1977* Tel: 2167. Telex: 251 usp sx

Primary Teachers' College, Malifa, Apia.

Secondary Teachers' College, Malifa, Apia. *1978*

Department of Education
P.O. Box 201, Apia.

YEMEN ARAB REPUBLIC
REPUBLIQUE ARABE DU YEMEN

*Gamiat Sana'a [Sana'a U.], P.O. Box 1247. Sana'a. *1970*
Tel: 200514. Telex: 2468

F : *arts, sc, com-eco, Sharia-law, ed, med, eng, agr.*
Ce : *lang.*

Supreme Student Committee—SSC (IUS)

*

Ministry of Education
Sana'a.
Tel: 274-552

Yemeni National Commission for Unesco
Ministry of Education, Sana'a.
Tel: 274-550

PEOPLE'S DEMOCRATIC REPUBLIC OF YEMEN
REPUBLIQUE DEMOCRATIQUE POPULAIRE DU YEMEN

University of Aden, P.O. Box 7039, Al Mansoora.   *1975*
Tel: 82434
F : *agr, eco, med, techn, law; ed* (Aden, Mukalla, Saber, Zingibar).

Central Council of Yemeni Students—CCYS (IUS)
P.O. Box 577, Aden.
               *

Ministry of Education
Madinat Asha-Ab, P.O. Box 7042, Aden.
Tel: 82-111
Unesco National Commission of the People's Democratic Republic of Yemen
Ministry of Education, Madinat Asha-Ab, P.O. Box 7042, Aden.
Tel: 82-111

YUGOSLAVIA
YOUGOSLAVIE

UNIVERSITIES—UNIVERSITES

*Univerzitet "Djuro Pucar Stari" u Banjoj Luci [U. de Banja Luka], Trg palih boraca 2, 78 000 Banja Luka.   *1975*
Tél: (78) 35018
F : élec, méc, techn, dr, éco.
A : péd.
E : tec sup (Bihai).
I : ch, gé, éco.
*Univerzitet u Beogradu**, Studentski trg 1, 11000 Beograd 6. (M. le Secrétaire général).
                              1838, 1905
Tél: (11) 635-153
F : phil, phill, math-nat, dr, agr, for, vét, éco, méd, gé civ, arc, élec, méc, mine-géol, mine-mét, techn-mét, phar, stom, pol, trans, phys, adm des aff, péd spé.
I : rech biol, rech nucl, rech phy, ch-techn-mét, agr, éd.
*Univerzitet u Bitola**, Bitola.   *1979*
Tél: (97) 23-788

F : éco, dr, techn, tour-hôtel.
E : agr, éd.
*Univerzitet "Svetozar Marković", Kragujevac**, B. Kidriča b.b., 34 000 Kragujevac.   *1976*
Tél: (34) 65-424
F : méc, éco, dr, nat-math; tec (Cačak).
* **Univerza "Edvarda Kardelja" v Ljubljani**, Trg revolucije 11, 61 000 Ljubljana.   *1595, 1919*
Tél: (61) 331-716. Fax: (61) 218567. Télex: 31573 elefak yu
F : biol-tec, arc-gé-géod, éco, méc, méd, dr, phil, nat-techn, socio-pol-jour.
A : mus, théât, ba, péd.
E : phys, mar.
*Univerza v Mariboru** [U. de Maribor], Krekova 2, 62 000 Maribor.
Tél: (62) 22-281
E : éco-com, tec, adm des aff, dr, agr.
*Univerzitet "Džemel Bijedić" u Mostaru** [U. de Mostar], Trg. 14 Februar b.b., 79 000 Mostar.

1977
Tél: (88) 39-140
F : dr, éco, méc, gé civ.
A : péd.
Ce : rech agr.
I : tabac (rech).
*Univerzitet u Nišu, Mike Paligorića 2, 18 000
Niš. *1965*
Tél: (18) 25-544
F : dr, éco, méd, électro, phil, méc, gé civ.
*Univerzitet u Novom Sadu, Veljka Vlahovića 3,
21 000 Novi Sad. *1960*
Tél: (21) 55-621
F : agr, dr, techn, math-nat, méd, éco, tec, phil,
phys, gé; péd-tec (Zrenianin).
*Sveučilište u Osijeku [U. de Osijek], Radićeva
13, 54 000 Osijek.
Tél: (54) 31-822
F : éco, agr-alim-techn, dr.
A : péd, mus.
D : méc-nav.
*Univerzitet Kosova u Prištini, Ulica, Maršala
Tita 53, 38000 Priština. *1971*
Tél: (38) 24-970
F : dr, éco, méd, phil, tec, math-nat; mine-géol
(Kosovska Mitrovica), agr, méd.
A : ba.
*Sveučilište u Rijeci, Ulica Aldo Negri 1, 51000
Rijeka. *1973*
Tél: (51) 25-682
F : méd, tec, éco, péd-ind, dr.
E : mar, éco.
A : péd, péd (Pula); péd (Gospić).
*Univerzitet u Sarajevu, Obala Vojvode Stepe 7,
71 000 Sarajevo. *1949*
Tél: (71) 211-216
F : arc-urb, éco, vét, méd, agr, for, dr, stom,
phil, math-nat, élec, méc, gé civ, pol, phys; mét
(Zenica).
E : éco-com, méd; éco-dom (Brčko)

A : péd, ba, mus.
*Univerzitet "Kiril i Metódij" u Skopju, bul.
"Krste Misirkov", 91 000 Skopje. *1949*
Tél: (91) 237-712
F : éco, agr, for, dr, méd, techn-mét, phil-hist,
phill, math-nat, arc, gé civ, élec-méc.
A : mus, éco (Prilep).
I : rech socio-pol-dr, éco, math.
*Sveučilište u Splitu, Livanjska 5, 58 000 Split.
1974
Tél: (58) 49-966
F : phil, élec-méc-nav, ch-techn, dr, éco, gé,
civ, tour-com.
E : éco, mar; mar (Dubrovnik).
A : péd; péd (Zadar).
I : cult-mar.
*Univerzitet "Veljko Vlahovic" u Titogradu,
Beogradska bb, 81 000 Titograd. *1974*
Tél: (81) 52-981
F : éco, dr, tec.
A : péd (Nikšić).
E : mar (Kotor).
I : rech biol-méd, hist, agr.
*Univerzitet u Tuzli, Rudarska 71 75 000 Tuzla.
1976
Tél: (75) 34-650
F : techn ch, gé mine-géol, gé de l'énergie, élec.
*Univerzitet Umetnosti [U. des Arts], Vuka
Karadžica, 12, 11 000 Beograd. *1957, 1973*
Tél: (11) 185-144
F : ba, arts app, dram, mus.
*Sveučilište u Zagrebu [U. de Zagreb], Trg
Maršala Tita 14, 41 000 Zagreb. *1669*
Tél: (41) 272-411
F : dr, éco, phil, math-nat, méd, stom, vét,
phar-biol-ch, arc, gé civ, géod, méc-nav, élec,
techn, mine-géol, agr, for, pol, orthophonie,
phys, com; infor (Varaždin).
I : rech méd, rech soc, phy.

Zajednica Jugoslovenskih Univerzitéta

L'Union des universités yougoslaves a été
constituée au cours de la Conférence interuniversitaire extraordinaire tenue les 28 et 29
janvier 1957 à Skopje.

L'Union représente l'association autogestionnaire d'universités unies librement et égales en
droits. Elle coordonne leurs intérêts particuliers
et communs et a pour but l'avancement de la
science et de la recherche ainsi que de l'éducation
et de l'enseignement. Elle examine aussi toutes
autres questions pouvant contribuer à une
activité plus fructueuse et au développement des
universités associées.

Parallèlement à ses activités générales dans le
cadre de la définition de la politique de l'enseignement supérieur de Yougoslavie, l'Union a
des tâches particulières: 1) suivre l'activité
scientifique et enseignante des universités et des
autres institutions d'enseignement supérieur
yougoslaves et assurer que cette activité soit au
niveau des réalisations scientifiques contemporaines, et qu'elle soit fondée sur les principes
marxistes et de la société autogestionnaire socialiste; 2) étudier l'organisation et l'association
autogestionnaire des institutions de l'enseignement supérieur et de leurs communautés; 3)
discuter et prendre positions sur: les questions de

coordination rationnelle du système des études, surtout entre facultés homologues et autres institutions de l'enseignement supérieur; des questions dont les données sont communes et unitaires et qui concernent la formation et la recherche, au sein des établissements d'enseignement supérieur, en matière de défense nationale générale; des questions de l'enseignement marxiste; des autres disciplines d'enseignement à caractère interdisciplinaire et de l'enseignement de la culture physique; des questions d'échange de travail, libre et autogestionnaire, entre les universités, et les institutions de l'enseignement supérieur, scientifiques et autres, et les organisations de travail associées; des critères pour la nomination des enseignants et des collaborateurs dans les institutions de l'enseignement supérieur; la coordination des critères pour la collation des grades académiques et scientifiques; des questions relatives à la situation matérielle et sociale des étudiants, des enseignants, des collaborateurs et des autres travailleurs; des questions communes d'organisation des universités, des institutions de l'enseignement supérieur et scientifique et surtout des questions portant sur leurs rapports mutuels; 4) stimuler et coordonner la participation des universités yougoslaves et des autres institutions de l'enseignement supérieur à la coopération internationale.

L'Union traite aussi toutes autres questions d'intérêt commun pour les universités, les facultés et les autres institutions de l'enseignement supérieur et prend les mesures nécessaires pour la réalisation de ces tâches.

Toutes les universités yougoslaves sont membres de l'Union, à savoir les universités de: Beograd, Bitola, Zagreb, Ljubljana, Skopje, Sarajevo, Novi Sad, Niš, Priština, Rijeka, Université des Arts, Beograd, Titograd, Split, Osijek, Maribor, Banja Luka, Kragujevac, Mostar et Tuzla.

La Skupština (l'Assemblée), organe suprême autogestionnaire de l'Union, est composée de: a) sept délégués de chaque université associée, dont au moins deux étudiants; b) un délégué de l'Association yougoslave des professeurs et maîtres de conférences des universités (SUUNiDNRJ) et un délégué de l'Union de la jeunesse socialiste yougoslave (SSOJ).

La Présidence de l'Union comprend les recteurs des universités associées, cinq délégués étudiants des universités dont ne sont pas issus le Président et les Vice-Présidents de l'Union, le Président de SUUNiDNRJ et un représentant de SSOJ.

L'Union a un Président (du rang de recteur), deux Vice-Présidents (du rang de recteur), un Vice-Président étudiant et un Secrétaire général. Au sein de l'Union travaillent neuf commis-

sions dont chacune est chargée d'un aspect particulier de ses activités. L'Union se charge de l'organisation du Séminaire international L'Université d'aujourd'hui et publie la revue "L'Université d'aujourd'hui."

The League of Yugoslav Universities was formed at an extraordinary interuniversity conference held on 28 and 29 January 1957 at Skopje. It is a self-administered free association of universities which enjoy equal rights. It co-ordinates their individual and common interests and its objective is the advancement of science and research, and of education and teaching. It also studies all other matters likely to contribute to more fruitful activity and to the development of associated universities.

In addition to its general responsibilities related to the formulation of policy for higher education in Yugoslavia, the League: 1) follows the scientific and teaching activities of the universities and other institutions of higher education ensuring that these are conducted at the level of modern scientific achievement, and that they are based on the principles of Marxism and a Socialist self-administering society; 2) studies the organization and self-administering association of the institutions of higher education and their members; 3) discusses and formulates opinions on: matters related to the rational co-ordination of the system of studies, especially between similar faculties and other institutions of higher education; questions of common interest concerning teaching and research in matters of national defence; questions concerning Marxist teaching, other fields of study of an interdisciplinary nature and the teaching of physical culture; questions relating to the free and self-administered exchange of work between university institutions of higher education and other scientific establishments and associated labour organizations; criteria for the appointment of academic staff and assistants; the co-ordination of criteria for the award of academic and scientific qualifications; questions relating to the material and social conditions of students, academic staff, and other workers; questions of common concern in matters of the organization of university institutions and scientific establishments, notably those related to their mutual relationships; 4) promotes and co-ordinates the participation of Yugoslav universities and other institutions of higher education in international co-operation.

The League also deals with all other matters of common interest to the universities, faculties and other institutions of higher education, and takes the necessary steps to deal with them. All the Yugoslav universities are members of the League: Belgrade, Bitola, Zagreb, Ljubljana, Skopje, Sarajevo, Novi Sad, Niš, Priština, Rijeka, University of the Arts, Belgrade, Titograd, Split, Osijek,

Maribor, Banja Luka, Kragujevac, Mostar, and Tuzla.

The Skupština (Assembly), the supreme self-administering organ of the League, is composed of: a) seven representatives of each member university, including at least two students; b) one representative of the Yugoslav Association of Professors and University Teachers (SUUNiDNRJ) and a representative of the League of Yugoslav Socialist Youth (SSOJ).

The executive of the League is comprised of the rectors of the associated universities, and five student representatives from universities other than those of which the President of SUUNiDNRJ and a representative of SSOJ are members.

The League has a President (a rector), two Vice-Presidents (rectors), a student Vice-President and a Secretary-General.

The League has nine commissions, each responsible for a particular aspect of its work. It is responsible for the organization of the International Seminar, The University Today, and publishes the journal "The University Today".
Président: Prof. Dr. Dragica Dodig.
Secrétaire général: Stamenka Uvalić-Trumbić.
Palmotićeva 22, 11000 Beograd.
  Tél: (11) 334-524

Co-ordination Committee of University Teachers' Association (IAUPL)
Correspondant: 18, rue du Docteur Roux, 75015 Paris.
  Tél: (33-1) 47-83-31-65
Union of Socialist Youth of Yugoslavia (USYY)
Bulevar Lenjina 6, Novi Beograd.
Travel Department of Yugoslav Youth and Students—YUS.
Moše Pijade 12/1, Beograd.
Student Christian Movement (WSCF)
Orthodox Theological Faculty, 2 July 7, 11000 Beograd.
United Nations Student Association of Yugoslavia (ISMUN)
c/o Matjaz Kos, Savezni Centar Klubova za UN, Cankarjeva 1/11, Ljubljana.
Institut federal pour la Coopération internationale dans le domaine de la Culture, de l'Education, de la Science et des Techniques
Kosancicev Venac 29, 1100 Beograd.
  Tél: (11) 625-955. Télex: 11661 zams yu

*

Commission yougoslave pour la coopération avec l'Unesco
Sekretarijat za obrazovanje i kultura SIV, Moše Pijade 8, Beograd.
  Tél: (11) 335-814. Cables: jugounesco belgrade

ZAIRE REPUBLIC
REPUBLIQUE DU ZAÏRE

UNIVERSITIES—UNIVERSITES

*Université de Kinshasa, B.P. 127, Kinshasa XI.   *1949, 1971, 1981*
Tél: 22-113. Télex: 21510
  F : méd-dent, phar, dr, ing, sc, éco.
Université de Kisangani, B.P. 2012, Kisangani.
                    1963, 1971, 1981

Tél: 2152. Télex: 19
  F : sc, éd-psyc, méd.
Université de Lubumbashi, B.P. 1825, Lubumbashi.   *1955, 1971, 1981*
Tél: 5403
  F : let, vét, soc-pol-adm, polytec, sc.

OTHER INSTITUTIONS—AUTRES INSTITUTIONS

Technical Education—Enseignement technique

Académie des Beaux-Arts, B.P. 8249, Kinshasa.
  Tél: 68476
Institut supérieur d'Etudes agronomiques de Bengamisa, B.P. 202, Kisangani.
  1968, 1971, 1981
Institut supérieur d'Etudes agronomiques de Mondongo, B.P. 60, Lisala. *1972, 1981*
Institut supérieur d'Arts et Métiers, B.P. 15.198, Kinshasa-Gombe. *1968, 1975, 1981*
Institut national des Arts, B.P. 8332, Kinshasa.
  1971, 1981
Institut des Bâtiments et des Travaux publics, B.P. 4731, Kinshasa. *1961, 1971, 1981*
Institut supérieur de Commerce, B.P. 16.596, Kinshasa. *1964, 1971, 1981*
Institut supérieur de Commerce, B.P. 2012, Kisangani. *1971, 1981*
Institut supérieur des Techniques médicales, B.P. 774, Kinshasa. *1971, 1981*
Institut supérieur d'Etudes sociales, B.P. 2849, Bukavu. *1971, 1981*
Institut supérieur d'Etudes sociales, B.P. 1575, Lubumbashi. *1971, 1981*
Institut supérieur de Statistique, B.P. 2471, Lubumbashi. *1967, 1971, 1981*
Institut supérieur des Techniques appliquées, B.P. 6593, Kinshasa. *1971, 1981*
  Tél: 23592
Institut supérieur des Techniques de l'Information, B.P. 14.998, Kinshasa. *1971, 1981*
  Tél: 25117

Teacher Training—Formation pedagogique

Institut de Formation des Cadres de l'Enseignement primaire, B.P. 711, Kisangani.
  1971, 1981
Institut pédagogique national, B.P. 8815, Kinshasa-Binza. *1961, 1971, 1981*
Institut supérieur pédagogique, B.P. 854, Bukavu. *1964, 1971, 1981*
Institut supérieur pédagogique, B.P. 340, Bunia.
  1968, 1971, 1981
Institut supérieur pédagogique, B.P. 282, Kananga. *1966, 1971, 1981*
Institut supérieur pédagogique, B.P. 258, Kikwit.
  1966
Institut supérieur pédagogique, B.P. 3580, Kinshasa-Gombe. *1961, 1971, 1981*
Institut supérieur pédagogique, B.P. 1514, Kisangani. *1967, 1971, 1981*
Institut supérieur pédagogique, B.P. 1796, Lubumbashi. *1959, 1971, 1981*
Institut supérieur pédagogique, B.P. 116, Mbandaka. *1971, 1981*
Institut supérieur pédagogique, B.P. 127, Mbanza-Ngungu. *1971, 1981*
Institut supérieur pédagogique, B.P. 682, Mbuji-Mayi. *1968, 1971, 1981*
Institut supérieur pédagogique technique, B.P. 3287, Kinshasa-Gombe. *1976, 1981*
Institut supérieur pédagogique technique, B.P. 75, Likasi. *1971, 1981*

Fédération zaïroise du MIEC (Pax Romana) B.P. 801, Kinshasa XI.

*

Département de l'Enseignement supérieur et universitaire, et de la Recherche scientifique, 10, avenue du Haut Commandement, B.P.
5429, Kinshasa/Gombé.
Tél: 27023. Télex: 21394
Commission nationale zaïroise pour l'Unesco
Commissariat d'Etat chargé de l'Education primaire et secondaire, Boîte postale 3163, Kinshasa/Gombe.
Tél: 30617

ZAMBIA
ZAMBIE

UNIVERSITIES—UNIVERSITES

*University of Zambia, P.O. Box 2379, Lusaka.
1965
Tel: 213221. Telex: 44370
S : *ed, eng, agr, mine, vet, hum-soc, law, med, nat, correspondence st, agr, extra-mural st.*
I : *African st, soc.*
LUANSHYA TECHNICAL AND VOCATIONAL

TEACHERS' COLLEGE, P.O. Box 90199, Lyanshya.
1975
D : *com, tec & ind arts, ed.*
The Copperbelt University, P.O. Box 21692, Kitwe.
1978, 1988
Tel: 210841. Cables: unzando kitwe
D : *bus-ind st, env st, techn, wood sc.*

OTHER INSTITUTIONS—AUTRES INSTITUTIONS

Evelyn Hone-College of Applied Arts and Commerce, P.O. Box 30029, Lusaka.
1963
Tel: 211557
D : *com, heal sc, jour, acc, bus st, hotel-catering, graph arts.*
Northern Technical College, P.O. Box KJ 250093, Millar Road, Ndola.
1964
Tel: 86211
D : *auto techn, structural fabrication techn, auto crafts, mec techn.*
Zambia Institute of Technology, P.O. Box 21993, Kitwe.
1973
Tel: 212243

D : *techn, elec, electro, telec, instrumentation, civ eng, bui, arc, surv, mine, ch, comp, app sc, met.*
Natural Resources Development College, P.O. Box CH99, Lusaka.
1965
National Institute of Public Administration, P.O. Box 31990, Lusaka.
1970
Tel: 216124
Zambia Air Services Training Institute, P.O. Box CH 198, Lusaka.
1970
Tel: 271087
D : *pilot training, maintenance techn, electro techn, meteo, traffic control & telec.*

World University Service (WUS)
  Chuundu House, Hewes Place, P.O. Box 50468, Lusaka.
  Tel: 214289
National Union of Zambian Students—NUZS (IUS)
  P.O. Box 1132, Lusaka.
University Christian Community (Pax Romana)
  University of Zambia, Kwacha 3/1, P.O. Box 2379, Lusaka.
Zambia Student Christian Movement (WSCF)
  c/o Bible House of Zambia, P.O. Box 31316, Lusaka.
  Tel: 3942

Ministry of Higher Education
  P.O. Box 50613, Lusaka.
  Tel: 219744
Department for Technical Education and Vocational Training
  Private Bag RW 16, Birdcage Walk, Lusaka.
  Tel: 212716. Cables: zamtec
Zambia National Commission for Unesco
  Ministry of Higher Education, P.O. Box 50619, Lusaka.
  Tel: 250095. Telex: 42621. Cables: zamnatcom unesco insaka.

*

ZIMBABWE
ZIMBABWE

*University of Zimbabwe, P.O. Box MP 167, Mount Pleasant, Harare. (The Registrar).
1955, 1970, 1980
Tel: 303211. telex: 4-152 zw
F : *arts, sc, ed, med, soc st, eng, agr, com-law, vet.*
Also associated teachers' colleges at: Belvedere, Bulawayo, Gwanda, Gweru, Harare, Masvingo, Morgenster, Mutare, Mutoko, Paulington, Seke.
Bulawayo Technical College, P.O. Box 1392, Bulawayo. *1961*
Tel: 63181
D : *bui, civ-mine, com, mec, elec, art-sc.*
S : *catering.*
Gweru Technical College, P.B. 137, Gweru.
Tel: 3583
D : *mec, auto eng, bus-sec, ed, elec.*
Harare Polytechnic, P.O. Box 8074, Causeway,

Harare. *1927*
Tel: 705951
D : *civ eng-bui, elec, mec, auto eng, sc techn, bus-sec, adult ed, mass ed, comp, printing-graphic arts, lib.*
Kushinga Phikelela Technical College, P.O. Box 3716, Marondera.
D : *bus ed, sec, cooperative st.*
Kwe-Kwe Technical College, P.B. 399, Kwe-Kwe.
Tel: 2991
D : *elec, mec, auto eng, bus-sec.*
Masvingoi Technical College, P.B. 800, Masvingo.
D : *bus-sec, auto, mec, elec.*
Mutare Technical College, P.B. 640, Mutare.
Tel: 63239
D : *auto eng, mec, elec, wood techn, bus-sec.*

Zimbabwe Association of University Women (IFUW)
P.O. Box MP 55, Mount Pleasant, Harare.
World University Service (WUS)
Department of Land Management, University of Zimbabwe, P.O. Box MP 167, Mount Pleasant, Harare.
Zimbabwe National Students Union—(ZINASU)
P.O. Box MP167, Mount Pleasant, Harara.
World University Service
Correspondent: Kingston Nyamapfene.
University of Zimbabwe, P.O. Box MP 167, Mount Pleasant, Harare.
Catholic Students' Society (Pax Romana)

University of Zimbabwe, Harare.
Student Christian Movement of Zimbabwe (WSCF)
P.O. Box 5836, Harare.

*

Ministry of Education
Harare.
Tel: 700791. Cables: "education"
Zimbabwe National Commission for Unesco
Ministry of Higher Education, Old Mutual Centre, P.O. Box U.A. 275, Union Avenue, Causeway, Harare.
Tel: 725430. Telex: 4235 zimgov zw

THE UNITED NATIONS UNIVERSITY
L'UNIVERSITE DES NATIONS UNIES

The Charter of the University, adopted by the General Assembly of the United Nations on 6 December 1973, specifies that it "shall enjoy autonomy within the framework of the United Nations" and that it shall enjoy "the academic freedom required for the achievement of its objectives, with particular reference to the choice of subjects and methods of research and training, and selection of persons and institutions to shape in its tasks, and freedom of expression."

Purposes

The University, which effectively came into being in the academic year 1975–76, is conceived as a worldwide network of advanced research and training institutions devoted to "pressing global problems of human survival, development and welfare." It is concerned with advanced research and training and dissemination of knowledge but does not provide courses of study leading to the award of degrees.

Its purpose is to give impetus, universality, and permanence to the search for practical knowledge needed to assure civilized survival. It seeks to bring together from East and West, North and South, the most knowledgeable experts, the most perceptive minds, and the most promising younger scholars for joint studies of maximum mutual value and worldwide applicability.

A central objective of the University is the continuing growth of vigorous academic and scientific communities everywhere and particularly in the developing countries. According to its charter, the University "shall endeavour to alleviate the intellectual isolation of persons in such communities in the developing countries which might otherwise become a reason for them moving to developed countries." Because so many of the world's most serious problems are concentrated in developing regions, the University, while serving the whole world, is strongly oriented toward the needs of developing countries.

La Charte de l'Université, adoptée par l'Assemblée générale des Nations Unies le 6 décembre 1973, précise qu'elle "jouit de l'autonomie dans le cadre de l'Organisation des Nations Unies" et "des libertés universitaires nécessaires à la réalisation de ses objectifs, notamment en ce qui concerne le choix des sujets et des méthodes de recherche et de formation, la désignation des personnes et institutions qui participeront à ses travaux et la liberté d'expression."

Objectifs

L'Université, dont la mise en place effective a eu lieu pendant l'année universitaire 1975–76, constitue un réseau mondial d'institutions de recherche et de formation de haut niveau se consacrant aux "problèmes mondiaux pressants de la survie, du développement et du bien-être de l'humanité." Elle se consacre à la recherche avancée, à la formation et à la diffusion du savoir mais elle ne dispense pas d'enseignement conduisant à l'obtention de diplômes. Son but est de donner l'impulsion, l'universalité et la permanence voulues à la recherche sur les connaissances pratiques nécessaires pour assurer la survie de la civilisation. Elle s'efforce de rassembler les plus grands spécialistes, les esprits les plus lucides et les jeunes chercheurs les plus prometteurs, venus de tous les horizons, pour les associer à des études dont les uns et les autres retireraient le maximum et qui seraient universellement applicables.

L'un des objectifs fondamentaux de l'Université est l'épanouissement en tous lieux et en particulier dans les pays en développement de solides communautés universitaires et scientifiques. Aux termes de sa Charte, l'Université "s'efforce d'atténuer l'isolement intellectuel des membres des communautés universitaires et scientifiques des pays en développement qui risquerait de les inciter à s'expatrier dans des pays développés.' Etant donné que la plupart des principaux problèmes qui se posent dans le monde sont concentrés dans les pays en développement, l'Université, tout en étant au service de l'humanité tout entière, se préoccupe particulièrement des besoins des pays en développement.

A formal agreement, approved by their respective governing bodies, provides for active co-operation between the United Nations University and the International Association of Universities wherever feasible and mutually desirable.

At present the University carries out research, training and knowledge dissemination in the areas of Peace, Development and Democracy; Global Economy; Global Life-Support Systems; Alternative Rural-Urban Configurations; and Science and Technology and Global Learning.

Organization

The governing body of the University, the Council, is made up of twenty-four distinguished educators and leading citizens, each from a different country, serving as individuals rather than governmental representatives. Council members serve for six-year terms and are appointed jointly by the Secretary-General of the United Nations and the Director-General of Unesco. The Rector of the University is also a member of the Council, and the Secretary-General of the United Nations, the Director-General of Unesco and the Director of Unitar are members *ex-officio*. The Chief Executive Officer is the Rector; he is appointed by the Secretary-General of the United Nations, with the concurrence of the Director-General of Unesco, from among a list of candidates submitted to him by the Council of the University.

The University, which has a small academic and administrative staff at its Headquarters in Tokyo, is working through a network of institutions in different parts of the world. The University now has 38 Associated Institutions, and collaborates with many other institutions of higher learning, through which it carries out its work in more than 60 countries. Between 1976 and June 1986, 1,178 UNU Fellowships were awarded. In 1984 the UNU established in Helsinki, Finland, the World Institute for Development Economics Research (WIDER), which is the first in the new worldwide network of research and training centres to be set up by the University. Other such research and training centres are in an advanced stage of planning.

Finance

The University relies on two types of financial support: endowment income (together with

Un accord en due forme, conclu avec l'approbation de leurs organes directeurs respectifs, prévoit une coopération active entre l'Université des Nations Unies et l'Association internationale des Universités dans tous les cas où une telle coopération paraîtra opportune et souhaitable pour les deux parties.

Actuellement l'Université effectue des recherches, dispense une formation et dissimine des connaissances dans les domaines suivants: la paix, le développement et le démocratie; l'économie mondiale; les systèmes globaux d'aide à la vie; les esquisses de solutions de remplacement aux problèmes en milieu rural/milieu urbain; et la science et la technologie et l'acquisition mondiale des connaisances.

Organisation

L'organe directeur de l'Université, le Conseil, est composé de vingt-quatre membres qui sont des éducateurs réputés et des personnalités éminentes, provenant de pays différents et siégeant à titre personnel et non en tant que représentants de leurs gouvernements respectifs. Les membres du Conseil sont nommés pour six ans conjointement par le Secrétaire général des Nations Unies et le Directeur général de l'Unesco. Le Recteur de l'Université est également membre du Conseil et le Secrétaire général des Nations Unies, le Directeur général de l'Unesco et le Directeur de l'Unitar sont membres de droit. L'administrateur principal de l'Université est le Recteur; il est nommé par le Secrétaire général des Nations Unies, avec l'approbation du Directeur général de l'Unesco, sur une liste de candidats qui lui est soumise par le Conseil de l'Université.

L'Université, qui a à son siège de Tokyo une petite équipe d'universitaires et d'administrateurs, déploie ses activités à l'aide d'un réseau d'institutions dans diverses parties du monde. L'Université compte maintenant 38 institutions associées et coopère avec un grand nombre d'autres établissements d'enseignement supérieur, ce qui lui permet d'exercer ses activités dans plus de soixante pays. Mille cent soixante dix-huit bourses de l'UNU ont été accordées entre 1976 et juin 1986. En 1984, l'UNU a créé à Helsinki, Finlande, l'Institut mondial de recherche en économie du développement (WIDER), le premier établissement créé par l'Université dans le nouveau réseau mondial des Centres de recherche et de formation. Les plans en vue de la création d'autres centres similaires de recherche et de formation en sont à un stade très avancé.

Finances

L'Université dépend de deux sources de financement: les revenus de la dotation (plus

other contributions to the annual operating budget); and project support.

The establishment of a substantial endowment fund is necessary to provide reliable support for the basic operations of the University. This is the surest guarantee of the University's viability, autonomy, quality and academic freedom. By the end of 1987 pledges to the endowment fund totalled some U.S. $192.2 million.

By the end of 1985 the governments of forty-four other countries had given or pledged financial support.

Rector: Heitor Gurgulino de Souza.

Vice-Rectors: Roland J. Fuchs; Kinhide Mushakoji.

Toho Seimei Building, 15–1 Shibuya 2–chome, Shibuya-ku, Tokyo, 150.

Tel: (3) 499-2811. telex: 25442 unatuniv j. Cables: unatuniv

d'autres contributions au budget annuel d'exploitation) et les subventions pour des projets.

L'établissement d'une dotation importante est nécessaire pour fonder les activités fondamentales de l'Université sur des bases solides. C'est pour l'Université la meilleure garantie de viabilité, d'autonomie, de qualité et de liberté académique. A la fin de l'année 1987, les engagements de verser des soutiens financiers à la dotation représentaient un montant d'environ 192.2 millions de dollars U.S.

A la fin de 1985, les gouvernements de quarante-quatre autres pays avaient apporté un soutien financier ou s'étaient engagés à le faire.

Recteur: Heitor Gurgulino Souza.

Vice-Recteurs: Roland J. Fuchs; Kinhide Mushakoji.

Toho Seimei Building, 15–1 Shibuya 2–Chome, Shibuya-ku, Tokyo, 150.

Tel: (3) 499-2811. Télex: 25442 unat univ j. Cables: unatuniv

THE EUROPEAN UNIVERSITY INSTITUTE
L'INSTITUT UNIVERSITAIRE EUROPEEN

The European University Institute is an international organization set up by the Member States of the European Communities. The idea was first launched in June 1955. The ensuing negotiations led to the signature by representatives of the six original Member States of the European Communities (Belgium, France, Germany, Italy, Luxembourg, Netherlands), on 19 April 1972, of the Convention setting up a European University Institute. Britain, Denmark, Ireland, as well as Greece and Spain, acceded later.

The Institute officially opened in autumn 1976 in the Badia Fiesolana. This famous building was made available by the Italian government.

The mission of the Institute is to contribute through its activities and through its influence to the development of Europe's cultural and academic heritage in its unity and in its diversity. It carries out this mission through teaching and research at the highest university level in the social and human sciences.

Structure

The Institute comprises three authorities:

— The High Council composed of two representatives of each Member State is responsible for the main guidance of the Institute, directs its activities and supervises its development. It is assisted by a Budget and Finance Committee which does the groundwork for its deliberations on budgetary and financial matters.
— The Principal of the Institute directs the Institute. He carries out or supervises the carrying out of acts and decisions pursuant to the Convention. He is responsible for the administration of the Institute and is assisted in his work by the Secretary.
— The Academic Council has general powers with regard to research and teaching, and among other things draws up the study and research programme. It is composed of the Principal, the Secretary, the tull-time professors, one representative of the research and

L'Institut universitaire européen est une organisation internationale fondée par les Etats membres des Communautés européennes. L'idée a été lancée pour la première fois en juin 1955. Les négociations qui suivirent ont abouti, le 19 avril 1972, à la signature, par les représentants des six Etats membres originaires des Communautés européennes (Belgique, France, Italie, Luxembourg, Pays-Bas, République fédérale d'Allemagne), de la Convention portant création d'un Institut universitaire européen. Le Danemark, le Royaume-Uni l'Irlande, la Grèce et l'Espagne y ont adhéré ultérieurement.

L'Institut a commencé à fonctionner à l'automne 1976 dans les bâtiments de la célèbre Badia Fiesolana, que le gouvernement italien a aménagés et mis à sa disposition.

La mission de l'Institut est de contribuer par son action et son rayonnement au développement du patrimoine culturel et scientifique de l'Europe, considéré dans son unité et dans sa diversité. Cette mission est accomplie par la voie de l'enseignement et de la recherche au niveau universitaire le plus élevé dans les domaines des sciences humaines et sociales.

Structure

Les structures de l'Institut comportent trois organes:

— Le Conseil supérieur, formé de deux représentants de chacun des États membres, est responsable de l'orientation principale de l'Institut; il règle le fonctionnement de celui-ci et veille à son développement. Il est assisté d'un Comité budgétaire et financier chargé de préparer ses délibérations dans les domaines budgétaire et financier.
— Le Président de l'Institut procède ou veille à ce titre à l'exécution des actes et décisions pris en application de la Convention. Chargé de l'administration de l'Institut il est assisté dans ses tâches par le Secrétaire général.
— Le Conseil académique possède une compétence générale en matière de recherche et d'enseignement et élabore notamment les programmes d'études et de recherche. Le Conseil académique est composé du Président, du Secrétaire général, des professeurs enseignant à plein temps, d'un représentant

administrative staff, representative of the research students and the Librarian.

Aims and Methods

Article 2 of the Convention lays down that "the aim of the Institute shall be to contribute, by its activities in the fields of higher education and research, to the development of the cultural and scientific heritage of Europe, as a whole and in its constituent parts. Its work shall also be concerned with the great movements and institutions which characterize the history and development of Europe. It shall take into account relations with cultures outside Europe. This aim shall be pursued through teaching and research at the highest university level." Research work is carried on through seminars. Some seminars are designed to offer the research students opportunities to present their problems and findings for discussion and criticism by other students and members of the academic staff. Other seminars in the Institute's research programme should help the research students to widen their range of interests both within their chosen discipline and within other related disciplines. Each department concentrates on a few major themes.

Article 2 of the Convention also states that "the Institute should also be a forum for the exchange and discussion of ideas and experience in subjects falling within the area of study and research with which it is concerned". With this in mind colloquia are organized at the Institute, bringing together small groups of people from the academic and scientific world and the members of the departments most directly concerned.

Research Student Admission and Length of Stay

The Institute takes in research students, in general nationals of the European Community Member States, intending to do a doctoral thesis at the Institute or who wish to obtain some additional training in the framework of their doctoral studies at another university. Students may also enrol for the one-year M.A. Programme in comparative European and international law and the M.A. course in Economics.

de chaque catégorie du personnel de recherche et administratif, de représentant des étudiants effectuant des travaux de recherche et du Bibliothécaire.

Objectifs et Méthodes

La Convention, dans son article 2, stipule que "l'Institut a pour mission de contribuer, par son action dans le domaine de l'enseignement supérieur et de la recherche, au développement du patrimoine culturel et scientifique de l'Europe considéré dans son unité et sa diversité. Les travaux portent également sur les grands mouvements et les institutions qui caractérisent l'Europe dans son histoire et son évolution. Ils tiennent compte des relations avec les civilisations extra-européennes. Cette mission est accomplie par la voie de l'enseignement et de la recherche au niveau universitaire le plus élevé". Les travaux de recherche sont effectués au sein de séminaires. Certains séminaires permettent aux étudiants effectuant des travaux de recherche d'exposer l'état de ces derniers, leur problématique, qui feront l'objet de discussions avec le corps enseignant et avec les autres étudiants. Les autres séminaires, entrant dans le cadre des programmes de recherche de l'Institut, aident les étudiants effectuant des travaux de recherche à élargir leurs centres d'intérêt au sein de la discipline choisie et dans les disciplines connexes. Chaque département concentre ses travaux sur quelques grands thèmes de recherche.

L'article 2 de la Convention stipule encore que "l'Institut doit être également le lieu de rencontre et de confrontation d'idées et d'expériences sur des sujets relevant des disciplines faisant l'objet de ses études et recherches". A ce titre, des colloques réunissant un petit groupe de personnalités des milieux universitaires et scientifiques en même temps que les membres des départements plus particulièrement intéressés sont organisés par l'Institut.

Admission des chercheurs

L'Institut accueille, pour des périodes allant de un à trois ans, des étudiants qui provenant généralement des pays de la Communauté européenne, effectuant des travaux de recherche et souhaitant soit préparer une thèse de doctorat à l'Institut, soit compléter leur formation de recherche dans le cadre des études de doctorat qu'ils effectuent dans une autre université. Les étudiants effectuant des travaux de recherche peuvent également s'inscrire au programme d'un an conduisant au "master's degree" en droit comparé européen et international et aux enseignements sanctionnés par un "master's degree" en sciences économiques.

590

Teaching and Research Programme

This programme is pursued in the four Departments, with a European, comparative and interdisciplinary approach: History and Civilization, Economics, Law, Political and Social Sciences.

History and Civilization
Contemporary History:
History of the European Community;
Economic History of Europe in the 19th and 20th centuries;
Political History of Europe in the 19th and 20th centuries;
Socio-cultural History of Europe in the 19th and 20th centuries.
Modern History:
Socio-economic History of Europe, from the 16th to the 19th century;
Political-social History, Ancien Régime;
Cultural-social History, History of ideas and mentalities, from the 15th to the 18th century.

Economics
European Economics:
European Economic Policy;
European Monetary Policy.
International Economics:
International Economic Relations;
International Monetary and Financial Relations.
Comparative Economics:
Comparative Economic Systems;
Centralized Economies and East/West Economic Relations.
Economic Theory:
Microeconomic Theory;
Macroeconomic Theory.

Law
European Law:
European Community Law;
Economic Law;
Administrative Law (Cultural Law);
Company Law.
International and Comparative Law:
Public International Law;
Labour and Social Law;
Comparative Law.
Legal Theory:
Legal Theory.

Political and Social Sciences
European Integration;
Mediterranean Studies;

Programme d'enseignement et de recherche

Ce programme est dispensé selon une approche européenne, comparative et interdisciplinaire dans les quatre départements ci-après: histoire et civilisation, sciences économiques, droit, sciences sociales et sciences politiques.

Histoire et civilisation
Histoire contemporaine:
Histoire de la Communauté européenne;
Histoire économique de l'Europe aux 19è et 20è siècles;
Histoire politique de l'Europe aux 19è et 20è siècles;
Histoire socio-culturelle de l'Europe aux 19è et 20è siècles.
Histoire moderne:
Histoire socio-économique de l'Europe, du 16 au 19è siècle;
Histoire sociale et politique de l'Ancien Régime;
Histoire socio-culturelle, histoire des idées et histoire des mentalités du 15è au 18è siècle.

Sciences économiques
Economie européenne:
Politique économique européenne;
Politique monétaire européenne.
Economie internationale:
Relations économiques internationales;
Relations financières et monétaires internationales.
Economie comparée:
Etude Comparative des systèmes économiques;
Economies centralisées et relations économiques Est-Ouest.
Théorie économique:
Théorie micro-économique;
Théorie macro-économique.

Sciences juridiques
Droit européen:
Droit communautaire européen;
Droit économique européen;
Droit administratif (droit de la culture);
Droit des sociétés.
Droit international et droit comparé:
Droit public international;
Droit du travail et droit social;
Droit comparé.
Théorie du droit.

Sciences sociales et sciences politiques
Intégration européenne;
Etudes méditerranéennes;

Comparative Government and Political Institutions
Sociology;
Social and Political Philosophy;
Public Policy Analysis;
Economic and social Policies.

Library
The library is fully computerized. It has at the moment some 310,000 documents, including microfilms. Some 3,000 periodicals are received.

Computing for Quantitative Research
The Institute has a PRIME 995511 computer for researchers wishing to do quantitative research.

Principal: Emile Noël
Secretary: Marcello Buzzonetti.
Badia Fiesolana, 50016 S. Domenico di Fiesole (Florence) (Italy).
Tel: (55) 50921. Fax: (55) 599887. Telex: 571528 iue. Cables univeur
Postal address: CP N° 2330, 1-50100 Firenze, Ferrovia (Italy).

Approche comparée des institutions gouvernementales et politiques;
Sociologie;
Philosophie sociale et politique;
Analyse des politiques publiques;
Politiques économiques et sociales.

Bibliothèque
La bibliothèque fonctionne selon un système automatisé. Elle possède actuellement l'équivalent d'environ 310.000 documents, y compris les microfilms, et est abonnée à environ 3.000 périodiques.

L'informatique pour la recherche quantitative
Les chercheurs désirant effectuer des recherches quantitatives et des traitements de textes ont accès à un ordinateur PRIME 995511.

Président: Emile Noël.
Secrétaire général: Marcello Buzzonetti.
Badia Fiesolana, 50016 S. Domenico di Fiesole (Florence) (Italie).
Tél: (55) 50921. Fax: (55) 599887. Télex: 571528 iue. Cables: univeur
Adresse postale: CP N° 2330, 1-50100 Firenze Ferrovia (Italie).

INTERNATIONAL
AND REGIONAL
ORGANIZATIONS

PART TWO
DEUXIEME PARTIE

ORGANISATIONS
INTERNATIONALES
ET REGIONALES

UNESCO AND THE UNIVERSITIES*

L'UNESCO ET LES UNIVERSITES*

Ever since its foundation in 1946, the United Nations Educational, Scientific and Cultural Organization has dealt with higher education and institutions of higher education. In 1948 it initiated and helped to organize an international university conference at Utrecht, followed by another at Nice in 1950, which led to the creation of the International Association of Universities (IAU). The Association's International Bureau (IUB) is housed in offices placed at its disposal by Unesco. Unesco also maintains formal consultative arrangements with other international university bodies and with international teachers' and students' organizations.

The Joint Unesco-International Association of Universities Research Programme in Higher Education was started in 1959, with a Joint Steering Committee, under the co-chairmanship of the Director-General of Unesco and the President of IAU. The Programme has sponsored studies and meetings, the most recent of which deal with the role of universities in environmental education and the impact of satellite technology on university teaching and research. Furthermore, the IAU-Unesco Information Centre for Higher Education provides extensive information services to the academic community.

Unesco is conscious that at present higher education is confronted with the major problem of its adaptation to the needs of those it serves, externally to the society in which it functions, and internally to its own institutions. The focus of Unesco's programmes is on the improvement of higher education through the promotion of innovation, regional and international co-operation, the mobility of students, teachers and researchers and the recognition of degrees and diplomas. Thus, the contribution of higher education to the development of the education

Depuis sa fondation en 1946, l'Organisation des Nations Unies pour l'Education, la Science et la Culture s'est occupée de l'enseignement supérieur et des institutions d'enseignement supérieur. En 1948, elle a pris l'initiative et aidé à l'organisation, d'abord d'une conférence universitaire à Utrecht, puis d'une autre conférence universitaire qui s'est tenue à Nice en 1950, et qui a conduit à la création de l'Association internationale des universités (AIU). Le Bureau International de l'Association (BIU) fonctionne dans des bureaux mis à sa disposition par l'Unesco. L'Unesco entretient également des relations consultatives officielles avec d'autres organismes universitaires internationaux et avec des organisations internationales d'enseignants et d'étudiants.

Les débuts du Programme conjoint Unesco-Association internationale des universités sur l'enseignement supérieur remontent à 1959. Pour l'exécution de ce programme, il a été créé un Comité mixte de direction sous la coprésidence du Directeur général de l'Unesco et du Président de l'AIU. Le programme a consisté essentiellement en études et réunions. Les activités les plus récentes traitent des universités et l'éducation pour l'environnement et l'impact de la technologie des satellites sur l'enseignement et la recherche universitaires. Le Centre d'information AIU-Unesco fournit des services en matière d'enseignement supérieur à la communauté académique.

L'Unesco est consciente du fait qu'aujourd'hui l'enseignement supérieur doit faire face au grave problème de son adaptation aux besoins de ceux qu'elle sert: à l'extérieur, la société dans laquelle elle fonctionne et, à l'intérieur, ses propres institutions. L'accent des programmes de l'Unesco est mis sur l'amélioration de l'enseignement supérieur, à travers l'encouragement des tendances novatrices de l'enseignement supérieur, la coopération régionale et internationale et la mobilité des étudiants, des enseignants et des chercheurs et la reconnais-

---

* French and English texts prepared by the Secretariat of Unesco.
* Textes anglais et français établis par le Secrétariat de l'Unesco.

system as a whole is an important issue. Other activities include higher distance learning, the evaluation of higher education, its links to the world of work and the development of higher education institutions. Since 1983 a series Papers in Higher Education has provided a forum for the analysis of key questions of higher education.

The activities designed to promote the mobility of persons concerned with higher education aim at increasing international co-operation, strengthening national training and research capacities and assisting specialists trained abroad to reintegrate into their own countries.

Certain activities are intended to improve harmonization between the standards which assure the recognition of training and skills acquired by individuals. They are designed to provide national, institutional and administrative authorities with information and legal instruments, which allow them to assess studies and competences and to decide on their recognition.

Unesco's efforts to standardize in this area have led to the adoption of the following conventions by Member States: Regional Convention on the Recognition of Studies, Diplomas and Degrees in Higher Education in Latin America and the Caribbean (Mexico, July 1974); Convention on the Recognition of Studies, Diplomas and Degrees in Higher Education in the Arab and European States bordering on the Mediterranean (Nice, December 1976); Convention on the Recognition of Studies, Diplomas and Degrees in Higher Education in the Arab States (Paris, December 1978); Convention on the Recognition of Studies, Diplomas and Degrees concerning Higher Education in the States belonging to the Europe Region (Paris, December 1979); Regional Convention on the Recognition of Studies, Certificates, Diplomas, Degrees and other Academic Qualifications in Higher Education in the African States (Arusha, Tanzania, December 1981); and Regional Convention on the Recognition of Studies, Diplomas and Degrees in Higher Education in Asia and the Pacific (Bangkok, December 1983).

sance des études et des diplômes. L'accent est également mis, dans ces programmes, sur l'intégration entre l'éducation, la formation et la recherche, ainsi que sur le rôle central qui revient à cet égard à l'enseignement supérieur. La contribution de l'enseignement supérieur à l'amélioration de l'éducation y trouve une place importante. Des activités ont été réalisées sur des questions prioritaires y compris l'éducation supérieure à distance, l'évaluation de l'enseignement supérieur et ses liens au monde du travail et le développement des universités. Depuis 1983 une série de documents intitulée *Cahiers de l'Enseignement Supérieur* a été établie pour analyser des questions importantes de l'enseignement supérieur.

Les activités portant sur la promotion de la mobilité des personnes engagées dans l'enseignement supérieur visent à en faire l'un des moyens d'intensifier la coopération internationale, d'assurer le renforcement des capacités nationales de formation et de recherche et de faciliter la réinsertion dans leur pays d'origine des spécialistes formés à l'étranger.

Certaines de ces activités ont pour but une meilleure harmonisation des normes qui régissent la reconnaissance des formations et des compétences que les personnes ont acquises. Elles sont destinées à mettre à la disposition des autorités compétentes, au niveau national comme au niveau institutionnel ou administratif, des informations et des instruments juridiques qui leur permettent d'évaluer les études et les compétences ainsi que de décider de leur reconnaissance.

L'action normative de l'Unesco dans ce domaine a abouti à l'adoption, par l'ensemble des Etats, des Conventions suivantes: Convention régionale sur la reconnaissance des études et des diplômes de l'enseignement supérieur en Amérique latine et dans les Caraïbes (Mexico, juillet 1974); Convention internationale sur la reconnaissance des études, des diplômes et des grades de l'enseignement supérieur dans les Etats arabes et les Etats européens riverains de la Méditerranée (Nice, décembre 1976); Convention sur la reconnaissance des études, des diplômes et des grades de l'enseignement supérieur dans les Etats arabes (Paris, décembre 1978); Convention sur la reconnaissance des études et des diplômes relatifs à l'enseignement supérieur dans les Etats de la région Europe (Paris, décembre 1979); Convention régionale sur la reconnaissance des études et des certificats, diplômes, grades et autres titres de l'enseignement supérieur dans les Etats d'Afrique (Arusha, Tanzanie, décembre 1981); et Convention régionale sur la reconnaissance des études, des diplômes et des grades de l'enseignement

The application of these Conventions is the responsibility of intergovernmental committees which meet regularly.

The Organization's efforts with regard to standardization are complemented by its interest in the problems of mobility. At the request of the Organization, the IAU undertook to revise and update the English and French versions of *World Guide to Higher Education: A Comparative Survey of Systems, Degrees and Qualifications.* The English edition appeared in 1982 and the French in 1983. A third edition is in preparation. With a view to strengthening the relations between education, training and research, a series of activities were undertaken concerning the establishment of *a co-operative network of higher education institutions dealing with the pedagogical inservice training of higher education personnel in the region of Latin America and the Caribbean (REDESLAC).* Three interregional workshops of REDESLAC have been held (Buenos Aires, 1985; San José, 1986; and Havana, 1988). Since 1986, similar networks are in the process of being established in the region of Europe and Africa. The European network on staff development has held meetings in Utrecht (1986), Aveiro, Portugal (1987) and plans another in Bucharest (1989). The following studies have been completed: *Three Case Studies on the Pedagogical Training of Higher Education Staff in Some Countries of French-speaking Africa, France, USSR; A Preliminary Study on the Nature and Scope of Instruction in Education Sciences in Higher Education Establishments; An International Inventory of Research Projects on Higher Education Problems Undertaken by Higher Education Establishments (preliminary version).*

In order to promote the principle of better integrated training and research, Unesco has compiled extensive documentation which analyses the data on needs, trends and available resources in these areas. Also, a regional workshop was organized in Montevideo, Uruguay, for national specialists responsible for training and research activities.

Within the framework of these activities, a study on the management and assessment of interdisciplinary training and research at university and postgraduate level was prepared. Two five-year national interdisciplinary pilot training projects were launched, in Mexico and the USSR.

supérieur en Asie et dans le Pacifique (Bangkok, décembre 1983).

La mise en application de ces Conventions est suivie par des Comités intergouvernementaux qui se réunissent régulièrement.

L'action normative de l'Organisation est soustendue par une réflexion sur les problèmes de la mobilité. L'AIU a préparé pour l'Organisation les versions anglaise et française mises à jour et révisées de l'ouvrage *Les études supérieures: présentation comparative des régimes d'enseignement et des diplômes.* La version anglaise a paru en 1982 et la version française en 1983. Une troisième édition est en préparation. En vue de renforcer l'interaction entre l'éducation, la formation et la recherche, une série d'activités a été entreprise concernant la création d'un *Réseau coopératif d'institutions de l'enseignement supérieur relatif à la formation continue pédagogique du personnel de l'enseignement supérieur dans la région de l'Amérique latine et les Caraïbes (REDESLAC).* Trois ateliers internationaux de REDESLAC ont eu lieu, à Buenos Aires en 1985, San José en 1986, et la Havane en 1988. Des réseaux similaires sont en cours de création dans les régions d'Europe et d'Afrique, depuis 1986. Le Réseau europé en pour la formation pédagogique des enseignants en enseignement supérieur a tenu des réunions à Utrecht en 1986 et à Aveiro, Portugal en 1987. Une réunion est prévue à Bucarest en 1989. Des études ont été publiées en 1986 sous les titres suivants: *Trois études de cas sur la formation pédagogique des enseignants d'enseignement supérieur dans quelques pays d'Afrique francophone, la France et l'URSS; Etude préliminaire sur la nature et l'importance de l'enseignement relatif aux sciences de l'éducation dans les établissements d'enseignement supérieur; Le répertoire international de projets de recherche sur les problèmes de l'enseignement supérieur entrepris par les établissements d'enseignement supérieur (version préliminaire).*

Afin de promouvoir le principe d'une meilleure intégration de la formation et de la recherche, l'Unesco produit une ample documentation qui traite de l'analyse des données sur les besoins, les tendances et les moyens disponibles. Egalement, un atelier régional a été organisé à Montevideo à l'intention des responsables locaux des activités de formation et de recherche.

Dans le cadre de ces activités, l'organisation et l'évaluation de la formation et de la recherche interdisciplinaires aux niveaux universitaire et postuniversitaire ont fait l'objet d'une étude. Deux projets pilotes quinquennaux de formation interdisciplinaire ont été mis en place à l'échelon national, au Mexique, et en URSS.

598

For the promotion of regional and international co-operation within higher education, Unesco is engaged in many different activites:

(a) The European Centre for Higher Education in Bucharest (CEPES), established in 1972, has constantly expanded the range of its activities as an information and referral centre and as a catalyst for the promotion of co-operation in higher education in the Europe Region. It has in particular sought to promote exchanges of experience, information, and innovation and to encourage the mobility of teachers, students and other specialists in higher education. CEPES also serves as the Secretariat of the Regional Committee for the Application of the Convention on the Recognition of Studies, Diplomas and Degrees Concerning Higher Education in the States Belonging to the Europe Region.

The quarterly review of CEPES, *Higher Education in Europe*, published in English, French and Russian, deals with major issues and trends in contemporary higher education and presents information on current developments and events in this field. The Centre has organized a large number of meetings and has undertaken studies on specific aspects of higher education in Europe. The following studies have been published: *Access to Higher Education in Europe; Inter–university Co–operation in the Europe Region; Higher Education and Economic Development in Europe (1975–1980) – A Statistical and Economic Study; Planning in Higher Education; Efficiency in Higher Education; Higher Education and Research; Alice in Academe – The Place of Women in Higher Education; University Teaching and the Training of Teachers.* In 1987, CEPES published (together with IBE) an *International Directory of Research Institutions on Higher Education.* CEPES has initiated a series of monographs on national systems of higher education which has covered thus far the following countries: Albania, Austria, Bulgaria, Byelorussian SSR, German Democratic Republic, Hungary, Netherlands, Norway, Poland, Switzerland, Ukrainian SSR, and United States of America. A large scale study on the terminology of higher education in the countries of the Europe Region has been completed; it comprises some 4500 terms most frequently used in relation to higher education in thirty-three countries of the region. Other studies which have been completed are: *The Introduction of New Information Technologies in Higher Education; Higher Education and Research In Europe: 1980–1985* (a new statistical study which, by comparison to the previous studies in

L'activité de l'Unesco pour la promotion de la coopération régionale et internationale dans le domaine de l'enseignement supérieur revêt des formes multiples:

a) Le Centre européen pour l'enseignement supérieur (CEPES, Bucarest), établi en 1972, a constamment élargi la gamme de ses activités en tant que centre d'information et d'orientation et comme catalyseur pour la promotion de la coopération dans le domaine de l'enseignement supérieur dans la région Europe. Il a cherché à promouvoir en particulier les échanges d'expérience, d'informations et les innovations et à encourager la mobilité des enseignants, des étudiants et d'autres spécialistes de l'enseignement supérieur. Le CEPES assure aussi le Secrétariat du Comité régional pour l'application de la Convention sur la reconnaissance des études et des diplômes relatifs à l'enseignement supérieur dans les Etats membres de la région Europe.

La revue trimestrielle du CEPES, *Enseignement supérieur en Europe*, publiée en anglais, français et russe, traite des questions et des tendances majeures dans l'enseignement supérieur contemporain et présente des informations sur les évolutions et les événements actuels dans ce domaine. Le Centre a organisé un grand nombre de réunions et a entrepris des études sur des aspects spécifiques de l'enseignement supérieur en Europe. Les études suivantes ont été publiées: *Accès à l'enseignement supérieur en Europe; La coopération interuniversitaire en Europe; L'enseignement supérieur et le développement économique en Europe (1975-1980) – Etude statistique et économique; "Planning in Higher Education"; "Efficiency in Higher Education; Higher Education and Research"; "Alice in Academe – The Place of Women in Higher Education"; Pédagogie universitaire et formation des enseignants.* En 1987 le CEPES a également publié (avec le BIE) un *Répertoire international des institutions de recherche sur l'enseignement supérieur.* Le CEPES a initié une série de monographies sur les systèmes nationaux d'enseignement supérieur qui comprend jusqu'à présent des monographies des pays suivants: Albanie, Autriche, Bulgarie, RSS de Biélorussie, Etats-Unis d'Amérique, Hongrie, Norvège, Pays-Bas, Pologne, République démocratique allemande, Suisse et RSS d'Ukraine. Une étude importante sur la Terminologie de l'enseignement supérieur dans les pays de la région Europe a été terminée; elle comprend quelque 4500 des termes les plus usités en relation avec l'enseignement supérieur dans 33 pays de la Région. Parmi les études parues on peut citer: *"The Introduction of New Information Technologies in Higher Education"; "Higher*

the series, also includes a statistical analysis of the share held by higher education in the national effort for R&D in the countries of the region); *Comparative Study of Higher Education Diplomas and Degrees in Europe and North America.*

CEPES has organized symposia dealing with: research on higher education (the Salamanca meetings of 1982 and 1986); university research and human problems; role of women in higher education; university teaching and the training of teachers; problems in comparing studies, diplomas and degrees in higher education; workshop for young academics doing research on higher education; relationship between general education, vocational training and further training in higher education. The Centre at present disposes of a computerized library and documentation unit with some 25,000 titles and is an active member of the International Network of Education, operated by IBE.

(b) The Regional Centre for Higher Education in Latin America and the Caribbean (CRESALC, Caracas) gathers and disseminates documentation and information concerning the different problems of higher education and research. It also carries out studies and surveys, and encourages contacts and exchanges between higher education specialists and officials in the region. The Centre publishes the bulletins *Higher Education* and *Abstract Bulletin* of publications on the main problems of higher education and bibliographies on this subject. It has organized meetings of experts and seminars on subjects such as: the role of universities in the development of the region; pedagogical training of higher education staff; reforms and innovations in higher education; problems regarding statistical information on higher education; higher education and the world of work; the university youth; resources and needs in research and teaching; graduate studies.

The Centre has also participated in meetings organized by other regional institutions on different areas of higher education. It has carried out studies and research projects on themes which include: the evaluation of the main reforms in higher education which aim to bring about

Education and Research in Europe: 1980-1985" (une nouvelle étude statistique qui, par rapport aux études antérieures de la série, comprend également des analyses statistiques de la contribution de l'enseignement supérieur à l'effort national pour la recherche et le développement dans les pays de la région); *"Comparative Study of Higher Education Diplomas and Degrees in Europe and North America".*

Le CEPES a organisé des symposiums sur les thèmes: la recherche sur l'enseignement supérieur (les réunions de Salamanque de 1982 et 1986); la recherche universitaire et les problèmes humains; le rôle des femmes dans l'enseignement supérieur; l'enseignement universitaire et la formation des enseignants; problèmes liés à la comparaison des études, des diplômes et des grades dans l'enseignement supérieur; atelier de formation pour les jeunes universitaires menant des recherches sur l'enseignement supérieur; la relation entre enseignement général, formation professionnelle et perfectionnement dans l'enseignement supérieur. A l'heure actuelle, le Centre dispose d'une bibliothèque et d'une unité de documentation informatisées avec quelques 25.000 titres et est un membre actif du Réseau international de l'éducation, mis en place par le BIE.

b) Le Centre régional pour l'enseignement supérieur en Amérique latine et dans la région des Caraïbes (CRESALC, Caracas), a pour fonctions: de réunir et de diffuser la documentation et les informations relatives aux différents problèmes de l'enseignement supérieur et de la recherche, de procéder à des études et à des enquêtes, et de favoriser les échanges et les contacts entre les responsables et les spécialistes de l'enseignement supérieur dans la région. Le Centre publie le bulletin *"Educación Superior"* et un *Résumé analytique* des ouvrages divers sur les problèmes de l'enseignement supérieur dans la région et des bibliographies en la matière. Il a organisé des réunions d'experts sur des sujets tels que: le rôle des universités dans le développement de la région, le perfectionnement pédagogique des enseignants universitaires, les réformes et innovations dans l'enseignement supérieur, la situation de l'information dans le domaine de l'enseignement supérieur, l'enseignement supérieur et le monde du travail, la jeunesse universitaire, les besoins et les ressources en matière de recherche et d'enseignement, les études postuniversitaires.

Le Centre a également participé à des réunions organisées par d'autres institutions régionales sur différents aspects de l'enseignement supérieur. Il a entrepris des études et des recherches sur des thèmes tels que l'évaluation des réformes visant à la démocratisation de l'enseignement supér-

its democratization; the development of post-graduate education; the social background and previous training of students; the present situation and future trends of higher education in several countries of the region; the participation of higher education in educational reforms and innovations; the present situation and means for improving statistical information on higher education; higher education and scientific and technological development; the conditions and status of higher education staff; the insertion of university graduates in the labour market. CRESALC provides on request technical assistance missions in a variety of fields.

(c) Unesco's Regional Offices undertake studies and research on the contribution of higher education institutions to the advancement of society. They organize consultations of experts in order to improve the quality of higher education and to harmonize the policies of Member States in this area. Through consultancy services and staff missions, the Regional Offices provide useful information which enhances the contribution of higher education to the solution of development problems, while promoting co-operation between different countries within this area of education.

(d) Thus, the Unesco Regional Office in Dakar (BREDA) has extended its activities to include further training for university teachers and managers of higher education institutions and establishments. Another of its priorities is training in new professional fields and activities have included the pedagogical training of higher education personnel; the management and use of informatics by higher education administrators; the use of informatics for scientific and technical data; technological assistance for the development of short-term training courses for new professions; project evaluation; and the role of higher education in cultural development and dissemination. The BREDA bulletin *EDUC-AFRICA* devoted two issues to higher education in 1987.

In 1986 a regional advisory committee on higher education in Africa was created to advise on the strategy to be adopted in order to improve the quality and relevance of higher education in the region. Furthermore, as a result of a regional colloquium at BREDA in 1987 on the improve-

ieur; le développement des études post-universitaires; l'origine socio-économique des étudiants et la formation préparatoire des étudiants; la situation actuelle de l'enseignement supérieur dans plusieurs pays de la région et la participation des personnels des institutions d'enseignement supérieur à la préparation et à la mise en oeuvre des réformes des systèmes d'éducation; la situation actuelle et les moyens d'amélioration de l'information statistique sur l'enseignement supérieur; l'enseignement supérieur et le développement scientifique et technique; la condition et le statut des enseignants universitaires; l'insertion des diplômés universitaires dans le marché du travail. Le CRESALC envoie sur demande des missions d'assistance technique.

c) Les bureaux régionaux de l'Unesco réalisent des études et des recherches sur la contribution des institutions d'enseignement supérieur au progrès de la société. Ils organisent des consultations d'experts destinées, d'une part, à améliorer la qualité des enseignements supérieurs et, d'autre part, à promouvoir et à harmoniser les politiques d'enseignement supérieur des Etats membres. Par des missions de consultants et des missions consultatives du personnel, les Bureaux régionaux apportent des informations utiles pour accroître la contribution de l'enseignement supérieur à la solution des problèmes du développement et encourager la coopération dans ce domaine entre les différents pays.

d) Ainsi, le Bureau régional de l'Unesco à Dakar (BREDA) a ajouté à ses activités celle du perfectionnement des enseignants des universités et des gestionnaires des institutions et établissements de l'enseignement supérieur. La formation dans les nouvelles filières professionnelles y représente une priorité. Quelques activités à souligner sont: la formation pédagogique du personnel d'enseignement supérieur, la formation en méthodes de gestion et d'utilisation de l'informatique à l'intention des administrateurs et des gestionnaires de l'enseignement supérieur, l'utilisation de l'informatique dans l'information scientifique et technique, le soutien technologique à des cours de formation de courte durée dans de nouvelles filières professionnelles, l'évaluation de projets et le rôle de l'enseignement supérieur dans le développement et la dissémination de la culture. Deux numéros du bulletin du BREDA, *EDUCAFRICA*, ont été consacrés à l'enseignement supérieur en 1987.

Un comité consultatif régional sur l'enseignement supérieur en Afrique a été créé en 1986 pour formuler des avis sur la stratégie à adopter pour améliorer la qualité et la pertinence de l'enseignement supérieur dans la région. Par ailleurs, l'organisation en mai 1987 au BREDA

ment of higher education in Africa a special programme was developed aiming at the improvement of higher level training, documentation exchange, and increased mobility in higher education.

(e) The Principal Regional Office for Asia and the Pacific, with the financial participation of the United Nations Development Programme (UNDP), aims to: promote inter-country exchange of experiences and expertise in innovative developments in higher education; contribute to the development and application of knowledge and techniques in the field of policy planning and management; contribute through special research studies to knowledge and understanding of the problems and emerging roles of higher education; and facilitate inter–country exchange of information and documentation. The emphasis of the programme has been on training of higher education personnel, development of training materials, carrying out research studies, and strengthening documentation and information services. A network of seventy universities, research institutions, grant commissions and other higher education institutions have been set up in seventeen countries within the framework of the regional programme, and have formed three consortia corresponding to the above programme areas.

In the field of distance education and open university, significant progress has been made, especially the establishment of the Asian Association of Open Universities (AAOU) and of a regional resource centre in distance education (both situated at STOU in Thailand), the co-operation of six universities in the production of three video programmes and of three universities in the production of a Master Degree course in human environment, and the production and distribution of the distance education newsletter *Never Too Far*.

Since 1984, several major regional and national symposia/seminars/workshops, study visits related to distance education, higher education planning and management, and academic staff development have been organized. More than 400 key persons from countries in this region have participated in one or more of these activities. A number of workshop reports have been published as monographs.

Recent publications include two research studies on equity, quality and cost in higher education (Australia and Republic of Korea), a combined report of research studies on higher

du Colloque régional sur l'amélioration de l'enseignement supérieur en Afrique a permis l'élaboration d'un programme spécial visant notamment "l'amélioration de la formation au niveau supérieur, l'échange de documentation, et l'accroissement de la mobilité" dans l'enseignement supérieur.

e) Le Bureau régional principal pour l'Asie et le Pacifique, avec la participation financière du Programme des Nations Unies pour le Développement (PNUD), vise à: promouvoir l'échange des expériences et de l'expertise en ce qui concerne les innovations en matière d'enseignement supérieur entre les pays de la région; contribuer au développement et à l'application des connaissances et des techniques dans les domaines de la politique, de la planification et de la gestion; contribuer par le moyen des études spéciales à la connaissance et à la compréhension des problèmes et du rôle de l'enseignement supérieur; et faciliter l'échange de l'information et de la documentation entre les pays de la région. Le programme met l'accent sur la formation du personnel de l'enseignement supérieur, le développement des matériels de formation, des études et le renforcement des services d'information et de documentation. Dans le cadre du Programme régional, un réseau de soixante-dix universités, centres de recherche et d'autres établissements de l'enseignement supérieur a été établi dans dix-sept pays et constitue trois groupes correspondant aux objectifs du programme.

En matière d'enseignement à distance et d'université ouverte, des progrès importants ont été réalisés, notamment: la création, en novembre 1987, de l'Association des universités ouvertes d'Asie (AAOU) et en 1988 d'un centre didactique sur l'enseignement à distance à STOU en Thaïlande. Une coopération entre six universités a permis la production de trois programmes vidéo, et trois universités ont collaboré à la production d'un programme de matrise en matière d'environnement humain. Le bulletin *"Never Too Far"* sur l'enseignement à distance continue à paraître.

Depuis 1984 plus de 400 responsables ont participé à des symposiums, séminaires, ateliers ou visites d'études au niveau régional ou national sur des sujets tels que l'enseignement à distance, la planification et la gestion de l'enseignement supérieur ou la formation continue des personnels de l'enseignement supérieur. Plusieurs rapports d'ateliers ont été publiés sous forme de monographies.

Parmi les publications récentes figurent deux études sur l'équité, la qualité et le coût en enseignement supérieur en Australie et dans la République de Corée, une synthèse de

education and development (carried out in four countries), a research study on the contribution of higher agricultural education to rural development and a monograph on pedagogical staff development. Several handbooks, manuals, case studies and monographs are under preparation by various universities and institutions on contract.

The second phase of UNDP supported project RAS/86/171 – Regional Technical Co-operation Programme in Higher Education for Development in Asia and the Pacific commenced in 1987 for four years.

(f) So as to develop co-operation in this field amongst the Arab States, Unesco has given financial support to the Arab Center for Higher Education, established by the Arab Educational, Cultural and Scientific Organization (ALECSO). Financial and technical support was also given to the Association of Arab Universities. Among the most important recent meetings and workshops organized by the Unesco Regional Office for Education in the Arab States (UNEDBAS) were a meeting on 'Distance Higher Education' in Bahrain in 1986, a workshop on 'The Application of Information Systems in the Management of Higher Education Institutions' in Amman in 1987, and a regional consultation meeting on 'Reinforcing the Links between Higher Education and the World of Work' in Cairo in 1988. UNEDBAS also provided financial support to various Arab universities for the organization of national training courses for administrators and university professors, and co-operated with ALECSO in organizing three conferences for Arab ministers of higher education.

Various studies were also undertaken by UNEDBAS on different topics related to higher education in the Arab Region. Titles include: *New Patterns of Higher Education Institutions Needed in the Arab Region by the Year 2000, Reinforcing Links between Higher Education and the World of Work and Challenges Facing the Future of Higher Education*. UNEDBAS is co-operating with the Association of Arab Universities in translating and publishing certain CEPES reviews and bulletins. Moreover, it has published the Arabic version of the *World Guide to Higher Education*.

(g) The International Bureau of Education (IBE, Geneva), founded in 1925 and an integral part of Unesco since 1969, has four main functions: to organize the biennial International

recherches sur l'enseignement supérieur et le développement dans quatre pays, une étude sur la contribution de l'enseignement supérieur agricole au développement rural et une monographie sur la formation continue des personnels enseignants dans l'enseignement supérieur. Plusieurs guides pratiques, manuels, études de cas et monographies sont en préparation.

La deuxième phase d'un projet financé par le PNUD (RAS/86/171) pour la coopération technique régionale en enseignement supérieur dans la région de l'Asie et du Pacifique, est en cours depuis 1987, pour une période de quatre ans.

f) Afin de développer la coopération dans ce domaine parmi les Etats arabes, l'Unesco a fourni un appui financier à l' "Arab Centre for Higher Education Research" qui a été établi par l'Organisation arabe pour l'éducation, la culture et la science (ALECSO) ainsi qu'un soutien financier et technique à l'Association des universités arabes. Parmi les réunions et ateliers récents les plus significatifs, organisés par le Bureau régional de l'Unesco pour les états arabes (UNEDBAS) figurent une réunion sur l'enseignement supérieur à distance (Bahrein, 1986), un atelier sur l'application des systèmes informatiques à la gestion des institutions d'enseignement supérieur (Amman, Jordanie, 1987), et une consultation régionale sur le renforcement des liens entre l'enseignement supérieur et le monde du travail (Le Caire, 1988). L'UNEDBAS a, par ailleurs, fourni un soutien financier à plusieurs universités arabes pour l'organisation de cours de formation au niveau national, destinés aux enseignants d'université et aux administrateurs. Il a coopéré également avec l'ALECSO pour la tenue de trois conférences de ministres arabes de l'enseignement supérieur.

Parmi les études effectuées par l'UNEDBAS sur des sujets relatifs à l'enseignement supérieur dans la région arabe, on peut citer: "*New Patterns of Higher Education Institutions Needed in the Arab Region by the Year 2000*" [Nouvelles configurations de l'enseignement supérieur requises dans la région arabe avant l'an 2000], "*Reinforcing Links between Higher Education and the World of Work*" [Renforcer les liens entre l'enseignement supérieur et le monde du travail], et "*Challenges Facing the Future of Higher Education*" [Les défis auxquels fait face l'enseignement supérieur]. L'UNEDBAS, en coopération avec l'Association des universités arabes, a traduit en arabe et publié certains ouvrages du CEPES, ainsi qu'une version arabe des *Etudes supérieures*.

g) Fondé en 1925, le Bureau international d'éducation (BIE, Genève) est partie intégrante de l'Unesco depuis 1969. Il a quatre fonctions principales: organiser la Conférence inter-

Conference on Education (ICE), which gives rise to the *International Yearbook of Education* (the theme of the forty-first session of the ICE, in 1988, was *Diversification of Post-secondary Education in Relation to Employment*); to undertake educational studies, particularly on comparative education; to collect and disseminate educational documentation and information, and to maintain an international educational library and exhibition. Thus it provides a broad basis for the conduct of educational studies by researchers from universities. Among its publications are some relating specifically to higher education such as: *International Directory of Higher Education Research Institutions; The Foreign Student Dilemma and Empirical Research in Education*. The IBE's Documentation Centre maintains a large data base of national and international publications and documents which is available for computer search through the many key words of higher education listed in the *Unesco: IBE Education Thesaurus* (at present available in English, French, Portuguese, Russian and Spanish editions).

(h) Established in 1963, the International Institute for Educational Planning (IIEP) launched its first major programme on higher education in 1969 with the research project *Planning the Development of Universities*, the objectives and methodology of which were decided upon in an international seminar. A survey covering eighty-five universities around the world provided the knowledge base at that time of the status of planning and management of universities. The results of the research were published in four volumes by Unesco. This was followed up by studies on lifelong education as a new function of higher education systems, as well as on its financing, curriculum planning and effectiveness. The results of this research were also published by Unesco in 1977.

During the period 1973-1984 the IIEP carried out a research project on higher education and employment with the objective of deriving implications for the planning of higher education in a particular country's socio-economic context and of identifying factors that would promote democratization in the fields of higher education and employment. Case studies were undertaken in twenty-one countries with the active participation of national researchers. Most of the results have been published along with a synthesis of these studies. The results of this research are now

nationale de l'éducation (CIE) qui a lieu tous les deux ans et dont découle l'*Annuaire international de l'éducation* (la 41e session de la CIE, en 1988, avait pour thème *la diversification de l'enseignement postsecondaire face à la situation de l'emploi*); entreprendre des études portant sur l'éducation et en particulier sur l'éducation comparée; recueillir et diffuser la documentation et l'information dans le domaine de l'éducation; et maintenir une bibliothèque et une exposition internationales de l'éducation. Le BIE offre donc aux chercheurs et aux universitaires d'importantes facilités pour entreprendre des études sur l'éducation. Parmi ses publications, il faut citer quelques-unes qui s'appliquent directement à l'enseignement supérieur: *Répertoire international des institutions de recherche sur l'enseignement supérieur; Les étudiants étrangers: un dilemme?*; et *La recherche empirique en éducation*. Le Centre de documentation du BIE dispose d'une grande base de données sur les publications et les documents nationaux et internationaux, qui est disponible pour la recherche informatisée grâce aux nombreux mots clefs sur l'enseignement supérieur qu'on trouve dans le *Thesaurus de l'éducation Unesco:BIE* (actuellement disponible en anglais, espagnol, français, portugais et russe).

h) L'Institut international de planification de l'éducation (IIPE), créé en 1963, lança son premier grand programme relatif à l'enseignement supérieur en 1969, avec un projet de recherche sur *la planification du développement des universités* dont les objectifs et la méthodologie furent déterminés à l'issue d'un séminaire international. Une enquête menée auprès de quatre-vingt-cinq universités de par le monde a fourni les informations de base sur les thèmes du statut de la planification et de la gestion des universités. Les résultats de cette recherche ont été publiés en quatre volumes par l'Unesco. Cette recherche fut suivie d'une autre sur l'éducation permanente (nouvelle fonction des systèmes d'enseignement supérieur), sur son financement, sur la planification des programmes et son efficacité, et dont les résultats ont été publiés en 1977.

Au cours de la période 1973-1984, l'IIPE a exécuté un programme de recherche sur l'enseignement supérieur et l'emploi dans le but d'analyser les implications de ce problème sur la planification de l'enseignement supérieur dans différents contextes, ainsi que d'identifier les facteurs qui tendent à promouvoir la démocratisation de l'enseignement supérieur et l'actualisation de l'emploi. Des études de cas sur vingt-et-un pays ont été entreprises avec la participation de chercheurs nationaux. Les résultats de ces recherches, dans leur majorité, ainsi qu'une

being used as training materials for national and regional intensive courses in education, employment and work.

IIEP contributed to the Unesco programme on the establishment of the new international order by publishing the book entitled *Higher Education and the New International Order* (1982). It has also conducted a series of studies on technical progress and its implications for education planning in general and higher education in particular. A synthesis of the several case studies has been published in two volumes. IIEP is undertaking several studies in the field of higher education, covering three main research themes: (1) educational planning and technological development; (2) the diversification of the educational field; and (3) the role of educational planning in the decision-making and implementation process. Countries being studied are: Algeria, Brazil, Cameroon, Congo, Costa Rica, France, German Democratic Republic, India, Indonesia, Mexico, Poland, Republic of Korea, Zambia and Zimbabwe. IIEP's training programme places special emphasis on higher education. A special training programme on new trends in this area and their implications for planning is included in the Annual Training Programme of the Institute.

(i) The establishment of a collective consultation with NGOs specialized in the domain of higher education has strengthened co-operation. A series of studies and round tables on key issues such as mobility, higher education and the world of work, women in higher education, the aspiration of students and the status of the professoriat have been carried out in collaboration with the *Association des universités partiellement ou entièrement de langue française* (AUPELF), the World Federation of Teachers' Union, the International Federation of University Women, the International Association of University Professors and Lecturers and the International Union of Students.

Unesco's involvement with higher education extends beyond the programmes of its Education Sector. Within the Science Sector, major emphasis is placed on the training of scientists for research, the development of effective university science teaching programmes as well as the education and training of engineers. For 1986/87, the university science teaching programme included activities under the Asian Physics Education Network, the International Network

synthèse de ces études, ont été publiés. Les résultats de cette recherche sont maintenant utilisés en tant que matériel didactique pour les cours intensifs nationaux et régionaux sur l'éducation, le travail et l'emploi.

L'IIPE a contribué au programme de l'Unesco sur le nouvel ordre international, par la publication d'un ouvrage intitulé *"Higher Education and the New International Order"* (1982). Il a mené une série d'études sur le progrès technique et ses implications dans la planification de l'éducation en général et de l'enseignement supérieur en particulier. Une synthèse de plusieurs études de cas a été publiée en deux volumes. L'IIPE a entrepris différentes études dans le domaine de l'enseignement supérieur sur trois thèmes principaux de recherche: 1) planification de l'éducation et développement technologique; 2) diversification dans le domaine de l'éducation; et 3) rôle de la planification de l'éducation dans le processus de prise de décision et de mise en oeuvre. Les études sont menées dans les pays suivants: Algérie, Brésil, Cameroun, Congo, Costa Rica, France, Inde, Indonésie, Mexique, Pologne, République démocratique allemande, République de Corée, Zambie et Zimbabwe. Le programme de formation de l'IIPE accorde une attention particulière à l'enseignement supérieur. Un programme de formation spécial sur les nouvelles tendances de l'enseignement supérieur et leurs implications sur la planification est inclus dans le Programme annuel de formation de l'Institut.

i) Une consultation collective avec des ONGs spécialisées en matière d'enseignement supérieur a permis de renforcer la coopération avec l'Unesco. Ce groupe, y compris l'Association des universités partiellement ou entièrement de langue française (AUPELF), la Fédération internationale syndicale de l'enseignement, la Fédération internationale des femmes diplômées des universités, l'Association internationale des professeurs et des maîtres de conférences des universités, l'Union internationale des étudiants, a collaboré afin de réaliser des études et des tables rondes sur des questions importantes telles que la mobilité, l'enseignement supérieur et le monde du travail, le statut des femmes, des professeurs et des étudiants.

Les activités de l'Unesco dans le domaine de l'enseignement supérieur débordent les programmes de son Secteur de l'Education. Dans les programmes du Secteur des Sciences l'accent est mis sur la formation des scientifiques en vue de la recherche, le développement de programmes d'enseignement scientifique universitaire efficaces ainsi que sur l'enseignement et la formation des ingénieurs. Pour 1986/87 le programme universitaire de formation scientifique com-

for Chemical Education, as well as programmes in biology and mathematics teaching at university level. Special attention is being paid to the local production of laboratory equipment and to interactions between universities and industry. The training of young scientists in research techniques and direct assistance to research workers in developing countries in the basic sciences are supported through organizations such as the International Organization for Chemical Science in Development (IOCD), International Cell Research Organization (ICRO), and International Brain Research Organization (IBRO). The Science Sector also carries out a major programme in computer sciences which includes programmes for computers in science education.

In addition to working with the various teaching commissions of the International Council of Scientific Unions (ICSU), contacts are maintained with universities in the arrangements of postgraduate training courses, provision of experts, fellowships and training courses.

As regards the education and training of engineers and higher technicians, a major new initiative has been undertaken to create cost-effective distance–learning packages, particularly in the fields of postgraduate training and up-dating courses. Unesco's first such postgraduate short course on 'Computational Techniques in Ocean Engineering' was recently created in association with the University of Padua and the International Technological University. This will be followed in 1989 by a one-year M.Sc. learning package on 'Technical Thermodynamics' produced by an international team of academics from the Moscow Power Engineering Institute, M.I.T. and Imperial College, London.

A major new network, the International Network of Centres for Computer Applications (INCCA), has been created, and the first issue of its journal has been published. New initiatives have been taken in the field of energy, including support for the development of solar-powered photo–voltaic devices for rural areas. International and regional meetings on various problems of higher engineering education are being conducted. Support is also given to the regional and international organizations concerned. Postgraduate courses for specialists in

prenait des activités s'inscrivant dans le Réseau asiatique d'enseignement de la physique et dans le Réseau international pour l'éducation et pour la formation en chimie, de même que des programmes d'enseignement en biologie et en mathématiques de niveau universitaire. Une attention spéciale est accordée à la production locale d'équipements pour laboratoires ainsi qu'aux interactions entre l'université et l'industrie. La formation de jeunes scientifiques en techniques de recherche et l'appui direct aux chercheurs dans les pays en développement, en sciences fondamentales, sont soutenues par l'intermédiaire d'organisations telles que l' "International Organization for Chemical Science in Development" (IOCD), l'Organisation internationale de recherche sur la cellule (ICRO), et l'Organisation internationale de recherche sur le cerveau (IBRO). Le Secteur des Sciences met également en oeuvre un grand programme en informatique, qui comprend des programmes sur l'utilisation des ordinateurs dans les sciences de l'éducation.

En complément au travail conjoint effectué par plusieurs Commissions d'enseignement du Conseil international des unions scientifiques (ICSU), des contacts ont été maintenus avec des universités en vue de l'organisation de cours de formation postgradués pour la préparation d'experts ainsi que de l'organisation de cours de formation et de programmes de bourses.

En ce qui concerne plus particulièrement la formation des ingénieurs et des techniciens de haut niveau, une initiative nouvelle importante a été prise afin de créer des ensembles pédagogiques économiques particulièrement pour des cours postuniversitaires et pour la formation continue. Le premier de ces cours de courte durée de niveau postuniversitaire sur les techniques de calcul en génie océanique a été créé récemment en collaboration avec l'Université de Padoue et l'Université technologique internationale. Il sera suivi en 1989 d'un cours du niveau de maîtrise sur la thermodynamique technique produit par une équipe internationale d'universitaires de l'institut de Moscou de génie énergétique et de l'Imperial College, Londres.

Un important nouveau réseau international, "The International Network of Centres for Computer Applications" (INCCA), a été créé. Le premier numéro de son journal est sorti récemment. Des initiatives nouvelles ont été prises dans le domaine de l'énergie, y compris un soutien au développement d'appareils photovoltages à puissance solaire destinés aux zones rurales. Des réunions régionales et internationales sur différents problèmes de formation supérieure d'ingénieurs sont organisées. Une assistance est fournie aux organisations région-

606

various technical and scientific disciplines have been organized.

Considerable attention has been given in recent years to the preparation of librarians, documentalists and archivists within the framework of university education. Unesco and UNDP have assisted in the establishment of regional schools at the University of Dakar, Makerere University (Kampala), the University of Ghana, and at the University of the West Indies (Mona, Kingston). A school of information science was established in Rabat. Unesco and UNDP assistance was provided to establish a nine-month postgraduate training course for science information specialists in South-East Asia at the University of the Philippines.

Since 1974, a postgraduate course for specialists in scientific and technical information and documentation has been given every year in France. Unesco is regularly providing consultant services for the planning or establishment of higher education programmes in the field of librarianship, information science and archives in Member States. Very recently, assistance has been provided through financing and consultant missions to the planning or establishment of regional training programmes in information sciences at postgraduate level in the People's Republic of China, at Addis Ababa University, Ibadan University, at the University Simón Bolívar (Caracas) and in Hanoi, Viet Nam, the latter two with financing from UNDP.

Unesco has also been and will continue to be active in preparing teaching materials of various kinds in the field of librarianship, information science and archives. In collaboration with AUPELF, preparatory activities for the creation of a coordinating centre for the university libraries of French-speaking countries of West Africa have been undertaken. University library manpower requirements have been assessed, the development of a university library network was proposed and, with the assistance of UNDP, investigations for future needs of university libraries in selected Member States were carried out.

In the field of preservation, presentation and enhancement of the cultural heritage, Unesco has given support to numerous activities devoted to the training of specialized personnel. Unesco has also provided fellowships for postgraduate studies in this field. Support has been given in the form of advisory services, financial contributions,

ales et internationales appropriées. Des cours destinés aux spécialistes des différentes disciplines scientifiques et techniques ont été organisés.

Une attention particulière a été accordée à la formation de bibliothécaires, de documentalistes et d'archivistes au niveau universitaire. L'Unesco et le PNUD ont aidé à l'établissement d'écoles régionales dans ce domaine aux universités de Dakar; de Makerere, Kampala; du Ghana, Accra; et des West Indies, Mona, Kingston. Une école des sciences de l'information a été établie à Rabat. L'Unesco et le PNUD ont apporté leur assistance pour la création d'un cours postuniversitaire pour spécialistes en sciences de l'information en Asie du Sud-Est à l'Université des Philippines.

Depuis 1974, un cours postuniversitaire pour la formation des spécialistes de l'information et de la documentation scientifiques se déroule chaque année en France. L'Unesco fournit régulièrement des services de consultation pour la planification ou la création de programmes de formation supérieure dans le domaine de la bibliothéconomie, des sciences de l'information et de l'archivistique. Tout récemment, une assistance, sous forme de financement et de missions de consultants, a été fournie en vue de la planification ou de la création de programmes régionaux de formation en matière de sciences de l'information au niveau postuniversitaire en République populaire de Chine, à l'Université d'Addis Ababa, à l'Université d'Ibadan, à l'Université Simón Bolívar, Caracas, et à l'Université de Hanoï, Viet Nam; les deux derniers programmes avec l'aide du PNUD.

L'Unesco a également été active – et continuera de l'être – dans la préparation de matériels didactiques de toutes sortes, dans le domaine de la bibliothéconomie, des sciences de l'information et de l'archivistique. En collaboration avec l'AUPELF, des activités préliminaires à la création d'un centre de coordination des bibliothèques universitaires des pays francophones d'Afrique de l'ouest sont entreprises. L'Unesco a apporté son concours à l'évaluation des besoins en personnel des bibliothèques universitaires ainsi qu'à un plan de développement d'un réseau de bibliothèques universitaires. Avec l'aide du PNUD, l'Unesco a entrepris des enquêtes sur les besoins futurs des bibliothèques universitaires dans certains Etats membres.

Dans le domaine de la préservation, la présentation et la mise en valeur du patrimoine culturel, l'Unesco a apporté son concours à de nombreuses activités pour la formation de personnels spécialisés. L'Unesco a également accordé des bourses postuniversitaires dans ce domaine. Un soutien a également été fourni, sous forme de

scholarships, and study tours or short-term internships at the national or regional level for the training, upgrading or retraining of activities organizers. Technical and financial assistance was given to activities of university, para-university or graduate-level centres such as the *Centre régional d'action culturelle*, Lomé; *Institut supérieur d'animation culturelle*, Tunis; Latin American and Caribbean Centre for Cultural Development, Caracas; the Centre for Cultural Resources and Training, New Delhi; the Research Institute for Cultural Development, Belgrade; Asian Cultural Centre for Unesco, Tokyo; and the SEAMO Project in Archaeology and Fine Arts (SPAFA), Bangkok.

In the fields of journalism and communication, Unesco has co-operated with universities and higher education institutions worldwide to establish or strengthen national and regional institutions dealing with training and research. Unesco and the International Programme for the Development of Communication (IPDC) have undertaken publication of a report on the state of communication in the world entitled *World Communication Report* foreseen in 1989 with French and Spanish versions to follow. This publication is intended as a statistical and descriptive summary of recent developments in the communication field. It is being compiled in close collaboration with other United Nations agencies, notably the International Telecommunication Union (ITU) and the Universal Postal Union (UPU), and is enlisting the collaboration of a wide variety of communication research institutions, universities and institutes of higher education, as well as non-governmental organizations and professional associations in all world regions. As part of this project, a reference and data base is being established which covers developments in the communication field, including information on research centres, programmes and publications.

Universities and institutes of higher education throughout the world are also involved in a series of collaborative research projects on the socio-cultural and economic impact of the new communication technologies, which extends throughout the period of Unesco's Second Medium-Term Plan (1984-1989). As part of this programme, a synthesis of ongoing research is to be published at regular intervals.

In the social and human sciences, collaboration with universities and other institutions of higher

services consultatifs, contributions financières, bourses, stages et voyages d'étude, à des activités de formation, de perfectionnement ou de re-cyclage des personnels du développement culturel, organisées au niveau national ou sous-régional. C'est ainsi qu'un appui technique et financier a été apporté aux activités de centres universitaires, parauniversitaires ou post-universitaires, nationaux ou régionaux, de formation (Centre régional d'action culturelle, Lomé; Institut supérieur d'animation culturelle, Tunis; Centre latinoaméricain et caraïbe pour le développement culturel, Caracas; "Centre for Cultural Resources and Training", New Delhi; Institut de recherche pour le développement culturel, Belgrade; "Asian Cultural Centre for Unesco", Tokyo; "SEAMEO Project in Arch-aeology and Fine Arts" (SPAFA), Bangkok, etc.).

L'Unesco a collaboré avec des universités à l'établissement ou au renforcement d'institutions nationales ou régionales spécialisées dans la formation et la recherche relatives à la communication et au journalisme. L'Unesco et le Programme international pour le développement de la communication (PIDC) ont entrepris conjointement l'élaboration d'un rapport sur l'état de la communication dans le monde, intitulé *Rapport sur la communication dans le monde*, qui sera publié à la fin de 1989. Cet ouvrage contiendra un résumé succinct de l'évolution récente de la communication, accompagné d'informations diverses et de statistiques. Sa préparation est assurée avec le concours de l'Union internationale des télécommunications (UIT) et de l'Union postale universelle (UPU), et bénéficie en outre de la collaboration de nombreuses institutions de recherche en matière de communication, d'universités et d'établisse-ments d'enseignement supérieur, ainsi que d'organisations non gouvernementales et d'associations professionnelles oeuvrant dans toutes les régions du monde. Dans le cadre de ce projet, il a été établi une base de données et de références portant sur l'évolution de la communication, les centres de formation, les programmes et les publications relatifs à la communication.

En outre, des universités et des établissements d'enseignement supérieur du monde entier participent à la mise en oeuvre de toute une série de projets conjoints de recherche sur l'impact socio-culturel et économique des nouvelles technologies de la communication; l'exécution de ces projets sera échelonnée sur toute la période couverte par le Deuxième Plan à moyen terme de l'Unesco (1984-1989). Des synthèses des recherches en cours seront publiées régul-ièrement dans le cadre de ce programme.

Dans le domaine des sciences sociales et

learning has continued to expand, particularly in the development of disciplines and cross-disciplinary approaches through training, research, and exchanges of information and documentation. At the same time, Unesco has increased its assistance to regional and sub-regional networks for research and training at the postgraduate level, to provide short-term study grants, and to develop textbooks and teaching materials appropriate to those regions. An important feature is the effort to reorient activities to applied fields and to the solution of crucial problems.

The regional networks have succeeded in establishing, not only within the region but also between regions, many linkages among social scientists in the universities and other institutions.

In the English-speaking Caribbean and Surinam, the Unesco-assisted consortium of graduate schools in the social sciences has inaugurated its graduate programme leading to higher degrees in the social sciences. Unesco continues to collaborate with the African Association of Universities (AAU). An inter-sectoral programme of population communication has been developed, thus allowing this subject to be integrated into courses at the Institute of Mass Communication of the University of the Philippines (Quezon City), the Department of Mass Communication of the University of Lagos, the Communication Faculty of the University of Cairo, and the Journalism and Mass Communication Department of the University of Yarmouk (Jordan). In addition, a programme of training courses in the management of population communication programmes has also been developed in collaboration with the Asia Pacific Institute for Broadcasting Development and the Arab States Broadcasting Union with faculty support from the Institutes of Management in Ahmedabad, Manila and Accra.

In collaboration with organizations such as the International Union of Architects (IUA) and the Union of African Architects (AUA), efforts have been made to strengthen and update the curriculum in several schools or faculties of architecture and urban planning in the developing countries and particularly in Africa. Training courses in this domain have been organized in Latin America in collaboration with the Latin American Faculty of Social Sciences (FLACSO), the Catholic University of Rio de Janeiro and the Nuevo León University; in Africa, thanks to the contributions, *inter alia*, of the universities of Abidjan, Kumasi, Khartoum, Rabat and Tunis; and in Asia, notably with the 'University of Life' in Manila.

Under the Regular Programme and the Pro-

humaines, la collaboration avec les universités et autres institutions d'enseignement supérieur continue à crotre, notamment par le développement de disciplines et d'approches interdisciplinaires pour la formation et la recherche. De même par l'échange d'informations et d'expériences, l'Unesco a intensifié son aide au développement des'structuresá: réseaux régionaux et sous-régionaux de coopération dans la recherche et dans l'enseignement au niveau postuniversitaire; elle accorde également des bourses de courte durée et aide à développer des manuels et des matériels pédagogiques pour ces régions.

Ces réseaux contribuent à l'établissement de nombreux liens régionaux et interrégionaux parmi des spécialistes des sciences sociales, des universités et autres institutions.

Dans les Caraïbes et au Surinam, le Consortium d'institutions universitaires dans les sciences sociales appliquées, assisté par l'Unesco, a inauguré son programme postuniversitaire, qui mène aux diplômes supérieurs. L'Unesco continue à collaborer avec l'Association des universités africaines (AAU). Un programme intersectoriel de communication relatif à la population a été développé, grce auquel des programmes relatifs à la population ont été intégrés aux cursus de l' "Institute of Mass Communication" de l'Université des Philippines (Quezon City), du "Department of Mass Communication" de l'Université de Lagos, de la Faculté des sciences de la communication de l'Université du Caire, et de la Faculté du journalisme et de la communication de l'Université de Yarmouk (Jordanie). Dans le domaine de l'information sur la population l'Unesco a établi, en collaboration avec l' "Asia Pacific Institute for Broadcasting development" et l' "Arab States Broadcasting Union", un programme de formation qui a le soutien des Instituts de gestion des Universités d'Ahmedabad, de Manille et d'Accra.

Les programmes de plusieurs écoles ou facultés d'architecture et d'urbanisme dans les pays en développement, notamment en Afrique, ont été renforcés et actualisés en collaboration avec des organisations telles que l'Union internationale des architectes (UIA) et l'Union des architectes de l'Afrique (AUA). Des cours de formation ont été organisés dans ce domaine, notamment en Amérique latine en collaboration avec la Faculté latino-américaine de sciences sociales (FLACSO), l'Université catholique de Rio de Janeiro et l'Université du Nuevo León; en Afrique, grâce aux contributions, entre autres, des Universités d'Abidjan, Kumasi, Khartoum, Rabat et Tunis; et en Asie surtout avec la "University of Life" à Manille.

Dans le cadre du Programme régulier et du

gramme of Participation in the activity of Member States, Unesco sent, at their request, high level international experts or teams of consultants, provided study grants, fellowships, financial assistance and equipment to help Member States in their efforts to improve and develop their systems of higher education, mostly in developing countries. Unesco also acted as the executing agency for large-scale and long-term projects relevant to higher education, financed by agencies such as the UNDP.

Another important aspect of Unesco's programmes is the provision of information about higher education and its institutions. Statistics concerning higher education are provided in *Education Statistics – Latest Year Available* (CSRE-56, 1988), *Unesco's Statistical Yearbook* (1987), *Unesco's Statistical Digest* (1987), *Female Participation in Higher Education – 1975-1982* (CSR-E-50, 1985), and *Statistics of Students Abroad 1974-1978* (1982).

Lastly, the publication *Studies Abroad* contains detailed information on scholarships, grants and other types of financial assistance, courses and training programmes which are offered to qualified candidates by international organizations and national institutions. The latest volume, No. XXVI, published in English, Spanish and French, covers the academic years 1989 to 1991.

Director-General: Federico Mayor.
7, place de Fontenoy, 75007 Paris.
   Tel: (33-1) 4568-1000
   Fax: (33-1) 4567-1690
   Telex: 204461 paris

Programme de participation aux activités des Etats membres, l'Unesco leur envoie, sur leur demande, des experts internationaux de haut niveau ou des équipes de consultants, leur offre des bourses, une assistance financière et des équipements pour les aider, notamment dans les pays en développement, dans leurs efforts pour améliorer et développer leur système: d'enseignement supérieur. L'Unesco est aussi chargée de l'exécution de projets à long terme ou importants par leurs dimensions, relatifs à l'enseignement supérieur et qui sont financés par des organismes tels que le Programme des Nations Unies pour le développement.

La diffusion d'informations sur l'enseignement supérieur et ses institutions constitue un autre aspect important du programme de l'Unesco. Des informations récentes sur l'enseignement supérieur figurent dans l'édition de 1985 de l'*Annuaire statistique de l'Unesco et Les statistiques des étudiants à l'étranger 1974-1978* (1982).

Enfin, la publication *Etudes à l'étranger* contient des renseignements détaillés sur les bourses, subventions et autres formes d'assistance financière, cours et programmes de formation offerts aux candidats qualifiés, par des organisations internationales et des institutions nationales. Le volume le plus récent (XXVI) est trilingue (anglais, espagnol et français) et couvre les années académiques 1989 à 1991.

Director général: Federico Mayor.
7, place de Fontenoy, 75007 Paris
   Tél: (33-1) 4568-1000
   Fax: (33-1) 4567-1690
   Télex: 204461 paris

THE INTERNATIONAL ASSOCIATION OF UNIVERSITIES (IAU)
and
THE INTERNATIONAL UNIVERSITIES BUREAU (IUB)

L'ASSOCIATION INTERNATIONALE DES UNIVERSITES (AIU)
et
LE BUREAU INTERNATIONAL DES UNIVERSITES (BIU)

HISTORY AND OBJECTIVES

Formally established in 1950, the International Association of Universities traces its origins to initiatives of the League of Nations which set up in 1923, within the framework of its International Committee of Intellectual Co-operation, the Institute of Intellectual Co-operation, and in 1933 the International Bureau of University Statistics. A Permanent Higher Education Committee was created in 1939, following a conference of university representatives in 1937.

These efforts, interrupted by World War II, were resumed by Unesco, whose General Conference decided in 1947 to convene a Preparatory Conference of University Representatives in 1948. In 1949, the International Universities Bureau was established at Unesco Headquarters to form a documentation centre on higher education and to prepare an International Conference in Nice in 1950, where representatives of 150 universities created the International Association of Universities (IAU).

According to its Constitution, the main objectives of the Association are to give expression to the 'obligation of universities as social institutions to promote, through teaching and research, the principles of freedom and justice, of human dignity and solidarity, and to develop material and moral aid on an international level', by providing 'a centre of co-operation at the international level among the universities and similar institutions of higher education of all countries, as well as among organizations in the field of higher education generally.' These objectives reflected the renewed sense of human interdependence and the need for mutual help which had emerged from the sufferings of the Second World War. Education seemed one of the surest safeguards against new dangers and the development of co-operation and solidarity among institutions of higher education, as widely as

HISTOIRE ET OBJECTIFS

L'Association internationale des Universités fut officiellement créée en 1950, mais ses origines remontent à des initiatives de la Société des Nations qui, dans le cadre de son Comité international de coopération intellectuelle, créa l'Institut de coopération intellectuelle en 1923, puis, en 1933, le Bureau international des statistiques universitaires. Un comité permanent de l'enseignement supérieur fut institué en 1939 à la suite d'une Conférence de représentants des universités, tenue en 1937.

Interrompus par la Seconde Guerre mondiale, ces efforts furent repris par l'Unesco, dont la Conférence générale décida en 1947 de réunir en 1948 une Conférence préparatoire de représentants des universités. En 1949, le Bureau International des Universités fut établi au siège de l'Unesco afin de créer un Centre de documentation sur l'enseignement supérieur et de préparer une Conférence internationale de Nice où, en 1950, les représentants de 150 universités fondèrent l'Association internationale des Universités (AIU).

Aux termes de ses Statuts, le principal objectif de l'Association est de concourir à l'accomplissement du 'devoir des universités, en tant qu'institutions sociales, de promouvoir par l'enseignement et la recherche les principes de liberté, de justice, de dignité et de solidarité humaines, et de développer l'entraide matérielle et morale sur un plan international', ceci en animant 'sur le plan international, la coopération entre les universités et les institutions d'enseignement supérieur similaires de tous les pays, ainsi qu'entre les organisations dont l'activité se rapporte de façon générale à l'enseignement supérieur'.

On a retrouvé là ce sens de l'interdépendance des hommes qu'avaient avivé les souffrances de la Seconde Guerre mondiale. L'éducation paraissait le meilleur rempart contre les nouvelles menaces et la promotion d'une coopération

possible in a divided world, seemed an urgent goal. Unesco, at the level of governmental co-operation, was seeking to serve these ideals.

The international situation has greatly changed since those early years. Development problems, in particular, have taken on an importance which could hardly have been foreseen. Universities have developed, and their Association with them. As institutions of higher education have come to occupy a leading place in social organization, they have also come under more critical scrutiny. The issues they now face seem to make co-operation between them more vital than ever.

MEMBERSHIP

Degree-conferring institutions whose main object is education and the advancement of knowledge, whether or not they bear the name of university, may be admitted to membership, but they must be at the level of higher education, as shown by the quality of their instruction and by the active participation of their staff in scientific and scholarly research.

Subject to appeal to the General conference, membership of the Association is granted or withdrawn, on the advice of the Director of the International Universities Bureau, by the Administrative Board which, under the terms of the Constitution, is empowered to admit at least one institution of higher learning from each country.

Member Institutions take part in the Association's activities individually and on a basis of complete equality; their participation in IAU is not formally based on national groupings, though full co-operation is maintained with these, chiefly through Rectors' Conferences, National Councils of Universities and similar bodies in countries where they exist. Membership has grown in consonance with the dynamic developments in higher education which have marked the last thirty years. It now includes most of the oldest and most famous universities in the world, as well as most of the younger institutions founded in the newly-independent and developing countries, whose influence is likely to grow constantly in the future. At present, the number of institutions admitted to membership of IAU has reached nearly 1000 in over 120 countries.

Membership dues range at present between US $700 and US $1,700 depending on the size of the institution. Through these contributions, Members ensure the independence of IAU.

Associate membership is granted to appropriate

systématique entre les établissements d'enseignement supérieur du monde entier s'imposait comme un objectif majeur. L'Unesco entendait poursuivre, au niveau de la co-opération entre Etats, les mêmes objectifs.

La situation internationale s'est profondément modifiée depuis ces premières années. Les problèmes du développement, notamment, ont pris une importance qu'on ne mesurait pas alors. Moteurs du développement, les universités se sont très considérablement développées et, avec elles, leur Association. Mais la place proéminente qu'elles vinrent à occuper dans les sociétés en fit bientôt des cibles voyantes pour la critique. Les problèmes qu'elles doivent affronter aujourd'hui rendent leur coopération plus indispensable que jamais.

MEMBRES

Peuvent devenir membres de l'Association les institutions conférant des diplômes et dont le but principal est l'éducation et l'avancement des connaissances, qu'elles aient ou non le nom d'université, à condition qu'elles se situent au niveau de l'enseignement supérieur, tel qu'il peut être attesté par la qualité des enseignements et par la participation active des professeurs à la recherche.

Sous réserve d'appel à la Conférence générale, la qualité de membre de l'Association est conférée ou retirée, sur l'avis du Directeur du Bureau international des Universités, par le Conseil d'administration, qui est habilité par les Statuts à admettre au moins une institution de haut enseignement par pays.

Les institutions membres participent aux activités de l'Association à titre individuel et sur un pied de complète égalité. Leur adhésion ne passe pas par l'intermédiaire de groupes ou organismes nationaux, encore que l'Association entretienne par ailleurs avec ces derniers une solide coopération, principalement par l'inter-médiaire des Conférences de Recteurs, des Conseils nationaux des Universités et d'autres organismes analogues dans les pays où ils existent. L'AIU s'est développée rapidement portée par la dynamique universitaire qui s'est affirmée dans le monde entier au cours des trente dernières années. Elle comprend à présent la plupart des universités les plus anciennes et les plus réputées du monde, mais aussi la plupart des institutions plus jeunes des pays en voie de développement ou ayant récemment accédé à l'indépendance, dont l'influence grandira sans doute à l'avenir. Actuellement le nombre d'institutions admises à la qualité de membre de l'AIU a atteint près de 1000 dans plus de 120 pays.

Les cotisations des membres sont actuellement

regional and international university organizations. The following nine university bodies are Associate Members and co-operate with IAU in many activities: Association of African Universities; Association of Arab Universities; Association of Commonwealth Universities; Association of Southeast Asian Institutions of Higher Learning; Association des Universités partiellement ou entièrement de langue française; Inter-American Organization for Higher Education; International Federation of Catholic Universities; Standing Conference of Rectors, Presidents and Vice-Chancellors of the European Universities; Unión de Universidades de América Latina.

comprises entre 700 et 1700 dollars, en fonction de la taille de l'institution. Par ces versements, les membres assurent l'indépendance de l'AIU.

La qualité de Membre associé est conférée à des organisations universitaires régionales et internationales qui en remplissent les conditions. Les neuf organismes universitaires suivants collaborent étroitement avec l'AIU en tant que Membres associés: Association of Commonwealth Universities; Association of Southeast Asian Institutions of Higher Learning; Association des Universités africaines; Association des Universités partiellement ou entièrement de langue française; Conférence permanente des Recteurs, Présidents et Vice-Chanceliers des Universités européennes; Fédération internationale des Universités catholiques; Organisation Universitaire interaméricaine; Unión de Universidades de América Latina; Union des Universités arabes.

ORGANIZATION

General Conference
The General Conference is composed of the representatives of the Members and Associate Members. Observers from international, regional and national bodies concerned with higher education attend by invitation. In appointing its representatives, each Member Institution acts in accordance with its own practices and may thus, if it so wishes, include among them junior members of academic staff, research workers and students.

The Conference meets once every five years. It determines the general policy of the Association and elects the President and the Members of the Administrative Board. In addition to exercising its constitutional functions and powers, the General Conference provides a regular opportunity for the world university community to mark its existence and to express both its diversity and its solidarity. Each Conference, in addition to internal matters related to higher education, is concerned with the role of universities in society under continually changing conditions. These are unique occasions for comparing situations in a setting in which differing points of view may be brought closer together.

1st General (Founding) Conference, Nice, December 1950; 2nd: Istanbul, September 1955; 3rd: Mexico, September 1960; 4th: Tokyo, September 1965; 5th: Montreal, September 1970; 6th: Moscow, August 1975; 7th: Manila, August 1980; 8th: Los Angeles, August 1985. 9th: Helsinki, August 1990.

President
The President of the Association is elected by the

ORGANISATION

La Conférence générale
La Conférence générale se compose des délégués des Membres et des Membres associés de l'AIU. Des observateurs d'organismes internationaux, régionaux et nationaux s'occupant d'enseignement supérieur y assistent sur invitation. Chaque institution membre désigne ses délégués conformément à ses propres règles et usages et peut ainsi, si elle le souhaite, faire figurer parmi eux de jeunes enseignants ou chercheurs et des étudiants.

La Confértence se réunit une fois tous les cinq ans. Elle définit la politique générale de l'Association et élit le Président et le Conseil d'administration. Outre l'exercice de ses fonctions statutaires, la Conférence générale fournit à la communauté universitaire mondiale une occasion régulière d'affirmer son existence et de manifester à la fois sa diversité et sa solidarité. Chaque Conférence, outre certains problèmes internes de l'enseignement supérieur, examine le rôle des universités dans la société, dont les conditions ne cessent pas de se modifier. La Conférence fournit ainsi une occasion unique de comparer les situations et peut favoriser le rapprochement de points de vue différents.

1ère Conférence générale (de fondation), Nice, décembre 1950; 2ème: Istanbul, septembre 1955; 3ème: Mexico, septembre 1960; 4ème: Tokyo, septembre 1965; 5ème: Montréal, septembre 1970; 6ème: Moscou, août 1975; 7ème: Manille, août 1980; 8ème: Los Angeles, août 1985. 9ème: Helsinki, août 1990.

Président
Le Président de l'Association est élu par la

General Conference. He is also the Chairman of the Administrative Board.

Administrative Board

The Administrative Board is composed of the President of the Association, of 16 to 20 members (with 16 to 20 deputy members) each from a university in a different country, and the Secretary-General. The two Vice-Presidents are elected by the Administrative Board from amongst its own members. The Board meets at least once a year, gives effect to the decisions of the General Conference and directs and controls the activities of the International Universities Bureau.

Among its main tasks, the Administrative Board adopts a working programme and budget presented by the Director of the Bureau, and takes decisions concerning membership and IAU external relations. It appoints among its members a number of Committees which examine special questions and prepare some of its decisions.

The Board's work is not exclusively administrative. Experience of high academic office in different parts of the world and personal concern for international co-operation enable its members to reach informed decisions concerning topics to be studied and, as a body, to act as an effective international forum on questions of higher education policy.

Leading personalities from 177 university institutions in 82 countries have served as members and deputy members of the Board since 1950.

International Universities Bureau (IUB)

The International Universities Bureau (IUB) was created in 1949 at Unesco Headquarters to set up an Information Centre on higher education, and since that time it has been housed at Unesco in Paris. After having prepared the Association's Founding Conference of 1950, the Bureau was placed under the authority of IAU for which it provides the permanent Secretariat. The Director of the Bureau acts as Secretary-General and Treasurer of the Association. Under the supervision of the Administrative Board, the Bureau is the principal instrument for the execution of the activities of the Association; its main tasks as defined by the Constitution are to: organize a centre for documentary material on all university questions of international interest; provide, by appropriate means, for the dissemination of this material; establish a basis for comparative university statistics and publish statistical documents conforming to this basis;

Conférence générale. Il est aussi le Président du Conseil d'administration.

Le Conseil d'administration

Le Conseil d'administration se compose du Président de l'Association, de 16 à 20 membres (avec 16 à 20 suppléants), tous issus d'universités de pays différents et du Secrétaire général. Les deux Vice-Présidents sont élus en son sein par le Conseil d'administration. Le Conseil se réunit au moins une fois par an. Il met en oeuvre les décisions de la Conférence générale, et dirige et réglemente les activités du Bureau international des Universités.

Parmi ses tâches principales, le Conseil d'administration adopte le Programme de travail et le Budget présentés par le Directeur du Bureau, et statue sur les questions concernant les Membres de l'Association, ainsi que ses relations extérieures. Il désigne en son sein un certain nombre de Comités qui étudient certaines questions particulières et préparent certaines de ses décisions.

Les travaux du Conseil ne sont pas de nature exclusivement administrative. L'expérience qu'ils ont de hautes responsabilités universitaires dans différentes parties du monde et leur engagement personnel envers la coopération internationale permettent à ses membres de choisir en toute connaissance de cause les thèmes d'étude de l'Association et collectivement de constituer un forum international sur les problèmes de la politique de l'enseignement supérieur.

Depuis 1950, des personnalités éminentes de 177 institutions universitaires appartenant à 82 pays ont siégé au Conseil comme Membres ou Membres suppléants.

Le Bureau international des Universités (BIU)

Le Bureau international des Universités (BIU) a été créé en 1949 au siège de l'Unesco pour mettre sur pied un Centre d'information et d'étude sur l'enseignement supérieur et continue, depuis cette date, à être abrité par l'Unesco à Paris. Après avoir préparé la Conférence de fondation de l'Association, en 1950, le Bureau a été rattaché à l'AIU dont il assure le Secrétariat permanent. Le Directeur du Bureau assume les fonctions de Secrétaire général et de Trésorier de l'Association. Sous le contrôle du Conseil d'Administration, le Bureau est le principal instrument d'exécution des programmes de l'Association. Ses tâches principales, telles qu'elles sont définies par les Statuts, sont les suivantes: organiser un Centre de documentation sur toutes les questions universitaires d'intérêt international; assurer, par les moyens appropriés, la diffusion de cette documentation; établir des normes de statistiques universitaires comparées,

614

establish machinery for facilitating the interchange of students and teachers; develop means for the better distribution and exchange of laboratory material, books and other equipment for university study and research; and undertake such other tasks as are compatible with the aims of the Association.

ACTIVITIES

IAU and its International Universities Bureau propose a variety of activities and services to its Member Institutions and to the international higher education community—teachers and researchers, administrators and students, policy and decision-makers.

Information

Under a signed Agreement with Unesco, IAU is operating at its International Universities Bureau the joint IAU/Unesco Information Centre on Higher Education. The Centre holds at present some 40,000 volumes and a large collection of unpublished materials. It receives about 300 periodicals dealing with higher education problems and policy from all parts of the world and keeps an up-to-date collection of some 4000 calendars and catalogues of major higher education institutions, as well as a collection of international and national directories and guides to higher education.

In order to facilitate access to this unique body of documentation and to play its role as a clearing-house on higher education and mobility, the Centre has been fully computerized, comprising a powerful micro-computer configuration and a link-up to Unesco's mainframe computer. Information is being processed using CDS/ISIS, a software developed by Unesco specially for international databases, of which a micro version is also available for use on personal computers. The technical co-operation with Unesco will provide opportunities for linking up and exchanging information in computerized form with other specialized databases within and outside Unesco. Three databases on higher education are at present being set up—a bibliographical and an institutional database, and a database on research on higher education.

The *bibliographical database* contains, in the first place, published and unpublished document-

et publier une documentation statistique conforme à ces normes; établir des services destinés à faciliter l'échange d'étudiants et de professeurs; mettre au point des mesures permettant d'améliorer la répartition et l'échange du matériel de laboratoire, des livres et autres instruments d'étude et de recherche, utilisés par l'enseignement supérieur; et entreprendre toutes autres tâches compatibles avec les buts de l'Association.

ACTIVITES

L'AIU et son Bureau international des Universités proposent divers services aux institutions membres, aux enseignants et chercheurs, aux administrateurs et étudiants, et aux responsables de la politique et décideurs.

Information

Le Bureau international des Universités administre le Centre AIU/Unesco d'Information sur l'Enseignement supérieur en vertu d'un accord signé avec l'Unesco.

A ce jour, le Centre contient près de 40.000 ouvrages et une importante collection de documents inédits. Il reçoit environ 300 périodiques spécialisés sur les problèmes et les politiques de l'enseignement supérieur du monde entier. Une collection de quelque 4.000 livrets de l'étudiant des principales institutions d'enseignement supérieur est régulièrement mise à jour. Le Centre possède également une collection de répertoires et de guides nationaux et internationaux de l'enseignement supérieur.

Afin de faciliter l'accès à cette collection unique de documents et de remplir plus efficacement son rôle de *clearing-house* sur l'enseignement supérieur et la mobilité, le Centre a été informatisé grâce à la mise en place d'un puissant ensemble micro relié à l'ordinateur central de l'Unesco. Le Bureau procède actuellement à l'informatisation des données qu'il possède en utilisant le système CDS/ISIS. Il s'agit d'un logiciel spécialement mis sur pied par l'Unesco pour les bases de données internationales dont il existe une version micro utilisable sur les microordinateurs. Ces aménagements techniques permettront d'entrer en liaison et d'échanger des informations avec d'autres bases de données spécialisées, tant au sein de l'Unesco qu'à l'extérieur ainsi qu'avec d'autres organisations et institutions. Trois bases de données sur l'enseignement supérieur sont en cours d'élaboration: une base bibliographique, une base institutionnelle et une base sur les recherches concernant l'enseignement supérieur.

La *base de données bibliographique* contient essentiellement les données documentaires

ation on higher education held by IUB. A bibliographical awareness service on higher education is being produced from this database, comprising literature published at the regional and national levels that is of interest in the international sphere. In this, IUB is working in collaboration with other regional or national documentation centres and specialists on higher education throughout the world. Closely linked to this bibliographical database, is the *database on institutions conducting research on higher education and their principal current projects*. Both are means to facilitate co-operation and exchanges within the scientific community investigating higher education from different viewpoints.

The *institutional database* contains detailed information on the systems of higher education and individual institutions in each country. The database is being updated on a regular basis and thus provides current information satisfying several types of needs: lists of institutions and their addresses by country or by subject speciality; more detailed information on the institutions and higher education systems; information on admissions criteria, programmes of study and on degrees and diplomas awarded by institutions of higher education; level of recognition of foreign degrees and diplomas within each country; and existing exchange agreements with other universities.

Mobility
—Collaboration for data networking with regional and national bodies which have already set up, or are planning to set up such databases, has been established within a very interesting international co-operative project called TRACE (Trans Regional Academic Mobility and Credential Evaluation).

TRACE has been conceived by a group of interested international education experts from several international and national academic bodies concerned with counselling students about studying abroad and with the evaluation of foreign academic and professional credentials. The aim is to provide a means of exchanging standardized higher education and professional training information through modern technology in order to avoid duplication in the area of data collection and updating.

publiées et inédites contenues dans le Centre de Documentation du BIU. A partir de cette base de données, des bibliographies sur l'enseignement supérieur préparées aux niveaux régional et national mais présentant un intérêt sur le plan international seront établies. Là aussi, il est prévu de travailler en coopération avec des centres de documentation régionaux ou nationaux et des spécialistes de l'enseignement supérieur du monde entier. La *base de données sur les institutions effectuant des recherches sur l'enseignement supérieur et leurs principaux projets de recherches en cours* est en étroite liaison avec cette base de données bibliographique. Ces deux bases constituent des moyens destinés à faciliter la coopération et les échanges au sein de la communauté universitaire réalisant des recherches sur l'enseignement supérieur sous différents angles.

La *base de données institutionnelle* contient des informations détaillées sur les systèmes d'enseignement supérieur et les institutions individuelles de chaque pays. Ces informations sont régulièrement mises à jour et répondent à divers besoins: listes d'institutions avec adresses par pays ou par spécialité; renseignements plus détaillés sur les institutions ou le système d'enseignement supérieur d'un pays; renseignements sur les conditions d'accès, sur les filières et programmes d'études ou sur les grades et diplômes conférés par les établissements d'enseignement supérieur; le niveau de reconnaissance des grades et diplômes étrangers dans les différents pays; et sur les accords de coopération existant avec d'autres universités.

Mobilité
—Dans ce contexte, une collaboration avec d'autres organes régionaux et nationaux ayant ce contexte, déjà mis sur pied de telles bases de données, ou sur le point de le faire, a été établie grâce à un projet international de coopération d'un grand intérêt appelé TRACE (Réseau transrégional sur la mobilité universitaire et l'évaluation des diplômes).

Le TRACE a été conçu par un groupe d'experts internationaux sur l'enseignement supérieur appartenant à plusieurs organes académiques internationaux et nationaux s'occupant d'orienter les étudiants dans leurs études à l'étranger et de procéder à l'évaluation des diplômes académiques et professionnels étrangers. Son but est de fournir un moyen d'échanger des renseignements normalisés sur les formations d'enseignement supérieur et professionnel en utilisant des moyens technologiques modernes, et d'éviter les doubles emplois en matière de collecte et de mise à jour de l'information.

Following discussions on the network's structure, the group conferred to IAU the task of co-ordinator and clearing-house for TRACE. As an association with worldwide membership and through its co-operation with Unesco, IAU is well placed to play a major role in such a joint venture. It has always been the Association's objective to contribute concretely to co-operation among universities and other institutions of higher education, and to assist in the advancement of international academic mobility. The TRACE project is in line with these objectives and will benefit all those involved in various forms of international collaboration and exchanges in tertiary education.

—Furthermore, IAU is organizing, in co-operation with the International Committee for the Study of Educational Exchange (ICSEE), a series of studies on academic exchanges between higher education institutions worldwide, with special attention to three major axes: co-operation between institutions of developed countries (in particular between East and West), between developed and developing countries and between developing countries.

—As a measure of practical support to academic mobility, IAU is also sponsoring the International Student Identity Card (ISIC), produced by the International Student Travel Confederation (ISTC) and the International Union of Students (IUS).

Studies and Research

In keeping with the global character of IAU, its studies and research programme focuses on issues of higher education and higher education policies which are either common to institutions and systems worldwide, or where a comparative analysis of different situations and approaches appears particularly interesting. Topics of recent IAU studies include: Contemporary Scientific and Technical Changes: their Impact on the Humanities in University Education; the Future of University Education; Universities and Regional Development; and under the joint Unesco/IAU research programme in higher education, Universities and Environmental Education; and The Impact of Satellite Communication on University Teaching and Research.

Meetings

As an international meeting place for higher education representatives and a forum for the discussion of their problems and concerns, IAU's recent meetings included, apart from the annual

Suite à des discussions sur la structure du réseau, le groupe a désigné l'AIU pour jouer le rôle de coordinateur et de *clearing-house* pour le TRACE. En tant qu'association mondiale et de par sa coopération avec l'Unesco, l'AIU est bien placée pour jouer un rôle important dans cette initiative conjointe. L'Association a toujours eu pour but d'apporter une contribution concrète à la coopération entre les universités et les autres établissements d'enseignement supérieur et d'aider à promouvoir la mobilité universitaire internationale. Le projet du TRACE reflète ces objectifs et servira tous ceux qui s'occupent de collaboration internationale et d'échanges dans l'enseignement tertiaire.

—En collaboration avec l'*International Committee for the Study of Educational Exchange* (ICSEE), l'AIU est également en train de mettre sur pied une série d'études sur les échanges universitaires entre les institutions d'enseignement supérieur dans le monde, en mettant l'accent sur trois domaines principaux: la coopération entre les institutions des pays développés (et plus particulièrement entre l'Est et l'Ouest), entre les pays développés et les pays en voie de développement, et entre les pays en voie de développement.

—Afin d'apporter un appui pratique à la mobilité universitaire, l'AIU parraine également la Carte d'Identité internationale d'Etudiant de la Confédération internationale des Voyages pour Etudiants (ISTC) et de l'Union internationale des Etudiants (UIE).

Etudes et recherches

Compte tenu du caractère global de l'AIU, son programme d'études et de recherches porte essentiellement sur les questions d'enseignement supérieur qui se posent aux établissements et aux systèmes du monde entier ou à propos desquelles une analyse comparative des diverses situations et approches semble présenter un intérêt particulier. Les thèmes récemment abordés par l'AIU comprennent: les mutations scientifiques et techniques contemporaines: leurs répercussions sur les sciences humaines dans la formation universitaire; l'avenir de la formation universitaire; les universités et le développement régional; et, dans le cadre du Programme conjoint Unesco-AIU d'études sur l'enseignement supérieur, les universités et l'éducation relative à l'environnement; et *The Impact of Satellite Communication on University Teaching and Research*.

Réunions

En tant que lieu de rencontre et forum de discussion international de leurs problèmes, et en dehors des réunions annuelles de son Conseil d'administration, l'AIU a compté parmi ses

Board Meetings, Seminars, Round Tables, Colloquia and Symposia on: the Future of University Education; the Role of Universities in Environmental Education; Universities and Health for all for the Year 2000; Universities and Regional Development; the International Responsibilities of Universities: Perspectives and Problems for the Coming Decade; Conflict Resolution and Education for Peace; the Role of Higher Education in National Economic Development; International University Co-operation—A Critical Analysis: Failures, Successes, Perspectives; the Responsibility of Universities in the Nuclear Age; Access to Higher Education. IAU has also organized, upon the request of the Director-General of Unesco, in 1988, a Consultation of University Leaders on Unesco's Mission and Future Activities.

In some cases, such meetings are linked to specific studies and research projects, others provide a sounding board for the expression of standpoints of the international higher education community with regard to major societal challenges, and still others are meant to open the dialogue between universities and their partners in the wider community.

Major meetings open to all Members are General Conferences (every five years, last one, Los Angeles, in 1985, next one, Helsinki, in 1990), and Mid-Term Conferences of Heads of Member Institutions (last one, Rio de Janeiro, in 1988).

Publications

Apart from the publication of the results of its studies and research projects and its meetings, IAU produces a number of other volumes, most of them in both English and French. Special mention should be made of the *International Handbook of Universities* and the *World List of Universities*, which are published under the authority of the Association, and the *World Guide to Higher Education*, a comparative survey of systems, degrees and qualifications, prepared by the Association and published by Unesco. These three reference works are updated regularly.

A quarterly international higher education journal, *Higher Education Policy*, provides a platform to the world community of higher education for sharing information, experience and ideas on the role of higher education in society today. In addition, a regular *Bulletin* is instrumental in the dissemination of information gathered and processed by the IUB. A full list of IAU publications is given on page 693.

réunions récentes des Tables rondes, des Colloques et des Symposiums sur les thèmes suivants: l'avenir de l'enseignement supérieur; le rôle des universités dans l'éducation relative à l'environnement; les universités et la santé pour tous d'ici l'an 2000; les universités et le développement régional; les responsabilités internationales des universités: perspectives et problèmes pour la prochaine décennie; la contribution des universités à la résolution des conflits et à l'education pour la paix; le rôle de l'enseignement supérieur dans le développement économique national; la coopération universitaire internationale—une analyse critique: échecs, réussites, perspectives; la responsabilité des universités à l'age nucléaire; l'accès à l'enseignement supérieur. En 1988, l'AIU a également organisé, à la demande du Directeur général de l'Unesco, une Consultation des Recteurs et des Responsables d'Universités sur les Programmes futurs de l'Unesco.

Certaines de ces réunions sont organisées en relation avec des études en cours, d'autres servent de caisse de résonance aux points de vue de la communauté internationale de l'enseignement supérieur sur d'importantes questions de société, d'autres encore visent à instaurer un dialogue entre les universités et leurs partenaires extérieurs.

Les grandes réunions, ouvertes à tous les membres, sont les Conférences générales (tous les cinq ans, la dernière à Los Angeles en 1985, la prochaine à Helsinki en 1990), et les Conférences intermédiaires de Chefs des institutions membres, (la dernière à Rio de Janeiro en 1988).

Publications

Outre ses études, et les comptes rendus de ses réunions, l'AIU publie également d'autres ouvrages, la plupart en anglais et en français. Il convient de mentionner l'*International Handbook of Universities* et la *Liste mondiale des Universités*, publies sous l'égide de l'Association, et *Les études supérieures*, présentation comparative des régimes d'enseignement et des diplômes, préparé par l'Association et publié par l'Unesco. Ces trois ouvrages sont régulièrement mis à jour.

La revue trimestrielle de l'AIU sur l'enseignement supérieur, *Higher Education Policy*, offre à la communauté universitaire mondiale une tribune lui permettant de procéder à des échanges d'informations, d'expériences, et d'idées sur le rôle de l'enseignement supérieur dans le monde d'aujourd'hui. En outre, un *Bulletin* fournira des informations recueillies et informatisées par le BIU.

La liste complète des publications de l'AIU figure en page 696.

Other Services

IAU and its international Universities Bureau see a major function in their acting as an agent and a catalyst in promoting international co-operation in higher education. They foster and facilitate international contacts through consultancies and good offices for exchanges on an institutional level, for visits of individual scholars to foreign universities, and for the exchange of publications and material for research and teaching purposes.

Through its co-operation with various partners active in the field, be they national or international, governmental or non-governmental, IUB discharges a unique function as an international clearing-house and referral centre on higher education.

CO-OPERATION WITH OTHER INTERNATIONAL ORGANIZATIONS

Unesco

IAU was created at the initiative of Unesco, and close co-operation was established from the start between the two organizations. The Association, as a non-governmental organization, has associate and consultative status with Unesco, and the latter provides office space for the Bureau. Since 1959, the two organizations have pooled efforts in a *Joint Unesco/IAU Research Programme in Higher Education*. Its purpose is to carry out, with the advantages of joint sponsorship, a programme of studies affecting the organization, structure and functioning of higher education institutions and systems in the changing conditions of the present day. The programme has so far included international studies of problems such as access to higher education, teaching and learning methods, and consequences of lifelong education for universities; and regional studies of the role of higher education in the development of countries in South-East Asia and of interuniversity co-operation in Africa. The South-East Asia study led, in 1970, to the creation of the Institute of Higher Education and Development (RIHED) supported by governments in the region. Assistance was given to Alecso and the Association of Arab Universities in planning their project to establish an Arab Regional Institute of Higher Education. The Joint Steering Committee also commissioned a study on Change and Innovation in Latin American Universities and a joint seminar on this theme took place at the National University of Mexico in 1978, in co-operation with the Union of Universities of Latin America. This was followed in 1980 by a symposium on the University of the Future. Following this, attention was directed to the role of universities in environ-

Autres services

L'AIU et son Bureau entendent jouer un rôle important de catalyseur dans le développement de la coopération universitaire internationale. Ils favorisent et facilitent les contacts internationaux en rendant divers services de consultation et de liaison destinés à faciliter les échanges entre institutions, les visites de chercheurs à des universités étrangères, et les échanges de publications et d'équipements pour la recherche et l'enseignement.

Par sa collaboration avec différents partenaires nationaux ou internationaux, gouvernementaux ou non gouvernementaux de ce domaine, le BIU joue un rôle unique de *clearing-house* international et de centre de référence sur l'enseignement supérieur.

COOPÉRATION AVEC D'AUTRES ORGANISATIONS INTERNATIONALES

Unesco

L'AIU a été créée à l'initiative de l'Unesco et une coopération étroite s'est instaurée dès l'origine entre les deux organisations. En tant qu'organisation non gouvernementale, l'Association jouit du statut d'association et de consultation avec l'Unesco, qui met des locaux à la disposition du Bureau. Depuis 1959, les deux organisations se sont associées au sein d'un Programme conjoint Unesco-AIU d'études sur l'enseignement supérieur.

Ce programme a pour objet d'effectuer, en profitant le plus possible des avantages que peut comporter le double patronage sous lequel il est placé, une série d'études concernant l'organisation, la structure et le fonctionnement des institutions ou des systèmes d'enseignement supérieur dans les conditions mouvantes du monde actuel. Le programme a jusqu'à présent comporté des études internationales sur des problèmes tels que l'accès à l'enseignement supérieur, les méthodes pédagogiques et les répercussions de l'éducation permanente pour les universités; et des études régionales sur le rôle de l'enseignement supérieur dans le développement des pays d'Asie du Sud-Est et sur la coopération interuniversitaire en Afrique. L'étude consacrée à l'Asie du Sud-Est a abouti en 1970 à la création, avec le soutien des gouvernements de la région, d'un Institut d'enseignement supérieur et de développement (RIHED). Elles ont offert leur concours à l'Alecso et à l'Union des universités arabes en vue de la réalisation d'un projet conçu par ces deux organisations et tendant à la création d'un Institut régional pour l'enseignement supérieur dans les pays arabes. Sous l'égide du Comité conjoint une étude a été entreprise sur le changement et l'innovation dans

mental education and a seminar was held in Budapest in October 1983. Lately, the Committee has assumed a larger mandate, covering the whole range of regular and project-oriented co-operation between the two organizations.

One of the aims of the Programme is to better identify the specific role of each organization in the pursuit of common purposes. A case in point is the striving for peace and international understanding through co-operation in science, culture and education—obviously a major concern for both organizations. The role of IAU with regard to Unesco could thus be seen as one of an intermediary, and this in two directions: to interpret to Unesco the needs and aspirations of higher education and to help Unesco carry out its programme and gain the support of higher education in its implementation. Apart from the on-going working relations, IAU and Unesco are regularly represented at each other's conferences and meetings. An historic moment in the development of the co-operation between the two organizations has been the signing of the agreement to establish a joint IAU/Unesco Information Centre on Higher Education (see Activities, Information above).

Other Organizations

IAU co-operates also closely with its Associate Members and regular joint Consultation Meetings are being held (Toledo, 1986; Cairo, 1989). Links have been established with a number of governmental and non-governmental bodies on an international and national level. Furthermore, a formal co-operation agreement exists with the United Nations University in Tokyo (see p. 585). Collaboration with other bodies is constantly being developed, and the International Universities Bureau increasingly acts as a clearing-house for various multicentred networks of international collaboration in higher education.

President: Dr. Justin Thorens.
Secretary-General: Dr. Franz Eberhard.
1, rue Miollis, 75732 Paris Cedex 15.
  Tel: (33–1) 45-68-25-45. Fax: (33-1) 47-34-76-05.
  Telex: 250615 iub f. Cables: univasoc

les universités d'Amérique latine et un séminaire conjoint s'est tenu sur ce thème à l'Université nationale du Mexique en 1978, en coopération avec l'Union des Universités d'Amérique latine. Cette réunion a été suivie en 1980 par un colloque sur l'Université de l'avenir. Après ce colloque une grande attention a été accordée au rôle de l'Université dans l'éducation relative à l'environnement et un séminaire s'est tenu à Budapest en octobre 1983. Le Comité a récemment reçu un mandat élargi couvrant toute la coopération régulière et prévue entre les deux organisations.

L'un des objectifs du Programme est de mieux cerner le rôle spécifique de chaque organisation dans la poursuite d'objectifs communs. La recherche de la paix et de la compréhension internationale par la coopération scientifique, culturelle et éducative, qui est, bien sûr, une préoccupation majeure des deux organisations, en est un exemple. L'un des rôles de l'AIU est de servir d'intermédiaire avec l'Unesco et ceci dans les deux sens: se faire l'interprète des besoins et des préoccupations de l'enseignement supérieur auprès de l'Unesco et aider l'Unesco à s'assurer de la collaboration de l'enseignement supérieur pour la mise en oeuvre de ses programmes.

En dehors des relations régulières de travail qu'elles entretiennent, l'AIU et l'Unesco sont représentées aux conférences et aux réunions qu'elles organisent. Un moment historique dans le développement de la coopération entre les deux organisations a été la signature d'un contrat créant un Centre AIU/Unesco d'Information sur l'Enseignement supérieur (voir Activités, section Information, ci-dessus).

Autres organisations

L'AIU coopère également très étroitement avec ses Membres associés et des réunions conjointes, de caractére consultatif, se tiennent (Tolède, 1986; Caire, 1989). Des liens ont été établis avec une série d'organismes gouvernementaux et non gouvernementaux, au plan national et international. En outre, un accord de coopération formel existe avec l'Université des Nations Unies à Tokyo (voir p. 585). La collaboration avec d'autres organismes se développe constamment et le Bureau international des Universités joue de plus en plus le rôle de 'plaque tournante' entre divers réseaux s'occupant de collaboration internationale dans le domaine de l'enseignement supérieur et comportant de nombreux centres.

Président: Dr. Justin Thorens.
Secrétaire général: Dr. Franz Eberhard.
1, rue Miollis, 75732 Paris Cedex 15.
  Tél: (33-1) 45-68-25-45. Fax: (33-1) 47-34-76-05.
  Télex: 250615 iub f. Cables: univasoc

ASSOCIATION OF AFRICAN UNIVERSITIES (AAU)
ASSOCIATION DES UNIVERSITES AFRICAINES

Associate Member of the International Association of Universities
Membre associé de l'Association internationale des Universités

The decision to create an Association of African Universities was taken at a Meeting of Heads of African Institutions of Higher Education held for this purpose at the University of Khartoum in September 1963. The International Association of Universities assisted in planning and making administrative arrangements for this meeting, and was invited to co-operate with the Interim Committee then set up to draft a constitution for the new Association. A founding conference, attended by the heads, or senior representatives, of 34 African university institutions, was held at Mohammed V University, Rabat, in November 1967. There the constitution was adopted and the first officers and members of the Executive Board of the Association were elected. The second General Conference of the Association was held by Lovanium University, Kinshasa, in November 1969, and new officers and a new Executive Board were elected to take office the following year.

The purposes of the Association are: *a*) to promote interchange, contact and co-operation among university institutions in Africa; *b*) to collect, classify and disseminate information on higher education and research, particularly in Africa; *c*) to promote co-operation among African institutions in curriculum development, and in the determination of equivalence of degrees; *d*) to encourage increased contact between its members and the international academic world; *e*) to study and make known the educational and related needs of African university institutions and, as far as practicable, to co-ordinate the means whereby those needs may be met; *f*) to encourage the development and wider use of African languages; and *g*) to organize, encourage and support seminars and conferences between African university teachers, administrators, and others dealing with problems of higher education in Africa.

La décision de créer une Association des universités africaines a été prise lors d'une réunion de chefs d'institutions d'enseignement supérieur africaines, qui se tint à cet effet à l'Université de Khartoum en septembre 1963. L'Association internationale des Universités a aidé à la planification et à l'organisation administrative de cette réunion, et elle a été invitée à coopérer avec le Comité intérimaire, constitué à cette époque afin d'élaborer un projet de statuts pour la nouvelle Association. Une conférence constitutive se tint à l'Université Mohammed V, Rabat, en novembre 1967, avec la participation des chefs ou des plus hauts représentants de trente-quatre institutions universitaires africaines. Elle adopta le projet de statuts et procéda à l'élection du premier bureau et des membres du Comité exécutif de l'Association. La deuxième Conférence générale de l'Association eut lieu à l'Université Lovanium, Kinshasa en novembre 1969. Elle élut des nouveaux responsables et un nouveau Conseil Exécutif qui devaient entrer en fonctions l'année suivante.

Les objectifs de l'Association sont: *a*) de promouvoir les échanges, les contacts et la coopération entre les institutions universitaires d'Afrique; *b*) de rassembler, de classer et de diffuser des informations sur l'enseignement supérieur et la recherche, particulièrement en Afrique; *c*) de promouvoir la collaboration des institutions africaines dans l'élaboration des programmes d'études et la détermination des équivalences de titres académiques; *d*) d'encourager le développement des contacts entre ses membres et le monde académique international; *e*) d'étudier et de faire connaître les besoins, dans les domaines de l'éducation et autres, des institutions universitaires africaines, et, autant que possible, de coordonner les moyens par lesquels ces besoins peuvent être satisfaits; *f*) d'encourager l'épanouissement et l'usage plus généralisé des langues africaines; et *g*) d'organiser, d'encourager et d'aider des séminaires et conférences réunissant des enseign-

In 1969, the Association set up a programme of scholarships tenable in African universities. Under an agreement with the Association, U.S.A.I.D. provided over $1 million over a period of one year for this; the British Government provides £25,000 and Canada $1 million for a period of 5 years. Germany contributed towards the Postgraduate Scholarship Programme. A number of African governments have also promised or are giving substantial contributions to the Association's Endowment Fund.

The programme provides for the granting at undergraduate, graduate and postgraduate levels of University scholarships and fellowships. One thousand and ten students, among whom are approximately 100 political refugees, have already received such grants; four training programmes for the intensive study of the English and French languages have been specially drawn up for both staff and students; exchanges of university professors and lecturers help to ensure the teaching of certain subjects, and the supervision of research projects. These exchange professors also serve on committees for examinations and the defence of theses and dissertations.

A Documentation Centre has been established in the Secretariat of the AAU. Its objective is to collect and disseminate information on higher education and research in African universities and to co-ordinate the activities of member universities.

The supreme governing body of the Association is the General Conference composed of the representatives of 88 member institutions. The President of the Association is elected by the General Conference and is also Chairman of the Executive Board. This body, which meets at least once every year, consists of the President, three Vice-Presidents and nine members, elected by the General Conference. Its members hold office for a period of four years. The Sixth General Conference took place at the Université des Sciences et de la Technologie Houari Boumediène, Algiers in November 1984, and the Seventh General Conference took place at Cairo University in January 1989.

Publications: *Newsletter* (quarterly); *List of Staff Vacancies in African Universities* (monthly); *New Acquisitions List* (biennially); *Reports*.

President: Prof. Rachid Haraoubia, Rector, Université des Sciences et de la Technologie Houari Boumediène, Algiers.

Vice-Presidents: Prof. J.M. Mwanza, Rector,

ants et des administrateurs des universités africaines, ainsi que toute personne intéressée par les problèmes de l'enseignement supérieur en Afrique.

En 1969, l'Association a créé un programme de bourses offertes dans des universités africaines. A ce titre, l'Agence américaine pour le Développement international a accordé, pendant un an, une subvention supérieure à un million de dollars, en vertu d'un accord conclu avec l'Association; le gouvernement britannique a octroyé de son côté vingt-cinq mille livres sterling, et le Canada un million de dollars pendant une période de cinq ans. L'Allemagne a contribué au Programme de bourses postgraduées. Un certain nombre de gouvernements africains ont également versé ou se sont engagés à verser d'importantes contributions à la Caisse de Dotation de l'Association.

Le programme attribue des bourses d'études supérieures (1er, 2e, et 3e cycles). Mille dix étudiants dont une centaine de réfugiés ont déjà bénéficié de ces bourses; quatre stages pour l'apprentissage rapide des langues anglaise et française ont été organisés à l'intention des professeurs et étudiants; les échanges de professeurs servent pour assurer des enseignements, l'encadrement des chercheurs ou la participation aux jurys d'examen ou de thèses.

Un Centre de Documentation a été créé au Secrétariat de l'Association. Il a pour objectif de rassembler et de diffuser des informations sur l'enseignement supérieur et la recherche dans les universités africaines et de coordonner les activités des universités membres.

L'organe suprême de l'Association est la Conférence générale composée des représentants des 88 institutions membres. Le Président de l'Association, qui est élu par la Conférence générale, est en même temps Président du Comité exécutif. Cet organisme, qui se réunit au moins une fois chaque année, est composé du Président, de trois Vice-Présidents et de neuf membres élus par la Conférence générale. Ses membres exercent leurs fonctions pendant une période de quatre ans. La sixième Conférence générale a eu lieu à l'Université des Sciences et de la Technologie Houari Boumediène, Alger en novembre 1984, et la septième Conférence générale a eu lieu à l'Université du Caire en janvier 1989.

Publications: *Newsletter* (trimestrielle); *List of Staff Vacancies in African Universities* (mensuelle); *New Acquisitions List* (tous les deux ans); *Reports*.

Président: Prof. Rachid Haraoubia, Recteur, Université des Sciences et de la Technologie Houari Boumediène, Alger.

Vice-Présidents: Prof. J.M. Mwanza, Recteur,

622

University of Zambia; Prof. H. Sindayigaya, Rector, Université du Burundi; Prof. C.A. Onwumechili, President, Anambra State University of Technology, Enugu (Nigeria).

Secretary-General: Prof. Lévy Makany. P.O. Box 5744, Accra-North (Ghana).

Tel: 65461 (ext. 620-625). Telex: 2284 adua gh.

Cables: afuniv

Université de Zambie; Prof. Hubert Sindayigaya, Recteur, Université du Burundi; Prof. C.A. Onwumechili, Président, Université de l'Etat de Technologie, Enugu d'Anambra (Nigeria).

Secrétaire général: Prof. Donald E. U. Ekong. P.O. Box 5744, Accra-Nord (Ghana).

Tél: 65461 (poste 620–625). Télex: 2284 adua gh. Cables: afuniv

ASSOCIATION OF ARAB UNIVERSITIES
UNION DES UNIVERSITES ARABES

Associate Member of the International Association of Universities
Membre associé de l'Association internationale des Universités

The Association of Arab Universities was founded in December 1964 and at present has seventy members in Algeria, Iraq, Jordan, Kuwait, Lebanon, Libya, Syria, Egypt, Sudan, Tunisia, Morocco, Saudi Arabia, Qatar, People's Democratic Republic of Yemen, United Arab Emirates, Occupied West Bank, Yemen Arab Republic, Bahrain, Somalia, and Mauritania.

Its principal aims are: to consolidate co-operation among Arab universities and institutions of higher education; to raise the standard of university education; to give due attention to applied research dealing with Arab problems and to relate research topics to plans for economic and social development; to preserve and spread the Arab cultural heritage; to sanction Arabic as the language of science and culture and to unify scientific and technical terminology; to encourage the establishment of new universities in Arab countries; to promote co-operation between Arab universities and other universities of the world; to co-ordinate the work of Arab universities in international organizations and congresses.

The supreme governing body of the Association is the Council of the Association of Arab Universities, which is composed of the rectors of member universities, or their representatives. The Council hold its meetings annually under the chairmanship of the host university, and it is the supreme organ of the Association. It is intrusted with the following duties: a) the formulation of the Association's general policy; b) the adoption of the Association's working programme and, when necessary, its amendment; c) the formulation of the general principles of the Association's budget; d) ratifying the financial, administrative and internal regulations; e) considering and deciding on applications by Arab Universities and instutitions of Higher Learning for membership; f) accepting donations, gifts and grants that are not in conflict with the objectives of the

L'Union des Universités arabes a été fondée en décembre 1964 et compte actuellement soixante-dix membres dans les pays suivants: Algérie, Irak, Jordanie, Koweit, Liban, Libye, Syrie, République arabe d'Egypte, Soudan, Tunisie, Maroc, Arabie saoudite, Qatar, République démocratique populaire du Yémen, Emirats Arabes Unis, la rive occidentale occupée, République arabe du Yémen, Bahrein, Somalie, et Mauritanie.

Ses objectifs principaux sont définis comme suit: resserrer la coopération entre les universités et les établissements d'enseignement supérieur; relever le niveau de l'enseignement universitaire; promouvoir les recherches appliquées traitant de problèmes arabes et rattacher ces recherches aux plans de développement économique et social; cultiver et diffuser le patrimoine de la culture arabe; consacrer la langue arabe comme langue de science et de culture et unifier la terminologie scientifique et technique; encourager la création de nouvelles universités dans les pays arabes; promouvoir la coopération entre les universités arabes et les autres universités du monde; co-ordonner l'action des universités arabes dans les organisations internationales et les congrès.

L'organe directeur suprême de l'Association est le Conseil de l'Union des Universités arabes, formé des recteurs des universités membres, ou de leurs représentants. Le Conseil se réunit chaque année sous la présidence de l'université hôte. Organe suprême de l'Association, il a pour fonctions: a) de définir la politique générale de l'Association; b) d'adopter le programme de travail de l'Association et, le cas échéant, ses modifications; c) de définir les principes généraux régissant le budget de l'Association; d) de ratifier les règlements financiers, administratifs et intérieurs; e) d'examiner les demandes d'adhésion présentées par les universités et institutions d'enseignement supérieur arabes et de prendre les décisions s'y rapportant; f) d'accepter des dons, des donations et des subventions dans la mesure où ils ne sont pas contraires aux objectifs

624

Association; g) ratifying means of investing the Association's funds in a manner that does not violate Islamic Law; h) ratifying the General Secretariat's Programme; i) considering all matters relevant to co-ordination, co-operation and the exchange of expertise amongst Arab universities in the fields of university organization: programmes of study; academic degrees; research; the exchange of faculty and students; athletic, social, cultural and artistic activities and other fields within the framework of the general policy of the Association.

So far the Council has held 21 meetings in different Arab universities.

The day-to-day business of the Association is entrusted to a general Secretariat, composed of the Secretary-General, two assistants and other supporting staff.

Secretary-General: Dr. Muhammed Faraj Doghaim.
Assistant Secretaries-General: Dr. Muhammad Majeed Al-Sa'eed; Dr. Muhammad Nabih Akel.
Secretariat-General: P.O. Box 401. Jubeyha-Amman (Jordan).
Tel: 845131. Fax: 832994. Telex: 23855 aaru jo.
Cables: ittihad jamiaat

de l'Association; g) d'approuver les modalités d'investissement des fonds de l'Association qui ne contreviennent pas au droit islamique; h) de ratifier le programme du Secrétariat général; i) d'étudier les thèmes et projets proposés par le Secrétariat général ou par n'importe quelle université membre et d'adopter les décisions les concernant; j) d'examiner toutes les questions relatives à la coordination, à la coopération et à l'échange d'expérience entre les universités arabes dans les domaines de l'administration universitaire, des programmes d'études, des grades et diplômes universitaires, de la recherche, des échanges d'enseignants et d'étudiants, des activités et manifestations sportives, culturelles, artistiques et sociales, ainsi que dans les autres activités entrant dans le cadre de la politique générale de l'Association. Le Conseil a jusqu'à présent tenu vingt-et-une réunions dans différentes universités arabes.

Secrétaire général: Dr. Muhammed Faraj Doghaim.
Secrétaires généraux adjoints: Dr. Muhammad Majeed Al-Sa'eed; Dr. Muhammad Nabih Akel.
Secrétariat général: P.O. Box (401), Jubeyha-Amman (Jordanie).
Tél: 845131. Fax: 832994. Télex: 23855 aaru jo.
Cables: ittihad jamiaat

ASSOCIATION OF COMMONWEALTH UNIVERSITIES (ACU)

Associate Member of the International Association of Universities
Membre associé de l'Association internationale des Universités

Founded in 1913, the Association is incorporated by Royal Charter and is the oldest international association of universities. Its Patron is H.M. The Queen, Head of the Commonwealth. The A.C.U. has (July 1988) 330 member universities in 29 Commonwealth countries or regions; 58% of them are in developing countries. Its affairs are controlled by a Council of executive heads (vice-chancellors and presidents) representing member universities in the different Commonwealth countries. Its core income comes from the annual subscriptions of its members but many of its activities are financed in other ways.

The Association works in a number of practical ways to implement its aim of promoting contact and co-operation between the universities of the Commonwealth.

Meetings
The A.C.U. holds three kinds of major meeting, providing university people from all parts of the Commonwealth with opportunities for personal contact and informal exchange of views and experience, as well as for formal discussions:

—quinquennial *Congresses*, to which each member institution is invited to send several delegates;
—*Conferences* confined to the executive heads of members, held twice in each five-year period;

—annual *Council meetings* which between Congresses normally become, in effect, interuniversity conferences when joint sessions are held with executive heads and academics in the country visited.

Fondée en 1913, l'Association s'est vu octroyer une Charte Royale et est placée sous le patronage de Sa Majesté la Reine, Chef du Commonwealth. L'ACU, la plus ancienne des associations d'universités, comptait en juillet 1988, 330 universités membres situées dans 29 pays ou régions du Commonwealth; 58% d'entre elles se trouvent dans des pays en voie de développement. Ses activités se déroulent sous la direction d'un Conseil de Chefs d'institutions (vice-chanceliers et présidents) représentant les universités membres dans les différents pays du Commonwealth. L'essentiel de ses ressources provient des cotisations annuelles de ses membres, mais un grand nombre de ses activités sont financées autrement.

L'Association cherche, par divers moyens pratiques, à réaliser son objectif, qui est de promouvoir le développement des contacts et de la coopération entre les universités du Commonwealth.

Réunions
L'ACU organise de grandes réunions offrant aux universitaires de tout le Commonwealth la possibilité de nouer des contacts personnels, de procéder à des échanges informels de vues et d'expériences, et de tenir des discussions de caractère officiel. Ces réunions sont de trois types:
—des *Congrès* quinquennaux auxquels chaque institution membre est invitée à se faire représenter par plusieurs déléguès;
—des *Conférences* réunissant uniquement les chefs des institutions membres (au nombre de deux pendant la période de cinq ans s'écoulant entre les Congrès);
—des *réunions annuelles du Conseil* qui deviennent, en effet, les années où il n'est pas organisé de Congrès, des conférences interuniversitaires lorsque se tiennent des réunions conjointes avec les chefs d'institutions et les universitaires du pays visité.

Information

The ACU provides information about Commonwealth universities and about access to them. It does so mainly through publications, the chief one being the 3,000-page *Commonwealth Universities Yearbook*. Others include: *Research Opportunities in Commonwealth Developing Countries—A Register*; *ACU Bulletin of Current Documentation*; *What Can We Do For Our Countries? the Contribution of Universities to National Development* (Report of proceedings of 14th ACU Congress); *Who's Who of Commonwealth University Vice-Chancellors, Presidents and Rectors*; *The Commonwealth of Universities: the Story of the ACU 1963–88* by Sir Hugh Springer and Alastair Niven; *Commonwealth University Situation Reports*; *Current documentation*; four handbooks on financial aid: *Awards for Commonwealth University Academic Staff*; *Grants for Study visits by University Administrators and Librarians*; *Scholarships Guide for Commonwealth Postgraduate Students*; and *Financial Aid for first Degree Study at Commonwealth Universities*; *Higher Education in the United Kingdom, a Handbook for Overseas Students* (Longmans for ACU); four handbooks on financial aid: *Awards for Commonwealth University Academic Staff*, *Grants for Study visits by University Administrators and Librarians*, Scholarships Guide for Commonwealth Postgraduate Students, and *Financial Aid for First Degree Study at Commonwealth Universities*; *Higher Education in the United Kingdom, a Handbook for Students and their Advisers* (Longmans for ACU); *University Entrance: The Official Guide*; *British Universities' Guide to Graduate Study*; *ACU Student Information Papers* about graduate study abroad. There is a Documentation Service, primarily for senior officers of member universities, a Personal Information Service, and a reference library of 15,000 volumes.

Academic Appointments

Acting for member institutions wishing to invite applications for vacant teaching and research posts from other countries, the Association maintains an Appointments Department through which, as such vacancies occur, they can be announced from London. In recent years, the Service has been consulted about more than 1,000 vacant posts a year. It also deals with many thousands of enquiries about specific vacancies which it has announced, as well as with a great

Information

L'Association fournit des renseignements sur les universités du Commonwealth et leurs conditions d'admission, principalement par ses publications, dont la plus importante est le *Commonwealth Universities Yearbook*, un ouvrage de 3.000 pages. Parmi ses autres publications, il convient de citer *Research Opportunities in Commonwealth Developing Countries—A Register; ACU Bulletin of Current Documentation; What Can We Do For Our Countries? the Contribution of Universities to National Development* (Actes du Quatorzième Congrès de l'ACU); *Who's Who of Commonwealth University Vice-Chancellors, Presidents and Rectors; The Commonwealth of Universities: the Story of the ACU 1963–88*, par Sir Hugh Springer et Alastair Niven; *Commonwealth University Situation Reports*; quatre ouvrages sur l'aide financière: *Awards for Commonwealth University Academic Staff; Grants for Study Visits by University Administrators and Librarians; Scholarships Guide for Commonwealth Postgraduate Students*; et *Financial Aid for First Degree Study at Commonwealth Universities; Higher Education in the United Kingdom, a Handbook for Overseas Students* (Longmans pour l'ACU); quatre ouvrages sur l'aide financière: *Awards for Commonwealth University Academic Staff; Grants for Study Visits by University Administrators and Librarians; Scholarships Guide for Commonwealth Postgraduate Students*; et *Financial Aid for First Degree Study at Commonwealth Universities; Higher Education in the United Kingdom, A Handbook for Overseas Students* (Longmans pour l'ACU) *University Entrance: The Official Guide; British Universities Guide to Graduate Study*, ainsi que les *ACU Student Information Papers* sur les études de postgraduation à l'étranger. L'ACU possède en outre un Service de documentation, essentiellement destiné aux principaux responsables des universités membres, un Service d'information personnel et une bibliothèque de référence contenant 15,000 volumes.

Nominations de personnel enseignant ou de chercheurs

Agissant pour les institutions membres désireuses de solliciter des candidatures d'autres pays pour des postes d'enseignement ou de recherche, l'Association dispose d'un service spécial pour les nominations de personnel grâce auquel les vacances qui se produisent peuvent être communiquées de Londres (ces dernières années, le Service a été consulté sur plus de mille vacances par an). Elle s'occupe également des

many general inquiries. It arranges, if asked, for overseas candidates to be assessed and for applicants in the United Kingdom or in Europe to be interviewed in London by independent committees of expert assessors who report to the universities concerned on the suitability of the candidates.

Scholarships and Fellowships

The Association provides the secretariat for the *Commonwealth Scholarship Commission in the United Kingdom*, the statutory body responsible for the administration in the U.K. of the Commonwealth Scholarship and Fellowship Plan. The Commission's main tasks are: to select Commonwealth Scholars, Commonwealth Academic Staff Fellows and holders of Commonwealth Medical Awards from overseas and place them in, or attach them to, universities and colleges in the U.K.; and to invite applications from U.K. candidates, and make nominations to the appropriate overseas agencies for Commonwealth Scholarships tenable in other countries. Since it was set up in 1960, the Commission has selected and placed at U.K. institutions nearly 8,000 Scholars and Fellows. More than 600 Commonwealth Scholarships have been awarded to U.K. students with tenure in another Commonwealth country. The Association prepares the annual report of the Plan's work throughout the Commonwealth and the Administrative Handbook on the Plan. It is also undertaking 'tracer studies' of former Commonwealth Scholars and Fellows.

The administration of the *Overseas Development Administration Shared Scholarship Scheme* (ODASSS) is now handled by the ACU. Under it, 150 new awards each year are available, with tenure in the UK, for work almost entirely at graduate taught course level, mainly for master's degrees.

On behalf of the Commonwealth Foundation, the Edward Boyle and the Lennox Boyd memorial trusts, the ACU administers Medical Electives Bursary schemes for senior medical students.

The Secretary General of the Association is executive secretary of the *Marshall Aid*

milliers de demandes concernant les vacances précises qu'elle a annoncées, ainsi que d'un grand nombre de demandes d'ordre général. Sur demande, elle prend des dispositions pour faire examiner les candidats étrangers et faire interviewer à Londres les candidats du Royaume-Uni ou d'Europe par des jurys indépendants qui soumettent aux universités intéressées un rapport sur l'aptitude des candidats à occuper les postes.

Bourses

L'Association assure le secrétariat de la *Commonwealth Scholarship Commission in the United Kingdom*, l'organisme officiellement chargé de l'administration dans ce pays du *Commonwealth Scholarship and Fellowship Plan*. Les fonctions principales de la Commission sont les suivantes: sélectionner des boursiers du Commonwealth, des enseignants boursiers du Commonwealth et des bénéficiaires à l'étranger des Fonds d'études médicales du Commonwealth et les affecter aux universités et collèges du Royaume-Uni; solliciter des candidatures au Royaume-Uni et faire des nominations aux organismes responsables des Bourses du Commonwealth valables dans d'autres pays. Depuis sa création en 1960, la Commission a sélectionné près de 8.500 boursiers et enseignants boursiers et les a affectés à des institutions du Royaume-Uni. Plus de six cent cinquante bourses permettant d'effectuer des études dans un autre pays du Commonwealth ont été octroyées à des étudiants britanniques. L'Association rédige le rapport annuel sur les activités et les progrès du Programme de Bourses du Commonwealth dans l'ensemble du Commonwealth, ainsi que le Répertoire administratif du Plan. Elle effectue également des 'études de localisation' des anciens chercheurs et boursiers ressortissants des pays du Commonwealth.

L'ACU administre maintenant l'*Overseas Development Administration Shared Scholarship Scheme* (ODASSS), qui prévoit l'octroi de 150 nouvelles bourses chaque année en vue de permettre à leurs titulaires d'effectuer des études au Royaume-Uni, se situant presqu'-entièrement au niveau des études avancées et principalement sanctionnées par un *master's degree*.

L'ACU gère, pour le compte de la Fondation du Commonwealth, de l'Edward Boyle et du Lennox Boyd Memorial Trusts, des programmes de bourses pour certains étudiants en médecine ayant atteint un stade avancé dans leurs études médicales.

Le Secrétaire général de l'Association est le Secrétaire exécutif de la *Marshall Aid Commem-*

Commemoration Commission which awards scholarships tenable at universities in the United Kingdom by students from the U.S.A.

The ACU runs two separate schemes for senior academic staff and administrators of Commonwealth universities. The first is for such senior academics as Deans, Assistant Vice-Chancellors and heads of service units who have leadership responsibilities for starting or developing a major section of their own university. It is funded by the Leverhulme Trust, Canadian International Development Agency (CIDA), and the ACU. The other is for administrators from university secretariats, libraries, etc.; its financial support comes from CIDA, and the ACU.

Tenable for short periods in developed or developing countries of the Commonwealth, the newly instituted ACU Development Fellowships are offered in subject areas where the needs of developing countries are particularly great. Movement of staff between industry/commerce/ public service and the universities, in both directions, is particularly encouraged.

Under the ACU/CIDA Women's Programme, the Association works with the Canadian International Development Agency to enhance the role of women in universities in developing countries of the Commonwealth. The first initiatives have been a training workshop in Bombay for women, academic and administrative, from South Asia and a special series of travelling fellowships for university women from Commonwealth developing countries.

The Association administers, on behalf of the Commonwealth Fund for Technical Co-operation, a programme of academic exchanges between member universities in developing countries of the Commonwealth. The Association also administers the *Third World Academic Exchange Fellowship* funded by the Times Higher Education Supplement.

The ACU is in close touch with national and regional inter-university organizations in Commonwealth countries, with the Commonwealth Secretariat, and with the International Association of Universities. It is in special relationship with Unesco.

oration Commission, qui octroie des bourses dans les universités britanniques à des étudiants des Etats-Unis.

L'ACU gère deux programmes distincts à l'intention du personnel académique et des administrateurs d'université des catégories les plus élevées qui sont ressortissants des pays du Commonwealth. Le premier s'adresse aux universitaires des catégories les plus élevées tels que les doyens, les vice-chanceliers adjoints et les chefs d'unités auxquels il incombe en priorité de créer ou de développer une section importante de leur propre université. Il est financé par le Leverhulme Trust, l'Agence canadienne de coopération pour le développement international (ACDI), et l'ACU. Le second est destiné aux administrateurs de secrétariats d'université, de bibliothèques, etc.; il reçoit son soutien financier de l'ACDI, et de l'ACU.

De création récente, les bourses de développement de l'ACU permettent d'effectuer de brefs séjours dans les pays développés ou en voie de développement du Commonwealth; elles sont octroyées dans des domaines où les besoins des pays en voie de développement sont particulièrement pressants. Les mouvements réciproques de personnel entre les milieux de l'industrie, du commerce, du service public et des universités sont vivement encouragés.

Dans le cadre du Programme ACU/ACDI pour les femmes, l'Association oeuvre, en coopération avec l'Agence canadienne de coopération pour le développement international (ACDI), en vue d'accroître le rôle des femmes dans les universités des pays en voie de développement du Commonwealth. Les premières initiatives ont été la tenue à Bombay d'un atelier de formation organisé à l'intention de femmes originaires de l'Asie méridionale et exerçant des fonctions soit dans l'université, soit dans l'administration, ainsi que la création d'une série spéciale de bourses de voyage pour les universitaires du sexe féminin originaires des pays en voie de développement du Commonwealth.

L'ACU gère, pour le compte du *Commonwealth Fund for Technical Co-operation*, un programme d'échanges universitaires entre les universités membres des pays en voie de développement du Commonwealth. L'Association gère également le *Third World Academic Exchange Fellowship* financé par le *Times Higher Education Supplement*.

L'Association entretient d'étroites relations avec les organisations universitaires nationales et régionales des pays du Commonwealth, avec le Secrétariat pour les pays du Commonwealth, et avec l'Association internationale des Universités. Elle bénéficie des relations consultatives avec l'Unesco.

Chairman (1988–89): Dr. Arnold Naimark (Canada).

Honorary Treasurer (1988–89): Dr. C.J. Maiden

Honorary Deputy Treasurer (1988–89): Prof. G.D. Sims (Sheffield).

Secretary General: Dr. Anastasios Christodoulou.

Deputy Secretary-General: Tom Craig.

Deputy Secretary-General (Commonwealth Awards and Appointments): Peter Hetherington.

John Foster House, 36 Gordon Square, London WC1H 0PF.

Tel: (1) 387-8572. Fax: (1) 387-2655. Cables: acumen london wc1

Président (1988–89): Dr. Arnold Naimark (Canada).

Trésorier honoraire (1988–89): Dr. C.J. Maiden (Australia).

Trésorier honoraire adjoint (1988–89): Prof. G.D. Sims (Sheffield).

Secrétaire général: Dr. Anastasios Christodoulou.

Secrétaire général adjoint: Tom Craig.

Secrétaire général adjoint (Bourses et nominations dans le Commonwealth): Peter Hetherington.

John Foster House, 36 Gordon Square, London WC1H 0PF.

Tél: (1) 387-8572. Fax: (1) 387-2655. Cables: acumen london wc1

ASSOCIATION OF SOUTHEAST ASIAN INSTITUTIONS OF HIGHER LEARNING (ASAIHL)

Associate Member of the International Association of Universities
Membre associé de l'Association internationale des Universités

The Association was founded as a non-governmental organization in 1956 at a meeting in Bangkok of the heads of eight State universities in Southeast Asia. Its purpose is to assist member institutions to strengthen themselves through mutual self-help and thus to achieve international distinction in teaching, research and public service. In so doing, the institutions contribute strength to their respective nations and to the entire region. Specifically, the Association exists to foster the development of the institutions themselves, the cultivation of a sense of regional identity and interdependence and liaison with other regional and international organizations concerned with research and teaching. It serves as a clearing-house of information; provides regular opportunities for the discussion of academic development and general university development; assists member institutions in the recruitment and placement of faculty and staff, exchanges of professors and students, and the development of co-operative arrangements on specific projects; provides advisory services of consultants; strengthens relationships with regional and international bodies, and keeps member institutions informed about development within them; and recognizes and acknowledges distinctive achievements among Southeast Asian institutions of higher education.

The membership of the Association includes about 100 university institutions in Australia, Brunei, Canada, Japan, Hong Kong, Indonesia, Malaysia, the Philippines, Singapore, Thailand and U.S.A. Its governing body is the General Conference, which meets at least once every two years. The first General Conference took place in Bangkok in 1957 and the second in Manila in 1959. The third General Conference was held in Kuala Lumpur in 1961, the fourth General

L'Association des institutions d'enseignement supérieur de l'Asie du Sud-Est a été fondée en 1956 comme organisation non gouvernementale au cours d'une réunion tenue à Bangkok par les chefs de huit universités d'Etat d'Asie du Sud-Est. Elle se propose d'aider les institutions membres à se développer par le moyen de l'assistance mutuelle et à atteindre par là un niveau international dans le domaine de l'enseignement, de la recherche et des services rendus au public. Les institutions contribuent ainsi à une expansion accrue tant de la région tout entière que de leurs pays respectifs. L'Association a notamment pour buts de promouvoir le développement des institutions elles-mêmes, de cultiver un sentiment d'identité régionale et d'interdépendance et de maintenir des liens avec d'autres organisations, régionales ou internationales s'occupant de recherche et d'enseignement. Elle fonctionne comme centre d'information; permet de discuter périodiquement de l'évolution des problèmes académiques et du développement général de l'université; apporte son aide aux institutions membres pour le recrutement et le placement de membres du corps enseignant, les échanges de professeurs et d'étudiants, et les accords de coopération sur des projets déterminés; fournit des services de consultants; resserre les liens avec les organismes régionaux ou internationaux; tient les institutions membres au courant de l'évolution qui s'y produit; et accorde son soutien et son appui aux réalisations les plus marquantes des institutions d'enseignement supérieur d'Asie du Sud-Est.

L'Association compte au nombre de ses membres environ 100 institutions universitaires d'Australie, de Brunei, du Canada, du Japon, de Hong-Kong, d'Indonésie, de Malaisie, des Philippines, de Singapour, de Thaïlande et des Etats-Unis. Son organe directeur est la Conférence générale qui se réunit au moins une fois tous les deux ans. La première Conférence générale a eu lieu à Bangkok en 1957 et la deuxième à Manille en 1959. La troisième a eu lieu à Kuala-

Conference in Bandung in 1963, the fifth General Conference in Bangkok in 1964, the sixth in Bangkok in 1966, the seventh in Manila in 1968, the eighth in Hong Kong in 1970, the ninth in Singapore in 1972, the tenth in Kuala Lumpur in 1974, and the eleventh in Jakarta in 1976. An Administrative Board composed of the President and Vice-President of the Association and one representative from each country which has a member institution, except those countries from which the President and Vice-President come, is elected by the General Conference and meets at least once a year.

President: Dr. Sujudi, Rector, University of Indonesia.

Secretary-General: Dr. Ninnat Olanvoravuth.

Ratasastra Building 2, Chulalongkorm University, Henri Dunant Road, Bangkok 10500.

Tel: 251-6966

Lumpur en 1961, la quatrième à Bandung en 1963, la cinquième à Bangkok en 1964, la sixième à Bangkok en 1966, la septième à Manille en 1968, la huitième à Hong-Kong en 1970, la neuvième à Singapour en 1972, la dixième à Kuala-Lumpur en 1974, et la onzième à Jakarta en 1976. Le Conseil d'administration, composé du Président et du Vice-Président de l'Association ainsi que d'un représentant de chacun des pays qui compte une institution membre, excepte ceux d'où viennent le Président et le Vice-Président, est élu par la Conférence générale et se réunit au moins une fois par an.

Président: Dr. Sujudi, Recteur, Université d'Indonésie.

Secrétaire général: Dr. Ninnat Olanvoravuth.

Ratasastra Building, Chulalongkorn University, Henri Dunant Road, Bangkok 10500.

Tél: 251-6966

ASSOCIATION DES UNIVERSITES PARTIELLEMENT OU ENTIEREMENT DE LANGUE FRANÇAISE (AUPELF)

Associate Member of the International Association of Universities
Membre associé de l'Association internationale des Universités

The Association was established in 1961 in Montreal. Since 1987, it has been endowed with the additional structure of a 'University of French-Speaking Networks' (UREF), a major project of the Summit of the Heads of State and of the governments of countries having in common the use of the French language. AUPELF is an international non-governmental association in consultative and associate relations with Unesco (Category A), which groups together institutions of higher education whose medium of instruction is French. It has a worldwide network of more than 200 partially or wholly French-language institutions and establishments of higher education together with 400 departments of French studies in non-francophone universities.

L'Association des universités partiellement ou entièrement de langue française (AUPELF) a été créée en 1961 à Montréal. Elle s'est dotée, depuis 1987, d'une Université des Réseaux d'Expression Française (UREF) qui est un projet majeur du Sommet des Chefs d'Etat et de Gouvernement des pays ayant en commun l'usage du français. C'est une association internationale non gouvernementale agréée par l'Unesco (statut A) qui regroupe l'ensemble des établissements d'enseignement supérieur utilisant le français. Son réseau est mondial et comprend plus de 200 institutions et réseaux institutionnels d'enseignement supérieur entièrement ou partiellement de langue française et 400 départements d'études françaises des universités non francophones.

Objectives

As a community of universities, AUPELF/UREF has as its main aim the development of an international conscience and spirit of co-operation to serve cultural plurality and scientific progress. To this end, it carries out the following tasks:

a) a constant reflection on the evolution of the university, on its role and place in national and international life, as well as on the structure and facilities of the university;

b) to establish ways of promoting the meeting of cultures and the role of the university as a vital element in socio-cultural development;

c) the continual improvement of the circulation of scientific information between member institutions;

d) to assure the availability of services to members, as well as the means of promoting exchange and international relations;

e) the organization of a cultural, scientific and technical French-speaking framework in the light of co-development.

Objectifs

Communauté d'institutions universitaires, l'AUPELF/UREF a pour objectif essentiel de développement d'une conscience internationale et d'un esprit de coopération au service de la pluralité culturelle et du progrès scientifique. A cette fin, elle se consacre notamment aux tâches suivantes:

a) une réflexion permanente sur l'évolution de l'université, sur son rôle et sa place dans la société nationale et internationale, ainsi que sur les structures et les moyens de l'université;

b) la mise en oeuvre de formules propres à promouvoir la rencontre des cultures et le rôle de l'université comme élément vital de développement socio-culturel;

c) l'amélioration constante de la circulation de l'information scientifique entre les institutions membres;

d) la mise à la disposition des membres de services ainsi que de formules d'échanges et de relations internationales;

e) l'aménagement de l'espace culturel, scientifique et technique d'expression française, dans la perspective du co-développement.

Organization

The organs of the Association are the General Assembly, the Administrative Board, the University Council of the University of French-Speaking Networks, the Scientific Council, the General Secretariat, and the General Delegation of UREF.

The General Assembly is the supreme body of AUPELF and meets every three years. It elects the President and the Administrative Board, approves the budget and defines the general policy of AUPELF/UREF. The Administrative Board, which is also the University Council, comprises 18 members (including the Chairman and three Vice-Chairmen) elected at the General Assembly from among representatives of the higher education and research establishments, which are titular members of the Association. It meets at least once a year and carries out the decisions of the General Assembly.

The Scientific Council, which comprises 12 members appointed by the Administrative Council and who are chosen in accordance with their personal scientific, cultural, technological or management experience. It is responsible for the evaluation and orientation of the Association's programme activities.

The General Secretariat has its headquarters at the University of Montreal and regional officers in Paris, for Europe, at the Université Cheikh Anta Diop, Senegal, for Africa, in Montreal, for North America and at Pétion-Ville, for the Caribbean region.

The General Delegation is responsible for the functioning of the University of French Speaking Networks.

Since 1968, AUPELF has operated an 'International University Co-operation Fund' (FICU) which gives active support to activities of multilaterial co-operation between member institutions. FICU is administered by a management committee of members of the AUPELF Administrative Board and governmental or private contributors. FICU meets annually and is governed by AUPELF.

Since 1983, AUPELF has also set up a databank of university and scientific information. This bank presently comprises five specialized files: an address base (12,000 addresses of universities, institutes, schools, faculties, university presses, departments of French studies, and national and international administrations specializing in educational, research or co-operation materials); a file of 'AUPELF member institutions' (description of member institutions with their areas of study and diplomas); a file of 'French language university periodicals' (900

Organisation

Les organes de l'Association sont l'Assemblée générale, le Conseil d'administration, le Conseil d'université de l'Université des réseaux d'expression française, le Conseil scientifique, le Secrétariat général et la Délégation générale de l'UREF.

L'Assemblée générale est l'instance suprême de l'Association qui se réunit tous les trois ans. Elle élit le Président et le Conseil d'administration, approuve le budget et définit la politique générale de l'AUPELF/UREF. Le Conseil d'administration qui est aussi le Conseil d'Université, est composé de dix-huit membres (dont le Président et trois Vice-Présidents) élus à l'Assemblée générale parmi les représentants des établissements d'enseignement supérieur et de recherche, membres titulaires de l'Association. Il se réunit au moins une fois l'an et exécute les décisions de l'Assemblée générale.

Le Conseil scientifique, qui comprend douze membres désignés par le Conseil d'administration, est composé de personnalités choisies en fonction de leur expérience personnelle scientifique, culturelle, technologique ou de gestion. Il est chargé d'une mission d'évaluation et d'orientation des activités de programme de l'Association.

Le Secrétariat général a son siège à l'Université de Montréal et des bureaux régionaux pour l'Europe à Paris, pour l'Afrique à l'Université Cheikh Anta Diop, pour l'Amérique du Nord au siège de Montréal et pour les Caraïbes à Pétion-Ville.

La Délégation générale a la responsabilité du fonctionnement de l'Université des réseaux d'expression française.

Depuis 1968, l'Association dispose d'un Fonds International de Coopération Universitaire (FICU) pour apporter un soutien concret aux activités de coopération multilatérale entre les institutions membres. Le FICU est administré par un comité de gestion composé de membres du Conseil d'administration de l'AUPELF et de l'ensemble des contributeurs gouvernementaux ou privés. Il se réunit une fois l'an et il est géré par l'AUPELF.

L'AUPELF a par ailleurs entrepris la création d'une banque de données universitaires et scientifiques depuis 1983. Cette banque comprend à ce jour 5 fichiers spécialisés: une base-adresses (12.000 adresses d'universités, instituts, écoles, facultés, presses universitaires, départements d'études françaises, administrations nationales ou internationales spécialisées en matière d'éducation, de recherche ou de coopération); le fichier "institutions membres de l'AUPELF" (description des universités et écoles membres, avec leurs filières de formation et leurs diplômes);

634

periodicals with publisher, editorial offices, contents, subscription rates); a file of 'French-speaking African teachers and researchers' (2,200 individual cards mentioning educational level, teaching and research activities); a file of 'Departments of French studies worldwide' (850 institutions with their academic potential and specialized diplomas).

le fichier "périodiques universitaires de langue française" (900 périodiques avec éditeur, rédaction, contenus, tarifs); le fichier "enseignements et chercheurs africains francophones" (2.200 fiches individuelles avec mention du niveau de formation, des activités d'enseignement et de recherche); le fichier "départements d'études françaises dans le monde entier" (850 établissements avec leur potentiel pédagogique et les diplômes spécialisés).

Finance

AUPELF is financially supported by: membership dues; proceeds from services; programme contracts concluded with national and international bodies; subventions from governments and co-operation agencies. UREF manages a multilaterial management fund, placed at its disposition by the Summit of Heads of State and governments.

President: Bakáry Touré, Université nationale de Côte d'Ivoire, (Paris XII).

Secretary-General: Maurice E. Beutler. B.P. 6128, Université de Montréal, Montréal, Qué., Canada H3C 3J7.

Tel: 343-66-30. Fax: 343-21-07. Telex: 556-09-55

European Office: 192, boulevard Saint-Germain, 75007 Paris.

Tel: 4222-9638. Fax: 4222-3948. Telex: 203543

African Office: B.P. 10017 Liberté, Dakar (Senegal).

Tel: 24-29-27. Fax: 25-34-58. Telex: 51267

Financement

Le financement de l'AUPELF est assuré par: les cotisations de ses membres; les produits de ses services; les contrats de programme conclus avec des organismes nationaux ou internationaux; les subventions de gouvernements et d'agences de coopération. L'UREF gère un fonds de gestion multilatérale mis à sa disposition par le Sommets des Chefs d'Etat et de Gouvernement.

Président: Bakáry Touré, Université national de Côte d'Ivoire.

Tél: 4390-00. Télex: 23469 recta ci

Secrétaire général: Maurice E. Beutler. B.P. 6128, Université de Montréal, Montréal, Qué, Canada H3C 3J7.

Tél: 343-66-30. Fax: 343-21-07. Télex: 556-09-55

Bureau européen: 192, boulevard Saint-Germain, 75007 Paris.

Tél: 4222-9638. Fax: 4222-3948. Télex: 203543

Bureau africain: B.P. 10017 Liberté, Dakar (Sénégal).

Tél: 24-29-27. Fax: 25-34-58. Télex: 51267

INTER-AMERICAN ORGANIZATION FOR HIGHER EDUCATION (IOHE)
ORGANISATION UNIVERSITAIRE INTERAMERICAINE (OUI)

Associate Member of the International Association of Universities
Membre associé de l'Association internationale des Universités

Realizing, after several years of study and observation, that the total absence of formal structures between the universities of North and South America prejudiced the organization and continuity of inter-American university co-operation, the representatives of Canadian, American and Mexican universities created the inter-American University Association (IUA) in April 1979.

The objective of this new Association was to intensify exchanges and to circulate information between agencies, institutions and people working in higher education and wishing to consolidate relations between their neighbours of the Americas. In collaboration with the organizations already in existence, the IUA wished, in the first place, to identify existing needs, and then participate in the execution of the most essential co-operation projects, while contributing to the cause of development and world peace.

During 1979 and 1980, the Association held several discussion meetings in both North and South America. Finally, after eighteen months of exploratory work, the Inter-American Organization for Higher Education (IOHE) was officially founded during the first Congress, held in Québec from October 13th to 16th, 1980.

Objectives

An international non-governmental organization (INGO), the Inter-American Organization for Higher Education is essentially dedicated to institutional co-operation and to the development of higher education in the Americas. It is a crossroads where the universities of the American continent meet to share their concerns and their resources in programmes of mutual interest.

According to its Statutes, the main objectives of the IOHE are: to promote and develop ties of solidarity and friendship among the universities

Constatant, après plusieurs années d'étude et d'observation, que l'absence totale de structures d'accueil entre les universités de l'Amérique du Nord et du Sud nuisait à l'organisation et à la continuité des efforts de coopération universitaire interaméricaine, des représentants d'universités canadiennes, américaines et mexicaines ont mis sur pied en avril 1979 l'Association universitaire interaméricaine (AUI).

L'objectif de cette nouvelle Association était d'intensifier les échanges et la circulation de l'information entre les organismes, institutions et personnes qui, se préoccupant du secteur universitaire, désiraient consolider les relations entre les peuples frères et voisins des Amériques. En collaboration avec les organisations déjà en place, l'AUI voulait d'abord identifier les besoins non comblés et ensuite participer à la mise en oeuvre des projets de coopération les plus essentiels contribuant ainsi au développement des pays et à la paix mondiale.

Elle a tenu en 1979 et 1980 plusieurs rencontres de réflexion tant en Amérique du Nord qu'en Amérique du Sud. Finalement, après dix-huit mois de travaux exploratoires, elle officiellement été fondée sous le nom d'Organisation universitaire interaméricaine (OUI) au cours du premier Congrès tenu à Québec, du 13 au 16 octobre 1980.

Objectifs

Organisme non gouvernemental international (ONGI), l'Organisation universitaire interaméricaine est essentiellement vouée à la coopération institutionnelle et au développement de l'enseignement supérieur dans les Amériques. Elle est un carrefour où se rencontrent les universités de l'Amérique du Nord et de l'Amérique du Sud pour partager leurs préoccupations et leurs ressources dans des programmes d'intérêt commun.

Selon les Statuts de Organisation universitaire interaméricaine, les principaux objectifs visés sont de: promouvoir et développer les liens de

of the Americas; to seek improved mutual understanding among universities of the Americas by identifying common needs, available resources and the potential for interinstitutional cooperation; and to bring together institutions of higher education by developing programmes of common interest in the fields of teaching, research and extension services. The General Assembly, the Board of Directors and the Advisory Council are the IOHE's main statutory authorities.

Members

The following may become members of the Inter-American Organization for Higher Education: universities and institutions of higher education of the Americas; national, regional and international university councils, associations, federations or similar institutions. The Inter-American Organization for Higher Education has progressively established itself in almost all the countries of the American continent and today has about 300 member universities, 250 of Latin American origin.

The members of the Organization are distributed in the following 8 administrative regions and 22 countries: Canada; U.S.A.; Mexico; Central America (Panama; Costa Rica; El Salvador; Nicaragua; Guatemala and Honduras); Caribbean (Guyana; Venezuela; Haiti; Republica Dominicana and Puerto Rico); Andean Countries (Chile; Bolivia; Peru; Ecuador and Colombia); Brazil and the Southern Cone (Argentina and Uruguay).

Development Programmes

Regionalization programme; Programme of seminars on regional problems; Inter-American University Communications and Information Network and the Institute of University Management and Leadership Programme.

Relations with the United Nations and other International and Regional Institutions

Since 1982, the Inter-American Organization for Higher Education is recognized as an international organization by Unesco, and it now has close relations with the Canadian Commission for Unesco, Ottawa (Canada), the Higher Education Division of Unesco, Paris, and regional organizations such as the Oficina

solidarité et d'amitié entre les universités des Amériques; rechercher une meilleure connaissance réciproque entre les universités des Amériques afin d'identifier leurs besoins communs, les ressources disponibles et les possibilités d'entraide institutionnelle, et regrouper les établissements universitaires des Amériques par le développement au niveau supérieur de programmes d'intérêt commun dans les domaines de l'enseignement, de la recherche et de la formation permanente. L'Assemblée générale des membres, le Conseil d'administration et le Conseil consultatif sont les principales instances administratives de l'Organisation.

Membres

Peuvent devenir membres réguliers de l'Organisation universitaire interaméricaine: les universités et les institutions d'enseignement supérieur des Amériques et les conseils, associations, fédérations et autres institutions analogues, à caractère international, national ou régional. Au cours des premières années de son existence, l'Organisation universitaire interaméricaine a consacré une large part de ses énergies au recrutement de membres et elle s'est progressivement implantée dans la presque totalité des pays du continent américain. Aujourd'hui, elle compte environ 300 universités affiliées, dont 250 d'origine latino-américaine.

Les membres de l'OUI sont répartis dans les 8 Régions administratives et les 22 pays suivants: Canada; Etats-Unis; Mexique; Amérique centrale (Panama, Costa Rica; El Salvador; Nicaragua; Guatemala et Honduras); Caraïbes (Guyane; Venezuela; Haïti; République dominicaine et Puerto Rico); Pays andins (Chili; Bolivie; Pérou; Equateur et Colombe); Brésil; Cône méridional de l'hémisphère austral (Argentine et Uruguay).

Programmes de développement

Les principaux programmes actuels de l'OUI sont: le Programme d'appui à la régionalisation; le Programme de séminaires sur des problématiques régionales (PSPR); le Réseau interaméricain de communication et d'information universitaires (RICIU) et l'Institut de gestion et de leadership universitaires (IGLU).

Relations avec les institutions spécialisées

Depuis 1982, l'Organisation universitaire interaméricaine est reconnue en tant qu'organisme international par l'Unesco. Elle s'est efforcée depuis lors d'entretenir d'étroites relations avec la Commission canadienne pour l'Unesco à Ottawa (Canada), la Division de l'enseignement supérieur, Paris (France) et d'autres organismes régionaux tels que le Bureau

Regional de Educación para América Latina y el Caribe (OREALC), Santiago (Chile) and the Centro Regional para la Educación Superior en América Latina y el Caribe (CRESALC), Caracas (Venezuela).

The Organization also has on-going relations with the offices of the United Nations Development Programme (UNDP) in Latin America. In August 1988, the Inter-American Organization for Higher Education was accepted as an Associate Member of the International Association of Universities (IAU). The IOHE and the Organization of American States (OAS) have agreed to establish general co-operation relations.

The IOHE seeks the support of foundations and international funding agencies in order to carry out its programmes. Finally, the general policy of the IOHE is to support all the initiatives of international organizations and national or regional associations for the development of higher education in the Americas, inasmuch as its resources and possibilities permit.

Publications

The Inter-American Organization for Higher Education publishes its newsletter *Interamerica* four times a year in two versions: French-English and Spanish-Portuguese for distribution to members and other interested persons. The IOHE also publishes a members' Directory, the Proceedings of its International Congresses, and other academic information and directive documents.

The Inter-American Organization for Higher Education is incorporated in Costa Rica.

President: Gilles Boulet.
Executive Director: Gilles Arès.
2875, boulevard Laurier, Sainte-Foy, Québec, Canada GIV 2M3.
  Tel: (418) 657-3551. Fax: (418) 657-3551 (ext. 2271). Telex: 051-31623

régional d'education pour l'Amérique latine (OREALC) Santiago, Chili et le Centre regional pour l'enseignement supérieur en Amérique latine et dans le Caraïbes (CRESALC) Caracas, (Venezuela).

De même, elle entretient des relations permanentes avec les différents bureaux du Programme des Nations Unies pour le Développement (PNUD) situés en Amérique latine. En août 1988, l'Organisation universitaire interaméricaine a été acceptée comme Membre Associé de l'Association internationale des Universités (AIU). L'OUI et L'Organisation des Etats américains (OEA) ont aussi convenu d'établir entre elles des relations de coopération générale.

L'OUI cherche l'appui des fondations et des agences de financement internationales pour la réalisation de ses programmes d'activités. Enfin, la politique générale de l'OUI est d'appuyer, dans la mesure de ses ressources et de ses possibilités, toutes les initiatives des organismes internationaux et des associations nationales ou régionales visant au développement de l'enseignement supérieur dans les Amériques.

Publications

L'Organisation universitaire interaméricaine publie quatre fois par an le bulletin *Interamerica*, bulletin d'information édité en deux versions: français-anglais et espagnol-portugais à l'intention de ses membres et des personnes ou organismes intéressés. Parmi les autres publications, il y a l'Annuaire des universités membres, les Actes des Congrès internationaux de l'OUI et des documents d'information, de réflexion ou d'orientation.

L'Organisation universitaire interaméricaine a légalement été constituée en societé et a son siège à San José (Costa Rica).

Président: Gilles Boulet.
Secrétaire général exécutif: Gilles Arès.
2875, boulevard Laurier, Sainte-Foy, Québec, Canada GIV 2M3.
  Tél: (418) 657-3551. Fax: (418) 657-3551 (poste 2271). Télex: 051-31623

INTERNATIONAL FEDERATION OF CATHOLIC UNIVERSITIES (IFCU)

FEDERATION INTERNATIONALE DES UNIVERSITES CATHOLIQUES (FIUC)

Associate Member of the International Association of Universities
Membre associé de l'Association internationale des Universités

The origins of this Federation date back to 1924, when, at the invitation of P.A. Gemelli (Milan) and D.J. Schrijnen (Nijmegen), a number of Rectors of Catholic Universities began to meet with the purpose of discussing specific questions of mutual interest.

On 29 June 1948, the "Foederatio Universitatum Catholicarum" was established at the Holy See, in Rome, by decree of the Sacred Congregation of Seminaries and Universities.

By his apostolic letter "Catholicas Studiorum Universitates", of 27 July, 1949, Pope Pius XII, recognized this Federation of Catholic Universities.

The first Statutes of the new Federation were approved by the Sacred Congregation of Seminaries and Universities on 11 January 1951. They were later revised following a resolution taken by the General Assembly in 1963. The text of the new Statutes was adopted by the General Assembly in Tokyo in 1965. These Statutes endow it with its new title—the International Federation of Catholic Universities—and with the status of an international non-governmental organization. Other amendments to the Statutes were adopted in subsequent assemblies. The Federation is a voluntary, non-governmental and self determinated organization.

The Federation now has 111 university members and 61 Associate Members: the latter include institutions, independent faculties and schools not attached to universities. The geographic distribution of members is: Africa, 1; Asia, 49; Australia, 2; North America, 36; Latin America, 46; Europe, 38. Associate Members have one vote at the General Assembly, whereas the member universities have two.

The Federation is governed by an Administrative Board, composed of the President, three Vice-Presidents, the Secretary-General, and ten Counsellors; Board Members are elected by the

Les origines de cette Fédération remontent à 1924 lorsque, à l'invitation de P.A. Gemelli (Milan) et de D.J. Schrijnen (Nimègue), plusieurs Recteurs d'Universités catholiques commencèrent à se réunir pour discuter de questions précises intéressant toutes les universités.

Le 29 juin 1948, la "Foederatio Universitatum Catholicarum" fut érigée auprès du Saint-Siège, à Rome, par décret de la Sacrée Congrégation des Séminaires et Universités.

Par la lettre apostolique "Catholicas Studiorum Universitates", en date du 27 juillet 1949, le Pape Pie XII reconnaissait cette Fédération des Universités catholiques.

Les premiers statuts de cette nouvelle Fédération furent approuvés par la Sacrée Congrégation des Séminaires et Universités le 11 janvier 1951. Ils furent révisés à la suite d'une décision prise par l'Assemblée générale en 1963. Le texte des nouveaux statuts fut adopté par l'Assemblée générale à Tokyo en 1965. Ces statuts donnent à la "Fédération internationale des Universités catholiques", avec son nouveau titre, le caractère d'une organisation internationale non gouvernementale. De nouvelles modifications des statuts furent adoptées par la suite. La Fédération est une organisation libre, non gouvernementale et autonome.

Actuellement la Fédération compte 111 universités membres et 61 membres associés: ces derniers sont des institutions d'enseignement supérieur, telles que facultés ou écoles, indépendantes des universités. La répartition géographique s'établit ainsi: Afrique, 1; Asie, 49; Australie, 2; Amérique du Nord, 36; Amérique Latine, 46; Europe, 38. Les membres associés ont une seule voix à l'Assemblée Générale, tandis que les universités membres disposent de deux voix.

La Fédération est dirigée par le Conseil d'administration, composé du Président, de trois Vice-Présidents, du Secrétaire général, et de dix Conseillers; les membres du Conseil sont élus par

General Assembly. The Administrative Board meets at least once a year.

The Federation has held fifteen General Assemblies: Rome 1949, Quebec 1952, Louvain 1955 and 1958, Rio de Janeiro 1960, Washington 1963, Tokyo 1965, Kinshasa 1968, Boston 1970, Salamanca 1973, New Delhi 1975, Pôrto Alegre 1978, Louvain-la-Neuve 1980, Toronto 1983, and Santo Domingo 1985.

The *purpose* of the Federation is "to work for the constant progress of knowledge and for the development of a more just and human society in the light of the Christian faith and the Gospel". Thus it has a threefold mission, intellectual, social, spiritual.

The ensuing *functions* are: 1) to promote collective reflection by providing a world forum in a variety of meetings; 2) to maintain representation on behalf of Catholic universities through liaison with international bodies; 3) to contribute to an effective collaboration among institutions by exchanges of all types; and 4) to provide information to members by selected means of communications.

Activities of the Federation take place at four levels: international or worldwide; regional or continental; sectoral or by faculties/schools; and interdisciplinary through research projects organized by the Center for Co-ordination of Research (Palazzo Frascara, Università Gregoriana, Piazza della Pilotta 4, 00187 Rome).

The *topics* of study have clustered principally around the following themes: a) University identity and government: mission, functions, specificity, autonomy, freedom, students and curriculum; b) Cultural issues: pluralism, values, inculturation; c) Economic questions: employment, multinational corporations; d) Social matters: Human rights, peace, development, population, New World order; e) Ethical problems: bioethics, technology and ethics.

Publications: *Planning of Education* (International Catholic Seminar) Louvain, 1964; *Monograph on Catholic Universities and the Modern World: The Cultural and Educational Aspects of Development*, by Rev. Theodore Hesburgh, 1964; *The Catholic University in the Modern World*: Report of the 8th General Assembly, Kinshasa; *The Catholic University and Development*: Report of the 9th General Assembly, Boston, 1970; *The Catholic University in the Modern World*: Congress of Catholic University Delegates, Rome, 1972; *The Spiritual Function of the Catholic University and its Function as a Critic*: Report of the 10th General Assembly, Salamanca, 1973; *The Co-ordination*

l'Assemblée générale. Le Conseil d'administration se réunit au moins une fois par an.

La Fédération a tenu quinze assemblées générales: 1949 à Rome, 1952 à Québec, 1955 et 1958 à Louvain, 1960 à Rio de Janeiro, 1963 à Washington, 1965 à Tokyo, 1968 à Kinshasa, 1970 à Boston, 1973 à Salamanque, 1975 à New Delhi, 1978 à Pôrto Alegre, 1980 à Louvain-la-Neuve, à Toronto, 1983, et à Santo Domingo 1985.

La *finalité* de la Fédération est de "contribuer, à la lumière de la foi chrétienne et grâce au ferment de l'Evangile, au progrès du Savoir et à l'élaboration d'un monde plus juste et plus humain". Elle a ainsi une triple mission, intellectuelle, sociale et spirituelle.

Les *fonctions* de la FIUC sont: 1) la promotion de la réflexion collective dans divers forums et assemblées; 2) la représentation au nom des universités catholiques par des liaisons auprès des organismes internationaux; 3) la collaboration efficace par un ensemble d'échanges entre les institutions; et 4) la diffusion d'informations aux membres par divers moyens de communication.

Les *activités* de la Fédération se situent à quatre niveaux: international ou mondial; régional ou national; sectoriel ou par disciplines; et interdisciplinaire à travers des projets de recherche organisés par le Centre de Coordination de la Recherche (Palazzo Frascara, Université Grégorienne, Piazza della Pilotta 4, 00187 Rome).

Les *sujets* d'étude se regroupent principalement autour des thèmes suivants: a) identité et gouvernement de l'université: mission, fonctions, spécificité; autonomie, liberté, étudiants et programme; b) enjeux culturels: pluralisme, valeurs, inculturation; c) questions économiques: emploi, multinationales, corporations; d) affaires sociales: droits humains, paix, développement, population, nouvel ordre mondial; e) problèmes éthiques: bioéthique, technologie et éthique.

Publications: *Planification de l'Education* (Séminaire catholique international) Louvain, 1964; *Monographie sur les universités catholiques et le monde moderne: L'Autonomie des Universités Catholiques*, par M. René Théry, Lille, 1965; *L'Université Catholique dans le monde moderne*: Rapport de la 8ème Assemblée Générale, Kinshasa, 1968; *Les Sciences économiques dans l'enseignement supérieur catholique*: Colloque de Barcelone, 1969; *L'Université Catholique et le Développement*: Rapport de la 9ème Assemblée Générale, Boston, 1970; *L'Université Catholique dans le monde moderne*: Congrès des délégués des universités catholiques, Rome, 1972; *Fonction*

of Research Work within the Church: Proceedings of a Colloquium organized by the IFCU at Grottaferrata, Italy, 1974; *The Participation of Catholic Universities in Research and Education in the Fields of Population and Human Development*: Report of the 11th General Assembly, New Delhi, 1975; *Population Problems: Colloquium of Diegem*, 1977; *The Catholic University, Instrument of Cultural Pluralism in the Service of Church and Society*: Report of the 12th General Assembly, Pôrto Alegre, 1978; *Medical Schools and Catholic Universities*: Beerse, 1980; *The Catholic University Facing the Ethical Problems of the Technological Society*: Report of the 13th General Assembly, Louvain-la-Neuve, 1980; *La ética ante la tecnología: una opción universitaria*, by Pierre Watté, 1982; *Human Rights: Research and Teaching*: IFCU Symposium, Salzburg, Austria, 1981; *Medical Schools and Catholic Universities*: IFCU Symposium, Lille, France, 1981; *Multinational Corporations and Regional Development: Conflicts and Convergences*, by L. Michaud, editor Herder, Roma, 1983 (Symposium of the Centre for Coordination of Interdisciplinary Research of IFCU, Sudbury, Canada, 1980); *The Peace Movements*: Proceedings of the Symposium organized by IFCU and the Club of Rome, Salzburg, 1983; *The Catholic University and the Search for a New World Order*: Report of the 14th General Assembly, Toronto, 1983; *Demographic Policies from a Christian View Point*: Proceedings of the Symposium in Rio de Janeiro, 1982, Franco Biffi (editor) IFCU - CCIR - Herder, Rome, 1984; *The Expectations of Youth and the Catholic University*: Report of the 15th General Assembly, Santo Domingo, 1985.

critique et spirituelle de l'Université Catholique: Rapport de la 10ème Assemblée Générale, Salamanque, 1973; *La coordination de la recherche dans l'Eglise*: Colloque de la FIUC à Grottaferrata, Italie, 1974; *La participation des Universités Catholiques à la recherche scientifique et à l'éducation dans les domaines de la population et du développement humain*: Rapport de la 11ème Assemblée Générale, New Delhi, 1975; *Problématique de la population*: Colloque de Diegem, 1977; *L'Université Catholique, voie du pluralisme culturel au service de l'Eglise et de la Société*: Rapport de la 12ème Assemblée Générale, Pôrto Alegre, 1978; *Le Pouvoir dans l'Entreprise*: 6èmes Journées Européennes des Instituts d'Enseignement Supérieur et des Sciences Economiques et de Gestion de la FIUC, Lyon, 1979; *Liberté, démocratie, projet universitaire*: Salamanque, 1979; *L'Université Catholique face aux problèmes éthiques de la société technologique*: Rapport de la 13ème Assemblée Générale, Louvain la Neuve, 1980; *Développement Economique et Social et Droit à l'Emploi*: 7èmes Journées Européennes, Madrid, 1981; *Droits Humains: Enseignement et Recherche*: Colloque de la FIUC, Salzburg, 1981; *Facultés de Médecine et Universités Catholiques*: Colloque de la FIUC, Lille, 1981; *Crise Economique et mutation des valeurs*: 8èmes Journées Européennes, Cergy-Pontoise, 1983; *Les Mouvements de la Paix*: Symposium organisé par la FIUC et le Club de Rome, Salzburg, 1983; *L'Université Catholique et la recherche d'un nouvel ordre international*: Rapport de la 14ème Assemblée Générale, Toronto, 1983; *Droits de l'Homme, Approche Chrétienne*: FIUC - CCRI - Herder, Rome, 1984; *Le Respect et la Liberté: Droits de l'Homme, Raison et Foi*, par Pierre Daubercies et Charles Lefèvre, FIUC - CCRI - Herder, Rome, 1985; *Les attentes de la Jeunesse et l'Université Catholique*: Rapport de la 15ème Assemblée Générale de Santo Domingo, 1985.

A news bulletin is issued 3 or 4 times a year. Other information publications are also available.

The official languages of the Federation are English, Spanish, and French.

President: Michel Falise, Rector, Fédération Universitaire et Polytechnique de Lille, France.

Secretary-General: Lucien Michaud, S.J.

Permanent Secretariat: 78A, rue de Sèvres, 75341 Paris Cedex 07.

Tel: (1) 4273-3625

Un bulletin de nouvelles brèves paraît 3 ou 4 fois par an. D'autres publications de type informatif sont disponibles.

Les langues officielles de la Fédération sont l'anglais, l'espagnol et le français.

Président: Michel Falise, Recteur, Fédération Universitaire et Polytechnique de Lille.

Secrétaire général: Lucien Michaud, S.J.

Secrétariat Permanent: 78A, rue de Sèvres, 75341 Paris Cedex 07.

Tél: (1) 4273-3625

STANDING CONFERENCE OF RECTORS, PRESIDENTS AND VICE-CHANCELLORS OF THE EUROPEAN UNIVERSITIES

CONFERENCE PERMANENTE DES RECTEURS, PRESIDENTS ET VICE-CHANCELIERS DES UNIVERSITES EUROPEENNES

Associate Member of the International Association of Universities
Membre associé de l'Association internationale des Universités

After the destruction caused by the Second World War resulting in the breakdown of academic links in Europe, an evident need was expressed for the renewal of the international dimension of university life. A first forum of university heads was convened in Cambridge in 1955, under the patronage of H.R.H. the Duke of Edinburgh. In 1959, in Dijon, a second European conference of the same kind agreed to create an association for interuniversity co-operation in Europe, the CRE, whose constitution was finally approved in Göttingen in 1964. In the course of the following general Assemblies (Geneva, 1969; Bologna, 1974; Helsinki, 1979; and Athens, 1984) the number of members increased to some 360 Rectors, Presidents and Vice-Chancellors from more than 20 European countries.

As a non-governmental international organization with its own constitution, dependent solely on its members, the CRE has the unique freedom to develop an institutional concept of the university as a place where knowledge is both imparted and improved.

Directed by a President, its governing structure includes a seven-member Bureau, a Permanent Committee of ·30 members, and a General Assembly. Through these organs, and as stated in its constitution, the CRE can express opinions and present recommendations to governments and to national, international and supranational organizations. As a non-governmental organization based in Geneva, it is nonetheless subject to Swiss law.

Aims and functions

Its aim is to promote co-operation among European universities. Its vocation is genuinely academic, strictly non-governmental, without

Après les destructions de la Deuxième Guerre Mondiale qui avaient brisé les liens de la culture en Europe, le renouvellement de la dimension internationale de la vie académique était un besoin prioritaire. Pour y répondre, une première rencontre de responsables d'unversities du continent fut organisée à Cambridge en 1955, sous le haut patronage de S.A.R. le Duc d'Edimbourg. En 1959, à Dijon, lors d'une deuxième réunion, les recteurs et vice-chanceliers décidèrent d'institutionaliser leur collaboration retrouvée en créant une association européenne de coopération interuniversitaire, association dont le statut fut approuvé lors d'une troisième assemblée, à Göttingen en 1964. Au fil des Assemblées générales suivantes (Genève, 1969; Bologne, 1974; Helsinki, 1979; et Athènes, 1984) le nombre des membres s'accrut à quelque 360 recteurs, présidents et vice-chanceliers venant de plus de 20 pays européens.

Organisation internationale non gouvernementale ne dépendant que de ses membres, la CRE se veut l'indépendance nécessaire à la promotion de l'Université comme fondement du développement et de la transmission de la connaissance.

Dirigée par un Président, l'association est administrée par un Bureau de sept membres issu d'un Comité Permanent d'une trentaine de personnes, lui responsable devant une Assemblée générale souveraine. Ces structures permettent à la CRE, comme le rappelle son statut, "d'exprimer son avis et de présenter ses recommandations aux gouvernements et aux organismes nationaux, internationaux et supranationaux" qui s'intéressent aux problèmes universitaires. Basée à Genève, l'association n'en est pas moins sujette au Code des obligations suisse.

Buts et fonctions

L'Association désire promouvoir la coopération entre universités européennes. De vocation authentiquement universitaire, strictement non

642

any political or economic restriction or affinity. It is in no way associated with any of the regional groupings to which some European States belong. Its concept of Europe is geographic.

Its functions include the following:
— to *provide a forum* for inter-European discussions and informal meetings;

— to *inform* members and other interested parties about developments in university policy throughout the continent;

— to *reflect* on the role of the university in European society;
— to *represent* the university's point of view to bodies concerned with higher education in Europe.

Its various programmes therefore attempt to identify common interests and problems so that the member Rectors, Presidents and Vice-Chancellors can become aware of the existing possibilities for mutual co-operation between their institutions.

Activities

MEETINGS: the *General Assembly*, open to all members and observers from national and international bodies of interuniversity co-operation, is convened once every five years in order to determine the general policy of the organization and to elect its President and other administrative organs. It can also draw up recommendations on the basis of its deliberations concerning general university policy; other *statutory meetings* include sessions of the Permanent Committee twice a year and of the Bureau every three months; the *biannual conferences*, limited to some hundred members, were introduced in order to promote regular contacts between university executive heads, whose role as such is discussed at each of these conferences in relation to a specific theme of topical interest, e.g., "Rationalization of the university", "Staff mobility", etc.; residential *training seminars*, run annually in conjunction with the OECD Programme for Institutional management in Higher Education (IMHE), are specially designed for small groups of newly appointed executive heads of universities in Europe; *occasional seminars*, organized by CRE on a consultancy basis at the request of national rectors' conferences, examine from an international, comparative point of view those university problems of particular concern to the host-country; *academic seminars*, supported by outside funding, are linked to joint university research projects sponsored by CRE. They aim to evaluate the state of research on university

gouvernementale donc, la CRE est un organisme sans affiliation politique, idéologique ni économique; c'est dire qu'elle ne se rattache à aucun des groupements régionaux dont font partie certains pays européens: sa conception de l'Europe est géographique.

Ses fonctions sont notamment:
— le *maintien d'un forum* où discuter informellement des problèmes de l'Europe universitaire;
— l'*information* des membres d'autres responsables de l'université quant à l'évolution des politiques concernant le monde académique européen;
— la *réflexion* quant au rôle de l'université dans la société européenne;
— la *représentation* du point de vue universitaire auprès des organismes responsables de l'enseignement supérieur en Europe.

Par conséquent, les activités de la CRE portent sur les problèmes d'intérêt commun à ses membres, recteurs, présidents et vice-chanceliers d'université, et définissent les lieux possibles d'une coopération accrue entre leurs établissements.

Activités

REUNIONS: les *Assemblées générales*, ouvertes à tous les membres comme à des observateurs venant d'organismes nationaux et internationaux de collaboration universitaire, sont convoquées tous les cinq ans pour fixer les grandes lignes de la politique de l'organisation, élire son Président et désigner ses organes administratifs. Elles prennent aussi des résolutions tirant parti de discussions sur les problèmes généraux de politique universitaire en Europe; les autres *réunions statutaires* sont celles du Comité permanent, deux fois l'an, et celles du Bureau, tous les trois mois; regroupant une centaine de membres environ, les *conférences semestrielles* permettent l'établissement de contacts réguliers entre dirigeants d'universités qui peuvent y confronter les différentes acceptions de leur mandat par rapport à des thèmes de discussion précis tels que, par exemple, "La rationalisation des universités" ou "La mobilité des enseignants"; projets conjoints de la CRE et du Programme de gestion des établissements d'enseignement supérieur de l'OCDE, les *séminaires de gestion* annuels, de type résidentiel, sont réservés à de petits groupes de dirigeants d'université nouvellement élus et désireux d'approfondir les aspects internationaux de leur tâche; préparés pour les conférences de recteurs nationales qui le demandent, les *séminaires ad hoc* apportent une dimension comparative européenne à l'examen de problèmes particulièrement urgents dans le pays hôte; soutenus par un financement extérieur, les

developments in a particular field of European interest.

PUBLICATIONS: *CRE-Action*, the Association's quarterly bulletin, publishes in particular the proceedings of the various conferences and seminars and presents on a regular basis information obtained from national rectors' conferences. Special issues are also prepared in collaboration with other journals such as the *European Journal of Education*, as well as with specialists in a given area, e.g., distance learning, academic mobility, regional development, etc.; *newsletters* are occasionally sent to members in order to draw their attention to important matters of international university life; the *proceedings* of the General Assemblies are published in book form for general distribution.

RESEARCH PROJECTS: parallel to the ongoing discussions of its regular meetings on the role of the university in European society, CRE supplements the general debate on the desirable profile to be attained by the European system of higher education by encouraging in-depth studies on very specific themes. By making use of the research network of its member institutions, this form of activity reflects the interdisciplinary and international nature of the European academic world.

A *pilot project* has thus been launched to examine the social identity of the European university through the ages and to determine the relevance of past developments for the present. It involves a network of historians, sociologists and political philosophers in some 40 member universities as well as an editorial board; the aim is to produce a series of publications on "The history of the European university".

REPRESENTATION: CRE has consultative status with Unesco (category B), with the United Nations Economic and Social Council (Roster) and has observer status at the Council of Europe (CC-PU, the Regular Conference on University Problems). It is also one of the eight Associate Members of the International Association of Universities and is a member of the Standing Committee of Non-Governmental Organizations (Unesco) in Paris.

Close working relations are moreover maintained with organizations such as the American Council on Education (Washington), the

colloques scientifiques relèvent de projets de recherche interuniversitaire patronnés par la CRE: leur objectif est de faire le bilan, dans des domaines précis, des travaux entrepris sur la raison d'être de l'université en Europe.

PUBLICATIONS: *CRE-Action*, bulletin trimestriel de l'Association, donne le compte rendu des diverses réunions de la Conférence permanente et diffuse les informations internationales fournies par les conférences de recteurs de chaque pays membre. Des numéros spéciaux sont l'occasion de collaborations avec d'autres revues telles que le *European Journal of Education* ou traitent, avec l'aide de spécialistes, de problèmes spécifiques de l'évolution universitaire en Europe, l'enseignement à distance, le développement régional ou la mobilité académique, par exemple; des *aide-mémoires* sont occasionnellement envoyés aux membres pour attirer leur attention sur des points importants du développement de la vie universitaire internationale; les *Actes* des Assemblées générales sont publiés sous forme de livre pour diffusion générale.

PROJETS DE RECHERCHE: pour approfondir la discussion habituellement poursuivie dans ses réunions régulières sur le rôle de l'université dans la société européenne, la CRE patronne des études portant sur des thèmes très précis de l'évolution attendue du système d'enseignement supérieur en Europe. A cet effet, elle s'appuie sur le réseau de recherche représenté par ses membres, utilisant au mieux leur diversité pour appréhender la nature interdisciplinaire et internationale du monde universitaire européen.

Un *projet-pilote* a été lancé pour étudier l'identité sociale de l'université européenne à travers les âges et tirer les enseignements du passé pour le développement actuel de l'institution. A cette recherche collaborent 40 universités-membres par le biais de chercheurs — historiens, sociologues et politologues intéressés par le sujet. Un groupe éditorial coordonne les travaux en vue de la publication d'une "Histoire de l'université en Europe".

REPRÉSENTATION: La CRE jouit du statut consultatif auprès de l'Unesco (Catégorie B), auprès du Conseil économique et social des Nations Unies (Roster) et a le statut d'observateur auprès de la Conférence régulière pour les problèmes universitaires (CC-PU) du Conseil de l'Europe. En outre, elle est l'un des huit membres associés de l'Association internationale des universités (AIU) et participe aux travaux du Comité permanent des organisations non gouvernementales auprès de l'Unesco à Paris.

Des liens étroits existent encore avec des organismes tels que le Conseil américain de l'éducation à Washington, le Centre européen

644

European Centre for Higher Education (CEPES, Bucharest), the European Institute of Education and Social Policy (Paris and Brussels), the Liaison Committee of Rectors' Conferences of Member States of the European Communities (Brussels), the Organization for Economic Co-operation and Development (OECD, Paris), the European Society for Engineering Education (SEFI, Brussels), as well as national bodies in Europe, especially the rectors' conferences.

Special activities

In order to affirm the specific contribution of universities to the development of universities to the development of European society, the CRE—with the support of outside funding agencies—is presently concerned to develop a dialogue with the world of industry, on the one hand, and with universities overseas, on the other.

The links with industry are of two kinds: firstly, the CRE is a member of the Steering Committee of PACE (European Programme of Advanced Continuing Education), which offers courses in advanced technology to specialized industries throughout Europe; these courses are provided by top university departments and transmitted to the firms via satellite. Secondly, in collaboration with the Roundtable of European Industrialists (ERT), the CRE is setting up a European University Forum, whose task will be to promote the European dimension of the interface between the academic community and the world of commerce and industry, particularly with a view to uniting Europe.

Finally, in conjunction with Latin American universities, the CRE is looking into the conditions necessary for the institutional development of the university as an agent of social change. Thanks to the support of bodies such as UNESCO, the European Community and the governments of Portugal and Spain, new forms of transatlantic co-operation are presently being worked out in this context.

Internal organization

CRE's only source of *income* derives from the dues paid in Swiss francs by its members. The subscription rate, which is the same for all members, is fixed by the General Assembly.

The *official languages* used are English and French; either may be spoken at CRE meetings.

A small *secretariat* of three persons, under the responsibility of a Secretary-General, is based in Geneva. It is provided with technical assistance by the University of Geneva.

President: Prof. Alfredo-Carmine Romanzi, Former Rector, University of Genoa.

pour l'enseignement supérieur à Bucarest, l'Institut européen d'éducation et de politique sociale à Paris et Bruxelles, le Comité de Liaison des conférences de recteurs des Etats membres de la Communauté européenne à Bruxelles, l'Organisation de coopération et de développement économiques à Paris, la Société européenne pour la formation des ingénieurs à Bruxelles comme, bien sûr, avec les conférences nationales de recteurs des divers pays européens.

Activités spéciales

Pour affirmer la contribution spécifique de l'université au développement de la société européenne, la CRE, avec l'appui de financements extérieurs importants, développe actuellement le dialogue avec le monde de l'industrie, d'une part, avec des universités d'outre-mer, d'autre part.

Les liens avec l'industrie sont de deux sortes: la CRE est membre du Comité directeur de PACE (le programme européen de formation continue avancée) qui offre des cours de haute technologie à des industries de pointe sur l'ensemble du continent, cours donnés dans les meilleurs centres universitaires et distribués dans les entreprises par satellite. En outre, en collaboration avec la Table ronde des industriels européens (ERT), elle organise un forum européen université-industrie où sera approfondie la dimension européenne de l'interface monde académique/monde économique, particulièrement en fonction de l'unification du continent.

Avec les universités latino-américaines, la CRE examine enfin les conditions nécessaires au développement de l'institution universitaire comme agent de changement social et ébauche à cet effet de nouveaux modes de coopération transatlantique grâce au soutien, notamment, de l'UNESCO, de la Communauté européenne et des gouvernements ibériques.

Organisation interne

Pour la CRE, la seule source régulière de *revenus* est représentée par la cotisation en francs suisses versée par ses membres. Son montant, qui est le même pour tous, est fixé par l'Assemblée générale.

Les *langues officielles* sont le français et l'anglais; dans les réunions, les interventions se font dans l'une de ces deux langues.

Trois personnes, dont un secrétaire général, assurent le *secrétariat* de la CRE. Le bureau bénéficie de l'assistance technique de l'Université de Genève.

Président: Prof. Alfredo-Carmine Romanzi, Ancien Recteur de l'Université de Gênes.

Treasurer: Prof. Marcel Guenin, Former Rector, University of Geneva.
Secretary-General: Dr. Andris Barblan. 10, Conseil Général, 1211 Geneva 4.
Tel: (22) 29-26-44. Fax: (22) 29-28-21. Telex: 428380. Cables: euruni genève

Trésorier: Prof. Marcel Guenin, Ancien Recteur de l'Université de Genève.
Secrétaire général: Dr. Andris Barblan. 10, Conseil Général, 1211 Genève 4.
Tél: (22) 29-26-44. Fax: (22) 29-28-21/ Télex: 428380. Cables: euruni genève

UNION DE UNIVERSIDADES DE AMERICA LATINA (UDUAL)

Associate Member of the International Association of Universities
Membre associé de l'Association internationale des Universités

The Union of Universities of Latin America was created in September 1949 by the First Congress of Universities of Latin America, which took place at Guatemala under the patronage of the Universidad de San Carlos de Guatemala. The Union seeks to aid in the development of university institutions in Latin America; to promote the cultural integration of Latin America; and to provide a documentation centre, a library, and a statistical and higher education planning centre for Latin America. The Union also maintains close relations with international cultural associations and acts as a regional centre for the ideals of world understanding and co-operation.

Membership of the Union is open to institutions of higher education which comply with the definition of a university contained in its by-laws. Other cultural institutions may be admitted to associate membership. In 1986 the Union comprised 155 members in 20 Latin American countries.

The Structure of the Union: The supreme organ of the Union is the General Assembly of member universities which meets every three years. Nine General Assemblies have been held: Guatemala, 1949; Chile, 1953; Argentina, 1959; Colombia, 1963; Peru, 1967; Dominican Republic, 1970; México, 1976 and 1979; and Colombia, 1986. The executive organ of the Union is the Executive Board (Consejo Ejecutivo) of 9 members (8 Rectors of Latin American universities, and the Secretary-General). When a member of the Board ceases to be the Rector or President of his university, a deputy member takes his place on the Board.

The Secretariat has its permanent headquarters in Mexico City. The General Secretariat has the following departments: Conferences, Statistics, Publications, Center of University Information and Documentation, and library.

Publications: The Union publishes annually a review "*Universidades*", and a quarterly newsletter "*Gaceta UDUAL*". Among its other publications, mention may be made of "*Censo Universitario Latinoamericano 1962–1965*,

L'Union des Universités d'Amérique latine a été créée en septembre 1949 par le Premier Congrès des Universités d'Amérique latine, qui a eu lieu au Guatemala sous le patronage de l'Université de San Carlos du Guatemala. L'Union cherche à contribuer au développement des institutions universitaires d'Amérique latine; à promouvoir l'intégration culturelle de l'Amérique latine; et à mettre à la disposition de l'Amérique latine un centre de documentation, une bibliothèque et un centre de renseignements statistiques et de planification de l'enseignement supérieur. L'Union entretient également d'étroites relations avec des associations internationales culturelles et elle est un centre régional où peuvent s'exprimer les idéaux de compréhension et de coopération internationales.

Peuvent devenir membres de l'Union les établissements d'enseignement supérieur qui répondent à la définition de l'Université contenue dans ses statuts. D'autres organismes culturels peuvent être admis en qualité de membres associés. En 1986, l'Union comptait 155 membres dans 20 pays d'Amérique latine.

Structure de l'Union: L'autorité suprême de l'Union est l'Assemblée générale des universités membres, qui se réunit tous les trois ans. Neuf Assemblées générales ont eu lieu: au Guatemala en 1949, au Chili en 1953, en Argentine en 1959, en Colombie en 1963, au Pérou en 1967, en République Dominicaine en 1970, au Mexique en 1976 et 1979, en Colombie en 1986. L'organe exécutif de l'Union est le Conseil exécutif (Consejo Ejecutivo) composé de neuf membres (huit recteurs d'universités latino-américaines, et le Secrétaire général). Lorsqu'un membre du Conseil n'est plus recteur ou président en fonction de l'université correspondante, un membre suppléant prend sa place au sein du Conseil.

Le Secrétariat a son siège social permanent à Mexico. Le Secrétariat général comprend les départements suivants: Conférences, Statistiques, Publications, Centre d'Information Universitaire et bibliothèque.

Publications: L'Union publie une revue annuellement "*Universidades*", et un bulletin trimestrielle "*Gaceta UDUAL*". Citons notamment, parmi ses autres publications, "*Censo Universitario Latinoamericano 1962–*

1966–1969, 1970, 1971, 1972–1973, 1974–1975, 1976–1977, 1979, 1981, 1983", México. "*Guía de Publicaciones Periódicas de Universidades Latinoamericanas*", México, 1967; "*Legislación Universitaria Latinoamericana (Análisis comparativo)*", México, 1967, "*Legislación Universitaria de América Latina*", México, 1973; "*Primera Conferencia Latinoamericana sobre Planeamiento Universitario*", México, 1970. "*Planeamiento y Universidad en América Latina*", (*Segunda Conferencia Latinoamericana sobre Planeamiento Universitario*), México, 1976. "*La Difusión Cultural y la Extensión Universitaria en el Cambio Social de América Latina*" (*Memoria de la II Conferencia Latinoamericana de Difusión Cultural y Extensión Universitaria*), México, 1976. "*Memoria de la V Asamblea General de la UDUAL*", México, 1969. "*Memoria de la VI Asamblea General de la UDUAL*", México, 1971. "*Memoria de la VII Conferencia de Escuelas de Medicina de América Latina*", México, 1972. "*El Médico que América Latina Necesita*" (*Memoria de la VIII Conferencia de Facultades y Escuelas de Medicina de América Latina*), México, 1974. "*Enseñanza del Derecho y Sociedad en Latinoamérica*" (*Memoria de la V Conferencia de Facultades y Escuelas de Derecho de América Latina*), México, 1975, "*Formación Integral de los Profesionales de la Salud*" (*Memoria de la IX Conferencia de Facultades y Escuelas de Medicina de América Latina*), México, 1977. "*Edificio de la UDUAL*", México, 1976. "*Examen de Una Década: Sociedad y Universidad 1962–1971*", México, 1976. "*Historia de la Unión de Universidades de América Latina a través de los Informes de sus Secretarios Generales a los Consejos Ejecutivos: (IaXX) y a las Asambleas Generales (IaVI)*", México, 1976. "*Economía y Desarrollo en América Latina*", (*Memoria de la VI Conferencia de Facultades y Escuelas de Economia de América Latina*), México, 1977. "*La Legislación Universitaria en la Solución de los Problemas de las Universidades Latinoamericanas*" (*Memoria de la I Conferencia Latinoamericana de Legislación Universitaria*), México, 1977. "*Perspectiva y Responsabilidad de la Universidad en América Latina*" (*Memoria de la VII Asamblea General de la UDUAL*), México, 1977. "*Las Facultades de Derecho en la Política de Desarrollo Latinoamericano*" (*Memoria de la VI Conferencia de Facultades y Escuelas de Derecho de América Latina*), Bogotá, 1977. "*La Práctica Médica y la Formación del Personal de la Salud*" (*Memoria de la X Conferencia de Facultades y Escuelas de Medicina de América Latina*), México, 1978. "*I Conferencia de Asociaciones y Consejos Nacionales y Subregionales de Universidades de América Latina*", México, 1978. "*Seminario sobre Nuevas*

1965, 1966–1969, 1970, 1971, 1972–1973, 1974–1975, 1976–1977, 1979, 1981, 1983", México. "*Guia de Publicaciones Periódicas de Universidades Latinoamericanas*", México, 1967; "*Legislación Universitaria Latinoamericana (Análisis comparativo)*", México, 1967, "*Legislación Universitaria de América Latina*"; México, 1973; "*Primera Conferencia Latinoamericana sobre Planeamiento Universitario*", México, 1970. "*Planeamiento y Universidad en América Latina*" (*Segunda Conferencia Latinoamericana sobre Planeamiento Universitario*), México, 1976. "*La Difusión Cultural y la Extensión Universitaria en el Cambio Social de América Latina*" (*Memoria de la II Conferencia Latinoamericana de Difusión cultural y Extensión Universitaria*), México, 1976. "*Memoria de la V Asamblea General de la UDUAL*", México, 1969. "*Memoria de la VI Asamblea General de la UDUAL*", México, 1971. "*Memoria de la VII Conferencia de Escuelas de Medicina de América Latina*", México, 1972. "*El Médico que América Latina Necesita*" (*Memoria de la VIII Conferencia de Facultades y Escuelas de Medicina de América Latina*), México, 1974. "*Enseñanza del Derecho y Sociedad en Latinoamérica*" (*Memoria de la V Conferencia de Facultades y Escuelas de Derecho de América Latina*), México, 1975, "*Formación Integral de los Profesionales de la Salud*" (*Memoria de la IX Conferencia de Facultades y Escuelas de Medicina de América Latina*), México, 1977. "*Edificio de la UDUAL*", México, 1976. "*Examen de Una Década: Sociedad y Universidad 1962–1971*", Mexico, 1976. "*Historia de la Unión de Universidades de América Latina a través de los Informes de sus Secretarios Generales a los Consejos Ejecutivos: (IaXX) y a las Asambleas Generales (IaVI)*", México, 1976. "*Economía y Desarrollo en América Latina*" (*Memoria de la VI Conferencia de Facultades y Escuelas de Economía de América Latina*), México, 1977. "*La Legislación Universitaria en la Solución de los Problemas de las Universidades Latinoamericanas*" (*Memoria de la I Conferencia Latinoamericana de Legislación Universitaria*), México, 1977. "*Perspectiva y Responsabilidad de la Universidad en América Latina*" (*Memoria de la VII Asamblea General de la UDUAL*), México, 1977. "*Las Facultades de Derecho en la Política de Desarrollo Latinoamericano*" (*Memoria de la VI Conferencia de Facultades y Escuelas de Derecho de América Latina*), Bogotá, 1977. "*La Práctica Médica y la Formación del Personal de la Salud*" (*Memoria de la X Conferencia de Facultades y Escuelas de Medicina de América Latina*), México, 1978. "*II Conferencia de Asociaciones y Consejos Nacionales y Subregionales de Universidades de América Latina*", México, 1978. "*Seminario*

648

Tendencias y Responsabilidades para las Universidades en Latinoamérica (*Unesco-AIU-UDUAL-UNAM*)", México, 1978. "*Unión y Confederación de los Pueblos Hispanoamericanos*", México, 1979. "*De la Universidad y su Problemática*", México, 1980. "*La Problemática de la Educación Universitaria en América Latina*", (*VIII Asamblea General*), México, 1980. "*La Relación entre las Facultades y Escuelas de Medicina y el Estado*", México, 1981. "*Opciones de posgrado en América Latina*", México, 1986. "*Coloquio Mundo Latinoamericano y Mundo de Habla Francesa (UDUAL-AUPELF)*", México, 1986. "*Ideas en Torno de Latinoamérica*", Vol. I y II, México, 1986.

The UDUAL has also edited a series of gramophone records under the auspices of the National University of Mexico. Bearing the general title '*Voz Viva de América Latina*' (Living Voice of Latin America), the series includes records of the messages of former leaders of Latin American thought as well as the voices of distinguished contemporary writers. The first 17 records are devoted to: Benito Juárez, José Marti, Rubén Darío, Pablo Neruda, Miguel Ángel Asturias, César Vallejo, Alejo Carpentier, Juan Carlos Onetti, Julio Cortázar, Gabriel Garcia Márquez, Manuel Rojas, Mario Vargas Llosa, Jorge Luis Borges, Ernesto Cardenal, Sara de Ibáñez, Augusto Monterroso, and Jorge Zalamea. New editions include "*Teatro Latinoamericano*", Luis Cardoza y Aragón, Faustino Sarmiento, José Lezama Lima, Léon de Greiff, Simón Bolívar, Julio Herrera y Reissig, Pedro Mir, "*De la Cultura Latinoamericana*", Nicolás Guillén, Carlos Solórzano, Darcy Ribeiro, Mario Benedetti, Concha Méndez, Julieta Campos, Hugo Gutiérrez Vega, Efrén C. del Pozo, Salvador Allende and José Donoso.

The Union has been admitted to consultative relations with Unesco (Category B).

President: Dr. Jorge Carpizo, Rector, Universidad Nacional Autónoma de México.
Secretary-General: Dr. José Luis Soberanes.
Apartado 70232, Ciudad Universitaria, 04510, México, D.F.
Tel: (5) 548-9786. Telex: 1764ll2 uual me

sobre Nuevas Tendencias y Responsabilidades para las Universidades en Latinoamérica (*Unesco-AIU-UDUAL-UNAM*)", México, 1978. "*Unión y Confederación de los Pueblos Hispanoamericanos*", México, 1979. "*De la Universidad y su Problemática*", México, 1980. "*La Problemática de la Educación Universitaria en América Latina*", (*VIII Asamblea General*), México, 1980. "*La Relación entre las Facultades y Escuelas de Medicina y el Estado*", México, 1981. "*Opciones de posgrado en América Latina*", México, 1986. "*Coloquio Mundo Latinoamericano y Mundo de Habla Francesa (UDUAL-AUPELF)*", México, 1986. "*Ideas en Torno de Latinoamérica*", Vol. I y II, México, 1986.

L'UDUAL a également dirigé, sous les auspices de l'Université nationale du Mexique, la parution d'une série de disques intitulés '*Voz Viva de América Latina*' (Voix vivante de l'Amérique latine). Cette série comporte des enregistrements de messages d'anciens dirigeants porte-parole des idéaux en faveur en Amérique latine, et des voix d'écrivains contemporains éminents. Les titres des dix-sept premiers disques sont les suivants: Benito Juárez, José Marti, Rubén Darío, Pablo Neruda, Miguel Angel Asturias, César Vallejo, Alejo Carpentier, Juan Carlos Onetti, Julio Cortázar, Gabriel Garcia Márquez, Manuel Rojas, Mario Vargas Llosa, Jorge Luis Borges, Ernesto Cardenal, Sara de Ibáñez, Augusto Monterroso, and Jorge Zalamea. Les nouvelles éditions comprennent notamment '*Teatro Latinoamericano*', Luis Cardoza y Aragón, Faustino Sarmiento, José Lezama Lima, Léon de Greiff, Simón Bolívar, Julio Herrera y Reissig, Pedro Mir, "*De la Cultura Latinoamericana*", Nicolás Guillén, Carlos Solórzano, Darcy Ribeiro, Mario Benedetti, Concha Méndez, Julieta Campos, Hugo Gutiérrez Vega, Efrén C. del Pozo, Salvador Allende et José Donoso.

L'Union a été admise aux relations consultatives avec l'Unesco (Catégorie B).

Président: Dr. Jorge Carpizo, Recteur, Universidad Nacional Autónoma de México.
Secrétaire général: Dr. José Luis Soberanes.
Apartado 70232, Ciudad Universitaria, 04510, México, D.F.
Tél: (5) 548-9786. Télex: 1764112 uual me

CONFERENCE OF RECTORS OF UNIVERSITIES OF BALKAN COUNTRIES

CONFERENCE DES RECTEURS DES UNIVERSITES DES PAYS BALKANIQUES

The first Conference of Rectors of Universities of Balkan Countries took place in Belgrade from 11 to 14 November 1982, following a recommendation made by the Ninth Conference of National Commissions of Unesco in the Balkan countries.

The purpose is to strengthen co-operation between universities in the region and between them and the Unesco European Centre for Higher Education (CEPES). Its members are the Rectors of Universities and University Institutions in Bulgaria, Greece, Romania, Turkey and Yugoslavia.

The Conference meets every two years. Each decides on the place of the next and appoints an Organizing Committee of which the Rector of the forthcoming host university is Chairman. Host to the First Conference was Professor V.M. Petrović, Rector of the University of Belgrade. Host to the Second, which took place in Sofia from 3 to 7 October 1984, was Professor G. Bliznakov, Rector of the University of Sofia. Host to the Third Conference, which took place in Thessaloniki from 26 to 30 November 1986, was the Rector of the Aristotle University of Thessaloniki. Host to the Fourth Conference, held in 1988 in Bucharest, and Chairman of the Organizing Committee was the Rector of the University of Bucharest.

A la suite d'une recommandation formulée par la neuvième Conférence des Commissions Nationales de l'Unesco dans les pays balkaniques, la première Conférence des Recteurs des Universités des Pays Balkaniques s'est tenue à Belgrade, du 11 au 14 novembre 1982.

L'objet de la Conférence est de renforcer la coopération des universités de la région aussi bien entre elles qu'avec le Centre Européen pour l'Enseignement Supérieur (CEPES) de l'Unesco. Elle se compose des recteurs des universités et des institutions universitaires de Bulgarie, de Grèce, de Roumanie, de Turquie, et de Yougoslavie.

La Conférence se réunit une fois tous les deux ans. A la fin de ses débats, elle décide du lieu de sa prochaine session et désigne un Comité d'Organisation présidé par le recteur de l'université qui doit accueillir cette session. L'hôte de la première Conférence était M. U.M. Petrović, Recteur de l'Université de Belgrade. L'hôte de la deuxième, qui a eu lieu à Sofia du 3 au 7 octobre 1984, a été M. G. Bliznakov, Recteur de l'Université de Sofia. L'hôte de la troisième Conférence, qui a eu lieu á Thessalonique du 26 au 30 novembre 1986, a été le Recteur de l'Université Aristote de Thessalonique. L'hôte de la quatrième Conférence, qui a eu lieu à Bucarest en 1988, a été le Recteur de l'Université de Bucarest qui présidera également son comité d'Organisation.

ASSOCIATION OF CARIBBEAN UNIVERSITIES AND RESEARCH INSTITUTES

ASSOCIATION DES UNIVERSITES ET INSTITUTS DE RECHERCHE DES CARAIBES

The Association was founded in November 1968 at a Conference held at the University of Puerto Rico and attended by heads and representatives of 19 universities and associated organizations from 14 Caribbean countries. The objectives of the Association are to foster contact and collaboration between member universities and institutions: a) through conferences and meetings of a general or specific nature; b) through the circulation of information by means of newsletters, bulletins, and handbooks or directories which contain statistics on enrolment, development plans, staffing (indicating recruitment possibilities), scholarships, admission requirements, building programmes, etc.; c) through collaboration between groups of Research Institutes and professional faculties, such as Medicine, Engineering, Agriculture, Education and Social Sciences; d) through facilitating co-operation and the pooling of institutional resources in research, and otherwise dealing with specific priority problems or areas of concern to promote increased efficiency and to expedite the attainment of results; e) through studies of the systems of higher education in the region through seminars, surveys, research papers and publications; and f) through encouraging the exchange of staff and students, particularly at the graduate level.

The Association now has 50 members in 14 countries.

The Association publishes a journal entitled *The Caribbean Education Bulletin*, which appears in January, May, and September.

President: Dr Jaime Viñas Román, Rector, Universidad "Pedro Henríquez Ureña", Santo Domingo.

Secretary-General: Dr. Thomas Matthews.

P.O. Box 11532, Caparra Heights Station, San Juan, Puerto Rico 00922.

L'Association a été fondée en novembre 1968 lors d'une Conférence tenue à l'Université de Porto-Rico et à laquelle assistaient les chefs et les représentants de 19 universités et organisations associées de 14 pays de la région des Caraïbes. Les objectifs de l'Association sont de promouvoir les contacts et la collaboration entre les universités et les institutions membres: a) en organisant des conférences et réunions de caractère général ou particulier; b) en diffusant des informations au moyen de communiqués, bulletins, annuaires ou répertoires contenant des statistiques sur les effectifs, les plans de développement, le personnel (en indiquant les possibilités de recrutement), les bourses, les conditions d'admission, les programmes de construction, etc.; c) en instaurant la collaboration entre des groupes de personnes travaillant dans des instituts de recherche et des étudiants des facultés, par exemple celles de médecine, des sciences de l'ingénieur, d'agriculture, d'éducation et des sciences sociales; d) en facilitant la coopération et la mise en commun des ressources des institutions en matière de recherche et, d'autre part, en traitant des problèmes ou des difficultés à examiner en priorité, afin de promouvoir un accroissement de l'efficacité et d'aboutir plus rapidement à des résultats; e) en étudiant les systèmes d'enseignement supérieur de la région au moyen de séminaires d'études, de documents relatifs à la recherche, et de publications; et f) en encourageant les échanges de personnel et d'étudiants, particulièrement au niveau des étudiants déjà diplômés.

L'Association compte maintenant 50 membres dans 14 pays.

L'Association publie une revue intitulée *The Caribbean Education Bulletin*, qui paraît en janvier, mai, et septembre.

Président: Dr. Jaime Viñas Román, Recteur, Universidad "Pedro Henríquez Ureña", Santo Domingo.

Secrétaire général: Dr. Thomas Matthews.

P.O. Box 11532, Caparra Heights Station, San Juan, Puerto Rico 00922.

CONFEDERACION UNIVERSITARIA CENTROAMERICANA

Founded in 1948, the Central American University Confederation is composed of the national universities of the following six countries: Costa Rica, El Salvador, Guatemala, Honduras, Nicaragua and Panamá. Its present guiding principles were approved by the twentieth ordinary meeting of CSUCA (Consejo Superior Universitario Centroamericano) and came into force on 1 June 1972. The members are: the University of El Salvador, the University of San Carlos of Guatemala, the National Autonomous University of Honduras, the National Autonomous University of Nicaragua, the University of Costa Rica, the National University of Costa Rica, and the University of Panamá.

The member universities of the Confederation are national and public in character, their educational and administrational autonomy being guaranteed in each country's constitution. Teachers, graduates and students are represented on their governing bodies.

The supreme authority of the Confederation is the Congress, composed of teachers and of students of the member universities. The Congress defines the Confederation's general policy. The Third Congress was held in September 1988, at the University of San Carlos, Guatemala.

The Higher Council is the body responsible for organizing and co-ordinating the Confederation's activities and meets three times a year; it is composed of fourteen members, seven are the Rectors of member universities and the others, the presidents of the national unions of students in each country.

The Secretariat-General is the executive and co-ordinating body. Directed by a Secretary-General who is aided by assistant secretaries and staff specialized in different fields, it carries out a series of different tasks; organization of technical plans for integrating in professional training, creation or modification of regional institutions, co-ordination of meetings of teachers and administrators, exchanges of documents and information, etc.

Within the framework of the Plan for the Regional Integration of Central American Higher Education, adopted in 1961, the Confederation

Fondée en 1948, la Confédération se compose des universités nationales des six pays suivants: Costa Rica, El Salvador, Guatemala, Honduras, Nicaragua et Panamá. Approuvés par la XXe réunion ordinaire du CSUCA (Consejo Superior Universitario Centroamericano), les principes de base sur lesquels elle s'appuie actuellement sont entrés en vigueur depuis le 1er juin 1972. Ses membres sont: l'Université de El Salvador, l'Université San Carlos du Guatemala, l'Université nationale autonome du Honduras, l'Université nationale autonome du Nicaragua, l'Université du Costa Rica, l'Université nationale du Costa Rica, et l'Université de Panamá.

Les universités membres de la Confédération sont nationales et de caractère public, les constitutions politiques des pays respectifs leur garantissant un régime d'autonomie, tant en matière d'enseignement que d'administration. Professeurs, diplômés et etudiants sont représentés au sein de leurs organes de gestion.

L'autorité suprême de la Confédération est le Congrés, formé à parts égales des professeurs et des étudiants des universités membres. Le Congrés décide de la politique générale de la Confédération. Le troisiéme Congrés a en lieu en septembre 1988, à l'Université de San Carlos, Guatemala.

Le Conseil supérieur est l'organe chargé de la programmation et de la coordination des activités de la Confédération et se réunit trois fois par an; il se compose de quatorze membres, dont sept sont des recteurs des universités membres et les autres sont présidents des unions nationales d'étudiants de chacun des pays.

Le Secrétariat général est l'organe d'exécution et de coordination. Sous la direction du Secrétaire général et avec l'aide des secrétaires adjoints et d'un ensemble de fonctionnaires spécialisés dans différents domaines, il accomplit une série de tâches diverses: organisation de plans techniques d'intégration au niveau des carrières professionnelles, création ou modification d'écoles regionales, coordination de réunions de professeurs et de fonctionnaires, échanges de documents et d'informations, etc.

Dans le cadre du Plan d'intégration régionale de l'enseignement supérieur centroaméricain, souscrit en 1961, la Confédération a favorisé la

has encouraged the creation of regional institutions. These are at a high academic level, serve the whole region and have been set up in the context of the needs of Central America. Duplication of effort and wastage of resources are thus avoided.

The Secretariat has recently been reorganized. Its present structure is as follows: The *Programa de Apoyo Docente* (Programme of teaching support) organizes courses, seminars and teaching specially to strengthen the systems of university postgraduate studies.

The Central American University Publishing House (EDUCA), founded in 1969, has initiated the systematic publication of books in the region and found suitable methods of distribution. It publishes books for students, cultural, reference, historical, literary and scientific works and has already published 200 titles with a total of 1,000,000 copies. It is located at the headquarters of the Secretariat-General.

The *Programa de Investigaciones* (Research Programme) supports and co-ordinates the research carried out by university research groups. It includes the following programmes: politics and strategies at State level; the family and living conditions; the power and participation of society; systems of production, distribution and consumption.

The *Unidad de Información, Planes y Programas* (Unit of Information, Planning and Programme) administers the system of internal information, and has undertaken the construction of a regional university network with the purpose of scientific information exchanges.

A Secretariat for student affairs is responsible for strengthening relations between the permanent agencies of the Confederation and the National Unions of Students, the Federation of University Students of Central America and international student organizations in general.

Publications: *Estudios Sociales Centroamericanos* (Quarterly); *Cuadernos de Investigación* (monthly); *Estadísticas Universitarias* (biannually).
President: Dr. Humberto López, Rector, Universidad Nacional Autónoma de Nicaragua.

Secretary-General: Dr. Rodrigo Fernández Vázquez.
Ciudad Universitaria "Rodrigo Facio", San José, Costa Rica.
Tel: 25-27-44. Telex: 3011 cosuca cr

création d'écoles régionales, centres de haut niveau académique au service de toute la région, et créés en fonction des besoins de l'Amérique centrale. Ainsi sont évités la duplication des efforts et le gaspillage des fonds.

Le Secrétariat général a été réorganisé récemment. Sa structure est à présent la suivante: Le *Programa de Apoyo Docente* (Programme de soutien de l'enseignement) organise des cours, séminaires et enseignements spécialement destinés à renforcer les systèmes d'études postgraduées des universités.

La Maison d'édition universitaire centroaméricaine (EDUCA), fondée en 1969, a institué pour la première fois la publication systématique de livres dans la région et a trouvé les instruments adéquats pour leur diffusion. Elle publie des livres à l'usage des étudiants, des ouvrages de culture et d'information générales, historiques, littéraires, scientifiques; son fonds d'édition dépasse 200 titres et totalise environ un million d'exemplaires. Son siège est situé au Secrétariat général.

Le *Programa de Investigaciones* (Programme de recherches) soutient et coordonne les recherches qu'effectuent les équipes de chercheurs des universités. Il comprend les programmes suivants: politiques et stratégies au niveau de l'Etat; famille et conditions de vie; pouvoir et participation de la société; systèmes de production, de distribution et de consommation.

L'*Unidad de Información, Planes y Programas* (Unité de l'Information, des Plans et des Programmes) administre le système d'information interne, et a entrepris la constitution d'un réseau universitaire régional en vue d'établir des échanges d'informations scientifiques.

Un Secrétariat annexe pour les affaires estudiantines a pour mission de veiller au renforcement des relations entre les organes permanents de la Confédération et les Unions nationales d'étudiants, la Fédération des étudiants des universités d'Amérique centrale et, en général, les organisations internationales d'étudiants.

Publications: *Estudios Sociales Centroamericanos* (trimestrielle); *Cuadernos de Investigación* (mensuelle); *Estadísticas Universitarias* (deux fois par an).
Président: Dr. Humberto López, Rector, Universidad Nacional Autónoma de Nicaragua.

Secrétaire général: Dr. Rodrigo Fernández Vázquez.
Ciudad Universitaria "Rodrigo Facio", San José, Costa Rica.
Tél: 25-27-44. Télex: 3011 cosuca cr

CONFERENCE OF THE SCANDINAVIAN RECTORS
CONFERENCE DES RECTEURS SCANDINAVES

In 1948 the Rector of the University of Copenhagen invited the rectors of the Scandinavian (Norwegian, Swedish, Danish and Finnish) universities to a meeting in Copenhagen to discuss questions of common interest and, in particular, the possibility of extending Scandinavian cooperation in matters concerning the universities. The initiative thus taken by the University of Copenhagen met with great interest, and it was decided to continue holding the meetings.

In 1972, a meeting of the rectors of the Scandinavian universities was held in Uppsala, Sweden. Only as from 1981 have there been regular meetings: in Aarhus, Denmark, in 1981 with the themes "The Scandinavian University Co-operation" and "The Recruitment of Researchers in the Scandinavian Countries"; in Oulu, Finland, in 1983 with the theme: "The University and the Region"; and in Lund, Sweden, in 1985 with the theme: "Balance Within the University"; and in Bergen, Norway, in 1988 with three themes: 1) Governing of Universities; 2) Nordic Universities and the EEC; and 3) Nordic Universities and the Third World". The next meeting will take place in Denmark in 1991.

The co-operation of the rectors of the Scandinavian universities has thus been provided with a more fixed framework, i.e., the rectors meet approximately every three years and contact meetings are held every 1½ years, in which the chairmen of the conference of rectors in the respective countries participate. In addition, the Conference of the Scandinavian Rectors has contact with the University in Iceland as well as with the Academy of the Faroe Islands.

Chairman (1988–1991): Prof. Ove Nathan, Rector, University of Copenhagen.
Secretariat: Danish Rectors' Conference.
Secretary-General: Ellen Hansen.
Frederiksholms Kanal 26, DK-1220 København K.
Tel: (1) 925-403. Fax: (1) 925-302. Telex: 16243 educ dk

En 1948, le Recteur de l'Université de Copenhague a invité les recteurs des universités scandinaves (norvégiennes, suédoises, danoises et finlandaises) à se réunir à Copenhague afin de débattre des questions d'intérêt commun et, en particulier, de la possibilité d'élargir la coopération scandinave en matière universitaire. L'initiative de l'Université de Copenhague fut accueillie avec un intérêt vif et il fut décidé de continuer à tenir de semblables réunions.

En 1972, une réunion des recteurs scandinaves s'est tenue à Uppsala, Suède. C'est seulement depuis 1981 que sont organisées des réunions périodiques, par exemple à Aarhus, Danemark, en 1981 avec pour thèmes "La coopération scandinave dans le domaine universitaire" et "Le recrutement de chercheurs dans les pays scandinaves"; à Oulu, Finlande, en 1983 sur le thème de "L'Université et la région"; à Lund, Suède, en 1985 sur le thème "L'équilibre au sein de l'Université"; et à Bergen, Norvège, en 1988 sur les thèmes: 1) Les administration de l'Université; 2) Les universités nordiques et le C.E.E.; et 3) Les universités nordiques et le tiers monde". La prochaine réunion aura lieu au Danemark en 1991.

La coopération des recteurs scandinaves se déroule ainsi dans le cadre d'une structure mieux définie: ils se réunissent environ tous les trois ans et des réunions de maintien des contacts se tiennent tous les dix-huit mois, auxquelles participent les présidents des Conférences de recteurs des pays respectifs. En outre, la Conférence des recteurs scandinaves a des contacts avec l'Université islandaise et avec l'Académie des Iles Féroé.

Président: (198–1991): Prof. Ove Nathan, Recteur de l'Université de Copenhague.
Le secretariat: Le Secretariat de la Conference des Recteurs Danoises.
Secrétaire général: Ellen Hansen.
Frederiksholms Kanal 26, DK-1220 København K.
Tél: (1) 925-403. Fax: (1) 925-302. Télex: 16243 educ dk

ORGANIZACION DE UNIVERSIDADES CATOLICAS DE AMERICA LATINA (ODUCAL)

ODUCAL was founded at Santiago de Chile with the first Constitutive Assembly, 7–12 September 1953. It was approved by Project No. 487/53 of the Sacred Congregation of Seminaries and Universities (Rome) on 25 November 1953.

The purpose of the organization is to promote the activities of Catholic higher education in Latin America, to assist in the cultural development of that region of the world, and to participate in educational progress. Its membership includes 24 Catholic universities in Argentina, Brazil, Chile, Colombia, Dominican Republic, Ecuador, Mexico, Nicaragua, Paraguay, Peru, Puerto Rico, and Venezuela.

Its Executive Board consists of a President, two Vice-Presidents and two Counsellors, who are Rectors of universities, and a Secretary-General.

ODUCAL held its first Congress and its second Assembly at the Catholic University of Chile, immediately following its Constituent Assembly; its second Congress and third Assembly at the Catholic University of Peru, from 12 to 17 September 1959; its third Congress and fourth Assembly at the Catholic University of Puerto Rico, Ciudad de Ponce, from 24 to 29 August 1963. Its fifth Assembly was held in Rio de Janeiro on 11 and 12 July 1971; its sixth Congress and seventh Assembly at Rio de Janeiro; its seventh Congress and eighth Assembly at Petropolis the 17 July 1973; its eighth Congress and ninth Assembly at Bogotá, from 12 to 14 July 1976; its ninth Congress and tenth Assembly at Valparaíso, from 19 to 21 March 1979; its tenth Congress and eleventh Assembly at San Miguel de Tucumán, from 13 to 15 May 1981; its eleventh Congress and twelfth Assembly at Santiago de los Caballeros, Dominican Republic, from 4 to 6 May 1983; its twelfth Congress and thirteenth Assembly at the Pontifical Catholic University "Santa María de los Buenos Aires", from 9 to 11 May 1985; its thirteenth Congress and fourteenth Assembly at the Universidad "Santo Tomás de Aquino", Bogotá, from 26 to 30 April 1988.

Publications: *Anuario; Sapientia; Universitas.*

L'ODUCAL a été fondée à Santiago du Chili, sa première Assemblée constitutive ayant eu lieu du 7 au 12 septembre 1953. Elle a été approuvée par le Projet n° 487/53 de la Sacrée Congrégation des Séminaires et des Universités (Rome), en date du 25 novembre 1953.

L'objet de l'organisation est de promouvoir les activités de l'enseignement supérieur catholique en Amérique latine, de soutenir le développement culturel de cette région du monde et de participer au progrès de l'éducation. Elle compte parmi ses membres 35 universités catholiques situées dans les pays suivants: Argentine, Bolivie, Brésil, Chili, Colombie, Equateur, Méxique, Nicaragua, Panamá, Paraguay, Pérou, Porto-Rico, République Dominicaine, Uruguay et Venezuela.

Son Conseil exécutif se compose d'un Président, de deux Vice-Présidents et de deux Conseillers Recteurs d'université; ainsi que d'un Secrétaire général.

L'ODUCAL a réuni son premier Congrès et sa deuxième Assemblée à l'Université catholique du Chili, immédiatement après l'Assemblée constitutive; son deuxième Congrès et sa troisième Assemblée à l'Université catholique du Pérou, du 12 au 17 septembre 1959; son troisième Congrès et sa quatrième Assemblée à l'Université catholique de Porto-Rico, Ciudad de Ponce, du 24 au 29 août 1963. Sa cinquième Assemblée s'est tenue à Rio de Janeiro les 11 et 12 juillet 1971; son sixième Congrès et sa septième Assemblée à Rio de Janeiro; son septième Congrès et sa huitième Assemblée à Petropolis le 17 juillet 1973; son huitième Congrès et sa neuvième Assemblée à Bogotá du 12 au 14 juillet 1976; son neuvième Congrès et sa dixième Assemblée à Valparaíso du 19 au 21 mars 1979; son dixième Congrès et sa onzième Assemblée à San Miguel de Tucumán du 13 au 15 mai 1981; son onzième Congrès et sa douzième Assemblée à Santiago de los Caballeros, République dominicaine, du 4 au 6 mai 1983; son douzième Congrès et sa treizième Assemblée à l'Université pontificale catholique "Santa María de los Buenos Aires", du 9 au 11 mai 1985; son treizième Congrès et sa quatorzième Assemblée à l'Université "Santo Tomás de Aquino", Bogotá, du 26 au 30 avril 1988.

Publications: *Anuario; Sapientia; Universitas.*

President: Dr. Anibal S. Fósbery, Rector, Universidad del Norte "Santo Tomás de Aquino", San Miguel de Tucumán (Argentina).
Tél: (81) 22-8805

Président: Dr. Anibal S. Fósbery, Recteur de la Universidad del Norte "Santo Tomás de Aquino", San Miguel de Tucumán (Argentine).
Tél: (81) 22-8805

STANDING CONFERENCE ON UNIVERSITY PROBLEMS
(Council of Europe)

CONFERENCE REGULIERE SUR LES PROBLEMES UNIVERSITAIRES
(Conseil de l'Europe)

The Standing Conference (CC-PU) was set up in 1978 by the Committee of Ministers of the Council of Europe (1) with the following specific terms of reference: to organize or encourage co-operation among European nations in the field of higher education and research; to promote relations among European universities and institutions of higher education and research.

The CC-PU groups together senior officials from Ministries of Education and academic representatives. It has observers from Yugoslavia and from European and international organizations working in this field. Its activities which are part of the Council of Europe's cultural programme under the European Cultural Convention, can be divided into three parts:

University policy
The aims of this part of the programme are to furnish Ministries of Education and academic authorities with studies and analyses relevant to their major concerns. Current topics include: the involvement of universities in adult and continuing education; university-industry relations in non-science fields; university and human rights; and new technologies, etc.

Academic mobility
The aim of this activity is to contribute towards the freedom of movement between institutions of

La Conférence régulière (CC-PU) créée en 1978 sur décision du Comité des Ministres du Conseil de l'Europe (2) a pour mandat: d'assurer ou de favoriser la coopération entre les nations européennes dans le domaine de l'enseignement supérieur et de la recherche; de promouvoir les relations entre les universités et les établissements d'enseignement supérieur et de la recherche.

La CC-PU regroupe des hauts fonctionnaires des Ministères de l'Education et des représentants des universités. Des observateurs de Yougoslavie ainsi que des organisations européennes et internationales oeuvrant dans ce domaine sont invités aux sessions de la CC-PU. Ses activités, qui font partie du programme culturel du Conseil de l'Europe dans le cadre de la Convention Culturelle Européenne, peuvent être divisées en trois volets:

Politique universitaire
Cette partie du programme a pour but de fournir aux Ministères de l'Education et aux responsables universitaires des études et des analyses répondant à leurs préoccupations principales. Parmi les sujets actuellement à l'étude figurent: l'université et la formation continue des adultes; les relations université-industrie en dehors des domaines scientifiques; l'université et les droits de l'homme; et les nouvelles technologies, etc.

Mobilité universitaire
Il s'agit ici de contribuer à la mobilité des étudiants, professeurs et chercheurs des établis-

---

(1) 24 member states: the 21 member states of the Council of Europe: Austria, Belgium, Cyprus, Denmark, Federal Republic of Germany, France, Greece, Iceland, Ireland, Italy, Liechtenstein, Luxembourg, Malta, Netherlands, Norway, Portugal, Spain, Sweden, Switzerland, Turkey, United Kingdom, as well as Finland, San Marino and the Holy See.

(2) 24 Etats membres: les 21 Etats membres du Conseil de l'Europe: Autriche, Belgique, Chypre, Danemark, Espagne, République Fédérale d'Allemagne, France, Grèce, Irlande, Italie, Liechtenstein, Luxembourg, Malte, Pays-Bas, Norvège, Portugal, Suède, Suisse, Turquie, Royaume-Uni, ainsi que Finalnde, Saint-Marin et Saint-Siège.

higher education and/or research by improving mobility information and by reducing legal, administrative and financial obstacles. Questions related to the mobility of students, academic teachers and researchers are considered.

European interuniversity co-operation

The main objective of this priority part of the programme is to encourage European institutions of higher education and research to co-operate in the improvement of postgraduate curricula by a continuous adjustment of training programmes. It is implemented through the organization of European intensive courses and/or European workshops. Participants in both activities are university teachers, postgraduate students, researchers and representatives of relevant professional branches.

The European Workshops aim at identifying areas where curriculum developments are needed and making recommendations for action at the European level.

The aim of the European Intensive Course is to implement new specialized training programmes in the framework of European interuniversity co-operation. Priority sectors have been identified in both natural (especially environmental) sciences and the humanities and social sciences.

The promotion of regional university co-operation is also under study.

Secretariat: Higher Education and Research Division, Council of Europe, 67006 Strasbourg Cedex (France).
Tel: 8861-4961. Telex: 870943. Cables: europa strasbourg

sements d'enseignement supérieur et/ou de recherche en améliorant l'information dans ce domaine et en aplannissant les obstacles d'ordre juridique, administratif et financier. Des questions relatives à la mobilité des étudiants, des enseignants et des chercheurs sont considérées.

Coopération interuniversitaire européenne

Cette partie prioritaire a essentiellement pour objet d'encourager les établissements européens d'enseignement supérieur et de recherche à coopérer pour améliorer les programmes de formation des étudiants diplômés (3e cycle) par une adaptation continue des programmes. Elle est mise en oeuvre par l'organisation de cours intensifs européens et/ou d'ateliers européens. Ces deux activités s'adressent aux professeurs d'université, aux étudiants diplômés (3e cycle), aux chercheurs et représentants des secteurs professionnels concernés.

Les ateliers européens ont pour objet d'identifier les domaines appelant des innovations en matière de programmes d'enseignement et de formation et de proposer des actions au niveau européen.

Les cours intensifs européens ont pour but la mise en oeuvre, dans le cadre d'une coopération interuniversitaire européenne, de nouveaux programmes de formation spécialisée. Des secteurs prioritaires ont été identifiés dans les sciences naturelles (notamment de l'environnement) ainsi que les sciences humaines et sociales.

La promotion de la coopération interuniversitaire transfrontière au niveau régional est également étudiée.

Secrétariat: Division de l'Enseignement supérieur et de la Recherche, Conseil de l'Europe, 67006 Strasbourg Cedex (France).
Tél: 8861-4961. Télex: 870943. Cables: europa strasbourg

WORLD ASSOCIATION FOR EDUCATIONAL RESEARCH
ASSOCIATION MONDIALE DES SCIENCES DE L'EDUCATION

The Association was founded at Gent in 1953 by Professors R.L. Plancke and R. Verbist. Its statutes were ratified in Oslo in 1961. The present title was adopted in Gent in 1977.

The aim of this non-profit Association is to foster the development, on an international level, of research in the field of education. It shall pursue this aim by the organization of international congresses, by the publication of scientific works or by the promotion of such publications, by exchange of information among its members or with third parties such as Unesco, by establishing centres of liaison, as well as by any other appropriate lawful means. Regular membership of the Association shall be open to those carrying out research in education at university level and to those qualified for appointment to carry out such research.

The General Assembly meets at least every four years. There are at present members in 49 countries. The Council of the Association is composed of a minimum of 20 members and a maximum of 30 members elected by the General Assembly.

President: Prof. A. de la Orden.

Permanent General Secretariat: Prof. Dr. M.-L. van Herreweghe, Rijksuniversiteit Gent, Pedagogisch Laboratorium, Henri Dunantlaan 1, 9000 Gent (Belgium).
Tel: (91) 254100

L'Association a été fondée à Gand en 1953 par les professeurs R.L. Plancke et R. Verbist. Ses statuts ont été ratifiés à Oslo en 1961. Sa dénomination actuelle a été adoptée à Gand en 1977.

L'Association, qui est dénuée de tout esprit de lucre, a pour objet de favoriser, sur le plan international, les recherches scientifiques dans le domaine des sciences de l'éducation. Elle poursuit cet objet par l'organisation de congrès internationaux, par l'édition ou l'encouragement de publications scientifiques, par l'échange d'informations entre ses membres ou avec des tiers tels que l'Unesco, par l'établissement de centres de contacts, ainsi que par tous autres moyens légaux appropriés. Peuvent être membres titulaires de l'Association: tout chercheur en science de l'éducation au niveau universitaire et tous ceux qui sont qualifiés à prendre une responsabilité dans une équipe de recherche.

L'Assemblée générale se réunit au moins tous les quatre ans. L'Association compte actuellement des membres dans 49 pays. Le Conseil de l'Association se compose au minimum de 20 membres et au maximum de 30 membres élus par l'Assemblée générale.

Président: Prof. Dr. A. de la Orden.

Secrétariat général permanent: Prof. Dr. M.-L. van Herreweghe, Rijksuniversiteit Gent, Pedagogisch Laboratorium, Henri Dunantlaan 1, 9000 Gand (Belgique).
Tél: (91) 254100

INTERNATIONAL ASSOCIATION FOR EDUCATIONAL AND VOCATIONAL INFORMATION (IAEVI)
ASSOCIATION INTERNATIONALE D'INFORMATION SCOLAIRE, UNIVERSITAIRE ET PROFESSIONNELLE (AIISUP)

Founded in 1956, IAEVI brings together organizations which, at the national or international level, endeavour to establish and disseminate information helpful to students of secondary and higher education in making an informed choice of profession.

The aims of IAEVI are based fundamentally on providing information to be used either directly or by the intermediary of national information and vocational services. Making use of the documentation collected by both public and private bodies and of statistics compiled by specialized agencies, it endeavours to help the public in presenting this information in a concise form.

To achieve this aim, IAEVI assures co-operation between all the national organizations concerned with making available to students and to the general public information on the choice of studies and careers, and encourages the establishment of similar bodies in countries where no initiative of this kind has yet been taken.

Making use of regular contacts between experts, it prepares a comparison between the methods employed in informing young people and their families of the facts and of the problems set by the choice of studies and of profession.

IAEVI is a consultative member of Unesco, category B, and of the UN. It is included on the special lists of the International Labour Office and of the International Bureau of Education.

Publications: *Informations universitaires et professionnelles internationales*: bi-monthly; and a collection: *Etudes et Rapports*.
President: L. Todorov.
20, rue de l'Estrapade, 75005 Paris.
Tel: (1) 4354-1027

Fondée en 1956, l'AIISUP groupe les organisations qui, dans les différents pays ou sur le plan international, se proposent d'établir et de diffuser une documentation susceptible de permettre aux élèves et étudiants de l'enseignement du second degré et de l'enseignement supérieur de décider de leur orientation en connaissance de cause.

L'AIISUP se définit essentiellement par une mission d'information auprès des utilisateurs, soit directement, soit par l'entremise des services nationaux d'information et d'orientation. Utilisant la documentation rassemblée tant par les organismes publics que privés, et les statistiques élaborées par les organismes spécialisés, elle se propose de toucher le public en présentant ces informations sous des formes simples.

Pour atteindre ce but, l'AIISUP assure une coopération entre tous les organismes nationaux préoccupés d'informer les usagers, l'enseignement et le public en général sur le choix des études et des carrières, et favorise la création d'organismes analogues dans les pays où aucun effort n'a encore été tenté en ce sens.

Elle procède, par des contacts réguliers entre les spécialistes, à la comparaison des méthodes qui sont employées pour informer la jeunesse et les familles des problèmes que pose le choix des études et de la profession.

L'AIISUP est membre consultatif de l'Unesco, catégorie B, et de l'ONU. Elle est inscrite sur la liste spéciale du Bureau international du Travail ainsi que du Bureau international de l'Education.

Publications: *Informations universitaires et professionnelles internationales*: bulletin bimestriel; et une collection: *Etudes et Rapports*.
Président: L. Todorov.
20, rue de l'Estrapade, 75005 Paris.
Tél: (1) 4354-1027

INTERNATIONAL COUNCIL FOR EDUCATIONAL DEVELOPMENT (ICED)

The Council (ICED) was established in October 1970 as an international and independent association of persons with a common concern for the future of education and its role in social and economic development.

ICED's major interests are strategies for educational development and the modernization and management of higher education. In each area it seeks to identify and analyse major educational problems shared by a number of countries, to make policy recommendations, and to consult, on request, with international and national organizations, both public and private.

ICED has examined the international dimension of higher education through a series of comparative studies: access to higher education in Western Germany and in the United States, with a comparison of problems in France, Canada, Sweden and the United Kingdom; a twelve-nation study on the design and management of systems of higher education; and a series of conferences and papers on the interrelated problems of youth, education, and employment.

The access study was made possible by a grant from the Volkswagen Foundation. The systems study was supported by a grant from the Krupp Foundation. The study on youth, education, and employment was supported by the Carnegie Corporation and the Carnegie Council on Policy Studies in Higher Education, and involves a variety of other agencies.

In the field of education for development, ICED works with international, binational, and national agencies, with universities and research groups, and with individual experts to analyse and recommend ways to strengthen education. While it is concerned with all levels of education, to date it has emphasized strategies to provide instruction outside of formal institutions. ICED has completed two studies on non-formal

Le Conseil international pour le Développement de l'Education (ICED) a été créée en octobre 1970 en tant qu'organisation internationale et indépendante réunissant des membres qui se préoccupent de l'avenir de l'éducation et de son rôle dans le développement économique et social.

Les principaux centres d'intérêt de l'ICED sont: les stratégies du développement de l'éducation; la modernisation et l'administration de l'enseignement supérieur. Il cherche dans chaque domaine à déterminer et à analyser les principaux problèmes d'enseignement communs à de nombreux pays, à formuler des recommandations en matière de politique éducative et à consulter, quand elles le demandent, les organisations nationales et internationales, qu'elles soient publiques ou privées.

L'ICED a étudié l'enseignement supérieur au niveau international dans une série d'études comparatives: l'accès à l'enseignement supérieur en République fédérale d'Allemagne et aux Etats-Unis, qui comporte des éléments de comparaison avec les problèmes tels qu'ils se posent en France, au Canada, en Suède et au Royaume-Uni: une étude portant sur douze pays et traitant de la conception et de l'administration des systèmes d'enseignement supérieur; et enfin une série de conférences et d'exposés sur les problèmes communs de la jeunesse, de l'enseignement et de l'emploi.

L'étude sur l'accès à l'enseignement a été menée à bien grâce à une subvention de la Fondation Volkswagen. L'étude sur les systèmes d'enseignement a été financée par une subvention de la Fondation Krupp. L'étude sur la jeunesse, l'enseignement et l'emploi a été financée par la Carnegie Corporation et le Carnegie Council on Policy Studies in Higher Education; divers autres organismes y ont participé.

Dans le domaine de la formation en vue du développement, l'ICED travaille en coopération avec des organismes internationaux, binationaux, avec des universités et des groupes de recherche, et avec des experts pour analyser les problèmes et formuler des recommandations sur les moyens de promouvoir l'éducation. Tout en s'occupant de tous les niveaux d'enseignement, l'ICED a jusqu'ici mis l'accent sur les stratégies

education—one for the World Bank and the second for Unicef. The World Bank study deals with out-of-school training programmes for adults and older adolescents—which can both train them for employment and improve productivity in rural areas. The Unicef study focuses on non-informal educational approaches to training youth to develop skills in functional literacy and numeracy, agricultural and non-agricultural occupations, home-making, child-rearing, health and nutrition.

ICED has now turned its efforts to a new project: finding new educational means for improving the quality of family life among the rural poor in developing countries.

A two-year study on Higher Education for Development linked ICED's two major areas of concern. It was sponsored by twelve international and national agencies that provide aid to education in developing countries. Teams of highly qualified educators in Africa, Asia and Latin America examined different ways in which higher education copes with such social concerns as public health, rural development, food, population, employment, and education and training at all levels. They examined some twenty-five innovative programmes and, in their final reports, suggested ways to spread their success or to avoid their pitfalls.

ICED as an institution has been generously supported by the Ford Foundation, the Exxon Foundation, the Charles E. Culpeper Foundation and the Johnson Foundation. Supporting grants beginning in 1970 have provided flexible funds for both institutional needs and exploratory studies, and supplementary funds for programmes supported by other agencies.

Publications: *A Global Approach to Higher Education* (Ladislav Cerych); *Higher Education: From Autonomy to Systems* (edited by James A. Perkins and Barbara Baird Israel); *Higher Education for National Development: One Model for Technical Assistance* (Kenneth W. Thompson); *The Structure of Higher Education: A World View* (Eric Ashby); *Higher Education in*

destinées à promouvoir l'enseignement en marge des institutions traditionnelles. L'ICED a achevé deux études sur l'enseignement extra-scolaire— la première pour la Banque mondiale et la seconde pour l'Unicef. L'étude effectuée à la requête de la Banque mondiale porte sur les programmes de formation extra-scolaire organisés à l'intention des adultes et des adolescents les plus âgés, et qui peuvent à la fois les former en vue d'un emploi et améliorer la productivité dans les régions rurales.

L'étude réalisée sur la demande de l'Unicef est axée sur les méthodes d'éducation extra-scolaires employées pour développer les connaissances des jeunes en matière d'alphabétisation fonctionnelle et de numération, de tâches agricoles et autres, d'économie domestique, de puériculture, de santé et de nutrition.

L'ICED axe maintenant ses efforts sur un nouveau projet, visant à trouver de nouveaux moyens d'enseignement pour améliorer la qualité de la vie familiale des paysans pauvres des pays en voie de développement.

Les deux objectifs principaux de l'ICED sont combinés dans une étude sur l'enseignement supérieur pour le développement, qui a duré deux ans. L'étude a été patronnée par douze organismes, internationaux et nationaux, octroyant aux pays en voie de développement une aide en matière d'éducation. Des équipes d'enseignants hautement qualifiés d'Afrique, d'Asie, et d'Amérique latine ont examiné comment l'enseignement supérieur contribue à la solution de problèmes sociaux tels que la santé publique, le développement rural, l'alimentation, la démographie, l'emploi et l'enseignement, et la formation à tous les niveaux. Ils ont étudié quelque vingt-cinq programmes novateurs et ont, dans leurs rapports finaux, suggéré des mesures visant à propager leur succès et à remédier à leurs défauts.

L'ICED reçoit, en tant qu'institution, un généreux soutien de la Fondation Ford, la Fondation Exxon, la Fondation Charles E. Culpeper et de la Fondation Johnson. Depuis 1970 des subventions accordées dans des conditions très souples ont pu être affectées soit aux besoins de l'institution soit à des études exploratoires. Des crédits de complément ont également été accordés pour des programmes subventionnés par d'autres organismes.

Publications: *A Global Approach to Higher Education* (Ladislav Cerych); *Higher Education: From Autonomy to Systems* (sous la direction de James A. Perkins et Barbara Baird Israel); *Higher Education for National Development: One Model for Technical Assistance* (Kenneth W. Thompson); *The Structure of Higher Education: A World View* (Eric Ashby); *Higher Education in*

Latin America: Current and Future (Alfonso Ocampo Londoño); *Is the University an Agent for Social Reform?* (James A. Perkins); *Seven Everyday Collisions in American Higher Education* (Harlan Cleveland); *Higher Education in Eastern Europe* (Jan Szczepanski); *Internationalizing Higher Education: A United States Approach* (Francis X. Sutton, F. Champion Ward, James A. Perkins and Bertil Östergren); *Higher Education in Developing Countries—A Select Bibliography* (Philip G. Altbach and David H. Kelly); *New Paths to Learning for Rural Children and Youth* (Philip H. Coombs); *Attacking Rural Poverty; How Non-Formal Education Can Help* (Philip H. Coombs, Manzoor Ahmed); *Education for Rural Development: Case Studies for Planners* (Manzoor Ahmed and Philip H. Coombs); *Higher Education and Social Change: Promising Experiments in Developing Countries, Volume I—Reports* (Kenneth W. Thompson and Barbara R. Fogel)—*Volume II—Case Studies* (Kenneth W. Thompson, Barbara R. Fogel and Helen E. Danner); *International Programs of U.S. Colleges and Universities: Priorities for the Seventies* (James A. Perkins); *Some Thoughts on Higher Education* (Soedjatmoko); *Systems of Higher Education: Australia* (Bruce Williams), *Canada* (Edward Sheffield, Duncan Campbell, Jeffrey Holmes, B.B. Kymlicka, and James Whitelaw), *France* (Alain Bienaymé), *Federal Republic of Germany* (Hansgert Peisert), *Iran* (M. Reza Vaghefi and Abdol Hossein Samii), *Japan* (Katsuya Narita), *Mexico* (Alfonso Rangel Guerra), *Poland* (Jan Szczepanski), *Sweden* (Bertil Östergren and Rune Premfors), *Thailand* (Sippanondha Ketudat), *United Kingdom* (Anthony R. Becher, Jack Embling, and Maurice Kogan), *United States* (Lyman A. Glenny, David D. Henry, and John R. Shea); *Cross-Country Topical Papers* (Howard R. Bowen, Burton R. Clark, Clark Kerr, Brian MacArthur, and John D. Millett); *Final Report* (Nell P. Eurich and James A. Perkins); *Recent Student Flows in Higher Education* (Ignace Hecquet, Christiane Verniers, and Ladislav Cerych); *Barriers to Higher Education in the Federal Republic of Germany* (Willi Becker); *Admissions to Medical Education in Ten Countries* (Barbara B. Burn, editor); *Admission to Higher Education in the United States: A German Critique* (Ulrich Teichler); *Innovations in Access to Higher Education: Ontario, Canada; England and Wales; and Sweden* (Robert M. Pike, Naomi E.S. McIntosh, and Urban Dahllöf); *Access Policy and Procedure and the Law in U.S. Higher Education* (Jenne K. Britell, William B. Schrader, Alice J. Irby, Simon V. Keochakian, and Larry Simon); *Access to Higher Education: Two Perspectives. A Comparative Study of the Federal*

Latin America: Current and Future (Alfonso Ocampo Londoño); *Is the University an Agent for Social Reform?* (James A. Perkins); *Seven Everyday Collisions in American Higher Education* (Harlan Cleveland); *Higher Education in Eastern Europe* (Jan Szczepanski); *Internationalizing Higher Education: A United States Approach* (Francis X. Sutton, F. Champion Ward, James A. Perkins et Bertil Östergren); *Higher Education in Developing Countries—A Select Bibliography* (Philip G. Altbach et David H. Kelly); *New Paths to Learning for Rural Children and Youth* (Philip H. Coombs); *Attacking Rural Poverty; How Non-Formal Education Can Help* (Philip H. Coombs, Manzoor Ahmed); *Education for Rural Development: Case Studies for Planners* (Manzoor Ahmed et Philip H. Coombs); *Higher Education and Social Change: Promising Experiments in Developing Countries, Volume I—Reports* (Kenneth W. Thompson et Barbara R. Fogel)—*Volume II—Case Studies* (Kenneth W. Thompson, Barbara R. Fogel et Helen E. Danner); *International Programs of U.S. Colleges and Universities: Priorities for the Seventies* (James A. Perkins); *Some Thoughts on Higher Education* (Soedjatmoko); *Systems of Higher Education: Australie* (Bruce Williams), *Canada* (Edward Sheffield, Duncan Campbell, Jeffrey Holmes, B.B. Kymlicka, et James Whitelaw), *France* (Alain Bienaymé), *République fédérale d'Allemagne* (Hansgert Peisert), *Iran* (M. Reza Vaghefi et Abdol Hossein Samii), *Japon* (Katsuya Narita), *Mexique* (Alfonso Rangel Guerra), *Pologne* (Jan Szczepanski), *Suède* (Bertil Östergren et Rune Premfors), *Thaïlande* (Sippanondha Ketudat), *Royaume-Uni* (Anthony R. Becher, Jack Embling, et Maurice Kogan), *Etats-Unis* (Lyman A. Glenny, David D. Henry, et John R. Shea); *Cross-Country Topical Papers* (Howard R. Bowen, Burton R. Clark, Clark Kerr, Brian MacArthur, et John D. Millett); *Final Report* (Nell P. Eurich et James A. Perkins); *Recent Student Flows in Higher Education* (Ignace Hecquet, Christiane Verniers, et Ladislav Cerych); *Barriers to Higher Education in the Federal Republic of Germany* (Willi Becker); *Admissions to Medical Education in Ten Countries* (Barbara B. Burn, éditeur); *Admission to Higher Education in the United States: A German Critique* (Ulrich Teichler); *Innovations in Access to Higher Education: Ontario, Canada; England and Wales; and Sweden* (Robert M. Pike, Naomi E.S. McIntosh, et Urban Dahllöf); *Access Policy and Procedure and the Law in U.S. Higher Education* (Jenne K. Britell, William B. Schrader, Alice J. Irby, Simon V. Keochakian, et Larry Simon); *Access to Higher Education: Two Perspectives. A Comparative Study of the Federal Republic of*

Republic of Germany and the United States of America (Final Report of the German—U.S. Study Group); *Design for Change: Higher Education in the Service of Developing Countries* (Barbara R. Fogel); *Comparative Higher Education Abroad: Bibliography and Analysis* (Philip G. Altbach); Conference Report: *Federal/State Responsibilities for Post-secondary Education: Australia and the United States* (Barbara B. Burn and Peter Karmel); *The Savar Project: Meeting the Rural Health Crisis in Bangladesh* (Manzoor Ahmed); *BRAC: Building Human Infrastructures to Serve the Rural Poor* (Bangladesh) (Manzoor Ahmed); *Social Work and Research Center: An Integrated Team Approach in India* (Pratima Kale and Philip H. Coombs); *Meeting the Basic Needs of the Rural Poor* (Philip H. Coombs); *The World Crisis in Education: The View from the Eighties* (Philip Coombs); *Perspectives on Comparative Education: A Survey of Research and Literature* (Philip G. Altbäch); *Privatization of Higher Education*; *International Trends and Issues* (Roger L. Geiger).

Chairman and Chief Executive Officer: James A. Perkins.

20 Nassau Street, Princeton, New Jersey 08540.

Tel: (609) 921-2440. Fax: (609) 683-7293

Vice-Chairman: Philip H. Coombs.

P.O. Box 217, Essex, Connecticut 06426.

Germany and the United States of America (Final Report of the German—U.S. Study Group); *Design for Change: Higher Education in the Service of Developing Countries* (Barbara R. Fogel); *Comparative Higher Education Abroad: Bibliography and Analysis* (Philip G. Altbach); Conference Report: *Federal/State Responsibilities for Post-secondary Education: Australia and the United States* (Barbara B. Burn et Peter Karmel); *The Savar Project: Meeting the Rural Health Crisis in Bangladesh* (Manzoor Ahmed); *BRAC: Building Human Infrastructures to Serve the Rural Poor* (Bangladesh) (Manzoor Ahmed); *Social Work and Research Center: An Integrated Team Approach in India* (Pratima Kale et Philip H. Coombs); *Meeting the Basic Needs of the Rural Poor* (Philip H. Coombs); *The World Crisis in education: The View from the Eighties* (Philip Coombs); *Perspectives on Comparative Education: A Survey of Research and Literature* (Philip G. Altbäch); *Privatization of Higher Education*; *International Trends and Issues* (Roger L. Geiger).

Président et Directeur exécutif: James A. Perkins.

20 Nassau Street, Princeton, New Jersey 08540.

Tél: (609) 921-2440. Fax: (609) 683-7293

Vice-Président: Philip H. Coombs.

P.O. Box 217, Essex, Connecticut 06426.

INTERNATIONAL ASSOCIATION OF UNIVERSITY PROFESSORS AND LECTURERS (IAUPL)

ASSOCIATION INTERNATIONALE DES PROFESSEURS ET MAITRES DE CONFERENCES DES UNIVERSITES

The Association gradually took shape by the amalgamation in 1944 of two sources: the movement towards co-operation among university personnel, expressed in the International University Conference inaugurated by the Association of University Teachers (U.K.) in 1934, and the activities and discussions of university teachers and research workers who were temporary inhabitants of Great Britain during the last World War, who, with some British colleagues, formed themselves into the Association of Professors and Lecturers of the Allied Countries in Great Britain.

IAUPL is a democratically constituted federal organization of the separate national associations of university teachers, and in some cases of the separate associations of teachers in single universities, who thereby collaborate in the international sphere. IAUPL comprises affiliated associations and individual members representing a total membership of some 60,000 university teachers. These are in Austria, Belgium, Denmark, Eire, Federal Republic of Germany, France, Finland, India, Israel, Italy, Lebanon, Madagascar, Malta, Mexico, Netherlands, South Africa, Switzerland, United Kingdom, Venezuela, and Yugoslavia. Each of the affiliated associations retains its identity and autonomy. The individual members are recruited where national, university, or college staff associations do not yet exist. It also has correspondents in countries where there are no affiliated associations.

The broad aims of IAUPL are the development of academic fraternity among university teachers of the various countries across national and faculty boundaries; the protection of the independence and freedom of teaching and research; the furtherance of the interests of university teachers; and the consideration of academic problems, whether initiated by the Association itself or referred to it by governments

L'Association a pris progressivement forme à la suite de la fusion en 1944 de deux mouvements: le mouvement de coopération du personnel des universités qui trouva son expression dans la Conférence universitaire internationale organisée par l'Association des enseignants des universités (Royaume-Uni) en 1934; et les activités et débats des enseignants et chercheurs universitaires qui résidèrent temporairement en Grande-Bretagne pendant la dernière guerre mondiale et se constituèrent, avec quelques collègues britanniques, en Association des Professeurs et Maîtres de Conférences des Pays alliés en Grande-Bretagne.

L'IAUPL est une organisation fédérale démocratiquement constituée d'associations nationales d'enseignants universitaires et, dans certains cas, d'associations d'enseignants existant au sein d'universités individuelles, qui collaborent ainsi à l'échelon international. L'IAUPL comprend des associations adhérentes et des membres individuels groupant un ensemble de quelque 60.000 enseignants universitaires des pays suivants: Afrique du Sud, Autriche, Belgique, Danemark, Finlande, France, Inde, Irlande, Israël, Italie, Liban, Madagascar, Malte, Mexique, Pays-Bas, République fédérale d'Allemagne, Royaume-Uni, Suisse, Venezuela, et Yougoslavie. Chacune des associations adhérentes conserve son identité et son autonomie. Les membres individuels sont recrutés là où il n'existe pas encore d'association du personnel à l'échelon national, de l'université, ou du collège. Elle possède des correspondants dans les pays où il n'existe pas d'associations adhérentes.

Les grands objectifs de l'IAUPL sont le développement de la fraternité académique entre enseignants universitaires par-delà les frontières nationales ou de facultés, la sauvegarde de l'indépendance et de la liberté de l'enseignement et de la recherche, la défense des intérêts des enseignants universitaires et l'examen des problèmes universitaires, soit à l'initiative de l'Association elle-même, soit à la demande de

or universities or by Unesco.

IAUPL is a non-governmental, non-political, non-sectarian body. It is recognized as holding consultative status by Unesco, and by other United Nations organizations. It works in friendly co-operation with similar organizations in other fields of university work and life.

Its academic programme has consisted of: the scheme for the establishment of an International Universities Bureau, 1948, and of an International Institute of Social Sciences, 1949; the report on Student Health Services, 1950, on Recurrent Long Leave, 1950; a continuing report on the Equivalences of University Degree Systems, 1948, 1950, 1953; a study on the Exchange of University Personnel, 1953, and their conditions of employment abroad, 1958; continuing reports on Academic Freedom; a comprehensive study of the conditions of Salary, Superannuation and Status of University Teachers in various countries as well as recruitment; an inquiry into the relations between Scientific Research in Universities and in Industry; studies on the recruitment of professors and lecturers to meet university expansion, and the necessity to maintain academic and economic standards; the place of the universities in training for professional and technical careers; university reform; new teaching methods; student participation in administration; training and information for teachers, etc. In 1982, IAUPL adopted a charter of rights and obligations of university teachers (Siena).

These and other topics of interest to all university teachers are discussed at international conferences which, since the war, have been held at Oxford, Brussels, Paris, Basle, Florence, Nice, Amsterdam, Vienna, Munich, Brussels, London, Istanbul, Jerusalem, Haifa, Herceg Novi (Yugoslavia) and Parma (Italy) in September 1972. In September 1965, IAUPL organized its First International Seminar on the Status of University Teachers (Vienna). A Round Table held at Pont-à-Mousson (1979) was on Agressions against the University Today. Between 1978 and 1983 two inquiries and a report (the social assessment of the University) were carried out for Unesco. A Round Table was held in Malta in October 1988 on "International Responsibilities of the University Professor: the Pax Academica".

A "European Liaison Committee", set up in 1973, has held several meetings in Paris, Germany, Brussels, Rotterdam, and London at which problems of particular relevance to

gouvernements, d'universités ou de l'Unesco.

L'IAUPL est un organisme non gouvernemental, non politique et non confessionnel. Elle bénéficie du statut consultatif auprès de l'Unesco et d'autres institutions des Nations Unies. Elle entretient une collaboration amicale avec les organisations analogues se consacrant à d'autres aspects du travail et de la vie universitaires.

Son œuvre proprement académique se compose comme suit: plan d'établissement d'un Bureau international des Universités, 1948, et d'un Institut international des Sciences sociales, 1949; rapport sur les services de santé universitaires, 1950, et sur le long congé périodique, 1950; rapport suivi sur les équivalences des systèmes de grades universitaires, 1948, 1950, 1953; étude sur l'échange de personnel universitaire, 1953, et sur les conditions d'emploi de ce personnel à l'étranger, 1958; rapports suivis sur la liberté académique; étude sur le traitement, la retraite et le statut des enseignants universitaires dans différents pays ainsi que sur le recrutement; enquête sur les relations entre la recherche scientifique à l'université et dans l'industrie; études sur le recrutement des professeurs et maîtres de conférences en fonction de l'expansion des universités et sur la nécessité du maintien de leurs niveaux académique et économique; enfin sur le rôle des universités dans la formation aux carrières libérales et techniques; réformes des universités; nouvelles méthodes pédagogiques; participation des étudiants à la gestion; formation et information des enseignants, etc. En 1982, l'IAUPL a adopté une Charte des droits et devoirs des enseignants universitaires (Sienne).

Ces sujets et d'autres d'intérêt commun à tous les enseignants universitaires sont débattus à des conférences internationales, tenues, depuis la guerre, à Oxford, Bruxelles, Paris, Bâle, Florence, Nice, Amsterdam, Vienne, Munich, Bruxelles, Londres, Istanboul, Jérusalem, Haïfa, Herceg Novi (Yougoslavie), et Parme (Italie) en septembre 1972. En septembre 1965, l'IAUPL a organisé le Premier Séminaire international sur la Condition de l'Enseignant universitaire (Vienne). Une Table Ronde de Pont-à-Mousson (1979) portait sur Les agressions contre l'Université d'aujourd'hui. Entre 1978 et 1983 deux enquêtes et un rapport (le bilan social de l'Université) ont été réalisés pour l'Unesco. Une Table Ronde s'est tenue du Malte en octobre 1988 sur le thème "Les responsabilités internationales du Professeur d'Université: la Pax Academica".

Depuis 1973 fonctionne un "Comité de Liaison Européen" dont plusieurs réunions à Paris, en Allemagne, à Bruxelles, à Rotterdam, et à Londres ont traité de problèmes plus spéciale-

666

Europe have been discussed with the collaboration of European organizations (Council of Europe, EEC).

Structure of the Association: Final authority rests in the Central Council, consisting of the representatives of the constituent national associations; the Executive Committee has 11 members, of whom 9 are elected by the Council and one is co-opted to ensure a more balanced geographical representation.

Periodical Publication: *Communication*.

Documentation Centre: University Library of Nancy (France).

President (1984–): R. Motmans.

Secretary-General: L.P. Laprévote.

18, rue du Docteur Roux, 75015 Paris.

 Tel: (1) 4783-3165

ment européens avec la collaboration d'organisations européennes (Conseil de l'Europe, CEE).

Structure de l'Association: L'autorité suprême est détenue par le Conseil central, composé de représentants désignés par les associations nationales adhérentes; le Comité exécutif compte 11 membres, dont 9 sont élus par le Conseil et un coopté en vue d'assurer une représentation géographique mieux équilibrée.

Publication périodique: *Communication*.

Centre de Documentation: Bibliothèque Universitaire de Nancy (France).

Président (1984–): R. Motmans.

Secrétaire général: L.P. Laprévote.

18, rue du Docteur Roux, 75015 Paris.

 Tel: (1) 4783-3165

NORDIC ASSOCIATION OF UNIVERSITY ADMINISTRATORS
ASSOCIATION NORDIQUE DES ADMINISTRATEURS D'UNIVERSITE

In 1976 administrators from universities and other institutions of higher education in Denmark, Finland, Norway and Sweden gathered for their first Scandinavian session in Røros, Norway. The need for a Nordic association had made itself felt over the years of attending the OECD and IMHE meetings. The Nordic administrators have always, to their great benefit, attended these meetings. The Scandinavian traditions, however, differ so much in many respects that a more specific association was called for. The Nordic Association of University Administrators was an immediate success, and to-day the association comprises members from Denmark, the Faroe Islands, Finland, Greenland, Iceland, Norway, and Sweden. About sixty universities and institutions of higher education are represented.

The structure of the association is centred round the annual sessions. Biannually, the sessions are also directors' meetings at which the plans for the following two-year period are discussed. The first two-year plan started in 1982, comprising a series of working groups to be set up. The first was on budget planning (1982); in 1983 groups on students counselling and on electronic data processing were started. 1985 saw the appearance of three additional groups: equivalence and transference of exams and degrees; administrative staff development; equipment and buildings.

The Nordic Association of University Administrators is in close contact with other Nordic associations on a university level and with international organizations, primarily OECD, IMHE, AIR, and IAU.

The Steering Committee consists of eight members who are directors of their respective Universities.
Chairman: Stig Møller, Director, Aarhus University.

Les administrateurs des universités et autres institutions d'enseignement supérieur du Danemark, de Finlande, de Norvège et de Suède ont tenu leur première réunion scandinave commune à Røros, Norvège, en 1976. La nécessité d'une Association nordique se faisait sentir au fil des ans, en raison de l'assistance aux réunions de l'OCDE et de l'IMHE, qui s'est toujours révélée très profitable pour les administrateurs nordiques. Le caractère nettement distinct des traditions scandinaves incitait à la création d'une association plus spécifique. L'Association nordique des administrateurs d'université a immédiatement été couronnée de succès; elle comprend aujourd'hui près de soixante membres, qui sont des universités et des institutions d'enseignement supérieur du Danemark, des Iles Féroé, de Finlande, du Groenland, d'Islande, de Norvège et de Suède.

La structure de l'Association repose sur les réunions annuelles. En outre, tous les deux ans, des réunions de directeurs sont organisées auxquelles on discute des plans et projets pour les deux prochaines années. Le premier plan biennal, qui a débuté en 1982, prévoyait la création d'une série de groupes de travail, le premier devant être celui de la planification budgétaire; les groupes s'occupant de l'orientation des étudiants et du traitement électronique de l'information ont été institués en 1983. Trois nouveaux groupes ont été créés en 1985: équivalence et reconnaissance d'examens et de diplômes; perfectionnement du personnel administratif; matériel et locaux.

L'Association nordique des administrateurs d'université est en relations étroites avec d'autres associations nordiques de niveau universitaire, ainsi qu'avec des organisations internationales (principalement l'OCDE, l'IMHE, l'AIR, et l'AIU).

Le Comité exécutif comprend huit membres, exerçant les fonctions de directeur dans les huit universités concernées.
Président: Stig Møller, Directeur de l'Université d'Aarhus.

Vice-Chairman: Roger Broo, Director, Aabo Academy, (Finland).

Secretariat: c/o Aarhus University, Administrationen, Ndr. Ringgade 1, 8000 Aarhus C (Denmark).
Tel: (6) 134311

Vice-président: Roger Broo, Directeur de l'Académie d'Aabo (Finlande).

Secrétariat: c/o Aarhus Universitet, Administrationen, Ndr. Ringgade 1, 8000 Aarhus C (Danemark).
Tel: (6) 134311

INTERNATIONAL FEDERATION OF UNIVERSITY WOMEN (IFUW)
FEDERATION INTERNATIONALE DES FEMMES DIPLOMEES DES UNIVERSITES (FIFDU)

The Federation is a worldwide organization of women who have had a university education. Membership is open to all qualified university women through National Associations which are affiliated in 50 countries: Argentina, Australia, Austria, Bangladesh, Belgium, Bolivia, Brazil, Canada, Costa Rica, Denmark, Egypt, El Salvador, Fiji, Finland, France, Germany (Federal Republic), Ghana, Great Britain, Greece, Hong Kong, Iceland, India, Indonesia, Ireland, Israel, Italy, Japan, Kenya, Korea, Lebanon, Luxemburg, Mexico, Netherlands, New Zealand, Nigeria, Norway, Pakistan, Peru, Philippines, Sierra Leone, South Africa, Spain, Sri Lanka, Sweden, Switzerland, Thailand, Turkey, U.S.A., Uruguay, Zimbabwe, with a total membership of approximately 200,000.

The aim of the Federation is to promote understanding and friendship among the university women of the world, irrespective of their race, nationality, religion or political opinions; to encourage international co-operation; to further the development of education; to represent university women in international organizations; and to encourage the full application of their knowledge and skills to the problems which arise at all levels of public life, whether local, national, regional or worldwide, and to encourage their participation in the solving of these problems. The Federation offers members research fellowships and an organization for combined action to improve the status of women in all respects and for study of some of the larger issues in the world today.

The work of the Federation is planned by a Conference of delegates of the national associations. The Conference meets every three years. Between Conferences there are meetings of the Council and of international Standing Committees responsible for special activities. The international headquarters office in Geneva acts as a co-ordination centre.

La Fédération est une organisation mondiale de femmes de formation universitaire. Peuvent y participer toutes les femmes universitaires qualifiées, par l'intermédiaire des sections nationales adhérentes qui se sont constituées dans 50 pays: Afrique du Sud, Allemagne (République fédérale), Argentine, Australie, Autriche, Bangladesh, Belgique, Bolivie, Brésil, Canada, Corée, Costa Rica, Danemark, Egypte, El Salvador, Espagne, Etats-Unis d'Amérique, Fidji, Finlande, France, Ghana, Grande-Bretagne, Grèce, Hong-Kong, Inde, Indonésie, Irlande, Islande, Israël, Italie, Japon, Kenya, Liban, Luxembourg, Mexique, Nigeria, Norvège, Nouvelle-Zélande, Pakistan, Pays-Bas, Pérou, Philippines, Sierra-Leone, Sri Lanka, Suède, Suisse, Thaïlande, Turquie, Uruguay, Zimbabwe — et groupent près de 200.000 membres.

L'objet de la Fédération est d'assurer l'entente et d'encourager l'amitié entre les femmes diplômées du monde entier, sans distinction de race, de nationalité, de religion, ou d'opinions politiques; de promouvoir l'esprit de coopération internationale; de favoriser le développement de l'enseignement; de représenter les femmes diplômées auprès des organisations internationales; et de les encourager à mettre tout leur savoir et leurs talents au service de l'étude des problèmes qui se posent à tous les niveaux de la vie publique, dans leurs communautés locales, nationales, régionales ou mondiale et encourager leur participation à la solution de ces problèmes. La Fédération offre à ses membres des bourses de recherche et un cadre d'action commune pour l'amélioration à tous égards du statut de la femme et pour l'étude de quelques-uns des plus grands problèmes du monde d'aujourd'hui.

Les tâches de la Fédération sont fixées par un Congrès des déléguées des associations nationales. Le Congrès se réunit tous les trois ans. Entre les Congrès il y a des réunions du Conseil et des Commissions permanentes internationales chargées de certaines activités spéciales. Le siège international de Genève joue le rôle de centre de coordination.

Periodical Publications: *Newsletter* (annually); *Communiqué* (1–2 times a year).

President (1986–89): Dr. Ritva-Liisa Karvetti (Finland).

Executive Secretary: Dorothy Davies.

37, Quai Wilson, 1201 Geneva.

  Tel: (22) 31-23-80

Publications périodiques: *Lettre de Nouvelles* (annuelle); et *Communiqué* (1–2 fois par an).

Présidente (1986–89): Dr. Ritva-Liisa Karvetti (Finlande).

Secrétaire générale: Dorothy Davies.

37, Quai Wilson, 1201 Genève.

  Tél: (22) 31-23-80

WORLD UNIVERSITY SERVICE (WUS)
ENTRAIDE UNIVERSITAIRE MONDIALE (EUM)

World University Service, founded in 1920, is an international non-governmental organization composed of a network of national committees all over the world. Its members are mainly staff and students in institutions of higher learning.

WUS believes that it is the poor and under-privileged who are denied justice, freedom and dignity and that these can only be achieved through the development of self-reliance and independence. It strives to involve those with access to higher education in a partnership with the poor and underprivileged to work jointly for social justice, human dignity and freedom.

WUS is involved in solidarity campaigns, literacy projects, community development, scholarship programmes and many others. The aim of each of these is to combat social, political and economic discrimination. The purpose of its assistance is to provide people with the resources, not to relieve but to change their situation.

The policy making body of the organization is the General Assembly of representatives of the national committees which meets once every three years. Each committee has one vote. The General Assembly takes all major policy decisions, reviews programmes and budgets, studies current activities of the Committees, examines future perspectives and elects an 11-member executive committee. This meets every six months and takes decisions during the period between meetings of the General Assembly. The Assembly appoints the General Secretary and executive staff of the International Secretariat in Geneva which is responsible for administering international programmes, for WUS relations with other organizations, and for liaison between the 61 national committees and contacts.

WUS maintains consultative status with several of the United Nations specialized agencies, such as Unesco, ECOSOC.

L'Entraide Universitaire Mondiale, fondée en 1920, est une organisation non gouvernementale internationale composée d'un réseau de comités nationaux partout dans le monde. La plupart des membres sont des enseignants et des étudiants d'institutions postsecondaires. L'EUM pense que ce sont les pauvres et économiquement faibles ne bénéficiant ni de la justice, ni de la liberté, ni de la dignité, qui ont besoin d'assistance et que ce n'est qu'à travers le développement de leur indépendance et de la faculté de ne compter que sur eux qu'ils arriveront à en bénéficier. Elle s'efforce d'engager ceux qui ont accès à l'éducation supérieure à lutter ensemble, en collaboration avec les moins privilégiés, pour la justice sociale, la dignité humaine et la liberté.

L'EUM s'engage dans des campagnes de solidarité, des projets d'alphabétisation, des programmes de développement de la commun-auté, des programmes de bourses et bien d'autres. Le but de chacun de ces programmes est de combattre la discrimination, qu'elle soit sociale, politique ou économique. Son assistance est destinée à aider les personnes en leur donnant les moyens de changer leur situation et non seule-ment de la soulager.

L'organisme responsable définissant la politique de l'EUM est l'Assemblée générale des représentants de chaque comité national qui se réunit tous les trois ans. Chaque comité dispose d'un vote. L'Assemblée générale prend toutes les décisions majeures concernant la politique de l'organisation, examine les programmes et les budgets, s'informe sur les perspectives d'avenir et sur les activités en cours des comités et élit un comité exécutif de onze membres qui se réunit tous les six mois et prend les décisions dans l'intervalle qui sépare les réunions de l'Assemblée. L'Assemblée générale nomme le Secrétaire général et le personnel dirigeant du Secrétariat international de Genève, qui a pour tâche d'administrer les programmes internationaux, d'assurer les relations de l'EUM avec les autres organisations et la liaison avec les 61 comités nationaux et contacts.

L'Entraide Universitaire Mondiale jouit du statut consultatif auprès de plusieurs institutions spécialisées de la famille des Nations Unies, telles que l'Unesco, et l'ECOSOC.

Periodical Publications: *WUS News; Annual Report; Conference and Seminar Reports; Special Studies.*
President: Hugo Miranda.
Treasurer: Caleb Fundanga.
General Secretary: Nigel Hartley.
5, chemin des Iris, 1216 Geneva.
Tel: (22) 98-87-11. Telex: 27273 wus ch.
Cables: interstud geneva

Publications périodiques: *Nouvelles de l'EUM; Rapport annuel; WUS Action; Comptes rendus des conférences et séminaires; Etudes spéciales; Conclusions des recherches.*
Président: Hugo Miranda.
Trésorier: Caleb Fundanga.
Secrétaire général: Nigel Hartley.
5, chemin des Iris, 1216 Genève.
Tél: (22) 98-87-11. Télex: 27273 wus ch.
Cables: interstud geneva

INTERNATIONAL UNION OF STUDENTS (IUS)
UNION INTERNATIONALE DES ETUDIANTS (UIE)

The International Union of Students was founded in August 1946 in Prague, by student organizations of 43 countries at the World Student Congress called by the International Preparatory Committee elected by the London International Students' Conference of November 1945.

Aims: according to the Constitution, as a representative international student organization which defends the rights and interests of students, the IUS shall strive for: peace, détente and disarmament; the right and possibility of all young people to enjoy primary, secondary and higher education; a better standard of education, academic freedom and student rights, the eradication of illiteracy and all forms of discrimination and in particular racial discrimination; the promotion of friendship, mutual understanding and co-operation among the students of the world and the unity of the world student community; the realization of the aspirations of students struggling against colonialism, neo-colonialism, and imperialism and for liberation and national independence and social progress, which are a prerequisite for the full development of education and national culture; the co-operation of students with other sections of the population and the development in students of a sense of responsibility towards society; world peace; international friendship among all peoples and the employment of advances in science and culture for the benefit of humanity.

Membership: The membership is based on the concept of national unions of students. There are two types of membership: full membership and associate membership. Organizations which do not qualify for full or associate membership but which desire to have working relations with the IUS may accept consultative status.

The IUS has 111 member organizations from 107 countries and territories of Europe, Asia, Africa, and Latin America since its 14th Congress which was held in Sofia, Bulgaria, from 11 to 16 April, 1984. The 15th Congress was held in Havana, Cuba, in November 1987.

Governing and Executive Bodies: The highest governing body of the IUS is the Congress, which meets at least once in three years.

L'Union internationale des Etudiants a été fondée en août 1946 à Prague, par les organisations étudiantes de 43 pays, réunies au Congrès mondial des Etudiants. Celui-ci avait été convoqué par le Comité étudiant international tenu à Londres en novembre 1945.

Buts: selon sa constitution d'organisation étudiante internationale représentative, chargée de défendre les droits et intérêts des étudiants, l'UIE déploie son action en faveur des objectifs suivants: paix, détente et désarmement; droit et possibilité pour tous les jeunes gens de bénéficier de l'enseignement primaire, secondaire et supérieur; élévation du niveau de l'enseignement, liberté et droits universitaires sans restriction aucune, élimination de l'analphabétisme et de toute forme de discrimination et en particulier de la discrimination raciale; encouragement de l'amitié, de la compréhension mutuelle, de la coopération entre les étudiants du monde, et de l'unité de la communauté étudiante; réalisation des aspirations des étudiants en lutte contre le néo-colonialisme, le colonialisme et l'impérialisme et pour la libération et l'indépendance nationales et le progrès social, qui sont une condition nécessaire au plein développement de l'enseignement et de la culture nationale; coopération des étudiants avec les autres couches de la population et développement chez eux du sens de leur responsabilité envers la société; paix mondiale; amitié entre tous les peuples et utilisation des progrès de la science et de la culture au profit de l'humanité.

Membres: les membres sont des unions nationales d'étudiants. Il y a deux sortes de membres: les membres titulaires et les membres associés. Les organisations n'appartenant à aucun de ces deux groupes et qui désirent collaborer avec l'UIE peuvent recevoir, si elles le veulent, un statut consultatif spécial.

L'UIE compte 111 organisations membres dans 107 pays et territoires d'Europe, d'Asie, d'Afrique et d'Amérique latine depuis son quatorzième Congrès, qui s'est tenu à Sofia, Bulgarie, du 11 au 16 avril 1984. Le quinzième Congrès s'est tenu à Havane, Cuba, en novembre 1987.

Organismes dirigeants et exécutifs: L'organe directeur suprême de l'UIE est le Congrès qui se réunit au moins une fois tous les trois ans.

The Congress elects amongst its own members the Executive Committee and the Finance Committee. The Executive Committee, which meets at least once a year, carries out the policies, decisions and projects adopted by the Congress.

The practical activities of the Executive Committee are carried out by the Secretariat, elected and mandated by the Congress of the IUS. The IUS Secretariat thus carries on the daily tasks of realizing all Congresses and Executive Committee programmes.

Activities: The IUS, either directly or in co-operation with other student organizations, in pursuit of its aims, organizes international student meetings, conferences and seminars both general and specialized, international student correspondence, a scholarship scheme, student travel and exchange, practical co-operation on a faculty basis, cultural activities and relief campaigns; sending of brigades; the collection of information concerning student problems and its dissemination throughout the world. The IUS activities are aimed at achieving and consolidating the reform and democratization of education, the respect of students' rights and interests; assuring the right to access to education and the struggle of eradication of illiteracy; the support of student struggles for their studying and living conditions and generally for the development of their societies and the establishment of a NIEO; the publication of official periodicals of the IUS; the organization or support of student sport activities; the support and encouragement of student contributions towards the establishment of better international understanding and the preservation of peace; all possible assistance to students of colonial, semi-colonial and dependent countries in support of their struggle for freedom and independence; the maintenance of the closest possible relations with other international organizations, particularly within the UN and Unesco system where it has consultative status; all other activities necessary to further the aims of the IUS; the annual distribution, in the framework of its scholarship scheme, of about 100 scholarships to student organizations.

Various worldwide campaigns are launched by the IUS—the major ones being "Education—a Right, Not a Privilege", "Students for Peace, against Nuclear War", and "Sport for All Students". The IUS activities are enriched by contributions from two specialized bodies: **International Student Travel Bureau** (ISTB) and **The International Student Research Centre** (ISRC), which has established useful contacts of exchange

Le Congrès élit parmi ses membres le Comité exécutif et la Commission des Finances. Le Comité exécutif, qui se réunit au moins une fois par an, se charge de mettre en application l'orientation, les décisions et les projets adoptés par le Congrès.

Les activités pratiques du Comité exécutif sont menées à bien par un Secrétariat—élu et mandaté par le Congrès de l'UIE. Le Secrétariat de l'UIE poursuit ainsi les tâches quotidiennes consistant à réaliser tous les programmes prescrits par les Congrès et les Comités exécutifs.

Activités: L'UIE, pour atteindre ses objectifs, organise directement ou en coopération avec d'autres unions étudiantes des réunions, conférences et séminaires étudiants internationaux présentant un caractère général ou spécialisé; une correspondance entre les étudiants du monde, un système de bourses, des voyages et échanges étudiants, une coopération effective entre les facultés, des activités culturelles et des campagnes d'aide; l'envoi de brigades; la collecte d'informations sur les problèmes étudiants et leur diffusion à travers le monde. Les activités de l'UIE visent à réaliser et à consolider la réforme et la démocratisation de l'éducation, à garantir le respect des droits et des intérêts des étudiants, à assurer le droit d'accès à l'éducation et à lutter pour la suppression de l'analphabétisme, à soutenir les luttes menées par les étudiants pour leurs conditions de vie et d'études et, de façon générale, pour le développement de leurs sociétés et l'instauration d'un nouvel ordre économique international; la publication de revues de l'UIE; des activités sportives qu'elle prépare ou encourage; le soutien et l'encouragement de contributions étudiantes à l'établissement d'une meilleure compréhension internationale et à la sauvegarde de la paix; toute l'assistance possible aux étudiants des pays coloniaux, semi-coloniaux et dépendants, pour les aider à lutter pour la liberté et l'indépendance; le maintien de relations très étroites avec d'autres organisations internationales, particulièrement celles de la famille des Nations Unies et l'Unesco auprès de laquelle l'UIE jouit du statut consultatif; toutes autres activités nécessaires à la promotion des buts de l'UIE; l'allocation annuelle par l'UIE, dans le cadre de son système de bourses, d'environ 100 bourses aux organisations étudiantes.

L'UIE organise diverses campagnes mondiales, dont les principales sont "L'éducation, un droit, et non un privilège", "Les étudiants au service de la Paix, contre la guerre nucléaire", et "Le sport pour tout". Les activités de l'UIE se développent grâce à la contribution de deux organes spécialisés, l'**International Student Travel Bureau** (ISTB) (Bureau international des voyages pour étudiants) et l'**International Student Research**

with a number of national, regional and international centres in almost all continents. These exchange contacts are centred around research and studies in problems of higher education. All library and documentary material is computerized.

Publications: *World Student News* (monthly) in English, French, Spanish, and German; *Democratization of Education* (quarterly) in English, French, and Spanish; *Young Cinema and Theatre* (quarterly) in English and French; and *Secretarial Reports* (monthly) in English, French, and Spanish. Also various regional and other Bulletins.

President: Josef Skála (Czechoslovakia).

General Secretary: Giorgos Michaelidis (Cyprus).

17th November Street, 110 01 Praha 01 (Czechoslovakia).

Tel: 2312812. Telex: 122858 ius prague. Cables: unistud prague

Centre (ISRC) (Centre international étudiant de recherche), qui a établi d'utiles contacts prévoyant l'organisation d'échanges avec un certain nombre de centres nationaux, régionaux et internationaux situés sur presque tous les continents. Ces contacts accompagnés d'échanges portent essentiellement sur la recherche et les études relatives aux problèmes qui se posent en matière d'enseignement supérieur. Tout le matériel de bibliothèque et de documentation est informatisé.

Publications: *Etudiants du monde* (mensuelle) en anglais, en français, en espagnol, et en allemand; *Démocratisation de l'enseignement* (trimestrielle) en anglais, en français et en espagnol; *Jeune Cinéma et Théâtre* (trimestrielle) en anglais et en français; et *Bulletin du Secrétariat* (mensuelle) en anglais, français, et espagnol. Egalement divers bulletins régionaux ou autres.

Président: Josef Skála (Tchécoslovaquie).

Secrétaire général: Giorgos Michaelidis (Chypre).

17th November Street, 110 01 Praha 01 (Tchécoslovaquie).

Tél: 2312812. Télex: 122858 ius prague. Cables: unistud prague

PAX ROMANA

Founded in Fribourg (Switzerland) in 1921 under the name of "Pax Romana—International Secretariat for Catholic Students", the Movement spread rapidly in Europe, then in the Americas, Asia and Africa. At the Assembly which it held in Rome in 1947, the organization abandoned its purely student character, and established two autonomous branches: *a*) Pax Romana—International Movement of Catholic Students; *b*) Pax Romana—International Catholic Movement for Intellectual and Cultural Affairs.

a) The International Movement of Catholic Students aims at awakening and developing the spirit of fraternal understanding between the federations of Catholic Students from different countries; at helping them in their activities and seeing to it that their members receive a sound Christian formation; ensuring the effective Christian presence in the university milieu and participating actively in international fora. The IMCS works within the perspective of transformation of society and the promotion of Human Rights, peace, justice and equality.

Members: 65 national federations in 60 countries.

Structure: The highest organ of the Movement is the Interfederal Assembly composed of two voting delegates from every national federation, which meets once every four years. The Directing Committee and the General Secretariat (in Fribourg) are the two other directing organs of the Movement. There are specialized Sub-Secretariats for the following questions: social formation, engineering students. Regional Secretariats carry out regional programmes of action—Asia: Hong Kong; Latin America: Lima; Europe: Brussels; Africa: Nairobi.
Secretary-General: Etienne Bisimwa.
171, rue de Rennes, 75006 Paris.
 Tel: (1) 4544-7074

b) The Graduate Branch of Pax Romana was constituted as an autonomous branch of the Movement in 1947. This movement aims at bringing together Catholic graduates so that they seek solutions to contemporary problems in keeping with Christian faith and ethics, and at facilitating contact and mutual aid between Catholic intellectuals and their organizations.

Fondé en 1921 à Fribourg (Suisse) sous le nom de "Pax Romana—Secrétariat international des Etudiants catholiques", le mouvement s'est vite propagé en Europe, puis en Amérique, en Asie et en Afrique. A l'Assemblée qu'elle a tenue à Rome en 1947, l'organisation a abandonné son caractère purement estudiantin en créant deux sections autonomes: *a*) Pax Romana—Mouvement International des Etudiants Catholiques; *b*) Pax Romana—Mouvement International des Intellectuels Catholiques.

a) Le *Movement International des Etudiants Catholiques* a pour but d'éveiller et de développer l'esprit de compréhension fraternelle entre les fédérations d'étudiants catholiques des différents pays; de les aider dans leurs activités et de veiller à ce que leurs membres reçoivent une sérieuse formation chrétienne; d'assurer une présence chrétienne efficace dans le milieu universitaire et d'avoir une participation active sur le plan international. Le MIEC travaille dans la perspective de transformation de la société et la promotion des droits de l'homme, de la paix, de la justice et de l'égalité.

Membres: 65 fédérations nationales dans 60 pays.

Structure: L'organe suprême du Mouvement est l'Assemblée interfédérale, composée de deux délégués de chaque fédération nationale, et qui se réunit tous les trois ans. Le Comité directeur et le Secrétariat général (à Fribourg) sont les deux autres organes directeurs du Mouvement. Des sous-secrétariats spécialisés traitent des questions suivantes: formation et action sociales, élèves-ingénieurs. Des secrétariats régionaux exécutent les programmes d'action régionaux: Asie: Hong-Kong; Amérique latine: Lima; Europe: Bruxelles; Afrique: Nairobi.
Secrétaire général: Etienne Bisimwa.
171, rue de Rennes, 75006 Paris.
 Tél: (1) 4544-7074

b) *Pax Romana en tant que Mouvement des intellectuels* a été constitué en 1947 comme branche autonome. Ce Mouvement se propose d'unir les diplômés catholiques dans la recherche des solutions aux problèmes de la vie moderne selon l'esprit de la foi et de la morale chrétienne et de faciliter les relations et l'entr'aide parmi les intellectuels catholiques et leurs organisations.

Members: 60 federations in 50 countries, with groups forming in 12 other countries, 6 professional groups (lawyers; secondary school teachers; scientists; artists; engineers, agriculturalists, economists, and political studies).

Structure: The highest body is the Plenary Assembly which meets once every four years. The Council, which is the executive organ, meets once a year, and is composed of the President, four Vice-Presidents (one for each continent), the Secretary-General and fourteen members elected by the Assembly. There are specialized secretariats for jurists, engineers, scientists, teachers, political questions, and artists. The General Secretariat is at Geneva.

President: William F. Neville.
Secretary-General: Victor P. Karunan.

The organ common to the two movements is the Committee of Pax Romana, composed of the President, the Secretary-General and two members of the Council/Directing Committee of each Movement. The World Congress, organized jointly by both Movements, takes place every six years. The last Congress was held in Fribourg in 1971 on the theme "Liberation of Man".

Regular publications: *Convergence* (published twice a year in two editions, English and French).

37–39, rue de Vermont, Boîte postale 85, 1211 Geneva (Switzerland).

Tel: (22) 33-67-40

Membres: 60 fédérations dans 50 pays; outre des groupes en formation dans 12 autres pays, 6 groupes professionnels (juristes; enseignants secondaires; scientifiques; artistes; ingénieurs, agronomes, cadres économiques et études politiques).

Structure: L'organe suprême est l'Assemblée plénière qui se réunit tous les quatre ans; le Conseil, organe exécutif se réunissant une fois par an, se compose du Président, de quatre Vice-Présidents (un par continent), du Secrétariat général, et de quatorze membres élus par l'Assemblée. Il existe des secrétariats spécialisés pour les juristes, les ingénieurs, les scientifiques, les enseignants, les questions politiques et les artistes. Le Secrétariat général est fixé à Genève.

Président: William F. Neville.
Secrétaire général: Victor P. Karunan.

L'organe commun aux deux Mouvements est le Comité de Pax Romana, composé du Président, du Secrétaire général et de deux membres du Conseil/Comité Directeur de chaque Mouvement. Le Congrès mondial, commun aux deux Mouvements, se tient tous les six ans. Le dernier Congrès, qui s'est tenu à Fribourg en 1971, a eu pour thème "Libération de l'homme".

Publications périodiques: *Convergence* (2 numéros par an) en français et en anglais.

37–39, rue de Vermont, Boîte postale 85, 1211 Genève (Suisse).

Tél: (22) 33-67-40

WORLD STUDENT CHRISTIAN FEDERATION (WSCF)
FEDERATION UNIVERSELLE DES ASSOCIATIONS CHRETIENNES D'ETUDIANTS (FUACE)

Founded in 1895, the WSCF is a federation of national Student Christian Movements, student sections of YMCAs and YWCAs, and denominational student movements. Among its members are students from all Christian confessions, but with a majority of Protestants and Orthodox. Its basic purpose is to form critical participants in the university through study of the biblical message and theology, and through action-oriented projects dealing with contemporary issues. It aims at bringing university movements into communication with one another, and also supports general efforts to serve all students in need, particularly in collaboration with the World University Service. It calls its members to strive for peace, libertation and justice in and among the nations, for the good of the university structure, life and community, for manifestation of the unity of the church, and to prepare themselves to serve as Christian witnesses in the academic world in their nation and throughout the whole world.

The WSCF is made up of movements in more than 100 countries.

The governing body of the WSCF is its General Assembly, which meets every four years, and consists of representatives of all movements. It elects the Executive Committee which is composed of 20 persons, including representatives of each of the six geographical regions of the Federation structure. The Executive Committee or the officers meet at least once a year.

Chairperson: Bishop Poulose Mar Poulose (India).

Co-Secretaries General: Ms. Chris Ledger (Australia); Manuel Quintero (Cuba).

Ecumenical Centre, 5 route des Morillons, 1218 Grand-Saconnex (Geneva).

Tel: (22) 98-89-53. Telex: 23423A oik ch. Cables: fuace

Fondée en 1895, c'est une fédération de mouvements nationaux d'étudiants chrétiens, de sections étudiantes des Unions chrétiennes de Jeunes Gens et de Jeunes Filles et de mouvements confessionnels. Il y a parmi ses membres des protestants et des orthodoxes. Son but essentiel est de former des étudiants d'université doués d'un esprit critique par l'étude du message de la Bible et de la théologie, ainsi que par des projets de caractère concret relatifs aux problèmes contemporains. Elle a pour but de mettre en rapport les mouvements universitaires, tout en soutenant les efforts généraux de secours aux étudiants, notamment en coopération avec l'Entr'aide universitaire mondiale. Elle demande à ses membres de travailler pour la paix, la libération et la justice parmi les nations, pour le bien de l'université, de son organisation, de sa vie et de sa communauté et pour la manifestation de l'unité de l'Eglise; elle prépare ses membres à servir en tant que témoins chrétiens dans le monde universitaire dans leur propre pays et dans le monde entier.

La FUACE se compose des mouvements de plus de 100 pays.

L'organe dirigeant de la FUACE est son Assemblée générale qui se réunit tous les quatre ans, et qui est composée de représentants de tous les mouvements membres. Il élit un Comité exécutif, qui se compose de 20 personnes, parmi lesquelles figurent les représentants de chacune des six régions géographiques couvertes par la Fédération. Le Comité exécutif ou le Bureau se réunissent au moins une fois par an.

Président: Bishop Poulose Mar Poulose (Inde).

Secrétaires généraux conjoints: Ms. Chris Ledger (Australie); Manuel Quintero (Cuba).

Ecumenical Centre, 5 route des Morillons, 1218 Grand-Saconnex (Genève).

Tél: (22) 98-89-53. Télex: 23423A oik ch. Cables: fuace

WORLD UNION OF JEWISH STUDENTS (WUJS)
UNION MONDIALE DES ETUDIANTS JUIFS (UMEJ)

The aims of the Union, since its foundation in 1924, are: to unite the national association of Jewish students in all countries; to represent Jewish students in academic life; to further and protect Jewish student interest and to ensure adequate representation of Jewish student opinion at meetings of international and other organizations; to co-operate with any organization which is concerned to promote the interests of students in general; to strengthen the ties of Jewish students with Israel; to organize activity on behalf of Jewish communities in distress.

Since the beginning of 1957, the activity of WUJS has considerably developed and has met with a large measure of success. Activities have been widely ranged; cultural guidance has been given to its unions; International Seminars, Holiday Schools and Camps have been arranged; students have benefited from exchange and travel schemes; instructive pamphlets and less specialized magazines have been published; consultative status as well as regular contacts both between the affiliated unions themselves and between other national and international bodies have been reinforced. WUJS operates Project Areivim, a unique service programme for Diaspora communities. Forty National Jewish Student Unions from all five continents are affiliated to, and cooperate in the framework of WUJS. In 1968, WUJS established the WUJS, Arad Institute for Post-Graduate Hebrew and Jewish studies, for University graduates interested in investigating the option of settling in Israel.

Every three years WUJS organizes an international Congress, with representation from 40 Jewish Student Unions throughout the world and many international student organizations. Apart from its World Secretariat office in Jerusalem, WUJS maintains its regional offices in Brussels, New York, Mexico City, Sydney, Johannesburg, and Tel Aviv.
During recent years several international educational seminars and conferences have been organized, as well as political activities regarding the cause of Jews in the USSR, Eastern Europe, Ethiopia and Yemen.

Les buts de l'Union, depuis sa création en 1924, sont: d'unir les associations nationales des étudiants juifs dans tous les pays; de représenter les étudiants juifs dans le monde académique; de servir et protéger les intérêts de l'étudiant juif et assurer une représentation adéquate de l'opinion de l'étudiant juif aux réunions des organisations internationales et autres; de collaborer avec toute organisation qui a pour but de servir les intérêts des étudiants en général; de resserrer les liens des étudiants juifs avec l'Israël; d'organiser des activités en faveur des communautés juives dans la détresse.

A partir de 1957, l'activité de l'UMEJ s'est sensiblement développée et a connu un succès considérable. Les activités ont pris une large extension: des séminaires internationaux, des écoles de vacances et des camps ont été organisés; des étudiants ont bénéficié de programmes d'échanges et de voyages; des brochures éducatives et des magazines sur des sujets variés ont été publiés; un statut consultatif a été maintenu à l'ONU et à l'Unesco; des contacts aussi bien entre les unions affiliées elles-mêmes qu'avec d'autres organismes nationaux et internationaux ont été renforcés. L'UMEJ administre le Projet Areivim, un programme de service pour les communautés juives unique en son genre. Quarante unions nationales d'étudiantes juifs des cinq continents sont affiliées et collaborent dans le cadre de l'UMEJ. En 1968, l'UMEJ a créé l'Institut UMEJ/Arad d'études hébraïques et juives de niveau post-gradué, à l'intention des diplômés d'université souhaitant s'enquérir des possibilités de s'installer en Israël.

Tous les trois ans l'UMEJ organise un Congrès international où sont représentées 40 unions nationales d'étudiants juifs dans le monde et de nombreuses organisations internationales étudiants. Outre son Secrétariat international à Jérusalem, l'UMEJ compte des bureaux régionaux à Bruxelles, New York, Mexico, Sydney, Johannesbourg, et Tel Aviv.
Au cours des dernières années plusieurs conférences et séminaires internationaux sur l'éducation ont été organisés; une action politique a également été entreprise en faveur des Juifs en URSS et en Europe de l'Est, en Ethiopie et au Yémen.

680

Publications: "Hofar" (quarterly journal); "WUJS Report" (bimonthly newsletter); "Deadline" (quarterly Ethiopian Jewry newsletter); "In Refusal" (quarterly Soviet Jewry newsletter); "The International Jewish Student Handbook".
Chairperson: Yosef Abramowitz.
Executive Director: Daniel Yossef.
P.O. Box 7914, 91077 Jerusalem.
Tel: (2) 637482. Fax: (2) 224153. Telex: 25615 (att. wujs)

Publications: "Hofar" (revue trimestrielle); "WUJS Report" (bulletin d'information, bimestriel); "Deadline" (bulletin trimestriel de la communanté juive d'Ethiopie); "In Refusal" (bulletin trimestriel de la communauté juive d'Union soviétique); "The International Jewish Student Handbook".
Président: Yosef Abramowitz.
Directeur exécutif: Daniel Yossef.
P.O. Box 7914, 91077 Jérusalem.
Tél: (2) 637482. Fax: (2) 224153. Télex: 25615 (att. wujs)

INTERNATIONAL YOUTH AND STUDENT MOVEMENT FOR THE UNITED NATIONS (ISMUN)

MOUVEMENT INTERNATIONAL DE LA JEUNESSE ET DES ETUDIANTS POUR LES NATIONS UNIES

The International Youth and Student Movement for the United Nations was created in August 1949 and since then developed into one of the main international non-governmental organizations working for the achievement of peace, justice and mutual understanding among peoples. The Movement maintains close links with the World Federation of United Nations Associations (WFUNA) and enjoys consultative status with the Economic and Social Council of the United Nations, Unesco and most of the other Specialized Agencies.

Aims: to work with students and young people for human rights, social equality, national independence, continuous development, for political, economic and cultural equality, and against colonialism and other forms of violation of human rights; and to work with students and young people to promote an informed public and a larger knowledge about the United Nations, its actual meaning and its potentialities. In doing so, ISMUN will encourage a continued critical attitude towards the world organization in order to promote its universality and effectiveness.

ISMUN is the only international student organization devoted exclusively to inspiring youth and students around the world with the principles and ideals of the United Nations and its Specialized Agencies. Thus the Movement concerns itself with all aspects of UN activities: political, social or economic. To reach its goals the Movement encourages the formation of United Nations Youth and Student Associations (UNYSAs) within all universities and other institutes of higher education and carries out a wide variety of activities both on the international and national level.

Members: Membership to the Movement is open to: a) National Youth and Student Associ-

Le Mouvement international de la Jeunesse et des Etudiants pour les Nations Unies fut créé au moins d'août 1949; depuis lors, il est devenu l'une des principales organisations internationales non gouvernementales travaillant pour la réalisation de la paix, de la justice et de la compréhension mutuelle entre les peuples. Le Mouvement garde des relations très étroites avec la Fédération Mondiale des Associations pour les Nations Unies (FMANU) et jouit du statut consultatif auprès du Conseil économique et social des Nations Unies, de l'Unesco et de la plupart des autres institutions spécialisées.

Objectifs: œuvrer, avec les étudiants et les jeunes en général, pour la défense des droits de l'homme, l'égalité sociale, l'indépendance nationale, le développement permanent, l'égalité politique, économique et culturelle, et lutter contre le colonialisme et les autres formes de violation des droits de l'homme; travailler avec les étudiants et les jeunes en général à promouvoir au sein du public une information plus complète sur les Nations Unies, sa signification réelle, et ses possibilités. Ce faisant, l'ISMUN favorise l'adoption d'une attitude critique à l'égard de cette organisation internationale afin de promouvoir son universalité et son efficacité.

L'ISMUN est la seule organisation estudiantine internationale qui se consacre exclusivement à faire connaître les principes et les idéaux des Nations Unies et de leurs institutions spécialisées à la jeunesse et aux étudiants dans le monde entier. Ainsi, le Mouvement s'intéresse à tous les aspects des activités des Nations Unies, qu'ils soient d'ordre politique, social ou économique. Pour atteindre son but, le Mouvement encourage la création d'Associations de jeunes et d'étudiants pour les Nations Unies (UNYSAs) dans toutes les universités et autres institutions d'enseignement supérieur et il a des activités très variées aux niveaux international aussi bien que national.

Membres: Peuvent être admises à la qualité de membre du Mouvement a) les Associations

ations for the United Nations, and b) National Unions of Students whose policies are connected with UN aims and not in contradiction with ISMUN general policies. The Movement at present has affiliated organizations in nearly 50 countries with different political, economic and social systems. Also the Youth Sections of Liberation Movements recognized by the United Nations are Associated Members of ISMUN.

Structure: the General Conference, held every eighteen months to two years, lays down the general lines of policy for the Movement, its educational programmes, finances, and external relations. The Conference also discusses its policy on political matters and holds an informal Political Forum for open discussion on one political problem before the UN. The Conference elects the Executive Committee which is composed of 12 members.

The Executive Committee administers the Movement between sessions of the General Conference, implements its decisions and gives guidance to the Secretariat. The Secretariat is directed by the Secretary-General, who is the main administration officer of the Movement.

Programme: a) International: Education about the United Nations System at youth and student level through seminars and study courses, participation in UN and Agency campaigns, preparation and distribution of information material, international exchanges, student campaigns, regional student institutions.

b) National: Seminars, courses, lectures, films, exhibitions, distribution of information on the UN, model sessions, work camps, marking of UN Day and Human Rights Day, political action, campaigns for development.

Publications: Quarterly *Bulletin*; background documents, information kits and working papers.
Secretary-General: Juan Carlos Giacosa.
c/o Palais des Nations, 1211 Geneva 10.
Tel: (22) 33-08-61

nationales de jeunes et d'étudiants pour les Nations Unies, et b) les Unions nationales d'étudiants dont les politiques correspondent aux objectifs des Nations Unies et ne sont pas en contradiction avec les politiques générales de l'ISMUN. Le Mouvement compte actuellement des organisations adhérentes dans près de 50 pays aux systèmes politiques, économiques et sociaux très différents. En outre, les Sections de jeunes des Mouvements de libération reconnus par les Nations Unies sont membres associés de l'ISMUN.

Structure: la Conférence générale, qui peut se réunir à intervalles de dix-huit mois à deux ans, fixe les lignes générales de la politique du Mouvement, son programme éducatif, son budget et ses relations extérieures. La Conférence débat également de la politique suivie sur les questions politiques et sert de cadre à un Forum politique non officiel destiné à permettre une discussion ouverte sur l'un des problèmes politiques soumis aux Nations Unies. La Conférence élit le Comité exécutif, composé de 12 membres.

Le Comité exécutif administre le Mouvement entre les sessions de la Conférence générale, exécute les décisions et donne des directives au Secrétariat. Le Secrétariat est dirigé par le Secrétariat général qui est le principal responsable administratif du Mouvement.

Programme: a) Au niveau international: Enseignement sur la famille des Nations Unies, dispensé à la jeunesse et aux étudiants par des séminaires et des cours, participation aux campagnes organisées par les Nations Unies et les institutions spécialisées, rédaction et distribution de matériel d'information, échanges internationaux, campagnes organisées par les étudiants, organisations régionales d'étudiants.

b) Au niveau national: Séminaires, cours, conférences, films, expositions, distribution de matériel d'information sur les Nations Unies, sessions modèles, camps de travail, célébration de la Journée des Nations Unies, de la Journée des Droits de l'Homme, action politique, campagnes pour le développement.

Publications: *Bulletin* trimestriel; documents de base, pochettes d'information, documents de travail.
Secrétaire général: Juan Carlos Giacosa.
c/o Palais des Nations, 1211 Genève 10.
Tél: (22) 33-08-61

CO-ORDINATING COMMITTEE FOR INTERNATIONAL VOLUNTARY SERVICE (CCIVS)
COMITE DE COORDINATION DU SERVICE VOLONTAIRE INTERNATIONAL (CCSVI)

The Co-ordinating Committee for International Voluntary Service, founded in 1948 on the initiative of Unesco with which it enjoys consultative status A, groups over 110 organizations having branches in different countries and promoting, each according to its individual capacity, voluntary service throughout the world. The Committee collects information on long and short-term voluntary service and through its publications disseminates and directs it to organizations and individuals. As a centre for co-ordination, it maintains liaison with the affiliated organizations and institutions associated with its work. The Committee initiates specific projects in response to and in accordance with the needs of voluntary service agencies and the challenge of the international situation; sponsors training projects and encourages the development of voluntary service in new areas; carries out surveys and research of interest to voluntary service organizers. The Committee also has consultative status with the ECOSOC.

Many of the volunteers are students or young graduates. In the developing areas, long-term volunteers are employed in their professional capacities as doctors, nurses, teachers, geologists, agriculturists, mechanics, engineers, youth leaders, and social workers.

Publications: *News from CCIVS; Workcamp Organisers 1988; New Trends in Voluntary Service 1983; Camp Leader's Handbook, 1987; Volunteering in Literary Work, 1985.*
President: Rao Chelikani.
Director: Alexei Kruglov.
CCIVS, Unesco, 1, rue Miollis, 75015 Paris.
  Tel: (1) 4568-2732. Telex: 204461 funesc (attn. ccivs)

Le Comité de Coordination du Service Volontaire International, fondé en 1948 à l'initiative de l'Unesco auprès duquel il bénéficie du statut consultatif A, réunit plus de 110 organisations membres ayant des branches dans différents pays et travaillant, chacune à sa manière, à la promotion du service volontaire dans le monde. Le Comité réunit des renseignements sur le service volontaire à long et à court terme, et par l'intermédiaire de ses publications diffusées aussi bien auprès des organisations que des particuliers. En tant que centre de coordination il maintient la liaison entre ses organisations membres ainsi qu'avec les institutions travaillant dans les mêmes domaines. En réponse aux besoins des organisations de service volontaire et aux impératifs de la situation internationale, le Comité lance des projets spécifiques, patronne des projets de formation et encourage le développement du service volontaire dans de nouvelles régions, entreprend des enquêtes et des recherches à l'intention des organisateurs de service volontaire. Le Comité bénéficie également d'un statut consultatif auprès de l'ECOSOC.

Un grand nombre de ces volontaires sont des étudiants ou de jeunes diplômés. Dans les régions en voie de développement, les volontaires à "long terme" sont employés selon leurs capacités professionnelles comme médecins, infirmières, professeurs, géologues, agriculteurs, mécaniciens, ingénieurs, animateurs de jeunes et travailleurs sociaux.

Publications: *Nouvelles du CCSVI; Organisateurs de Chantiers 1988; Nouvelles tendances du service volontaire; Manuel de l'Animateur de Chantier, 1987; Le Volontariat au Service de l'Alphabétisation, 1985.*
Président: Rao Chelikani.
Directeur: Alexei Kruglov.
CCSVI, Unesco, 1, rue Miollis, 75015 Paris.
  Tél: (1) 4568-2732. Télex: 204461 funesc (attn. ccsvi)

OTHER INTERNATIONAL ORGANIZATIONS CONCERNED WITH SPECIAL STUDENT INTERESTS

AUTRES ORGANISATIONS INTERNATIONALES S'OCCUPANT D'ACTIVITES ESTUDIANTINES PARTICULIERES

Union internationale d'hygiène et de médecine scolaires et universitaires/International Union of School and University Health and Medical Services
Château de Longchamp, Bois de Boulogne, 75016 Paris.
Tél: (1) 4505-2662

Association internationale des Etudiants en Sciences économiques et commerciales (AIESEC)/International Association of Students in Economics and Management
Président: Mathew de Villiers.
Washington Straat 40, 1050 Brussel.
Tél: (2) 648-8803. Télex: 65080 inac (attn aiesec intl)

Fédération internationale du Sport universitaire (FISU)/International University Sports Federation
Secrétaire général: Roch Campana.
12, rue Général Thys, 1050 Bruxelles.
Tél: (2) 640-6873. Télex: 64557 fisu b

International Association of Dental Students (IADS)
c/o L. Walters, Medical Protection Society, 50 Hallan Street, London W1N 6DE.
Tel: (1) 637-0541

International Association for the Exchange of Students for Technical Experience (IAESTE)
General Secretary: Dr. Bernardo J. Herold.
Instituto Superior Tecnico, Avenida Rovisco Pais, 1096 Lisboa Codex.
Tel: (1) 890844. Fax: (1) 899242 (attn. gs-iaste). Telex: 63423 intul p. Cables: iaeste lisboa

International Federation of Medical Students' Associations (IFMSA)/Fédération internationale des Associations d'Etudiants en Médecine (FIAEM)

Secretary-General: Fritz Mahrer.
General Secretariat: Liechtensteinstrasse 13, 1090 Vienna.
Tel: (222) 315566. Telex: 116706 oec a

International Pharmaceutical Students' Federation (IPSF)/Fédération internationale des Etudiants en Pharmacie
General Secretary: Ilan Kreiser.
11 Alexanderstraat, 2514 JL Den Haag.
Tel: (70) 631925

International Veterinary Students' Association (IVSA)/Association internationale des Etudiants vétérinaires
President: Dietmar Gerstnar.
Secretary: Yolanda Villagrasa.
c/o I.V.S.A. Information Office, Yalelaan 1, 3584 CL Utrecht (Netherlands).
Tel: 30-534694

International Student Research Centre (ISRC) (see p. 673)
Parizska 25, 110 01 Praha 1 (Czechoslovakia).
Tel: 2312812. Telex: 122858 ius

International Student Travel Bureau (ISTB)
Parizska 25, 110 01 Praha 1 (Czechoslovakia).
Tel: 2312812

International Student Travel Confederation (see p. 673)
Chairman: Einar Fryden.
Executive Secretary: Ursi Silberschmidt.
Weinbergstrasse 31, 8006 Zürich.
Tel: (1) 692769. Telex: 815729

Student Air Travel Association (SATA)
Gothersgade 30, 1123 København.
Tel: (1) 112155. Telex: 19279

UNIVERSITY VACATIONS — VACANCES UNIVERSITAIRES

The following table indicates the principal period of the year in which the full teaching activities of university institutions in different countries are largely suspended. For countries in which universities do not all follow the same academic year, the alternative major vacation period is indicated by a cross.

Le tableau ci-dessous indique, pour chaque pays, la période principale de l'année pendant laquelle les cours réguliers se trouvent généralement interrompus. Pour les pays où existent deux calendriers différents selon les universités, la deuxième période principale des vacances est désignée par une croix.

COUNTRY/PAYS	MONTH/MOIS											
	1	2	3	4	5	6	7	8	9	10	11	12
Afghanistan		–	–									
Albania						–	–	–				
Algeria							–	–	–			
Argentina	–	–										–
Australia	–	–										–
Austria							–	–	–			
Belgium							–	–	–			
Benin							–	–	–			
Bolivia	–	–	–									
Brazil	–	–										–
Bulgaria							–	–				
Burma							–	–				
Burundi							–	–	–			
Cambodia						–	–	–				
Cameroon							–	–	–			
Canada						–	–	–				
Central African Republic							–	–	–			
Chad					–	–	–					
Chile	–	–										–
Colombia	–											–
Congo (People's Republic of)							–	–	–			
Costa Rica	–	–										–
Côte d'Ivoire							–	–	–			
Cuba								–	–			
Czechoslovakia							–	–	–			
Denmark						–	–	–				
Dominican Republic	–											–
Ecuador		+	+	+				–	–	–		
Egypt							–	–	–			
El Salvador			–	–								
Ethiopia								–	–	–		
Finland						–	–	–				
France								–	–	–		
Gabon								–	–	–		
German Democratic Republic								–	–	–		
Germany, Federal Republic of								–	–	–		
Ghana							–	–	–			
Greece							–	–	–			
Guadeloupe							–	–	–			
Guatemala	–										–	–
Guinea							–	–	–			

685

Country/Pays	1	2	3	4	5	6	7	8	9	10	11	12
Guyana							−	−	−			
Haiti								−	−			
Holy See							−	−	−			
Honduras	−											−
Hong Kong							−	−				
Hungary							−	−				
Iceland							−	−				
India				−	−	−						
Indonesia	−										−	−
Iran							−	−	−			
Iraq						−	−	−				
Ireland							−	−				
Israel							−	−	−			
Italy						−	−	−				
Jamaica							−	−				
Japan							−	−				
Jordan						−	−	−				
Kenya							−	−	−			
Korea (Republic of)							−	−				
Kuwait							−	−				
Lao							−	−				
Lebanon							−	−				
Lesotho				−	−	−						
Liberia	−	−										−
Libya							−	−				
Madagascar							−	−				
Malawi							−	−				
Malaysia		−	−									
Mali							−	−				
Malta							−	−				
Martinique							−	−				
Mauritius			−	−	−							
Mexico	+						−	−			+	+
Mongolia							−	−				
Morocco							−	−				
Mozambique								−	−	−		
Nepal	−				+	+						−
Netherlands								−	−			
New Zealand	−	−									−	−
Nicaragua		−	−									
Nigeria							−	−	−			
Norway							−	−				
Pakistan				+	+	+	−	−	−			
Panama	+	+	−	−								
Paraguay	−	−										
Peru	−	−	−									
Philippines				−	−	−						
Poland							−	−				
Portugal								−	−			
Reunion							−	−				
Romania							−	−				
Rwanda							−	−				
Saudi Arabia							−	−				
Senegal							−	−				
Sierra Leone						−	−					
Singapore		−	−									
Somalia								−	−	−		

COUNTRY/PAYS	MONTH/MOIS											
	1	2	3	4	5	6	7	8	9	10	11	12
South Africa	–	–										–
Spain							–	–	–			
Sri Lanka				+			–	–	–			
Sudan				–	–	–						
Sweden						–	–	–				
Switzerland							–	–	–			
Syrian Arab Republic							–	–				
Taiwan							–	–				
Tanzania				–	–	–						
Thailand			–	–	–							
Togo								–	–	–	–	
Tunisia							–	–	–			
Turkey							–	–	–			
Uganda				–	–	–						
Union of Soviet Socialist Republics							–	–				
United Kingdom							–	–	–			
United States of America						–	–	–				
Uruguay	–	–										–
Venezuela	+					–	–	–				+
Viet Nam (Socialist Republic of)							–	–	–			
Yugoslavia							–	–	–			
Zaire Republic							–	–	–			
Zambia	–	–										–
Zimbabwe	–	–										–

APPENDIX — APPENDICE

INTERNATIONAL ASSOCIATION OF UNIVERSITIES
ASSOCIATION INTERNATIONALE DES UNIVERSITES

The origins, structure and activities of the Association are described on pages 610–619 of this volume.

Une note sur les origines, la structure et les activités de l'Association figure aux pages 610–619 du présent ouvrage.

IAU — INTERNATIONAL ASSOCIATION OF UNIVERSITIES PUBLICATIONS

Periodicals

† *Higher Education Policy*, Quarterly Journal, ISSN 0279-4631.

* *Bulletin of the International Association of Universities*. Bimonthly. ISSN 0020-6032.

Reference Works

‡ *International Handbook of Universities*. Eleventh Edition, 1989. xi + 1302 pages.
ISBN 92-9002-149-7
‡ *World List of Universities, Other Institutions of Higher Education and University Organizations*. Eighteenth Edition, 1990, xxiii + 706 pages.
ISBN 92-9002-048-2
Collection of Agreements Concerning the Equivalence of University Qualifications (on microfiches).

1966. vii + 655 pages (7 microfiches).
ISBN 92-9002-013-X
First Supplement.
1977. iv + 279 pages (3 microfiches).
ISBN 92-9002-031-8
Documents Concerning the Equivalence of University Qualifications.
1957. 280 loose leaves (microfilm).

Papers of the International Association of Universities

1. *Three Aspects of University Development Today*. 1953. 46 pages.
2. *Health at the University*. 1954. 76 pages.
3. *Student Mental Health*. 1958. 76 pages.
4. **University Education and Public Service*. 1959. 151 pages.
   ISBN 92–9002–102–0
5. **The Interplay of Scientific and Cultural Values in Higher Education Today*. 1960. 81 pages.
   ISBN 92–9002–103–9
6. **The Expansion of Higher Education*. 1960. 117 pages.
   ISBN 92–9002–104–7
7. *University Autonomy — Its Meaning Today*. 1965. 139 pages.
   ISBN 92–9002–110–1

8. *The Administration of Universities*. 1967. xiii + 99 pages.
   ISBN 92–9002–114–4
9. *International University Co-operation*. 1969. xvi + 161 pages.
   ISBN 92–9002–115–2
10. *The University and the Needs of Contemporary Society*. 1970. xv + 81 pages.
    ISBN 92–9002–116–0
11. *Problems of Integrated Higher Education — An International Case Study of the Gesamthochschule*. 1972. 85 pages.
    ISBN 92–9002–120–9
12. *The Social Responsibility of the University in Asian Countries — Obligations and Opportunities*. 1973. 124 pages.
    ISBN 92–9002–122–5

---

† May be ordered from: Kogan Page, 120 Pentonville Road, London, United Kingdom N1 9JN. Tel: (01) 278-0433.

* Published with the financial assistance of Unesco.

‡ May be ordered from: Globe Book Services Ltd., Stockton House, 1 Melbourne Place, London, United Kingdom WC2B 4LF. Tel: (01) 379 4687, or Stockton Press, 15 East 26th Street, New York, N.Y. 10010 U.S.A. Tel: (1-800) 221-2123 (Orders from U.S. and Canada).

13. *A Critical Approach to Inter-University Co-operation.* 1974. 138 pages.
ISBN 92–9002–124–1
14. *Differing Types of Higher Education.* 1977. 86 pages.
ISBN 92–9002–130–6
15. *The Right to Education and Access to Higher Education.* 1978. 107 pages.
ISBN 92–9002–132–2
16. *The Role of the University in Developing Countries: Its Responsibility towards the Natural and Cultural Environment.* 1979. 95 pages.
ISBN 92–9002–133–0

17. *Contemporary Scientific and Technical Changes: their Impact on the Humanities in University Education.* 1983. 80 pages.
ISBN 92–9002–140–3
18. *The Future of University Education.* 1983. 86 pages.
ISBN 92–9002–242–6
19. *Universities and Regional Development.* 1985. 47 pages.
ISBN 92–9002–144–6

Studies and Reports

The Staffing of Higher Education. 1960. 169 pages.
ISBN 92–9002–106–3
Some Economic Aspects of Educational Development in Europe. 1961. 144 pages.
ISBN 92–9002–108–X
Formal Programmes of International Co-operation between University Institutions. 1960. 39 pages in -4⁰ (published by Unesco).
Report of a Meeting of Heads of African Institutions of Higher Education, Khartoum, 16-19 September 1963. 1964. 107 pages.
ISBN 92–9002–109–8
*Report of the International Conference of Universities, Nice, December 1950. 1951. 162 pages.
Report of Proceedings, Second General Conference of the International Association of Universities, Istanbul, September 1955. 1956. 232 pages.
ISBN 92–9002–101–2
Report of Proceedings, Third General Conference of the International Association of Universities, Mexico, September 1960. 1961. 224 pages.
ISBN 92–9002–107–1
Report of the Fourth General Conference of the International Association of Universities, Tokyo, 31 August-6 September 1965. 1966. 264 pages.
ISBN 92–9002–112–8
Report of the Fifth General Conference of the International Association of Universiies, Montreal, 30 August-5 September 1970. 1971. 291 pages.
ISBN 92–9002–118–7

Report of the Sixth General Conference of the International Association of Universities, Moscow, 19-25 August 1975. 1977. 309 pages.
ISBN 92–9002–127–6
Report of the Seventh General Conference of the International Association of Universities, Manila, 25-30 August 1980. 1981. 322 pages.
ISBN 92–9002–137–3
Report of the Eighth General Conference of the International Association of Universities, Los Angeles, 12-17 August 1985. 1986. 203 pages.
ISBN 92–9002–146–2
Administrative Reports of the International Association of Universities: 1951–1954. 1955. 40 pages.
ISBN 92–9002–100–4
Idem: 1955–1959. 1960. 58 pages.
ISBN 92–9002–105–5
Idem: 1960–1964. 1965. 129 pages.
ISBN 92–9002–111–X
Idem: 1965–1969. 1970. 117 pages.
ISBN 92–9002–117–9
Idem: 1970–1974. 1975. 113 pages.
ISBN 92–9002–125–X
Idem: 1975–1979. 1980. 104 pages.
ISBN 92–9002–136–5
Idem: 1980–1984. 1985. 78 pages.
ISBN 92–9002–145–4

* Published with the financial assistance of Unesco.

Joint Unesco-IAU Research Programme in Higher Education (1)

The International Study of University Admissions:
Vol. I: *Access to Higher Education,* by Frank Bowles. 1963. 212 pages.
Bound: ISBN 92–3–100574–X
Paper: ISBN 92–3–100575–8
Vol. II: *National Studies.* 1965. 648 pages.
ISBN 92–3–100608–8
Higher Education and Development in South-East Asia:
Summary Report. 1965. 94 pages.
ISBN 92–3–100543–X
Higher Education and Development in South-East Asia:
Vol. I: *Director's Report,* by Howard Hayden. 1967. 508 pages.
ISBN 92–3–100651–7
Vol. II: *Country Profiles.* 1967. 615 pages.
ISBN 92–3–100650–9
Vol. II: Part 1. *High-level manpower for development,* by Guy Hunter. 1967. 184 pages.
ISBN 92–3–100649–5

Part 2. *Language policy and higher education,* by Richard Noss. 1967. 216 pages.
ISBN 92–3–100648–7
Teaching and Learning: An Introduction to New Methods and Resources in Higher Education, by N. MacKenzie, M. Eraut, H.C. Jones. 1970. 209 pages.
ISBN 92–3–100798–X
Second edition, revised. 1976. 224 pages.
ISBN 92–3–100798–X
Lifelong Education and University Resources (eight case studies). 1978. 193 pages.
ISBN 92–3–101397–1
New Trends and New Responsibilities for Universities in Latin America. 1980. 96 pages.
ISBN 92–3–101830–2
Universities and Environmental Education. 1986. 127 pages.
ISBN 92–3–102364–0

---

(1) Reports issued under this Programme are produced jointly by Unesco and IAU and may be purchased through national distributors of Unesco publications.

AIU — ASSOCIATION INTERNATIONALE DES UNIVERSITES PUBLICATIONS

Periodiques

† *Higher Education Policy*. Revue trimestrielle.
ISSN 0279-4631

* *Bulletin de l'Association internationale des universités*. Bimestriel.
ISSN 0020-6032.

Ouvrages de Reference

‡ *International Handbook of Universities*. Onzième édition, 1989. xi + 1302 pages.
ISBN 92–9002–149–7
‡ *Liste mondiale des universités, autres établissements d'enseignement supérieur et organisations universitaires*.
Dix-huitième édition, 1990, xxiii + 706 pages.
ISBN 92–9002–000–0

Recueil d'accords concernant l'équivalence des titres universitaires (sur microfiches). 1966. vii + 655 pages (7 microfiches).
ISBN 92–9002–013–X
Premier Supplément. 1977.
iv + 279 pages (3 microfiches).
ISBN 92–9002–031–8
Documentation concernant les équivalences des titres universitaires. 1957. 280 fiches (sur microfilm).

Cahiers de l'Association Internationale des Universites

1. *Trois aspects du développement de l'université d'aujourd'hui*. 1953. 47 pages.
2. *La santé à l'université*. 1954. 76 pages.
3. *La santé mentale à l'université*. 1958. 85 pages.
4. **L'université et la formation des cadres de la vie publique*. 1959. 162 pages.
ISBN 92–9002–202–7
5. **Le dialogue des sciences et des humanités dans l'enseignement supérieur d'aujourd'hui*. 1960. 86 pages.
ISBN 92–9002–203–5
6. **L'expansion de l'enseignement supérieur*. 1960. 132 pages.
ISBN 92–9002–204–3

7. *L'autonomie universitaire: sa signification aujourd'hui*. 1965. 139 pages.
ISBN 92–9002–210–8
8. *L'administration des universités*. 1967. xiii + 105 pages.
ISBN 92–9002–214–0
9. *La coopération universitaire internationale*. 1969. xvi + 173 pages.
ISBN 92–9002–215–9
10. *L'Université et les besoins de la société contemporaine*. 1970. xv + 83 pages.
ISBN 92–9002–216–7
11. *Problèmes d'intégration des enseignements supérieurs — Etude de cas internationale sur la Gesamthochschule*. 1972. 87 pages.
ISBN 92–9002–220–5

† Peut être commandé à: Kogan Page, 120 Pentonville Road, London, United Kingdom N1 9JN. Tel: (01) 278-0433.

* Publié avec le concours financier de l'Unesco.

‡ Peuvent être commandés à: Globe Book Services Ltd., Stockton House, 1 Melbourne Place, London, United Kingdom, WC2B 4LF. Tél: (01) 379-4687, or Stockton Press, 15 East 26th Street, New York, N.Y. 10010 U.S.A. Tél: (1-800) 221-2123 (Pour les Etats-Unis et Canada).

12. *La responsabilité sociale de l'Université dans les pays d'Asie—ses obligations et ses chances.* 1973. 130 pages.
    ISBN 92–9002–222–1
13. *Une approche critique de la coopération interuniversitaire.* 1974. 156 pages.
    ISBN 92–9002–224–8
14. *Les différents types d'enseignement supérieur.* 1977. 92 pages.
    ISBN 92–9002–230–6
15. *Le droit à l'éducation et l'accès à l'enseignement supérieur.* 1978. 112 pages.
    ISBN 92–9002–232–9

16. *Le rôle de l'université dans les pays en voie de développement: ses responsabilités envers l'environnement naturel et culturel.* 1979. 94 pages.
    ISBN 92–9002–233–7
17. *Les mutations scientifiques et techniques contemporaines: leurs répercussions sur les sciences humaines dans la formation universitaire.* 1983. 98 pages.
    ISBN 92–9002–240–X
18. *L'avenir de la formation universitaire.* 1983. 96 pages.
    ISBN 92–9002–242–6
19. *Les universités et leur développement régional.* 1984. 49 pages.
    ISBN 92–9002–244–2

Etudes et rapports

Le recrutement du personnel d'enseignement supérieur. 1960. 170 pages.
ISBN 92–9002–206–X

Quelques aspects économiques du développement de l'éducation en Europe. 1961. 150 pages.
ISBN 92–9002–208–6

Programmes officiels de coopération internationale entre institutions universitaires. 1960. 41 pages in-4 (publié par l'Unesco).

Rapport de la réunion des chefs d'institutions d'enseignement supérieur africains, Khartoum, 16-19 septembre 1963. 1964. 113 pages.
ISBN 92–9002–209–4

* *Rapport de la Conférence internationale des Universités, Nice, décembre 1950.* 1951. 164 pages.

Rapport de la Deuxième Conférence générale de l'Association internationale des Universités, Istanbul, septembre 1955. 1956. 240 pages.
ISBN 92–9002–201–9

Rapport de la Troisième Conférence générale de l'Association internationale des Universités, Mexico, septembre 1960. 1961. 232 pages.
ISBN 92–9002–207–8

Rapport de la Quatrième Conférence générale de l'Association internationale des Universités, Tokyo, 31 août-6 septembre 1965. 1966. 276 pages.
ISBN 92–9002–212–4

Rapport de la Cinquième Conférence générale de l'Association internationale des Universités, Montréal, 30 août-5 septembre 1970. 1971. 309 pages.
ISBN 92–9002–218–3
Rapport de la Sixième Conférence générale de l'Association internationale des Universités, Moscou, 19-25 août 1975. 1977. 328 pages.
ISBN 92–9002–227–2
Rapport de la Septième Conférence générale de l'Association internationale des Universités, Manille, 25-30 août 1980. 1981. 358 pages.
ISBN 92–9002–237–3
Rapport de la Huitième Conférence générale de l'Association internationale des Universités, Los Angeles, 12-17 août 1986. 1986. 217 pages.
ISBN 92–9002–246–9
Rapports administratifs de l'Association internationale des Universités: 1951–1954. 1955. 44 pages.
ISBN 92–9002–200–0
Idem: 1955–1959. 1960. 60 pages.
ISBN 92–9002–205–1
Idem: 1960–1964. 1965. 129 pages.
ISBN 92–9002–211–6
Idem: 1965–1969. 1970. 121 pages.
ISBN 92–9002–217–5
Idem: 1970–1974. 1975. 119 pages.
ISBN 92–9002–225–6
Idem: 1975–1979. 1980. 109 pages.
ISBN 92–9002–236–1
Idem: 1980–1984. 1985. 82 pages.
ISBN 92–9002–245–0

---

* Publié avec le concours financier de l'Unesco.

Programme Conjoint Unesco-AIU d'Études sur l'Enseignement Supérieur (1)

Etude internationale de l'admission à l'université:
Vol. I: *Accès à l'enseignement supérieur,* par Frank Bowles, 1964. 233 pages.
Relié: ISBN 92–3–200574–3
Broché: ISBN 92–3–200575–1
Vol. II: *National Studies.* 1965. 648 pages.
ISBN 92–3–100608–8
L'enseignement supérieur et le développement en Asie du Sud-Est:
Rapport sommaire. 1965. 94 pages.
ISBN 92–3–200543–3
L'enseignement supérieur et le développement en Asie du Sud-Est:
Vol. I: *Rapport du Directeur,* par Howard Hayden. 1969. 550 pages.
ISBN 92–3–200651–0
Vol. II: *Country Profiles.* 1967. 615 pages.
ISBN 92–3–100650–9
Vol. III: 1re partie: *Les cadres nécessaires au développement,* par Guy Hunter. 1969. 204 pages.
ISBN 92–3–200649–9

2e partie: *Politique linguistique et enseignement supérieur,* par Richard Noss. 1969. 235 pages.
ISBN 92–3–200648–0
Art d'enseigner et art d'apprendre: Introduction aux méthodes et matériels nouveaux dans l'enseignement supérieur, par N. MacKenzie, M. Eraut, H.C. Jones, 1971. 236 pages.
ISBN 92–3–200789–3
Education permanente et potentiel universitaire (huit études de cas). 1977. 202 pages.
ISBN 92–3–201397–5
Tendances et responsabilités nouvelles des universités en Amérique latine. 1980. 102 pages.
ISBN 92–3–201830–6

(1) Les rapports publiés dans le cadre de ce Programme sont édités conjointement par l'Unesco et l'AIU et ils sont en vente, dans les différents pays, chez les dépositaires des publications de l'Unesco.

INDEX—INDEX

PART ONE
PREMIERE PARTIE

**International Institutions —
Etablissements Internationaux**

PART TWO
DEUXIEME PARTIE

International and Regional Organizations —
Organisations internationales et régionales

706